HUMAN PARASITES

From Organisms to Molecular Biology

HUMAN PARASITES

From Organisms to Molecular Biology

Dunne Fong
Rutgers, The State University of New Jersey, USA

Marion M Chan
Temple University, USA

World Scientific

NEW JERSEY • LONDON • SINGAPORE • BEIJING • SHANGHAI • HONG KONG • TAIPEI • CHENNAI • TOKYO

Published by

World Scientific Publishing Co. Pte. Ltd.
5 Toh Tuck Link, Singapore 596224
USA office: 27 Warren Street, Suite 401-402, Hackensack, NJ 07601
UK office: 57 Shelton Street, Covent Garden, London WC2H 9HE

Library of Congress Cataloging-in-Publication Data
Names: Fong, Dunne, author. | Chan, Marion M., author.
Title: Human parasites : from organisms to molecular biology / Dunne Fong, Rutgers,
The State University of New Jersey, USA, Marion M. Chan, Temple University, USA.
Description: New Jersey : World Scientific, [2022] | Includes bibliographical references and index.
Identifiers: LCCN 2021043902 | ISBN 9789811236266 (hardcover) | ISBN 9789811236273 (ebook) |
ISBN 9789811236280 (ebook other)
Subjects: LCSH: Parasitic diseases. | Parasites--Genetics.
Classification: LCC RC119 .F66 2022 | DDC 616.9/6--dc23/eng/20211015
LC record available at https://lccn.loc.gov/2021043902

British Library Cataloguing-in-Publication Data
A catalogue record for this book is available from the British Library.

For any available supplementary material, please visit
https://www.worldscientific.com/worldscibooks/10.1142/12256#t=suppl

Typeset by Stallion Press
Email: enquiries@stallionpress.com

Printed in Singapore

Contents

Preface

Parasites threaten human health. Human parasites include species of protozoa, helminths, and arthropods, with the latter acting both as ectoparasites (living on human skin) and as vectors (carriers) of infectious agents. Phenomena such as climate change and globalization have led to the emergence/re-emergence of certain parasites, including zoonoses (parasites jumping species barrier to infect humans). Many parasitic diseases are grouped to be neglected tropical diseases (NTDs) by the World Health Organization (WHO).

As university instructors, we have the pleasure of introducing human parasites to many students: undergraduate and graduate students (graduate school), students in physician assistant and post-baccalaureate programs, and students in professional schools (medical school, dental school, and school of podiatric medicine). [Whereas Marion Chan has teaching experience with all students listed here, Dunne Fong's experience is limited to the first two groups. In 2021, Marion Chan received the Graduate/Non-MD Professional Program Teaching Award, an educational excellence award, at Lewis Katz School of Medicine, Temple University. In addition to parasitology, we teach other subjects: immunology, microbiology, and cell and molecular biology.] Our teaching experience has resulted in *Human Parasites: from Organisms to Molecular Biology*, a textbook designed for an upper level course in human parasitology.

Our goal for this textbook is to provide basic knowledge of the biology of parasitism. For the scope of this book, the initial chapters cover NTDs, definitions, principles, immunology, genomes, evolution, and phylogeny/classification. Chapters of specific groups follow, beginning from protozoa, to helminths, to arthropods, and ending with a discussion on the relationship between parasites and current global issues. [Presentation of each group is independent. Therefore, the order can vary as an instructor desires.]

For each group, we cover life cycle, diagnosis, treatment, and prevention. Human parasitic diseases are found in both the rich and the poor countries. Hence, we collect case reports from many countries to show the ubiquity of human parasites and to invoke interest in the readers who are more clinically inclined. We discuss history and genomes, from original discovery to current research. In history, then and now, science involves competitions/collaborations under various circumstances. [We mention both intentional/inadvertent self-inoculation of parasites by the investigators. We discuss paleoparasitology, such as fossil feces containing parasites.] In genomes, various techniques first developed elsewhere have been applied to human parasites (such as single cell transcriptomics/single cell atlas). As an extension to the standard reference list, we add websites from sources such as WHO, Centers for Disease Control and Prevention (CDC), and others so that the interested reader can easily access reports/relevant information.

In this textbook, the more essential information has been intentionally repeated, or presented in slightly differently ways, so as to make an impression on the reader. From our combined experience instructing courses, we find repetition to work well in helping students learn and retain information. In addition to our own introduction of research results, we often quote the investigators directly, allowing our readers to be familiar with primary publications and the researchers' own interpretations. As parasitism is a lifestyle, we place emphasis on nutrients (food and water) and resources. Additionally, aspects of parasitism as observed by artists, journalists, writers, and others are incorporated in select chapters. [We are pleased to include Chinese and Hindi characters in the book.] In all, these features make for a unique and genuine textbook.

This is an exciting time for the science of human parasites. The first vaccine for a parasite has just become available (against the deadly malaria protozoan parasite *Plasmodium falciparum*, fair efficacy, but a total of 4 doses are necessary). The infectious agents for sleeping sickness and guinea worm disease (caused by a protozoan and a helminth, respectively) are heading towards eradication. However, this is also a sad time, as the global population is facing the ongoing COVID-19 pandemic, with continuing variants/mutants of the original infectious agent (a virus). These old and new infectious diseases are real world health problems. We hope this book will arm/prepare the readers who want to take action.

Below, we show a photograph of the authors with a jar of tapeworm, taken on February 29, 2020 (right before the pandemic lockdown), while visiting the exhibit of Bill and Melinda Gates Foundation at Seattle, Washington (photo image courtesy of Grace Fong).

Acknowledgements

In the earlier days of our academic career, the internet was not yet invented (no *Google*, no *Grammarly*, no *Turnitin*), but we found a mentor in Robert Herman, who graciously and generously read and commented on our manuscripts and grant proposals. We express our sincere appreciation to Bob's friendship and sage advice. Dunne fondly remembers that he was invited to give a guest lecture of Bob's parasitology course each semester, with the topic: molecular biology of parasites (including antigenic variation of the protozoan parasite *Trypanosoma brucei*, an infectious agent of sleeping sickness). Many years later, Dunne was drafted to teach a parasitology course (after retirement and leaving the university of faculty members), because our team's research interests include the parasitic protozoan *Leishmania*. Another decade later, these teaching efforts and experience have morphed into the textbook titled *Human Parasites: from Organisms to Molecular Biology*.

For the writing of this book, we must first thank the many publishers for permission to reuse figures and tables from their journals and books. In our book, the life cycle of parasites are essential features, and we are exceedingly grateful to Keisha Simmons and Monica Parise (Division of Parasitic Diseases and Malaria, Center for Global Health, Centers for Disease Control and Prevention) at CDC for providing high-resolution images for our use.

We are grateful to the journal editors for allowing us to reuse published materials: Sung-Jong Hong, *The Korean Journal of Parasitology*; Tomas Scholz, *Folia Parasitologica*; Chandrawathani Panchadcharam, *Tropical Biomedicine*. We also thank the researchers for allowing us to reuse figures available on the internet: Zeynep Altun-Gultekin (Albert Einstein College of Medicine, for WormBase), Daniel Griffin (Columbia, for Parasites Without Borders), and Scott Weaver (University of Texas Medical Branch Galveston, for the online text *Medical Microbiology*).

In addition, we are grateful to the individual researchers who personally and promptly permitted our request to reuse their figures: Stephen Ambu (International Medical University, Malaysia), Sandra Barrios-de Pedro (Universidad Autónoma de Madrid, Spain), Richard Coico (SUNY Downstate Medical Center, New York), Youn-

Kyoung Goo (Kyungpook National University, Korea), Jens Anibal Juul (Stavanger University Hospital, Norway), Jae-Sook Ryu (Hanyang University College of Medicine, Korea), and Ananganallur Nagarajan Shriram (Unit of Vector Biology and Control, ICMR-Vector Control Research Centre, Ministry of Health & Family Welfare, India).

Although we have written many grant proposals, research papers, reviews, and even several book chapters, this endeavor is our first book. Therefore, we have sought for advice. Here, we give thanks to our colleagues: David Axelrod (Genetics, Rutgers) for help with the book contract, Joanna Burger and Gary Merrill (Cell Biology and Neuroscience, CBN, Rutgers) for sharing their knowledge of book publishing and writing, Peter Mickulas (Executive Editor, Rutgers University Press) for a different take from the angle of an academic publisher, Shu-Chan Hsu (CBN) for assistance with text improvement, and Anne Keating (Division of Life Sciences, Rutgers) for her insights on teaching parasitology. [Anne and Dunne teach human parasitology at different semesters of the academic year.]

We are indebted to numerous students who have commented on various draft chapters of the book. Dunne also appreciates graduate students in his seminars course, whose assignments have provided additional information for incorporation into the text. He thanks his teaching assistant (parasitology laboratory) Seth Bromagen for suggestions to improve aspects of parasites and ecology. Among the students, Dunne especially appreciates his graduate student Chase Christensen (currently at Infinity Biologix), Elmira Kirichenko (current 2021 fall semester seminar class participant), and undergraduate research students Nana Haruna (currently at Northwestern) and Anjana Ramesh, for their very careful reading of the select chapters (and providing corrections on facts and language).

We are indebted to Christopher Davis (Executive Editor, World Scientific Publishing) for securing us the book agreement. [We enjoyed meetings with Chris at Piscataway, NJ and Philadelphia, PA.] We wish to express our appreciation to the dedicated, experienced, and talented staff members at the World Scientific Publishing Company for the production of *Human Parasites: from Organisms to Molecular Biology*. Particular thanks are due to Ling Xiao, for her guidance in many steps along the way. We are indebted to others in the team, Sook Ling Pong, Yugarani, and especially to the typesetters for our last-minute changes (additions/updates).

We end our acknowledgments with a disclosure about the book cover. We received several drawings from Chin Choon Ng, the publisher's in-house designer, and decided on the current one. We had requested the incorporation of images of *Leishmania* expressing the green fluorescent protein (GFP) in the cover, based on our publication: Marion Chan, Chloe Bulinski, Kwang-Poo Chang, Dunne Fong, "A microplate assay for *Leishmania amazonensis* promastigotes expressing multimeric green fluorescent protein" *Parasitol Res.* 2003;89(4):266-71. These GFP-*Leishmania*, frozen in September 2003 and stored in a liquid nitrogen tank, were thawed in May 2021. The promastigote stage protozoans were alive and exhibited GFP fluorescence; they were fixed and imaged using spinning disk confocal microscopy. We thank Guoqiang Wang and Monica Driscoll (Molecular Biology and Biochemistry, Rutgers) for these GFP images (including a dividing promastigote as shown on the back cover). For the selection of cover design, we also wish to thank Grace Fong for her idea and comments.

1

Introduction to Parasites and Neglected Tropical Diseases

1.1 Biodiversity & Sustainable Food Systems

In January 2019, Sir David Attenborough, famous for his British Broadcast Company (BBC) nature documentaries (including *Life on Earth*), spoke at the World Economic Forum (WEF) held in Davos, Switzerland. At the forum, he said: "The Garden of Eden is no more. We have changed the world so much that scientists say we are in a new geological age: the Anthropocene, the age of humans." "There will be United Nations decisions on climate change, sustainable development and a new deal for nature. Together these will form our species' plan for a route through the Anthropocene."[1]

Anthropocene is explained as a geological epoch that is characterized by humanity being the dominating driver of change on Earth, as seen in the 2019 Lancet Commissions report on Food in the Anthropocene, by Walter Willett (Harvard T H Chan School of Public Health) and colleagues (19 commissioners and 18 coauthors, from 16 countries). Today, the world population is **7.8 billion**. The top 5 countries with the highest number of people, in order, are China, India, United States, Indonesia and Brazil. India is projected to overtake China in 2024. It is obvious that people require food and water to survive. Walter Willett and colleagues wrote: "food production is among the largest drivers of global environmental change by contributing to climate change, biodiversity loss, freshwater use, interference with the global nitrogen and phosphorus cycles, and land-system change (and chemical pollution)" (Willett *et al.* 2019). However, a win-win diet that is both healthy and environmentally sustainable is attainable within a safe operating space, even for an estimated global population of about 10 billion people by 2050. A universal healthy reference diet has been proposed, for an intake of 2,500 kcal/day, consisting of fruits, vegetables, whole grains, legumes, nuts and unsaturated oils, plus low to moderate amount of seafood and poultry (low or no red meat, no processed meat, added

[1] https://www.weforum.org/agenda/2019/01/david-attenborough-transcript-from-crystal-award-speech/

sugar, refined grains, and starchy vegetables). Please see Table 1.1 for the reference diet (Willett *et al.* 2019). For some consumers, red meat is an ethically and ecologically objectionable animal protein. As insects produce less greenhouse gases than livestock, entomophagy is an alternative. Insects have been favored cuisine in some cultures.

TABLE 1.1: The healthy reference diet. Possible ranges are included, for an intake of 2,500 kcal/day. Courtesy: W. Willett *et al. Lancet* 2019;393:447–492. Reproduced with permission from Elsevier.

	Macronutrient intake (possible range), g/day	**Caloric intake, kcal/day**
Whole grains*		
Rice, wheat, com, and other†	232 (total gains 0–60% of energy)	811
Tubers or starchy vegetables		
Potatoes and cassava	50 (0–100)	39
Vegetables		
All vegetables	300 (200–600)	—
Dark green vegetables	100	23
Red and orange vegetables	100	30
Other vegetables	100	25
Fruits		
All fruit	200 (100–300)	126
Dairy foods		
Whole milk or derivative equivalents (eg. cheese)	250 (0–500)	153
Protein sources‡		
Beef and lamb	7 (0–14)	15
Pork	7 (0–14)	15
Chicken and other poultry	29 (0–58)	62
Eggs	13 (0–25)	19
Fish§	28 (0–100)	40
Legumes		
Dry beans, lentils, and peas*	50 (0–100)	172
Soy foods	25 (0–50)	112
Peanuts	25 (0–75)	142
Tree nuts	25	149
Added fats		
Palm oil	6.8 (0–6.8)	60

TABLE 1.1: (*Continued*)

	Macronutrient intake (possible range), g/day	Caloric intake, kcal/day
Unsaturated oils¶	40 (20–80)	354
Dairy fats (included in milk)	0	0
Lard or tallow‖	5 (0–5)	36
Added sugars		
All sweeteners	31 (0–31)	120

For an individual, an optimal energy intake to maintain a healthy weight will depend on body size and level of physical activity. Processing of foods such as partial hydrogenation of oils, refining of grains, and addition of salt and preservatives can substantially affect health but is not addressed in this table. *Wheat, rice, dry beans, and lentils are dry, raw. †Mix and amount of grains can vary to maintain isocaloric intake. ‡Beef and lamb are exchangeable with pork and vice versa. Chicken and other poultry is exchangeable with eggs, fish, or plant protein sources. Legumes, peanuts, tree nuts, seeds, and soy are interchangeable. §Seafood consists of fish and shellfish (eg. mussels and shrimps) and originates from both captured animals and plants; the focus of this report is solely on animals. ¶Unsaturated oils are 20% each of olive, soybean, rapeseed, sunflower, and peanut oil. ‖Some lard or tallow are optional in instances when pigs or cattle are consumed.

1.2 Symbiosis & Parasitism

Every living organism needs nutrients. In ecology, this is the concept of trophic dynamics. [Trophic derives from the Greek word meaning "related to feeding and nutrition."] A trophic level describes the position that an organism occupies in the food chain: what an organism eats and what eats the organism. This results in a direct transfer of energy. Additionally, food chains may expand into food webs. Plants use sunlight for photosynthesis, hence they are the primary producers. Herbivores that eat plants are primary consumers, and carnivores that eat herbivores are secondary consumers. As seen in the universal healthy reference diet described above, humans eat plants and animals. Therefore, we are omnivores. In this sense, parasites are organisms that have chosen a unique parasitic lifestyle.

Symbiosis and parasitism can be viewed under such consideration of trophic interactions. Symbiosis means living together. William Trager (Rockefeller University) (1910–2005), with a lifelong work on malaria (as well as other protozoan parasites), must have had this in mind when he titled his book *Living Together: The Biology of Animal Parasitism* (1986, Plenum). In contrast to free-living lifestyle, any two organisms living in close association, commonly one living in or on the body of the other, are symbiotic. Interactions between symbionts may or may not involve energy transfer; there may be beneficial or harmful outcomes. Symbiotic relationship can be viewed in four ways: **phoresy, commensalism, mutualism** and **exploitation**. However, there are overlaps between the relationships, reflecting the diversity of lifestyles found in nature.

The first symbiotic relationship is phoresy (also known as, aka, phoresis), in which there is no trophic interaction; the organisms just travel together. Normally the smaller one, the phoront, is the hitchhiker. An example is bee pollination, with plant pollen attached to the bee's body (an unrelated note on the demise of honeybees: colony collapse disorder (CCD) that may be related to parasites and pesticides, especially neonicotinoids).

The second is commensalism, meaning "eating at the same table," in which there is indirect trophic interaction. Examples are remoras and sharks, hermit crabs and sea anemones, *Entamoeba gingivalis* and humans. [Please see Chapter 7 for amoebiasis.]

The third relationship is mutualism, in which there is direct trophic interaction (direct transfer of energy) with benefit, as both parties become advantageous. Examples are lichen (a combination of an alga and a fungus), coral, alga in cnidarians, termites and gut microflora, ruminants and microbiome, and the filarial worm *Brugia malayi* and bacterium *Wolbachia*. [Please see Chapter 18 for lymphatic filariasis.] Actually, the first example needs revision; the current understanding of lichen is a composite of three species, one algal and two fungal species (Tuovinen *et al.* 2019). Another interesting discovery is the presence of an apicomplexan within the coral, which is composed of an animal (Anthozoa) and symbiotic photosynthetic algae (the Symbiodiniaceae dinoflagellates). Members of apicomplexans are obligate intracellular parasites including the species that cause malaria. The coral apicomplexan has been named corallicolids; they contain the organelle apicoplast which retains four genes for chlorophyll biosynthesis. "Corallicolids thus share characteristics with both their parasitic and their free-living relatives, which suggests that they are evolutionary intermediates and implies the existence of a unique biochemistry" (Kwong *et al.* 2019). [Please see Chapter 9 for malaria.] Another important topic on mutualism is the **human microbiome**. Our bodies contain three times more microbial cells than human cells. Metabolism of microbiota in the gut benefits us (they produce branched chain amino acids and short chain fatty acids). The presence of parasites can alter the balance. Hence, the Parasite Microbiome Project has been proposed to investigate the microbiome dynamics within and across parasite-host interactions, "to propel the field of parasitology into the microbiome/metagenomic era" (Dheilly *et al.* 2017). The parasite-microbe-host triad may even influence cancer risk (Dheilly *et al.* 2019).

The fourth relationship is exploitation, in which there is direct trophic interaction with harm. For many hosts that are always killed, there is the predator. An example is a lion and the gazelle (an antelope). For a single host (or at least one stage of the life cycle), there is the parasitoid. An example is the female hymenopteran/dipteran (such as a wasp/a fly) laying an egg on the victim insects (such as a cockroach). For many hosts that are seldom killed, there is the micropredator. An example is the female mosquito, sucking blood. For a single host that seldom gets killed, there is the parasite. An example is the adult tapeworm living in the human gastrointestinal tract. [Please see Chapter 15 for taeniasis.] Please see Figure 1.1 for a view on the lifestyles of organisms (Bush *et al.* 2001).

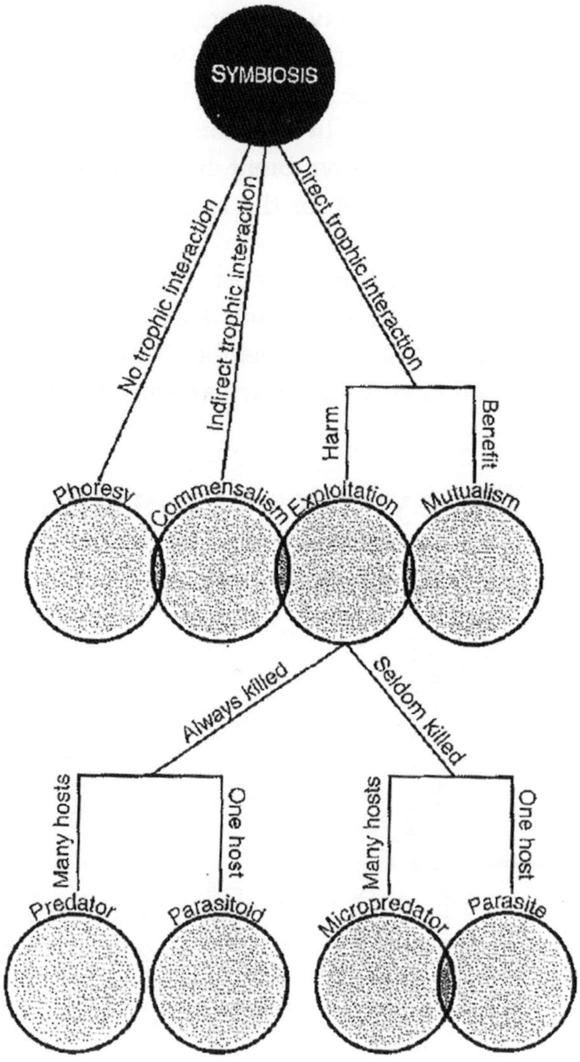

Fig. 1.1 ■ Lifestyles of organisms. An attempt to find "parasitism's place" within the context of symbiotic relationships. This is only one way of looking at parasitism and it is based, initially, on trophic relationships, followed by "harm," and finally, quantity of hosts involved. The final criterion, number of hosts attacked, is meaningful only if restricted to a single life-history stage. For example, adult parsitoids may attack many prey but their larvae live in, and consume, only a single individual. Likewise, a typical helminth parasite may have both intermediate and definitive hosts but each life-history stage will infect only a single host individual. We cannot emphasize too strongly that the overlap between many of the relationships reflects the extraordinary diversity of life styles found in nature. Seldom, if ever, can one classify a group of organisms exclusively. Courtesy: Bush *et al. Parasitism: The Diversity and Ecology of Animal Parasites* 2001. Reproduced with permission from Cambridge University Press.

There are other ways to view the lifestyles of organisms, each with a different emphasis. One very important outcome is whether there is benefit or harm to the host, to either increase or decrease host fitness. Please see Figure 1.2 for a view of the symbiosis continuum (Swain Ewald and Ewald 2018). In addition to host and symbiont, there is influence of the external environment on the symbiont. In this sense the parasite is the extreme obligate symbiont. Please see Figure 1.3 for the role of niche on the symbionts (Mestre *et al.* 2020).

A parasite takes energy (calorie) from its host. Take a moment to think back to the movie trilogy *The Matrix*, directed by Andy and Larry Wachowski (1999–2003 starring Keanu Reeves, plus *Matrix Resurrections* in December 2021). The films depicted machines harvesting humans for heat and energy, like how parasites take advantage of their human

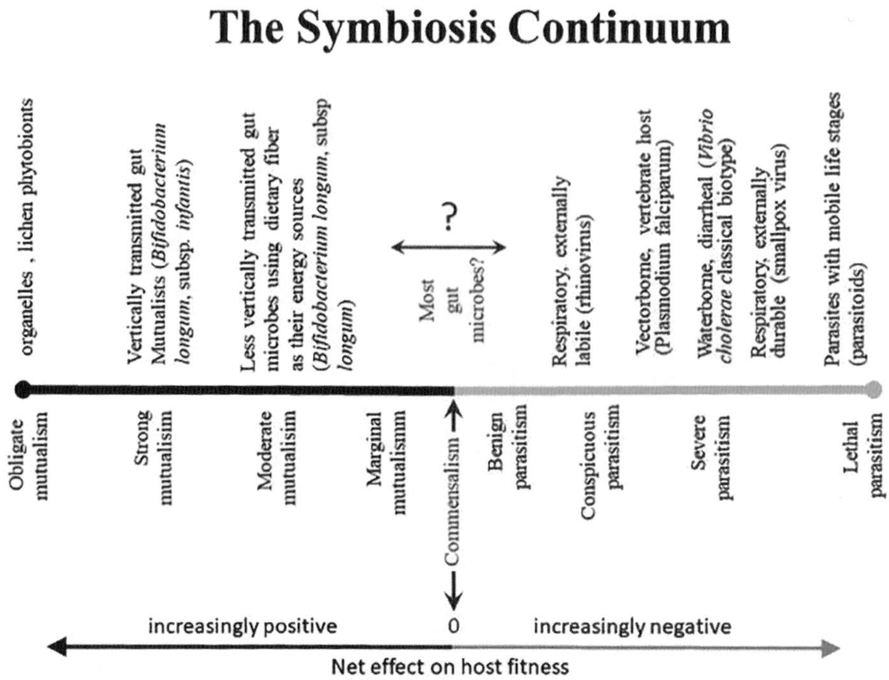

Fig. 1.2 ■ A continuum of symbiosis. Waterborne, vector-borne, and durable respiratory pathogens, and parasites with mobile stages of development can be transmitted from very sick hosts and therefore have probably been molded by natural selection to cause severe disease. The most severe parasites are those with mobile life history stages (often referred to as parasitoids), which can exploit their hosts to death during their parasitic stage and still reach new hosts through their mobile stage. Microbes evolve to mutualists when they can provide fitness benefits to their hosts, particularly when they are vertically transmitted and when their hosts provide them with nutrients that are different from their own cellular components (e.g., dietary plant fiber or milk oligosaccharides that their own cells do not normally produce). Courtesy: Swain Ewald H, Ewald P, *Yale J Biol Med* 2018;91:445–55. Reproduced with permission from *Yale Journal of Biology and Medicine*.

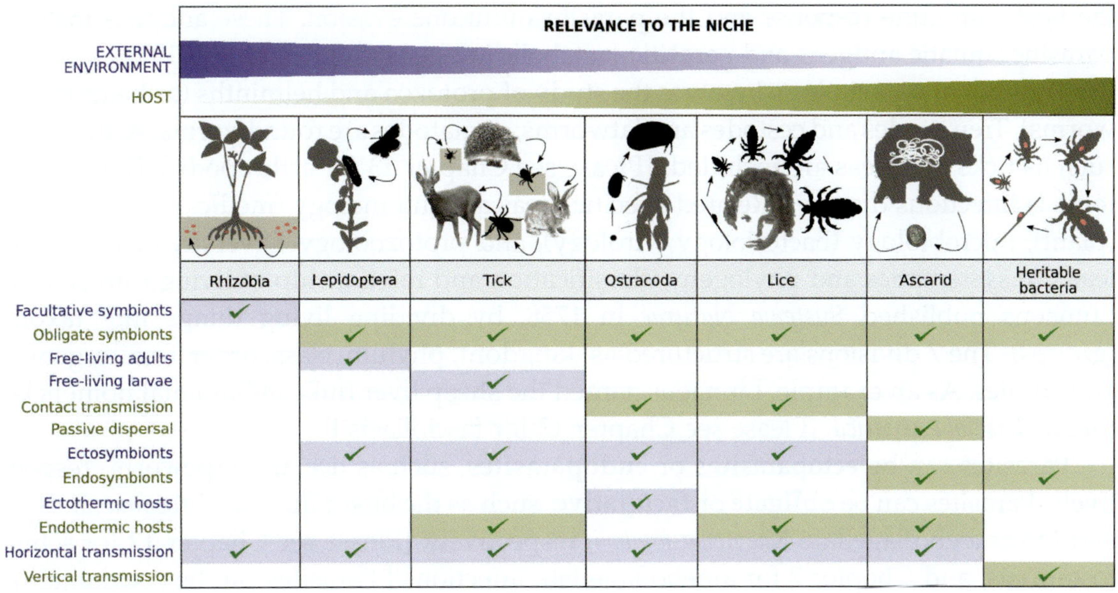

Fig. 1.3 ■ The role of niche on the symbionts. Variations in the relative relevance of the external environment and host traits to the symbiont's niche across systems, as illustrated by a variety of symbionts with different life cycles. Described from left to right, first, the soybean *Glycine max* takes up free-living bacteria *Bradyrhizobium* spp. from the soil (where they can live without the host) to establish an intracellular symbiosis in root nodules. Second, the lepidopteran *Aricia agestis* combines a larval symbiotic stage as caterpillar on the perennial plant *Helianthemum nummularium*, with an adult free-living stage as butterfly. Third, the three-host cycle of the tick *Ixodides ricinus* alternates feeding periods attached to hosts with long transitional free-living periods of larval development and host-seeking. Fourth, the ostracod *Ankylocythere sinuosa* lives on the exoskeleton of the crayfish *Procambarus clarkii*, and is transmitted by host-to-host contact or active dispersal through the water. Fifth, the louse *Pediculus humanus capitis* lives permanently on human hair and requires direct contact among hosts for transmission. Sixth, the parasitic nematode worm *Baylisascaris transfuga* is an endosymbiont of bears with no intermediate hosts and passive transmission through resistant eggs in host feces. Seventh, the bacterium *Candidatus Riesia pediculicola* is an intracellular endosymbiotic mutualist (of *Pediculus humanus capitis*); the endosymbiont colonizes internally the eggs of the female louse, thus its whole cycle (including transmission) occurs within the host. Courtesy: Mestre *et al. Biol Rev Camb Philos Soc* 2020;95:491–516. Reproduced with permission from Wiley.

hosts. As presented in *Schmidt & Roberts Foundations of Parasitology* (Roberts *et al.* 2013), energy is wasted in fevers caused by parasitic infections. Heat production of the human body increases by about 7.2% for each degree rise in Fahrenheit. The malaria-induced acute fever needs 5,000 calories in a day, equivalent to the entire energy demand equivalent to 2 days of hard labor. A parasite harms the host, either by mechanical injury to the host or by robbing the host's nutrition. In addition, exposure of parasitic antigens by the host leads to the host's immune response and the parasite's immune evasion. These antigens include parasitic somatic antigens and parasitic metabolic antigens (Bogitsh *et al.* 2019).

Traditional parasitology involves the study of protozoa and helminths (or helminthes, worms). Trematodes and cestodes are flatworms; nematodes are roundworms. Arthropods such as ticks and fleas are included. [Please see Chapter 23 for arthropods.] The general topic is infectious diseases. Related specific areas are entomology (medical), nematology (plant), microbiology (bacteriology/virology), and protozoology. Diversity of life forms leads to systematics and phylogeny, classification and relationship of living things. Carl Linnaeus published *Systema Naturae* in 1758, by dividing living things into taxons (groups). The 7 divisions are structured as: kingdom, phylum, class, order, family, genus, and species. As an example, Linnaeus named the sheep liver fluke in binomial nomenclature as *Fasciola hepatica*. [Please see Chapter 13 for fascioliasis.]

Parasites can be **ectoparasites** or **endoparasites**, such as lice and tapeworm, respectively. Parasites can be **obligate** or **facultative**, such as the blood fluke *Schistosoma mansoni* and the amoeboflagellate *Naegleria fowleri*, respectively. [Please see Chapter 12 for schistosomiasis, and Chapter 7 for ameboflagellate infections.] Parasites can be accidental or **incidental**, such as the roundworm *Toxocara canis* in humans instead of dogs. [Please see Chapter 22 for toxocariasis.] Under such instances, because of the lack of long co-evolutionary relationship, harm (virulence) to the accidental host can be severe. A **hyperparasite** is a parasite to a parasite. Robert Hegner titled his book *Big Fleas Have Little Fleas or Who's Who among the Protozoa* in 1938 (available online).[2] An example of a hyperparasite is a juvenile tapeworm in a flea. Danny Haelwaters (Harvard) and colleagues have investigated bats, bat flies and fungi. They wrote: "Bats are parasitized by numerous lineages of arthropods, of which bat flies (Diptera, Nycteribiidae and Streblidae) are the most conspicuous. Bat flies themselves can be parasitized by Laboulbeniales, fungal biotrophs of arthropods. This is known as hyperparasitism, a severely understudied phenomenon" (Haelewaters *et al.* 2018). Please see Figure 1.4 for bat parasites and hyperparasites (Haelewaters *et al.* 2018). [We shall re-visit Professor Hegner in Chapter 5.]

A parasite lives in its host. The hosts can be divided into **definitive host**, where the parasite reaches sexual maturity, such as adult tapeworm in the human gut, and **intermediate host**, such as the malaria parasite in human blood. Moreover, there is transport or **paratenic host**, whose function is to bridge ecological gaps. An example is the role of earthworm for the chicken nematode *Heterakis gallinarum*. Chickens get infected if they eat the nematode eggs in the soil, but the egg may be eaten by the earthworm, where the larval stages develop and wait for the chicken to eat the earthworm to infect its definitive host. Smaller size organisms that serve as a vehicle to transmit parasites are named **vectors**. An example is the female mosquito that sucks blood and transmits the malaria parasites. A related concept is host specificity, the parasite can infect either a single host or multiple hosts, and, within the host, various sites (cells, tissues, organs) provide a range of niches and diverse habitats for the parasite. An example of a single host is the

[2] https://hdl.handle.net/2027/uva.x002081533

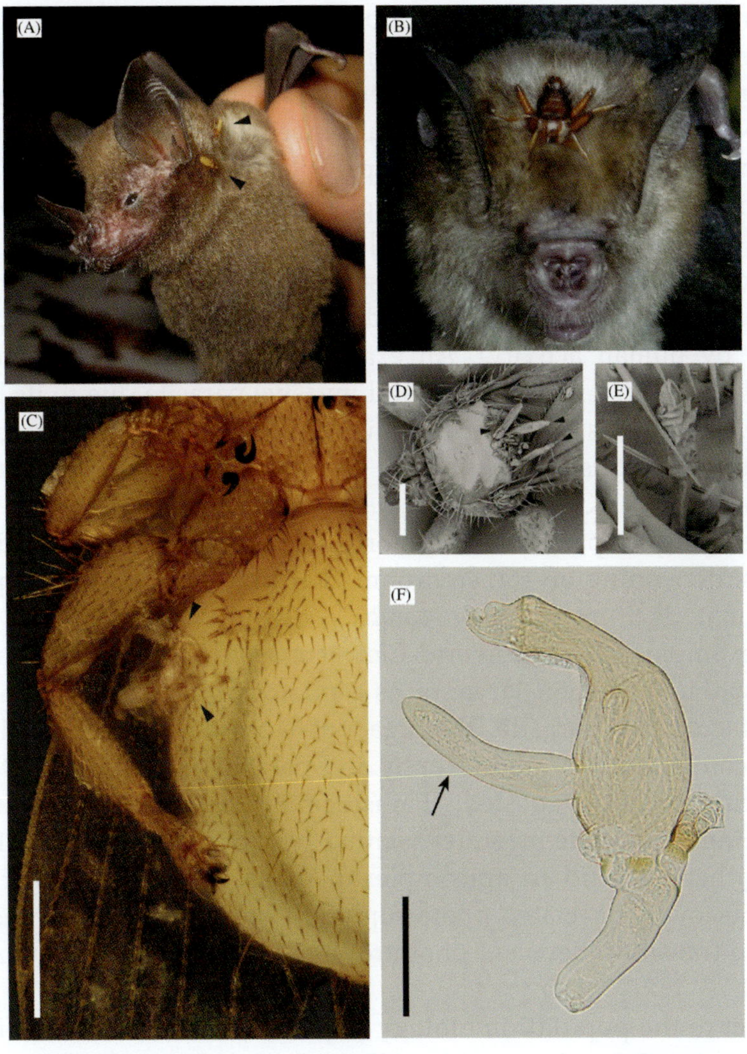

Fig. 1.4 ■ Lifestyles of parasites and hyperparasites: The Bat–Bat Fly–Laboulbeniales Tripartite System. (A) A *Carollia perspicillata* bat with two *Speiseria ambigua* bat flies (arrowheads), captured at La Virgen de Sarapiquí, Costa Rica. (B) A bat of the *Hipposideros caffer/ruber* complex with a single *Penicillidia* sp. on its head, from Forikrom, Ghana. Image provided by Julian Schmid. (C) *Trichobius joblingi* (from *Carollia perpicillata*), with thalli of an undescribed species of *Gloeandromyces* on its abdomen (arrowheads). Image provided by André De Kesel. (D, E) *Trichobius costalimai* (from *Phyllostomus discolor*), with thalli of *Nycteromyces streblidinus* on its thorax, from Peña Blanca Peninsula, Panama. Scanning electron microscopy images provided by Alena Maidel. *Nycteromyces* is dioecious, which means that (male) antheridia and (female) perithecia are housed on separate individuals. (D) Three female thalli are indicated by arrowheads. (E) Close-up of a single male thallus, forming antheridia that produce spermatia. (F) *Gloeandromyces* sp. nov., recognized by its finger-like projection at the perithecium (the spore-producing organ) and supported by sequence data (referred to as *Gloeandromyces* sp. nov. 3). Scale bars: (C, D) = 250 μm, (E, F) = 50 μm. Courtesy: Haelewaters *et al. Trends Parasitol* 2018;34:784–99. Reproduced with permission from Elsevier.

beef tapeworm whereas an example of multiple hosts is the parasitic protozoan *Toxoplasma gondii*. The nematode *Trichinella spiralis* has an adult stage in the intestine and larval stage in the skeletal muscle of its human host. There are **reservoir hosts** for diseases known as zoonoses. A zoonosis can be carried to humans by either **sylvatic** (wild) or domestic animals. As an example, different species of the parasitic protozoan *Leishmania* can be carried by dogs and wild mammals. [Please see Chapter 5 for leishmaniasis, Chapter 10 for toxoplasmosis, and Chapter 21 for trichinellosis.]

A parasite can invade a new species (host range increase) or expand its geographical territories. There are invasive species (including parasitic species; some may be brought to new places by human activity). An example is the Asian fish tapeworm (**AFT**), *Schyzocotyle acheilognathi*, a highly successful invasive parasite due to its broad environment tolerance. AFT infects a wide spectrum of freshwater fish, with its current number of hosts consisting of 312 fish species and 11 non-fish species. AFT has spread to all continents except Antarctica (Kuchta *et al.* 2018).

There is flexibility in parasitism. The organism can be parasitic and free-living at different times, depending on the environmental condition. One example is the soil-transmitted nematode *Strongyloides stercoralis*. [Please see Chapter 21 for strongyloidiasis.] Another example is the chromerid *Chromera velia*. The species lives either as an intracellular symbiont of coral larva, or as a phototrophic free-living alga. Likely an accidental or facultative parasite, the alga possesses a mixotrophic life style (photoparasitism, combination of phototrophy and parasitism). Miroslav Oborník (Czech Academy of Sciences) has suggested: "Parasitism is a heterotrophic strategy, with apicomplexans being among the most devastating parasites for humans. The presence of a nonphotosynthetic plastid in apicomplexan parasites suggests their phototrophic ancestry. The discovery of related phototrophic chromerids has unlocked the possibility to study the transition between phototrophy and parasitism in the Apicomplexa" (Oborník 2020).

With respect to the population biology of parasites, the numbers of parasites are of major importance. It has been said: "All species of worms are harmful when present in massive numbers" (Bogitsh *et al.* 2019). Consider a hypothetical sample of the mouse pinworm and its murine host: 10 mice and 100 worms. In this sample, the density is 10 worms per host (100/10). However, all 100 worms can be found in a single animal (1/10, the prevalence is 0.1) or worms can be equally distributed among all 10 animals (10/10, the prevalence becomes 1.0). Experimentally, a sampling unit is one individual host animal in a collection of such hosts. The density is the "average number of parasites per host in a sample of hosts, equal to the arithmetic mean." The intensity is the "number of parasites in an infected host (cannot be zero)." Prevalence is the "fraction or percentage of a single host species infected at a given time." The incidence is "the number of new infections per unit time divided by the number of uninfected hosts at the beginning of the measured time." Aggregated is "a situation in which most of the parasites occur in a relative minority of hosts and most host individuals are either uninfected or lightly infected" (definitions from Roberts *et al.* 2013). [Please see Chapter 21 for enterobiasis.]

Dynamics of population growth have initially been modeled in free-living organisms, and then adapted to parasite populations. Two types of population growth curves can be predicted.

The equation for exponential growth is:

$$dN/dt = rN$$

where N is the number of individuals at time t and r is the per capita rate of increase. These species are known as ***r*-selected**. This occurs under conditions that are variable for the species. The opportunistic species tend to have high fecundity, high density-independent mortality, and short life span. Parasitic protozoa such as *Giardia lamblia* seem to adopt this strategy. [Please see Chapter 6 for giardiasis.]

The equation for logistic or sigmoidal growth is:

$$dN/dt = rN(K - N/K)$$

where K is the carrying capacity of the habitat, or at that point in time when $dN/dt = 0$. The term $(K - N/K)$ means as N increases dN/dt decreases. It can be a measure of crowding. When $N = K$ the term will be 0. These species are ***K*-selected**. The equilibrium species tend to have low fecundity and low density-independent mortality, and longer life span. Parasitic worms such as the trematodes seem to adopt this strategy (Bush *et al.* 2001). [Please see Chapter 11 for trematodes.]

How about parasites with benefits? Before the discovery of antibiotics, malaria had been used to control syphilis. It was suggested that tertiary syphilis is rare in regions of Africa because of the high prevalence of malaria. For his interest in treating mental illness by inducing fever (pyrotherapy), the Austrian Julius Wagner-Jauregg won the 1927 Nobel in medicine for the treatment of neurosyphilis by inoculating malaria parasites to the patients (malariotherapy). This procedure is dangerous and no longer in use. Currently, there is the concept of hygiene hypothesis, as benefits related to infection of parasitic worms and other pathogens. [Please see Chapter 3 for parasites and immunity.]

Modern parasitology covers many areas: biology, biochemistry & molecular biology (genomics, proteomics, metabolomics), immunology & immunopathology, therapy & prevention, ecology & evolution. A multidisciplinary approach is required, as proposed by a group of German researchers. Please see Figure 1.5 for an illustration of this discussion (Kofer *et al.* 2017). In this textbook, we attempt to present a comprehensive picture of human parasites, from historical discovery to current molecular study.

1.3 Parasites & Politics

Parasitic diseases can be viewed as a global health issue. On May 5, 2009, US President Barack Obama announced his global health initiative. The following is the first paragraph of his statement: "In the 21st century, disease flows freely across borders and oceans, and, in recent days, the 2009 H1N1 virus has reminded us of the urgent need for

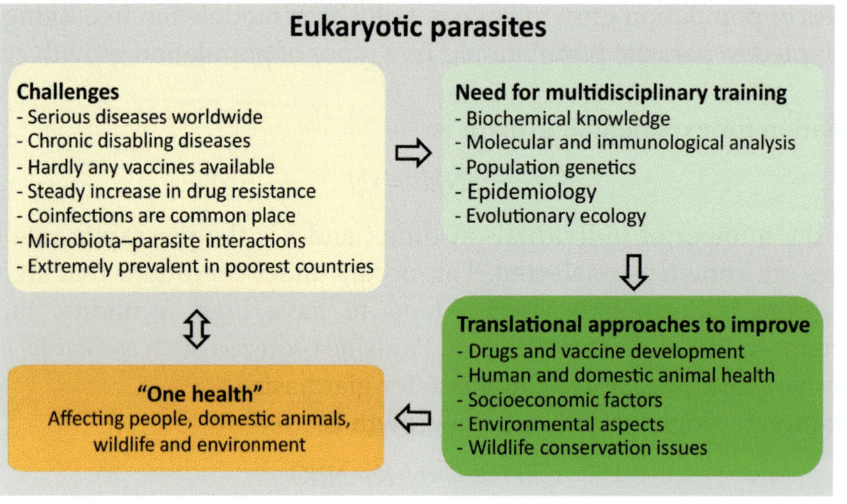

Fig. 1.5 ■ Training for modern parasitology. Challenges by eukaryotic parasites addressed by a multidisciplinary, translational structured training program. Courtesy: Kofer *et al. Trends Parasitol* 2017;33:423–5. Reproduced with permission from Elsevier.

action. We cannot wall ourselves off from the world and hope for the best, nor ignore the public health challenges beyond our borders. An outbreak in Indonesia can reach Indiana within days, and public health crises abroad can cause widespread suffering, conflict, and economic contraction. That is why I am asking Congress to approve my Fiscal Year 2010 Budget request of $8.6 billion — and $63 billion over six years — to shape a new, comprehensive global health strategy. We cannot simply confront individual preventable illnesses in isolation. The world is interconnected, and that demands an integrated approach to global health." [In hindsight, the avian flu pandemic did not happen, but COVID-19 pandemic did, causing global infections and deaths in 2020 and beyond.] The corresponding White House announcement explains the American Leadership on Global Health: "President Obama believes that it is in keeping with America's values and our history of compassion to lead an effort to solve some of the most serious problems facing the world's poorest people. Already, American leadership, sparked in large part by President George W. Bush and a bipartisan majority in Congress, has helped to save millions of lives from HIV/AIDS, malaria, and tuberculosis. Yet, even with that monumental progress, 26,000 children around the world die every day from extreme poverty and preventable diseases."[3]

Barack Obama's name has been immortalized in taxonomy by scientists who have named species after him. Among a total of 9 species, 2 are parasites, more than any of his

[3] https://obamawhitehouse.archives.gov/the-press-office/statement-president-global-health-initiative

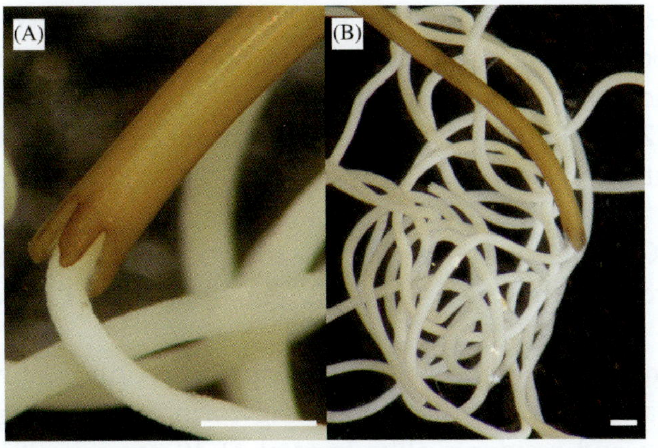

Fig. 1.6 ■ *Paragordius obamai* n. sp. female laying eggs. Female worm (brown) in the process of laying egg strings (white) containing eggs: (A) showing trilobed posterior end; (B) a worm and about 15% of total lifetime egg production. Scale bars = 2 mm. Courtesy: Hanelt *et al. PLoS One* 2012;7:e34472. Reproduced with permission from *PLoS One* with Creative Commons Attribution 4.0 (CC-BY) International License.

predecessors, as disclosed by Jessica Boddy in 2016[4] (a close second is Theodore Roosevelt with 7). A new species of African hairworm (15 cm adult) that infects crickets has been found to be the first parthenogenic species among the group. It was named *Paragordius obamai* in honor of Obama, as his father was from a Kenya town close by where the species was found. Please see Figure 1.6 for the female hairworm laying eggs (Hanelt *et al.* 2012). A new species of blood fluke that lives in the lung of Malaysian freshwater turtles was named *Baracktrema obamai*. This is the first proposal of a new genus of turtle blood fluke in 21 years (Roberts *et al.* 2016). A coauthor of the publication, Thomas Platt (Saint Mary's College, Notre Dame, Indiana), commented that the fluke reminded him of the POTUS (president of the United States) because of its resilience throughout its life cycle and for being: "it's long. It's thin. And it's cool as hell."[5]

Time magazine Person of the Year for 2019 was a climate activist, the Swedish high school student Greta Thunberg (then at age 16). Michael Darby (Natural History Museum, London) named a tiny beetle as *Nelloptodes gretae* sp. n. in her honor, for her outstanding contribution in raising awareness of environmental issues (the beetle was collected in 1965 by William Block in Nairobi, Kenya; the collection was donated to the museum in 1978). Taxonomists have various means in introducing their discoveries of new species (some prefer using their own names).[6]

[4] https://www.science.org/content/article/these-nine-different-creatures-have-been-named-after-barack-obama

[5] https://apnews.com/article/da385c1815934b909ba681c7b42773dc

[6] https://www.nhm.ac.uk/discover/news/2019/october/new-species-named-after-climate-activist-greta-thunberg.html

Parasites are seen in news announcements. After the Korean War (1950–1953), there exists North and South Korea (with official names Democratic People's Republic of Korea, and Republic of Korea, respectively), with the 38th parallel north Korean demilitarized zone (DMZ) in between. Defectors, including soldiers, have escaped from North Korea to South Korea. One such case involving a soldier at the Panmunjom truce village occurred in November 2017. The soldier was shot and had to be treated in a hospital in South Korea. Doctors treating the soldier found "an enormous number of parasites" (roundworms), the longest being 27 cm, in his gut. [Please see Chapter 20 for ascariasis.]

In USA, the islands forming the state of Hawaii are favorite destinations for vacationers, but there is "parasite in paradise." Rat lungworm disease, angiostrongyliasis, has sickened vacationers and residents alike (a total of 10 cases in 2018). Its intermediate hosts are snails and slugs; 80% of land snails are infected with the parasite. [Please see Chapter 22 for angiostrongyliasis.]

The rat lungworm case can serve as an example of range extension of parasites. Similarly, there are examples of range extension of parasitic vectors. In April 2019, the bloodsucking "kissing bug" became news when a girl in Delaware, USA was bitten. The incident was the first confirmed identification of the bug in that state, according to the US Center for Disease Control and Prevention (CDC). The insect vector is commonly known as "kissing bug" because it usually bites around the eyes and mouth, and can transmit the parasitic protozoan *Trypanosoma cruzi*, to cause Chagas' disease (alias American trypanosomiasis). [Please see Chapter 5 for trypanosomiasis.]

The parasitic wasps are useful in getting rid of moths. In February 2021, there was an announcement that an army of tiny, parasitic wasps (*Trichogramma evanescens*, 0.5 mm in size) will be unleashed inside the English stately home where Anne Boleyn was born (Blickling Hall, Norfolk, eastern England), in order to hunt out and eradicate moths that threaten the mansion's furniture and artifacts. The wasps will search out moth eggs and lay their own eggs inside them, so a new wasp hatches instead of a moth larva. Hilary Jarvis, assistant conservator, National Trust, commented: "We are really hoping this pioneering approach will provide a practical and sustainable method that any of our properties can use to deal with serious infestations."[7] [Please see Chapter 23 for arthropods.]

In sum, parasites are newsworthy.

1.4 Parasites in Arts & Sciences

Both the general public and scientists have been continuously fascinated by parasites, especially after parasites became popular subject of entertainment on television. Since 2009, the Animal Planet channel hosted the series *Monsters Inside Me*. Parasites and other

[7] https://www.cnn.com/travel/article/blickling-hall-wasps-moths-scli-gbr-intl/index.html

pathogens are depicted; the series continued, with its 8th season in 2017 (distributed by Animal Planet and Discovery Channel). Viewers become aware of examples of parasites attacking humans. [Some segments are freely available via YouTube and other internet sources.][8]

Images and caricatures of parasites appear frequently in movies, especially in science fiction horror films. One example is the 3D *Parasite* film (starring Demi Moore) in 1982. A more famous series is the 1979 *Alien* (starring Sigourney Weaver) as a part of the trilogy, a fourth installment, plus prequels and crossovers (*Alien vs. Predator* 2004). These are imaginary creatures infecting humans.

Parasitism is a lifestyle. Along this line, the movie *Parasite* (2019) directed by Bong Joon-ho, is the first Korean film to receive the Palme d'Or (the Golden Palm, highest award of the festival). The movie also won best picture and best director in the 2020 92nd Academy Awards. All hail the parasite!

We can venture into the literary world chasing the idea of parasites and lifestyle. The author and playwright Dame Daphne du Maurier (1907–1989), famous for her novel *Rebecca* (1957) with multiple film adaptations (from the 1940 film directed by Alfred Hitchcock to the 2020 film directed by Benjamin Wheatley, with a television miniseries directed by Jim O'Brien in between), wrote a novel titled *The Parasites* in 1949. Going further back, the writer Sir Arthur Conan Doyle (1859–1930), creator of Sherlock Holmes and Dr. (John) Watson (in books and short stories 1887–1927) wrote a novelette titled *The Parasite: A Story* in 1894 (available online).[9]

The actress of the first *Alien* also starred in the movie *Avatar* (2009), directed by James Cameron (famous for *Titanic* 1997) also with sequels coming (*Avatar 2* to be released in 2022). The plot involves the blue Na'vi people and humans who visit the alien planet in search of a resource referred to as unobtainium. The film may be seen in the light of imperialism/colonialism, and this provides a link to the study of parasites. A historical perspective of parasitology is intimately related to European imperialism. The topic is known as tropical medicine. The current medial text in this area is known as ***Manson's Tropical Diseases*** (by Jeremy Farrar, Peter Hotez, Thomas Junghanss, Gagandeep Kang, David Lalloo and Nicholas White) 23rd edition in 2013. The first edition was published in 1898; Sir Patrick Manson (1844–1922) was an important figure in parasitology. [Please see Chapter 18 for a discussion on Manson's contribution to elephantiasis.] For an artist's view of European colonization of Africa, please see Figure 1.7, an illustration titled *The sleeping sickness* by Gordon Ross (1873–1946) and published in 1911. The drawing shows a large, sleeping African man, together with European countries staking claims to portions of Africa (by planting flags of Belgium, England, France, Germany, Italy, Portugal, Spain, and Turkey). The illustration is from the Library of Congress.[10] [Please see Chapter 5 for sleeping sickness, aka human African trypanosomiasis.]

[8] https://www.animalplanet.com/show/monsters-inside-me-animal-planet

[9] http://www.gutenberg.org/ebooks/355

[10] https://www.loc.gov/item/2011649074/

Fig. 1.7 ■ The sleeping sickness. Illustration shows a large African man sitting, leaning against a tree, asleep; several European countries are staking claims to portions of Africa, planting flags labeled "England, Portugal, Belgium, Turkey, Italy, Germany, Spain, [and] France" all around the sleeping man. Courtesy: Ross G, *The Sleeping Sickness* 1911. Library of Congress, USA https://www.loc.gov/item/2011649074/.

Now, we move from the popular to the scientific. In 2013, The *Journal of Experimental Biology* hosted a special issue on neural parasitology. Shelley Adamo (Dalhousie University) and Joanne Webster (Imperial College London), guest editors, commented: "The ability of parasites to alter the behavior of their hosts fascinates both scientists and non-scientists alike. One reason that this topic resonates with so many is that it touches on core philosophical issues such as the existence of free will. If the mind is merely a machine, then it can be controlled by any entity that understands the code and has access to the machinery. This special issue of *The Journal of Experimental Biology* highlights some of the best-understood examples of parasite-induced changes in host brain and behavior, encompassing both invertebrate and vertebrate hosts and micro- and macro-parasites."[11] In introducing this topic, Carl Zimmer wrote: "How to control an army of zombies" for *The New York Times*.[12]

[11] https://jeb.biologists.org/content/216/1/1.article-info
[12] https://carlzimmer.com/how-to-control-an-army-of-zombies-245/

We want to introduce 2 unique parasitological situations from ornithology and ichthyology, namely **brood parasitism** and **sexual parasitism**. In some birds, the brood parasite female lays her eggs in host nests to evade parental care; interspecific brood parasitism thus becomes a breeding strategy. Cuckoo is a well-known example. There is evolution of tolerance to the parasite's behavior by the host (Medina & Langmore 2016). In deep sea anglerfish, there is sexual parasitism, permanent attachment of the smaller male to the bigger female fish. Swann *et al.* (2020) wrote: "Sexual parasitism has evolved as a distinctive mode of reproduction among deep-sea anglerfishes.... Pronounced modifications to immune facilities are associated with this reproductive trait." Loss of essential immune genes are seen in the males, such as activation-induced cytidine deaminase (AICDA, for optimal antibody synthesis) and recombination-activating genes (rag, for B- and T-cell receptor synthesis). The investigators concluded that modification of the immune system to curtail allogeneic reactions is important for sexual parasitism in deep sea fish. [Please see Chapter 3 for parasites and immunity.]

Parasites have been described by science journalists. Kathleen McAuliffe wrote *This is Your Brain on Parasites: How Tiny Creatures Manipulate Our Behavior and Shape Society* (2016, Houghton Mifflin Harcourt). Previously, Carl Zimmer wrote *Parasite Rex: Inside the Bizarre World of Nature's Most Dangerous Creatures* (2000, Free Press). The American writer Daisy Hernandez wrote *The Kissing Bug: A True Story of a Family, an Insect, and a Nation's Neglect of a Deadly Disease* (2021, Tin House Books).

Academic scientists have written popular treatises on parasites. Dickson D. Despommier wrote *People, Parasites, and Plowshares: Learning from Our Body's Most Terrifying Invaders* (2013, Columbia). Eugene H. Kaplan wrote *What's Eating You? People and Parasites* (2010, Princeton). Rosemary Drisdelle wrote *Parasites: Tales of Humanity's Most Unwelcome Guests* (2010, University of California). A personal account on human African trypanosomiasis was written by Peter Kennedy: *The Fatal Sleep: Africa's Killer Disease that Went Undiscovered for Centuries* (2007, Luath Press). A bit earlier, there are interesting books on parasites for the general public by Robert S. Desowitz (1926–2008), including *New Guinea Tapeworms and Jewish Grandmothers* (1981, Norton).

In this sense, parasites are intriguing to both the scientists and the general public. Some of the more significant and interesting discoveries in parasitology will be presented in this book. However, for readers who wish to pursue the historical record further, several monographs are recommended. B.H. Kean, Kenneth E. Mott and Adair J. Russell were editors of *Tropical Medicine and Parasitology: Classic Investigations, volumes I and II* (1978, Cornell). F.E.G. Cox was editor of *The Welcome Trust Illustrated History of Tropical Diseases* (1996, The Wellcome Trust, London). Gordon C. Cook wrote *Tropical Medicine: An Illustrated History of the Pioneers* (2007, Elsevier). Gerald W. Esch wrote *Parasites and Infectious Diseases: Discoveries by Serendipity, and Otherwise* (2007, Cambridge).

Information on human parasites can be accessed via the internet, but the reader should exercise care and caution. [These are days of "alternative facts" and "fake news." According to the Yale Law School librarian Fred Shapiro, the statement by Rudolph W.

Giuliani (former mayor of New York City) "truth isn't truth" is the most notable quote of 2018. Then, in 2019, there is the easy availability of deep fake video.] A reliable source of biomedical literature is **PubMed**, currently with over **30 million** citations. PubMed is a database sponsored by United States National Library of Medicine, National Institutes of Health. Other searchable places include Wikipedia and Google Scholar. Scientific journals reporting research on parasites are abundant. The literature of parasitology is distributed in primary international journals, with good science citation index scores, such as *Nature, Science, Proceedings of the National Academy of Sciences USA, New England Journal of Medicine* and *Journal of Experimental Medicine.* Currently, there is a discussion to "rethink the impact factor" (Wouters *et al.* 2019). Examples of specific parasitology journals include *American Journal of Tropical Medicine and Hygiene, Transactions of the Royal Society of Tropical Medicine and Hygiene, Acta Tropica, Journal of Parasitology, Experimental Parasitology, Parasite, Parasitology Research, Parasitology, Parasitology International, International Journal of Parasitology, Molecular and Biochemical Parasitology, Parasite Immunology, Parasites and Vectors, Veterinary Parasitology, Malaria Journal,* and many others. An example of an electronic journal is *PLoS Neglected Tropical Diseases,* by the Public Library of Science. An example of a review journal is *Trends in Parasitology* (renamed from *Parasitology Today*). An ongoing monograph series is *Advances in Parasitology* (from volume 1 in 1963 to volume 111 in 2021, Elsevier).

1.5 The United Nations: Millennium Development Goals (MDGs) & Sustainable Development Goals (SDGs)

In the year 2000 in New York City, the United Nations (UN) General Assembly convened and adopted a resolution known as UN Millennium Declaration, with 8 Millennium Development Goals (8 **MDGs**). They are:

1. to eradicate extreme poverty and hunger;
2. to achieve universal primary education;
3. to promote gender equality and empower women;
4. to reduce child mortality;
5. to improve maternal health;
6. to combat HIV/AIDS, malaria, and other diseases;
7. to ensure environmental sustainability;
8. to develop a global partnership for development.

These are 8 anti-poverty goals of the United Nations Development Programme (UNDP) with a target date of 2015. Human parasitic diseases are covered in MDG 6, "combat HIV/AIDS, malaria and other diseases." Among the world's population of 7.8

billion, an estimated 1 billion people live on less than US $1 per day, and another 2.7 billion on less than US $2 per day. Many of the people living on this income range suffer from parasitic diseases such as the soiled-transmitted helminths (STHs).

Progresses have been made, as noted in *The Millennium Development Goals Report 2015* by UN Secretary-General Ban Ki-moon.[13] Examples are given below for MDG 1 and 6.

For MDG 1, "extreme poverty has declined significantly over the last two decades. In 1990, nearly half of the population in the developing world lived on less than $1.25 per day; that proportion dropped from half to 14% in 2015. Globally, the number of people living in extreme poverty has declined by more than half, falling from 1.9 billion in 1990 to 836 million in 2015."

For MDG 6, "new HIV infections fell by approximately 40% between 2000 and 2013, from an estimated 3.5 million cases to 2.1 million. By June 2014, 13.6 million people living with HIV were receiving antiretroviral therapy (ART) globally, an immense increase from just 800,000 in 2003. ART averted 7.6 million deaths from AIDS between 1995 and 2013. Over 6.2 million malaria deaths have been averted between 2000 and 2015, primarily of children under five years of age in sub-Saharan Africa. The global malaria incidence rate has fallen by an estimated 37% and the mortality rate by 58%. More than 900 million insecticide-treated mosquito nets were delivered to malaria-endemic countries in sub-Saharan Africa between 2004 and 2014. Between 2000 and 2013, tuberculosis prevention, diagnosis and treatment interventions saved an estimated 37 million lives. The tuberculosis mortality rate fell by 45% and the prevalence rate by 41% between 1990 and 2013."

In the year 2015 UN General Assembly convened to adopt a resolution known as "Transforming our World: the 2030 Agenda for Sustainable Development" with 17 Sustainable Development Goals (17 **SDGs**). They are:

1. End poverty in all its forms everywhere.
2. End hunger, achieve food security and improved nutrition and promote sustainable agriculture.
3. Ensure healthy lives and promote well-being for all at all ages.
4. Ensure inclusive and equitable quality education and promote lifelong learning opportunities for all.
5. Achieve gender equality and empower all women and girls.
6. Ensure availability and sustainable management of water and sanitation for all.
7. Ensure access to affordable, reliable, sustainable and modern energy for all.
8. Promote sustained, inclusive and sustainable economic growth, full and productive employment and decent work for all.

---

[13] https://www.un.org/millenniumgoals/2015_MDG_Report/pdf/MDG%202015%20rev%20(July%201).pdf

9. Build resilient infrastructure, promote inclusive and sustainable industrialization and foster innovation.
10. Reduce inequality within and among countries.
11. Make cities and human settlements inclusive, safe, resilient and sustainable.
12. Ensure sustainable consumption and production patterns.
13. Take urgent action to combat climate change and its impacts.
14. Conserve and sustainably use the oceans, seas and marine resources for sustainable development.
15. Protect, restore and promote sustainable use of terrestrial ecosystems, sustainably manage forests, combat desertification, and halt and reverse land degradation and halt biodiversity loss.
16. Promote peaceful and inclusive societies for sustainable development, provide access to justice for all and build effective, accountable and inclusive institutions at all levels.
17. Strengthen the means of implementation and revitalize the global partnership for sustainable development.

There are signs of progress made, as seen in *The Sustainable Development Goals Report 2019*[14] by UN Secretary-General Antonio Guterres. In the introduction, he wrote: "The most urgent area for action is climate change. If we do not cut record-high greenhouse gas emissions now, global warming is projected to reach 1.5°C in the coming decades. As we are already seeing, the compounded effects will be catastrophic and irreversible: increasing ocean acidification, coastal erosion, extreme weather conditions, the frequency and severity of natural disasters, continuing land degradation, loss of vital species and the collapse of ecosystems. These effects, which will render many parts of the globe uninhabitable, will affect the poor the most. They will put food production at risk, leading to widespread food shortages and hunger, and potentially displace up to 140 million people by 2050. The clock for taking decisive actions on climate change is ticking."

For SDG 1, No poverty, "The decline of extreme poverty continues, but the pace has slowed, and the world is not on track to achieving the target of ending poverty by 2030. Extreme poverty today is concentrated and overwhelmingly affects rural populations. Increasingly, it is exacerbated by violent conflicts and climate change."

For SDG 2, Zero hunger, "Despite earlier extended progress, the number of people suffering from hunger has been on the rise since 2014. Stunting affects the growth and cognitive development of millions of children..."

The year 2020 saw the coronavirus disease 2019 (COVID-19). There is *The Sustainable Development Goals Report 2020*[15] by UN Secretary-General Antonio Guterres. He wrote in the Foreword: "before the COVID-19 pandemic, progress remained uneven and we were not on track to meet the Goals by 2030. ... Now, due to COVID-19, an unprecedented health, economic and social crisis is threatening lives and livelihoods, making the achieve-

[14] https://unstats.un.org/sdgs/report/2019/

[15] https://unstats.un.org/sdgs/report/2020/

ment of Goals even more challenging.... Health systems in many countries have been driven to the brink of collapse. The livelihood of half the global workforce has been severely affected. ... Although the novel coronavirus affects every person and community, it does not do so equally. Instead, it has exposed and exacerbated existing inequalities and injustices. In advanced economies, fatality rates have been highest among marginalized groups. In developing countries, the most vulnerable — including those employed in the informal economy, older people, children, persons with disabilities, indigenous people, migrants and refugees — risk being hit even harder."

For SDG 1, No poverty, "Even before the coronavirus disease (COVID-19) pandemic, progress towards Goal 1 had slowed, and the world was not on track to ending extreme poverty by 2030. Now, as the world anticipates the worst economic fallout since the Great Depression, tens of millions of people will be pushed back into poverty, undoing years of steady improvement."

For SDG 2, Zero hunger, "Eradicating hunger and achieving food security remains a challenge, more so in the wake of the COVID-19 crisis. At the global level, hunger and food insecurity have been on the rise, and malnutrition still affects millions of children. The situation is likely to get worse owing to economic slowdowns and disruptions caused by a pandemic-triggered recession. In addition to COVID-19, the desert locust upsurge in six Eastern African countries and Yemen — where 35 million people are already experiencing acute food insecurity — remains alarming."

SDG 3 is to "ensure healthy lives and promote well-being for all at all ages." This includes the control of infectious diseases, especially the group known as neglected tropical diseases (NTDs).

1.6 NTDs & Other Diseases

Kenneth Warren (1929-1996) first developed the concept of neglected tropical diseases (NTDs) in the 1970's. He drew attention to a large proportion of the global population who were poor, stigmatized, and were suffering from disabling, chronic diseases (Keating 2014; Croft, 2016). Warren first researched on schistosomiasis and later became Director of Health Sciences at the Rockefeller Foundation. In 1977, he presented a proposal to the board of trustees to encourage research on the great neglected diseases (**GNDs**) of mankind ("great" in terms of prevalence and "neglected" in terms of the involvement of major international scientists and financial support). [Conrad Keating wrote *Kenneth Warren and the Great Neglected Diseases of Mankind Programme: The Transformation of Geographical Medicine in the US and Beyond*, 2017 Springer.]

Ken Warren's GNDs gradually evolved into today's NTDs; furthermore, the number of diseases listed under the NTD umbrella continues to increase. In 2000, MDG 6 was introduced: "to combat HIV/AIDS, malaria, and other diseases." More international attention has been paid to the first two, and less to "other diseases." As commented in the only textbook on this topic, *Forgotten People, Forgotten Diseases* by Peter Hotez (2nd edition, 2013,

3rd edition available in October 2021, ASM Press): "This neglect is particularly true for a group of exotic-sounding tropical infections that represent a health and socioeconomic problem of extraordinary dimensions but one that world leaders and global health advocates are only now waking up to."

Under the UN banner, the World Health Organization (WHO) deals with global health. WHO initiated the sponsorship of Special Programme on Research and Training in Tropical Diseases (**TDR**) in 1974, with an aim to "to promote and conduct research equitably and to provide access to this knowledge and the resulting tools to the most vulnerable and hard-to-reach people" (quoted from "What have we learned from 40 years of supporting research and capacity building?" by Reeder and Guth 2015). John C. Reeder is the current TDR director. In addition to WHO, sponsorship of TDR includes the UNDP, the World Bank and the United Nations Children's Fund (UNICEF). The initial focus was 8 NTDs: "malaria, leprosy, schistosomiasis, leishmaniasis, onchocerciasis, lymphatic filariasis, Chagas' disease, and human African trypanosomiasis (HAT)." The first edition of Peter Hotez's book (2008) listed 13 NTDs: "ascariasis, trichuriasis, hookworm infection, schistosomiasis, lymphatic filariasis, trachoma, onchocerciasis, leishmaniasis, Chagas' disease, leprosy, HAT, Buruli ulcer, and dracunculiasis." In the second edition he listed 17 NTDs: "soil-transmitted helminth infections (ascariasis, hookworm infection, trichuriasis), schistosomiasis, lymphatic filariasis, dengue, food-borne trematode infections, onchocerciasis, trachoma, leishmaniasis, Chagas' disease, cysticercosis, leprosy, human echinococcosis, rabies, HAT, buruli ulcer, yaws and endemic treponematoses, and dracunculiasis."

In 2012, WHO published the NTD roadmap, *Accelerating work to overcome the global impact of neglected tropical diseases: a roadmap for implementation* by Margaret Chan, WHO Director-General.[16]

Reports on NTDs have been issued, one example is the Fourth Report, 2017, *Integrating neglected tropical diseases into global health and development* by Margaret Chan.[17] A continuing NTD roadmap was published in 2020, *Ending the neglect to attain the Sustainable Development Goals: A road map for neglected tropical diseases 2021–2030*.[18] [Please see Chapter 24 for further discussion on this topic.]

Below is the current list from the WHO, total to **20 NTDs** (chromoblastomycosis and other deep mycoses, scabies and other ectoparasites, and snakebite envenoming were added to the NTD portfolio in 2017):

- Buruli ulcer
- Chagas disease
- Dengue and Chikungunya
- Dracunculiasis (guinea-worm disease)
- Echinococcosis

[16] https://www.who.int/neglected_diseases/NTD_RoadMap_2012_Fullversion.pdf
[17] https://apps.who.int/iris/handle/10665/255011
[18] https://www.who.int/publications/i/item/9789240010352

- Foodborne trematodiases
- Human African trypanosomiasis (sleeping sickness)
- Leishmaniasis
- Leprosy (Hansen's disease)
- Lymphatic filariasis
- Mycetoma, chromoblastomycosis and other deep mycoses
- Onchocerciasis (river blindness)
- Rabies
- Scabies and other ectoparasites
- Schistosomiasis
- Soil-transmitted helminthiases
- Snakebite envenoming
- Taeniasis/Cysticercosis
- Trachoma
- Yaws (Endemic treponematoses)

The following are short descriptions of most NTDs from a former WHO website:

"**Dengue**: A mosquito-borne infection causing flu-like illness that may develop into severe dengue and cause lethal complications.

Rabies: A preventable viral disease transmitted to humans through the bites of infected dogs that is invariably fatal once symptoms develop.

Trachoma: A chlamydial infection transmitted through direct contact with the infectious eye or nasal discharge, or through indirect contact with unsafe living conditions and hygiene practices, which left untreated causes irreversible corneal opacities and blindness.

Buruli ulcer: A debilitating mycobacterial skin infection causing severe destruction of the skin, bone and soft tissue (*Mycobacterium ulcerans* infection).

Yaws: A chronic bacterial infection affecting mainly the skin and bone.

Leprosy: A complex disease caused by infection mainly of the skin, peripheral nerves, mucosa of the upper respiratory tract and eyes (Hansen disease).

Chagas disease: A life-threatening illness transmitted to humans through contact with vector insects (triatomine bugs), ingestion of contaminated food, infected blood transfusions, congenital transmission, organ transplantation or laboratory accidents.

Human African trypanosomiasis (sleeping sickness): A parasitic infection spread by the bites of tsetse flies that is almost 100% fatal without prompt diagnosis and treatment to prevent the parasites invading the central nervous system.

Leishmaniases: Disease transmitted through the bites of infected female sandflies that in its most severe (visceral) form attacks the internal organs and in its most prevalent (cutaneous) form causes face ulcers, disfiguring scars and disability.

Taeniasis and neurocysticercosis: An infection caused by adult tapeworms in human intestines; cysticercosis results when humans ingest tapeworm eggs that develop as larvae in tissues.

Dracunculiasis (guinea-worm disease): A nematode infection transmitted exclusively by drinking-water contaminated with parasite-infected water fleas.

Echinococcosis: Infection caused by the larval stages of tapeworms forming pathogenic cysts in humans and transmitted when ingesting eggs most commonly shed in feces of dogs and wild animals.

Foodborne trematodiases: Infection acquired by consuming fish, vegetables and crustaceans contaminated with larval parasites; clonorchiasis, opisthorchiasis and fascioliasis are the main diseases.

Lymphatic filariasis: Infection transmitted by mosquitoes causing abnormal enlargement of limbs and genitals from adult worms inhabiting and reproducing in the lymphatic system.

Onchocerciasis (river blindness): Infection transmitted by the bite of infected blackflies causing severe itching and eye lesions as the adult worm produces larvae and leading to visual impairment and permanent blindness.

Schistosomiasis: Trematode infections transmitted when larval forms released by freshwater snails penetrate human skin during contact with infested water (bilharziasis).

Soil-transmitted helminthiases: Nematode infections transmitted through soil contaminated by human feces causing anemia, vitamin A deficiency, stunted growth, malnutrition, intestinal obstruction and impaired development.

Mycetoma is a chronic, progressively destructive inflammatory skin disease which usually affects the lower limbs. Infection is thought to be caused by the inoculation, through a thorn prick or skin damage, or fungi or bacteria into the subcutaneous tissue."

Among the last inclusions is snakebite envenoming. In 2019, WHO has published *Snakebite envenoming: a strategy for prevention and control: executive summary*[19] "Snakebite is a neglected tropical disease which leads to more than 120,000 global deaths every year. … Although 5.4 million snakebites occur annually, only about half of them leads to envenoming (the clinical condition after bite from a venomous snake). Snake venoms are highly complex and diverse, which show inter-species as well as intra-species variation" (Bhaumik *et al.* 2020). "Local tissue necrosis, neurotoxic, and hemo-vasculotoxic effects

[19] https://apps.who.int/iris/handle/10665/312195

TABLE 1.2: Estimates for NTDs and other diseases. Data are collected from WHO, CDC, Hotez 2013, GBD 2017, and other sources [ND is no data].

Disease	Global prevalence	Death per year	Population at risk	Regions most affected
NTDs				
Ascariasis	804 million	60,000	4.2 billion	Cosmopolitan
Hookworms	472 million	65,000	3.2 billion	Cosmopolitan
Trichuriasis	477 million	10,000	3.2 billion	Cosmopolitan
Schistosomiasis	230 million	200,000	750 million	Africa
Lymphtic filariasis	51 million	20,000	893 million	India, Africa, East Asia Pacific
Foodborne trematodiasis	40 million	7,000	ND	Asia, Latin America
Trachoma	1.9 million	<500	137 million	Africa, Middle East
Onchocerciasis	20.9 million	<500	185 million	Africa, Latin America
Taeniasis/cysticercosis	12 million	ND	ND	Cosmopolitan except North America
Chagas'	7 million	10,000	25 million	Latin America
Leishmaniasis	10 million	50,000	350 million	India, Africa, Latin America
Echinococcosis	1 million	ND	ND	Cosmopolitan
Leprosy	208,619	6,000	ND	India, Africa, Latin America
HAT	876	ND	70 million	Africa
Buruli ulcer	2,713	ND	ND	Africa
Dracunculiasis	Near eradication	ND	ND	Africa
Dengue & chikungunya	400 million	ND	3.5 billion	Cosmopolitan
Rabies	15 million	59,000	ND	India, Africa
Yaws & treponematosis	80,472	ND	89 million	Africa, East & South Asia, Latin America
Mycetoma & deep mycosis	ND	ND	ND	Central & Latin America, Middle East, India
Scabies & ectoparasites	200 million	ND	ND	Cosmopolitan
Snakebite envenoming	5.4 million	120,000	ND	Cosmopolitan
Other Diseases				
HIV/AIDS	38 million	690,000	ND	Cosmopolitan
Malaria	219 million	435,000	3.5 billion	Africa
Tuberculosis	10 million	1.4 million	ND	Cosmopolitan
Amoebiasis	50 million	100,000	ND	Cosmopolitan

are well-recognized features… Acute pituitary insufficiency, hyponatremia resulting from natriuresis, and hypokalemia by the intracellular shift of potassium are emergencies that can occur after snakebite…. Awareness and knowledge of these conditions will decrease morbidity and mortality resulting from snakebite" (Bhattacharya *et al.* 2020).

In addition to NTDs, as shown in MDG 6, other major diseases are human immunodeficiency virus/acquired immunodeficiency disease (HIV/**AIDS**), **malaria** and **tuberculosis**. Another important parasitic disease is **amoebiasis**. Please see Table 1.2 for a summary of NTDs and other diseases, including estimates of global prevalence, deaths per year and population at risk. In the following chapters, the human parasites discussed will be protozoa and worms. This will include amoebiasis, malaria and the NTDs leishmaniasis, Chagas' disease, human African trypanosomiasis (sleeping sickness), soil transmitted helminth (STH) ascariasis (roundworm), hookworm infection and trichuriasis (whipworm), schistosomiasis (snail fever), lymphatic filariasis (elephantiasis), onchocerciasis (river blindness) and dracunculiasis (guinea worm).

While most NTDs are prevalent in developing countries, some are found in USA (Parise *et al.* 2014). A total of 5 parasitic infections remain significant health problems in the United States: Chagas disease, cysticercosis, toxocariasis, toxoplasmosis, and trichomoniasis. Estimated annual cases include 300 babies born with *Trypanosoma cruzi* infection, 1,000 hospitalizations for neurocysticercosis, 70 blindness due to ocular toxocariasis, 1.1 million new infections by *Trichomonas vaginalis*, and 60 million people with chronic infection by *Toxoplasma gondii* (potentially fatal in immunocompromised individuals, and potential birth defects in pregnancies). "These five diseases, which are among those that Centers for Disease Control and Prevention (CDC) refers to as neglected parasitic infections (**NPIs**) in the United States, have different epidemiologic profiles and modes of transmission and require tailored prevention and control strategies" (Parise *et al.* 2014).

NTDs are among the most common infections of the poorest people in developing countries. NTDs are endemic in rural areas, and some urban poor areas; therefore, to the politicians, out of sight, out of mind. NTDs are ancient ("biblical") with a long history in humans, as compared to emerging infections. Examples of agents of emerging infections are West Nile virus, Ebola virus, and coronaviruses for severe acute respiratory syndrome (SARS), Middle East respiratory syndrome (MERS), and COVID-19 (pneumonia and other symptoms from the novel coronavirus originated in Wuhan, China in 2019; the virus was named severe acute respiratory syndrome coronavirus 2, **SARS-CoV-2**). An open letter course titled *NTDs in the context of the COVID-19 pandemic: Impact and guidance* is available at the WHO site.[20] NTDs have a long historical heritage. Egyptian papyrus records described bloody urine from schistosomiasis and Aristotle described bladder worm stage of larval pork tapeworm. NTDs are chronic, may last for decades, can cause disability and disfigurement (blindness in onchocerciasis, limb enlargement in elephantiasis), so they are stigmatizing. Thus, people infected with NTDs may encounter problems in engagement with family members and others. Furthermore, NTDs have poverty

[20] https://openwho.org/courses/covid-19-ntd-en

promoting features. As an example, childhood education can be affected by cognition and intellectual impairment as a consequence of hookworm-associated iron deficiency and anemia. Major attributes of the NTDs are: "most prevalent among poor people, endemic in rural areas (some poor urban areas) of low-income countries, ancient (the biblical diseases"), chronic, disabling (growth delays, blindness, or disfigurement), associated with high disease burden but low mortality, stigmatizing, and poverty promoting" (Hotez 2013).

Here comes the World NTD Day, for NTD advocacy and resource mobilization. "Across health and development, world awareness days offer an annual opportunity to mobilize greater attention, action and investment on priority issues, particularly in the countries and communities most directly affected. NTDs were one of the few health and development issues that didn't have a dedicated advocacy milestone ... World NTD Day brings together civil society advocates, community leaders, global health experts and policymakers working across the diverse NTD landscape, and unifies partners behind our common goal: to Face NTDs and #EndTheNeglect.

- **30 January** is the anniversary of the landmark 2012 London Declaration on NTDs, which unified partners across sectors, countries and disease communities to push for greater investment and action on NTDs. World NTD Day not only honored this incredible show of support, but will inspire and rally partners each and every year behind the fight to #BeatNTDs.
- **2021** is the year the WHO will launch the #NTDRoadmap2030, with ambitious new goals to lead us into the next decade of collective action."[21]

The inaugural **World NTD Day**, Thursday January 30th 2020, was informally celebrated. On May 27th 2021, delegates participating in the virtual Seventy-fourth World Health Assembly endorsed a decision recognizing January 30th as World Neglected Tropical Diseases Day ('World NTD Day'). "World NTD Day is in appreciation of the work spearheaded by the United Arab Emirates along with other Member States and partners to inspire and incentivize communities to fight these debilitating diseases. I am confident this recognition will further motivate everyone to work across sectors to implement the new road map, which aims to free over a billion people from these diseases by 2030" (Dr Mwelecele Ntuli Malecela, Director, WHO Department of Control of Neglected Tropical Diseases).[22]

Regarding World NTD Day and the list of NTDs, please see Figure 1. 8 as a diagrammatic presentation of the WHO's 20 NTDs (Hotez *et al.* 2020a). Expanding from the WHO 20, additional diseases are recognized by *PLoS Neglected Tropical Diseases*, including "NTDs on the cusp" for infections by *Toxoplasma*, *Cryptosporidium*, *Cyclospora* and

[21] https://worldntdday.org/

[22] https://www.who.int/news/item/27-05-2021-world-health-assembly-adopts-decision-to-recognize-30-january-as-world-ntd-day

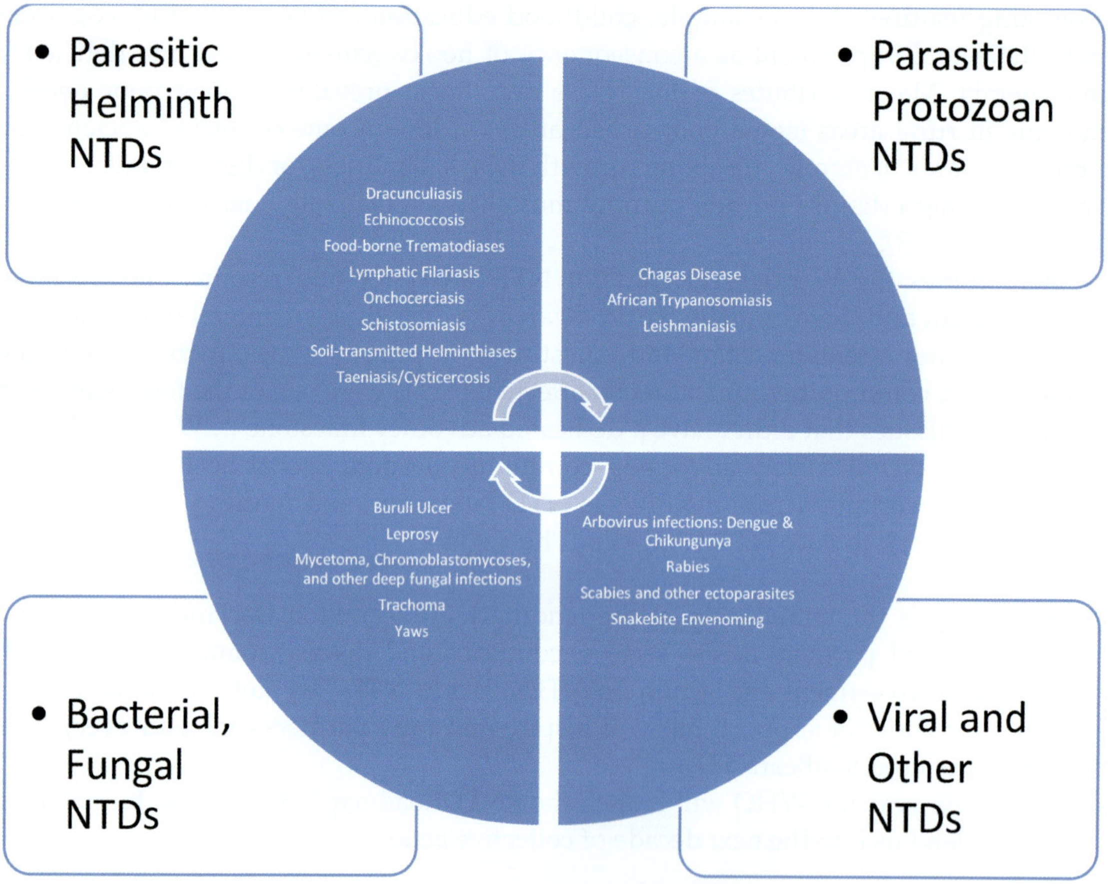

Fig. 1.8 ■ The WHO's list of 20 Neglected Tropical Diseases (NTDs). Courtesy: Hotez *et al. PLoS Negl Trop Dis* 2020;14:e0007999. Reproduced with permission from *PLoS Neglected Tropical Diseases* with Creative Commons Attribution 4.0 (CC-BY) International License.

Blastocystis protozoan species (Hotez *et al.* 2020b). [Please see Chapter 8 for *Blastocystis* and Chapter 10 for *Toxoplasma*, *Cryptosporidium*, and *Cyclospora*.]

The 2012 TDR's *Global report for research on infectious diseases of poverty*[23] was presented by Marie-Paule Kieny, Assistant Director-General of Innovation, Information, Evidence and Research at the WHO. Infectious diseases are caused by pathogens. This includes viruses, bacteria, fungi, parasites. "Infectious diseases of poverty" is "an umbrella term used to describe a number of diseases which are known to be more prevalent among poorer populations, rather than a definitive group of diseases. It is an overarching concept, recognizing the need to focus on the poor and vulnerable, who have less power to intervene. By the definition of what a NTD is by WHO, many such diseases are also considered as NTDs. Infectious diseases of poverty are not restricted to low and middle-

[23] https://apps.who.int/iris/bitstream/handle/10665/44850/9789241564489_eng.pdf?sequence=1

income countries, but manifest in poor populations globally. Apart from TB, malaria and HIV/AIDS, many other infectious diseases have not been high on the global agenda. However, an increasing number of organizations and partnerships are now engaged in their control." International agencies, governments, foundations and private sectors (such as the pharmaceutical industry) need to come together to combat NTDs and other diseases as an issue of global health. Examples are Drugs for Neglected Diseases Initiative (DNDi) and Medicines for Malaria Venture (MMV). The Bill and Melinda Gates Foundation in the United States and The Wellcome Trust in Great Britain are heavily involved in this area. As an example, the London-based Wellcome Trust announced, in May 2019, an initiative of 80 million pounds (about US $100 million) over 7 years on anti-venom research and other efforts in order to improve the treatment of snakebites in poor countries, in support to the newest NTD of WHO, namely snakebite envenoming.

1.7 NTDs, Disability-Adjusted Life Year (DALY) & Global Burden of Disease (GBD)

"Neglected tropical diseases represent the most common diseases for the 2.7 billion people living on less than US $2 per day" (Liese *et al.* 2010). There are rich countries and poor countries, but economic disparity still exists. Thus, this allows for rich countries to overpower their poor inhabitants. In the United States, a report in 2017 suggested that the 3 wealthiest people (Bill Gates, Jeff Bezos, Warren Buffett) own more wealth than the entire bottom half of the American population combined, a total of 160 million people. [In 2021 we add a 4th, Elon Musk, to the list of 3.] That is a widening wealth gap. A report by Oxfam in 2019 concluded that the world's 26 richest people own as many assets as the 3.8 billion people who make up the poorest 50% of the world's population.

Due to impaired immune responses and the lack of essential nutrition that result from hunger, impoverished people will continue to suffer from infectious diseases. The people of North Korea are a prime example for this type of suffering. In armed conflict zones, more children may die from inadequate water, sanitation, and hygiene (**WASH**) facilities than from violence. For example, diarrheal diseases are a contributor to the death preventable through WASH. The effects have extended signature within the epigenome of an affected individual. People with lower socioeconomic status have changes in their methylated CpG sites (an epigenetic marker), with increased methylation in 1,777 sites and decreased methylation in 769 sites. Thus, poverty leaves a mark on nearly 10% of the genome; it makes a lasting impact on a wide range of physiological systems and processes, leading to **health disparity** (McDade *et al.* 2019).

For global health, one health metric is the **DALY**. DALY can quantify the burden of disease resulted from mortality and morbidity. It was originally developed by Harvard

University for the World Bank in 1990; the WHO adopted the method in 1996. The DALY is now a key measure of the Global Burden of Disease **GBD**.

"One DALY represents the loss of the equivalent of one year of full health. DALYs for a disease or health condition are the sum of the years of life lost to due to premature mortality (YLLs) and the years lived with a disability (YLDs) due to prevalent cases of the disease or health condition in a population" (WHO).[24] Thus, one DALY can be thought of as one lost year of "healthy" life. The sum of these DALYs across the population, or the burden of disease, can be thought of as a measurement of the gap between current health status and an ideal health situation where the entire population lives to an advanced age, free of disease and disability. DALYs for a disease or health condition are calculated as the sum of the Years of Life Lost (YLL) due to premature mortality in the population and the Years Lost due to Disability (YLD) for people living with the health condition or its consequences.

$$\mathbf{DALY = YLL + YLD}$$

The YLL basically corresponds to the number of deaths multiplied by the standard life expectancy at the age at which death occurs. [One standard used was the life expectancy data from Japan.]

The basic formula for YLL is the following (for a given cause, age and sex).

$$\mathbf{YLL = N \times L}$$

- N = number of deaths
- L = standard life expectancy at age of death in years

To estimate YLD for a particular cause in a particular time period, the number of incident cases in that period is multiplied by the average duration of the disease and a weight factor that reflects the severity of the disease on a scale from 0 (perfect health) to 1 (dead). The basic formula for YLD is the following

$$\mathbf{YLD = I \times DW \times L}$$

- I = number of incident cases
- DW = disability weight
- L = average duration of the case until remission or death (years)

There are discussions on the standardization and comparability of the application of disability weight (DW) (Haagsma *et al.* 2014). There are comments on the proper use of DALY, because, in a way, this is "forced consistency" and "the DALY approach explicitly

[24] https://www.who.int/data/gho/indicator-metadata-registry/imr-details/158

presupposes that the lives of disabled people have less value than those of people without disabilities" (Arnesen and Nord 1999). "In recent years, it has become commonplace among the Global Burden of Disease (GBD) study authors to regard the disability-adjusted life year (DALY) primarily as a descriptive health metric. ... We identify numerous assumptions underlying the DALY and group them as descriptive or evaluative. We conclude that while the DALY model arguably has become more descriptive, it remains, by necessity, largely evaluative" (Solberg *et al.* 2020).

Christopher Murray (the Institute for Health Metrics and Evaluation, IHME, University of Washington, Seattle) and his international collaborators are the research group providing the GBD data (funded by the Gates Foundation). They want GBD 2.0 to be a continuously updated global resource. Actually, the full current name is Global Burden of Diseases, Injuries, and Risk Factors Study. Since social and economic development, measured with socio-demographic index (**SDI**), is highly correlated with health outcomes, SDI adjustments have been added to GBD analysis.

Beyond DALY, there are terms of quality-adjusted life year (**QALY**) and healthy life expectancy (**HALE**) in the consideration of systemic analysis of GBD globally, regionally, and nationally. This is a conclusion seen in a HALE report: "Over the past 20 years, fertility rates have been dropping steadily and life expectancy has been increasing, with few exceptions" (GBD 2019 Demographics Collaborators 2020). For GBD 2019 that covered 369 diseases in 204 countries, the conclusion is: "As disability becomes an increasingly large component of disease burden and a larger component of health expenditure, greater research and development investment is needed to identify new, more effective intervention strategies. With a rapidly aging global population, the demands on health services to deal with disabling outcomes, which increase with age, will require policy makers to anticipate these changes" (GBD 2019 Diseases and Injuries Collaborators 2020)

TABLE 1.3: DALYs of major diseases. DALY is disability-adjusted life year. HIV/AIDS is human immunodeficiency disease/acquired immunodeficient syndrome. TB is tuberculosis. NTDs are neglected tropical diseases. Data are derived from Hotez 2013; Murray *et al.* 2012; GBD 2015; GBD 2017.

	Annual DALYs (millions)			
Disease	**Hotez 2006**	**GBD 2010**	**GBD 2015**	**GBD 2017**
HIV/AIDS	84.5	81.5	66.7	65.9
Malaria	46.5	82.7	55.8	45.0
TB	34.7	49.4	40.3	45.0
NTDs	56.6	26.1	23.4	17.3

The previous GBD 2015 covered 195 different countries and territories for 315 causes by geography, sex and age groups. "Health is improving globally, but this means more populations are spending more time with functional health loss, an absolute expansion of morbidity. The proportion of life spent in ill health decreases somewhat with increasing SDI, a relative compression of morbidity, which supports continued efforts to elevate personal income, improve education, and limit fertility" (GBD 2015). A comparison of annual DALYs for NTDs and 3 major infectious diseases (HIV/AIDs, malaria, tuberculosis) is shown in Table 1.3 (data from Hotez 2013; Murray *et al.* 2012; GBD 2015, 2017); NTDs cause significant DALYs (although less than the other 3 infectious diseases).

Summary & Key Concepts

- Anthropocene is a geological time point where humanity is the main driving force of change on Earth.
- The 4 types of symbiotic relations are phoresy, commensalism, mutualism, and exploitation; parasites generally fall under the exploitation category.
- Parasites can be ectoparasites or endoparasites; they can be obligate or facultative, and accidental or incidental.
- For parasites and other information, use a reliable source of biomedical literature, such as PubMed. PubMed currently has over 30 million citations.
- UN had 8 MDGs in 2000 and 17 SDGs in 2015.
- WHO recognized a total of 20 NTDs.
- DALY has been used as a metric to compare different diseases including the NTDs.

References

Arnesen T, Nord E. The value of DALY life: Problems with ethics and validity of disability adjusted life years. *BMJ* 1999;319(7222):1423–5.

Bhattacharya S, Krishnamurthy A, Gopalakrishnan M, *et al.* Endocrine and metabolic manifestations of snakebite envenoming. *Am J Trop Med Hyg* 2020;103(4):1388–96.

Bhaumik S, Beri D, Lassi ZS, Jagnoor J. Interventions for the management of snakebite envenoming: An overview of systematic reviews. *PLoS Negl Trop Dis* 2020;14(10):e0008727.

Bogitsh BJ, Carter CE, Oeltmann TN. *Human Parasitology*, 5th ed., Academic Press, Elsevier, 2019.

Bush AO, Fernandez, Esch GW, Seed JR. *Parasitism: The Diversity and Ecology of Animal Parasites*, Cambridge, 2001.

Croft SL. Neglected tropical diseases in the genomics era: Re-evaluating the impact of new drugs and mass drug administration. *Genome Biol* 2016;17:46.

Dheilly NM, Ewald PW, Brindley PJ, Fichorova RN, Thomas F. Parasite-microbe-host interactions and cancer risk. *PLoS Pathog* 2019;15(8):e1007912.

Dheilly NM, Bolnick D, Bordenstein S, *et al.* Parasite microbiome project: Systematic investigation of microbiome dynamics within and across parasite-host interactions. *mSystems* 2017;2(4):e00050-17.

GBD 2015 Disease and Injury Incidence and Prevalence Collaborators. Global, regional, and national incidence, prevalence, and years lived with disability for 310 diseases and injuries, 1990–2015: A systematic analysis for the Global Burden of Disease Study 2015. *Lancet* 2016;388(10053):1545–1602.

GBD 2017 Disease and Injury Incidence and Prevalence Collaborators. Global, regional, and national incidence, prevalence, and years lived with disability for 354 diseases and injuries for 195 countries and territories, 1990–2017: A systematic analysis for the Global Burden of Disease Study 2017. *Lancet* 2018;392(10159):1789–858.

GBD 2019 Demographics Collaborators. Global age-sex-specific fertility, mortality, healthy life expectancy (HALE), and population estimates in 204 countries and territories, 1950–2019: A comprehensive demographic analysis for the Global Burden of Disease Study 2019. *Lancet* 2020;396(10258):1160–1203.

GBD 2019 Diseases and Injuries Collaborators. Global burden of 369 diseases and injuries in 204 countries and territories, 1990–2019: A systematic analysis for the Global Burden of Disease Study 2019. *Lancet* 2020;396(10258):1204–22.

Haelewaters D, Hiller T, Dick CW. Bats, bat flies, and fungi: A case of hyperparasitism. *Trends Parasitol* 2018;34(9):784–99.

Hanelt B, Bolek MG, Schmidt-Rhaesa A. Going solo: Discovery of the first parthenogenetic gordiid (Nematomorpha: Gordiida). *PLoS One* 2012;7(4):e34472.

Haagsma JA, Polinder S, Cassini A, Colzani E, Havelaar AH. Review of disability weight studies: Comparison of methodological choices and values. *Popul Health Metr* 2014;12:20.

Hegner R. *Big Fleas have Little Fleas or Who's Who among the Protozoa* 1938, Dover reprint 1968 (https://hdl.handle.net/2027/uva.x002081533).

Hotez PJ. *Forgotten People, Forgotten Diseases*, 2nd ed., ASM Press, 2013.

Hotez PJ, Aksoy S, Brindley PJ, Kamhawi S. World neglected tropical diseases day. *PLoS Negl Trop Dis* 2020a;14(1):e0007999.

Hotez PJ, Aksoy S, Brindley PJ, Kamhawi S. What constitutes a neglected tropical disease? *PLoS Negl Trop Dis* 2020b;14(1):e0008001.

Keating C. Ken Warren and the Rockefeller Foundation's great neglected diseases network, 1978–1988: The transformation of tropical and global medicine. *Mol Med* 2014;20(1): S24–30.

Kofer J, Hofer H, Hartmann S. Next-generation parasitologists: Structured training programs meet educational challenges. *Trends Parasitol* 2017;33(6):423–25.

Kuchta R, Choudhury A, Scholz T. Asian fish tapeworm: The most successful invasive parasite in freshwaters. *Trends Parasitol* 2018;34(6):511–23.

Kwong WK, Del Campo J, Mathur V, Vermeij MJA, Keeling PJ. A widespread coral-infecting apicomplexan with chlorophyll biosynthesis genes. *Nature* 2019;568(7750):103–107.

Liese B, Rosenberg M, Schratz A. Programmes, partnerships, and governance for elimination and control of neglected tropicaldiseases. *Lancet* 2010;375(9708):67–76.

McDade TW, Ryan CP, Jones MJ, *et al.* Genome-wide analysis of DNA methylation in relation to socioeconomic status during development and early adulthood. *Am J Phys Anthropol* 2019;169(1):3–11.

Medina I, Langmore NE. The evolution of acceptance and tolerance in hosts of avian brood parasites. *Biol Rev Camb Philos Soc* 2016;91(3):569–77.

Mestre A, Poulin R, Hortal J. A niche perspective on the range expansion of symbionts. *Biol Rev Camb Philos Soc* 2020;95(2):491–516.

Murray CJ, Vos T, Lozano R, *et al.* Disability-adjusted life years (DALYs) for 291 diseases and injuries in 21 regions, 1990–2010: A systematic analysis for the Global Burden of Disease Study 2010. *Lancet* 2012;380(9859):2197–223.

Oborník M. Photoparasitism as an intermediate state in the evolution of apicomplexan parasites. *Trends Parasitol* 2020;36(9):727–34.

Parise ME, Hotez PJ, Slutsker L. Neglected parasitic infections in the United States: Needs and opportunities. *Am J Trop Med Hyg* 2014;90(5):783–85.

Reeder JC, Guth JA. What have we learned from 40 years of supporting research and capacity building? *PLoS Negl Trop Dis* 2015;9(1):e3355.

Roberts JR, Platt TR, Orélis-Ribeiro R, Bullard SA. New genus of blood fluke (Digenea: Schistosomatoidea) from Malaysian freshwater turtles (Geoemydidae) and its phylogenetic position within schistosomatoidea. *J Parasitol* 2016;102(4):451–62.

Roberts LS, Janovy J, Jr. Nadler S. *Schmidt & Roberts Foundations of Parasitology*, 9th ed., McGraw Hill, 2013.

Ross, G. *The Sleeping Sickness/Gordon Ross*. Africa, 1911. N.Y.: Published by Keppler & Schwarzmann, Puck Building, 1911. [Photograph] Retrieved from the Library of Congress, https://www.loc.gov/item/2011649074/.

Solberg CT, Sørheim P, Müller KE, Gamlund E, Norheim OF, Barra M. The devils in the DALY: Prevailing evaluative assumptions. *Public Health Ethics* 2020;13(3):259–74.

Swain Ewald HA, Ewald PW. Natural selection, the microbiome, and public health. *Yale J Biol Med* 2018;91(4):445–55.

Swann JB, Holland SJ, Petersen M, Pietsch TW, Boehm T. The immunogenetics of sexual parasitism. *Science* 2020;369(6511):1608–15.

Tuovinen V, Ekman S, Thor G, Vanderpool D, Spribille T, Johannesson H. Two basidiomycete fungi in the cortex of wolf lichens. *Curr Biol* 2019;29(3):476–83.

Willett W, Rockström J, Loken B, *et al.* Food in the Anthropocene: The EAT-Lancet Commission on healthy diets from sustainable food systems. *Lancet* 2019;393(10170):447–92.

Wouters P, Sugimoto R, Larivière V, *et al.* Rethink impact factors: Find new ways to judge a journal. *Nature* 2019;569:621–3.

2

Evolution of Parasites and Potential Novel Therapies from Their Genomes

2.1 Biodiversity & Abundance of Parasites

In order to reduce human suffering and death due to parasitic diseases, there is an urgent need to deliver diagnostics, vaccines, and medications to vulnerable populations. Top priority must be given to those who live in dire economic conditions, especially those experiencing extreme hunger and poverty. In this chapter we shall consider several concepts: the diversity of life, the number of parasitic species currently known, conservation and evolution of parasites, and how the genomes of humans and parasites may provide novel targets for therapy and vaccines. There are also issues of biomedical ethics that are intimately associated with both the making and distributing of anti-parasitic drugs.

When considering biodiversity, the first question is: "how many species are present on Earth?" In their paper titled "Can we name Earth's species before they go extinct?" Mark Costello (University of Auckland, New Zealand) and colleagues estimated a total of **5 million** eukaryotic species on Earth, of which 1.5 million are named species, and the species are experiencing an extinction rate of 5% or less per decade (Costello *et al.* 2013). In another paper titled "How many species are there on Earth and in the ocean?" Camillo Mora (Dalhousie University, Halifax and University of Hawaii Honolulu) and colleagues estimated a total of **8.7 million** eukaryotic species on Earth, of which 2.2 million are marine species (Mora *et al.* 2011). The investigators have documented that the classification of species into higher taxonomic groups followed a consistent pattern from which the total number of species in any taxonomic group can be predicted; they concluded that "some 86% of the species on Earth and 91% in the ocean, still await description" (Mora *et al.* 2011).

The two studies on species diversity quoted above only mentioned eukaryotes. An entirely different picture emerges if prokaryotes are included in an analysis of biodiversity. The influence of prokaryotes on Earth's biodiversity is significant because they make

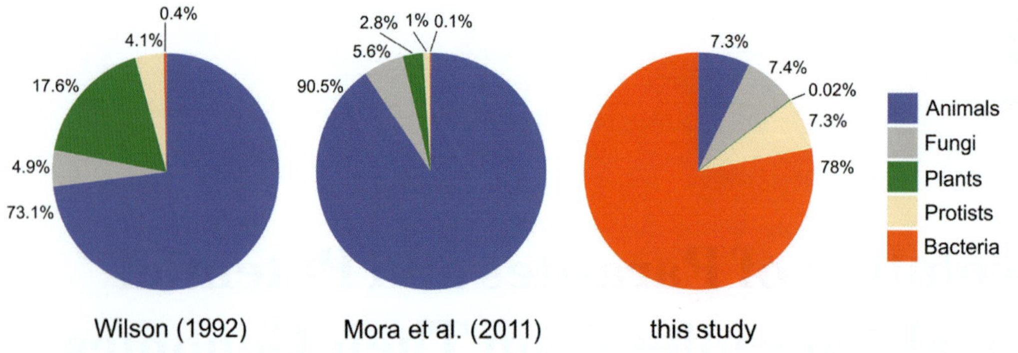

Fig. 2.1 ■ Traditional and new estimates of the pie of life. The pie on the left shows a traditional estimate of the relative richness of different groups of organisms based on numbers of described species (Wilson E, *The Diversity of Life*, Harvard, 1992), the middle shows an estimate based on projected richness of different groups (Mora *et al. PLoS Biol* 2011;9:e1001127), and the pie on the right shows estimates based on the projected richness of different groups in the present study. The pie on the right is estimated based on Scenario 1 (Table 1 of Larsen *et al.* 2017), but other scenarios and assumptions give very similar estimates of the relative richness of different groups (shown in Tables 1–4), even as total species richness changes. Courtesy: Larsen *et al. The Quarterly Review of Biology* 2017;92:229–65. Reproduced with permission from the University of Chicago Press.

up the majority of species in existence. In the paper titled "Inordinate fondness multiplies and redistributed: The number of species on Earth and the new pie of life," Brendon Larsen (University of Arizona Tucson) and colleagues provided an estimate ranging from **1 to 6 billion** species, the majority of which are prokaryotes (Larsen *et al.* 2017). These figures were based on all living things (excluding viruses, not quite "living things"); cryptic species are included (bacteria, fungi, and protozoa that live as endosymbionts within their respective host species). As a complement to the tree of life (showing evolutionary relationship or phylogeny among species), the investigators presented a pie of life, dominated by **bacteria** contributing **70–90%** of total species. Please see Figure 2.1 for species diversity (Larsen *et al.* 2017). [Please see Chapter 4 for classification and phylogeny of eukaryotes.]

Since we will be emphasizing human parasites in the upcoming chapters, it is interesting to ask: how many species of parasites are present on Earth? In his paper titled "Most of the species on Earth are parasites" Donald Windsor (Norwich, New York) wrote: "Parasitism is indeed a lifestyle and not a phylogenetic category. As such, parasites exploit all the free-living taxa" (Windsor 1998). In a comprehensive survey of the animal kingdom, Sara Weinstein and Armand Kuris (University of California Santa Barbara) found that parasitism has independently evolved at least **223 times** within 15 phyla: 13 times in Platyhelminthes, 18 times in Nematodes (these two phyla are crowded with human parasites), and 143 times in Arthropoda (including 87 times in class Insecta within this phylum). [Please see Chapter 23 for a discussion on arthropods.] Please see Figure 2.2 for evolution of parasitism (Weinstein & Kuris 2016). They concluded that: "Nearly half

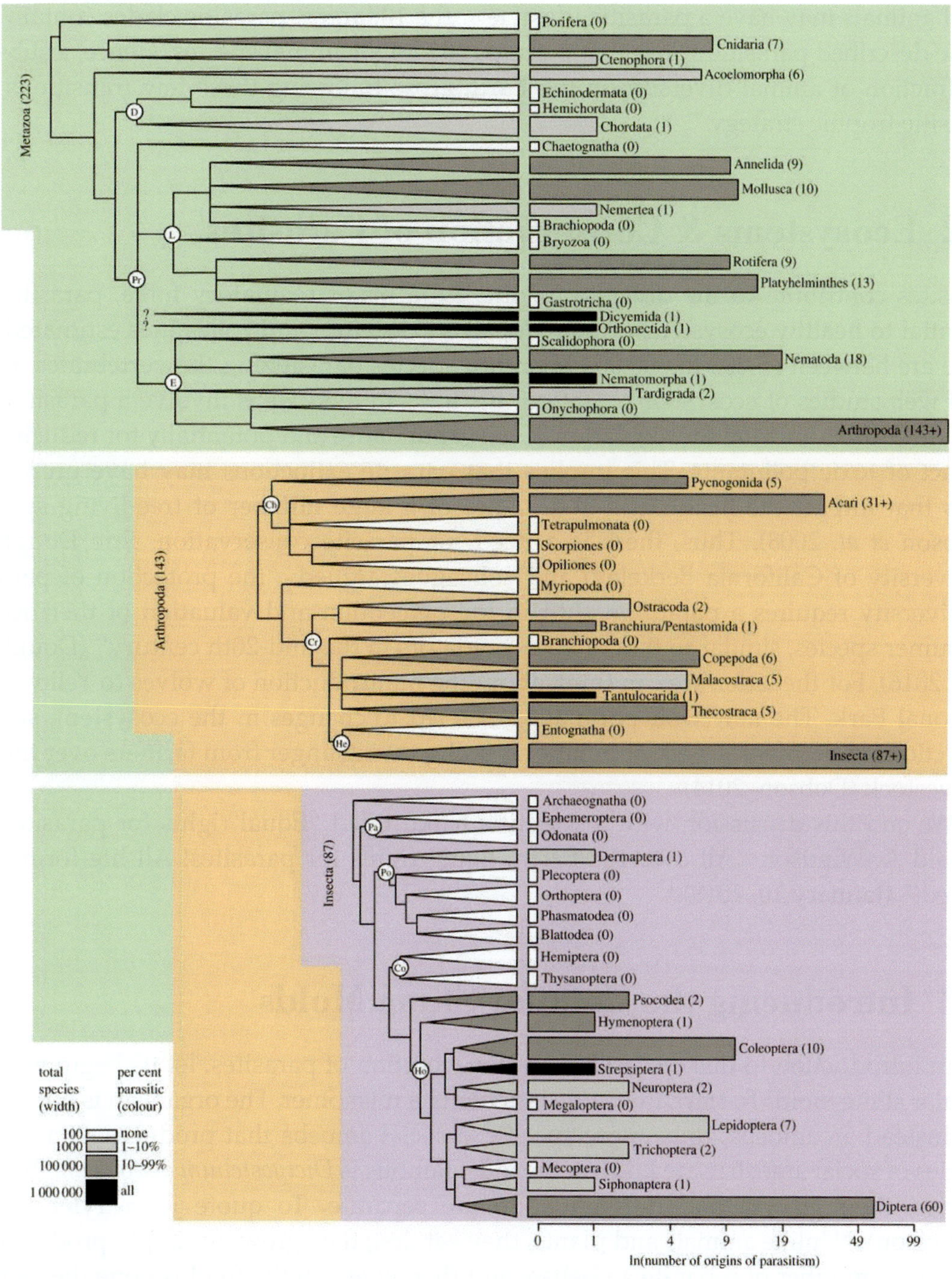

Fig. 2.2 ■ Origins of parasitism across Animalia. Bar plot of the natural log transformed number of independent acquisitions of parasitism within Metazoa, Arthropoda and Insecta, arranged according to taxonomic affiliation. Bar shading denotes the percent of the group that is parasitic and bar width is proportional to the log1000 transformed number of species per group. D, Deuterostomia; Pr, Protostomia; L, Lophotrochozoa; E, Ecdysozoa; Ch, Chelicerata; Cr, Crustacea; He, Hexapoda; Pa, Palaeoptera; Po, Polyneoptera; Co, Condylognatha; Ho, Holometabola. Courtesy: Weinstein S, Kuris A, *Biol Lett* 2016;12:20160324. Reproduced with permission from the Royal Society.

of all animals may have a parasitic lifestyle... the 10 largest parasitic clades contain 90% of the described parasitic species, or perhaps **40%** of all animal species. Hence, a substantial fraction of animal diversity on the Earth arose following these few transitions to a parasitic trophic strategy."

2.2 Ecosystems & Conservation of Parasites

Parasites contribute to the diversity of life. As a major regulatory force, parasites are essential to healthy ecosystems. Andy Dobson (Princeton) and colleagues estimated that there are between 75,000 to 300,000 helminth species parasitizing the vertebrates. In the food web studies of ecosystems, "75% of the links in food webs involve a parasitic species; these links are vital for regulation of host abundance and potentially for reducing the impact of toxic pollutants. This implies that parasite extinctions may have unforeseen costs that impact the health and abundance of a large number of free-living species" (Dobson *et al.* 2008). Thus, there is a need for parasite conservation. Eric Dougherty (University of California Berkeley) and colleagues argued: "the protection of parasitic biodiversity requires a paradigm shift in the perception and valuation of their role as consumer species, similar to that of apex predators in the mid-20th century" (Dougherty *et al.* 2016). For the latter, we can think about the reintroduction of wolves to Yellowstone National Park. The new wolf population has led to changes in the ecosystem, such as reductions in herbivorous elk populations, and growing anger from farmers over the loss of livestock (Dobson, 2014).

We end this discussion with a scientific haiku titled "Equal rights for parasites" by Donald A. Windsor: "All over the Earth, Equal rights for parasites! All life forms conserved!" (January 10, 2018).[1]

2.3 Introducing the Cellular Slime Molds

As an introduction to this discussion on the evolution of parasites, let us begin with the cellular slime mold. To start, the name is actually a misnomer. The organism is not a mold but instead an amoeba, to be more specific, a social amoeba that produces slime. Many species of social amoebae are known, the most famous is *Dictyostelium discoideum*. In these species, their growth and differentiation are separate. To quote John Tyler Bonner (Princeton): "Unlike animals and plants, they eat first; they grow by simply producing an increasing number of separate amoebae, and then when all the food is gone they stream together to become multicellular" (Bonner 2009). Chemotaxis is involved for this streaming, and the chemoattractant is cyclic AMP for *D. discoideum*. Amoebae aggregate to a motile, migratory slug. The slug finally differentiates into a fruiting body (aka a sorocarp),

[1] https://thescikuproject.com/2018/01/10/equal-rights-for-parasites-by-donald-a-windsor/

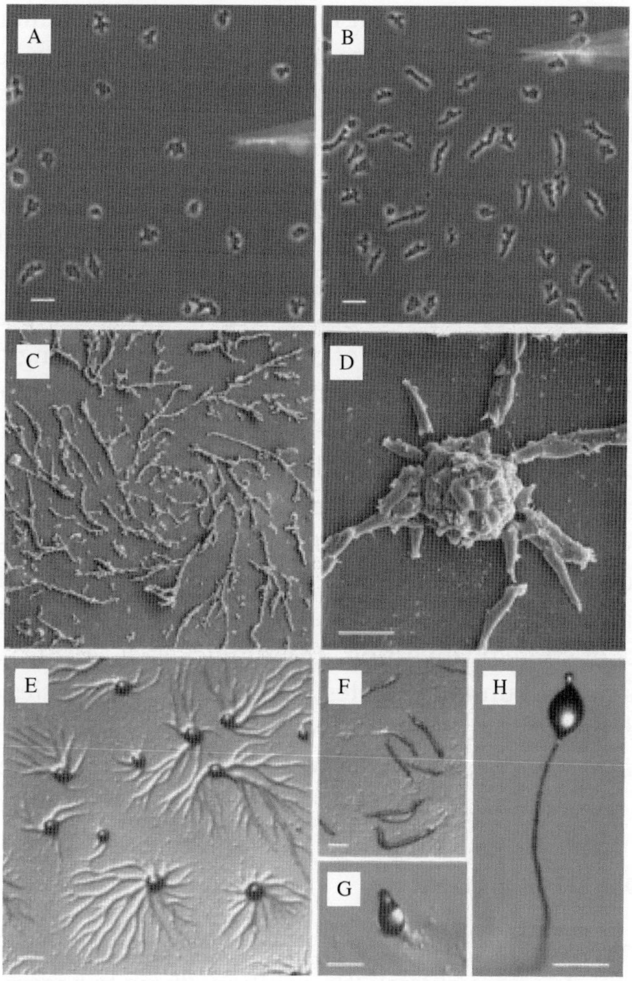

Fig. 2.3 ■ Stages of the *Dictyostelium discoideum* life cycle. (A and B) *Dictyostelium* cells chemotaxing toward cAMP released from a micropipette. Cells that have not yet sensed cAMP are shown in (A). Within 1 or 2 min the cells polarize (note the elongated cell shape) and migrate toward the source of chemoattractant (B). (C and D) Scanning electron micrograph of streaming *Dictyostelium* cells (C) and the formation of aggregates (D). (E) Formation of aggregation centers on an agar plate. (F) Slugs moving on an agar plate. (G) Culmination stage. (H) Fruiting body. Figures (C) and (D), courtesy of Günther Gerisch and Michael Claviez. The bars correspond to 10 μm in (A), (B) and (D), and 1 mm in (E)–(H). Courtesy: Müller-Taubenberger *et al. Eur J Cell Biol* 2013;92:45–53. Reproduced with permission from Elsevier.

containing stalked cells and spores. The stalk serves to facilitate spore dispersal; all stalked cells die during sorocarp formation — in this sense they are altruistic. Please see Figure 2.3 for the developmental stages of the cellular slime mold *Dictyostelium discoideum* (Müller-Taubenberger *et al.* 2013). The process is starvation-induced differentiation; protein degradation is involved. We have shown the use of chloroquine, an inhibitor of lysosomal acid hydrolase activity by raising lysosomal pH, would inhibit the differentiation; but the process continued in the presence of an added exogenous amino acid mixture, indicating the importance of proteolysis (protein degradation) for its metabolism and differentiation (Fong and Bonner 1979).

It is also known that *Dictyostelium* can have sex; when met, amoebae from compatible mating type strains will fuse to form macrocysts. One social amoeba species, *D. caveatum*, is carnivorous and will enter aggregate of a victim species and eat the victim amoebae. *D. mucoroides* is another species where different strains have been isolated. One such strain will only make spores even if it is mixed with a normal (sorocarp-forming) strain. These are "cheaters" that take advantage of other strains by utilizing their stalks. Another way to view this strain is to consider them as "auto-parasites" (Bonner 2009). Similar condition has been investigated in *D. discoideum*. "Microbes are surprisingly social organisms and are providing model systems for the study of the evolution of cooperation and conflict" (Noh *et al.* 2018). There is the concept of kin selection theory where individuals invest more into cooperation if their relatedness to group members is high. With respect to the controversy of altruism and conflict, social amoebae in the wild are both altruists and cheaters; "all individuals will sometimes appear to cooperate and sometimes cheat due to the dynamics of strategic investing" (Madgwick *et al.* 2018).

Amoeba species can be human parasites. We shall discuss species of obligate parasitic amoeba *Entamoeba histolytica* and other facultative species, such as the opportunistic free-living species *Acanthamoeba castellanii*. [Please see Chapter 7 for amoebiasis.]

2.4 Evolution of Parasites

Acknowledging that parasitism is a lifestyle and parasitism has evolved independently over 200 times in animal species, we ask the question: "how to become a parasite?" Based on analysis of 6 nematode genomes (including *Brugia malayi*, the agent for filariasis), Christoph Dieterich and Ralf Sommer (Max-Planck Institute for Developmental Biology, Tubingen, Germany) proposed a series of steps that needs to be taken to reach parasitism in nematodes. The process begins with a free-living state, a transition to **phoresy**, further progression to **necromeny**, and finally reaching parasitism (Dieterich and Sommer 2009). There exist two intermediate stages: phoretic species which hitch a ride (for transportation), and necromenic species that wait for the death of host to feed on the carcass and developing microbes. The authors mentioned the common theme of horizontal gene transfer (**HGT**), as well as the bacterial endosymbiont species *Wolbachia* found in some nematode species. Nematode genome comparison also shows HGT (from *Wolbachia* to nematodes), and the *Brugia* genome has lost essential genes but can afford to do so because of the endosymbiont. The parasitic nematode *Brugis malayi* has 11,515 genes, whereas the free-living *Caenorhabditis elegans* has 20,470 genes.

In order to explain the evolution of complex traits, the German evolutionary biologist Gunther Osche coined the term **pre-adaptation** in 1956. These changes are adaptation to the current environment of the organism and its life style. However, such adaptations might be co-opted to acquire a new function and facilitates the transfer to a new environment, thereby helping the organism to enter a new niche. This concept is hypothetical because one cannot foresee evolution. Pre-adaptation includes tolerance of low oxygen and toxins when nematodes associate with insects, as well as adapting a stationary period known as the dauer stage of nematodes. Recent evidence has shown conserved endocrine signaling mechanism between dauer stage of free-living *C. elegans* and infective larval 3 stage (iL3) of parasitic nematodes. So, some parasitic features evolved under free-living conditions (Dieterich and Sommer 2009).

Traditionally it is believed that parasites should evolve into less virulent forms, therefore, the most successful parasite is one that causes little harm to its host. This situation assumes a long-term relationship between the host and parasite to allow appropriate coevolution. Alternatively, there is the situation of parasite action known as host capture or **host switch**. For host capture, the parasite increases in host range (from original host A to new host B). Host capture may extend the parasite's host species diversity. In host switch (aka host shift), the parasite moves to a new host (from original host C to new host D). While host switch may also expand the parasite range, it becomes a necessity if the original host species suffers from morbidities, mortalities, or maybe facing extinction. Under such circumstances, a lack of host-parasite coevolution may mean an increase in virulence of the parasite in its new host. Thus, the various paths to parasitism may be related to the evolution of **virulence**. Virulence can be seen as the damage done to the host during its interaction with a parasite, and can be expressed, for example, as premature host death or decreased fecundity (capability of producing offspring). A related term is **pathogenicity**. As we put parasites as agents of infectious diseases, here, pathogenicity is "the broader term, which incorporates virulence. Virulence is seen as the severity of disease manifestation that can only be measured in infected individuals" (Thomas and Elkinton 2004). One definition is to see pathogenicity as the capacity to produce disease, and virulence as the severity of that disease. Virulence depends on action of the parasitic pathogen. "Pathogenic mechanisms that manipulate host immunity or escape from host defenses have particularly high sensitivity to parasite fitness and thus dominate as causes of parasite virulence. The high sensitivity of immunomodulation and immune escape arise because those mechanisms affect parasite survival within the host, the most sensitive of fitness components" (Frank and Schmid-Hempel 2008). [Please see Chapter 3 for parasites and immunity.]

Knowing that parasitism has evolved independently over 200 times in animal species, Robert Poulin and Haseeb Randhawa (University of Otago, New Zealand) noted that separate parasite lineages have converged over evolutionary time scale to share traits and exploit their hosts in similar ways. They found that: "at a phenotypic level, eukaryotic parasite lineages have all converged toward only 6 general **parasitic strategies:** parasitoid, parasitic castrator, directly transmitted parasite, trophically transmitted parasite, vector-transmitted parasite or micropredator" (Poulin and Randhawa 2015). A female parasitoid, e.g., hymenopteran insects, lays an egg on its host organism, and the embryo grows within the host. The larval parasite syphons nutrients from its host and can even alter host behavior but eventually causes death to the host when the parasite emerges as an adult. Parasitic castrators such as trematode juveniles within the molluscan host will inhibit the hosts' reproduction in order to promote its own reproductive cycle resulting in an increased parasite load within the host. Directly transmitted parasites such as the parasitic protozoan *Giardia lamblia* will infect a single host causing host pathology through reproduction and transmission of the parasites. [There is the concept of prevalence: a few hosts with aggregated abundance of parasites while others are free of parasites.] Trophically transmitted parasites such as the parasitic protozoan *Toxoplasma gondii* have multiple hosts; they can modify host behavior to induce host-to-host transmission. Vector transmitted parasites such as the parasitic protozoan *Leishmania donovani* have a host and a vector that are micropredators. Micropredators such as the dipteran insect female sand-fly will feed on host blood.

In addition to noting the strategies utilized by the parasites, the scientists also commented on the evolution of parasites based on their genomes. They noted "evidence of **parallel evolution** among unrelated parasite taxa with respect to genome reduction or compaction, and gene losses or gains" (Poulin and Randhawa 2015). Aspects of genome reduction, as well as gain and loss of genes among the human parasites whose genomes are known, will be discussed in the following chapters.

2.5 Genomes of Humans & Parasites

On June 26, 2000, US President Bill Clinton and British Prime Minister Tony Blair jointly announced the completion of the Human Genome Project (**HGP**). HGP, found in 1990 by US Department of Energy (DOE) and National Institutes of Health (NIH) with international collaboration between US, UK, Germany, France, Japan and China, ended with the draft human genome. Sequencing was done from clones derived by inserting the human DNA in bacterial artificial chromosome (BACs) and by whole genome shotgun cloning. This monumental task saw two groups race against one another to find the sequence. The international consortium was being challenged by Celera Genomics, a private company owned by J. Craig Venter. The haploid human genome has an estimate of **23,000** protein-coding genes (far fewer than previous expectation). There are non-coding RNA (ncRNA), regulatory sequences, and the increasingly important epigenome. In the first published human genome, repetitive sequences, centromeres, telomeres were not compiled or properly annotated. The very first draft has 92.3% of the genome sequenced; the cost of the project reached US $3 billion.

In their invited review titled "DNA sequencing at 40: past, present and future," Jay Shendure (University of Washington Seattle) and colleagues predicted: "the impact of DNA sequencing will be on a par with that of the microscope" (Shendure *et al.* 2017). In 1977, 2 techniques for DNA sequencing were available, namely the Maxam & Gilbert chemical cleavage procedure and the Sanger & Coulson chain termination method. The radioisotopes used in the original DNA sequencing were replaced with dyes for safety concerns. Because of its relative ease of use, the Sanger method became the first generation sequencing. This was followed by the second generation/next generation sequencing (NGS). Various biotech companies and academic scientists achieved massively parallel DNA sequencing, within a decade of NGS developments (Goodwin *et al.* 2016). Results are relatively short sequences after amplification and need computational capacity for assembly. Currently, the third generation sequencing is real time and uses single molecule sequencing strategies to obtain longer sequences. The first commercially available nanopore sequencing device, the MinION, was released in 2014 (Oxford Nanopore Technologies). It is an impressive small instrument capable of use in the field (Jain *et al.* 2016). Its capacity has been demonstrated in sequencing and assembly of a reference human genome (GM12878 from the Utah/CEPH pedigree), including ultra-long reads up to 882 kb in length. The long read covered 85.8% of the reference genome and enabled the assembly and phasing of its 4-Mb major histocompatibility complex (MHC) locus and telomere repeat lengths (Jain *et al.* 2018). Please see Figure 2.4 for DNA sequencing techniques (Shendure *et al.* 2017). Please see Kitts *et al.* (2016) for introducing the DNA sequencing and assembly database.[2]

The first sequenced genome was a mixture of human DNA. "The HGP's human genome was constructed from a mosaic of DNA donors, but mostly derived from one individual, from Buffalo, New York, who had roughly equal parts European and African ancestry" (Shendure *et al.* 2017). Individuals, including scientists and other public figures, have their DNA sequenced. The first was that of J. Craig Venter, founder of Celera, in 2007. The second sequencing costed $20 million and was conducted by the company 454 for James D. Watson (Nobel Laureate) in 2008. Others include Stephen Quake (Stanford Bioengineering) at under $50,000 but requiring comparison to the National Center for Biotechnology Information (NCBI) reference genome (Pushkarev *et al.* 2009), Bishop Desmond Tutu (1931–2021) (South Africa, in 2010), Henry Louis Gates Jr. (Harvard, *Finding Your Roots,* and other programs for Public Broadcasting Service, PBS, public television) and his father at estimated $300,000 (by the company Illumina). These are examples of whole-genome sequencing (**WGS**). A cheaper version is whole-exome sequencing (**WES**), selective sequencing of the 1–2% of the genome for protein-coding genes only. Current cost of WGS is towards **US $1,000** per genome because, at this level, clinical applications are possible. WGS of 100,000 individuals are in progress. Technical advances not only make genome availability more economical, but also allow studies of variants and polymorphisms, ancient genomes, and investigation into genomes of other species. Complete human genome and oral microbiome were recovered from an ancient "chewing gum" (5,700 years old piece of chewed birch pitch from Denmark). The individual was described as a female and "she likely had dark skin, dark brown hair and blue eyes" and the scientists also identified "DNA fragments from several bacterial and viral taxa, including Epstein-

[2] https://www.ncbi.nlm.nih.gov/assembly/

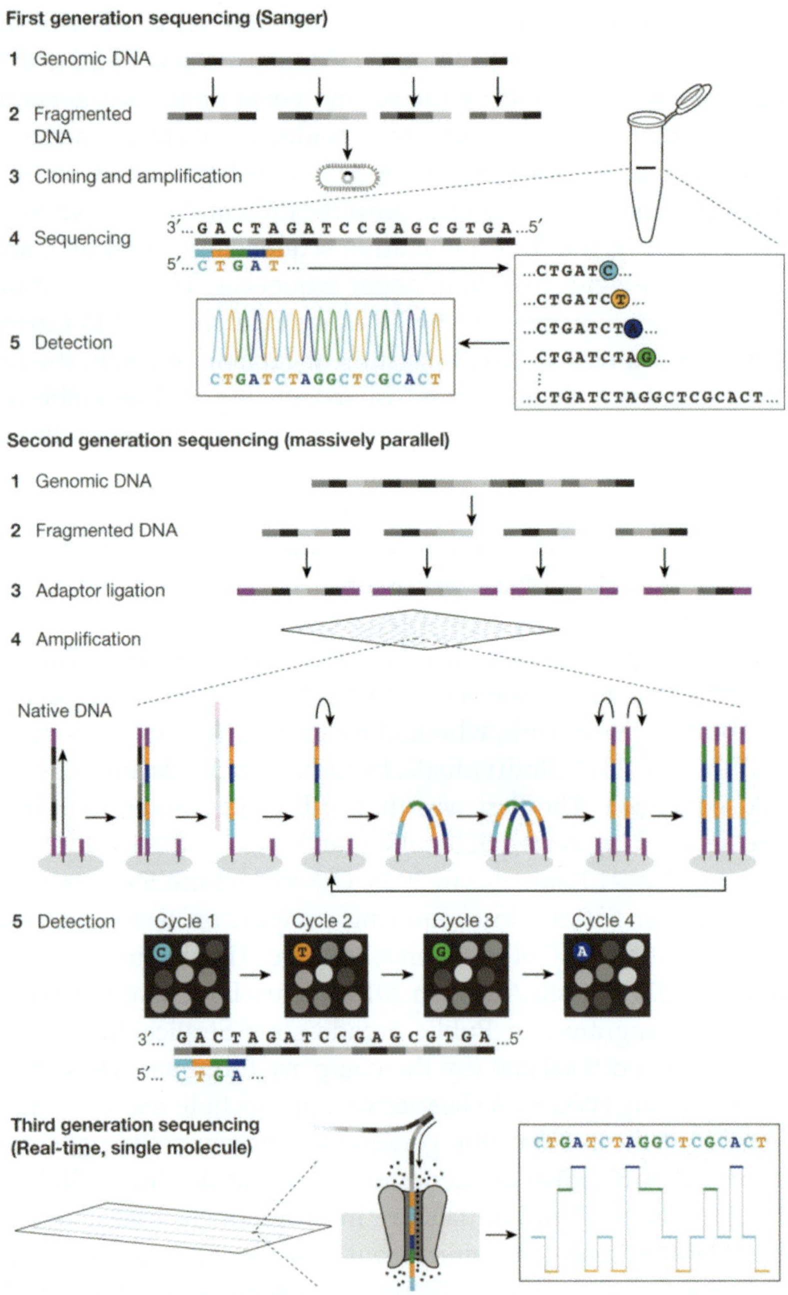

Fig. 2.4 ■ DNA sequencing techniques. Schematic examples of first, second and third generation sequencing are shown. Second generation sequencing is also referred to as next-generation sequencing (NGS). Courtesy: Shendure *et al. Nature* 2017;550:345–53. Reproduced with permission from Springer Nature.

Barr virus, as well as animal and plant DNA, which may have derived from a recent meal" (Jensen *et al.* 2019).

The cost of human WGS under $1,000 has been achieved. In a review of studies from 2005 to 2016 (a total of 32), "cost estimates for a single test ranged from $555 to $5,169 for WES and from $1,906 to $24,810 for WGS" (Schwarze *et al.* 2018). In 2016, a discussion on costs by National Human Genome Research Institute (NHGRI) concluded: "Based on the data collected from NHGRI-funded genome-sequencing groups, the cost to generate a high-quality 'draft' whole human genome sequence in mid-2015 was just above $4,000; by late in 2015, that figure had fallen below $1,500. The cost to generate a whole-exome sequence was generally below $1,000. Commercial prices for whole-genome and whole-exome sequences have often (but not always) been slightly below these numbers" (Kris Wetterstrand).[3,4] In 2017, Dante Labs offered WGS for $900, Beijing Genomics Institute (BGI) offered WGS from $600. Private companies, including Illumina, are competing to reach a new target for WGS of only $100. In 2020, Nebula Genomics has offered WGS for $299. In 2021, Dante Labs offered 30X WGS at $599. The application of WGS to clinical medicine is therefore feasible.

WGS has other applications, too. Here, we present one example: Infanticide vs. inherited cardiac arrhythmias. "In 2003, an Australian woman was convicted by a jury of smothering and killing her 4 children over a 10-year period. Each child died suddenly and unexpectedly during a sleep period, at ages ranging from 19 days to 18 months. In 2019 we were asked to investigate if a genetic cause could explain the children's deaths as part of an inquiry into the mother's convictions ... Whole genomes or exomes of the mother and her 4 children were sequenced ... a novel *CALM2* variant... Thus, calmodulinopathy emerges as a reasonable explanation for a natural cause of their deaths" (Brohus *et al.* 2021). The woman, Kathleen Folbigg, was sentenced on appeal to 30 years in prison with a non-parole period of 25 years, because of sudden infant death syndrome (SIDS)/sudden unexpected deaths in children (SUDC) of her 4 children. Carola Garcia de Vinuesa (Centre for Personalised Immunology, Australian National University) commented: "To my knowledge, this is the first case in which a court (anywhere in the world) has used whole genome sequencing to find evidence of a cause of death." The researchers found a new variant in the *CALM2* gene which controls how calcium is transported in and out of heart cells. Previous studies have shown the *CALM2* gene variants can cause heart problems in young children (as the best recognized causes of SIDS/SUDC). In this particular family, both daughters carried the same CALM2 mutation as the mother. Both boys carried bi-allelic rare missense mutations in the *BSN*, aka *Bassoon*, gene: one inherited from the mother, the other likely from the father (he refused to provide a sample to the researchers). This gene has been shown to cause early onset lethal epilepsy in mice when deleted. (One boy had experienced seizure before he died.) Based on the new data, an appeal was launched in the New South Wales Court of Appeal but was rejected on 24 March, 2021.[5]

[3] https://www.genome.gov/about-genomics/fact-sheets/Sequencing-Human-Genome-cost

[4] https://en.wikipedia.org/wiki/$1,000_genome

[5] https://en.wikipedia.org/wiki/Kathleen_Folbigg

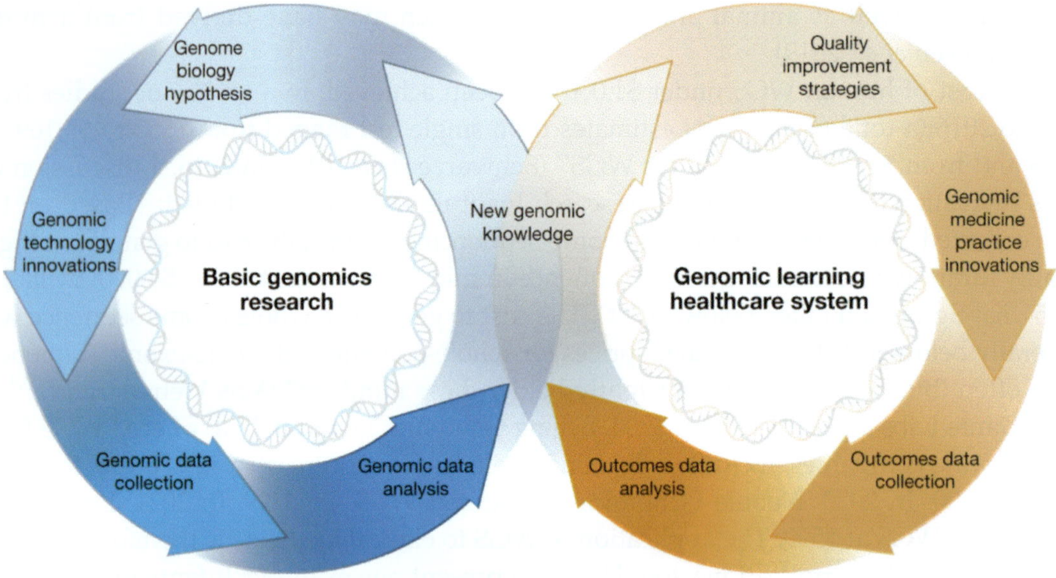

Fig. 2.5 ■ Virtuous cycles in human genomics research and clinical care. As human genomics has matured as a discipline, productive and connected virtuous cycles of activity have emerged, each self-improving with successive rounds of new advances. The cycle on the left reflects basic genomics research, in which technology innovations spur the collection and analysis of genomics research data, often yielding new knowledge and further hypotheses for testing. The cycle on the right reflects a genomic learning healthcare system, in which the implementation of new genomic medicine practice innovations allows for the collection and analysis of outcomes data, often yielding new genomic knowledge and additional genomics-based strategies for improving the quality of clinical care. Note that the new knowledge emerging from either the left or the right cycle has the potential to feed into the other, creating opportunities for 'bench to bedside' and 'bedside back to bench' progressions — both of which are expected to grow in the coming decade. Courtesy: Green *et al. Nature* 2020;586:683–92. Reproduced with permission from Springer Nature.

Three decades after the first human genome (the HGP), United States National Human Genome Research Institute (NHGRI) has developed strategic visions for the field for the 3rd time, "to capture, synthesize, and articulate the most compelling strategic opportunities for the next phase of genomics—with particular attention to elements that are most relevant to human health" (Green *et al.* 2020). Interacting virtuous cycles between genomics research and clinical medicine are foreseen. Please see Figure 2.5 for virtuous cycles in human genomics research and clinical care (Green *et al.* 2020). Eric Green (NHGRI) and colleagues stated: "Many of the details about what is needed to fulfil the promise of genomics have now come into focus. Major unsolved problems remain — among them determining the role for the vast majority of functional elements in the human genome (especially those outside of protein-coding regions), understanding the full spectrum of genomic variation (especially that implicated in human disease), developing data-science capabilities (especially those that keep pace with data generation), and improving healthcare through the implementation of genomic medicine (especially in the areas of prevention, diagnosis, and therapeutic development). The new decade also brings research questions related to the societal implications of genomics, including those related to social inequities, pointing to the continued importance of investigating the ethical, legal, and social issues related to genomics. But now more than ever, solutions to these problems seem to be within striking distance" (Green *et al.* 2020).

Whereas the human genome is important for clinical and other purposes, it was not the first multicellular organism to have its genome published. That honor belonged to the free-living nematode, *Caenorhabditis elegans*, with its genome completed in 1998. The worm possesses 20,470 protein-coding genes. The significance of this worm for developmental biologists is witnessed in the ability to trace each cell in the worm, ending with the adult hermaphrodite containing 969 somatic cells. The insightful choice was made by the Nobel Laureate Sidney Brenner, who coined the term Biopolis and was instrumental for biomedical research in Singapore, where he passed away on April 5, 2019.

With resequencing and analysis, the human genome is stated as the annotated and "final" genome. However, polymorphisms do exist, especially at the locus of MHC genes. This has become the reference human genome. Other annotated genomes include the one from mouse. Genomes of human parasites have become available after the human genome. The genome of the most virulent malaria parasite, *Plasmodium falciparum*, was published in 2002. Genomes of other protozoa and helminths followed (Pruitt *et al.* 2012).[6] "A genome contains all the genetic information of an organism and is the blueprint for various life events" (Lv *et al.* 2015). Genome mining offers potentials for the development of novel drugs, vaccine candidates, and diagnostic tools.

An important milestone for the comparative genomics of major parasitic worms was published in 2019 by the **International Helminth Genome Consortium**. Investigators from the Consortium have produced draft genomes from 45 worm species and predicted 0.8 million protein-coding genes, with 9,132–17,274 genes per species. By combining 36 published genomes with the new genomes (from 31 nematodes and 14 platyhelminthes), a total of **81 species** is a large genome collection available for use. One finding is about genome size. Genome size varies greatly within each phylum, from 42 to 700 Mb in nematodes, and from 104 to 1,259 Mb in platyhelminthes. Gene family births and hundreds of expanded gene families relevant to parasitism have been found, including ones that modulate host immune responses, enable parasite migration through host tissues, or allow the parasite to feed.

One prominent gene family comprises the **SCP/TAPS** (sperm-coating protein, SCP/testes-specific protein-1, Tpx-1/antigen 5, Ag5/pathogenesis related-1, Pr-1/Sc7, protein domain found in the prokaryote *Streptomyces coelicolor*; PF00188 at the protein family database[7]) genes that have been associated with parasitism through their abundance, secretion, and evidence of their role in immunomodulation (Cantacessi and Gasser 2012). (SCP is an acidic glycoprotein involved in sperm maturation during its passage through the epididymis.) The group is also known as the **CAP** (cysteine-rich secretory protein,

[6] http://www.ncbi.nlm.nih.gov/RefSeq/

[7] http://pfam.xfam.org/family/pf00188.

CRISP/antigen 5, Ag5/pathogenesis related-1, Pr-1) superfamily, that covers diverse groups of organisms, including CRISPs in male mammalian reproductive tract and reptilian venom secretory ducts, Ag5 in insects (saliva of mosquito and sand fly), and Pr-1 in plants (up-regulation after pathogen invasion, first discovered in tobacco mosaic virus, TMV-infected tobacco, *Nicotiana tabacum*). Protein members are also noted in model organisms such as *Caenorhabditis elegans*, fruit fly and yeast. As an example, humans possess 31 individual family members, including protease inhibitors and glioma pathogenesis related-1 (GLIPR1) (Gibbs *et al.* 2008). In parasitic helminths, as part of the larger SCP/TAPS superfamily, they are known as **VAL** (venom allergen-like) proteins, with substantial numbers in both platyhelminthes and nematodes. (Examples of VA proteins are VA 5 from vespid wasps and VA 3 from fire ants; VAs mediate allergic reactions to the bites by hymenopteran insects.) As an example, the blood fluke *Schistosoma mansoni* possesses 29 members (based on the genome), including at least 13 (SmVAL1 to SmVAL13) characterized members (some shown developmental regulation) (Cantacessi *et al.* 2009; Chalmers and Hoffmann 2012). SCP/TAPS protein structures have been investigated (by X-ray crystallography). A 15 kDa cysteine-rich CAP domain is present, despite limited sequence identity (among protein family members). The domain forms a characteristic alpha-beta-alpha sandwich fold (with further stabilization by disulfide bonds) plus additional flexible loop regions. For CRISP-like CAP domains, there are specific amino acids involved (2 glutamic acids and 2 histidines) for the binding of divalent cations (zinc, magnesium). Two distinct lipid-binding pockets in the CAT domain are seen: for the binding of sterols and fatty acids, respectively. Whereas many eukaryotic SCP/TAPS proteins only have one CAP domain, some parasitic CAP proteins have two covalently linked CAP domains (as seen in *Necator americanus Ancylostoma*-secreted protein-1, *Na*-ASP-1). One probable function is immune regulation. As an example, when the hookworm infective larval stage 3 (iL3) contacts humans, there is upregulation of CAP protein members. Hookworm SCP/TAPS members include ASPs (*Ancylostoma*-secreted proteins, or activation-associated secreted proteins), neutrophil inhibitory factor (NIF), and hookworm platelet inhibitor (HPI). Since the CAP domain is implicated in lipid binding and transport with its unique lipid-binding regions, such function may be important for immune modulation. As an example, recombinant *Na*-ASP-2 (possessing only one CAP domain) binds cholesterol, palmitic acid, and ascaroside (a glycolipid consisting of the sugar ascarylose with fatty acid side chain) in vitro (El Atab *et al.* 2020). In a review on this topic, Ruud Wilbers (Wageningen University, The Netherlands) and colleagues stated: "The ubiquitous presence and frequent dominance of VALs in helminth ES products - and their up-regulation during parasitic phases of the life cycle - point to a major role in host-parasite interactions ... Taken together, the pattern of animal-parasitic VAL evolution and expression suggests that most family members fulfill core functions at the host-parasite interface, with rapid diversification and adaptation to each host species ... Therefore, future research should focus on the specificity for different lipid ligands and how these ligands can be involved in the immunomodulatory properties of helminth VALs" (Wilbers *et al.* 2018) (ES, excretory secretory).

This rich data set allows study of evolutionary relationships. Investigators constructed a maximum-likelihood phylogeny based on analysis of a concatenated data matrix of 21,649 amino acid sites from 202 single-copy orthologous proteins present in at least 23 of the species. Please see Figure 2.6 for genome-wide phylogeny of helminths (International Helminth Genomes Consortium 2019). A phylogenetic tree is only as good as the data available. Thus, this phylogeny should be an improvement over previous ones. For example, one can compare relevant portions of this whole helminth phylogeny with the trematode tree based on ribosomal DNA genes (Figure 11.11 in Chapter 11).

On the topic of post-genomic progress in helminth parasitology, Paul McVeigh (Queen's University Belfast) commented: "The surge in availability of genomic tools for helminth parasites has revolutionized our ability to probe the biology of these pathogenic organisms without having to extrapolate from experiments performed in non-parasitic model systems. Genomics and transcriptomic data have provided new insights into the evolution and comparative genomics of helminth parasites, enabled new understanding of anthelmintic resistance and our ability to measure it in the field, new data on molecular interactions between parasites and hosts, and new molecular biomarkers enabling improved helminth diagnostics. We have also seen the development of transcriptomics towards the first applications of single cell RNA sequencing in whole flatworms. Ongoing development of functional genomics tools allow us to test hypotheses by editing the genomes and transcriptomes of helminth parasites, bringing new depths of understanding around these fascinating and pathogenically important worms" (McVeigh 2020).

Although all genomes of parasitic protozoa and helminths are known as "draft" genomes, they are readily available for various applications. We provide 3 examples: **ncRNAs, HGT**, and extracellular vesicles (**EVs**).

Protein-coding genes represent a very small portion of the whole genome. Human's 21,000 (or 23,000) protein-coding genes only make up 1% of the total genome. Some of the rest are transcribed into ncRNAs which may serve regulatory functions. In addition to the familiar ribosomal RNA (rRNAs) and transfer RNAs (tRNAs) for translation, there are other small and large RNAs, namely small nuclear RNAs (snRNAs), small nucleolar RNAs (snoRNAs), microRNA (miRNAs), and various long noncoding RNAs (lncRNAs). They may be involved in transcriptional and post-transcriptional regulation, and even spatial organization. Some ncRNAs have been shown to be associated with the epigenetic machinery and participate in parasite development and manipulation of host gene expression (Li *et al.* 2020). For host-parasite interactions, noncoding RNAs (ncRNAs) are (1) transmitted by the vector to possibly modulate vertebrate host responses and favor vector survival and (2) regulated in the host by parasites to favor parasite survival (Bensaoud *et al.* 2019).

Classical Mendelian inheritance transfers genes vertically within lineages. HGT, aka lateral gene transfer (LGT), moves genetic material between or among lineages. In 1998, Ford Doolittle (Dalhousie University), in a paper titled "You are what you eat: a gene transfer ratchet could account for bacterial genes in eukaryotic nuclear genomes," com-

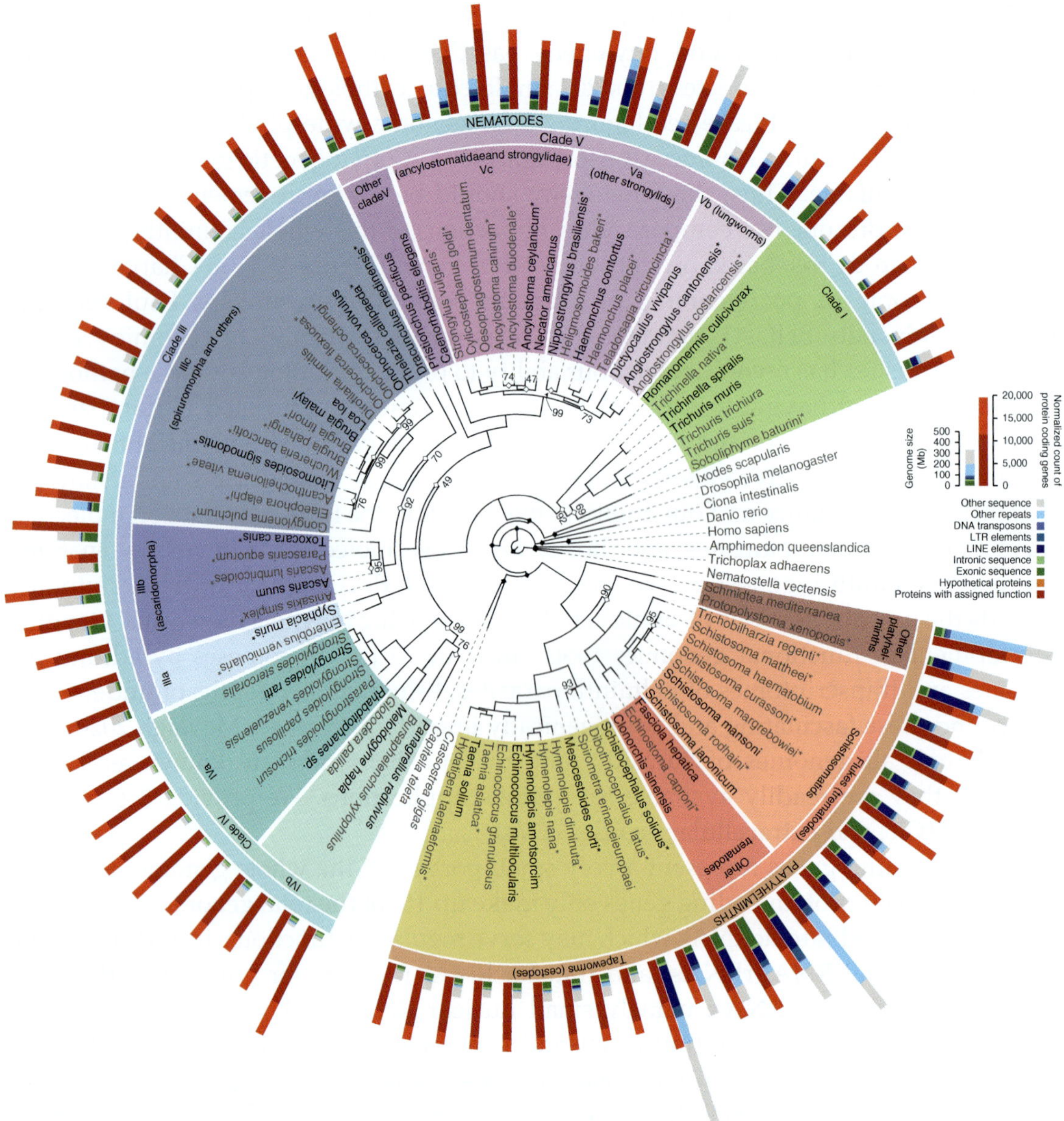

Fig. 2.6 ■ Genome-wide phylogeny of helminths. Maximum-likelihood phylogeny based on a partitioned analysis of a concatenated data matrix of 21,649 amino acid sites from 202 single-copy orthologous proteins present in at least 23 of the species. Values on marked nodes are bootstrap support values; all unmarked nodes were supported by 100 bootstrap replicates; nodes with solid marks were constrained in the analysis. Bar plots show genome sizes and total lengths of different genome features, and normalized gene count for proteins with inferred functions based on sequence similarity (having an assigned protein name), or those without (named 'hypothetical protein'). Species for which Coghlan et al. have sequenced genomes are marked with asterisks; 33 'tier 1' genomes are in black. LTR, long terminal repeat; LINE, long interspersed nuclear element. Courtesy: International Helminth Genomes Consortium. Coghlan *et al. Nat Genet* 2019;51:163–74. Reproduced with permission from *Nature Genetics* with Creative Commons Attribution 4.0 (CC-BY) International License.

mented: "Here I would like to suggest that their eating habits, not their sex habits, are most relevant to the understanding of 'lateral transfer' into the genomes of unicellular eukaryotes that survive through the ingestion of bacteria" (Doolittle 1998). One elegant example is the way eukaryotic microbes (including *Blastocystis*) have adapted to hypoxia by acquiring a gene involved in rhodoquinone biosynthesis via HGT (Stairs *et al.* 2018). [Please see Chapter 8 for more *Blastocystis* HGT.]

Intimate contact between parasites and their hosts affords substantial opportunities for HGT. Please see Figure 2.7 for putative HGT between parasites and hosts (Wijayawardena *et al.* 2013). Controversy often accompanies claims of HGT. Bhagya

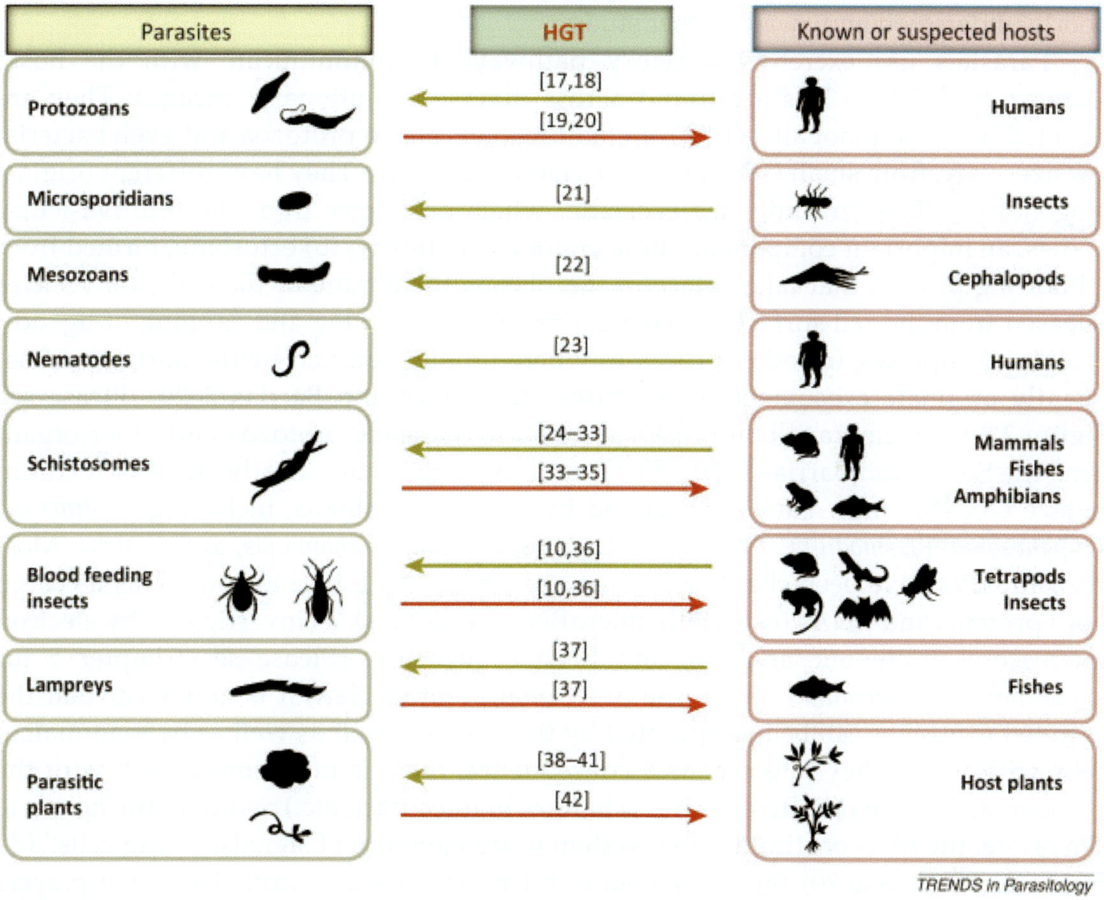

Fig. 2.7 ■ Putative horizontal gene transfer between parasites and hosts. The arrows indicate the inferred direction of HGT. Corresponding citations 10, 17, 18, 19, 20, 21, 22, 23, 24, 25, 26, 27, 28, 29, 30, 31, 32, 33, 34, 35, 36, 37, 38, 39, 40, 41, 42 are indicated on top of the arrows, and are available in Wijayawardena *et al.* (2013). Courtesy: Wijayawardena *et al.* *Trends Parasitol* 2013;29:329–38. Reproduced with permission from Elsevier.

Wijayawardena (Purdue University, West Lafayette, Indiana) and colleagues have analyzed 13 published cases on HGT in schistosomiasis and concluded that the reported cases of schistosome-associated HGT may be due to technical artifacts as opposed to biological reality (Wijayawardena *et al.* 2015). The availability of genomes from hosts and parasites allow further analysis with regard to the occurrence, prevalence, and overall importance of HGT in host-parasite coevolution. "LGT has played an important role in the adaptation of many successful parasite lineages to their host and interactions with other host-associated microbes" (Sibbald *et al.* 2020). HGT has played a role in the adaptation of eukaryotic microbes to new environments and conditions (such as *Blastocyst* in the mammalian gut). However, the "how" and "how often" (mechanisms and frequency) of HGT in eukaryotes (including parasitic protozoa and helminths) are still poorly understood and await further study.

"Parasites use excretory-secretory pathways to communicate with the host" (Nawaz *et al.* 2019). EVs are found across diverse evolutionary lineages. They are secreted by most, if not all, cells, from mammalian cells to protozoa and even bacteria. EV sizes vary, from small (100–200 nm) to large (>200 nm). They have different origins; biogenesis of EVs "includes (a) exosome, which originates from the multivesicular bodies, an important component of the endocytic pathway; (b) ectosome, formed from a budding process that takes place in the plasma membrane of the cells; (c) vesicles released from the cell surface following a process of patching and capping of ligand/receptor complexes; (d) other processes where tubules secreted by the parasite subsequently originate exosome-like structures" (de Souza and Barrias 2020). Please see Figure 2.8 for membrane-bound EVs secreted by parasitic protozoa and other organisms (de Souza and Barrias 2020). EVs found in protozoa are mostly small or medium in size (200–400 nm). They are secreted by parasitic protozoa, including *Leishmania, Trypanosoma, Plasmodium, Toxoplasma, Cryptosporidium, Trichomonas*, and *Giardia*. Most parasitic EVs have been characterized as exosomes, and found to contain as its cargo both proteins and RNAs (especially microRNAs, miRNAs), as investigated by electron microscopy, proteomic analysis, and RNA sequencing. [Please see Chapter 5 for exosomes of *Leishmania*.] "From the functional point of view, it is now clear that the secreted exosomes can be incorporated by the parasite itself as well as by mammalian cells with which they interact. As a consequence, there is interference both with the parasite (induction of differentiation, changes in infectivity, etc.) and with the host cell. Therefore, the EVs constitute a new system of transference of signals among cells" (de Souza and Barrias 2020). Similarly, helminth EVs have been identified as major players in the host-parasite interaction and provide a mechanism for the delivery of a range of parasite molecules (proteins, lipids, nucleic acids) to host cells. Using a total of 25 parasitic helminth genomes for analysis, it has been shown that helminths display phylum level divergence of proteins associated with loading RNA into exosomes. "Determining the expression patterns of these proteins, in combination with functional studies, could reveal which helminth proteins are the key drivers of EV biogen-

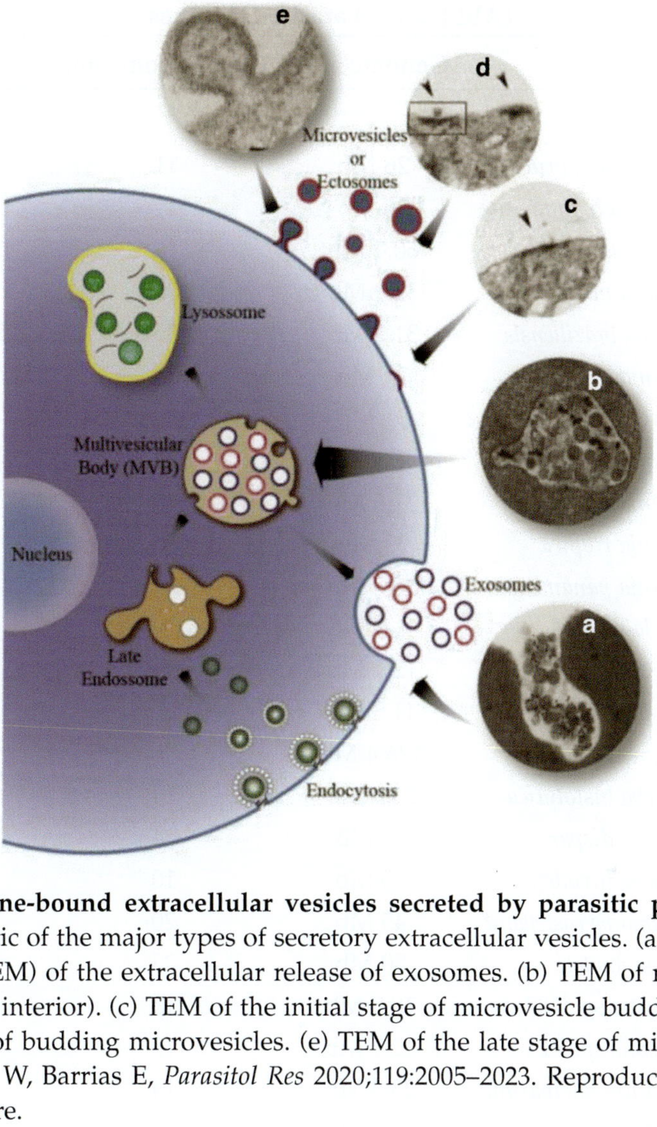

Fig. 2.8 ■ Membrane-bound extracellular vesicles secreted by parasitic protozoa and other organisms. Schematic of the major types of secretory extracellular vesicles. (a) Transmission electron microscopy (TEM) of the extracellular release of exosomes. (b) TEM of multivesicular body (note vesicles in the interior). (c) TEM of the initial stage of microvesicle budding. (d) TEM of the intermediate stage of budding microvesicles. (e) TEM of the late stage of microvesicle budding. Courtesy: de Souza W, Barrias E, *Parasitol Res* 2020;119:2005–2023. Reproduced with permission from Springer Nature.

esis and identify targets to block EV production for novel anti-parasitic therapies" (Bennett *et al.* 2020).

It has been said that the next big challenge is to determine the best way to translate the insights obtained from genomics into new, robust chemical leads that will form the basis of innovative drug discovery. One common application is to scan the genomes for potential drug targets. This is especially important when considering existing drugs for other human diseases that may be applicable to the parasitic protozoa and helminths (drug repurposing). Please see Table 2.1 for genomes of human parasitic protozoa and helminths.

TABLE 2.1: Parasite Genomes.

Year	Species	Genome size	Chromosome no.	Genes	Current
Protozoa					
2005	*Trypanosoma b. brucei*	26 Mb	11	9,068	11,703
2010	*Trypanosoma b. gambiense*	26 Mb	11	10,000	8,082
2005	*Trypanosoma cruzi*	60.4 Mb	41	22,570	10,596
2005	*Leishmania major*	32.9 Mb	36	8,272	9,378
2007	*Leishmania braziliensis*	31.2 Mb	35	8,153	8,493
2007	*Leishmania infantum*	32 Mb	36	8,154	8,748
2011	*Leishmania mexicana*	31 Mb	34	8,250	8,677
2011	*Leishmania donovani*	32.1 Mb	36	8,252	8,135
2011	*Leishmania tarentolae*	31.6 Mb	36	8,201	8,530
2014	*Leishmania tropica*	33 Mb	36	8,938	8,938
2015	*Leishmania panamensis*	30.7 Mb	35	8,246	8,778
2007	*Giardia lamblia A*	11.7 Mb	5	6,470	9,747
2009	*Giardia lamblia B*	12.1 Mb	5	4,691	4,562
2010	*Giardia lamblia E*	11.5 Mb	5	5,012	5,159
2007	*Trichomonas vaginalis*	176.4 Mb	6	59,681	98,611
2005	*Entamoeba histolytica*	23.8 Mb	14	9,938	8,333
2012	*Entamoeba dispar*	23 Mb	14	8,748	
2013	*Entamoeba invadens*	40 Mb	10	11,549	12,007
2013	*Acanthamoeba castellanii*	45 Mb	20	15,455	15,655
2014	*Naegleria fowleri*	30 Mb	23	17,252	13,252
2011	*Blastocystis sp.* ST7	18.8 Mb	15	6,020	
2015	*Blastocystis sp.* ST4	12.9 Mb	15	5,713	
2002	*Plasmodium falciparum*	23.3 Mb	14	5,268	5,712
2008	*Plasmodium vivax*	29.1 Mb	14	5,433	5,665
2008	*Plasmodium knowlesi*	24.4 Mb	14	5,188	5,483
2017	*Plasmodium malariae*	33.6 Mb	14	6,540	6,709
2017	*Plasmodium ovale curtisi*	33.5 Mb	14	7,132	7,280
2017	*Plasmodium ovale wallikeri*	33.5 Mb	14	7,052	
2012	*Babesia microti*	6.6 Mb	4	3,513	3,685
2014	*Babesia divergens*	9.5 Mb	4	4,134	4,187
2012	*Toxoplasma gondii*	66 Mb	14	8,322	8,920

TABLE 2.1: (*Continued*)

Year	Species	Genome size	Chromosome no.	Genes	Current
2004	*Cryptosporidium parvum*	9.1 Mb	8	3,807	4,020
2004	*Cryptosporidium hominis*	9.2 Mb	8	3,994	
2016	*Cyclospora cayetanensis*	44 Mb	?	7,457	7,455
Helminths					
2009	*Schistosoma mansoni*	381 Mb	16 (2n)	13,184	10,831
2009	*Schistosoma japonicum*	403 Mb	16 (2n)	13,469	12,738
2012	*Schistosoma hematobium*	385 Mb	16 (2n)	13,073	
2015	*Fasciola hepatica*	1.3 Gb	20 (2n)	15,740	15,739
2011	*Clonorchis sinensis*	516 Mb	14 (2n)	16,258	13,634
2014	*Opisthorchis viverrini*	634.5Mb	12 (2n)	16,356	
2019	*Opisthorchis felineus*	684 Mb	14 (2n)	21,036	
2018	*Paragonimus westermani*	1.1 Gb	22 (2n)	12,852	
2013	*Taenia solium*	122 Mb	18 (2n)	12,490	12,481
2016	*Taenia saginata*	169 Mb	18 (2n)	13,161	
2016	*Taenia asiatica*	168 Mb	18 (2n)	13,323	10,331
2014	*Diphyllobothrium latum*	531 Mb	18 (2n)	19,966	16,335
2019	*Hymenolepis diminuta*	166 Mb	12 (2n)	11,271	
2019	*Hymenolepis nana*	163 Mb	12 (2n)	13,777	
2013	*Echinococcus granulosus*	152 Mb	18 (2n)	10,231	10,245
2013	*Echinococcus multilocularis*	115 Mb	18 (2n)	10,345	10,150
2017	*Echinococcus canadensis*	115 Mb	18 (2n)	11,449	
2014	*Spirometra erinaceieuropaei*	1.26 Gb	18 (2n)	39,856	39,557
2007	*Brugia malayi*	94 Mb	10 (2n) 4A+XY	11,515	17,989
2015	*Brugia pahangi*	85.4 Mb	10 (2n) 4A+XY	9,687	14,674
2019	*Brugia timori*	65 Mb	10 (2n) 4A+XY	16,203	
2016	*Wuchereria bancrofti*	81.5 Mb	10 (2n) 4A+XY	13,247	13,134
2014	*Loa loa*	91.4 Mb	12 F, 11M (2n) 5A+X0	14,907	15,445
2017	*Onchocerca volvulus*	97 Mb	8 (2n) 3A+XY	12,143	11,300
2014	*Dracunculus medinensis*	103 Mb	?	10,969	
2014	*Necator americanus*	244 Mb	12F & 11M (2n)	19,151	19,153

(*Continued*)

TABLE 2.1: *(Continued)*

Year	Species	Genome size	Chromosome no.	Genes	Current
2014	*Ancylostoma duodenale*	333 Mb	12F & 11M (2n)	27,485	
2015	*Ancylostoma ceylanicum*	313 Mb	12F & 11M (2n)	30,738	15,892
2011	*Ascaris suum*	273 MB	24 (2n)	18,542	15,260
2014	*Ascaris lumbricoides*	317 Mb	24 (2n)	23,604	23,604
2014	*Trichuris trichiura*	75.2 Mb	8F & 7M (2n)	9,560	9,856
2014	*Trichuris suis*	83.6 M/87.2 F	6 (2n)	14,781 M/14,470 F	9,831
2016	*Strongyloides stercoralis*	42.6 Mb	3	13,098	11,244
2015	*Angiostrongylus cantonensis*	260 Mb	12 F & 11 M (2n)	17,482	14,520
2011	*Trichinella spiralis*	64 Mb	6 F & 5 M (2n)	15,808	16,380
2019	*Trichinella nativa*	49 Mb	12 F & 11 M (2n)	10,175	
2014	*Enterobius vermicularis*	150 Mb	?	12,895	
2014	*Anisakis simplex*	127 Mb	?	20,971	
2015	*Toxocara canis*	317 Mb	18	18,596	20,264

Source: Data from original publications, databases of parasitic protozoa, Eukaryotic Pathogens Database https://veupathdb.org/veupathdb/app International Helminth Genomes Consortium 2019 https://www.nature.com/articles/s41588-018-0262-1 and Nematode.net http://www.nematode.net/.

2.6 Therapy & Diagnosis of Parasitic Diseases

Parasitic diseases are infectious diseases caused by protozoa and helminths; they are subject to public health interventions. Steps taken to manage infections involve gaining control, elimination of disease, elimination of infection, and eradication/extinction of the infectious agent. We start with definitions: "**Control**: The reduction of disease incidence, prevalence, morbidity or mortality to a locally acceptable level as a result of deliberate efforts; continued intervention measures are required to maintain the reduction. Example: Diarrheal diseases. **Elimination of disease**: Reduction to zero of the incidence of a specified disease in a defined geographical area as a result of deliberate efforts; continued intervention measures are required. Example: Neonatal tetanus. **Elimination of infections**: Reduction to zero of the incidence of infection caused by a specific agent in a defined geographical area as a result of deliberate efforts; continued measures to prevent re-establishment of transmission are required. Examples: Measles, Poliomyelitis. **Eradication**: Permanent reduction to zero of the worldwide incidence of infection caused by a specific agent as a result of deliberate efforts; intervention measures are no longer needed. Example: Smallpox. **Extinction**: The specific infectious agent no longer exists in nature or in the laboratory. Example: none" (Dowdle 1998). Smallpox was eradicated in 1980; no cases of naturally occurring smallpox have happened since. The next example of eradication may belong to guinea worm disease (aka dracunculiasis). [Please see Chapter 19 for dracuculiasis.]

The London Declaration on Neglected Tropical Diseases signed on January 30, 2012 was an intervention into the spread of human parasitic diseases. The meeting was organized by Margaret Chan (Director-General of WHO) and Bill Gates (Bill & Melinda Gates Foundation), and attended by officials from WHO, World Bank, governments (including US and UK), and 13 leading pharmaceutical companies (including Merck and GlaxoSmithKline). "With the right commitment, coordination and collaboration, the public and private sectors will work together to enable the more than a billion people suffering from NTDs to lead healthier and more productive lives — helping the world's poorest build self-sufficiency. As partners, with our varied skills and contributions, we commit to doing our part to: • Sustain, expand and extend programmes that ensure the necessary supply of drugs and other interventions to help eradicate Guinea worm disease, and help eliminate by 2020 lymphatic filariasis, leprosy, sleeping sickness (human African trypanosomiasis) and blinding trachoma. • Sustain, expand and extend drug access programmes to ensure the necessary supply of drugs and other interventions to help control by 2020 schistosomiasis, soil-transmitted helminthes, Chagas disease, visceral leishmaniasis and river blindness (onchocerciasis)..."[8]

As noted in the declaration, these are a special arrangement known as public-private partnership (**PPP**) or product development partnership (**PDP**). These partnerships are set up because developing drugs for parasitic diseases are not of interest to pharmaceutical companies. Although important to the needs of countries with inhabitants suffering from parasitic diseases, the drugs are not profitable to the companies. There is no incentive to develop novel anti-parasitic drugs. Drug discovery is a high-risk, expensive and lengthy process. It may take over a decade; the costs are high. For one estimate, "after accounting for the costs of failed trials, the median capitalized research and development investment to bring a new drug to market was estimated at $985.3 million" (Wouters *et al.* 2020). For another, estimated costs for bringing a new drug to market amount to over US $2 billion: "total pre-approval cost estimate of $2,558 million (2013 dollars)" and post-approval R&D costs "increases the cost estimate to $2,870 million (2013 dollars)" (DiMasi *et al.* 2016).

Pharmaceutical companies protect their new drugs by getting patents before any drug development. However, another company may work to circumvent the patent in order to put the drug's analog on the market. Hence, when a new compound is patented, the filer includes an extensive list of all related compounds and their potential uses as "claims" in order to exclude potential competitors.

Drug development has several stages: target identification and validation, assay development, screening to identify hits, synthesis and assessment of analogs to develop structure-activity relationship (**SAR**) and identify leads, preclinical development and clinical evaluation. Criteria for hits, leads, and drug candidates must be identified. High throughput screening assays may be established. Assays can be based on parasite-specific targets,

[8] https://www.who.int/neglected_diseases/London_Declaration_NTDs.pdf?ua=1

such as an essential enzyme, or they can be based on phenotypes, such as growth/survival of the specific parasite (Pink *et al.* 2005). Parasitic diseases can be treated by drugs and prevented by vaccines. The concept of **selective toxicity** is for the drug to kill parasites while sparing the host. Development of drugs for neglected tropical diseases (NTDs) has to be designed to the needs of disease-control programs in the affected regions, i.e., field-driven. Critical needs for anti-parasitic drugs have to stress on low costs, short treatment regimens, and the ability to use the drugs safely in the absence of close medical supervision. For delivery of anti-parasitic drugs to the affected and potentially affected individuals, there can be mass drug administration (**MDA**) — treating all individuals in an area, and the more sophisticated mass screening and treatment (**MSAT**) (Croft 2016).

Various methods are possible for the drug development of parasitic diseases. Drugs have been developed by the piggy-back approach, by finding new use of existing drugs (repurposing/repositioning), by making combinations of existing drugs, and by improving current drugs. Novel venues have been attempted, notably open source drug discovery (Robertson *et al.* 2014). As an example, open collaboration on the internet has led to the technique getting the non-bitter active enantiomer of praziquantel (drug for schistosomiasis) (Woelfle *et al.* 2011). For the genomes and mechanisms of drug action for trypanosomes and malaria parasites, David Horn (University of Dundee) and Manoj Duraisingh (Harvard School of Public Health) commented: "A better understanding of drug transport (uptake and efflux), drug metabolism and the identification of drug targets, and mechanisms of drug resistance would facilitate the development of more effective therapies" (Horn and Duraisingh 2014). Drug discovery has been assisted by open sources of protein structures at the Protein Data Bank (**PDB**), as David Goodsell (Rutgers) and colleagues stated: "Recently published work showed that the PDB archival holdings facilitated discovery of 90% of the 210 new drugs approved by the US Food and Drug Administration 2010–2016" (Goodsell *et al.* 2020). For readers interested to know more, we recommend *The Drug Hunters* by Donald Kirsch and Ogi Ogas (2017) for an entertaining account of drug discovery. In the book Satoshi Omura and ivermectin were mentioned. Recognition of anti-parasitic drug discovery has led to the 2015 Nobel Prize in Physiology or Medicine — with one half jointly to William Campbell and Satoshi Ōmura for their discoveries concerning a novel therapy against infections caused by roundworm parasites, and the other half to Tu Youyou for her discoveries concerning a novel therapy against malaria.[9]

2.7 Parasitic Diseases & Bioethics

There is a term known as the **parasitologist's dilemma**. Parasites most commonly affect poor populations. If parasites are removed, there will be a potential for overpopulation. Is the removal of parasites really beneficial to that impacted population?

The situation is similar to sending aid to people in need. This has been viewed as short term relief. Population in poverty tends to have higher birth rates. Population and

[9] https://www.nobelprize.org/prizes/medicine/2015/summary/

subsistence can be traced to the original work of Thomas Robert Malthus. Malthus published *Principles of Populations* (first edition in 1798); his work influenced the thoughts of Charles Darwin and Alfred Russell Wallace on evolution.

The power of population is greater than the power of subsistence. Population increases in a geometrical ratio whereas subsistence increases in a linear ratio. Hence, part of the dilemma would suggest that there needs to exist negative checks on the population (such as wars and famines). Melinda Gates wrote, in *Myth Three: Saving lives leads to overpopulation*: "We make the future sustainable when we invest in the poor, not when we insist on their suffering."[10]

Currently, we are aware of *An Inconvenient Truth* (2006) and *An Inconvenient Sequel* (2017) (films by Al Gore on climatic change/global warming). We have concerns about the availability of resources like energy and clean water (think about the 2014 Flint water crisis: lead contamination in drinking water in the city of Flint in Michigan, USA).

Going back to the topic of parasitic diseases and their control, aspects of **bioethics** must be considered. There are multiple theories of ethics: utilitarianism (greatest good for the greatest numbers): deontology (respect for collective and individual duties), virtue ethics (cultivating accepted moral character), Rawlsian justice (the most vulnerable must not be made worse off), situation ethics (contextualized to local conditions), and intuitionism (what feels fundamentally fair and just). Is it ethical to use placebo controls against new drugs in clinical trials when some form of effective therapy exists and is the standard of care? What is exploitation? Is deciding to do a clinical trial in the United States versus in another country an economic or a biomedical ethics decision? These questions must be addressed with fairness, logic, and empathy.

Summary & Key Concepts

- Current estimate predicts a total of 8.7 million eukaryotic species on earth; the number is 10–30% of all living species (the majority of which are prokaryotic species).
- Parasitism has evolved independently at least 223 times in the animal kingdom (including 143 times in the arthropods).
- The cellular slime molds differentiate from individual amoebae to multicellular aggregate that develops into a fruiting body composed of spores and stalked cells; the latter die during stalk formation to aid in spore dispersal. Strains of amoebae only differentiate into spores and utilize another strain's stalk; these amoebae are "cheaters," aka "auto-parasites."
- Evolution of nematode parasitism shows a process of several steps: free-living, to phoresy, to necromeny, to parasitism.
- There are 6 general parasitic strategies: parasitoid, parasitic castrator, directly transmitted parasite, trophically transmitted parasite, vector-transmitted parasite, or micropredator.

[10] https://www.gatesfoundation.org/ideas/annual-letters/annual-letter-2014

- The human draft genome was first published in 2000; the first parasitic protozoan genome, for the malaria agent *Plasmodium falciparum*, was published in 2002; the first multicellular parasite genome, for the elephantiasis agent *Brugia malayi*, was published in 2007.
- The 2019 publication by the International Helminth Genome Consortium includes a total of 81 worm genomes.
- Genome mining offers potentials for the development of novel drugs, vaccine candidates, and diagnostic tools.

References

Bennett APS, de la Torre-Escudero E, Robinson MW. Helminth genome analysis reveals conservation of extracellular vesicle biogenesis pathways but divergence of RNA loading machinery between phyla. *Int J Parasitol* 2020;50(9):655–61.

Bensaoud C, Hackenberg M, Kotsyfakis M. Noncoding RNAs in parasite-vector-host interactions. *Trends Parasitol* 2019;35(9):715–24.

Bonner, JT. *The Social Amoebae: The Biology of Cellular Slime Molds*. Princeton, 2009.

Brohus M, Arsov T, Wallace DA, *et al*. Infanticide vs. inherited cardiac arrhythmias. *Europace* 2021;23(3):441–50.

Cantacessi C, Campbell BE, Visser A, *et al*. A portrait of the "SCP/TAPS" proteins of eukaryotes — developing a framework for fundamental research and biotechnological outcomes. *Biotechnol Adv* 2009;27(4):376–88.

Cantacessi C, Gasser RB. SCP/TAPS proteins in helminths — Where to from now? *Mol Cell Probes*. 2012;26(1):54–9.

Chalmers IW, Hoffmann KF. Platyhelminth Venom Allergen-Like (VAL) proteins: Revealing structural diversity, class-specific features and biological associations across the phylum. *Parasitology* 2012;139(10):1231–45.

Costello MJ, May RM, Stork NE. Can we name Earth's species before they go extinct? *Science* 2013;339(6118):413–6.

Croft SL. Neglected tropical diseases in the genomics era: re-evaluating the impact of new drugs and mass drug administration. *Genome Biol* 2016;17:46.

de Souza W, Barrias ES. Membrane-bound extracellular vesicles secreted by parasitic protozoa: Cellular structures involved in the communication between cells. *Parasitol Res* 2020;119(7): 2005–23.

Dieterich C, Sommer RJ. How to become a parasite — Lessons from the genomes of nematodes. *Trends Genet* 2009;25(5):203–9.

DiMasi JA, Grabowski HG, Hansen RW. Innovation in the pharmaceutical industry: New estimates of R&D costs. *J Health Econ* 2016;47:20–33.

Dobson AP. Yellowstone wolves and the forces that structure natural systems. *PLoS Biol* 2014;12(12):e1002025.

Dobson A, Lafferty KD, Kuris AM, Hechinger RF, Jetz W. Colloquium paper: homage to Linnaeus: How many parasites? How many hosts? *Proc Natl Acad Sci USA* 2008;105(1(1)):11482–9.

Doolittle WF. You are what you eat: A gene transfer ratchet could account for bacterial genes in eukaryotic nuclear genomes. *Trends Genet* 1998;14(8):307–11.

Dougherty ER, Carlson CJ, Bueno VM, *et al*. Paradigms for parasite conservation. *Conserv Biol* 2016;30(4):724–33.

Dowdle WR. The principles of disease elimination and eradication. *Bull World Health Organ* 1998;76(2(2)):22–5.

El Atab O, Darwiche R, Truax NJ, *et al*. *Necator americanus Ancylostoma* Secreted Protein-2 (Na-ASP-2) binds an ascaroside (ascr#3) in its fatty acid binding site. *Front Chem* 2020;8:608296.

Fong D, Bonner JT. Proteases in cellular slime mold development: Evidence for their involvement. *Proc Natl Acad Sci USA* 1979;76(12):6481–5.

Frank SA, Schmid-Hempel P. Mechanisms of pathogenesis and the evolution of parasite virulence. *J Evol Biol* 2008;21(2):396–404.

Gibbs GM, Roelants K, O'Bryan MK. The CAP superfamily: Cysteine-rich secretory proteins, antigen 5, and pathogenesis-related 1 proteins — roles in reproduction, cancer, and immune defense. *Endocr Rev* 2008;29(7):865–97.

Gilbert IH, Leroy D, Frearson JA. Finding new hits in neglected disease projects: Target or phenotypic based screening? *Current Topics in Medicinal Chemistry* 2011;11(10):1284–91.

Goodsell DS, Zardecki C, Di Costanzo L, *et al*. RCSB Protein Data Bank: Enabling biomedical research and drug discovery. *Protein Sci* 2020;29(1):52–65.

Goodwin S, McPherson JD, McCombie WR. Coming of age: Ten years of next-generation sequencing technologies. *Nat Rev Genet* 2016;17(6):333–51.

Goswami U. Some cytogenetical aspects of genus *Trichuris* (Nematoda). *Curr Sci* 1978;47(11): 368–371.

Green ED, Gunter C, Biesecker LG, *et al*. Strategic vision for improving human health at The Forefront of Genomics. *Nature* 2020;586(7831):683–92.

Horn D, Duraisingh MT. Antiparasitic chemotherapy: From genomes to mechanisms. *Annu Rev Pharmacol Toxicol* 2014;54:71–94.

International Helminth Genomes Consortium. Comparative genomics of the major parasitic worms. *Nat Genet* 2019;51(1):163–74.

Jain M, Olsen HE, Paten B, Akeson M. The Oxford Nanopore MinION: Delivery of nanopore sequencing to the genomics community. *Genome Biol*. 2016;17(1):239.

Jain M, Koren S, Miga KH, *et al*. Nanopore sequencing and assembly of a human genome with ultra-long reads. *Nat Biotechnol* 2018;36(4):338–345. doi: 10.1038/nbt.4060.

Jensen TZT, Niemann J, Iversen KH, *et al*. A 5700 year-old human genome and oral microbiome from chewed birch pitch. *Nat Commun* 2019;10(1):5520.

Kirsch DR, Ogas O. *The Drug Hunters*. Arcade, New York, 2017.

Kitts PA, Church DM, Thibaud-Nissen F, *et al*. Assembly: A resource for assembled genomes at NCBI. *Nucleic Acids Res*. 2016 Jan 4;44(D1):D73–80. doi: 10.1093/nar/gkv1226. Epub 2015 Nov 17.

Larsen BB, Miller EC, Rhodes MK, Wiens JJ. Inordinate fondness multiplied and redistributed: the number of species on Earth and the new pie of life. *The Quarterly Review of Biology* 2017;92(3):229–65.

Li Y, Baptista RP, Kissinger JC. Noncoding RNAs in apicomplexan parasites: An update. *Trends Parasitol* 2020;36(10):835–49.

Lv Z, Wu Z, Zhang L, *et al*. Genome mining offers a new starting point for parasitology research. *Parasitol Res* 2015;114(2):399–409.

McVeigh P. Post-genomic progress in helminth parasitology. *Parasitology* 2020;147(8):835–40.

Madgwick PG, Stewart B, Belcher LJ, Thompson CRL, Wolf JB. Strategic investment explains patterns of cooperation and cheating in a microbe. *Proc Natl Acad Sci USA* 2018;115(21):E4823–E4832.

Mora C, Tittensor DP, Adl S, Simpson AG, Worm B. How many species are there on Earth and in the ocean? *PLoS Biol* 2011;9(8):e1001127.

Müller-Taubenberger A, Kortholt A, Eichinger L. Simple system — Substantial share: The use of *Dictyostelium* in cell biology and molecular medicine. *Eur J Cell Biol* 2013;92(2):45–53.

Nawaz M, Malik MI, Hameed M, Zhou J. Research progress on the composition and function of parasite-derived exosomes. *Acta Trop* 2019;196:30–36.

Noh S, Geist KS, Tian X, Strassmann JE, Queller DC. Genetic signatures of microbial altruism and cheating in social amoebas in the wild. *Proc Natl Acad Sci USA* 2018;115(12):3096–3101.

Pink R, Hudson A, Mouriès MA, Bendig M. Opportunities and challenges in antiparasitic drug discovery. *Nat Rev Drug Discov* 2005;4(9):727–40.

Poulin R, Randhawa HS. Evolution of parasitism along convergent lines: From ecology to genomics. *Parasitology* 2015;142(1(1)):S6–S15.

Pruitt KD, Tatusova T, Brown GR, Maglott DR. NCBI Reference Sequences (RefSeq): Current status, new features and genome annotation policy. *Nucleic Acids Res* 2012;40(Database issue):D130–5.

Pushkarev D, Neff NF, Quake SR. Single-molecule sequencing of an individual human genome. *Nat Biotechnol* 2009;27(9):847–52.

Robertson MN, Ylioja PM, Williamson AE, *et al*. Open source drug discovery — A limited tutorial. *Parasitology* 2014;141(1):148–57.

Sanders JM, Monogue ML, Jodlowski TZ, Cutrell JB. Pharmacologic treatments for coronavirus disease 2019 (COVID-19): A review. *JAMA* 2020;323(18):1824–36.

Schwarze K, Buchanan J, Taylor JC, Wordsworth S. Are whole-exome and whole-genome sequencing approaches cost-effective? A systematic review of the literature. *Genet Med* 2018;20(10):1122–30.

Shendure J, Balasubramanian S, Church GM, *et al*. DNA sequencing at 40: Past, present and future. *Nature* 2017;550(7676):345–53.

Sibbald SJ, Eme L, Archibald JM, Roger AJ. Lateral gene transfer mechanisms and pan-genomes in eukaryotes. *Trends Parasitol* 2020;36(11):927–41.

Stairs CW, Eme L, Muñoz-Gómez SA, *et al*. Microbial eukaryotes have adapted to hypoxia by horizontal acquisitions of a gene involved in rhodoquinone biosynthesis. *Elife* 2018;7:e34292.

Thomas SR, Elkinton JS. Pathogenicity and virulence. *J Invertebr Pathol* 2004;85(3):146–51.

Weinstein SB, Kuris AM. Independent origins of parasitism in Animalia. *Biol Lett* 2016;12(7):20160324.

Wijayawardena BK, Minchella DJ, DeWoody JA. Hosts, parasites, and horizontal gene transfer. *Trends Parasitol* 2013;29(7):329–38.

Wijayawardena BK, Minchella DJ, DeWoody JA. Horizontal gene transfer in schistosomes: A critical assessment. *Mol Biochem Parasitol* 2015;201(1):57–65.

Wilbers RHP, Schneiter R, Holterman MHM, *et al*. Secreted venom allergen-like proteins of helminths: Conserved modulators of host responses in animals and plants. *PLoS Pathog* 2018;14(10):e1007300.

Windsor DA. Most of the species on Earth are parasites. *Int J Parasitol* 1998;28(12):1939–41.

Woelfle M, Seerden JP, de Gooijer J, Pouwer K, Olliaro P, Todd MH. Resolution of praziquantel. *PLoS Negl Trop Dis* 2011;5(9):e1260.

Wouters OJ, McKee M, Luyten J. Estimated research and development investment needed to bring a new medicine to market, 2009–2018. *JAMA* 2020;323(9):844–53.

3

Immunity and Immunopathology of Host-Parasite Interactions

3.1 Immunological Basis of Host-Parasite Interactions

Pathogens, including parasites, are agents that cause human diseases. Parasites induce the host immune response: infection and immunity. Parasites are capable of evading host immune response. This is seen in the famous example of antigenic variation practiced by trypanosomes, *Giardia*, and the malaria parasites. [More detailed discussions centered around species of human parasites will take place in later chapters.] For now, we focus on host immunity in general, and how it may spur an overzealous response that damages the host tissues (as seen in **immunopathology**).

Much of the diseases caused by parasites are directly related to host immune defense mechanisms. Parasites interact with the host's immunity and may cause an inflammatory response. Parasitic infections may result in traumatic effects on the host organism. Living parasites can syphon nutrition or produce toxins detrimental to the host. For example, *Giardia* and *Ascaris* infections may lead to malnutrition. For host-parasite interactions, the host may be susceptible or resistant; the parasite may be infective or non-infective. There exists the general concept of **tolerance**, maintenance of host health (fitness) at a given parasite burden (referring to the number of parasites in the host), parasite's virulence, and pathogenicity (Burgan *et al.* 2019). For immune response, there is the concept of **premunition**, the idea parasites are held in check by the host, who remains asymptomatic. The state of host immunity results in a persistent latent infection. Examples of premunition include malaria, toxoplasmiasis, and Chagas' disease. For the concept of **concomitant immunity**, a host is infected with one or a few parasites of the same species. These parasites may cause host morbidity, but in the meantime the host is immune towards further infections from other parasites of the same or closely related species. An example of concomitant immunity is witnessed during schistosomiasis.

Because a basic understanding of the immune response to parasites is important, a brief introduction of the host immune response is provided in discussion on inflammation,

TABLE 3.1: Overview of the defining features of innate and adaptive immunity. Courtesy: Marshall *et al. Allergy Asthma Clin Immunol* 2018;14(2):49. Reproduced with permission from *Allergy Asthma & Clinical Immunology* with Creative Commons Attribution 4.0 (CC-BY) International License.

	Innate immune system	Adaptive immune system
Cells	Hematopoietic cells: • Macrophages • Dendritic cells • Mast cells • Neutrophils • Basophils • Eosinophils • NK cells • T cells Non-hematopoietic cells • Epithelial cells (skin, airways, gastrointestinal tract)	Hematopoietic cells: • T cells • B cells
Molecules	• Cytokines • Complement • Proteins and glycoprotein	• Antibodies (Ig) • Cytokines
Response time	• Immediate	• Delayed by hours to days
Immunologic memory	• None: responses are the same with each exposure	• Responsiveness enhanced by repeated antigen exposure

innate, and adaptive immunity. Topics include molecules (pattern recognition receptors, antibodies), cells (macrophages, dendritic cells, T and B lymphocytes), and general immunity responses (type 1, 2 and 3) (Annunziato *et al.* 2015; Marshall *et al.* 2018; Abbas *et al.* 2020). In addition, parasites' actions on the immune system will be mentioned, as well as the hygiene hypothesis and the IgE antibody. Please see Table 3.1 for an overview of innate and adaptive immunity (Marshall *et al.* 2018).

3.2 Innate and Adaptive Immunity

Immunity involves the recognition of **self** and **non-self**. This capacity of differentiation/detection has been seen in the primitive invertebrate, the sponge (Porifera). Mammals have both innate and adaptive (acquired) immunity, and there are interactions, crosstalk, and synergism between the two. Phylogenetically, innate immunity is found in invertebrates, as phagocytes were first studied in the starfish larvae (echinoderms). Acquired immunity is found in jawed vertebrates, starting from cartilaginous fish (sharks, rays). The origin of the adult mammalian innate and adaptive immune cells comes from the bone marrow, where the presence of hematopoietic stem cells (**HSCs**) can both self-renew

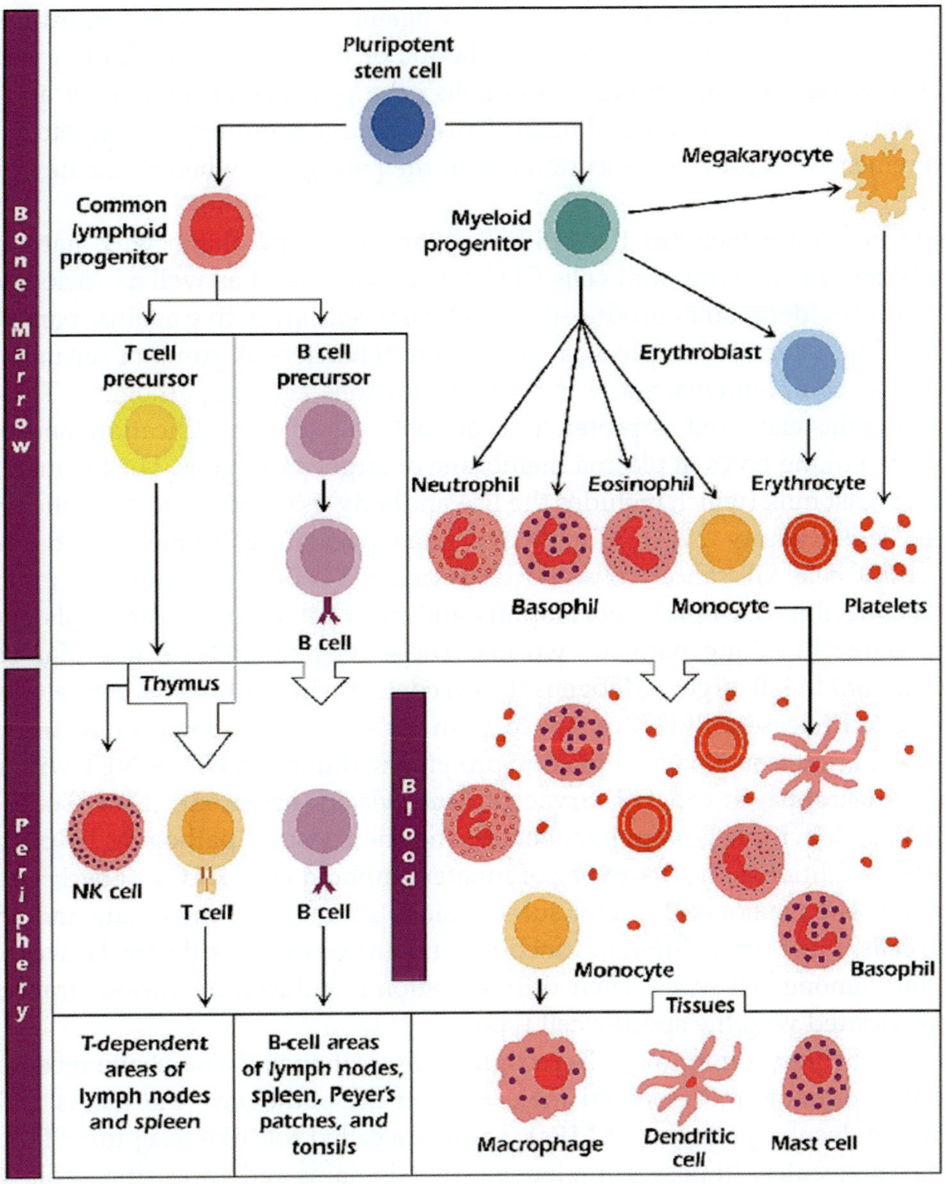

Fig. 3.1 ■ Immune cell differentiation. Developmental pathways of various hematopoietic cells from pluripotent bone marrow stem cells. Courtesy: Coico R, Sunshine G. *Immunology: A Short Course*, 5th ed., 2013. Reproduced with permission from Wiley and Richard Coico.

and differentiate into terminally differentiated cell types composed of all the cells for both innate and adaptive immunity. Please see Figure 3.1 for immune cell differentiation (Coico and Sunshine 2013).

The host immune defense consists of innate immunity, which mediates the initial protection against infections, and adaptive immunity, which develops more slowly and mediates the later, even more effective defense against infections. With regard to time of response, innate immunity takes minutes, hours, or days, whereas adaptive immunity takes days, weeks, or even months to establish the presence of memory B and T cells against the reintroduction of a pathogen. Thus, adaptive immunity has **memory** (allowing it to remember a previous encounter with the pathogen), whereas innate immunity does not.

Innate immunity includes the epithelial barrier (skin), phagocytes, natural killer (**NK**) cells, and innate lymphoid cells (ILCs). Salt from sweat as well as various antimicrobial peptides (**defensins**) produced by epithelial cells are active against parasites and pathogens. These function as physical and chemical barriers. A group of serum proteins, referred to as **complements**, serve important functions against pathogens. These are a series of proteins classified as proteinases, act with cascade amplification, and perform their role by poking holes in plasma membrane of target pathogens. For the mammalian newborn, breast milk (which includes the IgA antibody) is cytotoxic to parasitic protozoa such as *Giardia* (Kutty 2014). Circulatory monocytes differentiate into tissue macrophages. NK cells kill cancer cells and virus-infected cells. Other innate immune cells include neutrophils, basophils, eosinophils and mast cells. Both eosinophils and mast cells are active in killing parasitic worms. These cells can release granular contents (degranulation) to kill target pathogens. Upon contact with pathogens, activated neutrophils lyse, and release cellular content to form the neutrophil extracellular trap (**NET**). NET can kill *Leishmania* (via host histone proteins within the NET). A NET with neutrophils and macrophages can kill larvae of *Strongyloides* nematode (Díaz-Godínez and Carrero 2019). Macrophages are phagocytes, and they destroy pathogens by phagocytosis. A recent addition is the discovery of innate lymphoid cells (**ILCs**) (Eberl *et al.* 2015). Immunologists have noticed further sub-divisions among both the innate and adaptive immune cells, these serve different functions and are known as **subsets**. However, there is flexibility among cell types. Their differentiation is induced by various transcription factors associated with the specific cell types.

How do the innate immune cells recognize the pathogens? They have receptors that bind to the common and essential molecules on the pathogens, known as pathogen-associated molecular patterns (**PAMPs**). These are called toll-like receptors (**TLRs**), and 10 of these molecules, all possessing leucine-rich domains and appearing sickle-shaped, have been identified in humans. TLR-4 was first found in the insect *Drosophila*, where TLR-4 initiates the signal transduction pathway that ends in the production of an antifungal peptide, the 44-amino acid drosomycin. TLR-4 in mammals (mice and humans) works in the same manner to detect lipopolysaccharide (LPS) of Gram-negative bacteria. The concept of PAMPs has been extended to damaged host cell products (such as nuclear histones becoming extracellular) which are now known as damage-associated molecular patterns (DAMPs). Other recognition molecules of the innate immune cells have since been found. One group, named nucleotide oligomerization domain-like receptors (NOD-like receptors), can aggregate to form a structure known as an **inflammasome** (resulting in production of the proinflammatory cytokine interleukin-1 *beta*, IL-1β). Inflammasomes are cytosolic protein complexes that are assembled in response to cellular stress or upon sensing microbial molecules, culminating in cytokine processing and an inflammatory form of cell death (known as pyroptosis). An inflammasome consists of a sensor molecule, an adaptor protein, and an inflammatory caspase (a proteinase). Inflammasomes are activated in viral, bacterial, fungal, and parasitic diseases, including intracellular parasitic protozoa (*Leishmania, Trypanosoma cruzi, Plasmodium,* and *Toxoplasma*) (de Carvalho and Zamboni 2020).

For each TLR, NLR or other recognition receptor, there is a corresponding gene in the mammalian genome. This differs from adaptive immune cell receptors. An antibody is made from somatic recombination of various gene segments existing in the genome.

3.3 Inflammation

Inflammation is the vascularized tissue's response to injury or infection. Plasma proteins accumulate at the site of infection (or injury), as the local cells secrete chemoattractants and other molecules. Blood leukocytes migrate to the site as a consequence of this activity. Neutrophils and macrophages are concentrated at the site in attempts to remove the pathogen before starting tissue repair. Macrophages produce reactive oxygen and nitrogen intermediates (**ROIs** and RNIs) such as nitric oxide (**NO**) that are toxic to invading pathogens, via NADPH oxidase and inducible nitric oxide synthase (iNOS) pathways, respectively. Macrophages and surrounding cells also produce cytokines. **Cytokines** are small proteins exhibiting specific effects on the interactions, communication and behavior between cells (including immune cells). Cytokines have different functions. Interferon *gamma* (IFNγ) activates macrophages. An early proinflammatory cytokine IL-1β induces fever, as the body's response to infection. **Interleukins** are cytokine notations; different ILs serve different functions (there is functional redundancy among cytokines). The term interleukin comes from these phrases: "as a means of communication" and "deriving from the fact that many of these proteins are produced by leukocytes and act on leukocytes." While acute inflammation is a common result of innate immunity, chronic inflammation causes tissue damage and disease. Fibrosis or granulomas may form when inflammation cannot effectively remove the parasite or pathogen. Moreover, there is the concept of anti-inflammatory response, towards the resolution of chronic inflammation.

Macrophages exhibit proinflammatory or anti-inflammatory functions. These abilities are conveyed through different types of activation. The two subsets are the classically activated macrophages (**CAM**) and the alternately activated macrophages (**AAMs**). Both cell differentiation and cytokine expression are regulated by transcription factors. Nuclear factor *kappa* B (**NFκB**) is the major proinflammatory regulator. A second transcription factor, peroxisome proliferator-activated receptor *gamma* (**PPARγ**), is the major anti-inflammatory regulator. NFκB induces CAM; PPARγ induces AAM. CAMs are for pathogen destruction; AAMs are for tissue remodeling, wound healing and recovery. NFκB activates the expression of iNOS, whose product (NO) kills pathogens such as the intracellular *Leishmania*. PPARγ activates the expression of arginase, which degrades arginine, a precursor for the synthesis of NO. That PPAR is an important area of research can be seen in an online journal named *PPAR Research* (Hindawi Publishing, Egypt).

In some cases, activation of PPARγ will help parasite survival. We and our colleagues have conducted research on leishmaniasis. *Leishmania* parasites are killed by CAM production of NO (Chan *et al.* 2005). AAMs may help survival of the intracellular *Leishmania* parasite. *Leishmania* infection induced PPARγ in an experimental mice model. Furthermore, the dietary phytochemical **curcumin** (found in turmeric and curry) induced the anti-inflammatory transcription factor PPARγ; curcumin was shown to exacerbate visceral leishmaniasis in mice (Adapala and Chan 2008; Chan *et al.* 2012). Parasite infections may modulate gene expression of immune cells; PPARγ may serve as a balance for survival in parasitic infections (Chan *et al.* 2010).

3.4 B and T Lymphocytes

Adaptive immunity includes lymphocytes. B cells, first identified from bursa of chicken (an organ close to the cloaca) and bone marrow of mammals (also fetal liver), and T cells, from the thymus, are involved in specific recognition of pathogens (Gitlin and Nussenzweig 2015). Both **immunoglobulin** (Ig, aka antibody, B-cell receptor, BCR) and T cell receptor (**TCR**) genes are formed in the lymphocytes by somatic recombination of **gene segments** available in the germ line. It is important to note that multiple copies of gene segments allow for the generation of a diverse array (a vast number) of different BCRs and TCRs. There is the concept of **clonal selection theory**: initial availability of various immature lymphocytes (each exhibiting a different BCR or TCR) for the antigen to select particular (the best binding) clones for expansion. An **antigen** can be viewed as any molecule that can elicit an immune response (especially from B cells).

Adaptive immunity can be divided into **humoral** and **cell-mediated immunity**. Humoral immunity acts against extracellular pathogens, whereas cell mediated immunity acts against intracellular pathogens (such as virus and intracellular *Leishmania*). Adaptive immunity is specific, diverse against many antigens, has memory, and is non-reactive to self. B cells are activated to produce antibodies whereas T cells are activated to produce effector T cells. Effector T cells produce cytokines for immune functions. Some effector T cells are cytotoxic; they kill target cells, e.g., CD8 and NKT cells.

Humoral immunity consists of the primary and secondary antibody responses. The primary response takes longer time than the secondary response; the antibody peak is smaller in primary response; antibody types differ, IgM for primary and IgG (or IgE depending on specific situation such as helminth infection) for secondary response. A more efficacious, high-affinity antibody is present during the secondary response (via point mutations on the antigen-binding region of the gene as an outcome of the **affinity maturation** process). The types of antibodies are **IgM, IgG, IgA, IgE** and **IgD**, and the classification is based on antibody heavy chain isotypes/classes (**class switching** from IgM to another type). IgM is important for complement fixation; IgG is the major antibody. IgA is the secretory form, and IgE is for worms and allergies. IgD co-exists with IgM on early B cell surface; exact function is still unclear. An antibody molecule (such as IgG) is made up of 4 polypeptide chains (2 identical heavy chains and 2 identical light chains), each chain with a variable and a constant region (selected from different gene segments during somatic recombination events). Antibodies work in manners such as antibody-dependent cell-mediated cytotoxicity (**ADCC**), where an antibody-coated cell (such as a cancer cell) is recognized and killed by an immune cell, i.e., NK cells. Antibody-coated pathogens (**opsonization**) can be easily recognized and phagocytized by phagocytes, i.e., macrophages. Memory B cells allow the host to respond faster when encountering the same pathogen for a second time.

Cell-mediated immunity is implemented by T cells. CD8-expressing cytotoxic T lymphocytes (**CTL**) kill target cells. CD4-expressing T cells secrete cytokines and are known as helper T cells. [**CD** stands for cluster of differentiation, denoting the cell surface molecules of immune cells.] Helper T cells are divided into subsets: T helper1 (**Th1**), **Th2,** and **Th17** (these 3 are the main subsets; there are others). Regulatory T cells (**Treg**) serve to regulate the immune response. T follicular helper cells (**Tfh**) help B cells in the lymphoid follicles (within the lymph node) to generate improved antibodies (the affinity maturation step mentioned previously). Different cytokines are produced by different T cell types to perform their specific adaptive immune function. Memory T cells allow the host to respond faster when encountering the same pathogen for a second time.

3.5 Antigen Presentation

There is crosstalk between innate and adaptive immunity. This is accomplished through the concept of antigen presentation. Antigen presenting cells (**APCs**) include macrophages, dendritic cells (DCs) and B cells. B cells carry membrane bound immunoglobulins that can recognize any antigen, e.g., small molecules linked to a carrier protein, carbohydrates, proteins, etc. In contrast, T cells only recognize processed protein antigens as peptides, within the context of self and non-self, via the major histocompatibility antigens (MHCs) molecule on the surface of the APCs. Human MHCs are referred to as human leukocyte antigens (**HLAs**).

MHC denotes individuality within the species. There are two groups: **class I and class II MHCs**. Class I is present on the surface of all nucleated cells (absent in red blood cells). Class II is only found on APCs. An antigen is presented two different ways, depending on its source as either extracellular or intracellular. For MHC class II pathway, DC takes in an antigenic pathogen by endocytosis, and the pathogen's protein is degraded by **lysosomal acid proteinases** called cathepsins. The appropriately sized peptides are carried to the binding site (a "groove") on the MHC class II heterodimer protein for transfer to the cell surface enabling them to be presented to CD4 T cells. The CD4 protein and the TCR of the T cell recognize the peptide-MHC II complex. For MHC class I pathway, the cytosolic pathogenic antigen is degraded by proteinases in the **proteasome**. The appropriately sized peptide is transported to the lumen of the endoplasmic reticulum to join the newly

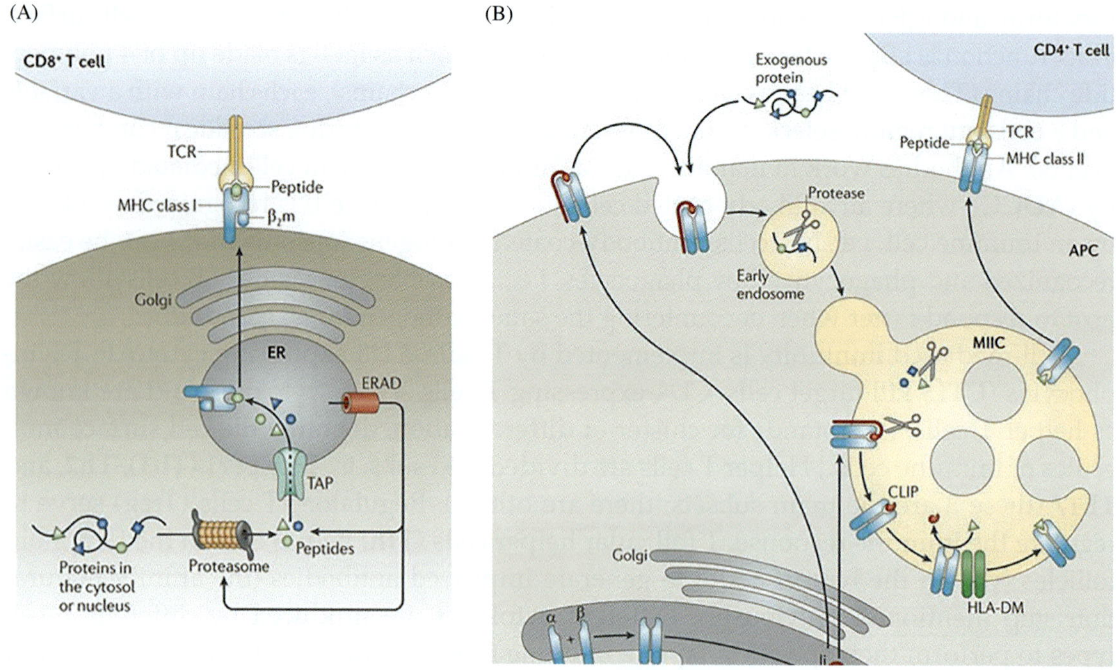

Fig. 3.2 ■ Antigen presentation. (A) Class I. The presentation of intracellular antigenic peptides by MHC class I molecules is the result of a series of reactions. First, antigens are degraded by the proteasome. Then, the resulting peptides are translocated via transporter associated with antigen presentation (TAP) into the endoplasmic reticulum (ER) lumen and loaded onto MHC class I molecules. Peptide–MHC class I complexes are released from the ER and transported via the Golgi to the plasma membrane for antigen presentation to CD8$^+$ T cells. β_2m, β_2-microglobulin; ERAD, ER-associated protein degradation; TCR, T cell receptor. (B) Class II. MHC class II α- and β-chains assemble in the endoplasmic reticulum (ER) and form a complex with the invariant chain (Ii). The Ii–MHC class II heterotrimer is transported through the Golgi to the MHC class II compartment (MIIC), either directly and/or via the plasma membrane. Endocytosed proteins and Ii are degraded by resident proteases in the MIIC. The class II-associated Ii peptide (CLIP) fragment of Ii remains in the peptide-binding groove of the MHC class II dimer and is exchanged for an antigenic peptide with the help of the dedicated chaperone HLA-DM. MHC class II molecules are then transported to the plasma membrane to present antigenic peptides to CD4$^+$ T cells. APC, antigen-presenting cell; TCR, T cell receptor. Courtesy: Neefjes *et al. Nat Rev Immunol* 2011;11:823–36. Reproduced with permission from Springer Nature.

synthesized MHC I heterodimer (sitting on the "groove" binding site). Peptide-MHC I complex is then transported to the cell surface for recognition by CD8 T cells. The CD8 protein and the TCR of the T cell recognize the peptide-MHC I complex. Please see Figures 3.2(A) and 3.2(B) for antigen presentation by Class I and II MHCs, respectively (Neefjes *et al.* 2011). This recognition of a foreign peptide within the context of self MHC spurs the T cell response to antigen presentation (known as **MHC restriction**). Antigen presentation involves APC-T cell interaction with MHC-TCR, followed by co-stimulation (the specific CD proteins, B-7 and CD28, for DC-T cell) and priming cytokine production (to induce T cell differentiation to the appropriate subset) (Jain and Pasare 2017). Activated DCs and mature T cells produce cytokines, while activated B cells produce antibodies. T helper cells can further stimulate B cells and DC. The process aims to destroy the pathogen and also establish memory of this pathogen attack.

3.6 Type 1, 2, & 3 Immunity

Different immune cells produce different cytokines to perform different functions. (However, there can be overlaps.) Interleukin-2 (IL-2), formerly known as T cell growth factor (TCGF), activates all T cells; IL-4 activates Th2; IL-5 activates eosinophils; and IL-10 suppresses Th1. Th2 cells give protective immunity against parasitic helminths. As discovered in a mouse infection model utilizing gene knockout towards IL-4 receptor of specific intestinal cell types, IL-4 and IL-13 were shown to be protective against lumen dwelling worms. The pair of interleukins induce intestinal epithelial cells (IEC) to differentiate into goblet cells; these cells secrete resistin-like molecule (RELM) as a means to inhibit the ability of worms to properly feed on host tissues, resulting in their spontaneous expulsion. The mechanism is independent of T or B cell function, or AAM activation (Herbert *et al.* 2009). The lab mouse has been the favorite animal model for immunologists. Here, we quote Bali Pulendran and Mark Davis (Stanford): "In the past decade there has been an explosion of new approaches and technologies to explore the human immune system with unprecedented precision." They quote Sydney Brenner, who remarked in 2008, "We don't have to look for a model organism anymore. Because we are the model organisms." The Stanford scientists wrote: "We propose that studying the immune system in humans, who are genetically diverse and afflicted by a multitude of diseases, offers both a direct link to medicine (i.e., 'translation') and the very real prospect of discovering fundamentally new human biology" (Pulendran and Davis 2020).

The first immune cell subsets were the separation of helper T cells into Th1 and Th2 (based on difference in cytokine production profiles). Differentiation of the 2 helper T subsets can be seen in the cutaneous leishmaniasis mice model using inbred strains. The susceptible BALB/c mice activate the Th2 differentiation and the mice die after *Leishmania major* infection. The resistant C57BL/6 mice activate the Th1 differentiation and the mice recover from leishmanial infection. Th1 and Th2 dichotomy has remained until the discovery of the third subset, Th17, helper T cells producing the cytokine IL-17. The importance of ILCs is seen during the initial immune response. ILCs can also be divided into 3 subsets (ILC1, ILC2, and ILC3) mirroring the 3 helper T cell subsets (Th1, Th2, and Th17). ILCs produce the same types of cytokines as the T helpers, except they appear much sooner in time (as innate cells and not adaptive cells). Linking the NK cells to CTLs (T cytotoxic, Tc), and the ILCs to Th subsets, the current view suggests the existence of 3 types of immune response. The response depends on appropriate tissue signals and cytokines as a result of the types of pathogens or conditions (Annunziato *et al.* 2015; Eberl *et al.* 2015).

Type 1 immunity targets intracellular microbes, viruses, and tumors. NK cells produce IFNγ and kill cancer cells or virus-infected cells. ILC1 and Th1 produce cytokines IFNγ and tumor necrosis factor *alpha* (TNFα) to activate macrophages (to CAM).

Type 2 immunity targets large parasites (helminths) and allergens. ILC2 and Th2 produce IL-4, IL -5, and IL-13 to activate macrophages (to AAM), and lead to tissue repair. In addition, type 2 response is involved in temperature changes, wound healing, and control of homeostasis (Lloyd and Snelgrove 2018).

Type 3 immunity targets extracellular microbes and fungi. ILC3 and Th17 produce IL-17, IL-22 and granulocyte macrophage-colony stimulating factor (GM-CSF) to induce phagocytosis and epithelial production of anti-microbial peptides. Please see Figure 3.3 for immunity types (Annunziato *et al.* 2015).

With different emphasis, we present another view. The immune system uses 2 distinct defense strategies against infections: microbe-directed pathogen **destruction** characterized by Type 1 immunity, and host-directed pathogen **containment** exemplified by Type

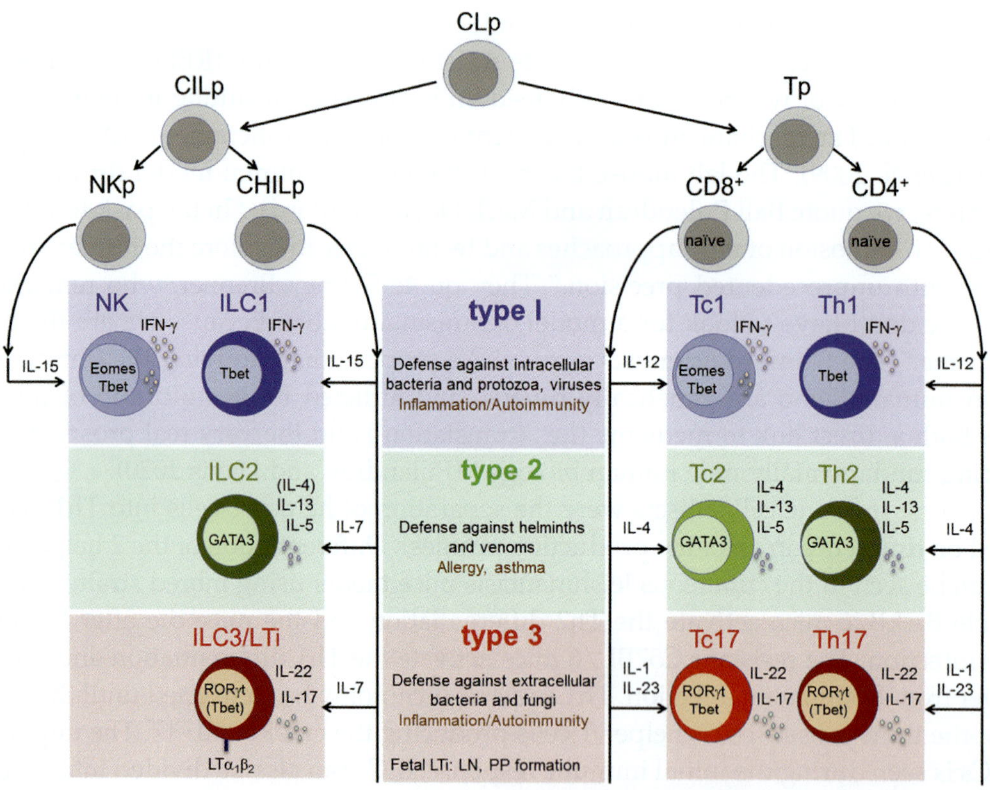

Fig. 3.3 ■ Type 1, 2, 3 Immunity. The 3 major types of innate and adaptive cell-mediated effector immunity. Type 1 immunity is composed of T-bet$^+$ IFN-γ–producing CD4$^+$ T_H1 cells and ILC1s and T-bet$^+$Eomes$^+$CD8$^+$ T_C1 and NK cells. Type 2 immunity is composed of GATA-3$^+$CD4$^+$ T_H2 cells, CD8$^+$ T_C2 cells, and ILC2s, which produce IL-4, IL-5, and IL-13. Type 3 immunity is composed of RORγt *(RORC)*$^+$CD4$^+$$T_H17$ cells, CD8$^+$ T_C17 cells, and ILC3s, producing IL-17, IL-22, or both. *CILp*, Common innate lymphoid precursor; *CLp*, common lymphoid precursor; *LN*, lymph node; *LTi*, lymphoid tissue inducer; *PP*, Peyer patch; *Tp*, T-cell progenitor. Courtesy: Annunziato *et al. J Allergy Clin Immunol* 2015;135:626–35. Reproduced with permission from Elsevier.

2 immunity in the induction of tissue repair. Similar to infectious diseases, a tumor progresses with self-propagating cancer cells inflicting host-tissue damage, and Type 2 immunity is involved (Liu *et al.* 2020).

The fact that the host immune response is important can be appreciated in the light of **opportunistic** parasitic infections. When the immune system is defective, either acquired or due to genetic predisposition, numerous parasitic infections may occur in the immune deficient host.

[We have only presented the basic knowledge in immunology relevant to our discussion on human parasites. For interested readers who want to learn more, there are other topics covered in a typical undergraduate immunology course, as recommended by the American Association of Immunologists. Please see Porter *et al.* 2021.]

3.7 Host Immune Response to Parasitic Infections

After an invasion by a parasite, the host immune system responds accordingly, starting from innate response and followed by acquired response. Different responses are activated, depending on whether the parasite is extracellular or intracellular (such as the extracellular *Trypanosoma brucei* and the intracellular *Trypanosoma cruzi*), especially for different species of parasitic protozoa. As most helminthic parasites are large, they tend to be extracellular (with exceptions such as *Trichinella* larvae within the mammalian hosts' nurse cells). [Please see Chapter 5 for trypanosomiasis and Chapter 21 for trichinellosis.]

In helminth infections, the host macrophages, a major population of tissue-resident mononuclear phagocytes, respond in a timely manner. Differentiated to become AAMs, they are induced early following tissue insult and parasite recognition, to amplify the early immune response initiated by epithelial cells and ILC2s, and to subsequently drive parasite expulsion. AAMs release effector molecules/chemokines to facilitate Type 2 immunity, recruit effector cells (eosinophils) and both directly and indirectly participate in parasite killing. Following tissue insult (resulted from migration of helminths), AAMs aim to repair damage by driving collagen deposition, angiogenesis and tissue remodeling through the release of wound-healing factors and support the activation, recruitment and differentiation of many other cell types (fibroblasts, endothelial cells). After repair at the damaged tissue site, AAMs limit excessive inflammation and fibrosis (via immunomodulatory cytokines, inhibitory receptor-ligand interactions, or arginase activity) (Coakley and Harris 2020).

For parasitic protozoa and helminths, one similar immune response by the host towards parasites that cannot be destroyed, is the formation of **granulomas**. "The appearance of granulomas, defined as organized and compact structures of macrophages and other immune cells, during various parasitic diseases is frequent, since these structures will only form when individual immune cells do not control the invading agent" (Giorgio *et al.* 2020). Granulomas are formed when immune cells cannot destroy the parasites. So, the next best way is to confine the parasites by creating a wall of immune cells surrounding/enclosing the central parasites. Please see Figure 3.4 for granulomas formation in chronic parasitic infections (Giorgio *et al.* 2020).

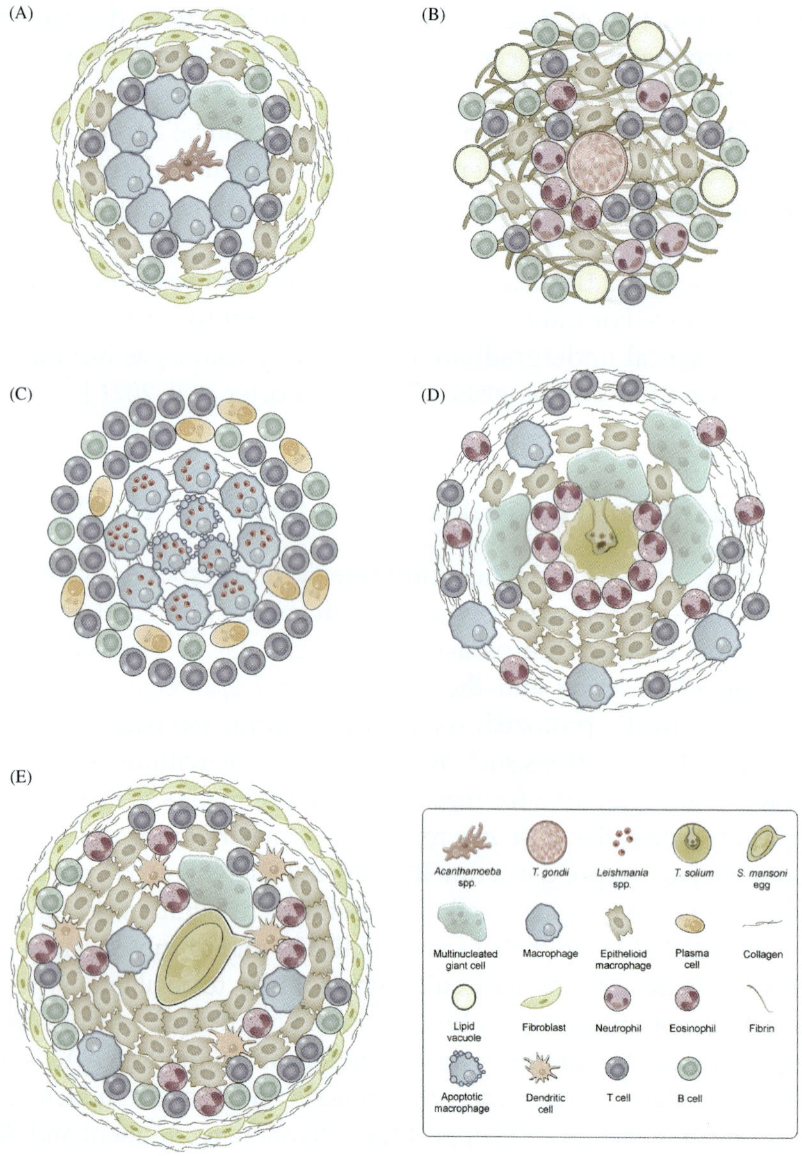

Fig. 3.4 ■ Granuloma formation due to chronic parasitic infections. The granuloma composition in some parasitic diseases. (A) GAE well-developed granuloma with ameba surrounded by multinucleated giant cell, epithelioid macrophages, macrophages, T and B cells, fibroblasts, and peripheral collagen fibers. (B) Toxoplasmosis less organized granuloma with parasites, macrophages, T and B cells, neutrophils, eosinophils, and lipid vacuoles surrounded by fibrin. (C) Leishmaniasis granuloma with focal dying infected macrophages, collagen fibers surrounded by infected macrophages, plasma cells, and T cells. (D) NCC granuloma with a dying *T. solium* cysticercus surrounded by eosinophils, multinucleated giant cells, epithelioid macrophages, macrophages, T cells, and collagen fibers. (E) Schistosomiasis mansoni granuloma with egg surrounded by macrophages, eosinophils, dendritic cells, and T and B cells. Fibroblasts and collagen fibers in the periphery present as signs of fibrosis. Courtesy: Giorgio *et al. Parasitol Res* 2020;119:3165–80. Reproduced with permission from Springer Nature.

3.8 Parasite Evasion & Modulation of Host Immunity

Different strategies are used by parasites/pathogens to evade host immune response. Parasites avoid host recognition, hide from host immune activity, change their antigenic composition, and suppress host immunity. In addition, there is the concept of **molecular mimicry**. Parasites produce molecules that the host can recognize as self. Parasites can even make proteins that are analogous to host immunosuppression cytokines.

There are many examples of parasites strategically targeting the host immunity. *Onchocerca vovulus* has cystatin on its surface, this is a proteinase inhibitor that blocks antigen presentation (inhibiting cathepsin activity). *Brugia malayi* secretes prostaglandin E2, an anti-inflammatory lipid molecule. *Schistosoma mansoni* has Ig-cleaving proteinase on its surface. It also has glutathione S-transferase, an enzyme that protects against ROI (detoxification). *Trichinella spiralis* secretes calreticulin and paramyosin that bind complement (inhibiting complement-mediated lysis) (Shao *et al.* 2019). *Plasmodium falciparum* produces hemozoin that inhibits DC function.

Parasites can cause host polymorphism and immunomodulation. Some immune genes are polymorphic. Genes such as TLRs and MHCs of APCs are structurally polymorphic. After an infection, DCs present antigens to immature T cells, and the T cells differentiate into effectors such as the T cell subsets Th1, Th2, Th17, or into Treg. Effectors may induce pathogen killing, allergy, or autoimmunity. Genes such as IL-2 and IL-4R (R, receptor) activate T cells, and ones such as IL-10 and transforming growth factor *beta* (TGFβ) activate Treg. Other cytokines such as IL-4, IL-13, and IFNγ also lead to effector function. All these genes may have single nucleotide polymorphisms (**SNPs**). These changes are seen in the promoter regions, introns, and 5′ and 3′ untranslated regions of the cytokine genes, resulting in quantitative changes to the level of the cytokine protein produced. Parasites maintain such SNP polymorphisms to control the intensity of an immune response (or the strength of a suppressive Treg effect). SNPs lead to structural polymorphisms that affect ligand binding, and regulatory polymorphisms that control cytokine levels (Maizels 2009). Please see Figure 3.5 for helminth products that are immune modulators (Maizels *et al.* 2018).

In immunology, specific MHC haplotypes are found in common with specific diseases. This observation has given rise to the concept of MHC and disease correlation. Some structurally polymorphic alleles of MHCs may come, not from ancestral humans, but from other humanoid lines, i.e., Neanderthals and Denisovans. Diversity of MHCs among the human population allows appropriate response to unknown infectious agents (such as novel parasites/pathogens), at least among some individuals, benefiting survival of the human species during an event of calamity. Most SNPs associated with helminth resistance go hand in hand with predisposition to allergic reactions. It has been shown that that the highest rate of SNP occurrence corresponds to geographic regions containing the greatest number of endemic helminth species. Indeed, 6 of the 9 risk alleles known to predispose to inflammatory bowel disease (IBD) are more frequent in pathogen-rich areas than other localities (Fumagalli *et al.* 2009).

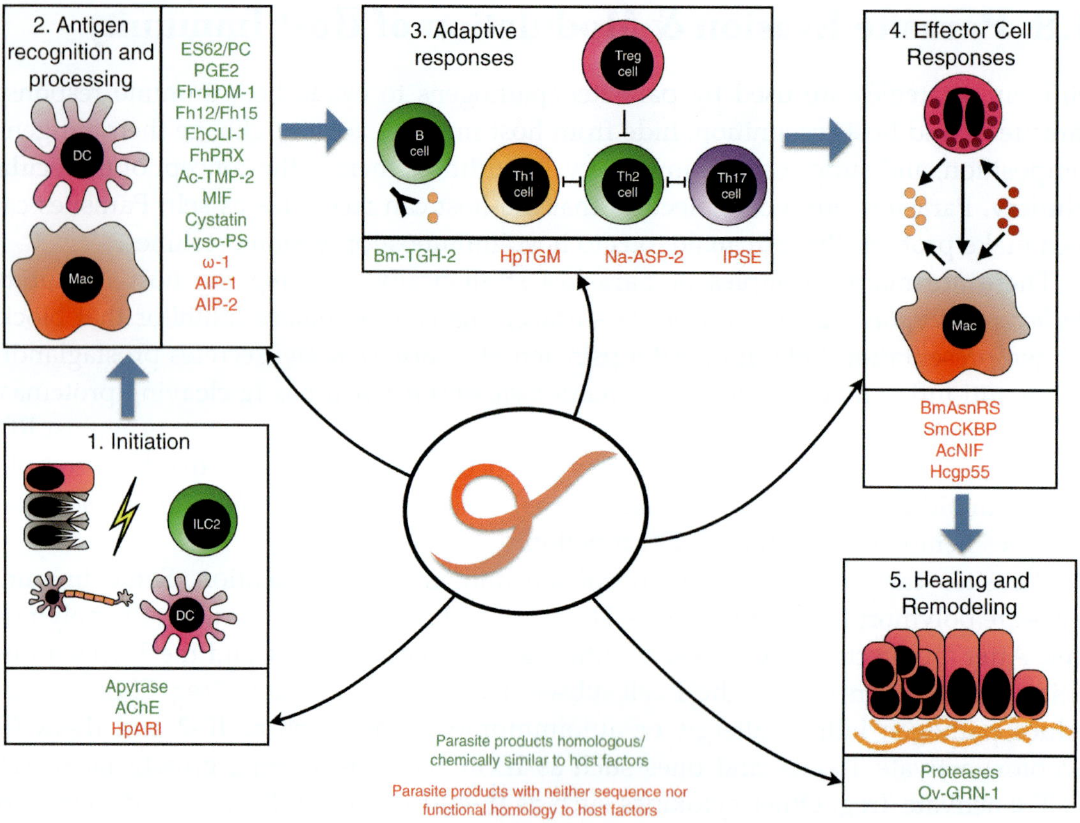

Fig. 3.5 ■ Helminth products as immune modulators. Helminth modulators act at all phases of the immune response. Modulatory proteins can be homologous to host genes (shared evolutionary ancestry, green) or show no homology (developed *de novo*, red). The immune response is divided into five phases: (1) initiation, innate recognition of damage and danger; (2) innate cell activation and antigen presentation; (3) adaptive immune responses; (4) effector immune responses; and (5) resolution and healing. Courtesy: Maizels *et al. Immunity* 2018;49:801–18. Reproduced with permission from *Immunity* with Creative Commons Attribution 4.0 (CC-BY) International License.

3.9 Hygiene Hypothesis

Long term coevolution between humans and their associated microbes and macro-organisms (helminth parasites) suggests that these infectious foreign agents may contribute to education of the immune system (including the maturation of regulatory T cells). In their absence, humans may become susceptible to both autoimmune and allergic disorders.

As noted above, parasites evade host immune response by avoiding immune detection, deflecting immune attack, and suppressing cellular immunity. The need to overcome suppressive mechanisms of parasites has led humans to make compensatory adjustments in immune genes that, in an environment where parasite infection is not endemic, may increase the likelihood of inappropriate responsiveness to self-antigens (autoimmunity) and environmental antigens (allergy). Therefore, there is coevolution between helminths and host immunity, which became the basis of the hygiene hypothesis: the lack of exposure to parasites in modern settings results in immune imbalance, augmenting susceptibility to the development of autoimmune and allergic conditions. By ridding the human immune system of interaction with helminths, one loses the potential for key regulatory interactions on which normal immunity may have evolved its dependence.

One origin of the hygiene hypothesis was a 1989 epidemiological study by David Strachen (London School of Hygiene and Tropical Medicine) encompassing 17,000 British children who were children born into a household with multiple siblings. These children were less susceptible to dermatitis and hay fever (allergy), presumably due to sharing of germs from older siblings; early childhood infections protect against allergy. Hygiene hypothesis may be a misnomer. Later, Graham Rook (University College London) suggested **"Old Friends" hypothesis** as replacement. Diseases of the modern era, including diabetes, multiple sclerosis, and allergies, involve the disruption of the immune-regulatory circuits, with the reason being a reduced exposure to organisms with which humans coevolved (Rook 2012). Comparing the immune system to computer terminology, it has software, but it needs data: exposure to a diverse set of microbes and macro-organisms. Rick Maizels (University of Edinburgh) has discussed **2 hygiene hypothesis**: (1) early in life to fix the set point — for infants the immune system is conditioned by environment, parasitic infections dampen the immune system against autoimmunity; (2) late in life to make the set point plastic — for children and adults the immune system is re-calibrated by exposure to various infectious agents (Maizels 2020). Other names have been proposed, e.g., microbiome depletion hypothesis, microbial diversity hypothesis (Scudellari 2017).

The hygiene hypothesis highlights the importance of microbiome. Gut microbiome varies for populations living in developed and developing countries, as seem in a study of microbiome of 200 infants and children (under 3 years) in different living conditions. For those living in an urban environment (Finland, Estonia), their gut microbiome contains an abundance of *Bacteroides*. For those living in a rural environment (Russia), their gut microbiome contains an abundance of *Escherichia coli*. The cell wall component (lipopolysaccharide, LPS is recognized by TLR-4) of *Bacteroides* inhibits the immune system whereas that of *E. coli* activates the immune system; the silent immune system may be prone to autoimmunity later in life (Scudellari 2017). The microbiome (used to be called normal flora) is composed of commensal species. The immune system has to learn what to tolerate and what to target. Commensal bacteria are important against autoimmunity (Bach 2018). With respect to the microbiome, there is the notion of **dysbiosis,** referring to an imbalance of the microbial flora. Dysbiosis is commonly found in the gut, but can also occur in other body localities, such as vagina, lung, and skin.

Infections by intestinal parasitic protozoa and helminths can influence the gut microbiome, as shown in animal models and in humans. For example, in Cameroon, *Entamoeba histolytica* infection changes the microbial species to an abundance of *Firmicutes*, with fewer *Bacteroides* as a consequence (Partida-Rodriguez *et al.* 2017). However, it must be noted that studies involving helminths and the microbiome in endemic populations tend to yield conflicting results, due to method variations and field work constraints (Cortes *et al.* 2019). It has been shown that, in a mouse model of IBD, nematode infection inhibits the inflammatory *Bacteroides* species and promotes the anti-inflammatory *Clostridium* species. Significantly, the difference is seen in urban and rural population samples in Malaysia. Deworming leads to a rise in *Bacteroides* (Ramanan *et al.* 2016). "Intestinal helminths, along with mutualistic microbes, have cohabited the intestine of mammals throughout evolution. ... This 'ménage à trois' situation ... Recent studies indicate that infection with intestinal helminths can and does impact the intestinal microbiome, with important consequences for each partner in this tripartite relationship" (Rapin and Harris 2018).

With respect to the hygiene hypothesis, there is the concept of **helminth therapy**: "re-worming the west" (McSorley *et al.* 2019). Please see Figure 3.6 for the suppression of autoimmunity and allergy by helminths through Type 2 immunity or regulatory immune response (Cruz *et al.* 2017). "However, it is worth noting that helminth parasites are not always benign infections, and that helminth immunomodulation can have stimulatory as well as suppressive effects on allergic responses" (McSorley *et al.* 2019).

Since individuals may not be happy with the intake of live parasites (the "icky" factor), an alternative approach is the application of helminth-derived molecules instead (Sobotková *et al.* 2019). Some products are being developed for their immune-regulatory activity; recombinant DNA expression in bacteria and yeasts has been applied (Nascimento Santos *et al.* 2017). These include proteases, protease inhibitors, cytokine homologs, heat shock proteins, and others. For example, the recombinant *Schistosoma mansoni* cathepsin B1 from yeast inhibits proinflammatory macrophage activation. In an experimental mouse model, *Schistosoma* cathepsin B1 induces expression of Th1, Th2, and Th17 helper T cells (proteolytic activity required for the induction). Th2 response to worm eggs leads to host survival and establishment of chronic infection. Acute infection induces a transient Th17 response (later down-regulated when oviposition starts). Th17 response is involved in the development of egg-induced pathology (Soloviova *et al.* 2019). Recombinant *Schistosoma japonicum* cystatin, a cysteine proteinase inhibitor, shows beneficial effects in sepsis-induced cardiomyopathy and diabetes mouse models (Gao *et al.* 2020; Yan *et al.* 2020). In the latter model, another *Schistosoma* molecule, recombinant aldolase, has the same positive effect (Yan *et al.* 2020). Similarly, recombinant macrophage migration inhibitory factor (MIF), r*Wba*MIF-2, from the filarial parasite, *Wuchereria bancrofti*, suppresses inflammation in a dextran sulphate sodium salt (DSS)-induced colitis mouse model (Ramani *et al.* 2020).

An expanding list of helminth-derived immune-regulatory molecules that may potentially be useful for treatments of allergy and autoimmunity is currently available (Maizels *et al.* 2018). Helminth modulators act on all phases of the immune response. Please see Figure 3.5 for helminth products as immune modulators (Maizels *et al.* 2018).

The significance of protozoa and helminths to immunology can be seen in a dedicated journal to this area of research: *Parasite Immunology* (Wiley).

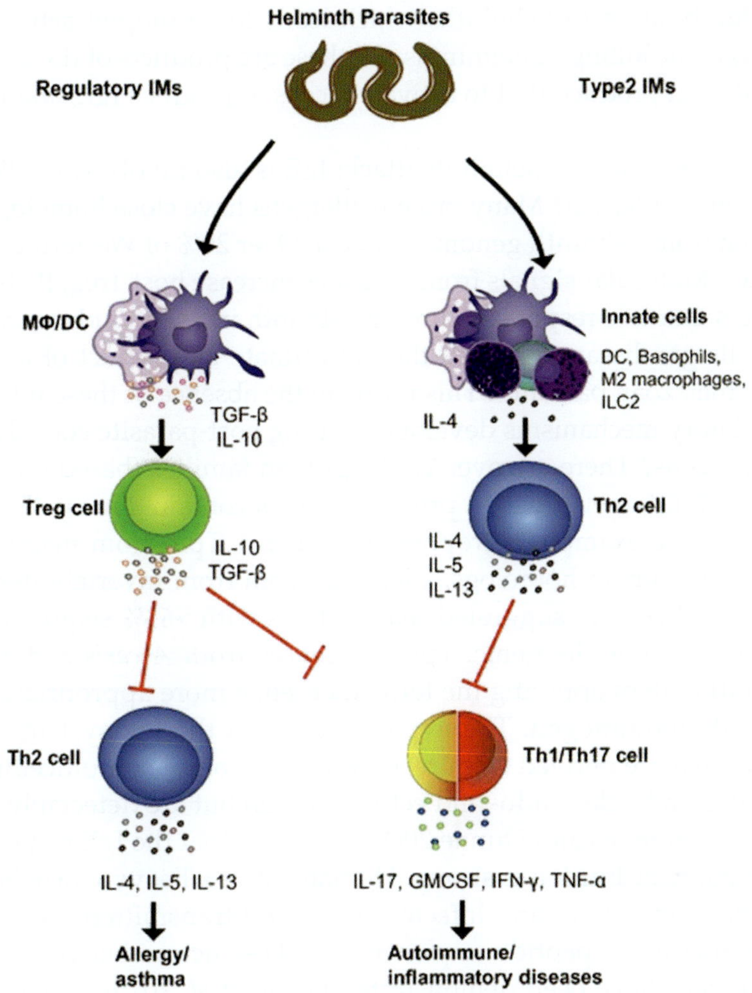

Fig. 3.6 ■ Suppression of autoimmunity and allergy by helminths through type 2 or regulatory immune response. Helminths suppress autoimmunity and allergy through type 2 or regulatory immune response. Immunomodulatory molecules *(IMs)* of parasites activate innate immune cells that promote either T_H2 or Treg cell responses. IMs that induce TGF-β and IL-10 production by dendritic cells or macrophages *(Mø)* prime IL-10–or TGF-β–producing Treg cells to suppress T_H2, T_H1, or T_H17 responses. A separate set of helminth-derived IMs activate type 2 innate cells, including basophils, M2 macrophages, and ILC2s, and induce innate IL-4 production, which drives differentiation of T_H2 cells. T_H2 cells and type 2 innate immune cells can suppress T_H1 and T_H17 responses. Courtesy: Cruz *et al.* *J Allergy Clin Immunol* 2017;140:1217–28. Reproduced with permission from Elsevier.

3.10 IgE in Allergy & Parasitic Infections

During allergic reactions, the mast cells become activated by binding to IgE via IgE receptors and degranulate to release histamines, which cause the person to sneeze. Mast cells also produce chemo-attractants to attract the eosinophils. **Eosinophils** also possess IgE receptors and IgE binding to helminths which leads to eosinophil activation to secrete molecules to target the killing of helminths. All these are products of ILC2 and Th2, which are immune cells that produce IL-4 to activate B cells to produce IgE, and IL-5 to activate eosinophils.

IgE is the host response to helminth attack; IgE is also involved in allergy. So, what makes an allergen an allergen? Many protein allergens have close homologs in metazoan parasites (as seen from helminth genome studies). Over 20% of Western populations suffer from allergies. Molecular signals from parasites increase host Treg, IL-10, and TGFβ in order to suppress immune response. Chronic helminth infection induces a modified Th2 environment. Allergic diseases may be the unfortunate by-product of an IgE-mediated defense against metazoan parasites. This is due to the absence of these infections and the absence of regulatory mechanisms developed during host-parasite coevolution.

What are allergens? There are over 10,000 protein families (based on 3D structures), and very few are IgE targets. Just 10 protein families contain almost 45% of all known protein allergens. One example is tropomyosin (Tpm). Tpm from mammals and birds are 90% identical to human homologs, allergenic Tpm from invertebrates are generally <55% identical. Studies have suggested that proteins with **>63%** sequence identity with human homologs are not allergenic. Tpm sequences from *Ascaris* and *Schistosoma* are known. Thus, rather than applying the term allergen, a more appropriate name may be **metazoan parasite immunogen**. The hypothesis is that the IgE system has evolved to target molecules that are derived from relatively large complex multicellular organisms (such as helminths and ticks, endo- and ecto-parasites) but are detectably different from the host itself (Fitzsimmons and Dunne 2009). Evidence that the IgE response evolved to limit metazoan parasitic burden is strong. Humans have a heavy worm burden, as over 1 billion of the population are infected with soil-transmitted helminths (STHs). Furthermore, similarity in peptide sequence and 3D structure between worm proteins and known allergens have been demonstrated (Tyagi *et al.* 2015). Environmental allergens share key properties with metazoan parasite immunogens that are targeted by IgE (this occurs at the epitope level, antigenic determinant portion of a protein). With respect to known allergenic proteins, tropomyosin is the most abundant, just ahead of the plant-specific Bet v 1 (for *Betula verrucosa*, white birch) in pollen. Allergen annotations are 3 letters from genus name, 1 from the species and then the order of allergen discovery. A Bet v 1 related protein has been identified and cloned from *Schistosoma mansoni*. The antigen has been shown to induce IgE and IgG4 (an IgG subclass) antibodies in endemic populations in Uganda. Another *Betula* allergenic protein (profilin) shows 3D structural similarity to an *Ascaris* protein. Please see Figure 3.7 for allergen and parasite antigen (Tyagi *et al.* 2015).

In the conclusion for IgE and hygiene hypothesis, a word of caution must be added. In some instances, helminth infections can enhance or lead to allergy; some worm antigens are allergens. The human roundworm *Ascaris lumbricoides* infection can cause asthma and pneumonitis (Briggs *et al.* 2016; Caraballo *et al.* 2019). Indeed, tropomyosin, Asc l 3, is an allergen. Many helminth species produce allergens (Caraballo and Coronado

(A)

```
Allergen       VGH-DGSVWAQSSSFPQFK (28-45)
               VG+ DGSVWA+S    +FK (Identical/similar(+)residues)
Worm protein   VGYPDGSVWARSEGDNEFK (24-42)
```

(B)

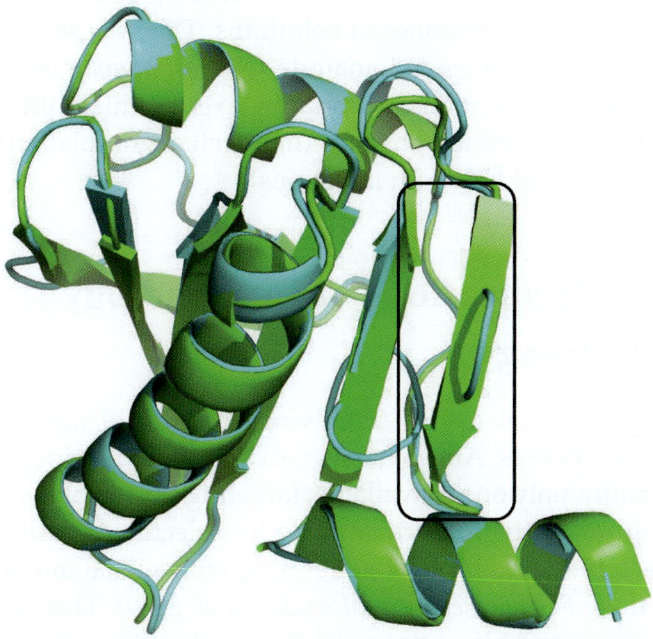

Fig. 3.7 ■ **Allergen and parasite antigen.** A. Sequence alignment of the epitopic region from profilin protein (allergenic) from *Betula pendula* (European white birch) (UniProt accession: P25816) and predicted epitopic-like region from the worm *Ascaris lumbricoides* (UniProt accession: F1LGV9). B. Superposition of the 3D structure of plant allergenic protein (PDB accession: 1CQA) (colored in green) and the 3D structural model of profilin protein from the worm *Ascaris lumbricoides* (in cyan). Epitope (allergen) and predicted epitopic-like regions (parasite protein) are depicted in the box. Courtesy: Tyagi *et al. PLoS Comput Biol* 2015;11:e1004546. Reproduced with permission from *PLoS Computational Biol*ogy with Creative Commons Attribution 4.0 (CC-BY) International License.

2018). One significant finding refers to the increasing allergy to *Anisakis simplex*, due to an increased consumption of marine fish. Allergic responses can be seen in ascariasis, anisakiasis, strongyloidiasis, and hydatidosis. [Please see these parasitic diseases in Chapters 20 to 22.]

Probably the most severe form of immunopathology is anaphylaxis, a potential lethal form of hypersensitivity in host immune response. So, are there any differences between IgE for environmental allergens and IgE for metazoan parasite immunogens? Earlier we mentioned immunoglobulin (Ig) class switching during secondary immune response, from IgM to IgA, IgG, or IgE. The process occurs in the lymph nodes with the aid of helper T cells known as Tfh (T follicular helper). Subsets of Tfh have been investigated, Tfh1, Tfh2, and Tfh13 (Gowthaman *et al.* 2019). The last one is a new discovery, Tfh13 produces IL-4, IL-5, and the signature cytokine IL-13. These cytokines induce differentiation of IgG1 producing B cells to produce high-affinity IgE, as a response to allergens. In contrast, **Tfh2** produces IL-4 and IL-21 to induce differentiation of IgM producing B cells generating low-affinity IgE in response to helminths. This was shown in mice using fungal allergen (*Alternaria*) and murine nematode (*Nippostrongylus brasiliensis*). Thus, low-affinity IgE for helminths does not induce anaphylaxis, but high-affinity IgE for allergens does. High-affinity IgE-induced anaphylaxis (mast cell degranulation) only happens with environmental allergens (not helminth infections).

3.11 Current Applications of Immunology to Parasitology

Immunoassays or serological assays (involving serum) are useful for immune-based diagnosis of parasitic diseases. Anti-parasite vaccines would be ideal in preventing parasitic diseases. Currently, only one is available, targeting the lethal malaria due to infection of *Plasmodium falciparum*. Attempts are ongoing for selecting parasitic antigens as potential vaccines, as seen in the example of generating monoclonal antibody to cathepsin B2 of the sheep liver fluke *Fasciola hepatica* (Norbury *et al.* 2019). This proteinase may play a role in immune evasion and also acts as the fluke's digestive enzyme. Cathepsin B and related cathepsin L are considered to be good targets for drugs and vaccines. "Monoclonal antibodies have a wide range of applications in basic and applied research as well as in the medical and pharmaceutical industries. Phage display antibody libraries offer an alternative to hybridoma technology for the generation of monoclonal antibodies and can be applied to high-throughput screening and facilitate the generation of novel antibodies" (Norbury *et al.* 2019). A single-chain variable fragment (**scFv**) phage display library from naïve mice was used to identify scFvs that can bind to antigens from adult *F. hepatica* homogenate, including one that binds cathepsin B2.

Immune-mediated diagnostic assays are widely used, such as a dipstick test for malaria antigen using monoclonal antibody on a nitrocellulose strip, and a dipstick assay for visceral leishmaniasis. Others include immunofluorescent assay (**IFA**) and enzyme-linked immunosorbent assay (**ELISA**). Non-immune molecular assays for diagnosis of parasitic diseases include ones based on polymerase chain reaction (**PCR**).

Summary & Key Concepts

- In immunopathology, host immunity may overreact to cause tissue damage.
- Immunity involves the recognition between self and non-self.
- The host immune defense consists of innate immunity, which mediates the initial

protection against infections, and adaptive immunity, which develops more slowly and mediates the later, even more effective defense against infections. Adaptive immunity's memory enables the immune system to remember when a previously encountered pathogen is reintroduced.

- Adult mammalian innate and adaptive immune cells are derived from the bone marrow. It is the location where HSCs can both self-renew and differentiate into terminally differentiated cell types.
- The TLR on the innate immune cell binds to the PAMP on the pathogen surface.
- The two macrophage subsets are the CAMs and the AAMs.
- Adaptive immunity can be divided into humoral and cell-mediated immunity. Humoral immunity consists of primary and secondary antibody responses and acts against extracellular pathogens. Cell-mediated immunity consists of T cell responses and acts against intracellular pathogens.
- The types of antibodies are IgM, IgG, IgA, IgE and IgD; this classification depends on the antibody heavy chain isotypes.
- Helper T cells are divided into subsets: T helper1 (Th1), Th2, and Th17. Regulatory T cells (Treg) serve to regulate the immune response. T follicular helper cells (Tfh) help B cells in the lymphoid follicles to generate improved antibodies.
- Long term coevolution between humans and associated microbes and helminths lead to the idea that these commensal and/or infectious agents may contribute to education/maturation of the immune system.
- Parasites evade host immune response by avoiding immune detection, deflecting immune attack, and suppressing cellular immunity.
- The hygiene hypothesis proposes a lack of exposure to parasites in modern settings results in immune imbalance, augmenting susceptibility to the development of autoimmune and allergic conditions.
- B cells can recognize any types of molecules but T cells can only recognize processed protein antigens as peptides via the major histocompatibility complexes (MHCs).
- Class I MHCs: in all nucleated cells, the cytosolic pathogen's protein antigen is degraded by proteinases in the proteasome. Class II MHCs: only on APCs, DC takes in the pathogen by endocytosis, its antigen is degraded by lysosomal acid proteinases named cathepsins.
- Type 1 immunity: targets intracellular microbes, viruses and tumors. NK cells kill cancer cells or virus-infected cells. ILC1 and Th1 produce cytokines IFNγ and TNFα to activate macrophages.
- Type 2 immunity: targets large parasites (helminths) and allergens. ILC2 and Th2 produce IL-4, IL-5, and IL-13 to activate macrophages.
- Type 3 immunity: targets extracellular microbes and fungi. ILC3 and Th17 produce IL-17, IL-22 and GM-CSF.
- Opportunistic infections: many parasitic infections occur in the immune-deficient hosts.
- Eosinophils possess IgE receptors. Binding of IgE to helminths causes eosinophil

activation, leading to secretion of molecules to kill helminths.

- Studies suggest that proteins with >63% sequence identity with human homologs are not allergenic.
- Immunoassays/serological assays are useful for immune-mediated diagnosis of parasitic diseases.

References

Abbas, AK, Lichtman, AH, Pillai, S. *Basic Immunology*, 6th ed. Elsevier, 2020.

Adapala N, Chan MM. Long-term use of an antiinflammatory, curcumin, suppressed type 1 immunity and exacerbated visceral leishmaniasis in a chronic experimental model. *Lab Invest* 2008;88(12):1329–39.

Akkaya M, Bansal A, Sheehan PW, *et al*. A single-nucleotide polymorphism in a *Plasmodium berghei* ApiAP2 transcription factor alters the development of host immunity. *Sci Adv* 2020;6(6):eaaw6957.

Annunziato F, Romagnani C, Romagnani S. The 3 major types of innate and adaptive cell-mediated effector immunity. *J Allergy Clin Immunol* 2015;135(3):626–35.

Bach JF. The hygiene hypothesis in autoimmunity: The role of pathogens and commensals. *Nat Rev Immunol* 2018;18(2):105–120.

Briggs N, Weatherhead J, Sastry KJ, Hotez PJ. The hygiene hypothesis and its inconvenient truths about helminth infections. *PLoS Negl Trop Dis* 2016;10(9):e0004944.

Burgan SC, Gervasi SS, Johnson LR, Martin LB. How individual variation in host tolerance affects competence to transmit parasites. *Physiol Biochem Zool* 2019;92(1):49–57.

Caraballo L, Coronado S. Parasite allergens. *Mol Immunol* 2018;100:113–119.

Caraballo L, Acevedo N, Zakzuk J. Ascariasis as a model to study the helminth/allergy relationships. *Parasite Immunol* 2019;41(6):e12595.

Chan MM, Adapala N, Chen C. Peroxisome proliferator-activated receptor-γ-mediated polarization of macrophages in *Leishmania* infection. *PPAR Res* 2012;2012:796235.

Chan MM, Adapala NS, Fong D. Curcumin overcomes the inhibitory effect of nitric oxide on *Leishmania*. *Parasitol Res* 2005;96(1):49–56.

Chan MM, Evans KW, Moore AR, Fong D. Peroxisome proliferator-activated receptor (PPAR): Balance for survival in parasitic infections. *Journal of Biomedicine & Biotechnology* 2010;2010, Article ID 828951.

Coakley G, Harris NL. Interactions between macrophages and helminths. *Parasite Immunol* 2020; 42(7):e12717.

Coico, R, Sunshine, G. *Immunology — A Short Course*, 5th ed. Wiley, 2013.

Cortés A, Peachey LE, Jenkins TP, Scotti R, Cantacessi C. Helminths and microbes within the vertebrate gut — Not all studies are created equal. *Parasitology*. 2019;146(11):1371–1378.

Cruz AA, Cooper PJ, Figueiredo CA, Alcantara-Neves NM, Rodrigues LC, Barreto ML. Global issues in allergy and immunology: Parasitic infections and allergy. *J Allergy Clin Immunol* 2017;140(5):1217–28.

de Carvalho RVH, Zamboni DS. Inflammasome activation in response to intracellular protozoan parasites. *Trends Parasitol* 2020 May;36(5):459–72.

Díaz-Godínez C, Carrero JC. The state of art of neutrophil extracellular traps in protozoan and helminthic infections. *Biosci Rep* 2019;39(1)pii: BSR20180916.

Eberl G, Colonna M, Di Santo JP, McKenzie AN. Innate lymphoid cells: A new paradigm in immunology. *Science*. 2015;348(6237):aaa6566.

Fitzsimmons CM, Dunne DW. Survival of the fittest: Allergology or parasitology? *Trends Parasitol*. 2009;25(10):447–51.

Fumagalli M, Pozzoli U, Cagliani R, *et al*. Parasites represent a major selective force for interleukin genes and shape the genetic predisposition to autoimmune conditions. *J Exp Med* 2009;206(6):1395–408.

Gao S, Li H, Xie H, *et al*. Therapeutic efficacy of *Schistosoma japonicum* cystatin on sepsis-induced cardiomyopathy in a mouse model. *Parasit Vectors* 2020;13(1):260.

Giorgio S, Gallo-Francisco PH, Roque GAS, Flóro E Silva M. Granulomas in parasitic diseases: the good and the bad. *Parasitol Res* 2020;119(10):3165–80.

Gitlin AD, Nussenzweig MC. Immunology: Fifty years of B lymphocytes. *Nature* 2015;517(7533):139–41.

Gowthaman U, Chen JS, Zhang B, *et al*. Identification of a T follicular helper cell subset that drives anaphylactic IgE. *Science*. 2019;365(6456)pii: eaaw6433.

Herbert DR, Yang JQ, Hogan SP, *et al*. Intestinal epithelial cell secretion of RELM-*beta* protects against gastrointestinal worm infection. *J Exp Med* 2009;206(13):2947–57.

Iwasaki A, Medzhitov R. Regulation of adaptive immunity by the innate immune system. *Science* 2010;327(5963):291–5.

Jain A, Pasare C. Innate control of adaptive immunity: Beyond the three-signal paradigm. *J Immunol* 2017;198(10):3791–800.

Kutty, PK. Breastfeeding and risk of parasitic infection — A review. *Asian Pac J Trop Biomed* 2014;4(11):847–58.

Liu M, Kuo F, Capistrano KJ, *et al*. TGF-*beta* suppresses type 2 immunity to cancer. *Nature* 2020;587(7832):115–120.

Lloyd CM, Snelgrove RJ. Type 2 immunity: Expanding our view. *Sci Immunol* 2018;3(25)pii: eaat1604.

Maizels RM. Parasite immunomodulation and polymorphisms of the immune system. *J Biol* 2009;8(7):62.

Maizels RM. Regulation of immunity and allergy by helminth parasites. *Allergy* 2020;75(3):524–34.

Maizels RM, McSorley HJ. Regulation of the host immune system by helminth parasites. *J Allergy Clin Immunol* 2016;138(3):666–75.

Maizels RM, Smits HH, McSorley HJ. Modulation of host immunity by helminths: The expanding repertoire of parasite effector molecules. *Immunity* 2018;49(5):801–18.

Marshall JS, Warrington R, Watson W, Kim HL. An introduction to immunology and immunopathology. *Allergy Asthma Clin Immunol* 2018;14(2):49.

McSorley HJ, Chayé MAM, Smits HH. Worms: Pernicious parasites or allies against allergies? *Parasite Immunol* 2019;41(6):e12574.

Nascimento Santos L, Carvalho Pacheco LG, Silva Pinheiro C, Alcantara-Neves NM. Recombinant proteins of helminths with immunoregulatory properties and their possible therapeutic use. *Acta Trop* 2017;166:202–11.

Neefjes J, Jongsma ML, Paul P, Bakke O. Towards a systems understanding of MHC class I and MHC class II antigen presentation. *Nat Rev Immunol* 2011;11(12):823–36.

Norbury LJ, Basałaj K, Bąska P, *et al*. Generation of a single-chain variable fragment phage display antibody library from naïve mice panned against *Fasciola hepatica* antigens. *Exp Parasitol* 2019;205:107737.

Partida-Rodríguez O, Serrano-Vázquez A, Nieves-Ramírez ME, *et al*. Human intestinal microbiota: Interaction between parasites and the host immune response. *Arch Med Res* 2017;48(8):690–700.

Porter E, Amiel E, Bose N, *et al*. American Association of Immunologists recommendations for an undergraduate course in immunology. *Immunohorizons*. 2021;5(6):448–65.

Pulendran B, Davis MM. The science and medicine of human immunology. *Science* 2020;369(6511):eaay4014.

Ramani S, Chauhan N, Khatri V, Vitali C, Kalyanasundaram R. *Wuchereria bancrofti* macrophage migration inhibitory factor-2 (rWbaMIF-2) ameliorates experimental colitis. Parasite *Immunol* 2020;42(4):e12698.

Ramanan D, Bowcutt R, Lee SC, *et al*. Helminth infection promotes colonization resistance via type 2 immunity. *Science* 2016;352(6285):608–12.

Rapin A, Harris NL. Helminth-bacterial interactions: Cause and consequence. *Trends Immunol* 2018;39(9):724–33.

Rook GA. A Darwinian view of the hygiene or "old friends" hypothesis. *Microbe* 2012;7(4):173–80.

Schmid-Hempel P. Parasite immune evasion: A momentous molecular war. *Trends Ecol Evol* 2008;23(6):318–26.

Scudellari M. News feature: Cleaning up the hygiene hypothesis. *Proc Natl Acad Sci USA*. 2017;114(7):1433–36.

Shao S, Sun X, Chen Y, Zhan B, Zhu X. Complement evasion: An effective strategy that parasites utilize to survive in the host. *Front Microbiol* 2019;10:532.

Sobotková K, Parker W, Levá J, Růžková J, Lukeš J, Jirků Pomajbíková K. Helminth therapy — From the parasite perspective. *Trends Parasitol* 2019;35(7):501–15.

Soloviova K, Fox EC, Dalton JP, Caffrey CR, Davies SJ. A secreted schistosome cathepsin B1 cysteine protease and acute schistosome infection induce a transient T helper 17 response. *PLoS Negl Trop Dis* 2019;13(1):e0007070.

Tyagi N, Farnell EJ, Fitzsimmons CM, *et al*. Comparisons of allergenic and metazoan parasite proteins: Allergy the price of immunity. *PLoS Comput Biol* 2015;11(10):e1004546.

Yan K, Wang B, Zhou H, *et al*. Amelioration of type 1 diabetes by recombinant fructose-1,6-bisphosphate aldolase and cystatin derived from *Schistosoma japonicum* in a murine model. *Parasitol Res* 2020;119(1):203–14.

4

Classification of Eukaryotes and Introduction to Protozoa

4.1 Classification of Living Things

Since historical times humans have classified other living things. As seen in the Bible (King James Version): "And out of the ground the Lord God formed every beast of the field, and every fowl of the air; and brought them unto Adam to see what he would call them: and whatsoever Adam called every living creature, that was the name thereof. And Adam gave names to all cattle, and to the fowl of the air, and to every beast of the field; but for Adam there was not found an help meet for him" (Genesis, Chapter 2 verses 19 and 20).

Classification orders living things according to similarities and differences between individual members. The term **taxonomy** refers to the science of identifying, naming and classifying organisms. Classification serves practical purposes as a key for field work and allows proper assignment after the discovery of a new organism. Classification, however, does not necessarily indicate the relationship among living things. The term **phylogeny** is used for evolutionary relatedness. Organisms are assembled into **clades**, which are groups of organisms descended from the same original ancestor. New molecular data supplement classic morphological observations, allowing scientists to incorporate phylogenetic relatedness into a modern synthesis: the current classification of living things.

The classification of living things has undergone multiple phases. In 1735, Carl Linnaeus, then soon to be professor at Uppsala University, Sweden, published *Systema Naturae* in the Netherlands and invented the **binomial nomenclature** system. Each living organism has its own unique genus and species name. These features remain in the current groupings: kingdom, phylum, class, order, family, genus, species. He originally proposed 2 kingdoms that became known as Animalia and Plantae but he actually had a third, for non-living things: the minerals.

In 1866, Ernest Haeckel (University of Jena, Germany) published *General Morphology of Organisms*, and added a third kingdom for the living things: Protista, including microbes (known as Monera), amoebae, and others. Haeckel suggested: "All organisms are the descendants of such autogenous Monerens," indicating he was thinking about phylogeny and evolution (Kutschera 2016). Haeckel was known for his many zoological studies, especially embryology. We recall the famous quote by Haeckel: "Ontogeny recapitulates phylogeny." He noted that stages of fetal development (ontogeny) seemed to repeat the evolutionary process of that particular organism (evolutionary relationship/ phylogeny).

In 1969, the American ecologist Robert Whittaker (Cornell University) (1920–1980) proposed 5 kingdoms, by adding 2 new ones. His classification of 5 kingdoms are: Monera (for bacteria), Protista, Plantae, Fungi, and Animalia (Whittaker 1969). In his view, evolutionary relations are better represented by this scheme, from Monera to Protista, later evolving into photosynthetic Plantae, absorptive nutrition Fungi, and finally ingestive nutrition Animalia.

In 1998, the British zoologist Thomas Cavalier-Smith (then at University of British Columbia, later Oxford) (1942–2021) proposed 2 superkingdoms and 6 kingdoms (Cavalier-Smith 1998). Prokaryota and Eukaryota are superkingdoms. The 6 kingdoms are: Bacteria, Protozoa, Animalia, Fungi, Plantae (land plants, plastids containing chlorophyll *a* and *b*), and **Chromista** (algae, chloroplasts containing chlorophyll *c*).

In 2015, Michael A. Ruggiero (Integrated Taxonomic Information System at Smithsonian Institution, Washington D.C.) and colleagues published "A higher level classification of all living things" (Ruggiero *et al.* 2015). Over **1.6 million** species of living things have been grouped in a unified, coherent, and hierarchically ranked system, titled the Catalogue of Life (**COL**), by over 3,000 taxonomists. The consensus classification has 2 superkingdoms and 7 kingdoms (an extension of Cavalier-Smith's 6 kingdoms). Prokaryota and Eukaryota are the two superkingdoms. Archaea and Bacteria are two kingdoms of Prokaryota (Archaea is the new kingdom). The same 5 kingdoms remain in the Eukaryota: Protozoa, Chromista, Fungi, Plantae, and Animalia. "The CoL classification will undergo review and revision at five-year intervals to consider changes as necessary" (Ruggiero *et al.* 2015).

The goal is to create a comprehensive list of all species on earth. "Principles for creating a single authoritative list of the world's species" (Garnett *et al.* 2020) requires international scientists' approval. The Catalogue of Life (COL) is a collaboration bringing together the effort and contributions of taxonomists and informaticians from around the world. COL aims to address the needs of researchers, policy-makers, environmental managers and the wider public for a consistent and up-to-date listing of all the world's known species. [Parasitic species discussed in this textbook are accessible at the COL site.][1]

An alternative classification of eukaryotes is based on supergroups (Adl *et al.* discussed later in this chapter). Ruggiero *et al.* commented: "The overarching higher level

[1] https://www.catalogueoflife.org/

classification used by the CoL, therefore, uses the standard formal categories, as it is intended to be simultaneously pragmatic and informative of both evolutionary relatedness and relative phylogenetic subordination. A classification should be biologically well-grounded and widely useful. In its simplicity, it provides less detail about relationships than a complete phylogeny but is still congruent with it. Our classification is not intended to compete with a cladification such as Adl *et al.*'s — both are valid ways of ordering the living world — but we would argue that theirs is less comprehensible to many in the public-domain user communities."

4.2 Taxonomy from Morphology to Molecular Biology

Classification of living things follows the advancement of experimental techniques. For example, motility of single cell organisms was observed under the light microscope. In 1880–1889, with emphasis on cellular **motility**, Otto Butschli (University of Heidelberg, Germany), divided protozoa into 4 groups: **Sarcodina** (amoebae), **Mastigophora** (flagellates), **Sporozoa** (parasites), and **Infusoria** (ciliates). Later scientists combined the first two groups, Sarcodina and Mastigophora, into one, **Sarcomastigophora**. The group Sporozoa was divided into 2: **Apicomplexa** and **Microsporidia**. The group Infusoria was renamed **Ciliophora**. The availability of electron microscope for biologists has enriched the knowledge of ultrastructure. Techniques of molecular biology have shown specific protein and gene sequences of the many species living on earth. All these technical advances have further improved our knowledge on the relationship among living things.

Early molecular studies used protein sequences such as cytochrome *c* and RNA sequences such as small subunit (SSU) ribosomal RNA. These are smaller size proteins and nucleic acids that do not change much among species because of their essential functions. With the current availability of complete genomes for the use of multiple proteins and genes, and with computational methods for gene alignments to reconstruct evolutionary histories, phylogenetic and phylogenomic analyses are available for further investigation into evolutionary relatedness among organisms. It should be known, however, that the data are not as complete as investigators would like to have, and there exists a lack of agreement among individuals about the proposed phylogenies (hence the need for consensus).

Biochemists compared sequences of the same gene or protein among organisms. By studying RNA sequences (5S, 16S ribosomal RNAs), the American microbiologist Carl Woese (University of Illinois) (1928–2012) used RNA sequence data to separate prokaryotes into **Eubacteria** (such as *Escherichia coli*) and **Archaea** (aka Archaebacteria) (such as the methanogens) in 1977. By studying mitochondrial proteins of eukaryotes and comparing to those of prokaryotes, the American physical chemist Margaret Dayhoff (Georgetown University, Washington D.C.) (1925–1983) used amino acid sequence alignment of ferredoxins, cytochrome *c* and others, to show evidence of protein evolution (molecular evolution), from 1966 onwards. Dayhoff invented the 1-letter code for amino acids for easier alignment and was the first to apply computer analysis to phylogeny (as an example, the amino acid arginine has Arg as its 3-letter code and R as its 1-letter code). She was a pioneer in the field of bioinformatics.

4.3 Origin of the Eukaryotic Cell

How did the prokaryotes evolve into eukaryotes? In 1967, the American biologist Lynn Margulis (then Boston University, later University of Massachusetts Amherst) (1938–2011) proposed the **endosymbiotic theory** as the origin of eukaryotes. Her paper, titled "The origin of mitosing eukaryotic cells" was published in the *Journal of Theoretical Biology* (after over 15 previous submissions and rejections). In 1970, Margulis published *Origin of Eukaryotic Cells* (Yale University Press). ["If at first you don't succeed, try, try, try again." These words were popularized by the British educational writer W. E. Hickson (1803–1870). The sentence was attributed to Robert the Bruce, king of Scots, speaking to his troops, against the English, at Bannockburn in 1314.]

Current understanding on Eubacteria and Archaea provides a more accurate picture on the origin of eukaryotic cells. A group of archaea studied by Swedish scientists (at Uppsala University and their collaborators) have been named Asgard archaea. Originally obtained from marine sediments, they have been divided into Odin, Thor, Loki and Hemidalla groups (all after Norse gods). From analysis of their genomes, the Asgard archaea prokaryotes possess many known eukaryotic features, including the presence of tubulin and actin-binding protein profilin, as well as endosomal sorting and membrane-trafficking components. These prokaryotes also have metabolic pathways such as carbon fixation and oxidation of organic substrates (Zaremba-Niedzwiedzka *et al.* 2017; Spang *et al.* 2019). The scientists proposed the origin of eukaryotes as a reverse flow model, a symbiogenetic model that involves electron or hydrogen flow from an organo-heterotrophic archaeal host to a bacterial symbiont.

These interesting Archaea prokaryotes, however, are difficult to culture until the 2020 success by Japanese scientists, after a decade of research (Imachi *et al.* 2020). Hiroyuki Imachi (Japan Agency for Marine-Earth Science and Technology) and collaborators used a methane-fed continuous-flow bioreactor to enrich deep sea sediments over 2,000 days, and reported growth of the first Archaeon. They named "***Candidatus Prometheoarchaeum syntrophicum*** strain MK-D1," as an extremely slow-growing, small coccal-shaped anaerobe that degrades amino acids (doubling time 14–25 days). In addition, the microbe can produce long, straight, or branched membrane protrusions. Based on these features the scientists proposed the entangle-engulf-enslave (E^3) model for eukaryogenesis. Please see Figure 4.1 for the first culture of an Archaeon (Imachi *et al.* 2020).

The last universal common ancestor (**LUCA**) became the first eukaryote when the **Asgard** archaea took in an **alpha proteobacterium** via its membrane protrusions to enslave the bacterium (future mitochondrion).

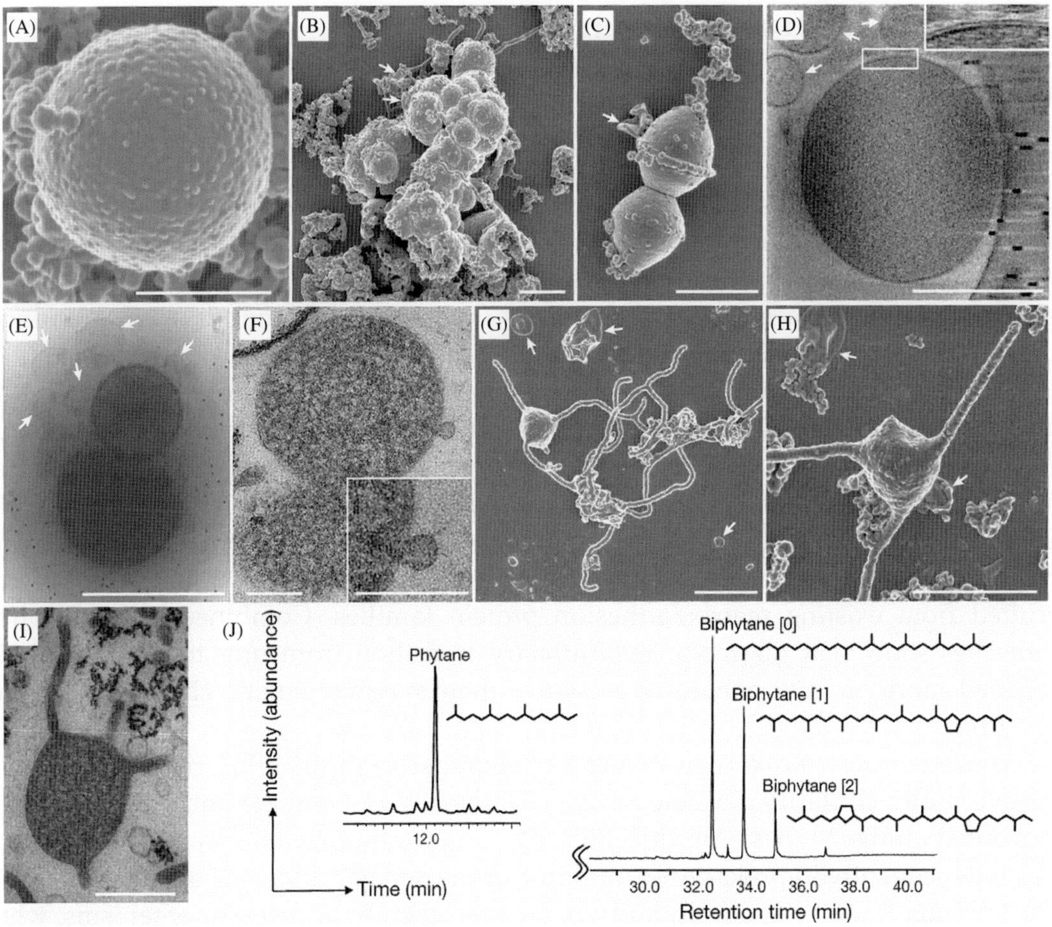

Fig. 4.1 ■ The first culture of an Archaeon. Microscopy characterization and lipid composition of MK-D1. A–C, SEM images of MK-D1. Single cell (A), aggregated cells covered with EPS-like materials (B) and a dividing cell with polar chains of blebs (C). D, Cryo-electron tomography image of MK-D1. The top-right inset image shows a magnification of the boxed area to show the cell envelope structure. E, Cryo-EM image of large membrane vesicles attached to and surrounding MK-D1 cells. F, Ultrathin section of an MK-D1 cell and a membrane vesicle. The bottom-right inset image shows a magnified view of the membrane vesicle. G, H, SEM images of MK-D1 cells producing long branching (G) and straight (H) membrane protrusions. I, Ultrathin section of a MK-D1 cell with protrusions. J, A total ion chromatogram of gas chromatography–mass spectrometry (GC–MS) for lipids extracted from a highly purified MK-D1 culture. The chemical structures of isoprenoids and their relative compositions are also shown. Scale bars, 1 μm (B, C, G, H), 500 nm (A, D, E, I) and 200 nm (F). A–C, G, H, SEM images are representative of n = 122 recorded images that were obtained from four independent observations from four culture samples. D, E, Cryo-EM images are representative of n = 14 recorded images that were taken from two independent observations from two culture samples. F, I, The ultrathin section images are representative of n = 131 recorded images that were obtained from six independent observations from six culture samples. White arrows in the images indicate large membrane vesicles. The lipid composition experiments were repeated twice and gave similar results. Courtesy: Imachi *et al. Nature* 2020;577:519–25. Reproduced with permission from *Nature* with Creative Commons Attribution 4.0 (CC-BY) International License.

4.4 Origin of Multicellularity

An important question to ask is how did the single eukaryotic cell evolve into a multicellular organism? The transition from unicellular to multicellular lifestyle has occurred multiple times, as seen in the lineages leading to plants, animals and fungi. Some unicellular amoeba species possess a multicellular developmental stage. Probably the most famous is the cellular slime mold/social amoeba *Dictyostelium discoideum* (first presented in Chapter 2). The amoebae feed on bacteria in the forest soil. Upon nutrient exhaustion they aggregate (using secreted cyclic AMP as the gathering signal) to form a multicellular slug stage (using adhesion proteins and slime, an extracellular matrix, to hold the cells together). The multicellular slug migrates and then differentiates into a fruiting body composed of stalked cells and spores (a process named culmination). Related species differentiate similarly; some species even use a different signal (the dipeptide, glorin, for the cellular slime mold species *Polysphondylium pallidum* in lieu of cyclic AMP) (McGrath 2018). In an analysis on gene expression, it is shown that "most genes required for multicellular development were already present in unicellular relatives or were recruited from existing matrix/adhesion protein families. Combined, these separate approaches show that the major evolutionary transition from uni- to multicellularity depended more on environmental pressures than massive genetic change" (Glöckner *et al.* 2016).

Dictyostelium discoideum is an example of **aggregative multicellularity**, as opposed to **cohesive multicellularity**. Pauline Schaap (University of Dundee) and colleagues have commented on the 2 types of multicellularity: "In fact, multicellularity evolved at many times independently in prokaryotes, and in 7 of the 8 major divisions of eukaryotes. The most common route to multicellularity is the one taken by sorocarpic organisms, which alternate between a unicellular feeding stage and a multicellular stage where starving cells aggregate to build a fruiting structure (sorocarp) with spores. … Sorocarpic multicellularity or aggregative multicellularity differs from all other forms of multicellularity, where cells stick together after division and feed in the multicellular stage. This type of cohesive multicellularity is common to green plants, red and brown algae and fungi, and encompasses all animals, which altogether have a more limited phylogenetic distribution" (Kawabe *et al.* 2019).

Environmental pressure induces multicellularity. As discussed above, starvation induces *Dictyostelium* amoebae towards aggregation and further differentiation. In the lab, the unicellular yeast *Saccharomyces cerevisiae* can be induced to become multicellular by size selection plus a single mutation that allows daughter cells to stick together (Pennisi 2018). In nature, an evolutionary pressure towards multicellularity can be **predation**. In a study of unicellular green alga *Chlamydomonas reinhardtii* under selection pressure by its predator *Paramecium tetraurelia*, predator-induced multicellular forms (algae form clusters and octads) are found after over 750 asexual generations, because the bigger forms are resistant to predation (Herron *et al.* 2019). Thus, in some instances, the origin of multicellularity can be selection by predation.

Multicellularity starts with **cell-to-cell adhesion**, followed by **cell-to-cell communication, cooperation**, and **specialization** (differentiation). For multicellularity of fungi and animals, the path may be a relatively simple three step process: unicellular, to colonial, to parenchymatous (unspecialized cells available for differentiation) (Niklas and Newman 2013; Niklas 2014). Multicellularity allows a bigger organism with division of labor (possessing a variety of tissues/organs for different functions).

For dividing animal cells to generate and maintain organized tissues, the mitotic spindle must be properly oriented relative to the position of surrounding cells. Cells that orient the spindle parallel to the epithelial plane can only expand the tissue (in a sheet composed of epithelial cells), whereas cells that rotate the orientation can leave the epithelium after division. At the molecular level, the origin of multicellularity has been hypothesized to come from gene duplication and novel use (repurposing) of a single protein in order to alter mitotic spindle orientation at the time of cell division (Anderson *et al.* 2016). The gene is guanylate kinase (GK). The duplicated version is named guanylate kinase protein-interaction domain (**GK-PID**). After gene duplication, a single mutation repurposed the protein and instead of its enzymatic activity, it became capable of binding other proteins (for its new function of linking the mitotic spindle to the cell surface). The GK enzyme catalyzes ATP + GMP to ADP + GDP. GK-PID links the microtubule kinesin motor (KHC73) with a cell surface protein (named Pins, partner of inscuteable, an example of concocted names for *Drosophila* mutations conceived by fly geneticists), thus affecting spindle orientation with this binding. Related proteins (orthologs) for GK, GK-PID, KHC73 and Pins have been found in both humans and **choanoflagellates** (the species *Salpingoeca rosetta*). Choanoflagellates are metazoa's closest unicellular cousins; they have both solitary and colonial forms (for feeding). Scientists can change the orientation of the choanoflagellate mitotic spindle by incorporating the GK-PID with a single amino acid residue mutation predicted for binding (from enzyme to scaffold). In this scenario, evolution of a protein complex involving 4 proteins (GK, GK-PID, KHC73 and Pins) resulted in multicellularity. Please see Figure 4.2 for the gene duplication as an origin of multicellularity (Anderson *et al.* 2016).

4.5 Classification of Eukaryotes

Eukaryotes have been classified based on phylogenetic and morphological data (to delineate monophyletic groups). Evolutionary relatedness has divided the eukaryotes into supergroups. In 2004, Canadians Alastair Simpson and Andrew Roger (both at Dalhousie University, Halifax) proposed "The real 'kingdoms' of eukaryotes" and described 6 Supergroups: **Opisthokonta, Amoebozoa, Plantae, Chromalveolata, Rhizaria,** and **Excavata** (Simpson and Roger 2004). Opisthokonta includes animals and fungi, as well as unicellular groups such as the choanoflagellates. Microsporidia has become members of fungi. Amoebozoa include classic free living and parasitic amoebae (such as *Entamoeba*) and cellular slime molds (*Dictyostelium*). Plantae includes species with "primary endosymbiosis"

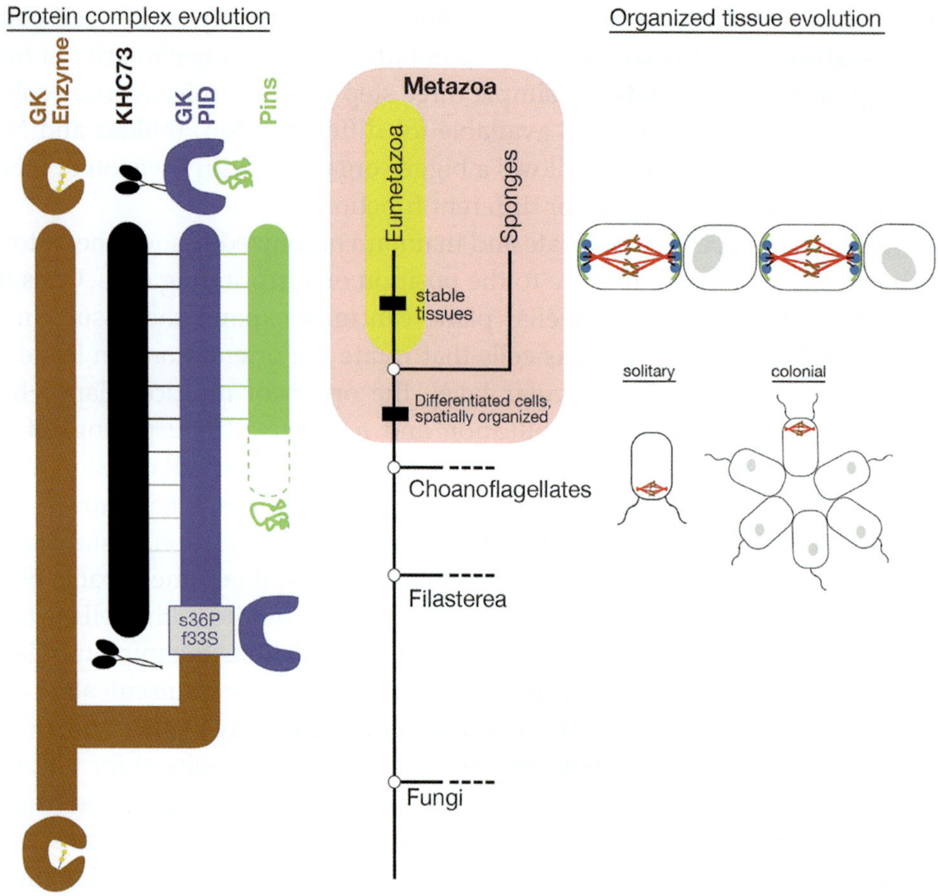

Fig. 4.2 ■ Gene duplication and the origin of multicellularity. Historical evolution of GK_{PID}-mediated spindle orientation complex. The center portion shows the phylogeny of Metazoa and closely related taxa. The origin of cell differentiation and spatially organized tissues is marked. The left portion shows major events in the evolution of the components of the spindle orientation complex reconstructed in this study. Duplication of an ancestral gk enzyme (brown) and the key mutations that led to the origin of a GK_{PID} (blue) that could bind other molecules in the complex are shown relative to the phylogeny's time scale. The apparent date of origin of KHC-73 (black) and Pins (green) are also shown. Dotted green line shows the origin of Pins in a form not yet bound by GK_{PID}. Solid green line shows GK_{PID}-binding form. Horizontal lines indicate binding between proteins. The right portion shows a schematic of the spindle orientation machinery in metazoans, which allows orientation relative to external cues from nearby cells, as well as spindle orientation relative to the internal cell axis as marked by the flagella in both solitary and colonial choanoflagellates. Courtesy: Anderson *et al. Elife* 2016;5:e10147. Reproduced with permission from *Elife* with Creative Commons Attribution 4.0 (CC-BY) International License.

and possess plastids. They are subdivided into 3 groups: land plants and green algae (*Chlamydomonas*), red algae (rhodophytes), and the glycophytes. Chromalveolata include species with "secondary endosymbiosis" in the eukaryotes already containing a primary plastid. Members include the unicellular algal groups dinoflagellates, cryptophytes and haplophytes, the stramenopiles (also known as heterokonts) with varying sizes from diatoms to kelps, the ciliates (*Paramecium*), and the apicomplexans (malaria parasite *Plasmodium*). Rhizaria supergroup classification is based on rRNA sequence data. Members include free-living foraminifera (marine amoebae) and radiolaria (heterotrophic amoebae and flagellates), and animal parasites (haplosporidia). Excavata are unicellular heterotrophic flagellates, including parasitic species that cause diseases (such as *Giardia* and *Trypanosoma*). Excavata is noted as the most contentious of the major supergroups: some studies indicating them as early branch of eukaryotes while others argue against the concept.

Classification of eukaryotes into supergroups has been maintained but further revised. As a substitute for the 1980 classification scheme for the Society of Protozoologists, Sina Adl (Dalhouse) and international colleagues kept 5 of the 6 supergroups (Adl *et al.* 2005): Amoebozoa, Opisthokonta, Rhizaria, Chromalveolata and Excavata; Plantae was replaced by **Archaeplastida**. In addition, there is a table showing genera with uncertain affiliation within the protists. The scientists concluded: "However, it should not be assumed that all contributors agreed on all points. The final synthesis is, nonetheless, a classification that we recommend as the basis for future revisions." This classification was accomplished on behalf of the International Society of Protozoologists.

From 2005 to 2021, there have been 2 revisions. This first revision was published in 2012. Sina Adl (now at University of Saskatchewan) and colleagues presented "The revised classification of eukaryotes" (Adl *et al.* 2012). Eukaryotes are divided into 5 supergroups: **Amoebozoa, Opisthokonta, SAR (Stramenopiles, Alveolata, Rhizaria), Archaeplastida** and **Excavata**. The old supergroup Chromalveolata was no longer recognized, and the new supergroup SAR included both members of Chromalveolata and the old Rhizaria supergroup. The scientists added 2 domains or super-supergroups (clusters known as taxa) to link the related supergroups. **Amorphea** means without form or shape; it combines 2 supergroups Amoebozoa and Opisthokonta, including mammals (*Homo sapiens*), fungi (*Neurospora*) and amoebae (*Dictyostelium*). **Diaphoretickes** means diversity in features; it combines 2 supergroups Archaeplastida and SAR, including plants (*Arabidopsis*) and ciliates (*Paramecium*). Previously, the terms **unikonts** and **bikonts** (1 and 2 cilia/flagella) had been used to differentiate the two groups but the scientists determined the differentiation to be "almost certainly incorrect." (However, unikonts and bikonts have been used by other scientists, for example, in the origin of eukaryote phylogeny study using bacterial genes, Derelle *et al.* 2015.) Excavata is an independent supergroup and not included in the 2 taxons. Similar to the original, the scientists have provided a table for protists of uncertain origins.

The third revision was published in 2019, titled "Revisions to the classification, nomenclature, and diversity of eukaryotes" (Adl *et al.* 2019). They stated: "In contrast to a phylogenetic tree, a classification system belongs to a community of users, and it is generated through discussions of the available evidence, for pragmatic purposes of teaching, curation, organizing data, archiving and communicating with a common language. It is a commonly agreed point of reference. It is not to be reimagined or re-done at will by one individual." The system is a consensus from a committee for the International Society of Protozoologists. The scientists commented on the classification of Ruggiero *et al.* (2015), discussed earlier, stating: "Another proposed classification of prokaryotes and eukaryotes was published recently (Ruggiero *et al.* 2015). This effort may be reasonable in their classification of the prokaryotes, but the eukaryote section does not pass standards of modern biology. Specifically, it is their refusal to use monophyly as a guiding principle…" Both Ruggiero *et al.* (2015) and Adl *et al.* (2019) are our current, best efforts at the classification of living things; they have applied various assumptions and they aim at different audiences.

The current eukaryote classification (Adl *et al.* 2019) is presented here in some detail. There are 2 domains: Amorphea and Diaphoretickes (same as before, but with addition of members). Amorphea includes supergroups CRuMs, Amoebozoa and **Obazoa**. Opisthokonta is classified under Obazoa (together with 2 other smaller groups) and contains Holozoa (including Choanoflagellata and Metazoa) and Nucletmycea. Diaphoretickes include supergroups Crypista, Haptista, Archaeplastida, and SAR (Stramenopiles, Alveolata and Rhizaria). New minor supergroups are Haptista, CRuMs, and Cryptista. Independent from the 2 domains (Amorphea and Diaphoretickes), the former supergroup Excavata has been deleted due to "loss of monophyly in the Excavata" and becomes the informal **"Excavates,"** which contains 2 major groups, Metamonada and Discoba. Below supergroups in the taxonomic hierarchy, groups and their genera are ranked by relatedness (being shown as levels of bullets, rankings, groupings in the classification scheme). The following is an introduction to the major groups, together with description of their parasitic members' genera.

Amoebozoa was from Luhe 1913 (Adl *et al.* noted priority, the scientist who first coined the term and described the organisms/group, later scientists make modifications/amendments, their names are omitted here, please consult Adl *et al.* for further details). Organisms generally show **amoeboid locomotion**, with fan-shaped pseudopodia. Members include the free-living species *Amoeba* and the social amoebae *Dictyostelium*. For human parasitic protozoa, there is the ranking **Archamoebea**, followed by the genus *Entamoeba*, with the description "cilia and kinetosomes absent; with mitosomes instead of classical mitochondria; peroxisomes absent; mitosis closed with endonuclear centrosome and spindle; reduced Golgi dictyosome." Another ranking is **Acanthopodida** (third rank, after Centramodebia, second rank) followed by *Acanthamoeba*, with the description "flattened with prominent subpseudopodia, flexible and tapering to a fine tip and sometimes furcated near their base (acanthopodia)…"

Opisthokonta members were first grouped together by Cavalier-Smith 1987. Organisms have a **single posterior flagellum** present in at least one life cycle stage (that may be secondarily lost) and flat mitochondrial cristae. Members include choanoflagellates, fungi and animals. Under Opisthokonta, is Holozoa, which includes Choanoflagellata (*Salpingoeca*) and **Metazoa**. All multicellular parasites (helminths/worms) belong to

Animalia within Metazoa. Also under Opisthokonta is Holomycota or Nucletmycea, true fungi (*Neurospora*), and the obligate intracellular parasites Microsporidia, including *Encephalitozoon*, an opportunistic human pathogen.

Archaeplastida members were described by Adl in 2005. Organisms have **photosynthetic plastid with chlorophyll *a*** resulting from a primary endosymbiont with a cyanobacterium. Under Archaeplastida are Glaucophyta (unicellular or colonial algae containing a unique plastid named cyanelle), Rhodophyceae (red algae) and Chloroplastida (plastids with thylakoids) including Embryophyta (land plants).

SAR members were described by Fabien Burki (then University of Geneva, now Uppsala University) in 2008 (Burki *et al.* 2008). The name is derived from acronym of the 3 groups united in this clade: **Stramenopiles, Alveolata,** and **Rhizaria**. The 3 are grouped together as a supergroup due to available phylogenetic relatedness data.

The S in SAR stands for Stramenopiles. Stramenopiles (first rank) is from David Patterson 1989 (then University of Bristol, now Marine Biological Laboratory and University of Sydney), as defined by "motile cells typically bi-ciliate, typically with **heterokont** ciliation — anterior cilium with tripartite mastigonemes in two opposite rows and a posterior usually smooth cilium; tubular mitochondrial cristae; typically, four microtubular kinetosomal roots." Stramenopiles include diatoms, water molds, and kelps. There is Opalinea (at fifth rank), including *Opalina* (intestinal parasites of frogs/toads) and *Blastocystis* (another fifth rank) with a single species of human pathogen *Blastocystis*, with description "rounded aciliated yeast-like cells, anaerobic commensals/parasites of intestinal tracts; cilia secondarily lost. Environmental samples and from mammalian, avian, and reptile hosts, many without specific host."

A in SAR stands for Alveolata. Alveolata (first rank) is from Cavalier-Smith 1991, with description "**cortical alveolae**, sometimes secondarily lost; with ciliary pit or micropore; mitochondrial cristae tubular or ampulliform." Alveolata is mainly composed of **Dinoflagellata, Apicomplexa,** and **Ciliophora** (all second ranks). Alveolata also includes Perkinsidae (a different second rank), with the oyster parasite *Perkinsus*. Dinoflagellata composes of dinoflagellates (plankton). Apicomplexa Levine 1980 is described to have "at least one stage of the life cycle with flattened subpellicular vesicles and an apical complex consisting of one or more polar rings, rhoptries, micronemes, conoid and subpellicular microtubules ... mostly parasitic." Apicomplexa includes many species of parasitic protozoa. Within Aconoidsida (third rank) with "apical complex lacking conoid in asexual motile stages," Haemospororida Danilewsky 1885 (fourth rank) includes *Plasmodium* (malaria parasites) and Piroplasmorida Wenyon 1926 (a different fourth rank) includes *Babesia*. Within Conoidasida Levine 1988 (another third rank) with "complete apical complex, including a closed conoid in all or most asexual motile stages," Coccidia Leuckart 1879 (fourth rank) includes *Cyclospora, Eimeria, Toxoplasma*; and Gregarinasina Dufour 1828 (a different fourth rank) includes *Cryptosporidium*, with description "oocysts and meronts with attachment 'feeder' organelle ... epicellular localization in host cell." Ciliophora Doflein 1901 is named for "cells with nuclear dimorphism, including a typically polygenomic macronucleus and at least one diploid micronucleus," that includes the ciliates

(*Paramecium*). Within Ciliophora, Balantidiidae (ninth rank), after Vestibuliderida (eighth rank), with description "endocommensals in fish and herbivorous placental mammals, except for marsupials," includes *Balantidium, Neobalantidium. Balantidium* is the only known human pathogen of ciliates.

The R in SAR stands for Rhizaria. Rhizaria Cavalier-Smith 2002 members have cells "with fine pseudopodia varying as simple, branching, or anastomosing patterns, often supported by microtubules in those groups examined by electron microscopy." The group was originally identified almost exclusively from molecular phylogenetic reconstruction. It includes foraminifera and radiolarian, groups of ecological interests (they form fossils with silicate and calcite mineral deposits, important for paleoclimatology), and Acetosporea (third rank), Haplosporida (fourth rank), including *Haplosporidium nelsoni*, an oyster parasite. We studied SSU rRNA gene sequence of *Perkinsus* (belong to A or SAR) and *Haplosporidium* (belong to R of SAR) in collaboration with colleagues at Haskins Lab/Rutgers Shellfish Research Lab in southern New Jersey (Fong *et al.* 1993a, 1993b & Ko *et al.* 1995, 1999).

The supergroup **Excavata** was originally from Cavalier-Smith 2002. In the current classification, the group is known informally as **"Excavates."** [The term used: Incertae sedis Eukarya: Excavates ("Excavates" are of uncertain placement). Taxonomists used the term for a taxonomic group where its broader relationships are unknown or undefined. Other have referred these groups as "enigmatic taxa."] Organisms belonging to the "Excavates" have shared common feeding structure, a typical **suspension feeding groove** (cytostome). Within the "Excavates," there is monophyly for 2 groups (first rank): **Metamonada** and **Discoba**.

Metamonada Grasse 1952 is described as "anaerobic/microaerophilic, either with modified mitochondria that lack cristae, are non-respiratory, and lack a genome (e.g., hydrogenosomes or mitosomes), or without mitochondria..." There is Diplomonadida (third rank, after Fornicata, second rank) "two nuclei" and Giardiinae (fourth rank) that includes *Giardia*. Parabasalia Honigberg 1973 (a different second rank) for "cells with a parabasal apparatus..." Trichomonadida Kirby 1947 (third rank) includes *Trichomonas* and *Pentatrichomonas*.

Discoba is defined as "a grouping robustly recovered in multigene phylogenetic analyses, containing Heterolobosea, Euglenozoa, Jakobida, and Tsukubamonadida; ancestrally bi-ciliate." Vahlkampfiidae (fifth rank, after Heterolobosea, Tetramitia, Eutetramitia, second, third, fourth rank, respectively), which are "ciliated amoebae or amoeboid without cilium ... nucleolus persists through mitosis; single nucleus," includes *Naegleria* and *Paravahlkampfia*. In Euglenozoa (second rank), defined as "cells with two cilia, occasionally one, rarely more, inserted into an apical/subapical ciliary pocket; with rare exceptions, emergent cilia with heteromorphic paraxonemal rods; usually with tubular feeding apparatus associated with ciliary apparatus; basic ciliary apparatus pattern consisting of two functional kinetosomes and three asymmetrically arranged microtubular roots; single mitochondrion mostly with discoidal cristae," and Kinetoplastea Honigberg 1963 (third rank) as "cells with a kinetoplast, which is a large mass of mitochondrial DNA; apomorphy: kinetoplast; mitochondrial RNA editing; trans-splicing of splice leader RNA; polycistronic transcription," species include *Trypanosoma, Leishmania, Leptomonas, Phytomonas.* (Molecular features will be discussed in the Chapter 5, on trypanosomatid protozoa.)

There are 3 new minor supergroups. **CRuMs** links orphan taxa together based on molecular data, including swimming flagellates, filose amoebae and gliding cells. The term is derived from the groups Collodictyonids, Rigifilida, and Mantamonas. **Cryptista** includes the cryptomonads, algae with red algal-derived plastids. **Haptista** includes marine photosynthetic haptophytes and fresh water heterotrophic centrohelids. Parasitic protozoa are absent in these 3 minor supergroups.

Please see Figure 4.3 for a diagrammatic representation of classification (Adl *et al.* 2019). New features in Adl *et al.* (2019) include a table of PCR primers for SS RNA analysis, a trophic functional group discussion and several tables, including one with Chinese terminology of protist groups (as appendices). To present the information in a different manner, please see Figure 4.4 and Table 4.1 to show our emphasis on parasitic protozoa and their relationship in phylogeny and classification.

Using molecular phylogenetics, lab culture of unicellular organisms from marine and other sources, novel supergroups have been discovered (hence the primer table provided to encourage future field work). Most organisms are heterotrophic flagellates, others are heterotrophic amoebae, heterotrophic amoeboflagellates, and unicellular algae (hence the trophic discussion in the revised classification). New findings lead to enrichment of the eukaryotic phylogenetic tree (Burki *et al.* 2020). As an example, the heterotrophic flagellate group Hemimastigophora is found to be a new supergroup (Lax *et al.* 2018). Keeling and Burki (2019) commented: "The tree is not completely resolved, and contentious problems remain, but many well-established supergroups now encompass much more diversity than the traditional kingdoms. Some of the most exciting recent developments come from the discovery of branches in the tree that we previously had no inkling even existed, many of which are of great ecological or evolutionary interest. These new branches highlight the need for more exploration..."

Internet web sources are available for eukaryote classification.[2–3]

4.6 Protozoan Form and Function

The term **protist** is used to describe eukaryotes with a unicellular level of organization, without cell differentiation into tissues. As seen above, several monophyletic lineages have been identified within the protists. The traditional kingdoms, Animalia, Fungi and Plantae are recognized as being derived from within monophyletic protist lineages. Each eukaryotic microbe possesses a nucleus (which is absent in the prokaryote). In Adl *et al.* (2019), the current eukaryote classification depends on phylogenetic/evolutionary

[2] The catalog of life project can be found in https://www.catalogueoflife.org/

[3] The universal taxonomy for eukaryotes can be found in https://unieuk.org/

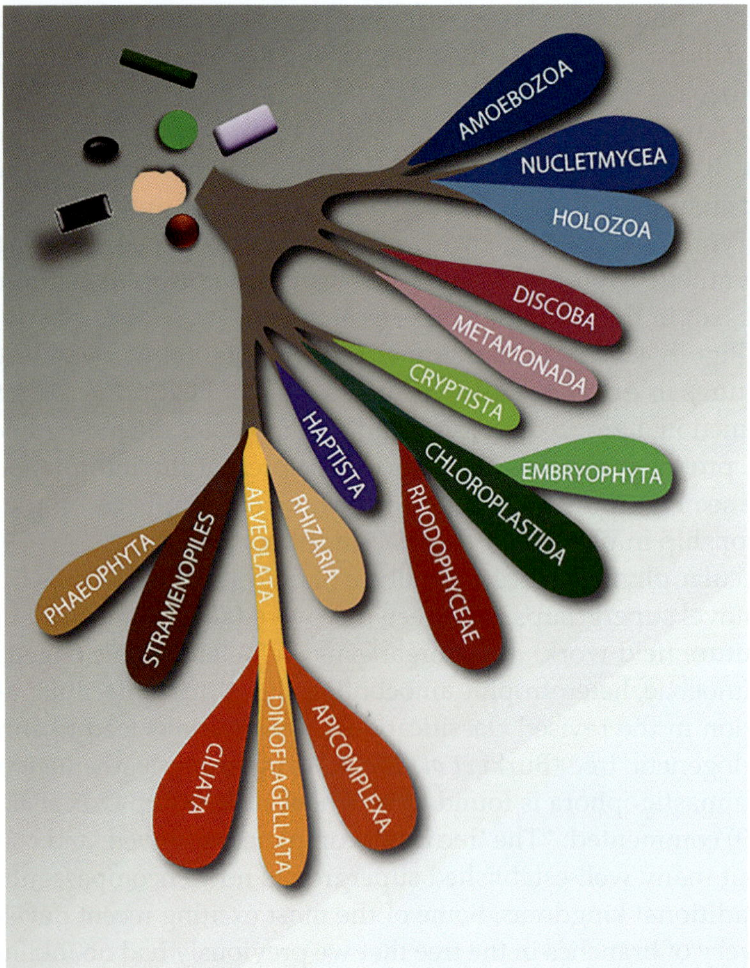

Fig. 4.3 ■ Classification of eukaryotes as supergroups. Overview of the diversity of protists among eukaryotes. Amoebozoa, Nucletmycea, and Holozoa together form the Amorphea; The Diaphoretickes includes Crypista, Chloroplastida and Embryophyta, Rhodophyceae, Haptista, Rhizaria, Alveolata (Apicomplexa, Dinoflagellata, Ciliata), Stramenopiles and Phaeophyta. Courtesy: Adl *et al. J Eukaryot Microbiol* 2019;66:4–119. Reproduced with permission from *The Journal of Eukaryotic Microbiology* with Creative Commons Attribution 4.0 (CC-BY) International License.

relatedness among organisms. Eukaryotic characteristics include: a cytoskeleton made up of microtubules/microfilaments, with 9+2 axoneme flagellum/cilium, an endomembrane system with ER/Golgi/lysosomes, nuclear envelopes; genome in chromosomes contained with the membrane-bound nucleus; mitochondria descended of bacterial endosymbiont; and translation using 80S ribosomes (S stands for Svedverg unit), as compared to the smaller 70S prokaryotic ribosomes.

Protozoa were first seen by Anthony van Leeuwenhoek. In 1681 he found *Giardia* in his own diarrheal stool. So, the first protozoan seen was a parasitic species. Probably

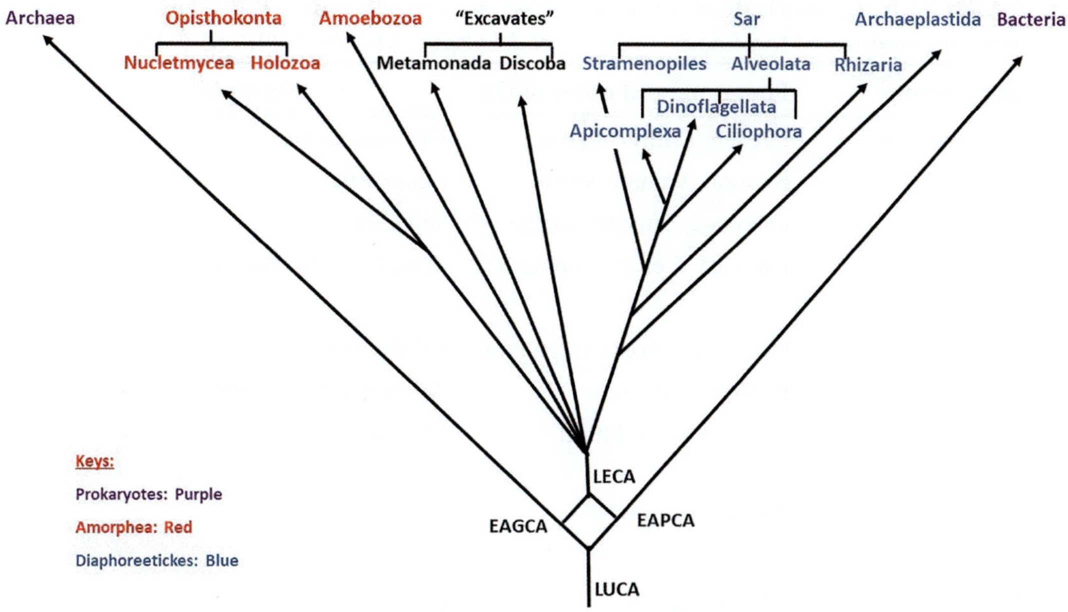

Fig. 4.4 ■ Proposed evolutionary relationship of life on earth. Both prokaryotes and eukaryotes are included, but only major eukaryotic supergroups are shown. LUCA is last universal common ancestor; LECA is last eukaryotic common ancestor. EAGCA is eukaryote-Asgard common ancestor; EAPCA is eukaryote-alphaproteobacterium common ancestor. Prokaryotes are colored in purple. Eukaryotes of the domain Amorphea are colored in red. Eukaryotes of the domain Diaphoretickes are colored in blue. Members of the informal supergroup "Excavates" are in black. (Adapted from multiple sources, including Adl *et al. J Eukaryot Microbiol* 2019;66:4–119; Burki *et al. Trends Ecol Evol* 2020;35:43–55; McInerney J, O'Connell M. *Nature* 2017:541:297–299; White M, Suvorova E. *Trends Parasitol* 2018:34: 759–771; Wiser M. *Protozoa and Human Disease*, Garland, 2011.)

the best known free-living protozoan is *Amoeba proteus*. Comparison of an amoeba (protozoan) and the human macrophage (mammalian cell) shows organelle commonality between the two. There is one nucleus and many types of organelles, including mitochondria, Golgi, rough/smooth endoplasmic reticulum (RER/SER), lysosomes and peroxisomes. Cytosol separates into ectoplasm and endoplasm. There are pseudopodia; their different shapes have been used in amoebae classification. For each protozoan species and different mammalian cell types, there are various adaptive and functional structural additions/modifications. A human sperm cell or *Leishmania* promastigote has a flagellum, with its 9+2 microtubule rings made up of tubulins, and the base is the kinetosome/basal body.

There are specialized features, such as the subpellicular microtubules of *Leishmania*. The pellicle is a cell surface protective structure, prominent in ciliates such as *Paramecium*. *Leishmania* has a single flagellum and *Paramecium* has many cilia. Cilia and flagella are structurally the same, except for the differences in length. Unique structures have been found in various protozoan species, such as the microtubule-based **axostyle** in *Trichomonas*, and **contractile vacuoles** for osmoregulation in *Balantidium*.

TABLE 4.1: Classification of eukaryotes as supergroups. (With emphasis on parasitic protozoa. Modified from Adl *et al. J Eukaryot Microbiol*, 2019;66:4–119.)

Supergroup	First rank and other ranks	Examples
Amoebozoa	Evosea, Eumycetozoa	*Dictyostelium*
	Evosea, Archamoebea	*Entamoeba*
	Discosea, Thecamoebida	*Sappinia*
	Discisea, Centramoebia	*Acanthamoeba, Balamuthia*
Opisthokonta	Holozoa, Choanoflagellata	*Salpingoeca*
	Holozoa, Metazoa	Animalia, helminths
	Nucletmycea, Fungi	Microsporidia, *Encephalitozoon*
Archaeplastida	Chloroplastida	Plantae
Sar	Stramenopiles	*Blastocystis*
	Alveolata, Perkinsidae	*Perkinsus*
	Alveolata, Apicomplexa	*Plasmodium, Babesia, Toxoplasma, Cryptosporidium, Cyclospora*
	Alveolata, Ciliophora	*Balantidium*
	Rhizaria, Ascetosporea	*Haplosporidium*
"Excavates"	Metamonada, Fornicata	*Giardia*
	Metamonada, Parabasalia	*Trichomonas*
	Discoba, Heterolobosea	*Naegleria, Paravahlkampfia*
	Discoba, Euglenozoa	*Trypanosoma, Leishmania*

A protozoan may proceed to a resistant stage via encystment to form a **cyst**, especially in adverse environments. Protozoa have different forms of reproduction. A protozoan can divide by binary fission, from 1 to 2. For some species, there can be multiple fissions, from 1 to many, known as **schizogony** or **merogony**, and **gametogony**, as seen in the malaria parasite *Plasmodium*.

Protozoa adapt to various environments and live at various trophic levels. Parasitic protozoa include obligate and facultative species. Their parasitic lifestyles affect humans. Their roles as human pathogens will be presented in the following chapters.

Summary & Key Concepts

- Taxonomy, classification of living things, is the scientific organization of all life on earth.
- Biochemical and genetic analyses provide scientists to track the phylogenetic history of a particular species.
- Current theory suggests endosymbiosis led to development of the eukaryotic cell.
- Environmental pressures and genetic predispositions allowed for multicellular organisms to evolve.
- Based on phylogenetic and morphological data, eukaryotes are currently classified into 2 domains (super-supergroups): Amorphea (without form) and Diaphoretickes (diversity in features).
- The major supergroups are Amoebozoa, Obazoa (including Opisthokonta), SAR (Stramenopiles, Alveolata, Rhizaria), Archaeplastida and "Excavates."
- Supergroups contain groups and their constituent genera, which are ranked by relatedness.
- Classification models are consistently updated as more data becomes available and new species are discovered.
- Protists possess eukaryotic characteristics but most have a unicellular level of organization.

References

Adl SM, Simpson AG, Farmer MA, *et al.* The new higher level classification of eukaryotes with emphasis on the taxonomy of protists. *J Eukaryot Microbiol* 2005;52(5):399–451.

Adl SM, Simpson AG, Lane CE, *et al.* The revised classification of eukaryotes. *J Eukaryot Microbiol* 2012;59(5):429–93. Erratum in: *J Eukaryot Microbiol* 2013;60(3):321.

Adl SM, Bass D, Lane CE, *et al.* Revisions to the classification, nomenclature, and diversity of eukaryotes. *J Eukaryot Microbiol* 2019;66(1):4–119.

Anderson DP, Whitney DS, Hanson-Smith V, *et al.* Evolution of an ancient protein function involved in organized multicellularity in animals. *Elife* 2016;5:e10147.

Bass BL. *RNA Editing*, Oxford, 2001.

Burki F, Shalchian-Tabrizi K, Pawlowski J. Phylogenomics reveals a new 'megagroup' including most photosynthetic eukaryotes. *Biol Lett* 2008;4(4):366–9.

Burki F, Roger AJ, Brown MW, Simpson AGB. The new tree of eukaryotes. *Trends Ecol Evol* 2020;35(1):43–55.

Cavalier-Smith T. A revised six-kingdom system of life. *Biol Rev Camb Philos Soc* 1998;73(3):203–66.

Derelle R, Torruella G, Klimeš V, *et al.* Bacterial proteins pinpoint a single eukaryotic root. *Proc Natl Acad Sci USA* 2015;112(7):E693–9.

Embley TM, Martin W. Eukaryotic evolution, changes and challenges. *Nature* 2006;440(7084):623–30.

Fong D, Chan MM, Rodriguez R, *et al.* Small subunit ribosomal RNA gene sequence of the parasitic protozoan *Haplosporidium nelsoni* provides a molecular probe for the oyster MSX disease. *Mol Biochem Parasitol* 1993a;62(1):139–42.

Fong D, Rodriguez R, Koo K, *et al.* Small subunit ribosomal RNA gene sequence of the oyster parasite *Perkinsus marinus*. *Mol Mar Biol Biotechnol* 1993b;2(6):346–50.

Garnett ST, Christidis L, Conix S, *et al.* Principles for creating a single authoritative list of the world's species. *PLoS Biol* 2020;18(7):e3000736.

Glöckner G, Lawal HM, Felder M, *et al.* The multicellularity genes of dictyostelid social amoebas. *Nat Commun* 2016;7:12085.

Herron MD, Borin JM, Boswell JC, *et al.* De novo origins of multicellularity in response to predation. *Sci Rep* 2019;9(1):2328.

Imachi H, Nobu MK, Nakahara N, *et al.* Isolation of an archaeon at the prokaryote–eukaryote interface. *Nature* 2020;577(7791):519–25.

Kawabe Y, Du Q, Schilde C, Schaap P. Evolution of multicellularity in Dictyostelia. *Int J Dev Biol* 2019;63(8–9–10):359–69.

Keeling PJ, Burki F. Progress towards the tree of eukaryotes. *Curr Biol* 2019;29(16):R808–R817.

Ko YT, Ford SE, Fong D. Characterization of the small subunit ribosomal RNA gene of the oyster parasite *Haplosporidium costale*. *Mol Mar Biol Biotechnol* 1995;4(3):236–40.

Ko YT, Chan MM, Ford SE, Fong D. A PCR-ELISA method for direct detection of the oyster pathogen *Haplosporidium nelsoni*. *Mar Biotechnol (NY)* 1999;1(2):147–54.

Kutschera U. Haeckel's 1866 tree of life and the origin of eukaryotes. *Nat Microbiol* 2016;1(8):16114.

Lax G, Eglit Y, Eme L, Bertrand EM, Roger AJ, Simpson AGB. Hemimastigophora is a novel supra-kingdom-level lineage of eukaryotes. *Nature* 2018;564(7736):410–14.

Levine ND. "Taxonomy of the Sporozoa". *J Parasitol* 1970;56 (4, Sect. 2, Part 1: Supplement: Proceedings Of the Second International Congress of Parasitology):208–9.

McGrath C. Highlight: Origins of multicellularity revealed by single-celled amoebae. *Genome Biol Evol* 2018;10(2):705–6.

McInerney JO, O'Connell MJ. Microbiology: Mind the gaps in cellular evolution. *Nature* 2017;541(7637):297–9.

Niklas KJ. The evolutionary-developmental origins of multicellularity. *Am J Bot* 2014;101(1):6–25.

Niklas KJ, Newman SA. The origins of multicellular organisms. *Evol Dev* 2013;15(1):41–52.

Pennisi E. The power of many. *Science* 2018;360(6396):1388–91.

Ruggiero MA, Gordon DP, Orrell TM, *et al.* A higher level classification of all living organisms. *PLoS One* 2015;10(4):e0119248. Erratum in: *PLoS One* 2015;10(6):e0130114.

Simpson AG, Roger AJ. The real 'kingdoms' of eukaryotes. *Curr Biol* 2004; 14(17):R693–6.

Spang A, Stairs CW, Dombrowski N, *et al.* Proposal of the reverse flow model for the origin of the eukaryotic cell based on comparative analyses of Asgard archaeal metabolism. *Nat Microbiol* 2019;4(7):1138–48.

Whittaker RH. New concepts of kingdoms or organisms. Evolutionary relations are better represented by new classifications than by the traditional two kingdoms. *Science* 1969;163(3863):150–60.

White MW, Suvorova ES. Apicomplexa cell cycles: Something old, borrowed, lost, and new. *Trends Parasitol* 2018;34(9):759–71.

Wiser MF. *Protozoa and Human Disease*, Garland, 2011.

Zaremba-Niedzwiedzka K, Caceres EF, Saw JH, *et al.* Asgard archaea illuminate the origin of eukaryotic cellular complexity. *Nature* 2017;541(7637):353–8.

5

Trypanosomiasis and Leishmaniasis by Kinetoplastid Flagellates

5.1 Introducing Kinetoplastid Protozoa

Kinetoplastid flagellates are agents for neglected tropical diseases (NTDs), namely human African trypanosomiasis (HAT or sleeping sickness), American trypanosomiasis (Chagas' disease), and cutaneous, mucocutaneous, and visceral leishmaniasis. In 2012, WHO published Technical Report Series 975, titled "Research priorities for Chagas disease, human African trypanosomiasis and leishmaniasis."[1]

In the current Adl *et al.* (2019) classification of eukaryotes, the kinetoplastid protozoa belong to the "**Excavates**" (a demotion from the previous supergroup Excavata by adding brackets). Within the "Excavates," they belong to **Euglenozoa**, which includes the photosynthetic protozoan *Euglena* (with secondarily obtained chloroplast, for photosynthesis). Within Euglenozoa, they belong to Kinetoplastea, protozoa with kinetoplasts. Members of this group include free-living species (such as the genus *Bodo*) and the ones that belong to Trypanosomatida, which include parasites of plants (such as *Phytomonas*) and animals (frogs, fish, lizards, mammals). [Trypanosomes are found in birds where they seem to be harmless (Zídková *et al.* 2012).] A unique characteristic feature is the presence of a single **kinetoplast**. This structure is the circular DNA portion of the single mitochondrion in the trypanosomatid protozoan. The presence of DNA can be demonstrated by light microscopy, using Giemsa stain. Both nucleus and the kinetoplast are stained color purple, the existence of extranuclear DNA was first convincingly demonstrated in the kinetoplastid protozoa. Kinetoplast is located close to the kinetosome (aka basal body, or centriole). The structure was named kinetoplast because of the original speculation for a function in motility. This close association is important for kinetoplast division during cell division; the

[1] https://apps.who.int/iris/bitstream/handle/10665/77472/WHO_TRS_975_eng.pdf;jsessionid=70FD42B91CAF3B1E6BAA8EC95EBCC375?sequence=1

organelle is maintained by special proteins (known as components of tripartite attachment complex, **TAC**) (Mensa-Wilmot *et al.* 2019). A flagellum ends in the basal body. The kinetoplastid flagellum has an associated structure, named paraflagellar (or paraxial) rod. In some species or developmental stages, the flagellum may be attached to the cell surface, leading to a structure known as an **undulating membrane**; some scientists have described this structure as a "fin" of the protozoan. Some developmental forms possess a prominent surface coat known as glycocalyx. In addition, all kinetoplastid protozoa possess unique organelles, named **glycosome**, the location where glycolysis takes place. This feature is different from other organisms whose glycolytic process takes place in the cytosol. These unique characteristics may serve as potential targets for chemotherapy against all species of kinetoplastid protozoan parasites.

Kinetoplastid protozoa have several different forms, depending on their location of nucleus and kinetoplast. The flagellum is the anterior (front) portion of the protozoan, and the relative location of kinetoplast to the nucleus differs in different developmental stages. The main forms are **amastigote, promastigote, epimastigote** and **trypomastigotes** (Sharma *et al.* 2009). Amastigotes and promastigotes are seen in *Leishmania* species; epimastigotes and trypomastigotes are seen in *Trypanosoma brucei*. Other forms found in other species are ignored in this discussion, because they are absent in human pathogens. Please see Figure 5.1 for trypanosomatid forms (Sinclair and de Graffenried 2019). In addition to the flagellum that contains microtubules, different forms of the trypanosomatids are protected and shaped by a layer of subpellicular microtubules underneath the plasma membrane.

The kinetoplastid protozoa are also known as **hemoflagellates**. They cannot synthesize heme and thus require heme for survival. Typical laboratory culture conditions for these protozoa contain blood or blood components (for heme in hemoglobin). While this information is true for most species, there is at least one exception. The species *Phytomonas serpens* can survive without heme (Kořený *et al.* 2012). Because of the importance of trypanosomes in human diseases, these protozoa are also known as trypanosomatids. The trypanosomatids that cause human diseases are **heteroxenous**, that is, they infect both vertebrates (animals and humans) and invertebrates (insect vectors). Different vectors carry different species. The carrier for *Trypanosoma brucei* is the **tsetse fly** (both adult males and females suck blood). The carrier for *Trypanosoma cruzi* is the assassin or **kissing bug** (adults of either sex, as well as juveniles or nymphs, all stages suck blood). The carrier for *Leishmania* species is the **sand fly** (only adult females suck blood for ovulation, just like female mosquitoes and malaria).

Some trypanosomatids are **monoxenous**, associated only with a single host, such as *Leptomonas* living in cat flea (however, can be found in AIDS patients as **opportunistic infections**). Development of trypanosomatids in the insect gut can be divided into **Salivaria**, or anterior station, such as *Trypanosoma brucei*, in the anterior portion of insect digestive tract, or **Stercoraria**, or posterior station, such as *Trypanosoma cruzi*, in the posterior portion of insect digestive tract. In addition, kinetoplastid protozoa can be pleomorphic or polymorphic. The bloodstream form of trypomastigotes of *Trypanosoma brucei*

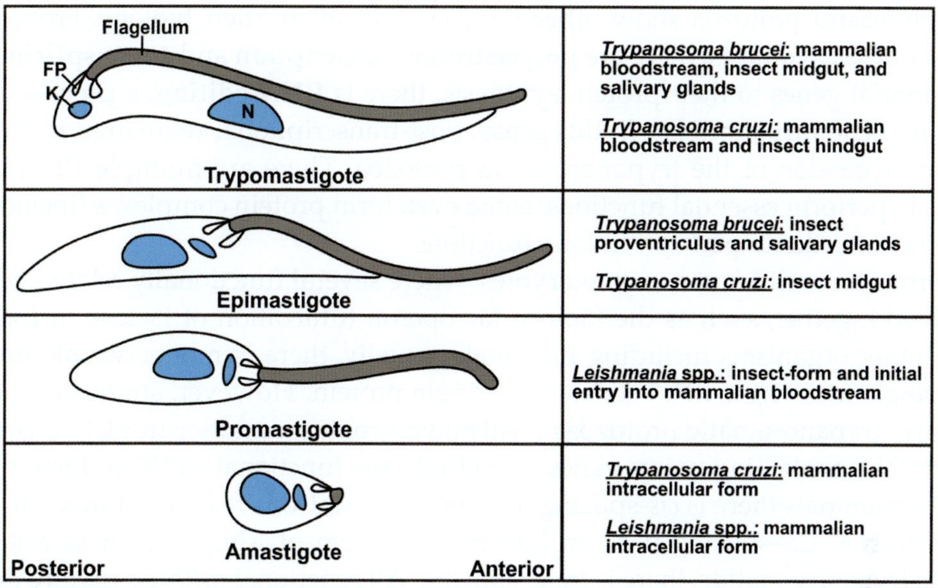

Fig. 5.1 ■ Trypanosomatid forms. The primary morphologies of human-infectious trypanosomatid parasites. Left. Schematic of cell structure and topological order of single-copy organelles in each morphology. The trypomastigote form is characterized by the posterior localization of the mitochondrial DNA aggregate, called the kinetoplast (K), to that of the nucleus (N). An attached flagellum exits from the flagellar pocket (FP) near the cell posterior. In the epimastigote form, the kinetoplast is anterior to the nucleus. While the flagellum is still attached to the cell surface, it also has a long, cell-free overhang. The promastigote form has a similar arrangement of DNA-containing organelles as the epimastigote, but the flagellum is unattached after exiting the flagellar pocket at the cell anterior. The kinetoplast is also positioned anterior to the nucleus in the smaller, more-spherical amastigote form. The flagellum is short and nonmotile, and barely protrudes from the flagellar pocket. Right. A list of the life-cycle stages in which the human-infectious trypanosomatids adopt these morphologies. Courtesy: Sinclair A, de Graffenried C. *Trends Parasitol* 2019;35:760–77. Reproduced with permission from Elsevier.

can be long-slender or short-stumpy, the latter believed to be pre-adaptation for tsetse environment.

5.2 Molecular Cell Biology

In addition to unique structures (kinetoplast, glycosome), trypanosomatid protozoa have a unique molecule known as **trypanothione**. In lieu of glutathione of the mammals (for detoxification purpose), they possess trypanothione, two glutathione molecules linked by a spermidine. The enzyme trypanothione reductase is involved in the metabolism and this pathway is a potential drug target (Wiser 2011).

Kinetoplastid protozoa show other unusual features in their biology. From nuclear genes to mRNA synthesis, there are **polycistronic transcription** and ***trans*-splicing**. From mitochondrial genes to their protein synthesis, there is **RNA editing**, a process to make mature mitochondrial mRNA. In this sense, post-transcriptional regulation is important for gene expression of the trypanosomatid protozoa. There are multiple RNA-binding proteins to perform essential functions; some even form protein complexes (including the editosome) in order to perform unique functions.

Operons are well known in prokaryotes, where several functionally related genes are transcribed together, such as the famous lac operon (utilization of lactose in *Escherichia coli*). In other organisms including mammals, usually, there is monocistronic transcription; a single messenger RNA codes for a single protein. However, studies on the transcription of trypanosomatid protozoa reveal polycistronic (or multicistronic) transcription. A pre-mRNA containing many genes is spliced into functional mRNAs for individual genes. In mammals there is *cis*-splicing, to remove the introns from pre-mRNA to get the mature mRNA. *Cis*-splicing uses an intermediate form of RNA known as a lariat (or lasso). In trypanosomatids, there is *trans*-splicing. All functional mRNAs require the addition of a **spliced leader** (aka mini-exon) RNA (SLRNA), which is coded from elsewhere in the genome. *Trans*-splicing seems to use similar mechanisms as *cis*-splicing to achieve the joining of two RNAs, except with a Y-shaped intermediate RNA molecule (Bitar *et al.* 2013). Please see Figure 5.2 for trypanosome gene expression (Clayton 2019).

Although first discovered in *Trypanosoma brucei* by comparing the cloned DNA sequences between complementary RNA (cRNA) and genomic DNA of the variant surface glycoprotein (VSG) gene (for antigenic variation, discussed later in this chapter) and showing an additional 39 bases at the 5′ end of mature VSG mRNA, trans-splicing has since been detected in many other species, although not to the extent of trypanosomatids. Examples include *Euglena gracilis*, *Hydra littoralis*, *Ciona intestinalis* (a primitive chordate), *Schistosoma mansoni*, and *Caenorhabditis elegans*. Please see Figure 5.3 for a variety of *trans*-splicing organisms (Lasda and Blumenthal 2011).

Another trypanosomatid surprise is RNA editing for mitochondrial organelle gene expression. The kinetoplast contains DNA (**kDNA**). It is composed of concatemeric circles of DNA of two types: 20 to 50 **maxicircles** (20 to 38 kilobases, kb, in size), and 5,000 to 10,000 **minicircles** (0.5 to 1 kb). Maxicircle DNA contains mitochondrial genes, but for quite a while the function of minicircle DNA was unclear. When the mitochondrial genes of mature mRNA were compared to the genomic sequence in recombinant DNA clones, sequence differences were found. For example, there was an addition of 4 uridines (U) in the mature mRNA for the COXII (cytochrome c oxidase II, aka MT-CO2) gene. The purpose of RNA editing is to achieve mature mitochondrial RNAs. Editosomes are assemblies containing guide RNAs (**gRNAs**), which are gene products of the minicircles, which guide and edit the transcripts from the maxicircles. A model of cleavage-ligation for RNA editing has been proposed. Pre-mRNA binds gRNA, followed by endonuclease cut, addition or deletion of U (hundreds of U's per transcript), and then linking together by RNA ligase. In trypanosomatid RNA editing of mitochondrial genes, the process involves the

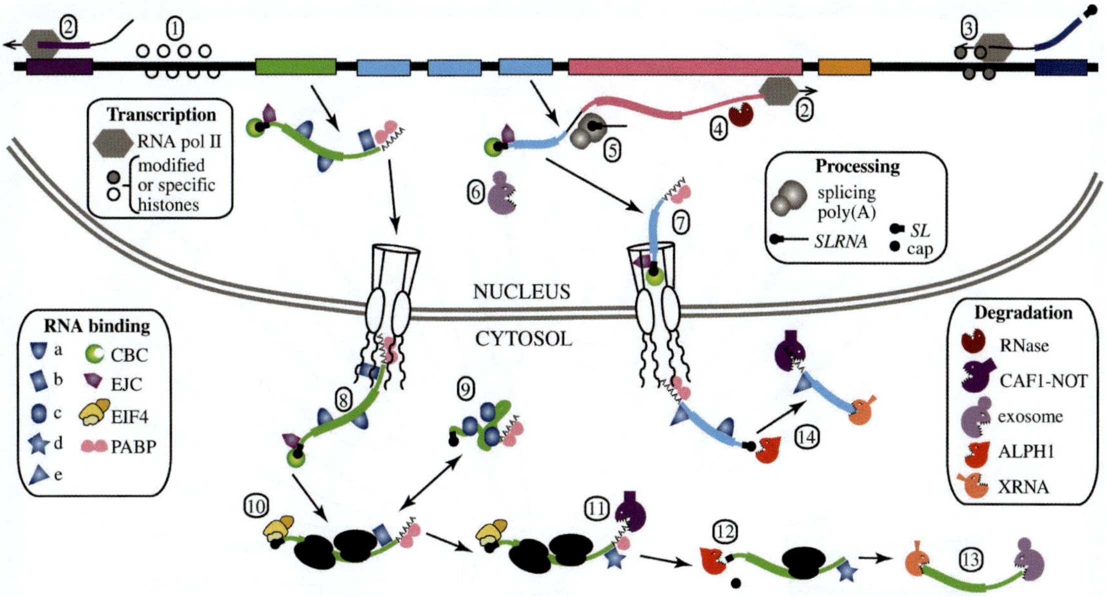

Fig. 5.2 ■ Gene expression in kinetoplastids. The thick line at the top represents the genome, and each colored block is represented in a mature mRNA. The corresponding mRNAs are shown with the coding regions thicker than the untranslated regions. The numbered steps are described in the text. 1: Modified histones in an RNA polymerase II initiation region. 2: RNA polymerase II elongation. 3: RNA polymerase II termination. 4: Endonuclease cleavage of precursor (postulated). 5: *Trans*-splicing and polyadenylation. 6: Incompletely processed mRNAs can be degraded by the exosome. 7: Export of a completed mRNA, with bound poly(A) binding protein (PABP), exon junction complex (EJC) and nuclear cap-binding complex (CBC). (Note that we do not know which, if any, splice junctions are bound by the EJC, and also that mRNA export can commence before the 3′-end is complete.) 8: Emergence of a mature mRNA including proteins on the coding region (a) and a specific, stabilizing protein (b) bound to the 3′-untranslated region (3′-UTR). 9: Binding by a silencing or aggregating RNA-binding protein (c) and condensation into granules. 10: Binding of EIF4E, EIF4G and EIF4A, and translation. 11: Protein (b) is replaced by a destabilizing RNA-binding protein (d) and deadenylation starts. 12: Decapping by ALPH1. 13: Degradation by XRNA and the exosome. 14: Rapid decay pathway — immediate decapping promoted by protein (e). Many of the proteins involved are listed in electronic supplementary material, table S1. Courtesy: Clayton C. *Open Biol* 2019;9:190072. Reproduced with permission from *Open Biology* with Creative Commons Attribution 4.0 (CC-BY) International License.

addition or deletion of uridines in order to produce functional mRNAs for the mitochondrial proteins (Zimmer *et al.* 2018). Please see Figure 5.4 for trypanosome mitochondrial RNA editing (Aphasizheva *et al.* 2020).

First discovered in kinetoplastid protozoa, RNA editing is found in other organisms. For example, there is editing in plant mitochondria and chloroplasts, in the true slime mold *Physarum polycephalum*, and even in mammals. However, mechanisms differ. For

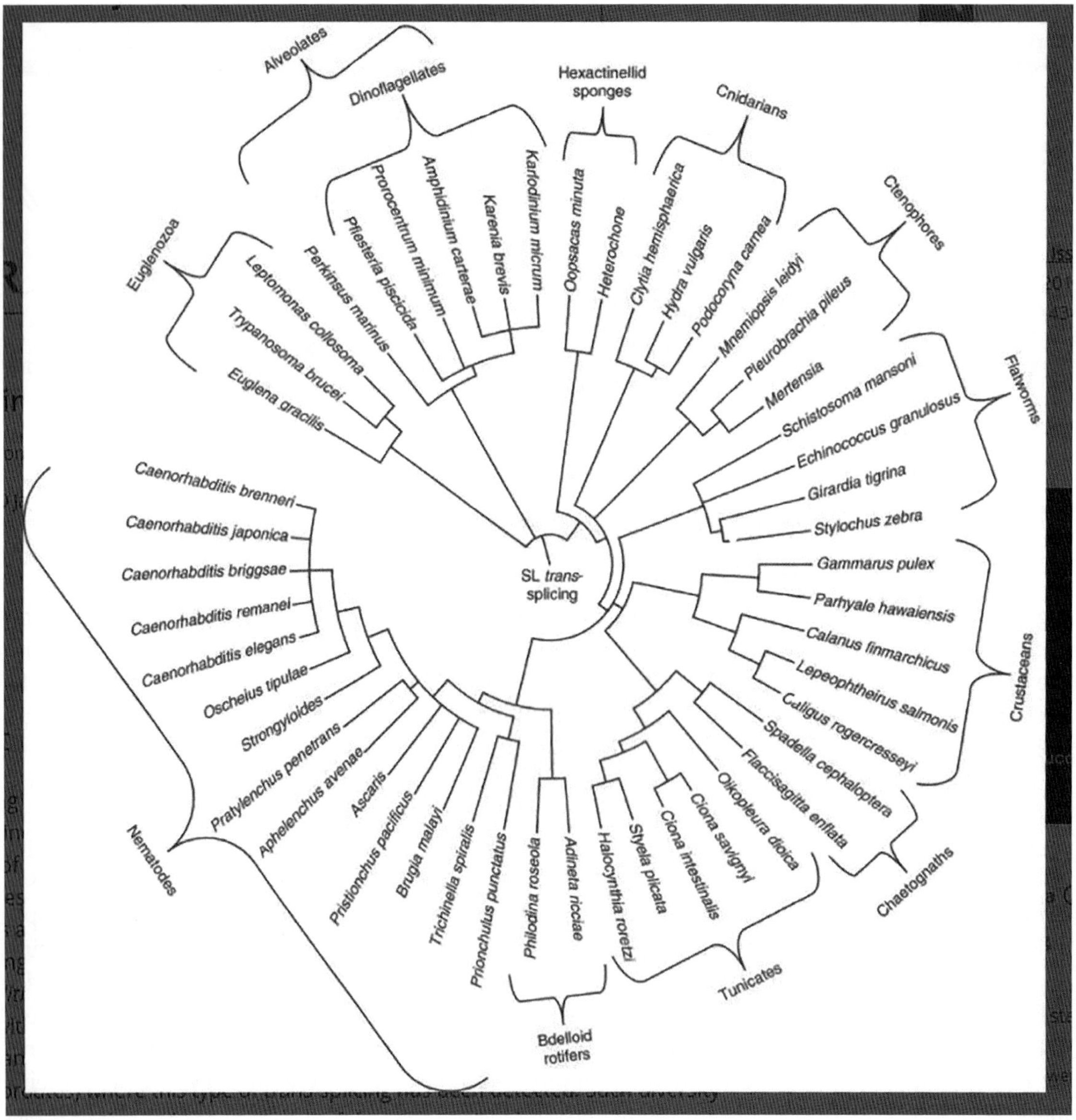

Fig. 5.3 ■ Spliced leader RNA *trans*-splicing in many species. Spliced leader (SL) *trans*-splicing organisms. Circular tree of selected species that have SL *trans*-splicing. Tree is based on NCBI taxonomy classification of numerous SL *trans*-splicing organisms. It is not necessarily representative of phylogenetic relationships and branch lengths are arbitrary. Drawn using Interactive Tree of Life (iTOL) according to Ref [89]. Courtesy: Lasda E, Blumenthal T. *Wiley Interdiscip Rev RNA* 2011;2:417–34. Reproduced with permission from John Wiley and Sons.

example, in humans, there is cytidine deamination of apolipoprotein B, with C to U conversion in the nucleus.

The unicellular trypanosomatids belong to the group Euglenozoa; all are obligate parasites. They infect plants, invertebrates, and vertebrates (including humans). Genomes

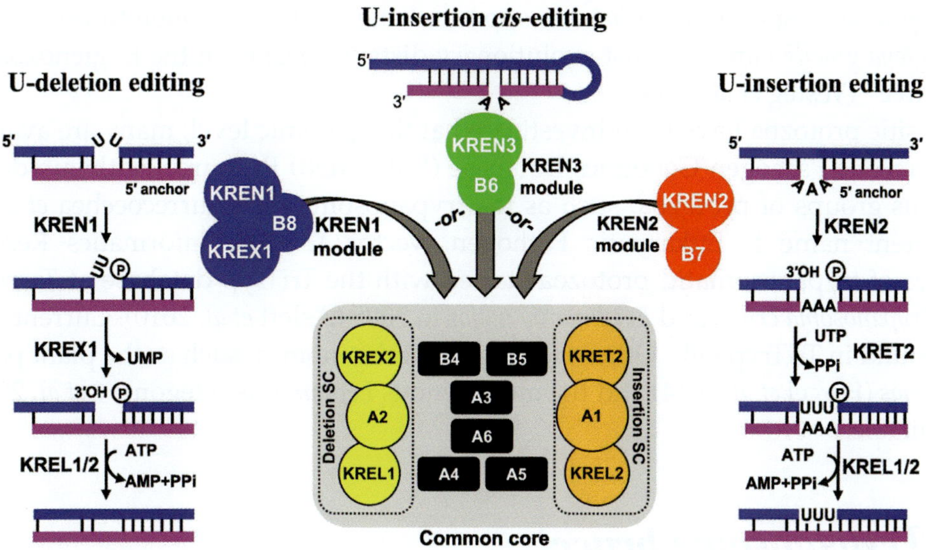

Fig. 5.4 ■ Trypanosome RNA editing. Schematic diagram of RNA-editing catalytic complex (RECC) isoforms and editing reactions. *Trans*-guided insertion and deletion, and *cis*-guided insertion substrates are juxtaposed with corresponding endonuclease modules and 12 common core proteins, with catalytic pathways outlined. Abbreviations: 5′ anchor, 5′ part of the guide-RNA that hybridizes with pre-edited mRNA; A, KREPA; B, KREPB; SC, subcomplex. See Table 1 for protein designations. Courtesy: Aphasizheva *et al. Trends Parasitol* 2020;36:337–55. Reproduced with permission from Elsevier.

of human trypanosomatids, as well as ones infecting other hosts, plus the free-living relative *Bodo saltans*, are all known. Features previously described for the parasitic trypanosomatids (glycosome and trypanothione, cell surface molecules amastin and gp63, spliced leader *trans*-splicing, poly-cistronic transcription, and RNA editing) are already present in the *Bodo* genome (but not mitochondrial circular kDNA network). "Robust phylogenetic reconstructions across Euglenozoa are now possible and place the results of parasite-focused studies into an evolutionary context. Here we discuss recent advances in identifying the factors shaping the evolution of Euglenozoa, focusing on ancestral features generally considered parasite-specific. Remarkably, most of these predate the transition(s) to parasitism, suggesting that the presence of certain preconditions makes a significant lifestyle change more likely" (Butenko *et al.* 2020). These findings seem to provide molecular data as proof for the concept of preadaptation (discussed in Chapter 2). Further analysis on the phylogeny may shed light on possible reductionist pathways for parasitism in the Euglenozoans.

"Parasitic trypanosomatids and phototrophic euglenids are among the most extensively studied euglenozoans. The phototrophic euglenid lineage arose relatively recently through secondary endosymbiosis between a phagotrophic euglenid and a prasinophyte green alga that evolved into the euglenid secondary chloroplast. The parasitic trypanosomatids (i.e., *Trypanosoma* spp. and *Leishmania* spp.) and the freshwater phototrophic euglenids (i.e., *Euglena gracilis*) are the most evolutionary distant lineages in the Euglenozoa phylogenetic tree" (Vesteg *et al.* 2019).

Parasitic protozoa have been investigated at the genomic level; many are available in the Eukaryotic Pathogen Genomics Database (EuPathDB) Resource, with sub-databases of various groups of protozoa, such as the trypanosomatids (Aurrecoechea *et al.* 2017). The current name is Eukaryotic Pathogen, Vector & Host Informatics Resources.[2] Genomes of trypanosomatid protozoa started with the TriTryp database of *Trypanosoma brucei*, *Trypanosoma cruzi*, and *Leishmania major* in 2005 (Aslett *et al.* 2010). Current updates can be found in TriTryp DB.[3] Other trypanosomatid genomes, such as the plant pathogen *Phytomonas* (Porcel *et al.* 2014) and the monoxenous *Leptomonas* (Flegontov *et al.* 2016), are also available.

5.3 *Trypanosoma brucei*

Another name for **HAT** is **sleeping sickness**, a disease caused by infection of the trypanosomatid protozoan *Trypanosoma brucei*. [Trypanosma comes from the Greek word for trypanon, denoting a corkscrew, a drill, or an auger, referring to the movement of this protozoan (due to its undulating membrane with surface-attached flagellum in the trypomastigotes of the bloodstream); soma means body; brucei is after David Bruce, who first identified trypanosomes as the cattle pathogen.]

HAT is restricted to sub-Sahara Africa. In 1995, about 25,000 cases were detected, with an estimated 300,000 undetected cases and 60 million people at risk of HAT infection. One prevalence estimate was 50,000 to 70,000, plus 10,000 new cases per year. In the last decade of the 20th century, the number of reported HAT cases reached to 50,000 new cases per year. Surveillance and control activities against HAT were reinforced at the beginning of the 21st century. Since then, there has been a steady decrease in HAT cases. HAT was included in the WHO NTD roadmap of diseases targeted for elimination by 2020. The WHO definition of **elimination** for HAT is that the incidence is less than 1 new case per 10,000 in at least 90% of foci and with fewer than 2,000 cases reported globally. According to this definition, the criteria for elimination was achieved in **2017**, because only 1,446 cases were reported that year (the previous year 2016 had 2,200 HAT cases). For both 2018 and 2019, under 1000 cases were reported too. For 2018, there were 977 cases (953 Tbg and 24 Tbr). For 2019, the number was 876. WHO's aims: the elimination of HAT as a public health problem by 2020 and the interruption of transmission by 2030, are on track.

Historically, HAT was troublesome to the European colonial powers. Various control measures were applied, and, under certain circumstances, had some degree of success. The prevalence was at a minimum of 4,435 cases in Africa in 1964. However, post-1960s,

[2] https://veupathdb.org/veupathdb/app
[3] https://tritrypdb.org/tritrypdb/app

disease control interventions were constrained due to conflicts, insecurity, and other social instability factors which largely resulted from the emergence of independent African states from their former European colonizers. Political turmoil led to HAT resurgence in the 1980s and 1990s. HAT cases in 1998 were 37,385 new cases and total estimated 300,000 cases (Domagalska and Dujardin 2020). At that time, the status of HAT triggered attention from the health authorities in endemic countries alongside bilateral and multilateral agencies. The WHO coordinated international partners working in HAT control, raised awareness and political will, and brought new resources from the public and private sectors to support national control programs. This resulted in a substantial, steady reduction in the number of HAT cases, reaching the historical lowest figure in 2019. However, "almost 150 confirmed HAT cases were reported in non-endemic countries in the last three decades" (Gao *et al.* 2020).

Two types of HAT are known, by 2 subspecies (some scientists prefer species instead); they are carried by different species of tsetse flies. For the more chronic West African or Gambian HAT, ***Trypanosoma brucei gambiense*** (Tbg) is carried by ***Glossina palpalis*** and related species ("riverine" flies). For the more acute East African or Rhodesian HAT, ***Trypanosoma brucei rhodesiense*** (Tbr) is carried by ***Glossina morsitans*** and related species ("savannah" flies). [Gambiense is after Gambia, the country in West Africa. The former British colony Rhodesia became today's Zimbabwe, but the colonial name stays in the parasite's nomenclature.] A total of over 20 tsetse fly species are involved in the transmission. Over **98%** of the cases are West African HAT, with anthroponotic transmission (fly-human-fly), the rest (2%) are East African HAT, with zoonotic transmission (animal reservoirs). The only country where both HATs can be found is Uganda. The cattle disease, **nagana**, is caused by ***Trypanosoma brucei brucei*** and other species (*T. congolense, T. vivax*). The trypanosomes causing HATs and nagana are all morphologically identical, but disease patterns differ.

5.3.1 History

Sleeping sickness, aka HAT, has been linked to European colonial ambitions in Africa. European countries started the first generation of schools of tropical medicine because of such novel diseases, in Antwerp (Belgium), Basel (Switzerland), Hamburg (Germany), Lisbon (Portugal), Liverpool and London (England) during the late 19th and early 20th century (Hotez 2013). In 2011, Peter Hotez became the founding dean of the National School of Tropical Medicine at Baylor College of Medicine, Houston, Texas, the first such school in the United States. Sleeping sickness was described in 14th century Arabian texts, mentioning a despotic emperor of Mali who died of this disease. The scientific discovery of the involved parasitic protozoans is based on the works of David Bruce.

The first disease investigated was a cattle disease. David Bruce wrote: "The term 'Fly Disease' has of course been given on the supposition that the disease is caused by the bite of the Tsetse Fly, and the term Nagana from the symptoms presented by the animals suffering from the disease, the word Nagana meaning in Zulu, to be in low or depressed spirits" (*1895 Report to the Governor of Natal and Zululand, Sir Walter Hely-Hutchinson*). Imported livestock got sick. In 1894 an outbreak of nagana occurred in South Africa. Hely-Hutchinson who was previously the Governor of Malta where he got to know David Bruce, a surgeon-major of the British army, who had found the cause of Malta fever to be a bacterium in contaminated goat milk (today known as brucellosis caused by *Brucella*), arranged to have Bruce to investigate. With Mary, wife and assistant (a microbiologist trained under Robert Koch), Bruce used stained blood films of infected animals and found the trypanosome. Mary accompanied David in all his fieldwork and David, at his deathbed, asked that her part in his scientific work always receive due acknowledgment. On 27 November, 1931, David Bruce died while Mary Bruce's funeral service was in progress (Cook 2007; Kean *et al.* 1978).

David Bruce, as mentioned in his report, was aware of a disease named surra, found in horses and camels, and reported by Griffith Evans from India in 1881. Bruce wrote: "the constant occurrence in the blood of an infusorial parasite, either identical with or closely resembling the *Trypanosoma evansi* found in Surra, a disease of India and Burmah" (now Myanmar). Bruce concluded that nagana and fly disease were the same, as quoted above. At the time a second disease, fly disease, also against livestock, was a disease not seen above an altitude of 3,000 feet above sea level. The Bruces did experiments by moving dogs and oxen to lower altitudes, and found the same parasites. They identified the trypanosomes in the blood (even before surra, trypanosomes had been found in the blood of fish and frogs by investigators in the 1840s). [Trypanosomes have been found in fish, amphibians, birds, and mammals. The latter include human, cattle, horse, camel, even elephant. An elephant in Thailand was cured of trypanosomiasis by a wildlife veterinarian in 2009. This 31-year-old bull elephant, Plai Thang, had an unexpected reunion with Pattarapol Maneeon 12 years later; he still recognized the vet in 2021. An elephant never forgets![4]] The Bruces showed that tsetse fly bite may or may not cause disease, fly carries disease from host to host, the infected fly bite will infect a horse. As the local people knew that game animals were related to fly disease, they killed indigenous mammals and found trypanosomes in their blood, hence solved the case for the reservoir.

In 1901, an outbreak of sleeping sickness occurred in Uganda. This epidemic in British East Africa, 1902–1905, was estimated to kill 250,000. The Royal Society sent out a commission of 3, including 2 who were protégés of Patrick Manson, of filaria and mosquito fame (including Aldo Castellani with no experience in tropical medicine). The 2 set up labs and the third did fieldwork; they found enlarged cervical lymph nodes in sleeping sickness patients. This is still known today as **Winterbottom's sign**, first described by Thomas Winterbottom in 1803, who was a physician to the colony of Sierra Leone. Actually, slave traders of the 16th to 18th century routinely threw overboard captives with such signs during trans-Atlantic voyages, as individuals destined for early death. In 1903,

[4] https://www.dailymail.co.uk/news/article-9363135/Heartwarming-moment-elephant-recognises-vet-treated-12-years-Thailand.html

Castellani isolated the bacterium *Streptococcus* and also found trypanosomes in cerebrospinal fluid (CSF) of sleeping sickness patients.

A second commission was dispatched to Africa in 1903 (including David Bruce). This is a story of ego and priority in scientific research. Castellani told Bruce his findings and insisted that he would be the sole discoverer of CSF trypanosomes. The two crossed paths for a month. They found no protozoa in 12 control samples, but protozoa in 20 out of 34 sleeping sickness patients. A report was presented by Castellani to the Royal Society. Bruce later made a confirmatory report, stating: "At the time of the arrival of this commission, he did not consider that this trypanosome had any causal relationship to the disease…As Dr Castellani has not entered into any detail respecting these matters in his reports, it is thought advisable to supplement his account with the above, as the history of the discovery of the cause of any important disease must always be of interest." Bruce also thought tsetse to be the vector, and contacted missionaries and government agencies throughout Uganda to ask them to collect tsetse flies. The idea was to compare distribution of the insect vector and the sleeping sickness disease, and they showed **sympatry** (the two existing in the same geographic area) (Esch, 2007; Kean *et al.* 1978).

The first trypanosome in humans, in a European sailor, was found in 1901 by Joseph Everett Dutton in Gambia (today's *Trypanosoma brucei gambiense*). Mr. Kelly, master of government steamer on the River Gambia, became sick and was treated by Robert Michael Forde, a colonial surgeon at Gambia. Ford found trypanosomes in the patient's blood. At first, Forde did not recognize the parasite until he invited a visiting parasitologist (Dutton, Liverpool School of Tropical Medicine) to take a look. Dutton became the first to observe trypanosomes in a human patient and named *Trypanosoma gambiense*. Dutton later found trypanosomes in natives' blood (but without symptoms); he was also known for discovering the bacterial agent of African tick fever (relapsing fever, by the spirochete *Borrelia duttoni*). Dutton himself died of the same fever at age 31 (Cook 2007).

5.3.2 Life cycle

The life cycle of African trypanosomiasis is between mammals and tsetse flies in sub-Saharan Africa. The life cycle of this parasitic protozoan and others can be obtained from Centers for Disease Control and Prevention (CDC)[5] (Division of Parasitic Diseases and Malaria, DPDM) with A–Z index of parasites[6] as well as the CDC public health image library (PHIL)[7] available for searches.

Please see Figure 5.5 for the life cycle, from CDC.[8]

[5] https://www.cdc.gov/dpdx/index.html

[6] https://www.cdc.gov/dpdx/az.html

[7] https://phil.cdc.gov

[8] https://www.cdc.gov/dpdx/trypanosomiasisafrican/index.html

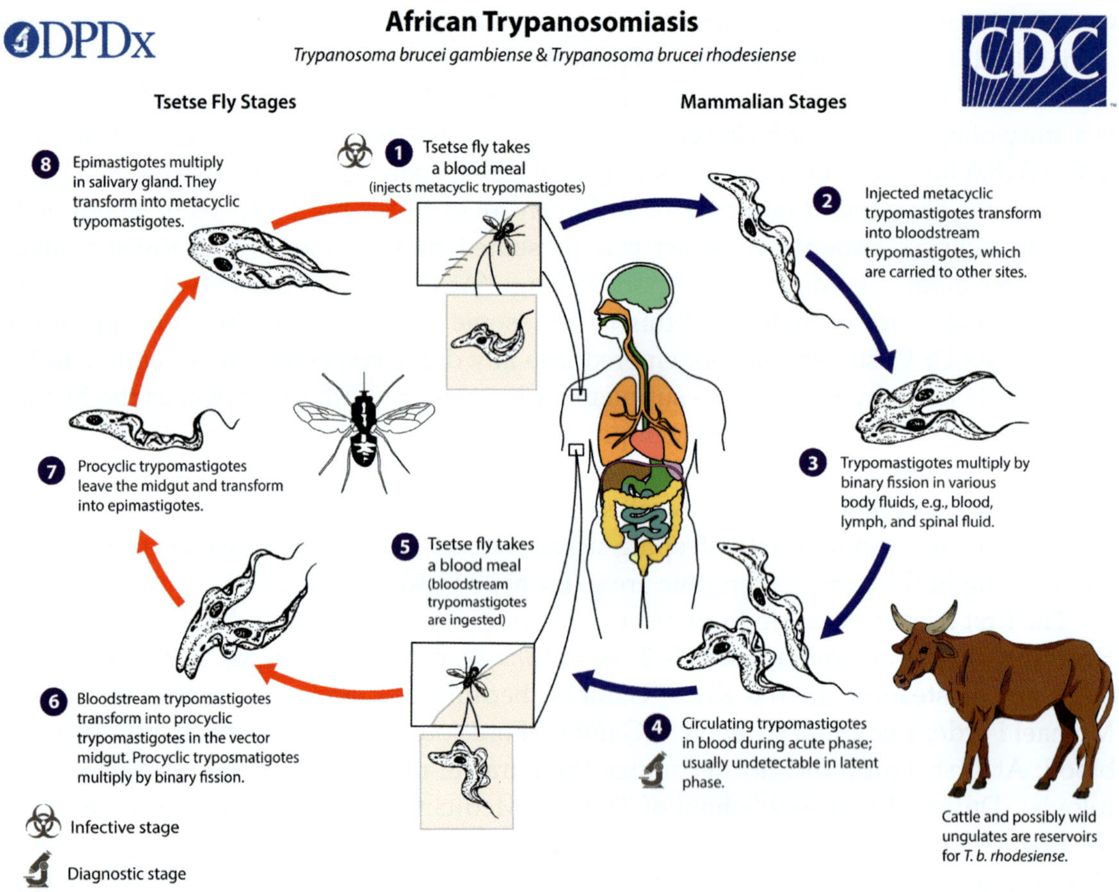

Fig. 5.5 ■ Life cycle *Trypanosoma brucei*. During a blood meal on the mammalian host, an infected tsetse fly (genus *Glossina*) injects metacyclic trypomastigotes into skin tissue. The parasites enter the lymphatic system and pass into the bloodstream ❶. Inside the host, they transform into bloodstream trypomastigotes ❷, are carried to other sites throughout the body, reach other body fluids (e.g., lymph, spinal fluid), and continue the replication by binary fission ❸. The entire life cycle of African trypanosomes is represented by extracellular stages. The tsetse fly becomes infected with bloodstream trypomastigotes when taking a blood meal on an infected mammalian host ❹, ❺. In the fly's midgut, the parasites transform into procyclic trypomastigotes, multiply by binary fission ❻, leave the midgut, and transform into epimastigotes ❼. The epimastigotes reach the fly's salivary glands and continue multiplication by binary fission ❽. The cycle in the fly takes approximately 3 weeks. Rarely, *T. b. gambiense* may be acquired congenitally if the mother is infected during pregnancy. Courtesy of CDC. Reproduced from https://www.cdc.gov/dpdx/trypanosomiasisafrican/index.html.

The entire life cycle of the trypanosome is **extracellular** (Cayla *et al.* 2019). The trypomastigotes are found in blood and other body fluids, including cerebrospinal fluid (CSF) of brain and spinal cord. Additional reservoirs of trypanosomes inside the mammal hosts have been found, including the skin and the **adipose tissue**, as major extravascular parasite niches (Capewell *et al.* 2016). The adipose tissue forms show extensive remodeling of parasite gene expression in this lipid-rich environment, including upregulation of fatty acid β-oxidation enzymes as functional adaptation (Trindade *et al.* 2016).

In the tsetse fly, trypanosome starts with procyclic trypomastigotes (with procyclin on the cell surface), then differentiate to epimastigotes in the gut (binary fission, cell division), and to infective metacyclic trypomastigotes in the salivary gland of the tsetse fly. *Glossina palpalis gambiensis* can transmit all *Trypanosoma* spp., particularly *Trypanosoma brucei gambiense* in humans and *Trypanosoma vivax* in cattle. It picks up the bloodstream form of trypanosomes from a host and injects the metacyclic form into the skin of another host after an extrinsic cycle of 10–30 days (Bouyer 2020).

The trypanosomes are normally diploid. Using mating-compatible pairs, a haploid stage with evidence of meiosis has been found in the insect salivary gland before the metacyclic or infective stage, with a unique morphology described as the "promastigote-like" stage (Peacock *et al.* 2014).

5.3.3 Pathology

East African or **Rhodesian HAT** is the more acute form, with wild animal reservoirs, and the patients die within one year. West African or **Gambian HAT** is the more chronic form. Parasites survive for years in blood and lymph before the central nervous system (CNS) involvement. Although the domestic pig may be a reservoir, there is no major animal reservoir of this disease (fly-human-fly). The bloodstream forms depend primarily on glycolysis, using **glucose** for energy. In contrast, the fly forms depend on the Krebs cycle, using the amino acid **proline** for energy, because proline is the reserve energy source for insect flight. These features show specific adaptation of trypanosomes to their vertebrate and invertebrate hosts.

For pathology, tsetse bite leaves a chancre; trypanosomes first enter the blood, then lymph, and later cerebrospinal fluid. The two stages of trypanosomiasis are the early **hemolymphatic** phase and the late neurological or **meningo-encephalitic** phase. Winterbottom sign denotes cervical lymph node swelling of HAT. For Gambian HAT, there may exist some degree of trypano-tolerance, since untreated human infections are not 100% fatal (Jamonneau *et al.* 2012).

As already discussed, *Trypanosoma brucei* causes HAT. Three subspecies are involved: *T. brucei gambiense* (Tbg) and *T. b. rhodesiense* (Tbr) in humans, and *T. b. brucei* (Tbb) in the cattle. Molecular markers subdivided Tbg into two groups: Tbg1 and Tbg2, of which the latter is different from Tbg1 and Tbr (absence of the SRA gene), but indistinguishable from Tbb. [Tbg2 is considered to be a zoonotic form of HAT in West Africa.] Tbg2 was found mainly in Ivory Coast (Côte d'Ivoire) between 1978 and 1992; the latest Tbg2, in Ghana in 2013. A list of Tbg2 (human-infective strains of *T. brucei brucei*) from West and Central Africa had 29 patients as confirmed by isozyme, PCR and other analytical methods (Jamonneau *et al.* 2019).

We provide case reports/case studies of protozoan and metazoan parasites (in this and later chapters) because they should be of interest to individuals interested in medicine/medical practice. A case of HAT in an 11-year-old girl detected in 2017 in Ivory Coast was described in detail, even tracing from her birth to her diagnosis. She was successfully treated (NECT, Nifurtimox Eflornithine Combination Therapy) and the whole affair costed Euro 5,668.84. At the time of diagnosis, the patient was positive in both serological and molecular tests and trypanosomes were detected in blood and cerebrospinal fluid. She suffered neurological disorders. The first disease symptoms had appeared 3 years prior but there were misdiagnoses. The failure to diagnose HAT for such a long time caused significant health deterioration, as well as financial burden for her family. This case study "illustrates the complexity of detecting the last HAT cases due to complex diagnosis and the progressive disinterest and unawareness by both health professionals and the population. It confirms the need of implementing passive surveillance in combination with continued sensitization and health staff training" (Koné *et al.* 2020).

A case of a 56-year-old male admitted to a university hospital in Paris because of somnolence, confusion, decreased concentration, gait instability and weight loss (for 2 months) was documented. The patient emigrated to France 6 years ago and had spent his holidays in Mali in 2016. Although his non-contrast brain computed tomography (CT) was normal, his magnetic resonance imaging (MRI) revealed hyposignal of the dentate nuclei (DN) on fluid-attenuated inversion recovery (FLAIR) sequence. He had fever; his consciousness deteriorated. Blood and CSF PCR were positive for *Trypanosoma* sp.; blood smears and bone marrow aspirates showed numerous trypanosomes. The patient was treated with nifurtimox and eflornithine. "The present case shows a correlation between the clinical and radiological findings: involvement of the cerebellum, including the DN, was correlated with clinical findings of somnolence, memory, and gait impairment" (Boukobza *et al.* 2020).

5.3.4 Diagnosis

Diagnosis can be done with protozoa present in blood and (later) cerebrospinal fluid (CSF).

5.3.5 Therapy

Drugs for HAT are mostly quite old and inadequate (Steverding 2010). Developed from the synthetic dyestuff industry, the compound **suramin**, first reported in 1916, is still being used. Trypanosomatid glycolysis takes place in glycosomes, suramin inhibits the glycerophosphate oxidase system of glycolysis. It was based on the work of Paul Ehrlich, who found the dyes trypan red and trypan blue. The compound **pentamidine**, first reported in 1936, acts against kinetoplastid DNA synthesis. The drug **melarsoprol**, first reported in 1949, developed by Ernest Friedheim, is an organo-arsenic compound, works against late stages, but is toxic. Melarsoprol acts by attacking the sulfhydryl group and may act on the critical enzyme pyruvate kinase. In some patients it can cause post-treatment reactive encephalopathy (**PTRE**). Drug resistance to melarsoprol, first noticed in the 1970's, has become widespread in the 1990's. Mechanisms of drug resistance are due to mutations in aquaglyceroporin (AQP2), a parasite solute and drug transporter (Fairlamb and Horn 2018). The newer drug **eflornithine**, reported in 1991, was a byproduct of cancer research (piggyback research). Also known as difluoro-methyl ornithine (**DFMO**), it is an inhibitor of ornithine decarboxylase (ODC), the first enzyme of polyamine synthesis, which makes trypanothione. DFMO works for Gambian HAT, because the half-life of its target *gambiense* ODC is long, 18–19 h (it does not work for short half-lives of ODC from *rhodesiense* 4 h or human cancer cells, its original intended target).

New drugs are being developed and approved. In 2009, there was nifurtimox-eflornithine combination therapy (**NECT**) as an improved treatment for sleeping sickness patients (nifurtimox is being used for Chagas' disease, which will be discussed in the next section). This was achieved by the non-profit organization DNDi.[9] Drugs for Neglected Diseases international (**DNDi**) is an organization with the participation of Brazil, France, India, Kenya and Malaysia, with WHO TDR as an observer (including Doctors Without Borders or Médecins Sans Frontières, MSF, Oswaldo Cruz Foundation or FIOCRUZ). Another HAT drug, **fexinidazole**, is effective against late-stage Gambian HAT (Mesu *et al.* 2018). Fexinidazole is the first oral treatment for HAT. Other drugs and targets such as proteasomes are being investigated for the kinetoplastid protozoa (Khare *et al.* 2016).

5.3.6 Genome

The Trytryp genomes were first published in 2005 in *Science*. The genome of *T. b. brucei* was included (Berriman *et al.* 2005); this was followed by the genome of *T. b. gambiense* (Jackson *et al.* 2010). Genomes of these two, together with other trypanosomes (free-living and parasitic species) and leishmanias, are updated and available at the TriTryp DB.[10] Examples include the avirulent *T. rangeli* (Stoco *et al.* 2014) and the African crocodile trypanosome *T. grayi* (Kelly *et al.* 2014).

Trypanosoma brucei is diploid. It has **11 pairs** of megabase sized chromosomes, about 5 (range of 1–10) intermediate-sized and about 100 mini-chromosomes (30–700 kb). The 11 chromosomes were sequenced; later, different strains were also sequenced (Müller *et al.* 2018). Please see Figure 5.6 for gene organization of the 11 chromosomes (including the variant surface glycoprotein, VSG genes and pseudogenes) (Müller *et al.* 2018). Repetitive DNA sequences are found at the telomeres, composed of **TTAGGG** repeats, which are the same as the repeats in vertebrates (including humans).

A first analysis has reported **9,068** genes, about 900 pseudogenes, 1,700 *brucei* specific genes, and **806** variant surface glycoprotein (VSG) genes (TREU927 strain, the current

[9] https://www.dndi.org/about-dndi/

[10] https://tritrypdb.org/tritrypdb/

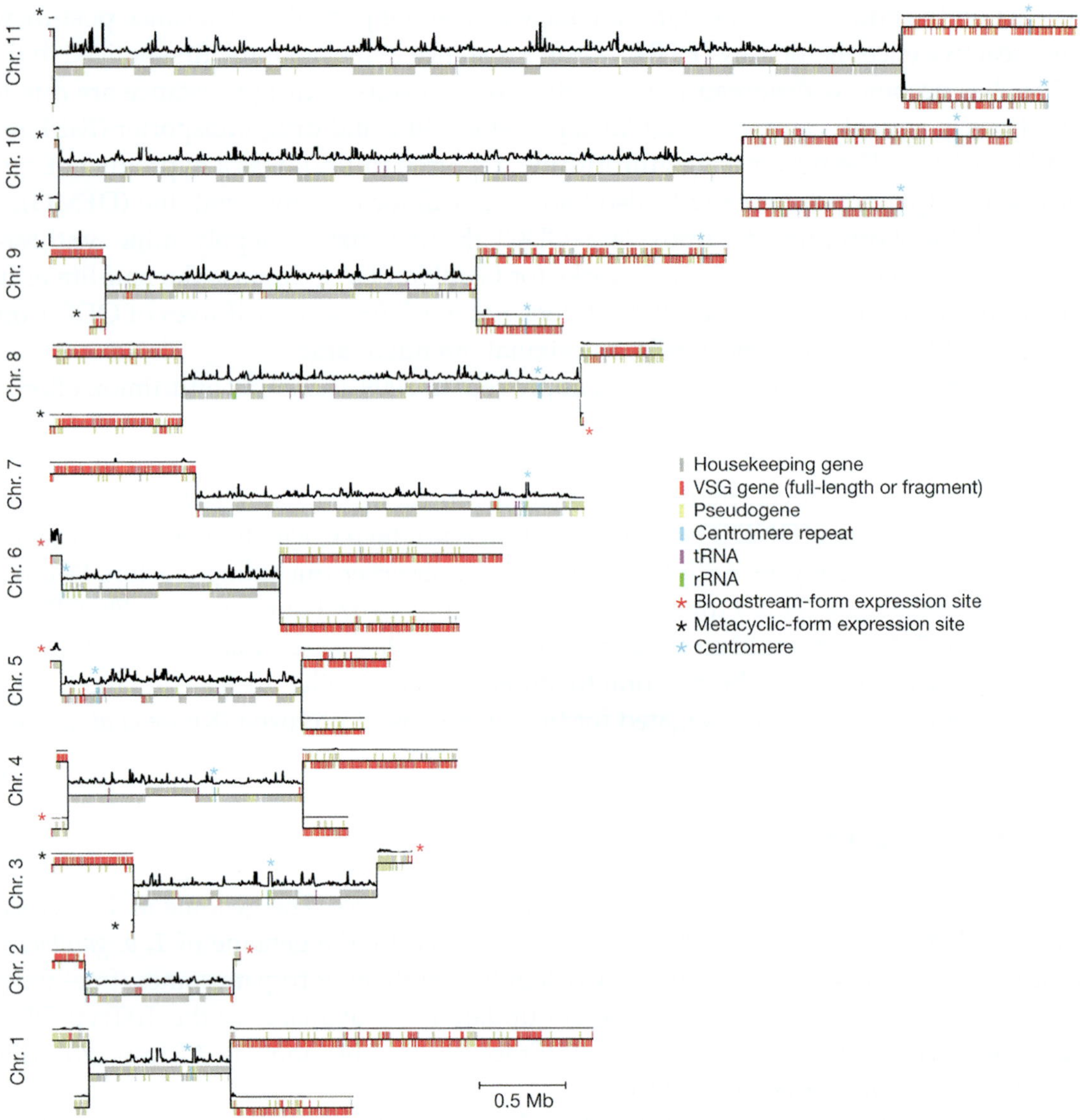

Fig. 5.6 ■ *Trypanomosoma brucei* chromosomes and VSG gene location. Long-read and Hi-C-based de novo assembly of the *T. brucei* Lister 427 genome. Only one of the two homologous chromosomes (chr.) is depicted for the homozygous chromosomal core regions (22.71 Mb). Both chromosomes are shown for the heterozygous subtelomeric regions (19.54 Mb). Relative transcript levels (window size, 5,001 bp; step size, 101 bp) are shown as a black line above each chromosome. BESs and MESs were assigned to the respective subtelomeric region if an unambiguous assignment based on DNA interaction data was possible. Centromeres were assigned based on KKT2 ChIP–seq data. Courtesy: Müller *et al. Nature* 2018;563:121–5. Reproduced with permission from *Nature* with Creative Commons Attribution 4.0 (CC-BY) International License.

estimate of protein-coding genes for *brucei*: **11,703** for TREU927 and 9,313/17,243 for Lister strain 427). Whole chromosome shotgun, bacterial artificial chromosome (BAC) walking methods were used. It seems that trypanosomes emphasize microtubule-based functions (although microfilament and associated proteins are present). There is flagellum, and **paraflagellar rod**, which is seen only in *Trypanosoma* and *Euglena*. Tubulin includes α, β, γ, δ, ε, and ζ (zeta); both δ and ε tubulins are involved in the basal body. Comparison between coding regions of *T. b. brucei* and *T. b. gambiense* shows **99.2%** sequence identity (9,898 in *gambiense* then; **8,082** now).

One interesting feature from the trypanosomatid genomes, and those of other parasitic protozoa, is the concept of lateral gene transfer (or horizontal gene transfer, **LGT/HGT**) (Alsmark *et al.* 2013). Genes of prokaryotic or eukaryotic origins were incorporated by protozoan species for their own use. It seems the ecological niche of the protozoa influences their gene transfer choice. There were 46 potential LGT cases for *Trypanosoma brucei*, 49 for *T. cruzi*, and 68 for *Leishmania major* (but 149 for *Trichomonas vaginalis*, to be discussed in Chapter 6).

Knowledge from the trypanosomatid genome has been applied in novel means of trypanosome targeting. One method is RNA interference (**RNAi**), a small RNA complementary to mRNA will bind to it and inhibit its translation. First seen in *Caenorhabditis elegans*, RNAi has led to 2006 Nobel Prize for Andrew Fire (Stanford) and Craig Mello (University of Massachusetts Medical School). Using the RNAi technique targeting specific proteins of the paraflagellar rod, it has been shown that flagellar motility is essential for viability of the bloodstream trypomastigotes (Broadhead *et al.* 2006). With appropriate targets (such as paraflagellar rod proteins) using RNAi, there is a trypanosome with incomplete cell division. Thus, this approach may be a method for therapy.

[RNAi therapeutics are being clinically tested, such as targeting age-related macular degeneration, AMD, vision improvement. However, the lack of early success has led to withdrawal from RNAi research by major pharmaceutical companies. To date, 3 RNAi-based drugs have been approved by the FDA to Alnylam Pharmaceuticals: the first in 2018 for its transthyretin-directed patisiran (brand name Onpattro) to treat the rare and deadly genetic disorder hereditary transthyretin-mediated amyloidosis; the second in 2019 for givosiran (Givlaari) to treat acute hepatic porphyria (AHP); and the third in 2020 for lumasiran (Oxlumo) to treat primary hyperoxaluria type 1 (PH1), a rare genetic disorder which causes recurrent kidney stones and loss of kidney function.]

Knowledge from the trypanosomatid genome has been applied to confirm and seek drug targets, by a genome-wide RNA interference screen (Alsford *et al.* 2012). Using a tetracycline-inducible RNA interference library of 750,000 clones covering 99% of 7,500 genes, with each gene targeted by 5 RNAi sequences, targets of current drugs are revealed as clones that survive by the absence of the target gene via RNAi. The experiments provide a better understanding of drug targets, as well as novel targets, such as the invariant surface glycoprotein (ISG75) for suramin. Thus, "genomics decodes drug action" (Fairlamb 2012).

5.3.7 Antigenic variation

An interesting feature is the antigenic variation of trypanosomes, a way for the parasite to evade host immune response. IgM against special VSGs are detected in the mammalian blood. The surface of bloodstream trypanosomes is covered with one particular variant surface glycoprotein (**VSG**). In the blood, the *Trypanosoma* trypomastigote has 10^7 VSG molecules on its cell surface. The molecules form a thick coat of glycocalyx protecting the protozoan. VSG works as homodimers and has a glycosylphosphatidylinositol (GPI) linkage to the plasma membrane. Transcription of VSG is done by RNA polymerase I (normally only for ribosomal RNA gene transcription, as found in mammal), with *trans*-splicing (adding a 39 base spliced leader) and polyadenylation. VSG expression is only seen on the trypanosome surface in the mammal; the trypanosome surface is coated with procyclin in the tsetse fly.

Both genes and pseudogenes for VSG are present in the genome. A functional VSG has 436–582 amino acids; in the genome there are sequences that code for half (about 250) of the VSG proteins. An analysis of the VSGnome of the Lister 427 strain reveals 2,563 sequences (gene segments coding 150 amino acids or larger) including 325 functional genes (Cross *et al*. 2014). Genes are located in the subtelomeric region. A typical VSG expression site consists of a promoter, followed by expression site-associated genes (**ESAGs**), repeats (70 base pair repeat), a single VSG gene, and telomeric sequence (TTAGGG repeats). There are 14 different expression sites (ESs) for the bloodstream form, but at any one time only one site, known as the expression site body (**ESB**), is active and has transcription of the single VSG gene. As VSG is transcribed by RNA polymerase I, an extra-nucleolar polymerase I is probably only present and active in the single ESB, but not in the other ESs. There are 12 ESAGs, some with unknown function, others code for transferrin receptors (for iron uptake) and adenylate cyclase (for parasite survival against host innate immunity).

VSGs are activated during infection at a rate of up to one activation event per 100 cell doublings. Antigenic variation requires transcription of a single VSG gene, silencing of all other VSG genes, and periodic switching of the expressed gene, typically via DNA recombination with duplicative translocation of a new VSG gene to the active site known as ESB. Thus, the mechanism may be viewed as the classic cassette-based model (as seen in yeast mating type switch). Different ways to bring the VSG gene to the expression site are possible. Gene conversion consists of array VSG conversion, telomeric VSG conversion, and segmental VSG conversion. There is also transcriptional switch. Please see Figure 5.7 for VSG expression (Stockdale *et al*. 2008).

VSG expression is also regulated by epigenetic means. The methyltransferase disruptor of telomeric silencing 1 (Dot1) mutation in trypanosomes leads to the expression of silent VSGs (Stockdale *et al*. 2008). Similarly, the deletion of histone variants (H3.V and H4.V) also leads to silent VSG expression (Müller *et al*. 2018).

In summary, telomeric location, epigenetic controls, and monoallelic transcription by RNA polymerase I at an extranucleolar site are prominent features of VSG genes and their

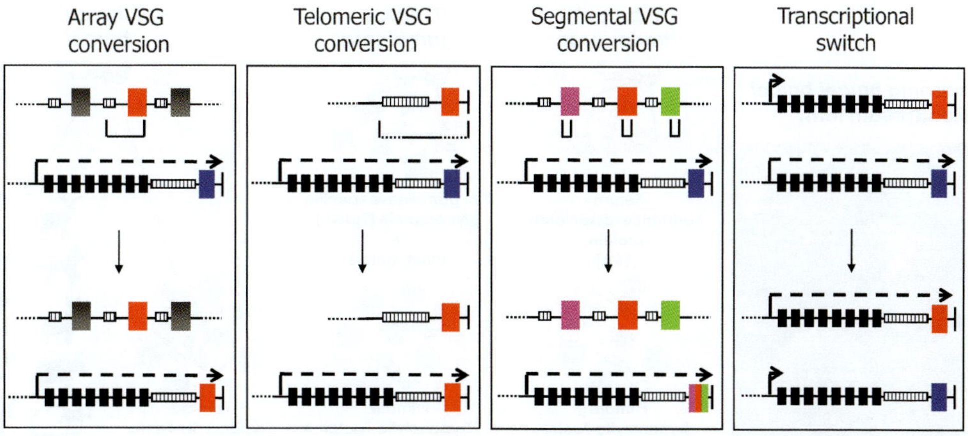

Fig. 5.7 ■ Antigenic variation and VSG expression. Mechanisms of *VSG* switching during antigenic variation in *T. brucei*. The *VSG* gene expressed prior to a switch (indicated by a blue box) is transcribed from an expression site (ES) that is found at the telomere (vertical black line) of a chromosome (horizontal black line); active transcription of the ES is indicated by a dotted arrow, *ESAG*s are depicted by black boxes, and 70-bp repeat sequence is shown as a hatched box. Gene conversion to generate a *VSG* switch can occur by copying a silent *VSG* (red box) from a subtelomeric array into the ES, replacing the resident *VSG*; the amount of sequence copied during gene conversion is illustrated, and normally encompasses the *VSG* ORF and extends upstream to the 70-bp repeats. The silent *VSG* donor can also be telomeric (either in a mini chromosome or in an inactive ES); here, the downstream limit of conversion can extend to the telomere repeats, while the upstream limit can either be in the 70-bp repeats or the *ESAG*s (if the donor is in an ES). Segmental *VSG* conversion involves the copying of sequence from multiple, normally nonfunctional *VSG*s (pink, red, or green boxes) to generate a novel mosaic *VSG* in the ES. In transcriptional *VSG* switching, recombination appears not to be involved; instead, limited transcription at a silent *VSG* ES (indicated by a small arrow) becomes activated to generate fully active transcription, while the previously active ES is silenced. Courtesy: Stockdale *et al. PLoS Biol* 2008;6:e185. Reproduced with permission from *PLoS Biology* with Creative Commons Attribution 4.0 (CC-BY) International License.

expression, with telomeres, chromatin structure, and nuclear organization all making vitally important contributions to monoallelic gene expression's control and switching.

5.3.8 HAT and human genetics

Trypanosoma brucei gambiense and *Trypanosoma brucei rhodesiense* are agents of sleeping sickness, while *Trypanosoma brucei brucei* is an agent of nagana. Among the 3 subspecies, the first 2 are not killed, but the third is, by human serum high-density lipoprotein (HDL). A minor class of HDL is the trypanosome lytic factor-1 (**TLF-1**), made up of haptoglobin-related protein (HRP), apolipoprotein L1 (Apo-L1), and Apo-A1. Trypanosomes take in

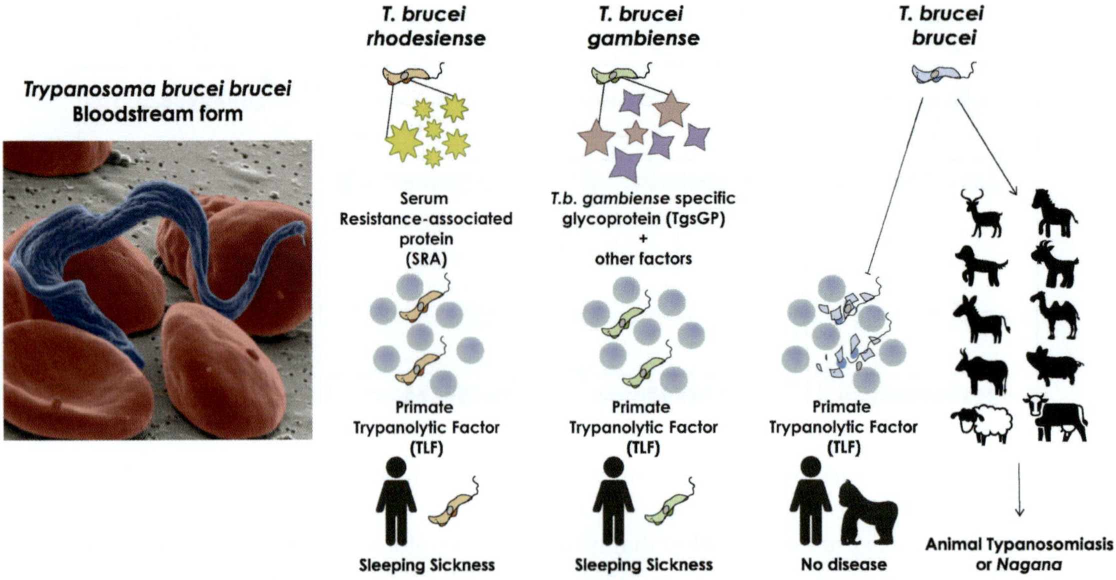

Fig. 5.8 ■ Trypanosomes causing HAT. Courtesy: Romero-Meza G, Mugnier M. *Trends Parasitol* 2020;36:571–2. Reproduced with permission from Elsevier.

the TLF-1 by endocytosis via the haptoglobin/hemoglobin receptor; Apo-L1 permeabilization of the lysosomal membrane results in chloride ion influx and osmotic lysis of the trypanosome (Matthews 2015).

Resistance to TLF-1 is seen in sleeping sickness-causing parasites. For *Trypanosoma brucei rhodesiense* there is the protein named serum resistance-associated (**SRA**). It is an ESAG derived from a truncated VSG and binds to Apo-L1 to inhibit its lysosomal pore-forming activity. Checking the genome of *Trypanosoma brucei gambiense*, SRA is absent but it has decreased haptoglobin/hemoglobin receptor expression. In addition, there is another VSG derived protein, *T. gambiense*-specific glycoprotein (**TgsGP**), which is localized to the flagellar pocket (site for endocytosis) and acts to stabilize parasite lysosomal membrane to avoid parasite lysis (Capewell *et al.* 2013). Please see Figure 5.8 for trypanosome resistance to human serum proteins (Romero-Meza and Mugnier 2020).

African Americans have a higher rate of kidney disease than European Americans. Focal segmental glomerulosclerosis (**FSGS**) and hypertension-attributed end-stage kidney disease (**H-ESKD**) are associated with two independent sequence variants in the Apo-L1 gene (on chromosome 22). These variants can lyse *Trypanosoma brucei rhodesiense*, leading the investigators to conclude: "We speculate that evolution of a critical survival factor in Africa may have contributed to the high rates of renal disease in African Americans" (Genovese *et al.* 2010). [A related and more famous example is malaria and sickle cell anemia, discussed in Chapter 9.]

5.3.9 Vector control

Control of West African HAT relies on case detection and treatment, plus vector control. Control of East African HAT is more complicated, it involves the control of animal reservoirs and vector control. One way of vector control is sterile insect technique (**SIT**); irradiated male *Glossina* flies are released to mate with females, several generations of SIT treatment plus insecticide spray are found to be effective for control of tsetse flies. The flies are attracted to blue-black color and such traps have been made to capture tsetse flies (Wiser 2011; Torr and Vale 2015).

5.4 *Trypanosoma cruzi*

Chagas' disease is endemic in southern USA and 21 countries across Latin America. It has been carried to other places by immigrants from these areas (including the United States, Spain, as the "globalization of Chagas' disease") (Lidani *et al.* 2019). The global prevalence of **Chagas' disease**, aka American trypanosomiasis (**AT**), is estimated to be **7 million**, with 50,000 new cases annually, 14,000 annual deaths, and 70 million individuals at risk (Moretti *et al.* 2020). CDC estimates 300,000 infected individuals living in the United States. Regional control programs have been successful, from 700,000 new AT cases per year in 1980–1985 to 38,593 AT cases in 2010 (Domagalska and Dujardin 2020).

The AT pathogen is *Trypanosoma cruzi*; its carrier is the bloodsucking insects with various names: assassin bug, kissing bug (bite around the face), conenose bug (for its pointed heads), reduviid or triatomine bugs (from its family name in classification), as well as local names such as barbeiro (barber bug) and vinchuca (local language meaning "that which falls to the ground").

Trypanosoma cruzi has been recovered from mummies discovered in the Andes Mountains (in Peru and Chile). Charles Darwin came into contact with the kissing bug during his voyage of the Beagle (1831–1835). He wrote: "At night I experienced an attack (for it deserves no less name) of Benchuca, a species of Reduvius, the great black bug of the Pampas. It is most disgusting to feel soft wingless insects, about an inch long, crawling over one's body. Before sucking they are quite thin, but afterwards they become round and bloated with blood, and in this state are easily crushed. One which I caught at Iquique (for they are found in Chile and Peru) was very empty. When placed on a table, and though surrounded by people, if a finger was presented, the bold insect would immediately protrude its sucker, make a charge, and, if allowed, draw blood. No pain was caused by the wound. It was curious to watch its body during the act of sucking, as in less than ten minutes it changed from being as flat as a wafer to a globular form." Darwin had gastrointestinal problems. It has been suggested by some that Darwin might have suffered from Chagas' disease, although this is probably not true. Darwin's illness may have other causes or even, psychosomatic origins. The first description of the South American trypanosome parasite and the related disease was reported by Carlos Chagas (hence Chagas' disease).

5.4.1 History

Carlos Chagas published on AT in 1909. As descendants of immigrants from Portugal to Brazil, the family owned a small coffee farm, but Carlos' mother became a young widow with 4 kids. At first, Carlos tried to be a mining engineer (according to his mother's wishes), but did not like it. Influenced by an uncle who was a doctor, Carlos Chagas switched to medicine; he even wrote a thesis on the hematological aspect of malaria, under the direction of Oswaldo Cruz. Cruz was a famous scientist whose research institute became The Oswaldo Cruz Institute, and a foundation, still the preeminent research center in Brazil today (FIOCRUZ, Oswaldo Cruz Foundation). Initially working elsewhere, Chagas was invited to join the institute, and was sent by Cruz, the director and his former mentor, to coordinate the malaria campaign, in a small town in the Amazons, 350 miles from Rio de Janeiro, because the government had planned to build railways. Chagas spent 2 years living in a railroad car that doubled as a clinic. Soon, he found patients suffering from a disease different from malaria. This disease seemed to be related to the bloodsucking insects that harbored a flagellated protozoan. Chagas found trypanosomes in the blood of a 22-month-old girl named Berenice, who was suffering from fever together with enlargement of liver, spleen and lymph nodes, plus facial edema (swelling), symptoms of acute AT. He even found trypanosomes in the cat living in her house. Chagas described 27 cases of acute and over 100 cases of chronic disease and published his findings in 1909. At 27 years after Chagas' death, Berenice was found again in 1961, as a grandmother of 3, and her AT diagnosis was confirmed. Berenice died in 1981 (at age 73), but parasite strains isolated from her (at age 55 and 71) are still available (as *Trypanosoma cruzi* Berenice strains Be-62 and Be-78) (Cruz *et al.* 2006). Carlos Chagas named his new trypanosome *Schizotrypanum cruzi*, in honor of his mentor Cruz; he thought he saw schizogony in the lung. This turns out to be incorrect; some suggested he might have seen the fungal pathogen *Pneumocystis* instead. Chagas believed that the trypanosomes were carried to the host via bloodsucking. This turns out to be incorrect, as shown by the French scientist Alexandre Brumpt in 1912. The protozoa were deposited in the feces during feeding; hence we have *Trypanosoma cruzi*, belonging to Stercoraria. In 1912 Chagas also found armadillo as a sylvatic reservoir host. AT is zoonotic; other reservoirs include the opossum (Steverding 2014).

5.4.2 Life cycle

Please see Figure 5.9 for the life cycle, from CDC.[11]

Besides kissing bug bloodsucking, AT can be transmitted via blood transfusion, organ transplant, mother-to-child, and intake of contaminated food (Coura 2015). In 1955 the first case of indigenous AT was reported in USA. In 1998, 5 cases of transfusion

[11] https://www.cdc.gov/dpdx/trypanosomiasisamerican/index.html

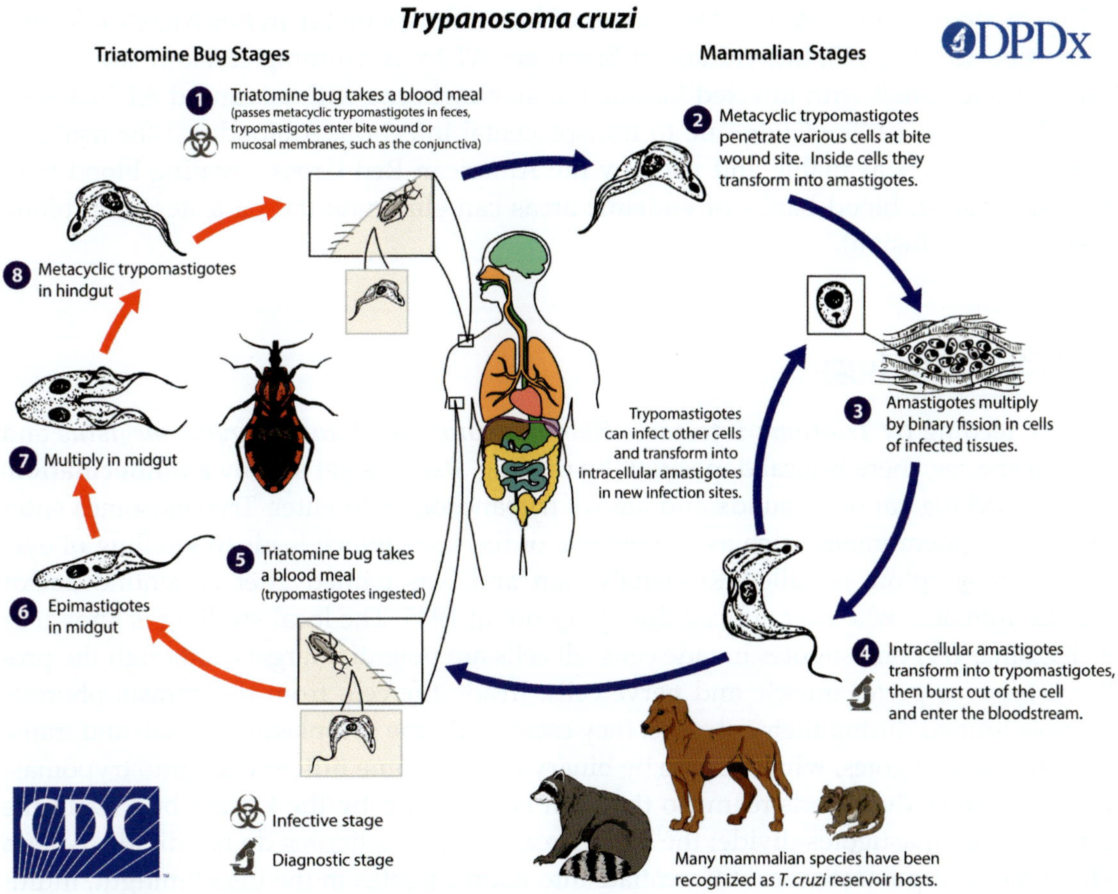

Fig. 5.9 ■ Life cycle *Trypanosoma cruzi*. An infected triatomine insect vector (or "kissing" bug) takes a blood meal and releases trypomastigotes in its feces near the site of the bite wound. Trypomastigotes enter the host through the bite wound or intact mucosal membranes, such as the conjunctiva ❶. Inside the host, the trypomastigotes invade cells near the site of inoculation, where they differentiate into intracellular amastigotes ❷. The amastigotes multiply by binary fission ❸ and differentiate into trypomastigotes, and then are released into the circulation as bloodstream trypomastigotes ❹. Trypomastigotes infect cells from a variety of tissues and transform into intracellular amastigotes in new infection sites. Clinical manifestations can result from this infective cycle. The bloodstream trypomastigotes do not replicate (different from the African trypanosomes). Replication resumes only when the parasites enter another cell or are ingested by another vector. The "kissing" bug becomes infected by feeding on human or animal blood that contains circulating parasites ❺. The ingested trypomastigotes transform into epimastigotes in the vector's midgut ❻. The parasites multiply and differentiate in the midgut ❼ and differentiate into infective metacyclic trypomastigotes in the hindgut ❽. Other less common routes of transmission include blood transfusions, organ transplantation, transplacental transmission, and foodborne transmission (via food/drink contaminated with the vector and/or its feces). Courtesy of CDC. Reproduced from https://www.cdc.gov/dpdx/trypanosomiasisamerican/index.html.

AT were reported in USA. In 2006, 2 cases of heart transplant AT in Los Angeles County were reported. In 2005, individuals in Brazil got AT by consuming contaminated sugar cane juice (crushed with infected kissing bugs). Newborns with advanced AT had been found in countries like Chile due to transplacental infection. A blood test for trypanosome antibody is available and used by the American Red Cross. Treating blood with **crystal violet** in blood banks of endemic areas can eliminate the parasites from blood (used for transfusion).

5.4.3 Pathology

During feeding by ***Triatoma infestans, Rhodnius proxilus, Panstrongylus megistus*** and related species, there is fecal deposition by the bug. Patients get sick by **autoinoculation**: their scratching causes wounds and allows trypanosomes to enter. Trypanosomes enter via mucous membranes, such as conjunctiva of the eyes, which leads to swelling of eyelids. This symptom is called **Romana's sign** and was named after Argentine doctor Cecelio Romana, who first noticed this symptom in 1935. The local swelling is known as a chagoma. Trypomastigotes invade cells; all cells are potential targets, although the protozoa seem to prefer muscle and nerve cells. Inside the cell, from the parasitophorous vacuole formed during their entrance, they escape into the cytoplasm (cytosol) and transform into amastigotes, which divide by binary fission. Some differentiate into trypomastigotes to enter the bloodstream, so they can be taken up by the kissing bug. Only the intracellular amastigotes divide; the bloodstream trypomastigotes do not divide. After a blood meal, trypomastigotes differentiate into epimastigotes in the insect midgut, multiply there and then differentiate into trypomastigotes in the hind gut for re-infection. (In **opossum**, this marsupial mammal possesses an anal gland, where both the metacyclic trypomastigotes and epimastigotes normally found in the insect vectors are present for transmission.)

Amastigotes may accumulate in the host cells and tissues. Such masses are named pseudocysts. In acute AT, there may be inflammation of the heart, **myocarditis**. The acute phase is usually asymptomatic. It can happen at any age and parasites can be found in the peripheral circulation. From the acute phase, **30%** of AT becomes chronic. The chronic phase manifests in about 20 years from the first infection, with low parasite burden. In chronic AT, there is **mega syndrome**, with megacolon and megaesophagus, where the autonomous nerve is not properly functional under such cases (Wiser 2011; Moretti *et al.* 2020). In addition, Chagas' disease is the cause of 70% of cardiac deaths of young adults in endemic areas (**cardiomyopathy**). Autoantibodies against heart myosin, for example, have been found. Autoimmunity in AT is controversial, because such antibodies appear soon after infection, and chronic disease carries on for years.

Experiments in mice with *Trypanosoma cruzi* and heart transplant have been performed. Mice take up syngeneic hearts but not allogeneic hearts. However, in chronic infection, mice reject syngeneic heart, as a result of parasite-induced inflammation. The normal response to AT, to be effective, is cellular immunity. Macrophages produce nitric oxide (NO) that kills intracellular amastigotes.

The question of tissue tropism has also been investigated with mice. "*T. cruzi* does not exhibit a tissue-specific tropism, revealing characteristics of a pan-infective species able to invade tissues of ectodermal, mesodermal, and endodermal embryonic origin, irrespective of the parasite's lineage, infective form, route of entry, or size of the inoculum causing the host's infection" (Añez and Crisante 2020). The trypanosome has been recovered from brain, heart, liver, spleen, muscle, intestine and skin.

An interesting question is: despite the prevalence of kissing bugs, there is not that many AT in North America (Buhaya *et al.* 2015). One hypothesis is that these bugs are zoophilic, while the ones in South America are anthropophilic. Another hypothesis is that the North American species may feed and defecate at different times. AT is common in Central and South America. In USA, autochthonous transmission has been described but is thought to be rare. A total of 11 kissing bug species are found naturally in 29 states (10 species are known to harbor *T. cruzi*), but it appears that only 4 species have been associated with human dwellings. One study conducted in Arizona has shown that despite a high proportion of kissing bugs being infected with *T. cruzi* (>50%) and residents frequently being bitten, none had confirmatory serologic evidence of Chagas disease, except a likely autochthonous case from a young woman who tested positive for *T. cruzi* infection at blood donation. Northern American mammals infected with *T. cruzi* include the domestic pets, as well as the sylvatic species — raccoon, opossum, skunk, fox, coyote, wood rat and other rodents, white-tailed deer, and armadillo. Even a zoo-housed red panda from Kansas had a lethal case of AT. Thus, North American kissing bugs may be behaving differently compared with their relatives from Mexico, and Central and South America, therefore less likely to be effective at transmitting *T. cruzi* to humans through fecal contamination of a mucous membrane or bite (Beatty and Klotz 2020).

5.4.4 Diagnosis

For acute infection, presence of parasites in the blood can be used as a diagnosis. This is not possible in chronic infection. Serological tests are available. The definitive test is **xenodiagnosis**, first reported by Brumpt in 1912, allowing lab bred bugs to feed on patients followed by detection of trypanosomes in the bugs in 10 to 30 days.

5.4.5 Therapy

Nifurtimox is the drug of choice; it works by targeting the essential flavin-containing cellular enzymes. This nitro drug, actually a pro-drug, is activated by the trypanosome (Patterson and Wyllie 2014). Another drug is **benznidazole**, which may be involved in the inhibition of nucleic acid synthesis and double-stranded DNA breaks in parasitic DNA

(Rajão *et al.* 2014). Rick Tarleton (University of Georgia, Athens) and colleagues have reported a modified drug regimen to clear active and dormant parasites in a mouse model using fluorescent protein-tagged trypanosomes. "Once per week administration of benznidazole at a dose 2.5 to 5 times the standard daily dose rapidly eliminated actively replicating parasites and ultimately eradicated the residual, transiently dormant parasite population in mice" (Bustamante *et al.* 2020). This method using a currently available drug to therapeutically override dormancy may be clinically applicable in the future.

There are ongoing efforts for new drug development. One example is K-777, a vinyl sulfone protease inhibitor, targeting the cysteine proteinase cruzipain of the protozoan; it was tested by DNDi but stopped in 2013 due to potential toxicity in dogs and primates. [However, it should be mentioned that cysteine proteinases of many parasitic protozoa are potential drug targets. Cysteine proteinases and their inhibitors serve multiple functions, from protein degradation to immune modulation (Siqueira-Neto *et al.* 2018). Our research group was the first to clone the human lysosomal cysteine proteinase cathepsin B (Fong *et al.* 1986).]

Additional drugs are being developed, including nitroimidazoles (fexinidazole the HAT drug being adapted for AT), the pan-kinetoplastid benzoxaboroles, and proteasome inhibitors (Kratz 2019). DNDi has other projects to develop drugs for AT, HAT, leishmaniasis, and malaria.

5.4.6 Genome

Common features of trypanosomatid protozoa include *trans*-splicing, RNA editing, and polycistronic transcription. The *Trypanosoma cruzi* genome, published in 2005, suggests the presence of about **12,000** genes (gene number is **10,596** for CL Brenner Esmeraldo-like strain, and **11,106** for CL Brenner Non-Esmeraldo-like strain in TriTrypDB) (El-Sayed *et al.* 2005). Because the strain chosen for sequencing is a hybrid strain from known subgroups, the number of chromosomes was not originally determined. A later study reported that *Trypanosoma cruzi* has **41** chromosome pairs (Weatherly *et al.* 2009). One important finding is the abundance of large gene families of surface proteins, including both genes and pseudogenes: **trans-sialidase** 1,430 total genes (with 693 pseudogenes), mucin-associated surface protein (MASP) 1,377 (433), and mucin 863 (201). These surface molecules may assist the parasite to evade host immune response; they may inhibit host innate and adaptive immunity (such as antigen presentation and function of CD4 T cells) (Flávia Nardy *et al.* 2015). As MASP is a novel family for the protozoan, it can be a potential drug target. In addition to the conventional myosins, there is a family of novel kinetoplastid myosins.

Another protein of interest is *Trypanosoma cruzi* **calreticulin** (TcCalr). TcCalr can be considered a virulence factor; its knock-out leads to a non-viable trypanosome. This multifunctional, endoplasmic reticulum (ER)-resident chaperone will mediate host–parasite interactions, once it is translocated to the external microenvironment. TcCalr binds complement component (C1) to inactivate the host complement pathway; it also binds mannose-binding lectin (MBL), an important pattern-recognition receptor of the complement system. Interestingly, *T. cruzi* infection may confer protection against tumorigenesis. The reason probably is its inhibition of angiogenesis. Homologs of TcCalr are seen in other parasitic protozoa and worms, where they may act in a similar manner. Recombinant TcCalr has anti-angiogenic and immunomodulatory properties; it may provide new pharmacological/immunological interventions in the areas of Chagas' disease and experimental cancer (Ramírez-Toloza *et al.* 2020).

Genetic loci analysis has divided *Trypanosoma cruzi* from the original 2 group (I and II) into **6** groups, distinct typing units (**DTUs**): type TcI (from the original I) and type TcII to TcVI (all from the original II) (Flores-López and Machado 2011). TcI came from opossums and the rest from placental mammals of South America. The AT pathogen evolved from a bat trypanosome ***Trypanosoma marinkellei*** found in South American bats ("bat seeding hypothesis"), as TcBat is closely related to TcI of opossums (Wiser 2011; Steverding 2014).

5.4.7 Vector control

Vector control is effective in some countries. In lieu of DDT, the choice is **pyrethroid**, a synthetic insecticide that is related to the natural pyrethrum, found in *Chrysanthemum*. There are countries that have been declared free of vectorial and transfusional transmission of AT, e.g., Uruguay in 1997 and Chile in 1999. Today the country with the most cases of AT is Bolivia, the landlocked South American country. One interesting development by the Spanish chemist Pilar Mateo has been the use of paints containing insect growth regulators (together with insecticidal and acaricidal molecules) to vanquish the bugs from village huts, these "parasite paints" (Inesfly paint) are being field-tested in Bolivia.[12]

We have introduced the idea of parasites controlling host behavior (please see Chapter 1). This feature has been reported in *Trypanosoma cruzi* and its insect vector. Alex Córdoba-Aguilar (National Autonomous University of Mexico) and colleagues have written about "Zombie bugs? Manipulation of kissing bug behavior by the parasite *Trypanosoma cruzi*" (Ramírez-González *et al.* 2019) and "Chagas bugs and *Trypanosoma cruzi*: Puppets and puppeteer?" (Córdoba-Aguilar 2020). The **parasite manipulation hypothesis** states that the parasite modifies host's behavior thereby increasing the probability that the parasite will pass from an intermediate host to its final host. The scientists have found the kissing bug *Triatoma* young instars were more active and likely to detect human odor when they were infected by the trypanosomes. "Two major factors that can drive the evolution of triatomines and *T. cruzi* are global change and the use of insecticides" (Córdoba-Aguilar 2020).

[12] https://inesfly.com/en/dra-pilar-mateo-herrero/

5.5 *Leishmania*

The NTDs sleeping sickness and Chagas' disease by *Trypanosoma* protozoa are restricted in geographical location (sub-Sahara Africa, Central and South America, respectively), the NTD leishmaniasis by *Leishmania* species is found in many countries, spanning a wide range of terrains. The insect vector responsible for the spread of leishmaniasis is the female sand fly (***Phlebotomus*** and mainly ***Lutzomyia*** genera for the Old and New World, respectively). [Vector name can be either sand fly or sandfly. Here, we use sand fly.]

HAT is caused by *Trypanosoma brucei gambiense* and *T. b. rhodiense* (2 subspecies). AT is caused by *T. cruzi* (a single species). In contrast, many species of *Leishmania* cause different forms of leishmaniases. An interesting question is how come there are so many species of *Leishmania*. Hypotheses have been proposed about the origin of *Leishmania*. The parasite initially associated only with the insect vector; it then became parasite to the rodent whose blood was sucked by the female sand fly, as well as other mammals (even reptiles). Three hypotheses have been presented: (1) Palearctic origin — based on fossil evidence of sand fly and rodent, the parasite evolved in Central Asia region, crossed land bridges, and distributed to become many related species; (2) Neotropical origin — based on the greatest diversity of *Leishmania* species seen in South America (as compared to the Old World), this location had to be the origin of this parasite, and then followed by global expansion; (3) Neotropical African or Supercontinent origin — splitting of the supercontinent Gondwana ended up with Africa and South America, the *Leishmania* origin was in the east Africa portion and continental split led to further evolution and speciation (Akhoundi *et al.* 2016; Steverding 2017). Please see Figure 5.10 for *Leishmania* distribution (Akhoundi *et al.* 2016). [*Sergentomyia*, mentioned in the figure, is another genus of sand flies that feed on reptiles and mammals.]

Leishmania parasites are agents of a spectrum of diseases — ranging from self-healing cutaneous to fatal visceral infections. Three major clinical forms are visceral, cutaneous and mucocutaneous leishmaniasis (**VL**, **CL**, and **MCL**). Leishmaniasis has a global prevalence of **10 million**, with 50,000 annual deaths (26,000 to 65,000). Over 350 million people are at risk for the disease, and approximately 50,000 to 90,000 cases of VL and 0.7 to 1.2 million cases of CL occur each year. Out of 200 countries and territories (according to WHO), leishmaniasis is endemic in more than 98 countries, distributed throughout Africa, Asia, and Latin America. Over 90% of global cases of VL occur in Brazil, Ethiopia, Sudan, South Sudan, India, and Bangladesh; 84% of global cases of CL occur in Afghanistan, Algeria, Brazil, Colombia, Iraq, Pakistan, Peru, the Syrian Arab Republic, Tunisia, and Yemen (in 2016). "Visceral and cutaneous leishmaniasis incidence ranges were estimated by country and epidemiological region based on reported incidence, underreporting rates if available, and the judgment of national and international experts. … Based on these estimates, approximately **0.2 to 0.4 million VL cases** and **0.7 to 1.2 million CL cases** occur each year" (Alvar *et al.* 2012). Sakib Burza (London School of Hygiene & Tropical Medicine) and colleagues commented: "Leishmaniasis is a poverty-related disease with two main clinical forms: visceral leishmaniasis and cutaneous leishmaniasis. An estimated 0.7–1 million new cases of leishmaniasis per year are reported from nearly 100 endemic coun-

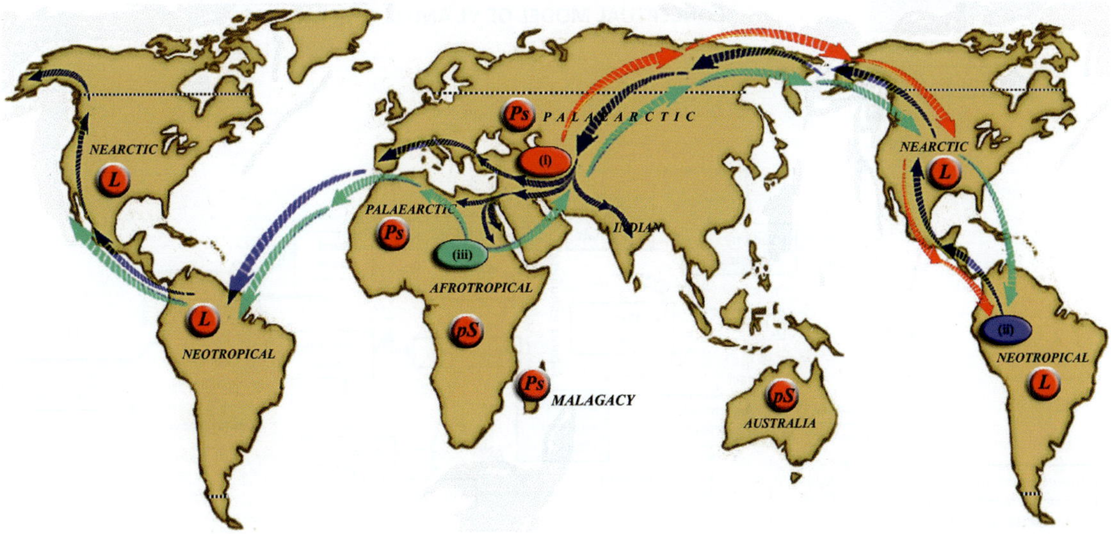

Fig. 5.10 ■ *Leishmania* distribution. Possible routes of dissemination of *Leishmania*. (i). Red arrow: Palearctic origin of *Leishmania* (Lysenko [142], Kerr [136,144], Kerr *et al.* [145]). (ii) Blue arrow: Neotropical origin of *Leishmania* (Croan *et al.* [150], Noyes [149], Noyes *et al.* [83], Lukeš *et al.* [146]). (iii) Green arrow: Neotropical/African origin of *Leishmania* (Momen and Cupolillo [139]). Distribution of medically important sandflies is highlighted by red symbols. *L*: *Lutzomyia*, *P*: *Phlebotomus*, *S*: *Sergentomyia*, *PS*: Relative density and diversity of *Phlebotomus* as compared to *Sergentomyia*. Courtesy: Akhoundi *et al. PLoS Negl Trop Dis* 2016;10:e0004349. Reproduced with permission from *PLoS Neglected Tropical Diseases* with Creative Commons Attribution 4.0 (CC-BY) International License.

tries ... Increased conflict in endemic areas of cutaneous leishmaniasis and forced displacement has resulted in a surge in these endemic areas as well as clinics across the world" (Burza *et al.* 2018) [Increase in leishmaniasis in Syria was mentioned in the article.]

VL is caused by *Leishmania donovani* and *L. infantum* (the New World species formerly named *L. chagasi* has been shown to be identical to the Old World *L. infantum*; the parasite was transplanted from Europe, possibly Portugal). MCL is caused by *L. braziliensis*, *L. guyanensis*, and related species; geographically MCL is restricted to South America. CL is caused by a multitude of species, including *L. tropica*, *L. major*, *L. mexicana* and others. Over 50 species of *Leishmania* are known and about 20 species can be human pathogens, most as zoonoses. Anthroponotic transmission (fly-human-fly) is common in VL caused by *Leishmania donovani*. In addition to sylvatic animal reservoirs, feral dogs act as reservoirs for some species (Dantas-Torres *et al.* 2019).

Compared to HAT and AT, leishmaniasis is a complex disease, transmitted by sand flies, and mainly affects the poor and neglected populations. VL, CL, and MCL involve many parasite species, different vector species, as well as various mammalian hosts, for consideration of leishmaniasis as a zoonosis. There are environmental and social risk factors that impact the disease incidence. Many socioeconomic, environmental, and climate variables affect leishmaniasis. One example is the possibility of vector adaptation to urban

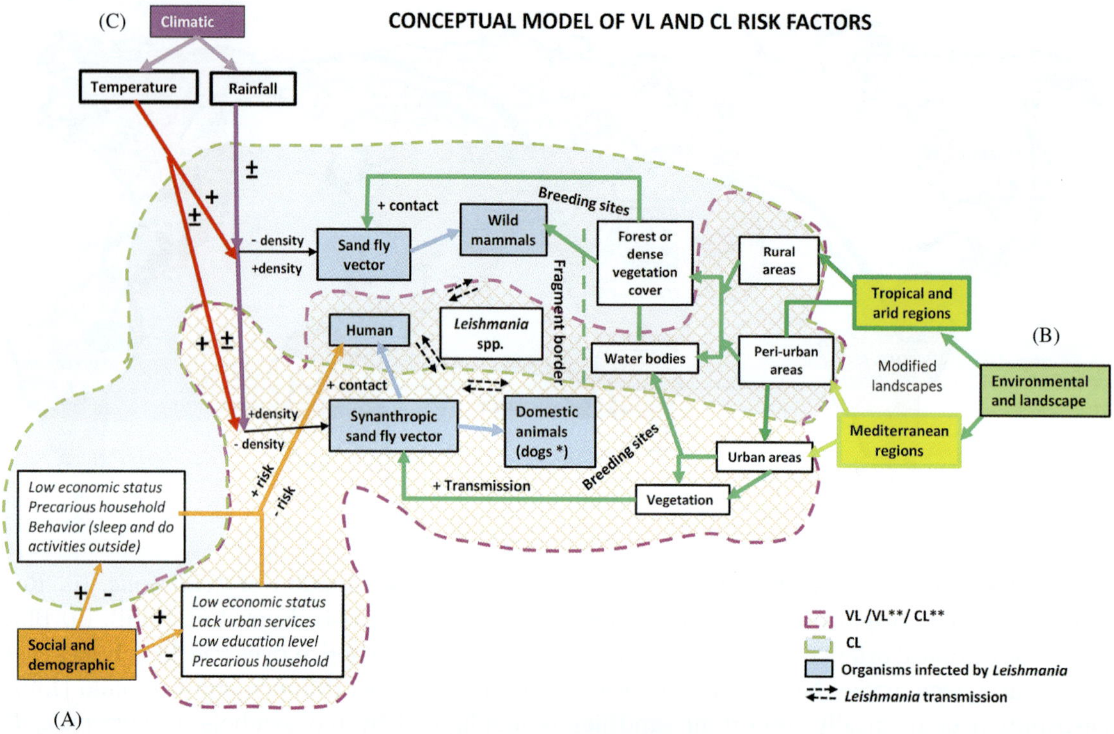

Fig. 5.11 ■ Risk factors for leishmaniasis. Interaction of risk factors which influence the incidence of visceral (VL) and cutaneous leishmaniasis (CL). Arrows show factors that influence transmission: (A) orange = socioeconomic factors; (B) green = environmental factors; (C) climatic factors: brown = temperature; purple = rainfall. (±) Represent intermediate values of temperature and rainfall. (*) Dogs are susceptible to some species responsible of VL especially in the New World. Segmented green line represents vegetation border between landscape components. (**) Anthroponotic leishmaniasis. Courtesy: Valero N, Uriarte M. *Parasitol Res* 2020;119:365–84. Reproduced with permission from Springer Nature.

environments in developing countries where populations with low socioeconomic status are particularly vulnerable to the disease (Valero and Uriarte 2020). Please see Figure 5.11 for risk factors of leishmaniasis (Valero and Uriarte 2020).

5.5.1 History

Fossil record showed the presence of *Leishmania*-like parasites and blood of reptilian origin in a female sand fly trapped within Burmese amber of the Cretaceous age; the parasite was aptly named *Paleoleishmania* (Poinar and Poinar 2004). [Paleoparasitology is the study of parasites in ancient material, which provided new information on the evolution, paleoepidemiology, ecology and phylogenetics of infectious diseases (Araujo *et al.* 2013).]

CL is the most widespread of leishmaniasis. Its aliases include **oriental sore**, Delhi sore, Aleppo evil, Baghdad boil, and other names. Its medical aspect was published in

1898 by a Russian military surgeon: Peter Fokitsch Borovsky was studying Sart sore, and correctly referred to as caused by a protozoan. Borovsky wrote: "Owing to the peripheral position of the nucleus and to the presence of processes like flagella, we are inclined to refer the parasites described by us to the class of protozoa" (Kean *et al.* 1978).

VL is known as **kala azar**, the word in Urdu and Hindi means **black fever**. To the British in India at the time, kala azar was known as dum dum fever (Dum Dum located about 7 miles from Calcutta, now Kolkata). VL was first published in 1903. Lieutenant-General Sir William Boog Leishman, a Scot who studied at the University of Glasgow, in 1900 observed spleen specimens from a patient that had died of kala azar. ("Private J.B. 2nd Royal Irish Rifle, aged 23... necropsy, made 38 hours after death... spleen was greatly enlarged... I was struck by the curious appearance, among the spleen cells and red corpuscles, of enormous numbers of small round or ovoid bodies, 2 to 3 μ in diameter, which corresponded to nothing I had previously met with or had seen figured or described.") Leishman later became a professor at the Army Medical School. Another individual, Colonel Charles Donovan, an Irish who studied in Dublin hospitals, worked at the Indian Medical Service and confirmed Leishman's observation in 1903. Donovan later became a professor at Madras University, and after retirement studied birds and butterflies of Ireland. Both manuscripts were sent to *British Medical Journal*. The editor, Ronald Ross, realized the similarity, as both were describing the possibility of trypanosomiasis in India. Ross named the parasite *Leishmania donovani* in their honor. Leishman also perfected a staining method, similar to Giemsa stain that stains the nucleic acid. The stained amastigotes became known as Leishman–Donovan bodies, **LD bodies**. The two papers were published in *BMJ* in 1903 (Leishman's in volume 1 and Donovan's in volume 2). In 1908, mammals, especially dogs, were shown to be capable of infection by *L. donovani*. Thus, dogs can serve as reservoirs. In 1942, in India, VL transmission by the sand fly *Phlebotomus* was demonstrated using human volunteers. The authors were Swaminath, Shortt, and Anderson; the journal was *Indian Journal of Medical Research*. Actually, this was the winning team led by Henry Shortt (then Colonel with the Indian Medical Service, later reader at University of London) in Assam in the race to discover the insect vector for VL (two other teams were based in Calcutta and in China). "It is curious that Shortt was not the senior author of the paper reporting the successful experiments: it was C.S. Swaminath, an assistant entomologist and a junior member of the research staff. The contribution to the human experiments — if any — of the third author, Swaminath's superior officer Lieutenant-Colonel L.A.P. Anderson, is uncertain" (Killick-Kendrick 2013). [Of course, such experiments would not be allowed to proceed today.]

5.5.2 Life cycle

Please see Figure 5.12 for the life cycle, from CDC.[13]

Species of *Leishmania* are carried by different species of sand flies. Only female sand flies transmit *Leishmania* during bloodsucking. Males prefer plant juices. During the

[13] https://www.cdc.gov/dpdx/leishmaniasis/index.html

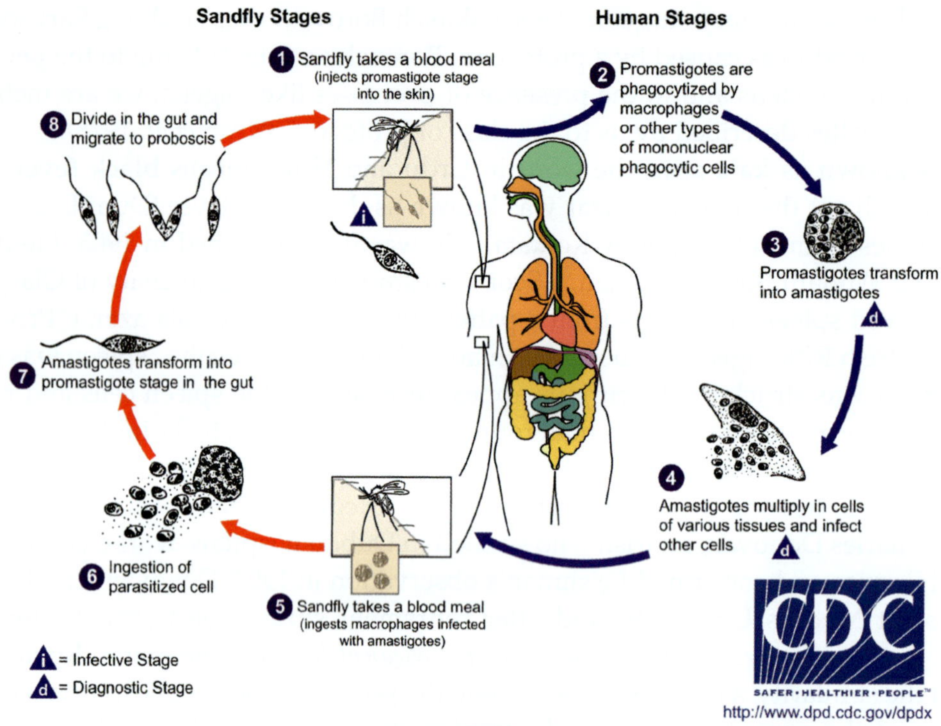

Fig. 5.12 ■ Life cycle of *Leishmania* species. Leishmaniasis is transmitted by the bite of infected female phlebotomine sandflies. The sandflies inject the infective stage (i.e., promastigotes) from their proboscis during blood meals ❶. Promastigotes that reach the puncture wound are phagocytized by macrophages ❷ and other types of mononuclear phagocytic cells. Promastigotes transform in these cells into the tissue stage of the parasite (i.e., amastigotes) ❸, which multiply by simple division and proceed to infect other mononuclear phagocytic cells ❹. Parasite, host, and other factors affect whether the infection becomes symptomatic and whether cutaneous or visceral leishmaniasis results. Sandflies become infected by ingesting infected cells during blood meals (❺, ❻). In sandflies, amastigotes transform into promastigotes, develop in the gut ❼ (in the hindgut for leishmanial organisms in the *Viannia* subgenus; in the midgut for organisms in the *Leishmania* subgenus), and migrate to the proboscis ❽. Courtesy of CDC. Reproduced from https://www.cdc.gov/dpdx/leishmaniasis/index.html.

development of promastigotes in the sand fly gut, some researchers classify the ones that develop in the midgut as *Leishmania* and the ones in the hindgut as genus *Viannia*. *L. braziliensis* becomes *Viannia braziliensis*, or *L. (V.) braziliensis*. *Leishmania* infection of the insect vector may confer benefits to the sand fly; the fly becomes less susceptible to bacterial infection, such as the insect pathogen *Serratia marcescens* (Sant'Anna *et al*. 2014). Therefore, there are **tripartite** interactions, the sand fly, the protozoan, and the microbiome. "The bacterial components of the microbiota can interfere with *Leishmania* development inside the sand fly vector" (Campolina *et al*. 2020).

Leishmania has 2 developmental stages: extracellular **promastigotes** in the sand fly gut and intracellular **amastigotes** within the phagolysosome of a macrophage (from the

Human immune responses to *Leishmania infantum* infection			
Asymptomatic	Presence of specific anti-*Leishmania* antibodies	Positive in skin test	Respond to *Leishmania* antigen *in vitro* (Il-2, IFNγ, and Il-12)
Diseased	Hypergammaglobulinemia	Negative in skin test	Lack of response to *Leishmania* antigens *in vitro*
Cured	Long-term specific anti-*Leishmania* antibodies	Positive in skin test	Recovery of cellular immunity to *Leishmania* antigens *in vitro*

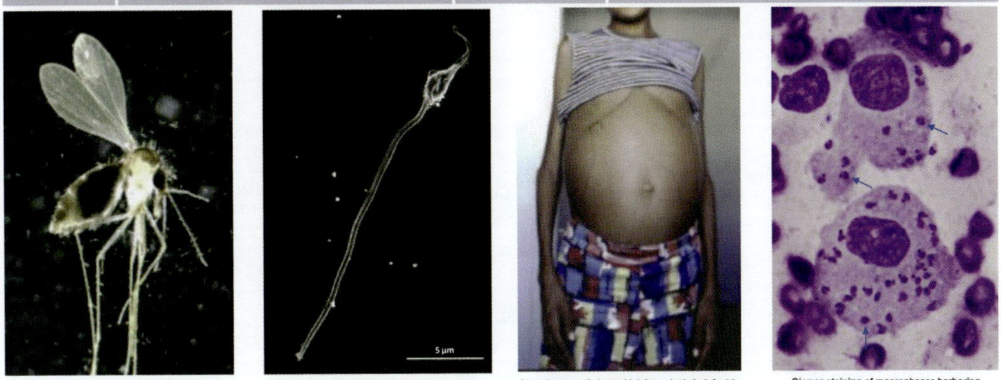

Fig. 5.13 ■ ***Leishmania infantum* leishmaniasis.** Courtesy: Serafim *et al. Trends Parasitol* 2020;36: 80–81. Reproduced with permission from Elsevier.

mammalian host). A promastigote possesses the organelles nucleus, kinetoplast within the mitochondrion, lysosome, endoplasmic reticulum, glycosome, acidocalcisome (for calcium and phosphate storage), plasma membrane with subpellicular microtubules, and a flagellum ending with the flagellar pocket. Whereas promastigote has a long flagellum, amastigote has a flagellum stump (tiny flagellum). In addition, amastigote possesses megasome (modified lysosome with cysteine proteinases). An interesting question is: how can the amastigote survive within the lysosome, which is a very hostile environment (full of acid hydrolases for digestion of molecules)? It seems that the amastigote is protected by a surface coat that the lysosomal enzymes cannot penetrate/attack (lipophosphoglycan, LPG). The parasite is sheltered within phagolysosome-like structures called parasitophorous vacuoles (**PVs**) where the promastigote differentiates into the round-shaped amastigote form that multiplies and propagates in the mammalian host organism. In species such as *Leishmania amazonensis*, PVs are fluid-filled and large; they can be isolated by density gradient centrifugation (using Ficoll) for further study (Real 2020).

Please see Figure 5.13 for *Leishmania infantum* leishmaniasis (Serafim *et al.* 2020). Animation of the *Leishmania* parasite is available (by Liquid Jigsaw, one from the archive: the original Leishmaniasis life cycle animation created for the Wellcome Trust).[14] Please see Figure 5.14 for illustrations of organelles of *Leishmania* promastigotes and amastigotes (Teixeira *et al.* 2013).

[14]https://www.youtube.com/watch?v=ubCUjNW1Sco

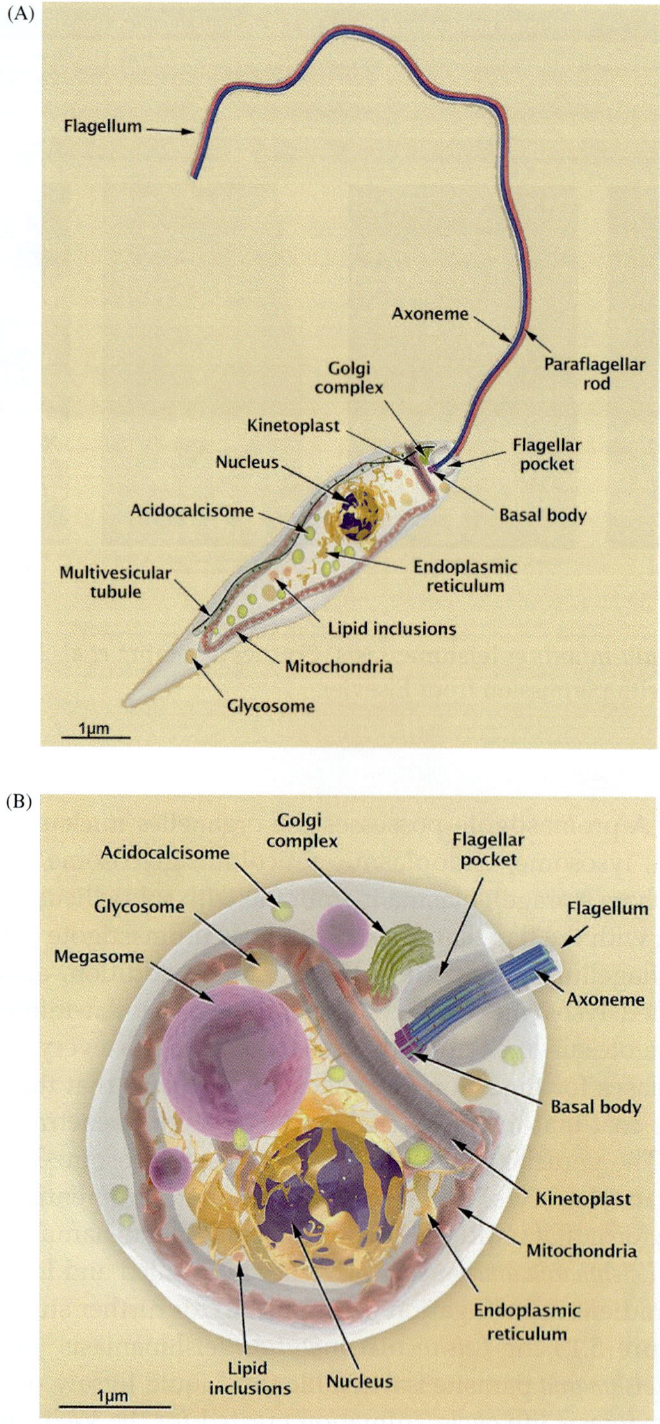

Fig. 5.14 ■ Structural organization of *Leishmania* promastigote and amastigote. Schematic 3D representations of the organelles found in the *Leishmania* promastigote (A) and amastigote (B). Courtesy: Teixeira *et al. PLoS Pathog.* 2013;9:e1003594. Reproduced with permission from *PLoS Pathogens* with Creative Commons Attribution 4.0 (CC-BY) International License.

5.5.3 Pathology

Cutaneous infection can be self-curing. CL is the most common clinical form, but the self-healing skin lesion is a slow process that takes 8 months to 2 years. Mucocutaneous infection can result in the loss of soft tissues. Visceral infection can lead to hepatosplenomegaly; VL is potentially fatal. A *Leishmania* RNA virus-1 (LRV1), found in *Leishmania braziliensis* and *L. guyanensis* (both belonging to the *Vannia* subgenus), is recognized by the host innate immune response and causes more severe MCL (Ives *et al.* 2011). Leishmaniasis is also an opportunistic infection in patients with HIV.

Because the amastigotes in the mammalian host live intracellularly, the host immune response to leishmaniasis depends on the T cells. *L. major* gives the best indication for T cell subsets in immunology. In inbred mice studies, in the susceptible strain BALB/c the response is **Th2** and the mice die of CL, whereas in the resistant strain C57BL/6 the response is **Th1** and the animals can get rid of *Leishmania* (Heinzel *et al.* 1989). This early finding has been extended. "Depending on the parasite strain/species/host model studied the Th2 response could either promote infection or at best be irrelevant to disease progression ... In the ideal scenario following infection with *Leishmania* infection Th1 responses are induced sufficient to control infection initially while regulatory mechanisms are necessary laterly to prevent excessive pathology, maintain a latent (sub-clinical) infection and immunity to re-infection. Perturbation of this balance results in either progressive or chronic disease" (Alexander and Brombacher 2012).

The immune response to leishmaniasis depends on the macrophage subsets. Both classically activated and alternatively activated macrophages (**CAM, AAM**) may be the innate immune response to the parasite. The subset development depends on the activity of transcription factors: pro-inflammatory nuclear factor *kappa* B (NFκB) and the anti-inflammatory peroxisome proliferator-activated receptor *gamma* (PPARγ). PPARγ is a transcriptional factor that suppresses the immune response, whereas NFκB is the transcription factor that induces the inflammatory response (inducing pro-inflammatory cytokine production). In addition to the regulation of gene expression, PPARγ may sequester NFκB so the latter is not available to activate cytokine gene expression. *Leishmania* lives within lysosomes of macrophages. NFκB induces the differentiation of CAM; CAM can kill amastigotes via NO produced by inducible nitric oxide synthase (iNOS) (Lamb 2012). For *Leishmania amazonensis*, the amastigotes demonstrate an **immune subversion** strategy to target host cell epigenetic regulation to establish conditions beneficial for parasite survival, via a decreased expression of activating and increased expression of de-activating components of the pro-inflammatory pathways. Amastigotes target histone H3 modification of the host macrophages. Changes in transcript abundance correlate with histone H3K9/14 hypoacetylation and H3K4 hypo-trimethylation in infected primary and lesional macrophages at promoters of NFκB-related, pro-inflammatory genes (Lecoeur *et al.* 2020). In a comment on this phenomenon, *Leishmania* has become "a maestro in epigenetic manipulation of macrophage inflammasomes" (Kamhawi and Serafim 2020).

PPARγ activates AAM. AAM can enhance parasite survival by producing arginase, an enzyme that degrades arginine, the precursor for NO. Phytochemicals such as curcumin (in turmeric) activate PPAR. VL is endemic in regions of India (especially in the state of Bihar); the Indian population has used lots of turmeric (both in cuisine and Ayurvedic medicine). In murine VL model, we have shown that curcumin treatment exacerbates *Leishmania donovani* parasite growth (Adapala and Chan 2008; Chan *et al.* 2012). PPAR ligands such as rosiglitazone (Avandia) and pioglitazone (Actos) are drugs for type 2 diabetes. Treatment of rosiglitazone has been reported to enhance survival in murine cerebral malaria (Serghides 2012). These findings suggest that, for some parasitic diseases, an overzealous immune response contributes to pathology (immunopathology) (Chan *et al.* 2010; Chan and Fong 2012).

Leishmania prefers a Th2 environment for survival. Helminth infections tend to enhance Th2 environment too. Experiments with mice infected with a murine nematode (*Heligmosomoides polygyrus*), followed with a secondary infection by *Leishmania donovani*, has shown that the worm infection also exacerbates VL (Classon *et al.* 2019). Leishmaniasis persistence is associated with arginase expression by neutrophils and AAMs, as well as possible T-cell suppression and/or exhaustion, thus preventing the development of a protective immune response (Pessenda and da Silva 2020).

The presence of *Leishmania* and cancer in the same tissue sample may be merely fortuitous, but there may exist a relationship between leishmaniasis and cancer. Both show worldwide prevalence. The clinical outcome for both diseases is under the control of innate and adaptive immunity, and both are characterized by an impaired Th1 response. The Th2 cytokine microenvironment occurring in progressive leishmaniasis can potentially promote tumor cell proliferation, and vice versa. Furthermore, because aspects of subclinical CL and VL sometimes closely resemble the symptoms observed in various neoplasms, leishmaniasis may be misdiagnosed as cancer (Schwing *et al.* 2019).

Leishmania infection may co-exist with other infectious diseases. An example is a case report of VL/HIV co-infection in Brazil. On October 11, 2017, a 40-year-old male presented at a health service with high fever, chills, asthenia, pale skin, lower limb edema, hepatomegaly, and splenomegaly. VL was confirmed by direct examination, plus serological and molecular tests, with expert diagnosis at FIOCRUZ to demonstrate positive ELISA (rK39) for anti-leishmanial antibodies, positive direct agglutination test (DAT) for VL, positive urinary antigen for VL (KAtex), and positive real-time PCR (qPCR). This patient was already known to the health service since 2014, for HIV treatment (tenofovir/lamivudine/efavirenz) and he also had treatment for erythema nodosum leprosum (an immune-mediated complication of leprosy, characterized by the presence of multiple inflammatory cutaneous nodules and systemic symptoms such as fever, malaise, arthritis, iritis, neuritis and lymphadenitis) (with thalidomide, prednisone) since 2015. His serum levels of Th1/Th2 cytokines were measured, and treated for VL (liposomal amphotericin B) with good clinical response, until VL recurred 6 months later. The treatment was reinitiated (liposomal amphotericin B); the patient showed clinical improvement with important recovery of $CD4^+$ T-lymphocyte count. This case of VL-HIV co-infection occurred in a hyper-endemic area for VL and leprosy (Aquino *et al.* 2020).

Leishmaniasis may be misdiagnosed as another infectious disease. A case report documented a 21-year-old male presented at a London hospital with fever, weight loss, night sweats, and abdominal discomfort (for 2 weeks). Born in the United Kingdom but had lived between UK and Spain (Barcelona, Valencia), he had traveled once to Morocco for vacation (2 years prior). A pastry factory worker owning a healthy pet dog, his case of VL was initially diagnosed as Q fever (based on positive *Coxiella burnetii* serology, probably a false positive) and he showed a partial response to doxycycline treatment. He had hepatomegaly and splenomegaly. His bone marrow sample, sent on day 11 and data returned on day 33, confirmed positive diagnosis of VL (PCR result showing *Leishmania donovani* complex DNA). The patient was successfully treated with liposomal amphotericin B (AmBisome). The case has shown "the potential pitfalls in diagnosing VL ... The role of doxycycline as an adjunctive agent for treating VL merits further study" (Dhariwal *et al.* 2020).

Several case reports of CL, MCL, and VL are discussed below. For CL, a couple (31-old-male, 30-year-old female) traveled to Costa Rica for honeymoon (hiking, rafting, camping) and had skin lesions 2 weeks back to Colorado, USA (both had reported insect bites). Their skin biopsy specimen by PCR revealed the presence of *Leishmania panamensis* (by CDC). Both were completely cured with systemic therapy of oral miltefosine (Impavido). "We suggest that miltefosine represents an important therapeutic alternative in the treatment of cutaneous lesions caused by *L. panamensis* and in preventing mucosal involvement" (Mann *et al.* 2020).

For MCL, aka mucosal leishmaniasis (**ML**), the disease is rare in USA, with a total of 8 documented civilian cases (7 from the New World). The last 2 cases were reported in New York City (Murray *et al.* 2020). Case 1 involved a 77-year-old Syrian male who had lived in NYC for 50 years (had not returned to Syria) and, after 3 months of nasal stuffiness plus a sense of swelling, had received an otolaryngology evaluation to reveal the presence of a nasal mass. Tissue sample PCR indicated infection by *Leishmania tropica*. The patient received oral miltefosine and was cured after 2 months. This is the first case of Old World MCL in USA. Case 2 involved a 45-year-old male, who, in 1995 (23 years before presentation), studied wildlife ecology in the Amazon rainforest in Bolivia. There, he developed a right neck skin lesion (cutaneous infection) and was treated with sodium stibogluconate. Back in NYC, he developed lesions many years later, initially of the uvula, soft palate, and posterior pharynx and subsequently the larynx. His uvula tissue showed chronic inflammation with granulomas and intracellular amastigotes; tissue culture and analysis performed at the CDC identified *L. (Viannia) braziliensis*. He was treated with miltefosine, recovered but had recurrence (11 months later) and was treated with liposomal amphotericin B. For MCL, "retreatment may be required and recurrence after apparent clinical cure is always a possibility — Patient 2 is a clear-cut example of this clinical problem. In patients with ML who show improvement or healing after treatment, most relapses occur within the first 2 years, thus the importance of close clinical follow-up" (Murray *et al.* 2020). Another case report in Brazil also showed pharyngeal involvement with the same infectious agent *L. braziliensis*. A 46-year-old male from Bahia, Brazil, a rural worker, started with CL symptom of lesion in his left leg and also nodular lesions in the oropharynx and rhinopharynx. He was treated with IV Glucantime, and antimony therapy healed his oropharyngeal lesion in one month, but not the leg lesion. He was followed with amphotericin B, and the lesion healed in 12 months. The patient's cytokine evaluation showed the initial lack of production of interferon (IFN)-γ, interleukin (IL)-1β, and IL-17 but showed enhancement of cytokine levels after cure. "Classically, ML is secondary to the skin lesion" (Figueiredo *et al.* 2020).

As already mentioned, VL can be fatal if untreated. A representative case of VL was documented from West Bank, Palestine. The case involved a 2-year-old female child suffering from recurrent fever, weakness, and abdominal discomfort associated with loss of appetite. She had hepatomegaly. Her diagnosis of VL was made by demonstrating amastigotes in a Giemsa-stained smear from a bone marrow aspirate followed by genotyping by PCR and sequencing (the agent was *L. infantum*). She recovered after intravenous Pentostam (sodium stibogluconate) therapy. The investigators did an epidemiological description of the situation surrounding this case. They collected 17 sand flies from the indoor corners of her house and serum was collected from 39 dogs (reservoir host). All sand flies were females except 2 and none contained *L. infantum* parasite DNA in their gut. Of the 39 dog sera, 6 (15.4%) were positive for anti-leishmanial antibodies (with 3 dogs showing some VL symptoms, the other 3 asymptomatic). Seropositive dogs were quelled (according to protocol). "In conclusion, early detection of VL infection followed by appropriate treatment protocols is essential to saving the patient" (Al-Jawabreh *et al.* 2020).

Leishmaniasis is caused by an intracellular pathogen in mammal hosts, and requires T cell action to destroy these foreign organisms. For an immunocompromised patient, VL can be difficult to treat. A case report from Brazil documented a 46-year-old black male from the endemic VL region of Rio Grande do Norte state, and had continued fever for almost 1.5 years, plus a remarkable medical history for a splenectomy performed 20 years prior (due to an abdominal gunshot wound), together with alcohol consumption and daily 2 packs of cigarettes. This splenectomized male was diagnosed with disseminated VL in the liver, bone marrow, lymph nodes, and gastrointestinal tract. In addition, his stool samples were positive for *Entamoeba* cysts. He was treated for intestinal amoebiasis (metronidazole, teclozine) and leishmaniasis (liposomal amphotericin B, L-AmB), with clinical improvement and fever disappearance. However, he had relapse, but was finally, successfully treated with a drug combination (L-AmB, meglumine antimoniate, and pentamidine isethionate) — still asymptomatic after 12 months. "Despite our promising result, the anti-*Leishmania* drug triple combination therapy should be restricted to VL cases that are difficult to treat in view of the possible dangers related to toxicity. ... It should be reserved for refractory cases, especially when L-AmB treatment has failed. This regimen will potentially avoid resistance to L-AmB, which today is the most efficient drug for VL treatment" (Vechi *et al.* 2020).

Another VL case was documented in Australia. A 61-year-old male presented with 7 months of fevers, night sweats, fatigue, and weight loss. The patient had extensive travel history, including a 3-week trip to southern Italy (12 months prior) and a trip to India (6 years prior). In addition, his medical history included multiple sclerosis (MS) that had been managed with fingolimod (for 6 years). His bone marrow aspirate revealed numerous intracellular and extracellular *Leishmania* amastigotes. Whole community shotgun metagenomic sequencing of DNA extracted from an aspirate was undertaken on the Illumina NextSeq, generating 121,364,564 sequencing reads. After removing human genome sequences, 905,743/121,364,564 (0.7%) nonhuman sequencing reads remained, of which 294,673/905,743 (32.5%) were classified as *Leishmania* reads. Species confirmation of *L. infantum* was performed by in silico reconstruction of the hsp 70 gene and whole genome phylogenetic comparisons of the reconstructed draft genome sequences with publicly available *Leishmania* genomes. The finding correlated with the patient's acquisition of *L. infantum* in Italy instead of *L. donovani* in India. He was treated with liposomal amphotericin B for over 2 months, and remained well 6 months after treatment cessation. "This case of fingolimod-associated VL in a returned traveler from Italy illustrates the need for vigilance for the emergence of rare, opportunistic infections in patients on novel immunosuppressive agents, particularly following travel to endemic areas. The application of metagenomic sequencing has the potential to identify and speciate *Leishmania* in cases of VL; however, further assessment is required using more readily obtained clinical samples such as blood" (Williams *et al.* 2020).

5.5.4 Diagnosis

For CL and MCL, parasites can be detected in lesions. For VL, parasites can be observed in biopsy samples from spleen or bone marrow. For detection of leishmaniasis, diagnostic methods can be microbiological, immunological, or molecular (Kumar *et al.* 2020). Clinical samples can be cultured for the appearance of promastigotes. An early and famous one is Novy, MacNeal, and Nicolle (**NNN**) media of blood agar and salt, used to show similarities between the kala azar and oriental sore parasites (Kazanjian 2017). Another diagnostic method is a measurement of delayed-type hypersensitivity (DTH) named leishmanin skin test (**LST**), aka Montenegro test (first introduced in 1926 by J. Montenegro in Brazil), an intradermal injection of killed promastigotes for detection of the size of DTH response 48 hours later (an induration, over 5 mm in diameter, occurs in a positive reaction). A positive response indicates either past or present *Leishmania* infection (da Costa *et al.* 1996). LST is a skin hypersensitivity test (local inflammatory response at the injection site); it is similar to the better known TB test using purified protein derivative (PPD) to check exposure to *Mycobacterium tuberculosis*.

As an alternative to LST, in lieu of skin response, whole blood stimulation assay (**WBA**) checks the proliferation response of peripheral blood mononuclear cells (PBMCs) after stimulation with *Leishmania* antigens. A cell proliferation assay (CPA) has been modified to measure the cellular immune response to *Leishmania* antigens, by the detection of cytokine/chemokine production levels after stimulation in vitro. WBA and cytokine assays are quick, easy, and inexpensive tools workable in the field. One example is the interferon *gamma* release assay (IGRA), cell-based test to detect IFNγ or other cytokines/chemokines after stimulation in vitro. Presence of cytokines and chemokines are assayed by cytometric bead array (CBA), a system that enables simultaneous measurement of multiple analytes in sample volumes too small for traditional immunoassays (Morgan *et al.* 2004). For leishmaniasis, the levels of analytes detected in the plasma of WBA are useful as biomarkers of infection/exposure and cure/relapse. Such a panel of expression in WBA has identified IL-2 as a preferential biomarker of infection/exposure to *Leishmania* infection. The monocyte chemotactic protein 1 has been shown as a potential biomarker of response to *L. infantum* (Ibarra-Meneses *et al.* 2017 and 2020).

Other serological diagnostic tests have been developed. Compared to CL and MCL, VL is the most severe and potentially fatal. That being said, in regions endemic for VL, most infected individuals remain asymptomatic. "Faster, simpler, more sensitive, and more robust field tools are needed for early diagnosis of VL and monitoring of patients during and after drug treatment" (Ibarra-Meneses *et al.* 2020). Immunochromatographic test (**ICT**) uses simple cellulose-based strip devices with crude or recombinant leishmanial antigen to detect the presence of *Leishmania*-specific antibodies in sera or blood samples. Rapid rK39-ICT and rK28-ICT are available for case detection. The rK28 antigen-based RDT (rapid diagnostic test) has even been used to detect antibodies in patient urine (Ghosh *et al.* 2016). Direct agglutination test (DAT) uses whole fixed and stained *Leishmania* promastigotes to measure *Leishmania*-specific serum antibodies. The antibodies will agglutinate the promastigotes forming a film whereas antibody absence allows the promastigotes to settle to the bottom of the test well.

Molecular diagnosis of *Leishmania* is another approach. Polymerase chain reaction (PCR) or quantitative PCR (qPCR) is useful and sensitive but requires a DNA thermal cycler (an instrument necessary for temperature shifts) and the diagnosis takes time. A related technique that combines simplicity, rapidity, and high sensitivity is the loop-mediated isothermal amplification (**LAMP**). In lieu of the Taq DNA polymerase (thermophilic enzyme), the displacement activity of Bst-polymerase requires no changes in temperature for denaturation of the DNA and hybridization with the primers; only a thermoblock or incubator is necessary for the DNA amplification process (Nzelu *et al.* 2019). Eiken Chemical Co. and the Foundation for Innovative New Diagnostics (FIND) have developed a kit for the diagnosis of leishmaniasis known as Loopamp Leishmania detection in an easy-to-use format, with all reagents lyophilized in the lid of the reaction tube for transport and/or storage (no cold chain needed) (Ibarra-Meneses *et al.* 2020).

In sum, serological and molecular diagnosis techniques, such as the rK28-ICT and the *Leishmania* Loopamp detection kit, are fast, simple, and robust tools and allow early diagnosis of VL in endemic areas without the need for large blood samples or complex facilities (Ibarra-Meneses *et al.* 2020).

5.5.5 Therapy

Drugs for leishmaniasis are old. Based on pentavalent antimony, the two standard drugs are **sodium stibogluconate** (Pentostam) and **meglumine antimoniate** (Glucantime); they have been used as first-line treatment for VL for over half a century. The exact mechanism is not known, but may involve energy production and trypanothione metabolism. Drug-resistant parasites have arisen. One such case was described using modern advances in technology of genomics, proteomics, and transcriptomics. The clinical isolate (HVZ) was obtained from bone marrow puncture fluid of a patient treated with 4 courses of antimonials and then relapsed. This clinical isolate was used in drug-resistance testing, whole genome resequencing and proteome profiling, together with reference controls. The isolate showed higher-level virulence and clear resistance to antimonials in promastigote culture, infected macrophages and animal experiments. Sequencing showed genetic variations (86 copy number variations, 271 frameshift mutations in protein-coding genes, including a C to T mutation in a tRNA that might change its secondary structure). Proteomic analysis showed 69 exclusively detected proteins and 82 consistently down/upregulated proteins. "High-level pathogenicity and evident antimony-resistance were confirmed for the HCZ isolate of *L. donovani*. Integrative genomic, proteomic and phenotypic studies of the resistant HCZ isolate and reference sensitive strains (DD8 and 9044) of *L. donovani* revealed genetic variations likely associated with nucleotide binding, fatty acid metabolism, oxidation-reduction and transport of drugs" (Zheng *et al.* 2020). It should be noted that, although the findings have confirmed drug resistance, the exact molecular mechanism of Sb (antimonial) drug resistance has not yet been pinpointed in this study.

For leishmaniasis, a drug of choice is **amphotericin B liposome** (AmBisome). The target is *Leishmania* membrane lipid biosynthesis. Both *Leishmania* and fungi share a similar pathway; amphotericin B was originally developed as an antifungal. Sometimes, a drug combination, including amphotericin B, is necessary to treat leishmaniasis. This situation was shown in a case of leishmaniasis AIDS co-infection in Brazil. A 46-year-old male resident in the municipality of Maranhãozinho–Maranhão state, had an ulcerated lesion in the left upper limb in 2017 and was diagnosed HIV positive in 2019. The patient was infected with *L. amazonensis* (diagnosis by PCR and RFLP) and had diffuse cutaneous leishmaniasis (DCL), a rare type of leishmaniasis characterized by diffuse skin lesions. For co-infection, therapeutic regimen was the combination of antiretroviral (lamivudine, tenofovir, and dolutegravir), prophylactic therapy for pneumocystosis and toxoplasmosis (sulfamethoxazole, trimethoprim), and anti-leishmanial (liposomal amphotericin B, AmB-L). There were relapses of DCL, his treatment was AmB-L alternated with pentamidine the first time, and later with AmB-L and Glucantime. The patient remained on weekly prophylactic use of Glucantime. It is known that patients with DCL may be refractory to antileishmanial treatment. The situation worsens in cases of HIV coinfection, where higher rates of therapeutic failure and relapse are observed despite ongoing antiretroviral treatment. The investigators concluded: "In areas of high CL and HIV-endemic conditions, particularly in the Brazilian Amazon region, it is possible to obtain reports of patients infected by both pathogens simultaneously manifesting atypical clinical signs, as occurred in this report. Thus, the health team should be aware of these cases, which require appropriate treatment and continuous clinical follow-up of the patient" (Corrêa Soares *et al.* 2020).

A newer drug is **miltefosine** (Impavido), a compound originally proposed to treat cancer. This hexadecylphosphocholine is the only oral drug currently registered for the treatment of leishmaniasis; it is useful for all clinical forms. Mitelfosine was approved in India (2002), Germany (2004), and USA (by FDA as an orphan drug in 2006). A case report of CL has shown drug resistance to mitelfosine. A 67-year-old white male was probably bitten by an infected sand fly on his residential farm in central Texas. From his initial visit to his primary care physician in September 2016 until the followed up period in June 2018, approximately 26 months after initial onset of symptoms, the patient's lesions remained refractory to treatment. After confirmation of CL (CDC confirmation, NNN medium agar with RPMI FBS overlay for promastigote growth, and PCR), he received two consecutive 28-day courses of oral miltefosine (150 mg/day) followed by a 28-day course of oral ketoconazole (600 mg/day) in November 2017, and then two consecutive 42-day courses of oral ketoconazole (600 mg/day), followed by an additional 28-day course of oral miltefosine (150 mg/day). While all therapies were well tolerated, still there was no cure. "In the United States, phlebotomine sand flies carrying *Leishmania Leishmania mexicana* are endemic along the southern border. However, relatively little is known about the enzootic and zoonotic transmission of *L. (L.) mexicana* within the United States, and autochthonous cases of the consequent disease are rarely reported. ... We also investigated sand fly vectors around the patient's residence. ... The *L. (L.) mexicana* genotype from the patient was identical to one found in a positive sand fly. Moreover, this genotype presented the same single-nucleotide polymorphisms as other historical CL cases acquired in Texas over the last 10 years, but distinct from those originating in Mexico and Central America. ... The majority of which were *Lutzomyia (Dampfomyia) anthophora* (n = 190), of which four specimens tested positive for *Leishmania* and two blood-fed specimens showed the presence of a human blood meal. This study highlights the complexity of clinical management of CL in a setting where the disease is infrequently encountered" (Kipp *et al.* 2020). The investigators claimed 2 "firsts": "The detection of human blood in *Lu. (D.) anthophora* is the first documentation of anthropophagy in this species. This is the first report of wild-caught, naturally infected sand flies found in association with an autochthonous case of human leishmaniasis and the specific strain of *Leishmania (Leishmania) mexicana* in the United States" (Kipp *et al.* 2020).

Another drug is the antibiotic **paromomycin**, originally shown to be anti-leishmanial in the 1960s but abandoned because of a lack of profitability for drug development. The Institute for One World Health, a nonprofit drug company located in San Francisco, re-introduced the compound; it was approved in India in 2006 for VL therapy. Concerning paromomycin and drug resistance, we and our collaborators have studied the sequence of SSU RNA and found that *Leishmania* paromomycin resistance is not based on mutation in sequences found in other resistant prokaryotes (Fong *et al.* 1994).

For VL, after drug treatment, there is post kala-azar dermal leishmaniasis (previously named post kala-azar dermal leishmanoid). **PKDL** is a late skin manifestation. About 2.5% to 20% of patients recovered from VL develop PKDL. "These individuals with PKDL represent an important but largely neglected reservoir of infection that perpetuates anthroponotic *Leishmania donovani* transmission in the Indian subcontinent (ISC), and can jeopardize the VL elimination program as these cases can infect the sand flies and spread the endemic. Therefore, it becomes imperative to eradicate PKDL as a part of the VL elimination program" (Gedda *et al.* 2020). Strategies to track/treat PKDL have been proposed and discussed (Moulik *et al.* 2021).

There are efforts at novel drug developments. One specific example is CDC-2-related kinase 12 (CRK12); the lead compound was shown to be active in murine models of VL (Wyllie *et al.* 2018). Metabolic pathways essential for the survival of parasites can be exploited as potential drug targets against leishmaniasis. Examples include sterol biosynthesis, glycolysis, redox metabolism, folate biosynthesis, kinases and others (Raj *et al.* 2020). Saravanan Vijayakumar (Rajendra Memorial Research Institute of Medical Science, Indian Council for Medical Research, Patna, Bihar, India) and colleagues have created LeishInDB, a web-accessible resource of small molecule inhibitors having a varying degree of activity towards *Leishmania* sp. The database includes searchable information of >7,000 small molecules collected from >600 literature. The comprehensive information of inhibitors includes activity details (IC50, EC50, Ki), information on species and form of *Leishmania* the inhibitor is active against, as well as details about their protein target (with links to TriTrypDB) (Vijayakumar *et al.* 2019).[15]

Antibodies may be useful for therapy. Camels and llamas possess unique antibodies known as single-domain antibodies (**sdAb**) or nanobodies. They are the variable domains of the camel heavy-chain antibodies (HCAbs), which are reduced in structure due to the lack of light chains. Enas Abu Alshamat (Damascus University, Syria) and colleagues had constructed an immune library from a camel immunized with *Leishmania tropica*. Nanobodies from the library were displayed on the tips of M13 bacteriophage (phage display library) and selected by 3 rounds of panning against *L. tropica* antigens. The anti-*L. tropica* phage nanobodies were capable of detecting *Leishmania*. They analyzed 5 and found all 5 were more specific to *L. tropica* than to *L. major*, but could equally recognize the lysate and the outer surface of the intact cells from the two main stages of the parasite. Because of its role in *Leishmania* life cycle, gp63 (glycoprotein 63 kDa, metalloproteinase) was considered a potential antigen candidate for nanobodies, and bioinformatics predicted such interaction. All nanobodies decreased the number of infected macrophages and the amastigotes within them. Their conclusion: "Such anti-*leishmania* nanobodies, with outstanding characteristics and important target, can be of great use in the development of promising treatment strategies against leishmaniasis" (Abu Alshamat *et al.* 2020).

5.5.6 Genome

The first *Leishmania* genome was published together with the other two trypanosomes. This genome is from *Leishmania major* Friedlin strain (Ivens *et al.* 2005). It consists of a

[15] http://leishindb.biomedinformri.com/

haploid genome of 33 Mb in size from 36 chromosomes, with 911 RNA genes, 39 pseudogenes, and 8,272 protein-coding genes (current update to 8,402, one third as hypothetical proteins with unknown function, a situation similar to genomes from many protozoan organisms). Many protein-encoding genes belong to families; they are often organized in tandem gene arrays (including the tubulin genes).

Soon after *L. major*, the genomes of both *L. infantum* and *L. braziliensis* were published (Peacock *et al.* 2007). Both *L. major* and *L. infantum* have 36 chromosomes, *L. braziliensis* has 35. For protein-coding genes, the numbers are *L. major*, 8,258; *L. infantum*, 8,154; *L. braziliensis*, 8,153. Although retrotransposons are only found in the genome of *L. braziliensis* (plus RNAi genes), the three genomes show marked conservation of synteny. A surprise is that only **200** genes are found to differ between VL, CL and MCL. This may mean that, either the genome does not reflect clinical presentation (pathology), or that gene expression level may be important under such conditions (variation in gene copy number).

Many *Leishmania* genomes followed. *Leishmania mexicana* has 34 chromosomes and 8,250 protein-coding genes (Rogers *et al.* 2011). The differences in the haploid chromosome number between species known so far arose from fusion events between members of the set of 36 chromosomes. Other genomes are available: *Leishmania amazonensis* (Real *et al.* 2013; Valdivia *et al.* 2017, the latter from dog reservoir), *L. panamensis* (Llanes *et al.* 2015), *L. adleri* (Coughlan *et al.* 2017), and *L. tarentolae* (Raymond *et al.* 2011). The last 2 are lizard parasites; they have been grouped into ***Sauroleishmania***. These genomes and others are available in the TriTrypDB.[16]

The typical genome is **32–35 Mb** haploid size within **24–36** chromosomes and has **8,000–9,000** protein-coding genes. Field isolates show extensive variation in chromosome and gene copy numbers. In this sense, *Leishmania* may be considered as aneuploid rather than diploid organisms, as extra chromosomes (supernumerary chromosomes) may be present in the same or different isolates, showing genetic plasticity (Downing *et al.* 2011; Cantacessi *et al.* 2015). A transcriptomics study of *Leishmania mexicana* has shown differential expression of 3,832 genes between amastigotes and promastigotes, as well as upregulated expression of amastigote genes in the isolate with a tetraploid chromosome 30, thus linking "this whole chromosome duplication event and adaptation to the vertebrate host in this group" (Fiebig *et al.* 2015).

Whereas genomes of many *Leishmania* species are now available, the mitochondrial genome has not been investigated in detail until 2019 (Camacho *et al.* 2019). The parasitic trypanosomatid mitochondrial genome consists of concatemers (maxi and minicircircle DNA) in a network, as discussed earlier. This feature is only found in the parasitic species; it is absent in the free-living *Bodo saltans*. Whether this is somehow involved in parasitism is not yet known, but the complex structural and repetitive nature of kinetoplast DNA (kDNA) delayed their sequencing. With improvements in next generation sequencing (NGS) and bioinformatics genome assembly, "the maxicircle molecules and the plethora of minicircle classes for *Leishmania major*, *Leishmania infantum* and *Leishmania*

[16] https://tritrypdb.org/tritrypdb/app/search/organism/GenomeDataTypes/result

braziliensis have been characterized" (Camacho *et al.* 2019). For *Leishmania major*, 53,340,123 paired-end reads generated from whole-DNA sequencing, were mapped to the reference genome. For those that did not map, the left overs were 3,793,390 pair-end reads; they were analyzed by de novo assembly, as well as comparisons to published sequence and genes (mitochondrial genome and transcriptome of the lizard parasite *L. tarentolae*) (Simpson *et al.* 2015). For *L. major* (Friedlin) a total of 97 **minicircles** were assembled, size range between 660–876 nucleotides (nt) and average size is **691** nt. *L. major* **maxicircle** DNA shows a continuous contig of **18,998** nt in length, with repeated AT-rich sequences at the extremities of the assembled contig. Maxicircles are also assembled in 2 other species: 17,897 nt for *L. infantum* and 17,771 nt for *L. braziliensis*. All 3 maxicircles show remarkable conservation in structure and gene sequence, to each other and to the *L. tarentolae* maxicircle (used as reference for gene annotation). Please see Figure 5.15 for maxicircle gene arrangement of *Leishmania* species (Camacho *et al.* 2019).

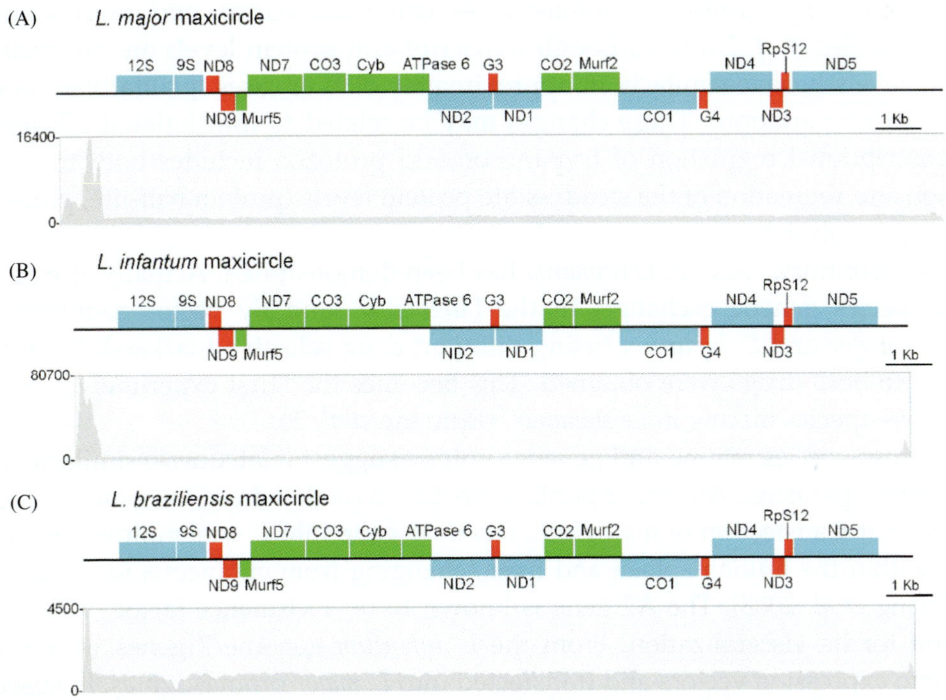

Fig. 5.15 ■ Maxicircle gene arrangement of *Leishmania* species. Diagram of the assembled contigs corresponding to the *L. major* (A), *L. infantum* (B) and *L. braziliensis* (C) maxicircles. The nomenclature and abbreviations of genes are those established for *L. tarentolae* [5]. Blue, green and red boxes are used to indicate non-edited genes, edited genes and pan-edited genes, respectively. The graph, below each gene map, shows the read depth, i.e., the number of reads aligned in a given position along the assembled contig sequence (linear scale). Courtesy: Camacho *et al. Genes (Basel)* 2019;10:758. Reproduced with permission from *Genes (Basel)* with Creative Commons Attribution 4.0 (CC-BY) International License.

Published *Leishmania* genomes are followed by post-genomic research and applications. As an example, PCR primers have been designed as molecular targets to analyze the New World *Leishmania* species (Conter *et al.* 2019). Based on the TriTryp genomes, TrypTag is a project with an aim to successfully generate subcellular localization database of every protein encoded in the *T. brucei* genome. The project has been extended to *Leishmania mexicana*, by constructing fluorescently tagged proteins as "cellular landmarks" for locations and organelles of amastigotes and promastigotes (Halliday *et al.* 2019). Gene editing and RNA interference techniques can knockout genes. *Leishmania* and other trypanosomatid genomes contain genes with known and unknown functions (open reading frames ORFs coding putative proteins). To accelerate the dissection of gene function, a streamlined pipeline for CRISPR-Cas9 gene editing, LeishGEdit, has been established. For high-throughput mutant screens, the pipeline has added the capacity of barcoding mutants with unique 17-nucleotide barcodes, to allow loss-of-function screens in mixed populations (Beneke and Gluenz 2020). The pipeline is available online.[17]

Before CRISPR and gene editing become popular, transcriptional analysis was performed in sand fly-*Leishmania* promastigotes using microarray and RNA-sequencing analyses (Alcolea *et al.* 2019). Although transcript and protein levels are not well correlated, the levels behave similarly in approximately 60% of cases qualitatively (increase, decrease, or no variation). These changes may be related to translational efficiency. So, post-transcriptional regulation of trypanosomatid protozoa includes both translational regulation and regulation of the steady-state protein levels (protein half-life, protein degradation/proteolysis).

In the laboratory, "sex" in *Leishmania* has been demonstrated. Actually, it was shown as cross-species genetic exchange. In the *Lutzomyia* sand fly vector co-infected with *Leishmania major* and *L. infantum* (using different drug selective markers), hybrids with resistance to both drugs were obtained. This becomes the "first experimental confirmation of cross-species mating in *Leishmania*" (Romano *et al.* 2014).

Both cross-species mating and genetic synteny suggest relatedness/similarity among the *Leishmania* parasites. An earlier publication, based on data from the genome, has demonstrated that transfection of a single *L. infantum* gene into *L. major* allows the latter to survive within the human spleen and liver (changing from cutaneous to visceral infection) (Zhang *et al.* 2008). The A2 gene is known to be a virulence factor of *L. donovani*, important for its visceralization. From the *L. infantum* genome 7 genes were selected, cloned into expression vectors and transfected into *L. major* promastigotes. In susceptible BALB/c mice, 1 of the 7 resulted in the survival of transfected *L. major* in both the spleen and liver of the mouse. The gene used is Li1040, so a single gene can induce visceralization. The gene product is an endosomal protein transport complex member. A detailed study has shown that such a gene is present in *L. major*, suggesting the level of gene expression may influence leishmanial pathology.

[17] www.leishgedit.net

A difference in glucose metabolism between *L. donovani* and *L. major* may also determine visceralization (Zhang *et al.* 2013). In trypanosomatid protozoa, the unique organelle glycosome is the site of glycolysis. The first 7 steps of the pathway, from glucose to 3-phosphoglycerate, are localized in the glycosome, including step 6, catalyzed by the enzyme glyceraldehyde-3-phosphate dehydrogenase (GAPDH). However, in *L. donovani* and *L. mexicana*, there exists a second cytosolic GAPDH (**cGADPH**). The gene is absent in *L. braziliensis*, and has become a pseudogene in *L. major.* For functional analysis of cGADPH, the gene was either deleted in *L. donovani* or added back to *L. major.* The *L. donovani* cGAPDH-null mutant consumed less glucose and proliferated more slowly than the wild-type parasite in culture, and displayed reduced infectivity in visceral organs of experimentally infected mice. Adding a functional cGAPDH gene to *L. major*, in contrast, had an adverse effect on its growth in glucose-containing medium (so it had to change to become a pseudogene).

Similarly, a natural case was reported in American soldiers participating in the Operation Desert Storm 1990–1991, the Gulf War of President George Herbert Walker Bush (Magill *et al.* 1993). Eight soldiers had signs of VL (but no symptom of cutaneous involvement) and the agent was *L. tropica*, normally causing CL, here showed visceralization among infected American soldiers.

After the genomes of infectious agents of Sleeping Sickness, Chagas' disease, and leishmaniasis, a genome of the free-living trypanosomatid ***Bodo saltans***, became available. The protozoan possesses **18,943 genes**, as compared to 9,068 for *Trypanosoma brucei* TREU927, 8,272 for *Leishmania major* Friedlin, and 10,834 for *T. cruzi* Non-Esmeraldo (Jackson *et al.* 2016). The results suggest **genomic "streamlining"** in the parasites, including the loss of functional redundancy. In addition, there are innovations: expansion of transport genes in the parasites and various cell surface proteins in different parasites, as independent derivations from a common ancestral form, named "bodonin," a gene family with 394 members (Jackson *et al.* 2016).

5.5.7 Exosomes

Exosomes are membrane vesicles best defined as extracellular vesicles, 20–150 nm in diameter, that are released from cells upon fusion of an intermediate endocytic compartment, the multivesicular body (MVB), with the plasma membrane. First discovered in reticulocytes and thought of having a garbage bin function, current view has elevated exosome roles and functions. Exosomes are involved in cell-cell communication and the transmission of disease states, with their cargoes of proteins and RNAs. The microRNA (miRNA) and long noncoding RNA (lncRNA) within exosomes may serve regulatory functions. Exosomes have been investigated in cancer, including cancer metastasis (Wu *et al.* 2019).

The role of exosomes in parasitology is an area of current research. For *Leishmania*, exosomes from infected macrophages may show an immune-suppressive function (inhibiting TNFα, activating IL-10). Over 300 proteins have been identified as exosome cargo from *L. donovani*. Experimentally, during temperature shift for promastigotes of *L. mexicana*, there is an increase in the production of exosomes (Dong *et al.* 2019).

Here, we use *Leishmania* exosomes as an example. Exosomes, collected from amastigote and promastigote *L. infantum*-conditioned medium by ultracentrifugation, were characterized by the presence of exosome proteins (HSP70, HSP83/90), and then used to treat human monocytes/macrophages. Changes in motility and cytokine expression were observed, suggesting exosomes can create a Th2 environment favorable to the protozoan. "Since *L. infantum* exosomes demonstrated the capacity to modulate the chemotactic behavior of the cells studied and cytokines production, they could contribute in the disease establishment and may be considered an appropriate candidate for a vaccine therapy in prophylaxis and treatment" (Castelli *et al.* 2019).

Many parasitic protozoa and helminths release exosomes for host-parasite interaction (Jones *et al.* 2018; Nawaz *et al.* 2019; Wu *et al.* 2019). Excretory/secretory (**E/P**) products, abundant in parasitic worms, can be exosome components for the modulation of host immune response.

5.5.8 Vaccines

Currently, vaccines are not yet available but many attempts are ongoing. For historical context, let us start with leishmanization (**LZ**). LZ is an intradermal inoculation of live *Leishmania* to induce an artificial CL lesion in a covered part of the human body (to protect against further natural CL lesion development). It has been a practice for endemic area populations in the Middle East. "Exudate of an active CL lesion was collected from a lesion using a sharp instrument like a knife and inoculated into a CL naïve individual usually a child in a covered part of the body, inoculation usually induced a CL lesion and upon healing the person was protected against further natural infection for the rest of life" (Mohebali *et al.* 2019). Later, with the NNN medium available, cultured promastigotes were used for LZ. LZ is the deliberate inoculation of live wild type parasites, except without the disease exacerbating factors associated with sand fly bites (saliva proteins including the vasodilator maxadilan). LZ has been shown to reduce CL incidence in endemic areas (Iran, Israel and former Soviet Union countries). Please see Figure 5.16 for a pre-World War II view on LZ by Robert Hegner, as depicted in his book titled *Big fleas have little fleas; or, Who's who among the protozoa* (Hegner 1938).[18] [Robert William Hegner (1880–1942) was a professor at Johns Hopkins University.]

A typical vaccine can be a killed pathogen or a subunit vaccine, which may be recombinant proteins (or synthetic mRNAs) derived from the pathogen. Effective vaccines against *Leishmania* parasites are a goal for the scientific community working with both canine and human leishmaniases. Although a human vaccine is still not available, the dog vaccine is already here. **CaniLeish®** vaccine (Virbac), licensed in Europe in 2011, is a

[18] https://hdl.handle.net/2027/uva.x002081533

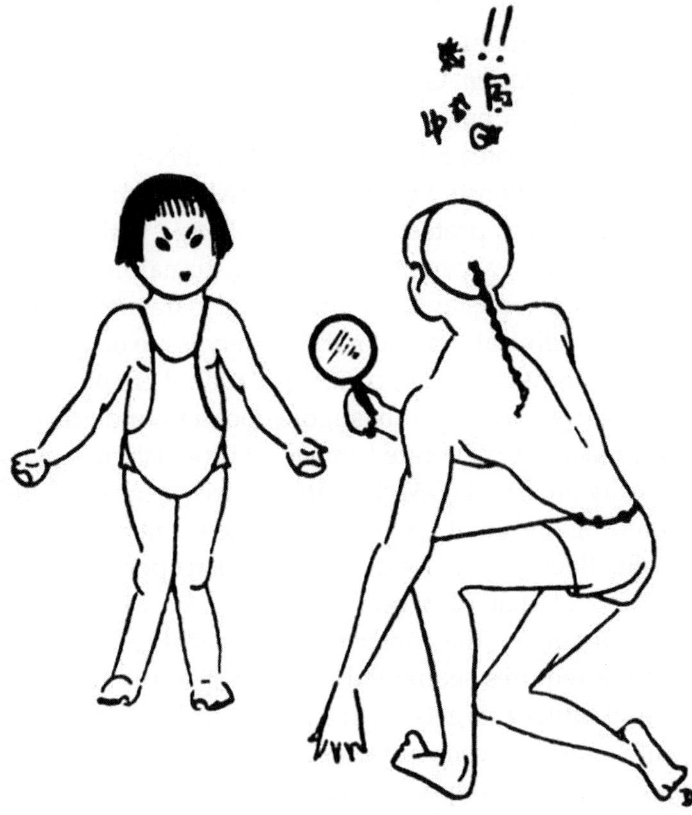

Fig. 5.16 ■ Pre-World War II view on leishmanization. Oriental sore. "Where," says this distracted mother, "can I find a spot to vaccinate against oriental sore that will not be exposed when my little girl grows up?" Hegner R. *Big fleas have little fleas; or, Who's who among the protozoa*, Baltimore, The Williams & Wilkins Company, 1938. 1969 Dover reprint. Public Domain. Google-digitized: HathiTrust Digital Library. Courtesy of HathiTrust. Reproduced from https://hdl.handle.net/2027/uva.x002081533.

second-generation vaccine, composed of purified E/S proteins of *L. infantum* (LiESP) with saponin adjuvant (QA-21) from a purified fraction of *Quillaja saponaria*, with pre-licensing field trial of 68.4% efficacy in the prevention of clinical signs and the reduction of developing active disease by 3.6 times (Velez *et al.* 2020).

Whereas E/S proteins have been developed as canine vaccine, live vaccines are being considered for humans. "There is now a broad consent among *Leishmania* researchers that the perseverance of parasite is very essential for eliciting a protective immune response and may perhaps be attained by live attenuated parasite vaccination" (Pandey *et al.* 2020). Live attenuated vaccines for VL and CL are being investigated (Pandey *et al.* 2020; Zabala-Penafiel *et al.* 2020). However, there is a concern: the live attenuated vaccine pathogen may revert back to wild type, as happened in polio vaccine-derived polio outbreaks (Ming *et al.* 2020).

An approach towards the live attenuated vaccine is in vitro selection with the aminoglycoside antibiotic gentamicin, a technique that has been used to attenuate *L. major*, *L. mexicana* and *L. infantum*. Gentamicin binds to the 30S ribosomal subunit and targets the RNase P complex in eukaryotes. Attenuated promastigotes were unable to survive as intracellular amastigotes but elicited higher IFN-γ and lower IL-4 and IL-10 secretions for Th1 immune response. Furthermore, BALB/c mice immunized with gentamicin-attenuated *L. major* were protected upon challenge with virulent parasites. The gentamicin-attenuated *L. major* vaccine is undergoing human trials. However, it should be pointed out that antibiotic resistance in attenuated parasite strains may create hindrance during actual use in clinical trials. Possible safety issue of vaccine strain transmissibility by the sand fly vector is an added concern (Zabala-Penafiel *et al.* 2020).

All antibiotic-selected *Leishmania* promastigotes possess undefined genetic modifications; an improved approach is to generate *Leishmania* promastigotes with defined genetic modifications. Genetically modified (**GM**) live attenuated vaccine involves genetic alteration of the genes, including ones that are indispensable for intracellular survival and/or virulence of the parasite. [Here, think about the public's response to GM food, notably in Europe.] However, it is not that easy and needs further work in the laboratory. As *Leishmania* is a diploid organism, the construction of genetically modified null mutant-based attenuated vaccine requires sequential disruption of the two alleles of *Leishmania* genes. Examples for null mutant targets include genes for the bifunctional dihydrofolate reductase/thymidylate synthase, centrin (a centrosome protein), heat shock protein 70, lipophosphoglycans-2 (LPG), the Asp-Glu-Ala-Asp (DEAD) box RNA helicase, and p27 gene (*Ldp*27, amastigote-specific protein of cytochrome c oxidase complex associated with oxidative phosphorylation) (Mohebali *et al.* 2019). For CL, knockouts of cysteine protease a/b, LPG, and paraflagellar rod-2 have resulted in parasites yielding decreased lesions in rodent models (hamster, mouse) (Pandey *et al.* 2020; Zabala-Penafiel *et al.* 2020).

As stated multiple times, VL is the most severe disease among all clinical forms. For a potential VL vaccine, "some problems should be kept in mind or to be solved before a VL vaccine becomes a reality: (a) good knowledge on protective antigens; (b) genetic variation in the host may vary the response to antigen; (c) a particular vaccine may exacerbate the disease associated with infection due to malnourished or starving, AIDS, etc.; (d) tropical countries, people rarely suffer from single disease and many have lower immunocompetence; (e) a judicious choice of adjuvant for appropriate Th1 response; (f) use of nature's adjuvant, *that is*, soluble cytokines which are known to promote Th1 responses, *that is*, IL-12" (Mohebali *et al.* 2019).

Hira Nakhasi (Division of Emerging and Transfusion Transmitted Diseases, Center for Biologics Evaluation and Research, CBER, Food and Drug Administration, FDA) and colleagues have "produced a dermotropic live attenuated centrin gene deleted *Leishmania major* (LmCen−/−) vaccine under Good Laboratory Practices and demonstrated that a single intradermal injection confers robust and durable protection against lethal VL transmitted naturally via bites of *L. donovani*-infected sand flies and prevents mortality" (Karmakar *et al.* 2021). Using CRISPR gene editing technique, a markerless, attenuated

Leishmania major was created and named LmCen−/− (using the Friedlin strain, whose genome was first reported in 2005). "Spleen cells from LmCen−/− immunized and *L. donovani* challenged hamsters produced significantly higher Th1-associated cytokines including IFN-γ, TNF-α, and reduced expression of the anti-inflammatory cytokines like IL-10, IL-21, compared to non-immunized challenged animals. ... This study demonstrates that the LmCen−/− parasites are safe and efficacious against VL and is a strong candidate vaccine to be tested in a human clinical trial" (Karmakar *et al.* 2021). This GLP vaccine is scalable and allows easy adaptation to human trials.

Every type of vaccine has pros and cons. Subunit vaccines are preferable for no worries with avirulent strain reversion, but they can be less immunogenic than the attenuated whole cell vaccine. As an example, during the COVID-19 pandemic, although both types are being considered, the subunit vaccines have moved much faster, with RNA and DNA vaccines and some obtaining FDA Emergency Use Authorization (EUA) in under 1 year. [COVID-19 mRNA-based vaccines are the first time that RNA vaccines are used in humans.] COVID-19 subunit vaccines in almost all cases target a single protein, the surface S (spike) protein of SARS-CoV-2, albeit with modification by inserting two proline residues to stabilize the protein from mammalian cellular degradation and to form a stable pre-fusion homotrimer to induce host immunity (Krammer 2020).

The search for potential *Leishmania* vaccines can go via routes of in silico, in vitro, in vivo, or combinations of the 3. A typical *Leishmania* genome codes for about 8,000 proteins (including ones with unknown functions). A conserved, hypothetical protein (LiHyE), suggested as an antigenic marker for both canine and human VL, was cloned after PCR from *L. infantum* DNA and expressed in *Escherichia coli*. The recombinant protein was evaluated regarding its immunogenicity and protective efficacy in mice against *L. infantum* infection. Vaccination with recombinant LiHyE in liposome induced effective protection in the mice, showing reductions of parasite load in spleen, liver and other sites. The protection was associated with Th1 immunity (high IFN-γ, IL-12, GM-CSF; low IL-4, IL-10). Recombinant LiHyE also stimulated lymphoproliferation in treated patients' and healthy subjects' peripheral blood mononuclear cells (PBMCs), with high IFN-γ level. "In conclusion, rLiHyE could be considered for future studies as a vaccine candidate against VL" (Ribeiro *et al.* 2020).

In a second example, there is the finding of a dominant naturally processed peptide (PEPCK 335–351) derived from *Leishmania* glycosomal phosphoenolpyruvate carboxykinase (gPEPCK). PEPCK is conserved in all pathogenic *Leishmania*, expressed in glycosomes of promastigotes and amastigotes, and elicited strong $CD4^+$ T cell response in infected mice and humans to produce IL-2, IFNγ, and TNFα, as Th1 immune response. Experimentally, DNA expressing full-length PEPCK, or rPEPCK peptide induced strong, durable, cross-species protection in both resistant and susceptible mice. Thus, here is a path towards a broadly cross-species protective vaccine against different forms of leishmaniases (Mou *et al.* 2015).

With respect to subunit vaccines for *Leishmania*, functions of most proteins are unknown (open reading frames, ORFs), judicious picking of appropriate targets is a necessity. As an example, Jinlei He (Sichuan University, Chengdu, China) and colleagues applied bioinformatics analytical and epitope prediction tools to 4 *Leishmania donovani* proteins: Amastin, serine/threonine protein phosphatase 2B catalytic subunit A2 (CaNA2), kinetoplastid membrane protein-11 (Kmp-11) and protein disulfide isomerase (PDI). [We have already mentioned that amastin is present in both parasitic trypanosomatids and the free-living *Bodo*.] All 4 proteins are VL vaccine candidates (or possible drug targets). A total of 11 bioinformatics tools were used to analyze different aspects of the proteins, including amino acid composition, topology, signal peptide, secondary structure, surface properties, phosphorylation sites and kinases, protein binding sites, 3D homology modeling, B cell epitopes, MHC class and epitopes and protein-protein interactions. The scientists concluded: "Based on the above findings, we believe that among the pathogen proteins, the proteins with random coil structures, high flexibility, important phosphorylation sites and extensive interaction with other proteins should be the key proteins for drug and vaccine research" (He *et al.* 2019).

"Given the drawbacks with chemotherapy and vector control, a prophylactic vaccine for leishmaniasis is an attractive goal" (Zabala-Penafiel *et al.* 2020). "An ideal anti-leishmanial vaccine should meet following specific criteria: (a) safety, (b) affordability and stability, (c) should provide protective and long-term immunity, (d) stable at room temperature, (e) should be effective as a prophylactic as well as a therapeutic vaccine, (f) should be effective against a wide range of *Leishmania* species, (g) a single dose of vaccine should provide robust and long-lasting immunity. So far, various efforts have been made in order to develop potential and cost-effective vaccines" (Mohebali *et al.* 2019).

A first-in-human dose escalation Phase I trial in 20 healthy volunteers was performed using a third generation vaccine, ChAd63-KH, designed for VL and PKDL. Using the chimpanzee adenovirus 63 (**ChAd63**) as a carrier, containing a synthetic **haspb** gene (hydrophilic acylated surface protein B, synthetic gene encoding the conserved N and C termini bordering 10 repeats, as the haspb contains multiple polymorphic 11–14 AA repeats) inked to a **kmp11** gene (kinetoplast membrane protein 11) via a **viral 2A** sequence (from tetravirus and serves to self-cleavage of the translated bi-protein to 2 separate proteins although ChAd63-KH has been constructed to code a single mRNA). Its role as therapeutic vaccine was previously shown with a similar vaccine (Ad5-KH); a single vaccination inhibited splenic parasite growth by 66% in infected mice. The chimp adeno vaccine was designed to specifically activate $CD8^+$ T cells (cytotoxic T lymphocytes). Phase I trial was successful: ChAd63-KH has effectively elicited IFNγ production in innate response, and robust $CD8^+$ T cell response. "The results of this study support the further development of ChAd63-KH as a novel third generation vaccine for VL and PKDL" (Osman *et al.* 2017).

"Leishmaniasis is widely regarded as a vaccine-preventable disease" (Ashwin *et al.* 2021). One approach under consideration is controlled human infection model (**CHIM**) — a means to provide a pathway for accelerating vaccine development and to more fully understand disease pathogenesis and correlates of protection. The isolation, characterization, and GMP manufacture of 2 clinical strains of *Leishmania major* from Israel have been developed for future CHIM (Ashwin *et al.* 2021).

Someday the vaccine will come. [Very, very soon.]

5.5.9 The trifluralin story

We conclude this chapter on the trypanosomatid protozoa with a personal touch: our research on dinitroaniline herbicides and *Leishmania*. We discovered that the herbicide trifluralin is a chemical compound potentially useful for targeting leishmaniasis. The cytoskeleton of this parasitic protozoan is made up of microtubules, which have become drug targets in cancer (such as taxol) and helminths (mebendazole) (Majumder 2008; Fennell *et al.* 2008; Dostál and Libusová 2014). The subpellicular microtubules covering the *Leishmania* give its shape. *Leishmania* differentiates from the flagellated promastigote to non-motile amastigotes. Using radioactive methionine incorporation to indicate novel protein synthesis, tubulin biosynthesis was shown to correspond to the differentiated state (Fong and Chang 1981). Over a decade ahead of the *Leishmania* genome project, we cloned and sequenced the beta-tubulin gene of *Leishmania mexicana amazonensis* (Fong and Lee 1988). Sequence comparison showed a similarity to plant tubulin instead of animals. This finding led us to identify the herbicide, trifluralin, for the killing of *Leishmania* promastigotes and amastigotes, but not affecting host macrophages (Chan and Fong 1990). Please see Figure 5.17 for tubulin sequence comparison and the chemical structure of trifluralin (Chan and Fong 1994). In vivo trifluralin worked in a murine cutaneous leishmaniasis model (Chan *et al.* 1993a). Trifluralin and related herbicides (such as the more water-soluble oryzalin) showed anti-leishmanial activity, even for drug-resistant variants (Chan *et al.* 1993b; Chan *et al.* 1995). Sublethal dose of oryzalin inhibited promastigote division in vitro, leading to a multi-flagellated round cell (Chan *et al.* 1991). However, the chemical structure of dinitroaniline has been scrutinized as potentially carcinogenic to humans. Not being medicinal chemists, we have not followed up but we maintain a keen interest in this topic. [Maybe a talented reader with expertise in medicinal chemistry and pharmacology can synthesize a mononitoaniline, or another compound, that is potent towards leishmaniasis but not human cells. Such compounds would have potential for other parasitic diseases.]

Following our initial publication, other investigators joined in. Inhibitory activity of dinitroaniline herbicides against different parasitic protozoa have been reported, including *Leishmania donovani* (Carvalheiro *et al.* 2009), *Trypanosoma brucei* (by our collaborators, Chan *et al.* 1993a), *Trypanosoma cruzi* (Zaidenberg *et al.* 2006, but with toxicity, Zaidenberg *et al.* 2007), *Entamoeba histolytica* (Makioka *et al.* 2000), *Naegleria fowleri* (Wang *et al.* 1995), *Plasmodium falciparum* ((Kaidoh *et al.* 1995; Fennell *et al.* 2006; against the liver stage parasite, Dempsey *et al.* 2013; Soleilhac *et al.* 2018), *Toxoplasma gondii* (Stokkermans *et al.* 1996); *Cryptosporidium parvum* (Mead *et al.* 2003) and *Babesia* (Silva *et al.* 2013). Oryzalin-resistant *Toxoplasma* mutants have been isolated and characterized. The affected gene was specific amino acid residual changes in alpha-tubulin (Lyons-Abbott *et al.* 2010; Ma *et al.* 2010; Morrissette 2015). [We cloned and sequenced the *Leishmania* beta-tubulin gene and reported its sequence similarity to the beta-tubulin of *Arabidopsis thaliana*, thale cress, a model used in plant molecular biology.] A novel alkyl phosphocholine-dinitroaniline hybrid molecule inhibits *Leishmania amazonensis* (Godinho *et al.* 2013). Trifluralin analog

```
        1                                                    50
Arabi   MREILHIQGG QCGNQIGAKF WEVVCAEHGI DPTGRYTGDS DLQLERINVY
Leish   MREIVSCQAG QCGNQIGSKF WEVIADEHGV DPTGSYQGDS DLQLERINVY
Human   MREIVHLQAG QCGNQIGAKF WEVISDEHGI DPTGTYHGDS DLQLERINVY

        51                                                  100
Arabi   YNEASCGRFV PRAVLMDLEP GTMDSLRSGP YGQTFRPDNF VFGQSGAGNN
Leish   FDESAGGRYV PRAVLMDLEP GTMDSVRAGP YGQLFRPDNF IFGQSGAGNN
Human   YNEATGGKYV PRAVLVDLEP GTMDSVRSGP FGQIFRPDNF VFGQSGAGNN
                        ^
        101                                                 150
Arabi   WAKGHYTEGA ELIDSVLDVV RKEAENCDCL QGFQVCHSLG GGTGSGMGTL
Leish   WAKGHYTEGA ELIDSVLDVC RKEAESCDCL QGFQLSHSLG GGTGSGMGTL
Human   WAKGHYTEGA ELVDSVLDVV RKEAESCDCL QGFQLTHSLG GGTGSGMGTL
                     ^
        151                                                 200
Arabi   LISKIREEYP DRMMLTFSVF PSPKVSDTVV EPYNATLSVH QLVENADECM
Leish   LISKLREEYP DRIMMTFSVI PSPRVSDTVV EPYNTTLSVH QLVENSDESM
Human   LISKIREEYP DRIMNTFSVV PSPKVSDTVV EPYNATLSVH QLVENTDETY

        201                                                 250
Arabi   VLDNEALYDI CFRTLKLTTP SFGDLNHLIS ATMSGVTCCL RFPGQLNSDL
Leish   CIDNEALYDI CFRTLKLTTP TFGDLNHLVA AVMSGVTCCL RFPGQLNSDL
Human   CIDNEALYDI CFRTLKLTTP TYGDLNHLVS ATMSGVTTCL RFPGQLNADL
                               ^                ^
        251                                                 300
Arabi   R.KLAVNLIP FPRLHFFMVG FAPLTSRGSQ QYR.SLTVPE LTQQMWDSKN
Leish   RNRLAVNLVP FPRLHFFMMG FAPLTSRGSQ EYRQGLSVAD VTQQMFDAKN
Human   R.KLAVNMVP FPRLHFFMPG FAPLTSRGSQ QYR.ALTVPE LTQQMFDAKN

        301                                                 350
Arabi   MMCAADPRHG RYLTASAMFR GKMSTKEVDE QMLNVQNKNS SYFVEWIPNN
Leish   MMQAADPRHG RYLTASALFR GRMSTKEVDE QMLNVQNKNS SYFIEWIPNN
Human   MMAACDPRHG RYLTVAAVFR GRMSMKEVDE QMLNVQNKNS SYFVEWIPNN
            ^          ^          ^
        351                                                 400
Arabi   VKSTVCDIPP TGLKMASTFI GNSTSIQEMF RRVSEQFTAM FRRKAFLHWY
Leish   IKSSICDIPP KGLKMSVTFI GNNTCIQEMF RRVGEQFTGM FRRKRFLHWY
Human   VKTAVCDIPP RGLKMSATFI GNSTAIQELF KRISEQFTAM FRRKAFLHWY
                                         ^ ^
        401                                                 450
Arabi   TGEGMDEMEF TEAESNMNDL VSEYQQYQDA TADEEGDYED EEEGEYQQEE
Leish   TGEGMDEMEF TEAESNMNDL VSEYQQYQDA TVEEEGEFDE EEEAY*....
Human   TGEGMDEMEF TEAESNMNDL VSEYQQYQDA TAEEEGEFEE EAEEEVA*..

        451
Arabi   EY*
Leish   ...
Human   ...
```

Fig. 1. The amino acid sequence of β-tubulin from Arabidopsis thaliana *(Arabi, TUB2)*[44], Leishmania mexicana amazonensis *(Leish)*[7] *and human (Human, β-2)*[45]*. Cys is encoded at position 238 of the* Leishmania *and plant sequences whereas Thr is encoded in the human counterpart; at position 305, Ala is encoded instead of Cys. Arrowheads denote consensus residues showing identity between plants and* Leishmania*, but not with vertebrates*[14]*.*

(A)

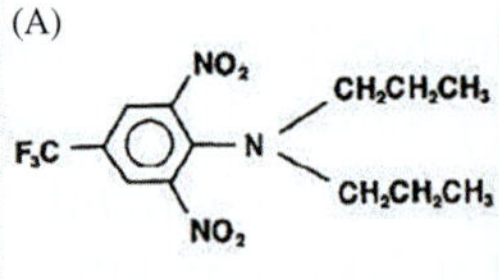

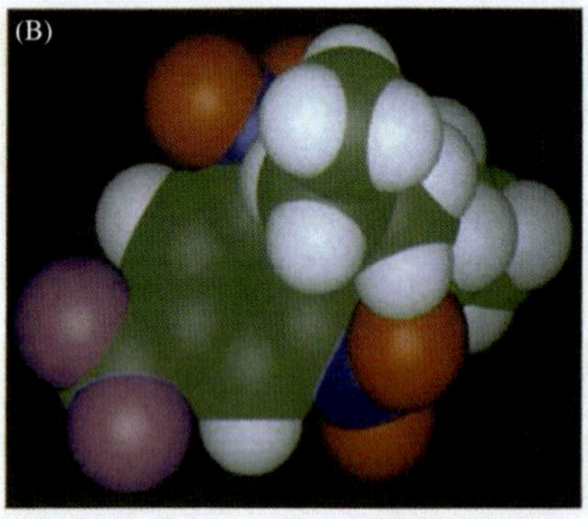

Fig. 2. Chemical formula (a) and molecular model (b) of trifluralin. The molecular modeling program Insight (version 2.0) was used to build the trifluralin molecule. Color code: C, green; F, purple; H, white; N, blue; O, red.

Fig. 5.17 ■ Plant microtubule inhibitors against trypanosomatids. Top. Comparison of β tubulin among species. **Bottom**. Structure of the herbicide trifluralin. Courtesy of the authors. Chan M, Fong D. *Parasitol Today* 1994;10:448–51. Reproduced with permission from Elsevier.

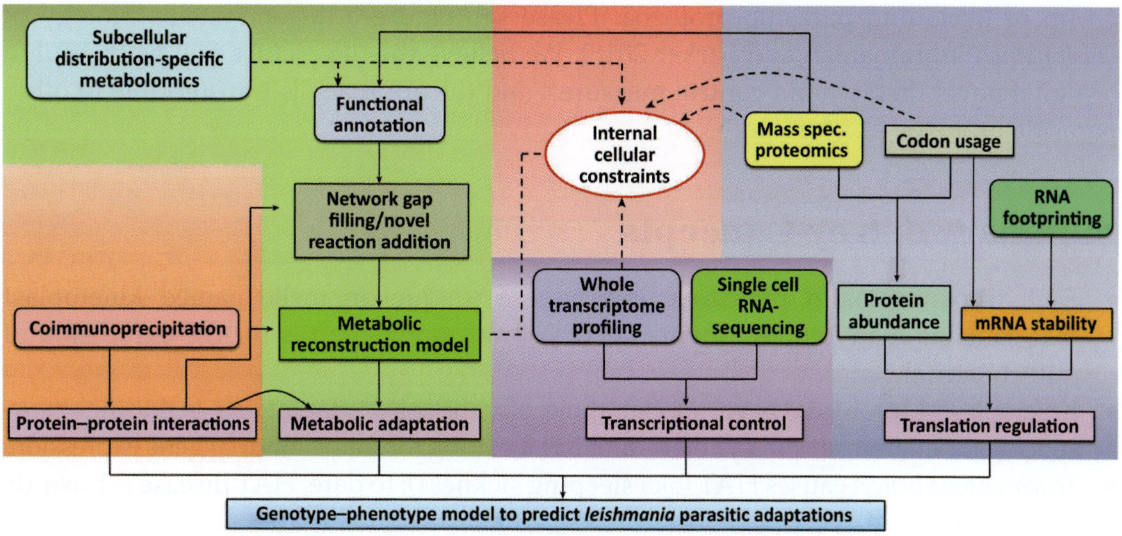

Fig. 5.18 ■ Systems biology of *Leishmania*. Systematic Integration of Discrete Genotype and Phenotype Features (as Obtained from Multi-omics Datasets) for Understanding within-Host Adaptations of the *Leishmania* Parasite. These features represent different levels of biological organization or modules, namely, transcription (purple gradient), translation (blue gradient), protein–protein interactions (orange gradient), and adaptive *Leishmania* metabolism (green gradient). The features from these different modules can be integrated as cellular constraints within a metabolic reconstruction model (broken arrows leading towards the red shaded area and end in the metabolic reconstruction model) and/or as a genotype–phenotype model that can predict associations between different features and their effect on parasite adaptations. Courtesy: Subramanian A, Sarkar R. *Trends Parasitol* 2018;34:1068–81. Reproduced with permission from Elsevier.

within liposomes works in the *Leishmania infantum* infection mouse model (Carvalheiro *et al.* 2015). Extending from parasitic protozoa to metazoans, trifluralin and oryzalin can act against the free-living model nematode *Caenorhabditis elegans*. Both egg and larval development were found to be inhibited by the 2 compounds. Thus, dinitroanilines are promising lead molecules for the development of new compounds for the treatment of helminthiasis (Sant'anna *et al.* 2016).

To recap, there is a definite anti-parasitic protozoal activity in trifluralin and related dinitroaniline compounds. The criteria for approving herbicides by the US Environmental Protection Agency (EPA) and those for human medication by the US Food and Drug Administration (FDA) are different, with the latter more stringent and should be so. [Human cells and organs affected by dinitroaniline herbicides are discussed by Leonard *et al.* (2019).] If it is possible to rid the putative toxic portion by appropriate synthesis, we may still be able to construct an efficacious trifluralin-derived compound to target the parasitic protozoa.

Our trifluralin study is but one small part of research on the *Leishmania* parasite. We end this chapter with a larger view. Current investigations on systems biology of *Leishmania*, from genotypes to phenotypes, will generate a better understanding of this group of intriguing parasitic protozoa. Please see Figure 5.18 for systems biology of *Leishmania* (Subramanian and Sarkar 2018). We believe the big picture will be fruitful in bringing novel therapy and control measures, and the approach is transferrable to other parasitic protozoa and helminths.

Summary & Key Concepts

- Each trypanosomatid protozoan possesses a unique organelle named kinetoplast that contains many copies of circular DNA and its function is for the expression of mitochondrial genes.
- Kinetoplastid protozoa have special molecular biology adaptations including *trans*-splicing for nuclear mRNA synthesis and RNA editing for mitochondrial gene expression.
- *Trypanosoma brucei* causes HAT (aka sleeping sickness); to date, HAT disease is towards elimination.
- HAT is carried by the insect vector tsetse flies (*Glossina* species).
- Antigenic variation of *T. brucei* allows its evasion of host immune response by changing the surface coat protein named variant surface glycoprotein (VSG).
- *Trypanosoma cruzi* causes American trypanosomiasis (AT, aka Chagas' disease); to date there are still many infected as well as an expansion of people at risk.
- AT is carried by the insect vector kissing bugs (*Triatoma* and other species).
- Leishmaniasis is an emerging and re-emerging parasitic disease with three clinical manifestations named cutaneous, mucocutaneous, and visceral leishmaniasis, with about 20 species infecting humans.
- *Leishmania* species are carried by the insect vector sand flies (only the females of *Phlebotomus* and *Lutzomyia* species suck blood).
- Genomic studies indicate a difference of only 200 genes among 3 species of *Leishmania* that show different clinical patterns.
- *Leishmania* exosomes, as well as excretory/secretory products from other parasites, may function in parasite-host interactions and modulate host immune response.
- Leishmanization uses live parasites to prevent cutaneous leishmaniasis; *Leishmania* vaccines are being actively pursued.
- The dinitroaniline herbicide trifluralin and its related compounds have been shown to be active against *Leishmania* and other protozoan parasites. They may have potential for future drug development.

References

Abu Alshamat E, Kweider M, Abbady AQ. Camel nanobodies: Promising molecular tools against leishmaniasis. *Parasite Immunol* 2020;42(9):e12718.

Adapala N, Chan MM. Long-term use of an antiinflammatory, curcumin, suppressed type 1 immunity and exacerbated visceral leishmaniasis in a chronic experimental model. *Lab Invest* 2008;88(12):1329–39.

Adl SM, Bass D, Lane CE, *et al.* Revisions to the classification, nomenclature, and diversity of eukaryotes. *J Eukaryot Microbiol* 2019;66(1):4–119.

Akhoundi M, Kuhls K, Cannet A, *et al.* A historical overview of the classification, evolution, and dispersion of *Leishmania* parasites and sandflies. *PLoS Negl Trop Dis* 2016;10(3):e0004349.

Alcolea PJ, Alonso A, Molina R, Jiménez M, Myler PJ, Larraga V. Functional genomics in sand fly-derived *Leishmania* promastigotes. *PLoS Negl Trop Dis* 2019 May;13(5):e0007288

Alexander J, Brombacher F. T helper1/t helper2 cells and resistance/susceptibility to leishmania infection: is this paradigm still relevant? *Front Immunol* 2012;3:80.

Al-Jawabreh A, Ereqat S, Dumaidi K, *et al.* Case report: Autochthonous case of human visceral Leishmaniasis in the West Bank, Palestine. *Am J Trop Med Hyg* 2020;103(4):1490–92.

Alsford S, Eckert S, Baker N, *et al.* High-throughput decoding of antitrypanosomal drug efficacy and resistance. *Nature* 2012;482(7384):232–6.

Alsmark C, Foster PG, Sicheritz-Ponten T, Nakjang S, Martin Embley T, Hirt RP. Patterns of prokaryotic lateral gene transfers affecting parasitic microbial eukaryotes. *Genome Biol* 2013;14(2):R19.

Alvar J, Vélez ID, Bern C, et al.; WHO Leishmaniasis Control Team. Leishmaniasis worldwide and global estimates of its incidence. *PLoS One* 2012;7(5):e35671.

Añez N, Crisante G. The tissue specific tropism in *Trypanosoma cruzi*. Is it true? *Acta Trop* 2020;213:105736.

Aphasizheva I, Alfonzo J, Carnes J, *et al.* Lexis and grammar of mitochondrial RNA processing in trypanosomes. *Trends Parasitol* 2020;36(4):337–55.

Aquino SR, Diniz LFB, Queiroz IT, *et al.* Case report: Severe visceral Leishmaniasis in a patient with HIV coinfection undergoing treatment for erythema nodosum leprosum. *Am J Trop Med Hyg* 2020;103(6):2253–56.

Araújo A, Reinhard K, Ferreira LF, Pucu E, Chieffi PP. Paleoparasitology: the origin of human parasites. *Arq Neuropsiquiatr*. 2013;71(9B):722–6.

Ashwin H, Sadlova J, Vojtkova B, *et al.* Characterization of a new *Leishmania major* strain for use in a controlled human infection model. *Nat Commun* 2021;12(1):215.

Aslett M, Aurrecoechea C, Berriman M, *et al.* TriTrypDB: A functional genomic resource for the Trypanosomatidae. *Nucleic Acids Res* 2010;38(Database issue):D457–62.

Aurrecoechea C, Barreto A, Basenko EY, *et al.* EuPathDB: The eukaryotic pathogen genomics database resource. *Nucleic Acids Res* 2017;45(D1):D581–91.

Bass BL. *RNA Editing*, Oxford, 2001.

Beatty NL, Klotz SA. autochthonous chagas disease in the united states: how are people getting infected? *Am J Trop Med Hyg* 2020;103(3):967–9.

Beneke T, Gluenz E. Bar-seq strategies for the LeishGEdit toolbox. *Mol Biochem Parasitol* 2020;239:111295.

Berriman M, Ghedin E, Hertz-Fowler C, *et al.* The genome of the African trypanosome *Trypanosoma brucei*. *Science* 2005;309(5733):416–22.

Bitar M, Boroni M, Macedo AM, Machado CR, Franco GR. The spliced leader trans-splicing mechanism in different organisms: Molecular details and possible biological roles. *Front Genet* 2013;4:199.

Boukobza M, Lariven S, Houzé S, Laissy JP. Unusual MRI findings in African *Trypanosoma brucei gambiense* Trypanosomiasis: Dentate nuclei and hypothalamic lesions. *Am J Trop Med Hyg* 2020;102(1):5–6.

Bouyer J. *Glossina palpalis gambiensis* (Tsetse Fly). *Trends Parasitol* 2020;36(10):864–865.

Broadhead R, Dawe HR, Farr H, *et al*. Flagellar motility is required for the viability of the bloodstream trypanosome. *Nature* 2006;440(7081):224–7.

Buhaya MH, Galvan S, Maldonado RA. Incidence of *Trypanosoma cruzi* infection in triatomines collected at Indio Mountains Research Station. *Acta Trop*. 2015;150:97–9.

Burza S, Croft SL, Boelaert M. Leishmaniasis. *Lancet* 2018;392(10151):951–970.

Bustamante JM, Sanchez-Valdez F, Padilla AM, White B, Wang W, Tarleton RL. A modified drug regimen clears active and dormant trypanosomes in mouse models of Chagas disease. *Sci Transl Med* 2020;12(567):eabb7656.

Butenko A, Hammond M, Field MC, Ginger ML, Yurchenko V, Lukeš J. Reductionist pathways for parasitism in euglenozoans? Expanded datasets provide new insights. *Trends Parasitol* 2020:S1471–4922(20)30264–6.

Camacho E, Rastrojo A, Sanchiz Á, González-de la Fuente S, Aguado B, Requena JM. *Leishmania* mitochondrial genomes: Maxicircle structure and heterogeneity of minicircles. *Genes (Basel)* 2019;10(10):758.

Campolina TB, Villegas LEM, Monteiro CC, Pimenta PFP, Secundino NFC. Tripartite interactions: *Leishmania*, microbiota and *Lutzomyia longipalpis*. *PLoS Negl Trop Dis* 2020;14(10):e0008666.

Cantacessi C, Dantas-Torres F, Nolan MJ, Otranto D. The past, present, and future of *Leishmania* genomics and transcriptomics. *Trends Parasitol* 2015;31(3):100–108.

Capewell P, Clucas C, DeJesus E, *et al*. The TgsGP gene is essential for resistance to human serum in *Trypanosoma brucei gambiense*. *PLoS Pathog* 2013;9(10):e1003686.

Capewell P, Cren-Travaillé C, Marchesi F, *et al*. The skin is a significant but overlooked anatomical reservoir for vector-borne African trypanosomes. *Elife* 2016;5:e17716.

Carvalheiro M, Esteves MA, Santos-Mateus D, *et al*. Hemisynthetic trifluralin analogues incorporated in liposomes for the treatment of leishmanial infections. *Eur J Pharm Biopharm* 2015;93:346–52.

Carvalheiro M, Jorge J, Eleutério C, *et al*. Trifluralin liposomal formulations active against *Leishmania donovani* infections. *Eur J Pharm Biopharm* 2009;71(2):292–6.

Castelli G, Bruno F, Saieva L, *et al*. Exosome secretion by *Leishmania infantum* modulate the chemotactic behavior and cytokinic expression creating an environment permissive for early infection. *Exp Parasitol* 2019;198:39–45.

Cayla M, Rojas F, Silvester E, Venter F, Matthews KR. African trypanosomes. *Parasit Vectors* 2019;12(1):190.

Chan MM, Adapala N, Chen C. Peroxisome proliferator-activated receptor-γ-mediated polarization of macrophages in *Leishmania* infection. *PPAR Res* 2012;2012:796235.

Chan MM, Evans KW, Moore AR, Fong D. Peroxisome proliferator-activated receptor (PPAR): Balance for survival in parasitic infections. *J Biomed Biotechnol* 2010;2010:828951.

Chan MM, Fong D. Inhibition of leishmanias but not host macrophages by the antitubulin herbicide trifluralin. *Science* 1990;249(4971):924–6.

Chan MM, Fong D. Plant microtubule inhibitors against trypanosomatids. *Parasitol Today* 1994;10(11):448–51.

Chan MM, Fong D. The interplay of PPARs with parasites and related intracellular pathogens. *PPAR Res* 2012;2012:624845.

Chan MM, Grogl M, Callahan H, Fong D. Efficacy of the herbicide trifluralin against four P-glycoprotein-expressing strains of *Leishmania*. *Antimicrob Agents Chemother* 1995;39(7):1609–11.

Chan MM, Grogl M, Chen CC, Bienen EJ, Fong D. Herbicides to curb human parasitic infections: In vitro and in vivo effects of trifluralin on the trypanosomatid protozoans. *Proc Natl Acad Sci U S A* 1993a;90(12):5657–61.

Chan MM, Triemer RE, Fong Effect of the anti-microtubule drug oryzalin on growth and differentiation of the parasitic protozoan *Leishmania mexicana*. *Differentiation* 1991;46(1):15–21.

Chan MM, Tzeng J, Emge TJ, Ho CT, Fong D. Structure-function analysis of antimicrotubule dinitroanilines against promastigotes of the parasitic protozoan Leishmania mexicana. *Antimicrob Agents Chemother* 1993b Sep;37(9):1909–13.

Classon C, Feng X, Eidsmo L, Nylén S. Intestinal nematode infection exacerbates experimental visceral leishmaniasis. *Parasite Immunol* 2019;41(4):e12618.

Clayton C. Regulation of gene expression in trypanosomatids: living with polycistronic transcription. *Open Biol* 2019;9(6):190072.

Conter CC, Mota CA, Dos Santos BA, *et al.* PCR primers designed for new world *Leishmania*: A systematic review. *Exp Parasitol* 2019;207:107773

Cook GC. *Tropical Medicine: An Illustrated History of the Pioneers*, Elsevier, 2007.

Córdoba-Aguilar A. Chagas bugs and *Trypanosoma cruzi*: Puppets and puppeteer? *Acta Trop* 2020;211:105600. (capital Trypanosoma)

Corrêa Soares GH, Silva ABSD, *et al.* Case Report: Coinfection by *Leishmania amazonensis* and HIV in a Brazilian diffuse cutaneous Leishmaniasis patient. *Am J Trop Med Hyg* 2020;103(3):1076–1080.

Coughlan S, Mulhair P, Sanders M, Schonian G, Cotton JA, Downing T. The genome of *Leishmania adleri* from a mammalian host highlights chromosome fission in *Sauroleishmania*. *Sci Rep* 2017;7:43747

Coura JR. The main sceneries of Chagas disease transmission. The vectors, blood and oral transmissions — A comprehensive review. *Mem Inst Oswaldo Cruz* 2015;110(3):277–82.

Cox FE. History of human parasitology. *Clin Microbiol Rev* 2002;15(4):595–612.

Cox, F.E.G. (ed). *The Wellcome Trust Illustrated History of Tropical Diseases*. The Wellcome Trust. London, 1996.

Cross GA, Kim HS, Wickstead B. Capturing the variant surface glycoprotein repertoire (the VSGnome) of *Trypanosoma brucei* Lister 427. *Mol Biochem Parasitol* 2014;195(1):59–73.

Cruz RE, Macedo AM, Barnabé C, *et al.* Further genetic characterization of the two *Trypanosoma cruzi* Berenice strains (Be-62 and Be-78) isolated from the first human case of Chagas disease (Chagas, 1909). *Acta Trop* 2006;97(3):239–46

da Costa CA, de Toledo VP, enaro O, Williams P, Mayrink W. Montenegro skin test — Evaluation of the composition and stability of the antigen preparation. *Mem Inst Oswaldo Cruz* 1996;91(2):193–4.

Dantas-Torres F, Miró G, Bowman DD, Gradoni L, Otranto D. Culling dogs for zoonotic visceral Leishmaniasis control: The wind of change. *Trends Parasitol* 2019;35(2):97–101.

Dempsey E, Prudêncio M, Fennell BJ, Gomes-Santos CS, Barlow JW, Bell A. Antimitotic herbicides bind to an unidentified site on malarial parasite tubulin and block development of liver-stage *Plasmodium* parasites. *Mol Biochem Parasitol* 2013;188(2):116–27.

Dhariwal A, Jawad S, Bicanic T. Case report: Visceral Leishmaniasis falsely diagnosed as Q fever. *Am J Trop Med Hyg* 2020;103(5):1927–29.

Domagalska MA, Dujardin JC. Next-generation molecular surveillance of TriTryp diseases. *Trends Parasitol* 2020;36(4):356–67.

Dong G, Filho AL, Olivier M. Modulation of host-pathogen communication by extracellular vesicles (EVs) of the protozoan parasite *Leishmania*. *Front Cell Infect Microbiol* 2019;9:100.

Dostál V, Libusová L. Microtubule drugs: Action, selectivity, and resistance across the kingdoms of life. *Protoplasma* 2014;251(5):991–1005.

Downing T, Imamura H, Decuypere S, *et al.* Whole genome sequencing of multiple *Leishmania donovani* clinical isolates provides insights into population structure and mechanisms of drug resistance. *Genome Res* 2011 Dec;21(12):2143–56.

El-Sayed NM, Myler PJ, Bartholomeu DC, *et al.* The genome sequence of *Trypanosoma cruzi,* etiologic agent of Chagas disease. *Science* 2005;309(5733):409–15.

Esch GW. *Parasites and Infectious Disease,* Cambridge, 2007.

Esteves MA, Fragiadaki I, Lopes R, Scoulica E, Cruz ME. Synthesis and biological evaluation of trifluralin analogues as antileishmanial agents. *Bioorg Med Chem* 2010;18(1):274–81.

Fairlamb AH, Horn D. Melarsoprol resistance in African Trypanosomiasis. *Trends Parasitol* 2018;34(6):481–92.

Fairlamb AH. Infectious disease: Genomics decodes drug action. *Nature* 2012;482(7384):167–9.

Fennell B, Naughton J, Barlow J, *et al.* Microtubules as antiparasitic drug targets. *Expert Opin Drug Discov* 2008;3(5):501–18.

Fennell BJ, Naughton JA, Dempsey E, Bell A. Cellular and molecular actions of dinitroaniline and phosphorothioamidate herbicides on *Plasmodium falciparum*: Tubulin as a specific antimalarial target. *Mol Biochem Parasitol* 2006;145(2):226–38.

Fiebig M, Kelly S, Gluenz E. Comparative life cycle transcriptomics revises *Leishmania mexicana* genome annotation and links a chromosome duplication with parasitism of vertebrates. *PLoS Pathog* 2015;11(10):e1005186

Figueiredo LP, Almeida LDC, Magalhães A, Arruda S, Lessa MM, Carvalho EM. Case report: Unusual presentation of pharyngeal mucosal Leishmaniasis due to *Leishmania* (*Viannia*) *braziliensis*. *Am J Trop Med Hyg* 2020;103(4):1493–95.

Flávia Nardy A, Freire-de-Lima CG, Morrot A. Immune evasion strategies of *Trypanosoma cruzi*. *J Immunol Res* 2015;2015:178947.

Flegontov P, Butenko A, Firsov S, *et al.* Genome of *Leptomonas pyrrhocoris*: A high-quality reference for monoxenous trypanosomatids and new insights into evolution of Leishmania. *Sci Rep* 2016;6:23704.

Flores-López CA, Machado CA. Analyses of 32 loci clarify phylogenetic relationships among *Trypanosoma cruzi* lineages and support a single hybridization prior to human contact. *PLoS Negl Trop Dis* 2011;5(8):e1272.

Fong D, Calhoun DH, Hsieh WT, Lee B, Wells RD. Isolation of a cDNA clone for the human lysosomal proteinase cathepsin B. *Proc Natl Acad Sci U S A* 1986;83(9):2909–13.

Fong D, Chan MM, Rodriguez R, Gately LJ, Berman JD, Grogl M. Paromomycin resistance in *Leishmania tropica*: lack of correlation with mutation in the small subunit ribosomal RNA gene. *Am J Trop Med Hyg* 1994;51(6):758–66.

Fong D, Chang KP. Tubulin biosynthesis in the developmental cycle of a parasitic protozoan, *Leishmania mexicana*: Changes during differentiation of motile and nonmotile stages. *Proc Natl Acad Sci U S A* 1981;78(12):7624–8.

Fong D, Lee B. Beta tubulin gene of the parasitic protozoan *Leishmania mexicana*. *Mol Biochem Parasitol* 1988;31(1):97–106.

Gao JM, Qian ZY, Hide G, Lai DH, Lun ZR, Wu ZD. Human African trypanosomiasis: The current situation in endemic regions and the risks for non-endemic regions from imported cases. *Parasitology* 2020;147(9):922–31.

Gedda MR, Singh B, Kumar D, Singh AK, Madhukar P, Upadhyay S, Singh OP, Sundar S. Post kala-azar dermal leishmaniasis: A threat to elimination program. *PLoS Negl Trop Dis* 2020;14(7):e0008221.

Genovese G, Friedman DJ, Ross MD, *et al.* Association of trypanolytic ApoL1 variants with kidney disease in African Americans. *Science* 2010;329(5993):841–5.

Ghosh P, Bhaskar KR, Hossain F, *et al.* Evaluation of diagnostic performance of rK28 ELISA using urine for diagnosis of visceral leishmaniasis. *Parasit Vectors* 2016;9(1):383.

Godinho JL, Georgikopoulou K, Calogeropoulou T, de Souza W, Rodrigues JC. A novel alkyl phosphocholine-dinitroaniline hybrid molecule exhibits biological activity in vitro against *Leishmania amazonensis*. *Exp Parasitol* 2013;135(1):153–65.

Günzl A. The pre-mRNA splicing machinery of trypanosomes: complex or simplified? *Eukaryot Cell* 2010;9(8):1159–70.

Halliday C, Billington K, Wang Z, *et al.* Cellular landmarks of *Trypanosoma brucei* and *Leishmania mexicana*. *Mol Biochem Parasitol* 2019;230:24–36.

He J, Huang F, Li J, Chen Q, Chen D, Chen J. Bioinformatics analysis of four proteins of *Leishmania donovani* to guide epitopes vaccine design and drug targets selection. *Acta Trop* 2019;191:50–59.

Hegner, R. *Big fleas have little fleas; or, Who's who among the protozoa.* Baltimore, The Williams & Wilkins Company, 1938. https://hdl.handle.net/2027/uva.x002081533

Heinzel FP, Sadick MD, Holaday BJ, Coffman RL, Locksley RM. Reciprocal expression of interferon gamma or interleukin 4 during the resolution or progression of murine leishmaniasis. Evidence for expansion of distinct helper T cell subsets. *J Exp Med* 1989;169(1):59–72.

Hotez P. *Forgotten People, Forgotten Diseases: The Neglected Tropical Diseases and Their Impact on Global Health and Development*, 2nd ed. ASM Press, 2013.

Ibarra-Meneses AV, Moreno J, Carrillo E. New strategies and biomarkers for the control of visceral Leishmaniasis. *Trends Parasitol* 2020;36(1):29–38.

Ibarra-Meneses AV, Sanchez C, Alvar J, Moreno J, Carrillo E. Monocyte chemotactic protein 1 in plasma from soluble *Leishmania* antigen-stimulated whole blood as a potential biomarker of the cellular immune response to *Leishmania infantum*. *Front Immunol* 2017;8:1208.

Ivens AC, Peacock CS, Worthey EA, *et al.* The genome of the kinetoplastid parasite, *Leishmania major*. *Science* 2005;309(5733):436–42.

Ives A, Ronet C, Prevel F, *et al.* *Leishmania* RNA virus controls the severity of mucocutaneous leishmaniasis. *Science* 2011;331(6018):775–8.

Jackson AP, Otto TD, Aslett M, *et al.* Kinetoplastid phylogenomics reveals the evolutionary innovations associated with the origins of parasitism. *Curr Biol* 2016;26(2):161–72.

Jackson AP, Sanders M, Berry A, *et al.* The genome sequence of *Trypanosoma brucei gambiense*, causative agent of chronic human african trypanosomiasis. *PLoS Negl Trop Dis* 2010;4(4):e658.

Jamonneau V, Ilboudo H, Kaboré J, *et al.* Untreated human infections by *Trypanosoma brucei gambiense* are not 100% fatal. *PLoS Negl Trop Dis* 2012;6(6):e1691.

Jamonneau V, Truc P, Grébaut P, *et al.* *Trypanosoma brucei gambiense* group 2: The unusual suspect. *Trends Parasitol* 2019;35(12):983–95.

Jones LB, Bell CR, Bibb KE, Gu L, Coats MT, Matthews QL. Pathogens and their effect on exosome biogenesis and composition. *Biomedicines* 2018;6(3)pii:E79.

Kaidoh T, Nath J, Fujioka H, Okoye V, Aikawa M. Effect and localization of trifluralin in *Plasmodium falciparum* gametocytes: an electron microscopic study. *J Eukaryot Microbiol.* 1995;42(1):61–4.

Kamhawi S, Serafim TD. *Leishmania:* A maestro in epigenetic manipulation of macrophage inflammasomes. *Trends Parasitol* 2020;36(6):498–501.

Karmakar S, Ismail N, Oliveira F, *et al.*, Preclinical validation of a live attenuated dermotropic *Leishmania* vaccine against vector transmitted fatal visceral leishmaniasis. *Commun Biol.* 2021;4(1):929

Kazanjian PH. *Frederick Novy and the Development of Bacteriology in Medicine.* Rutgers, New Brunswick, 2017.

Kean BH, Mott KE, Russell AJ (eds.). *Tropical Medicine and Parasitology. Classic Investigations.* Volume I and II, Cornell, Ithaca, 1978.

Kelly S, Ivens A, Manna PT, Gibson W, Field MC. A draft genome for the African crocodilian trypanosome *Trypanosoma grayi. Sci Data* 2014;1:140024.

Khare S, Nagle AS, Biggart A, *et al.* Proteasome inhibition for treatment of leishmaniasis, Chagas disease and sleeping sickness. *Nature* 2016;537(7619):229–33.

Killick-Kendrick R. The race to discover the insect vector of kala-azar: A great saga of tropical medicine 1903–1942. *Bull Soc Pathol Exot* 2013;106(2):131–7.

Kipp EJ, de Almeida M, Marcet PL, *et al.* An atypical case of autochthonous cutaneous Leishmaniasis associated with naturally infected phlebotomine sand flies in Texas, United States. *Am J Trop Med Hyg* 2020;103(4):1496–501.

Koné M, N'Gouan EK, Kaba D, *et al.* The complex health seeking pathway of a human African trypanosomiasis patient in Côte d'Ivoire underlines the need of setting up passive surveillance systems. *PLoS Negl Trop Dis* 2020;14(9):e0008588.

Kořený L, Sobotka R, Kovářová J, *et al.* Aerobic kinetoplastid flagellate *Phytomonas* does not require heme for viability. *Proc Natl Acad Sci U S A* 2012;109(10):3808–13.

Krammer F. SARS-CoV-2 vaccines in development. *Nature* 2020;586(7830):516–27.

Krasner RI. *20th Century Microbe Hunters.* Jones & Bartlett, Boston, 2008.

Kratz JM. Drug discovery for chagas disease: A viewpoint. *Acta Trop* 2019;198:105107.

Kumar A, Pandey SC, Samant M. A spotlight on the diagnostic methods of a fatal disease visceral Leishmaniasis. *Parasite Immunol* 2020:e12727.

Lamb T (ed). *Immunity to Parasitic Infection*, Wiley, 2012.

Lasda EL, Blumenthal T. Trans-splicing. *Wiley Interdiscip Rev RNA* 2011;2(3):417–34.

Lecoeur H, Prina E, Rosazza T, *et al.* Targeting macrophage histone h3 modification as a *Leishmania* strategy to dampen the NF-kappaB/NLRP3-mediated inflammatory response. *Cell Rep* 2020;30(6):1870–82.

Leonard JA, Nelms M, Craig E, *et al.* A weight of evidence approach to investigate potential common mechanisms in pesticide groups to support cumulative risk assessment: A case study with dinitroaniline pesticides. *Regul Toxicol Pharmacol* 2019;107:104419.

Lidani KCF, Andrade FA, Bavia L, *et al.* Chagas disease: From discovery to a worldwide health problem. *Front Public Health* 2019;7:166.

Llanes A, Restrepo CM, Del Vecchio G, Anguizola FJ, Lleonart R. The genome of *Leishmania panamensis:* Insights into genomics of the L. (Viannia) subgenus. *Sci Rep* 2015;5:8550.

Lyons-Abbott S, Sackett DL, Wloga D, *et al.* α-Tubulin mutations alter oryzalin affinity and microtubule assembly properties to confer dinitroaniline resistance. *Eukaryot Cell* 2010 Dec;9(12):1825–34.

Ma C, Tran J, Gu F, *et al.* Dinitroaniline activity in *Toxoplasma gondii* expressing wild-type or mutant alpha-tubulin. *Antimicrob Agents Chemother* 2010;54(4):1453–60.

Magill AJ, Grögl M, Gasser RA Jr, Sun W, Oster CN. Visceral infection caused by *Leishmania tropica* in veterans of Operation Desert Storm. *N Engl J Med* 1993;328(19):1383–7.

Majumder HK (ed). *Drug Targets in Kinetoplastid Parasites. Advances in Experimental Medicine and Biology Vel 625*. Springer, New York, Landes, Austin, 2008.

Makioka A, Kumagai M, Ohtomo H, Kobayashi S, Takeuchi T. Effect of dinitroaniline herbicides on the growth of *Entamoeba histolytica*. *J Parasitol* 2000;86(3):607–10.

Mann S, Phupitakphol T, Davis B, *et al*. Case report: Cutaneous Leishmaniasis due to *Leishmania (Viannia) panamensis* in two travelers successfully treated with miltefosine. *Am J Trop Med Hyg* 2020;103(3):1081–4.

Marr JJ, Nilson TW, Komuniecki RW. *Molecular Medical Parasitology*. Academic Press, 2003.

Matthews KR. 25 years of African trypanosome research: From description to molecular dissection and new drug discovery. *Mol Biochem Parasitol* 2015;200(1–2):30–40.

Mead JR, Fauq AH, Khan MA, McNair N. Efficacy of glycoconjugated dinitroanilines against *Cryptosporidium parvum*. *J Eukaryot Microbiol* 2003;50 Suppl:550–2.

Mehlhorn H. *Human Parasites: Diagnosis, Treatment, Prevention*. Springer, 2016.

Mensa-Wilmot K, Hoffman B, Wiedeman J, Sullenberger C, Sharma A. Kinetoplast division factors in a Trypanosome. *Trends Parasitol* 2019;35(2):119–128.

Mesu VKBK, Kalonji WM, Bardonneau C, *et al*. Oral fexinidazole for late-stage African *Trypanosoma brucei gambiense* trypanosomiasis: A pivotal multicentre, randomised, non-inferiority trial. *Lancet* 2018;391(10116):144–154. Erratum in: *Lancet* 2018;391(10116): 124.

Ming LC, Hussain Z, Yeoh SF, Koh D, Lee KS. Circulating vaccine-derived poliovirus: A menace to the end game of polio eradication. *Global Health* 2020;16(1):63.

Mohebali M, Nadim A, Khamesipour A. An overview of leishmanization experience: A successful control measure and a tool to evaluate candidate vaccines. *Acta Trop* 2019;200:105173.

Moretti NS, Mortara RA, Schenkman S. *Trypanosoma cruzi*. *Trends Parasitol* 2020;36(4):404–405.

Morgan E, Varro R, Sepulveda H, *et al*. Cytometric bead array: A multiplexed assay platform with applications in various areas of biology. *Clin Immunol* 2004;110(3):252–66.

Morrissette N. Targeting *Toxoplasma* tubules: tubulin, microtubules, and associated proteins in a human pathogen. *Eukaryot Cell* 2015;14(1):2–12.

Mou Z, Li J, Boussoffara T, *et al*. Identification of broadly conserved cross-species protective *Leishmania* antigen and its responding $CD4^+$ T cells. *Sci Transl Med* 2015;7(310):310ra167

Moulik S, Sengupta S, Chatterjee M. Molecular tracking of the *Leishmania* parasite. *Front Cell Infect Microbiol* 2021;11:623437.

Müller LSM, Cosentino RO, Förstner KU, *et al*. Genome organization and DNA accessibility control antigenic variation in trypanosomes. *Nature* 2018;563(7729):121–5.

Murray HW, Eiras DP, Kirkman LA, Chai RL, Caplivski D. Case report: Mucosal Leishmaniasis in New York City. *Am J Trop Med Hyg* 2020;102(6):1319–22.

Nawaz M, Malik MI, Hameed M, Zhou J. Research progress on the composition and function of parasite-derived exosomes. *Acta Trop* 2019;196:30–36.

Nzelu CO, Kato H, Peters NC. Loop-mediated isothermal amplification (LAMP): An advanced molecular point-of-care technique for the detection of Leishmania infection. *PLoS Negl Trop Dis* 2019;13(11):e0007698.

Osman M, Mistry A, Keding A, et al. A third generation vaccine for human visceral leishmaniasis and post kala azar dermal Leishmaniasis: First-in-human trial of ChAd63-KH. *PLoS Negl Trop Dis* 2017;11(5):e0005527.

Pandey SC, Kumar A, Samant M. Genetically modified live attenuated vaccine: A potential strategy to combat visceral leishmaniasis. *Parasite Immunol* 2020;42(9):e12732.

Patterson S, Wyllie S. Nitro drugs for the treatment of trypanosomatid diseases: Past, present, and future prospects. *Trends Parasitol* 2014;30(6):289–98.

Peacock CS, Seeger K, Harris D, *et al.* Comparative genomic analysis of three *Leishmania* species that cause diverse human disease. *Nat Genet* 2007;39(7):839–47.

Peacock L, Bailey M, Carrington M, Gibson W. Meiosis and haploid gametes in the pathogen *Trypanosoma brucei. Curr Biol* 2014;24(2):181–6.

Pessenda G, da Silva JS. Arginase and its mechanisms in *Leishmania* persistence. *Parasite Immunol* 2020;42(7):e12722.

Poinar G Jr, Poinar R. *Paleoleishmania proterus* n. gen., n. sp., (Trypanosomatidae: Kinetoplastida) from Cretaceous Burmese amber. *Protist* 2004;155(3):305–10.

Porcel BM, Denoeud F, Opperdoes F, *et al.* The streamlined genome of *Phytomonas* spp. relative to human pathogenic kinetoplastids reveals a parasite tailored for plants. *PLoS Genet* 2014;10(2):e1004007.

Raj S, Sasidharan S, Balaji SN, Saudagar P. An overview of biochemically characterized drug targets in metabolic pathways of *Leishmania* parasite. *Parasitol Res* 2020;119(7):2025–37.

Rajão MA, Furtado C, Alves CL, *et al.* Unveiling benznidazole's mechanism of action through overexpression of DNA repair proteins in *Trypanosoma cruzi. Environ Mol Mutagen* 2014;55(4):309–21.

Ramírez-González MG, Flores-Villegas AL, Salazar-Schettino PM, Gutiérrez-Cabrera AE, Rojas-Ortega E, Córdoba-Aguilar A. Zombie bugs? Manipulation of kissing bug behavior by the parasite *Trypanosoma cruzi. Acta Trop* 2019;200:105177.

Ramírez-Toloza G, Sosoniuk-Roche E, Valck C, Aguilar-Guzmán L, Ferreira VP, Ferreira A. *Trypanosoma cruzi* Calreticulin: Immune evasion, infectivity, and tumorigenesis. *Trends Parasitol* 2020;36(4):368–81.

Raymond F, Boisvert S, Roy G, *et al.* Genome sequencing of the lizard parasite *Leishmania tarentolae* reveals loss of genes associated to the intracellular stage of human pathogenic species. *Nucleic Acids Res* 2012;40(3):1131–47.

Real F, Vidal RO, Carazzolle MF, *et al.* The genome sequence of *Leishmania (Leishmania) amazonensis:* Functional annotation and extended analysis of gene models. *DNA Res* 2013;20(6):567–81.

Real F. Isolation of intact *Leishmania amazonensis* large parasitophorous vacuoles from infected macrophages by density gradient fractionation. *Exp Parasitol* 2020;218:107989.

Ribeiro PAF, Dias DS, Lage DP, *et al.* Evaluation of the protective efficacy of a *Leishmania* protein associated with distinct adjuvants against visceral leishmaniasis and in vitro immunogenicity in human cells. *Parasitol Res* 2020;119(8):2609–22.

Rogers MB, Hilley JD, Dickens NJ, *et al.* Chromosome and gene copy number variation allow major structural change between species and strains of *Leishmania. Genome Res* 2011;21(12): 2129–42.

Romano A, Inbar E, Debrabant A, *et al.* Cross-species genetic exchange between visceral and cutaneous strains of *Leishmania* in the sand fly vector. *Proc Natl Acad Sci U S A* 2014;111(47):16808–13.

Romero-Meza G, Mugnier MR. *Trypanosoma brucei. Trends Parasitol* 2020;36(6):571–2.

Sant'Anna MR, Diaz-Albiter H, Aguiar-Martins K, *et al.* Colonisation resistance in the sand fly gut: *Leishmania* protects *Lutzomyia longipalpis* from bacterial infection. *Parasit Vectors* 2014;7:329.

Sant'anna V, de Souza W, Vommaro RC. Anthelmintic effect of herbicidal dinitroanilines on the nematode model *Caenorhabditis elegans. Exp Parasitol* 2016;167:43–9.

Sarıgöl Kılıç Z, Aydın S, Ündeğer Bucurgat Ü, Başaran N. In vitro genotoxicity assessment of dinitroaniline herbicides pendimethalin and trifluralin. *Food Chem Toxicol* 2018;113:90–98.

Schwede A, Carrington M. Bloodstream form Trypanosome plasma membrane proteins: antigenic variation and invariant antigens. *Parasitology* 2010;137(14):2029–39.

Schwing A, Pomares C, Majoor A, Boyer L, Marty P, Michel G. *Leishmania* infection: Misdiagnosis as cancer and tumor-promoting potential. *Acta Trop* 2019;197:104855.

Serafim TD, Iniguez E, Oliveira F. *Leishmania infantum. Trends Parasitol* 2020;36(1):80–81.

Serghides L. The case for the use of PPARγ agonists as an adjunctive therapy for cerebral malaria. *PPAR Res* 2012;2012:513865.

Sharma R, Gluenz E, Peacock L, Gibson W, Gull K, Carrington M. The heart of darkness: Growth and form of *Trypanosoma brucei* in the tsetse fly. *Trends Parasitol* 2009;25(11):517–24.

Silva MG, Domingos A, Esteves MA, Cruz ME, Suarez CE. Evaluation of the growth-inhibitory effect of trifluralin analogues on in vitro cultured *Babesia bovis* parasites. *Int J Parasitol Drugs Drug Resist* 2013;3:59–68.

Simpson L, Douglass SM, Lake JA, Pellegrini M, Li F. Comparison of the mitochondrial genomes and steady state transcriptomes of two strains of the Trypanosomatid parasite, *Leishmania tarentolae. PLoS Negl Trop Dis* 2015;9(7):e0003841.

Sinclair AN, de Graffenried CL. More than microtubules: The structure and function of the subpellicular array in Trypanosomatids. *Trends Parasitol* 2019;35(10):760–77.

Siqueira-Neto JL, Debnath A, McCall LI, *et al.* Cysteine proteases in protozoan parasites. *PLoS Negl Trop Dis* 2018;12(8):e0006512.

Soleilhac E, Brillet-Guéguen L, Roussel V, *et al*. Specific targeting of plant and apicomplexa parasite tubulin through differential screening using in silico and assay-based approaches. *Int J Mol Sci* 2018;19(10):3085.

Steverding D. The development of drugs for treatment of sleeping sickness: A historical review. *Parasit Vectors* 2010;3(1):15.

Steverding D. The history of African trypanosomiasis. *Parasit Vectors* 2008;1(1):3.

Steverding D. The history of Chagas disease. *Parasit Vectors* 2014;7:317.

Steverding D. The history of leishmaniasis. *Parasit Vectors* 2017;10(1):82.

Stockdale C, Swiderski MR, Barry JD, McCulloch R. Antigenic variation in *Trypanosoma brucei:* Joining the DOTs. *PLoS Biol* 2008 Jul 29;6(7):e185.

Stoco PH, Wagner G, Talavera-Lopez C, *et al.*Genome of the avirulent human-infective trypanosome — *Trypanosoma rangeli. PLoS Negl Trop Dis* 2014;8(9):e3176.

Stokkermans TJ, Schwartzman JD, Keenan K, Morrissette NS, Tilney LG, Roos DS. Inhibition of *Toxoplasma gondii* replication by dinitroaniline herbicides. *Exp Parasitol* 1996;84(3):355–70.

Subramanian A, Sarkar RR. Perspectives on *Leishmania* species and stage-specific adaptive mechanisms. *Trends Parasitol* 2018;34(12):1068–81.

Teixeira DE, Benchimol M, Rodrigues JC, Crepaldi PH, Pimenta PF, de Souza W. The cell biology of *Leishmania:* How to teach using animations. *PLoS Pathog* 2013;9(10):e1003594.

Torr SJ, Vale GA. Know your foe: Lessons from the analysis of tsetse fly behaviour. *Trends Parasitol* 2015;31(3):95–9.

Trindade S, Rijo-Ferreira F, Carvalho T, *et al. Trypanosoma brucei* parasites occupy and functionally adapt to the adipose tissue in mice. *Cell Host Microbe* 2016;19(6):837–48.

Valdivia HO, Almeida LV, Roatt BM, *et al.* Comparative genomics of canine-isolated *Leishmania (Leishmania) amazonensis* from an endemic focus of visceral leishmaniasis in Governador Valadares, southeastern Brazil. *Sci Rep* 2017;7:40804.

Valero NNH, Uriarte M. Environmental and socioeconomic risk factors associated with visceral and cutaneous leishmaniasis: A systematic review. *Parasitol Res* 2020;119(2):365–84.

Vechi HT, Sousa ASV, Cunha MAD, Shaw JJ, Luz KG. Case report: Combination therapy with liposomal amphotericin B, N-methyl meglumine antimoniate, and pentamidine isethionate for disseminated visceral leishmaniasis in a splenectomized adult patient. *Am J Trop Med Hyg* 2020;102(2):268–73.

Velez R, Domenech E, Cairó J, Gállego M. The impact of canine leishmaniasis vaccination with Canileish® in *Leishmania infantum* infection seroprevalence studies. *Acta Trop* 2020;202:105259.

Vesteg M, Hadariová L, Horváth A, Estraño CE, Schwartzbach SD, Krajčovič J. Comparative molecular cell biology of phototrophic euglenids and parasitic trypanosomatids sheds light on the ancestor of Euglenozoa. *Biol Rev Camb Philos Soc* 2019;94(5):1701–21.

Vijayakumar S, Kant V, Das P. LeishInDB: A web-accessible resource for small molecule inhibitors against *Leishmania* sp. *Acta Trop* 2019;190:375–9.

Walochnik, J, Duchene, M (eds). *Molecular Parasitology: Protozoan Parasites and Their Molecules.* Springer, 2016.

Wang A, Band RN, Kopachik W. Effects of trifluralin on growth and differentiation of the amoeboflagellate *Naegleria. FEMS Microbiol Lett* 1995;127:99–103.

Weatherly DB, Boehlke C, Tarleton RL. Chromosome level assembly of the hybrid *Trypanosoma cruzi* genome. *BMC Genomics* 2009;10:255.

Williams E, Isles NS, Seemann T, *et al.* Case report: Confirmation by metagenomic sequencing of visceral Leishmaniasis in an immunosuppressed returned traveler. *Am J Trop Med Hyg* 2020;103(5):1930–33.

Wiser MF. *Protozoa and Human Disease*. Garland, 2011.

Wu M, Wang G, Hu W, Yao Y, Yu XF. Emerging roles and therapeutic value of exosomes in cancer metastasis. *Mol Cancer* 2019;18(1):53.

Wu Z, Wang L, Li J, Wang L, Wu Z, Sun X. Extracellular vesicle-mediated communication within host-parasite interactions. *Front Immunol* 2019;9:3066.

Wyllie S, Thomas M, Patterson S, *et al.* Cyclin-dependent kinase 12 is a drug target for visceral leishmaniasis. *Nature* 2018;560(7717):192–7.

Zabala-Peñafiel A, Todd D, Daneshvar H, Burchmore R. The potential of live attenuated vaccines against cutaneous Leishmaniasis. *Exp Parasitol* 2020;210:107849.

Zaidenberg A, Luong T, Lirussi D, *et al.* Treatment of experimental chronic chagas disease with trifluralin. *Basic Clin Pharmacol Toxicol* 2006;98(4):351–6.

Zaidenberg A, Marra C, Luong T, *et al.* Trifluralin toxicity in a Chagas disease mouse model. *Basic Clin Pharmacol Toxicol* 2007;101(2):90–5.

Zhang WW, McCall LI, Matlashewski G. Role of cytosolic glyceraldehyde-3-phosphate dehydrogenase in visceral organ infection by *Leishmania donovani. Eukaryot Cell* 2013;12(1):70–7.

Zhang WW, Peacock CS, Matlashewski G. A genomic-based approach combining in vivo selection in mice to identify a novel virulence gene in *Leishmania. PLoS Negl Trop Dis* 2008;2(6):e248.

Zheng Z, Chen J, Ma G, Satoskar AR, Li J. Integrative genomic, proteomic and phenotypic studies of *Leishmania donovani* strains revealed genetic features associated with virulence and antimony-resistance. *Parasit Vectors* 2020;13(1):510.

Zídková L, Cepicka I, Szabová J, Svobodová M. Biodiversity of avian trypanosomes. *Infect Genet Evol* 2012;12(1):102–12.

Zimmer SL, Simpson RM, Read LK. High throughput sequencing revolution reveals conserved fundamentals of U-indel editing. *Wiley Interdiscip Rev RNA* 2018:e1487.

6

Giardiasis and Trichomoniasis by Other Flagellates

6.1 Introductory Remarks

Both *Giardia* and *Trichomonas* are ancient species by phylogenetic analysis. They belong to the "**Excavates,**" formerly known as the supergroup Excavata, which includes *Trypanosoma* and *Leishmania*. Although they are not on the list of neglected tropical diseases (NTDs), these flagellates cause diseases worldwide. *Giardia lamblia* is a leading cause of waterborne and foodborne diarrheal disease. For giardiasis, it is estimated that over 200 million people infected annually (Karanis *et al.* 2007); another estimate yielded a somewhat lower number, **184 million** (Torgerson *et al.* 2015). For trichomoniasis, the prevalence is **156 million** (Rowley *et al.* 2019). *Trichomonas vaginalis* flagellate is the agent responsible for the most abundant non-viral sexually transmitted disease (**STD**). Giardiasis and trichomoniasis, while causing morbidities, are never fatal (as compared to other protozoan infections, such as the agent for visceral leishmaniasis *Leishmania donovani*). The same drug, **metronidazole,** is used to treat the two parasitic diseases. In both, there are asymptomatic cases. However, at the genomic level, *Giardia* exhibits a compact genome (with a small number of genes) as opposed to *Trichomonas* which displays the opposite. Please see GiardiaDB (database) and TrichDB for current updates.[1,2]

6.2 *Giardia*

Classification of this parasitic protozoan makes it a member of the **diplomonad** protozoa, ones with 2 nuclei. *Giardia* has a **trophozoite** and a **cyst** stage. The *Giardia* trophozoite has

[1] https://giardiadb.org/giardiadb/
[2] https://trichdb.org/trichdb/

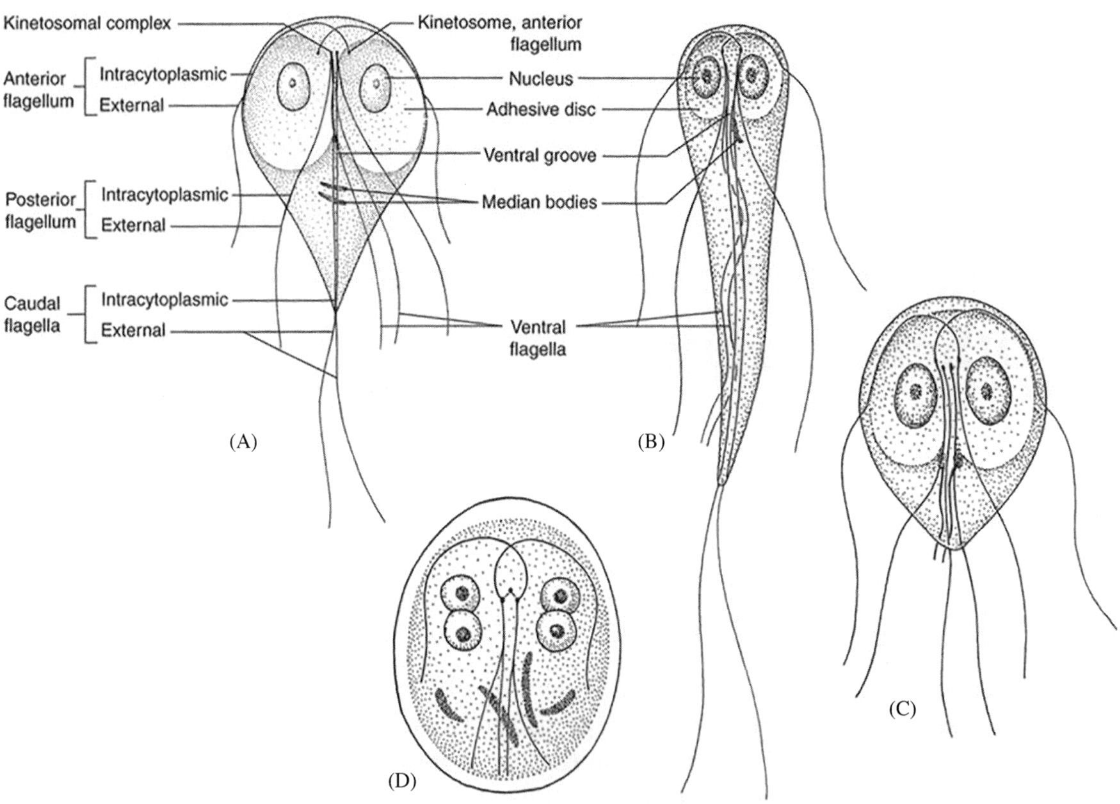

Fig. 6.1 ■ Diagram of *Giardia lamblia, G. agilis* and *G. muris* trophozoite and *G. lamblia* cyst. *Giardia* species and life cycle stages. (A) *Giardia lamblia* trophozoite, 10–15 μm long; (B) *G. agilis* from amphibians, about 20 μm long; (C) *G. muris* from mice, approximately the same size as *G. lamblia* but with a relatively broad body; (D) Cyst of *G. lamblia*. These cysts are 8–12 μm long; karyosomes of all 4 cyst nuclei, as well as several intracytoplasmic axonomenes and median bodies are visible. Courtesy: Roberts *et al. Foundations of Parasitology*, 9th ed., 2013. Reproduced with permission from McGraw-Hill.

been described as an owl face, an old man with glasses, or a smiling face; trophozoites have also been described as "tear drops in the duodenum" (Javed *et al.* 2019). In addition to 2 identical nuclei, it has 4 pairs of flagella located anterior/posterior/ventral/caudal, a ventral **adhesive disc**, and 2 curved rods known as median bodies. Please see Figure 6.1 for diagram of *Giardia lamblia* trophozoite and cyst (Roberts *et al.* 2013), Figure 6.2(A) for *Giardia* trophozoites as seen by scanning electron microscopy (Gutiérrez-Gutiérrez *et al.* 2017), and Figure 6.2(B) for a detailed view of its unique organelle, the ventral disc, as seen by 3-D negative staining and cryo-electron tomography (Brown *et al.* 2016). Furthermore, *Giardia* possesses unusual organelles known as mitosomes (mitochondrial relic, first discovered in *Entamoeba*). [Please see Chapter 7 for amoebiasis.] The mature cyst contains 4 nuclei; each cyst will produce two trophozoites.

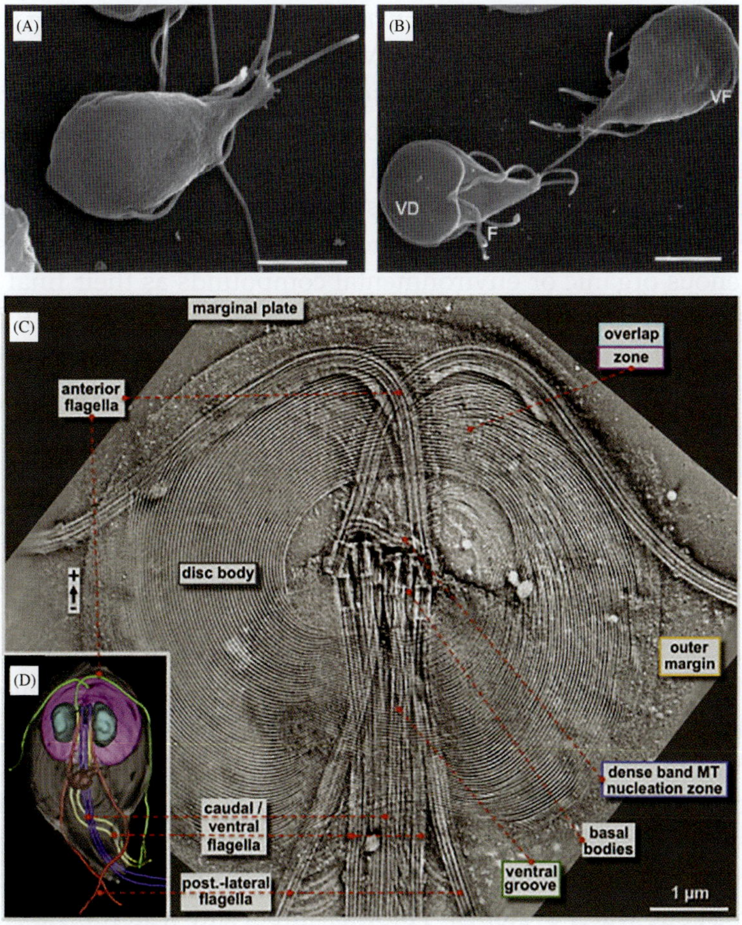

Fig. 6.2 ■ SEM micrographs of *Giardia lamblia* trophozoites. (A & B) Bar = 5 and 10 μm. (VD = ventral disk; F = Flagella and VF = ventrolateral flange). Courtesy: Gutiérrez-Gutiérrez *et al. Acta Trop* 2017;172: 113–21. Reproduced with permission from Elsevier. (C & D), the *Giardia lamblia* ventral disc: 4 × 4 tomogram montage of an entire *Giardia* ventral disc and some of its associated cytoskeletal structures such as flagella and the marginal plate. (C) Approximately 180 nm thick slice through a tomographic reconstruction obtained from a negatively stained, *Giardia* cytoskeleton preparation. The most prominent features are the highly ordered array of microtubule–microribbon complexes of the ventral disc that start at the dense band MT nucleation zone or the inner disc edge, and end at the outer margin or the ventral overlap zone. Furthermore, four pairs of flagella originate from basal bodies arranged at the center of the spiral. One pair (anterior flagella) points towards the front of the cell, and then curves outwards. All other flagella leave the cell towards the posterior end. The ventral disc microtubules form a large right-handed spiral assembly with an overlap zone at the top right. (D) 3-D reconstructions of *Giardia lamblia*. SEM and microtomy 3-D reconstruction approach reveals the overall architecture of the *Giardia* cell with the ventral disc (pink) the nuclei (cyan), the median body (brown) and the four flagellar pairs in green (anterior), blue (caudal), yellow (ventral) and red (post-lateral). Courtesy: Brown *et al. J Struct Biol* 2016;194:38–48. Reproduced with permission from Elsevier.

The mitosome, found in *Giardia* and *Entamoeba,* is an example of organelles known as mitochondrion-related organelles (**MROs**). Mitochondria originated from an endosymbiotic event commencing with the engulfment of an ancestral α-proteobacterium by the first eukaryotic ancestor. Mitochondria are categorized into 5 classes based on energy metabolism, with classes 1–4 as ATP-producing and class 5 as non-ATP-producing. The "aerobic mitochondrion" belongs to class 1 as it possesses an electron transport chain (ETC) and exclusively uses oxygen as its terminal electron acceptor. Classes 2, 3, and 4 are organelles that use endogenous organic or environmental compounds as their final electron acceptor. They consist of the "anaerobic mitochondrion" (which possesses an ETC and does not produce hydrogen), the "hydrogen-producing mitochondrion" (which possesses an ETC and produces hydrogen), and the "**hydrogenosome**" (which lacks an ETC and produces hydrogen), respectively. The "**mitosome**" is categorized as a class 5 mitochondrion since it completely lacks the ability to produce ATP. The organelles belonging to classes 3, 4, and 5 are generally called MROs and are found among parasitic protozoa. *Trichomonas* possesses hydrogenosomes; *Blastocystis* possesses hydrogen-producing mitochondria. Adaptation to parasitism includes the reductive evolution from aerobic mitochondria to MROs (Santos *et al.* 2018).

The presence of *Giardia* is of concern to the Environmental Protection Agency (EPA), as seen in its "*Giardia*: drinking water fact sheet".[3] Reported *Giardia* levels have ranged from 10,000–100,000 cysts/L in untreated sewage, 10–100 cysts/L in treated sewage, and 10 or few cysts/L in surface water sources and tap water. As little as **10** "human-sourced" cysts can cause an infection. Contraction of giardiasis is via the **fecal–oral** route. The US Centers for Disease Control and Prevention (CDC) has recognized *Giardia* to be the most frequent waterborne etiologic agent. As such, *Giardia* has taken the top spot of 10 causes of outbreaks in public water systems.[4] Another important waterborne etiologic agent is *Cryptosporidium parvum*, an apicomplexan parasitic protozoan. [Please see Chapter 10 for cryptosporidiosis.] An analysis of 325 water-associated outbreaks of parasitic protozoan disease has shown that 60% occurred in the US and over 20% in Britain. *Giardia lamblia* and *Cryptosporidium parvum* account for the majority of outbreaks (132; 40.6% and 165; 50.8%, respectively) (Karanis *et al.* 2007).

For giardiasis, children under the age of 5 and women of childbearing age are at higher risk. *Giardia* infects humans and other vertebrates. Isolates of *Giardia* have been divided into genotypes (also known as assemblages) based on molecular epidemiological grouping. These **8 assemblages** are referred to by letter code **A to H** (even with further subgroups). Assemblage A and B have broad host range (lack of host specificity), including beavers and humans. Other assemblages have restricted host range: C and D for dogs, E for ungulates such as pigs, F for cats, G for rats, and H for seals and seagulls. Please see Table 6.1 for *Giardia* host assemblages (Capewell *et al.* 2021).

[3] https://www.epa.gov/sites/production/files/2015-10/documents/giardia-factsheet.pdf

[4] https://www.cdc.gov/healthywater/drinking/public/water_diseases.html

TABLE 6.1: *Giardia lamblia* host assemblages. Courtesy: Capewell *et al.* *Trends Parasitol* 2021;37:142–53. Reproduced with permission from Elsevier.

Giardia assemblage/ sub-assemblage	Host	Proposed nomenclature
A I, II, III	Humans, non-human primates, canines, felines, other mammals	*G. duodenalis*
B	Humans, non-human primates, canines, felines, other mammals	*Giardia enterica*
C	Canines	*Giardia canis*
D	Canines	*G. canis*
E	Livestock	*Giardia bovis*
F	Felines	*Giardia cati*
G	Rodents	*Giardia simondi*
H	Marine mammals	

Giardiasis is also known as "**beaver fever**" or "**hiker's diarrhea**." Beavers may serve as animal reservoirs (zoonosis). *Giardia* cysts are resistant. A small fraction of cysts can withstand a single freeze-thaw cycle. Cysts can survive for 2 to 3 months in water temperatures of less than 10°C, and at 21°C, cysts remain viable for almost a month. Boiling water is effective in destroying cysts, as is treating water by **iodination**. [Using the iodination approach begins by taking 6 g of iodine crystal and dissolving it with 60 mL of water in an amber bottle, allowing to stand for 2 hr. For drinking water, take 12.5 mL of iodine solution to 1 L water and let stand for 15 min. If water is cloudy use double strength.] Common chlorination in water treatment process does not kill *Giardia* cysts, but filtration can remove them.

6.2.1 History

Giardia was the first parasitic protozoan seen by scientists. The Dutch microbiologist Anthony von Leeuwenhoek (businessman and scientist) wrote a letter to Robert Hooke (secretary of the Royal Society) dated November 4, 1681, stating that he saw protozoa in a sample of his stool with his hand-made lens: "**animalcules** a-moving very prettily; some of them a bit bigger, others a bit less, than a blood-globule, but all of one and the same make. Their bodies were somewhat longer than broad, and their belly, which was flat-like, furnisht with sundry little paws… they made but slow progress." A better description with illustrations was presented by Vilem Lambl (University of Prague) in 1859, from the stool of a 5-year-old girl. Lambl wrote: "Form: similar to a tadpole. At the blunt end, there is a suction bowl, in whose depth two nuclei-like formations gleam through," and named *Cercomonas intestinalis*. The name was changed to *Lamblia intestinalis* by Raphael Blanchard. In 1915, the American parasitologist Charles Wardell Stiles named ***Giardia lamblia*** in honor of Alfred Giard of Paris (a revered French zoologist) and Vilem Lambl of Prague. *Giardia lamblia* is also known as ***Giardia intestinalis*** or ***Giardia duodenalis*** (names showing duodenum, the small intestine region where the trophozoites reside). The importance of this parasitic protozoan was first recognized during World War I (1914–1918). There were 187 cases of giardiasis among 1,300 British soldiers returning from the battle of Gallipoli (in Turkey). The afflicted soldiers suffered from diarrhea and passed cysts, which; when fed to lab animals (kittens and mice), developed the same symptom. Later, in 1926, Reginald Miller at London's Paddington Green Children's Hospital showed that giardiasis would impair growth and development in chronically infected children, due to malabsorption of nutrients. Thus, *Giardia* is a human pathogen (Kean *et al.* 1978; Cox 1996; Lipoldová 2014).

6.2.2 Life cycle

Please see Figure 6.3 for the life cycle, from CDC.[5]

As the term "**fomite**" is used in the figure legend from CDC, we define fomite as any nonliving object or substance capable of carrying infectious agents. The life cycle follows the path from trophozoite to cyst to trophozoite.

6.2.3 Pathology

As little as 10 cysts can cause an infection. Giardiasis may be asymptomatic; it may cause acute or chronic diarrhea, with potential for persistent and recurrent infections (an average of over 6 months) in infants. There may be flatulence, greasy stool, abdominal cramps, bloating; more serious is the possibility of suffering from malabsorption (Bartelt and Sartor 2015). Innate immune response includes nitric oxide (NO) destruction of the parasite, and adaptive immune response includes *Giardia*-specific IgA and T cells.

In adults, *Giardia* infection causes self-limited diarrhea. In infants, persistent *Giardia* infection has been associated with reduced weight gain and linear growth (height-for-age). These features have been replicated in a neonatal mouse model (Riba *et al.* 2020). *G. lamblia* induces bile secretion because it uses the bile constituent phosphatidylcholine as a substrate for growth. *Giardia* infection can alter the gut microbiome, including an increase in Coriobacteriaceae (can very efficiently deconjugate bile acids) and lead to elevated energy consumption and dysregulated lipid metabolism, resulting in reduced adipose tissue, body weight gain, and growth in the infected mice. The investigators wrote: "Our results indicate that this enteropathogen's modulation of bile acid metabolism

---

[5] https://www.cdc.gov/dpdx/giardiasis/index.html

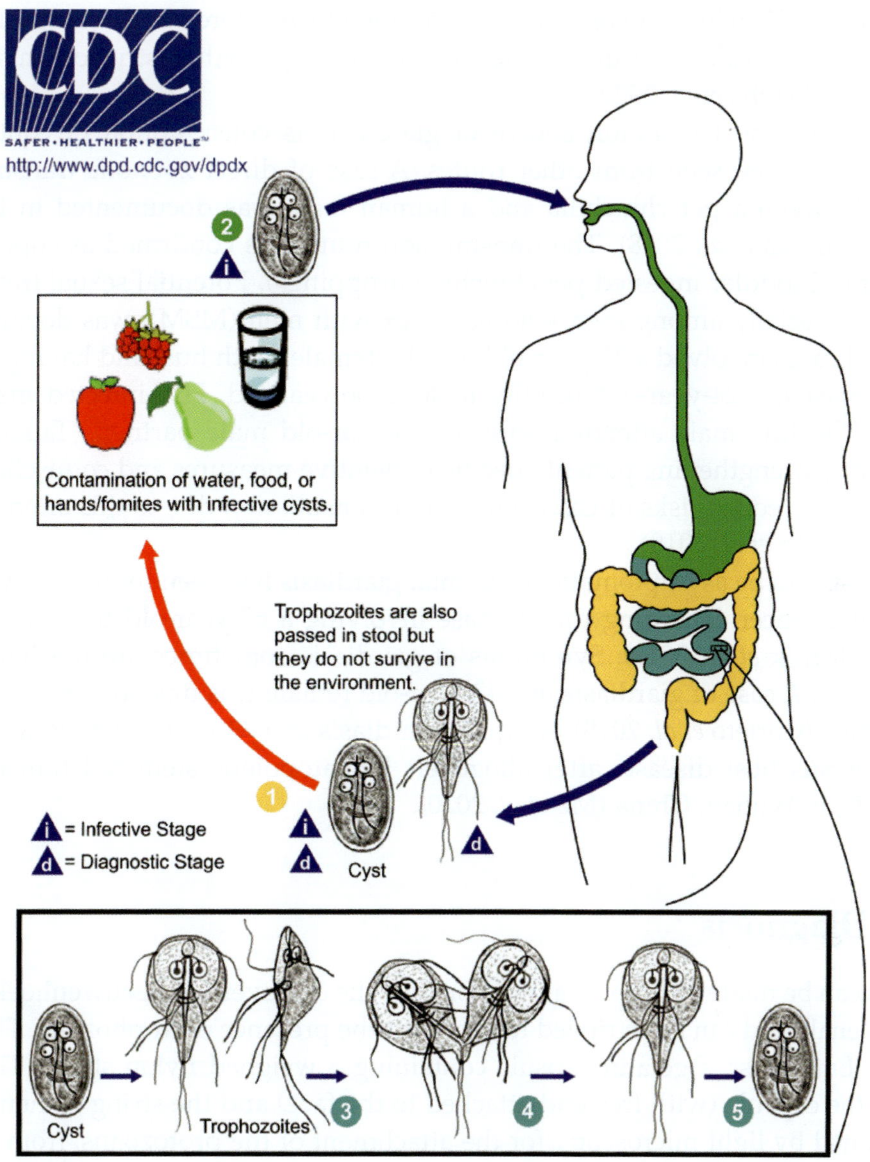

Fig. 6.3 ■ Life cycle of *Giardia lamblia*. Cysts are resistant forms and are responsible for transmission of giardiasis. Both cysts and trophozoites can be found in the feces (diagnostic stages) ①. The cysts are hardy and can survive several months in cold water. Infection occurs by the ingestion of cysts in contaminated water, food, or by the fecal-oral route (hands or fomites) ②. In the small intestine, excystation releases trophozoites (each cyst produces two trophozoites) ③. Trophozoites multiply by longitudinal binary fission, remaining in the lumen of the proximal small bowel where they can be free or attached to the mucosa by a ventral sucking disk ④. Encystation occurs as the parasites transit toward the colon. The cyst is the stage found most commonly in nondiarrheal feces ⑤. Because the cysts are infectious when passed in the stool or shortly afterward, person-to-person transmission is possible. While animals are infected with *Giardia*, their importance as a reservoir is unclear. Reproduced with permission from Centers for Disease Control and Prevention (CDC), USA. https://www.cdc.gov/dpdx/giardiasis/index.html

and lipid metabolism in the neonatal mouse host led to an altered body composition, suggesting how *G. lamblia* infection could contribute to growth restriction in infants in endemic areas" (Riba *et al.* 2020).

Whereas the most common source of giardiasis is consumption of contaminated water, rare cases are seen from other routes. A case of direct zoonotic transmission of giardiasis between a pet chinchilla and a human male was documented in the Czech Republic (Tůmová *et al.* 2018). The transmission route was confirmed as coprophagous (the 1-year-old toddler ingested pet chinchilla droppings). Potential sexual transmission of *Giardia*, especially among men who have sex with men (MSM), was documented in Cuba. The 4 cases involved a 35-year-old healthy female (with husband having asymptomatic giardiasis), a 24-year-old healthy male, a 56-year-old, HIV-infected male, and a 21-year-old healthy male attended with his 28-year-old male partner. "Talking openly with patients, strengthening patient-specific preventive measures and counseling appear to be needed to reduce risks of *Giardia* infection transmission due to this often neglected route" (Escobedo *et al.* 2018).

Giardiasis can be asymptomatic. Incidental giardiasis has been found in several cases of pancreatic cancer, including the 4th case involving a 67-year-old male in the Czech Republic (Hurník *et al.* 2019). Symptoms of giardiasis sometimes are misdiagnosed as other diseases. A case of giardiasis in a 42-year-old female was mistook for celiac disease (CD) in Rome (Corleto *et al.* 2018). A case of giardiasis in a 23-year-old male was mistook for graft versus host disease, after allogeneic hematopoietic stem cell transplantation (allo-HSCT), in Wuhan, China (Ma *et al.* 2020).

6.2.4 Diagnosis

Diagnosis can be made by stool examination, like the discovery of Leeuwenhoek. In addition, duodenal fluid can be retrieved to check for the presence of trophozoite. The "**string test**" uses Enterotest, a gelatin capsule containing a weighed nylon string. The patient swallows the capsule (with free end attached to the face) and the string is then retrieved and examined by light microscopy for the attachment of the protozoans, from duodenal fluid.

6.2.5 Therapy

The drug used as treatment is metronidazole (Flagyl). This drug, 5-nitroimidazole, has been in use since 1959. It needs to be activated (a prodrug) and is effective against many anaerobic parasitic protozoa, as well as anaerobic bacteria. Reduction of metronidazole, however, only takes place under very low concentrations of oxygen, explaining why metronidazole is exclusively toxic to microaerophilic and anaerobic microbes. Enzymes such as thioredoxin reductase (TrxR) and nitroreductase are involved. Metronidazole has a pleiotropic mode of action; it reacts with many molecules, causing DNA damage and inhibiting TrxR in *Giardia* and *Trichomonas* by the formation of metronidazole-cysteine adducts. Drug resistance in parasitic protozoa has been detected (Leitsch 2019).

Giardiasis resistant to the standard metronidazole treatment has been documented, as seen in the case report of a 39-year-old man from Bogota, Columbia. After several unsuccessful trials of drugs and drug combinations, the patient was finally cured by combination therapy of nitazoxanide and metronidazole. His case developed from January 2015 (stool sample with cysts and trophozoites present), to February 2016 (no cysts for the first time), to October 2016 (no trophozoites for the first time); his stool remained free of *Giardia* in May 2019. "When treatment failure is confirmed, it is necessary to switch to second-line regimens" (Iza *et al.* 2019).

6.2.6 Genome

The *Giardia* genome was published in 2007 by Mitchell Sogin (Marine Biological Laboratory at Woods Hole, Massachusetts) and his colleagues (Morrison *et al.* 2007). *Giardia* has a compact genome, hence "genetic minimalism." *Giardia* has 5 chromosomes, a genome size of 11.7 Mb and **6,470** protein-coding genes (as open reading frames, **ORF**) (current number is **9,667** protein-coding genes for this reference strain in GiardiaDB). Evidence for transcription of 4,787 genes was provided (by serial analysis of gene expression, SAGE, and cDNA sequencing). While tubulin-based microtubule cytoskeleton is important, myosin gene is absent (important for actin-myosin based microfilament cytoskeleton). This has led the investigators to speculate that a non-myosin adhesion-dependent cytokinesis mechanism may exist in *Giardia* (like the one present in the cellular slime mold *Dictyostelium*). Unique cytoskeleton proteins are named α and β giardins (annexin and striated fiber assembling homologs, respectively). From prokaryote donors, there is evidence of lateral gene transfer (**LGT**), aka horizontal gene transfer (**HGT**). During LGT, an organism incorporates genetic material from a second organism without being the offspring of that organism (the second organism is always a different species, as seen in a protozoan taking in genes from bacterial species). Attached to the intestinal mucosa, *Giardia* had picked up over 100 genes from prokaryotes for its own use; these genes are bacterial and archaeal homologs. LGT genes allow *Giardia* to utilize the amino acid arginine, with the acquired arginine deiminase, ornithine carbamoyl transferase, and carbamate kinase (arginine dihydrolase pathway, also seen in *Trichomonas*). The protozoan uses arginine (in addition to glucose) for metabolism. By depriving arginine, which is the substrate for nitric oxide (NO) synthesis by the host's inducible nitric oxide synthase (iNOS), NO will not be available to destroy the protozoa. *Giardia* salvages purines, pyrimidines and lipids from its environment instead of synthesis. The protozoan secretes proteins ("the secretome"); some of which become virulence factors. The most abundant are the cysteine proteases, cathepsin B-like proteolytic enzymes. They degrade host immunoglobulins and chemokines, disrupt intestinal epithelial junction complexes and cause intestinal epithelial cell apoptosis; cysteine proteases are "the teeth behind the smile" (Allain *et al.* 2019). [We appreciate the importance of cathepsin B. It is the major cysteine protease within the lysosome. Our research group was the first to isolate and report the sequence of a cDNA clone of human cathepsin B, Fong *et al.* 1986.] Another secretory product is the extracellular matrix protein *Giardia* tenascin (Dubourg *et al.* 2018). Both cysteine protease and tenascin are composed of gene families, with multiple members in the *Giardia* genome.

The first *Giardia* genome came from the isolate WB-C6, belonging to assemblage A (to be more specific, the subgroup AI), other known genomes include members of assemblages A, B and E (with one from a piglet). There are considerable differences in the available *Giardia* genomes. Similarity between protein-coding genes from A and B (isolate GS) assemblages are only **78%.** Some investigators consider assembly B should be treated as a different species. The phylogenetic distance based on the whole genome between assemblage C and D was about the same as between assemblage A and B, and the assemblage C and D isolates were more closely related to assemblage B than to assemblage A (Buret *et al.* 2020). Since the *Giardia* genome is compact (12 Mb), it has been utilized in whole genome amplification (**WGA**) (Weisz *et al.* 2019). The availability of high quality genomic DNA in sufficient amounts to perform next generation sequencing (NGS) experiments is challenging for pathogens that cannot be cultivated in vitro (such as *Giardia*).

Whereas *Giardia lamblia* is a human pathogen, there is another diplomonad protozoan of importance to aquaculture. The flagellate ***Spironucleus salmonicida*** ("the salmonid killer") causes systemic infections in farmed Atlantic salmon, Chinook salmon, and Arctic char. Its genome bears similarity to ones from *Giardia* (Xu *et al.* 2014).

The mouse equivalent (as rodent model of giardiasis) is ***Giardia muris***. Its genome was published to confirm the compact nature of these diplomonad protozoa (Xu *et al.* 2020). It has 5 chromosomes, 9.8 Mb of DNA, and 4,653 protein-coding genes (the paper shares revised data for *G. lamblia*, with 12.6 Mb DNA and 4,963 protein-coding genes). Human and murine *Giardia* species "share many known or predicted virulence factors, including cysteine proteases and a large repertoire of cysteine-rich surface proteins involved in antigenic variation. ... Additionally, *G. muris* encodes proteins that might be used to modulate the prokaryotic microbiota. The responsible genes have been introduced in the *Giardia* genus via LGT from prokaryotic sources" (Xu *et al.* 2020). An example is quorum-quenching N-acyl-homoserine lactonase. The murine *Giardia* genome is even more compact than the human one (lacking introns, genes closed together with each other).

6.2.7 Antigenic variation

Like *Trypanosoma brucei*, *Giardia lamblia* exhibits antigenic variation, but it uses a different mechanism (Prucca and Lujan 2009). The basis is RNA interference (**RNAi**). The proteins involved are the variant-specific surface proteins (**VSPs**); they are cysteine-rich proteins (with CXXC motifs) on the *Giardia* cell surface, covering all spaces including the flagella. The amino variant portion is followed by a relatively conserved membrane-spanning region and then an invariant cytoplasmic tail at the carboxyl terminal. VSPs vary from 20–200 kDa in size. At any one time, only 1 VSP protein, from a total of about **220** VSP genes, is expressed on the cell surface. The VSP genes are found in small clusters, ranging in size from 2–9 copies, scattered throughout the genome. The frequency of change of surface antigens is isolate- and VSP-dependent, averages between 6 and 16 generations. So, how does the trophozoite change its coat? It is via post-transcriptional regulation. For this model, many VSP genes are all expressed as mRNAs at first. An RNA-dependent RNA polymerase (RdRP) makes complimentary copies to these mRNAs, with the exception of one mRNA. The double strand RNAs are then degraded in RNA-mediated silencing complex (RISC). This results in only 1 single-stranded mRNA for VSP protein remaining and available for translation; the one mRNA that has never received a complimentary copy earlier. This finding suggests that RNAi has an ancient history. Experimental knockdown of RISC or RdRP results in a protozoan expressing multiple copies of VSP genes on its surface. Such protozoa expressing many VSPs may serve as a vaccine, as seen in animal experiments using gerbils. Bioengineered oral vaccination shows success in mice, with chimeric virus particles decorating with VSPs and influenza hemagglutinin (HA) and neuraminidase (NA) genes. However, for antigenic variation, there are additional regulatory steps, including chromatin remodeling and small non-coding RNAs. The former involves histone deacetylase and the latter include microRNAs (**miRNAs**) and small interfering RNAs (**siRNAs)**. It has been shown that 5 miRNAs can target 178 of the 220 VSP genes, to inhibit VSP translation. Please see Figure 6.4 for *Giardia* antigenic variation (Prucca *et al.* 2011).

6.3 *Trichomonas*

Classification of this parasitic protozoan makes it a member of the **parabasalid** protozoa, ones possessing parabasal apparatuses. A parabasal apparatus contains "two or more striated parabasal fibers connecting the Golgi apparatus to the ciliary apparatus." Within the parabasalids, it belongs to the trichomonad protozoa, ones with 3 to 5 anterior flagella and 1 posterior flagellum.

Distribution of the pathogenic species *Trichomonas vaginalis* is cosmopolitan. In fact, trichomoniasis is the most abundant non-viral STD. For 2008, WHO estimates showed 498.9 million new cases of curable sexually transmitted infections (STIs) worldwide for individuals aged 15 to 49 years, with 276.4 million of those cases resulting from *Trichomonas vaginalis*. The trichomoniasis estimate number is the combined figure of estimates for bacterial STDs from both *Chlamydia trachomatis* and *Neisseria gonorrhoeae*. Another bacterial STD is caused by the syphilis agent *Treponema pallidum*. Viral STDs are infections by human papilloma virus, herpes virus, and human immunodeficiency virus (HIV).

The life cycle is composed of only one stage, trophozoites (no cysts). Morphology of *Trichomonas vaginalis* is pyriform (pear-shaped), it has 4 + 1 flagella, parabasal body and parabasal fibril, and an axial **axostyle** (a tube made up of cytoskeleton). The 4 anterior

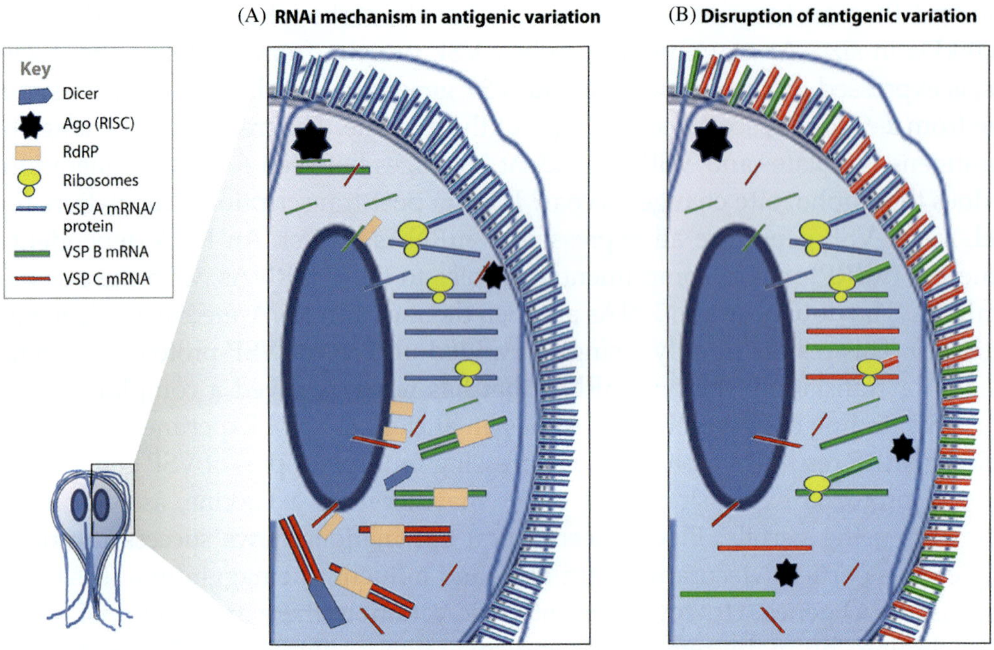

Fig. 6.4 ■ Antigenic variation of *Giardia*. Schematic of the mechanism controlling antigenic variation in *Giardia*. (A) In wild-type cells, many VSP mRNAs are generated in the nuclei of the parasite and transported to the cytoplasm. There, RdRP generates antisense VSP mRNAs, producing VSP dsRNA complexes. *Giardia* Dicer (and possible Ago) detects these dsRNAs, cleaving them into 25–27-nt-long small RNAs. Only one VSP transcript bypasses the silencing process by a still unknown mechanism, accumulates in the cytoplasm, and is then translated into the VSP that will be expressed on the trophozoite surface. (B) In cells in which the RNAi pathway has been disrupted (for example, Dicer's expression has been knocked down), many VSP transcripts achieve a steady-state level that allows the simultaneous expression of many VSPs on the surface of individual trophozoites. Abbreviations: Ago, Argonaute protein; dsRNA, double-stranded RNA; mRNA, messenger RNA; RdRP, RNA-dependent RNA polymerase; RNAi, RNA interference; RISC, RNA-induced silencing complex; VSP, variant-specific surface protein. Courtesy: Prucca *et al. Annu Rev Microbiol* 2011;65:611–30. Reproduced with permission from Annual Reviews, Inc.

flagella are free, whereas the 1 posterior flagellum (recurrent flagellum) is linked to the cell membrane (undulating membrane) and supported by a structure known as costa. Its single nucleus has an endosome (nucleolus-like structure). There are rows of hydrogenosomes (unique organelles) along axostyle, costa, and in other locations. The hydrogenosome was discovered by Donald Lindmark and Miklos Muller (Rockefeller University) in 1973; it converts glycolytic end-products to hydrogen. Please see Figure 6.5 for a diagrammatic representation of trichomonads infecting humans (Roberts *et al.* 2013), and Figure 6.6 for morphology by scanning electron microscopy (showing a longer axostyle in fresh patient isolates as compared to lab strains) (Cheon *et al.* 2013).

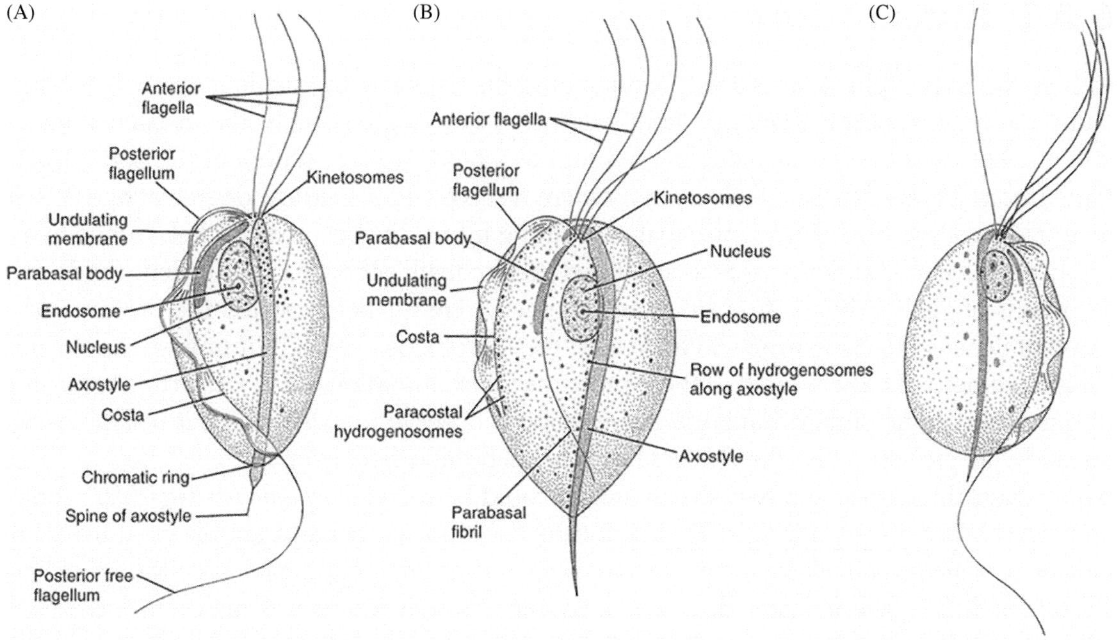

Fig. 6.5 ■ Diagram of *Tritrichomonas foetus, Trichomonas vaginalis* and *Pentatrichomonas hominis*. Morphology of trichomonads. A. *Tritrichomonas foetus*, 10–25 μm long; B. *Trichomonas vaginalis*, 7–32 μm long; C. *Pentatrichomonas hominis*, 8–20 μm long. The hydrogenosomes are not always in a defined row. Courtesy: Roberts *et al. Foundations of Parasitology*, 9th ed., 2013. Reproduced with permission from McGraw-Hill.

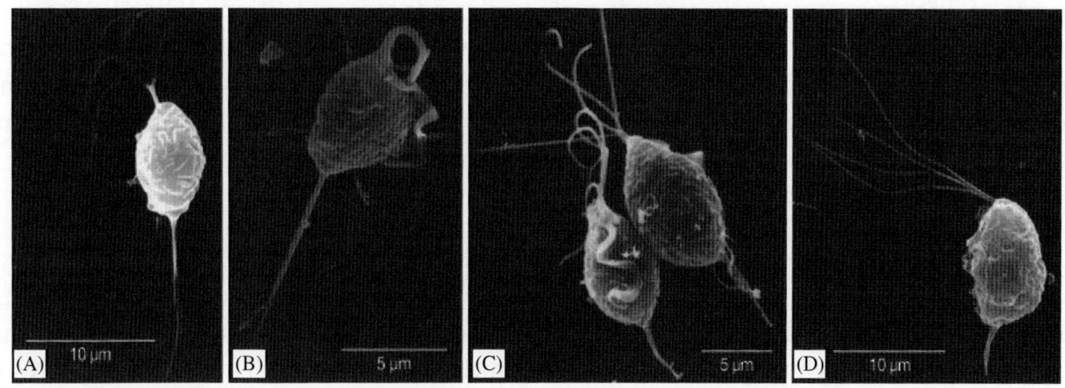

Fig. 6.6 ■ Scanning electron microscopy of *Trichomonas vaginalis*. Two fresh isolates of *T. vaginalis* (A, B) collected from vaginitis cases have longer axostyles than isolates KT9 (C) and KT4 (D) cultured for more than a year in TYM. Courtesy: Cheon *et al. Korean J Parasitol* 2013;51:243–6. Reproduced with permission from *The Korean Journal of Parasitology*, Sung-Jong Hong and Jae-Sook Ryu.

6.3.1 History

In 1836 the French physician Alfred Donne found the flagellate in purulent vaginal secretion and male urogenital tract. Donne initially earned a law degree due to the insistence by his parents. His own interest in medicine led him to attend medical school at the Sorbonne in Paris (today Paris-Sorbonne University), where he received a medical degree at age 30. He invented a collapsible microscope capable of fitting into a doctor's coat pocket. Donne had a publication at the Academy of Sciences titled "Animalculi observed in purulent fluids and secretions of genital organs from men and women." He further reported the protozoa as a cause of venereal disease, in 1837. He wrote: "these protozoa… exist in immense numbers in certain women… I have submitted these protozoa for examination to Mr. Dujardin. According to this observer, no similar infusoria has ever been observed or described; it resembles the *Monas* by its proboscis and the *Tricodes* by its hairs, but it differs from both by 'uniting' these two organs, thus forming a new genus which could be called *Tricho-monas vaginale*." Today its name is *Trichomonas vaginalis* (Trichos means hair, monas means a simple creature, vaginale being the location where the protozoan is found). Donne might have seen the spirochete *Treponema* and he would later discover leukemia through the use of his own microscope (Thorburn 1974).

6.3.2 Life cycle

Please see Figure 6.7 for the life cycle, from CDC.[6]

The life cycle is trophozoite to trophozoite, as there is no cyst stage. The protozoan divides by binary fission. Although the life cycle only involves trophozoites, there are reports of *Trichomonas vaginalis* pseudocysts under adverse conditions (Dias-Lopes *et al.* 2017). Hydrogenosome metabolism involves the essential iron-sulfur (Fe-S) proteins, removal of iron with a chelator (2,2-dipyridyl) leads to unfavorable growth conditions. Trophozoites stop dividing and their morphology change to spherical non-proliferating and non-motile pseudocysts, a process reversible with iron supplements.

6.3.3 Pathology

Trichomonas vaginalis is the agent for a very common, sexually transmitted, infection that may sometimes be asymptomatic or cause vaginitis and urethritis. The protozoan lives in the human urogenital system. The infection can be asymptomatic, as seen in almost all infected males and about half of infected females. Normal vaginal condition has a pH ranging from 4–4.5, maintained by *Lactobacillus* (normal flora or microbiota), *Trichomonas* infection raises the pH to 5–6. Transmission is via sexual intercourse. Newborns may be infected during passage through the birth canal, also, potentially, in vitro fertilization (IVF), because trophozoites survive the cryopreservation of human semen. Symptoms

[6] https://www.cdc.gov/dpdx/trichomoniasis/index.html

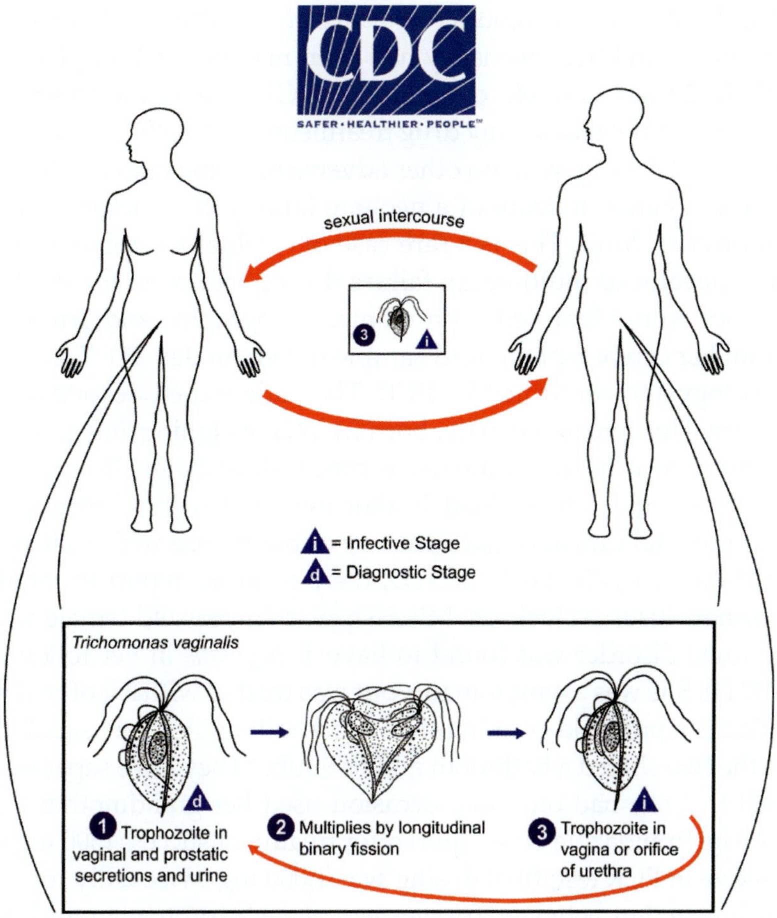

Fig. 6.7 ■ Life cycle of *Trichomonas vaginalis*. *Trichomonas vaginalis* resides in the female lower genital tract and the male urethra and prostate ❶, where it replicates by binary fission ❷. The parasite does not appear to have a cyst form, and does not survive well in the external environment. *Trichomonas vaginalis* is transmitted among humans, its only known host, primarily by sexual intercourse ❸. Reproduced with permission from Centers for Disease Control and Prevention (CDC), USA. https://www.cdc.gov/dpdx/trichomoniasis/index.html

include vaginal itching, burning sensation during urination, and slimy whitish-yellowish blood-tinged discharges. *Trichomonas vaginalis* causes inflammation (vaginitis). Trichomoniasis is a risk factor for adverse pregnancy outcome and HIV infection; it may even be a risk factor for cervical and prostate cancer. Human immune response after infection includes the immunoglobulins IgG and IgA (Schwebke and Burgess 2004).

T. vaginalis has been associated with adverse obstetric outcomes such as preterm delivery, low birth weight and premature rupture of membranes. *T. vaginalis* can be vertically transmitted at birth. A recommended treatment is a 2 g metronidazole oral single dose, even for asymptomatic patients. This treatment is effective against *Trichomonas* and its use is safe during pregnancy. A case of non-treated *T. vaginalis* infection and severe preterm labor with positive obstetrical outcome was reported (Salakos *et al.* 2018). A 33-year-old female from Paris became pregnant and her pregnancy had been marked by 4 hospitalizations for preterm labor at 24, 27, 29 and 32 weeks of gestation (WG). Because the patient was allergic to nitroimidazoles, she did not receive any drug treatment. She finally gave birth at 34 WG and 5 days to a baby girl of 2,980 g, with no other adverse outcome than small prematurity.

A case in the US ended in death of a neonate (at day 22): *Trichomonas vaginalis* brain abscess (Hamilton *et al.* 2018). This is a rare case of cerebral trichomoniasis. The neonate had seizures and developed multi-organ failure during treatment for staphylococcal sepsis. Brain abscesses were identified with cranial sonography, and *Trichomonas vaginalis* was isolated from her cerebrospinal fluid sample (taken on day 21). *T. vaginalis* was identified by morphology and confirmed by PCR. The patient died despite undergoing metronidazole therapy. This female neonate, born 24 WG, weighing 740 g, was transferred 2 hours after delivery to a neonatal intensive care unit at Baton Rouge, Louisiana. Her mother was a 28-year-old female (had 2 abortions and 6 live births prior) who had received limited prenatal care and had a history of heroin use with recurrent cellulitis.

Whereas trichomoniasis is mostly a STD, there is a case report of familial nonsexual transmission (Bishop 2020). At Jackson, Mississippi, a 26-year-old female with a history of chronic autoimmune disorder was found to have *T. vaginalis* in her follow up of urinary tract infection (UTI). She was asymptomatic, but was treated with 2 g of oral metronidazole (but no cure). This is a probable grandmother to granddaughter nonsexual transmission of *Trichomonas*, as the two shared a bathroom and bathtub. "They have separate soaps, but the patient admitted that she had on a rare occasion used her grandmother's soap" (Bishop 2020). High-dose metronidazole was required for treatment success (500 mg twice daily for 7 days, still positive in PCR test; final dosing was 1,000 mg twice daily for 7 days).

There is an interaction between *Trichomonas vaginalis* protozoan and the host tissue. Upon contact, the pear-shaped cell rapidly differentiates into an amoeboid form (pancake-liked) but retaining the flagella. The protozoan binds tightly to the vaginal epithelial cells by changes in cytoskeletal proteins (fimbrin, actin bundling protein). In addition, the protozoan secretes exosomes (with 215 cargo proteins) to modulate its environment. Some isolates have an endogenous virus, a double-stranded RNA virus known as *Trichomonas vaginalis* virus (**TVV**) and some are associated with the prokaryote **mycoplasma** (*Mycoplasma hominis* and another species known as "Candidatus *Mycoplasma girerdii*") (Fettweis *et al.* 2014; Hirt and Sherrard 2015). *Mycoplasma hominis* resides and replicates within the protozoan, and *T. vaginalis* is able to pass the bacterial infection to both mycoplasma-free protozoan isolates and human epithelial cells (Dessì *et al.* 2019). Metabolic interactions with mycoplasma enhance the growth and weaken the macrophage-mediated killing of *T. vaginalis* (Aquino *et al.* 2020). Trichomoniasis leads to dysbiosis of the vagina, as characterized by the loss of protective Lactobacilli.

Thus, *Trichomonas vaginalis* is a human pathogen. Humans also harbor commensal trichomonad species. The two species are ***Trichomonas tenax*** in the mouth (transmitted by kissing) and ***Pentatrichomonas*** (formerly *Trichomonas*) ***hominis*** in the intestine; both are non-pathogenic and feed on bacteria in their respective niches.

6.3.4 Diagnosis

Diagnosis is by the presence of trophozoites in secretion samples. In addition, InPouch TV culture system can be used to start anaerobic culture of the protozoa.

A case of fortuitous diagnosis of trichomoniasis by PCR using panfungal primers was reported (Dupont *et al.* 2020). An 18-year-old female had pelvic pain and metrorrhagia (abnormal bleeding from the uterus). Her vaginal discharge was sampled for suspicion of upper genital tract infection, and classical bacteriological procedures confirmed *Chlamydia trachomatis*, *Mycoplasma hominis*, and *Gardnerella vaginalis*. Thus, she was diagnosed for salpingitis (inflammation of the fallopian tubes, caused by bacterial infection). Another sample was sent to the mycology laboratory in search of yeasts. Mistakenly processed with the panfungal PCR, *T. vaginalis* infection was assessed fortuitously by PCR-sequencing using panfungal primers (NL1/NL4 targeting the D1/D2 domain of the 28S rDNA) on her vaginal swab. This cross-reactivity of panfungal primers was further confirmed using a specific *T. vaginalis* PCR as well as comparison to a reference strain *T. vaginalis*. Fungal primers targeting eukaryotic organisms are likely to hybridize with rDNA of other eukaryote species. "Such cross-reactivity of panfungal primers has been previously reported with non-fungal eukaryotes (*Taenia solium*, *Strongyloides stercoralis* or *Toxoplasma gondii* DNA). This case highlights the usefulness of broad range molecular tools that can take advantage of this cross-reactivity in order to diagnose unsuspected pathogens" (Dupont *et al.* 2020).

6.3.5 Therapy

The drug used as treatment is metronidazole (Flagyl). A related **tinidazole** is used for resistant protozoan infection. As a prodrug, it needs to be converted to toxic nitro-radicals via reduction by ferredoxin within the hydrogenosome. Drug resistance has been found in isolates and involves metronidazole activation (nitroreductase), accumulation (multi-drug resistant, MDR, pumps) and detoxification (nitroimidazole reductase) (Bradic *et al.* 2017). In addition to oral treatment, intravaginal administration is also available (Bouchemal *et al.* 2017). It is necessary to treat both partners simultaneously.

Metronidazole-resistant trichomoniasis is an uncommon condition that presents significant therapeutic challenges. Alternative treatment for trichomoniasis is possible. Combination therapy with high-dose oral tinidazole and vaginal paromomycin cream has been uniformly successful, as shown in a case report of a 49-year-old woman with a 5-month history of unrelenting *Trichomonas* infection and treated at Drexel Vaginitis Center in Philadelphia (Henien *et al.* 2019).

6.3.6 Genome

Like *Giardia*, the *Trichomonas* genome was published in 2007, from The Institute for Genome Research (TIGR), by Jane Carlton (currently at New York University) and colleagues (Carlton *et al.* 2007). *Trichomonas* has 6 chromosome pairs, a large genome of 176 Mb in size with **59,681** predicted genes (ORFs), and 25,949 evidence supported genes (current number is **98,611** genes and 97,474 protein-coding genes at the TrichDB). There are **152** cases of possible **LGT**; for example, a new way to make cysteine, by a prokaryotic cysteine synthase. In addition, **65%** of the genome is repetitive. It is the first eukaryotic genome with no glycosyl-phosphatidylinositol (GPI) anchor biosynthetic pathway. Like the *Giardia* genome, it has no myosin. However, it has abundant copies of surface proteins, with gene families of GP63-like leishmanolysin (77 members), cysteine proteinases (117) and Bsp-A-like genes (658). A study has shown the protozoan can express long non-coding RNAs (**lncRNAs**) and pseudogenes (Woehle *et al.* 2014). The authors hypothesized "the numerous lncRNAs could offer a large pool for potential innovation from which novel proteins or regulatory RNA units could evolve."

It is believed that *T. vaginalis* suffered a bottleneck during its entrance into urogenital environment, while the other trichomonad species live in enteric environment. It collected genomes including LGTs. The genome size corresponds to the cell volume, as *T. vaginalis* is larger than the other commensal species (*T. tenax* and *P. hominis*). [Sizes of trophozoites: *T. vaginalis*, 10–30 μm; *T. tenax*, 5–16 μm; *Pentatrichomonas hominis*, 8–20 μm.]

Different trichomonad species have different hosts. Host species include cockroaches, termites, amphibians, reptiles, birds, cattle, and humans. Phylogenetic analysis suggests a close relationship between the human *Trichomonas vaginalis* to the avian *Trichinomonas gallinae* (a pathogen for pigeon and hawk). The cattle pathogen ***Tritrichomonas foetus*** induces cattle abortion. Thus, it is a species of major agricultural importance.

6.3.7 Tv BspA-like gene family

Current analysis suggests the presence of **911** copies of Tv BspA-like (*Treponema pallidum* leucine-rich repeats, LRRs) proteins. The 911 number includes gene family members for both the secreted and cell surface forms, as well as pseudogenes (Noel *et al.* 2010). Structurally, the amino terminal end contains the LRRs. There may be proline-rich repeats (PRRs) and other repeats, followed by a trans-membrane sequence and a short cytoplasmic carboxyl end. BspA-like protein was first identified in the periodontal bacterial pathogen *Bacteroides forsythus* that causes periodontitis, the antigen is known as the 98 kDa surface protein **BspA** (*Bacteroides* surface protein A). These proteins are commonly found on the bacterial surface, for binding to mammalian proteins (such as fibronectin and fibrinogen), and serve cell-cell adhesion purpose on the host-pathogen interface. This type of bacterial adhesion is seen in both archaea and bacteria. To date, besides *Trichomonas*, BspA-like proteins have only been found in another parasitic protozoan, *Entamoeba*. For *Trichomonas vaginalis*, this is the largest gene family encoding potential extracellular proteins for this protozoan. Please see Figure 6.8 for *Trichomonas* BspA proteins (Hirt *et al.* 2007).

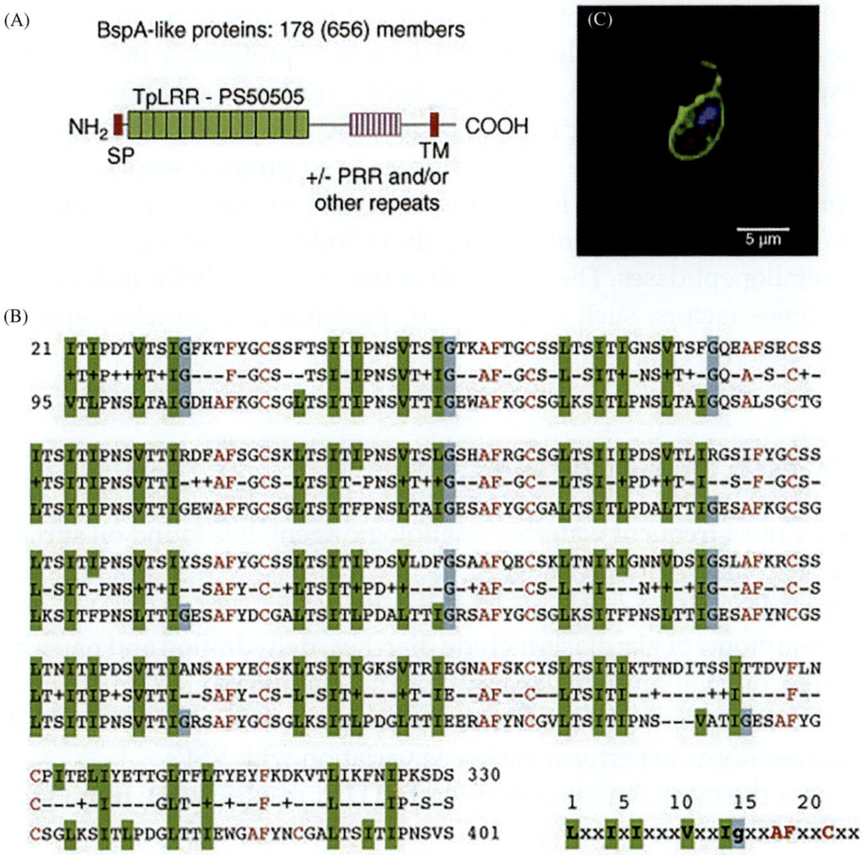

Fig. 6.8 ■ ***Trichomonas vaginalis* BspA-like proteins. (a)** The structural organization of BspA-like proteins with a TM domain (178 entries for a total of 656 entries) is shown with the TpLRR domain (green rectangle — 14 repeats are shown here). Other repeats are also often present such as proline-rich repeats (PRR) or serine and threonine-rich repeats (pink rectangle). Some BspA-like proteins also have detectable signal peptides. Most hypothetical BspA-like proteins have no TM. Some of these have a signal peptide, which could be either secreted or anchored to the membrane in an unknown fashion or could be derived from pseudogenes. **(b)** BlastP alignment (E-value = $2e^{-78}$, identity = 52%) between one *T. vaginalis* BspA-like protein (top sequence, TvBspA625, accession: AAM51159) and BspA from *Tannerella forsythensis* (accession: AAC82625 — note that the species former name was *Bacteroides forsythus*) showing the high level of sequence identity between their shared TpLRR. The first and last aligned residues for each protein are indicated. The TpLRR consensus sequence, made of 23 residues (with some known variation in length), is also shown (bottom right). The conserved residues (identical or similar) defined in the consensus sequence are highlighted in the same way in the alignment. The + and – signs indicate similar and distinct amino acid residues, respectively. **(c)** Indirect immunocytochemistry on fixed and permeabilized *T. vaginalis* cells using confocal microscopy demonstrating the expression and cellular localization of one BspA-like protein (TvBspA-625) using a specific mouse anti-peptide antisera (green) compared with the localization of malic enzyme (a classic hydrogenosomal marker — using a specific rabbit antisera — red) and the nucleus (DAPI staining — blue) (Noel *et al.* unpublished). Courtesy: Hirt *et al. Trends Parasitol* 2007;23, 540–7. Reproduced with permission from Elsevier.

Among the total secretome of *Trichomonas vaginalis* (using a strain isolated from a symptomatic patient in axenic culture) consisting of 89 proteins, 4 are leucine-rich repeat protein of BspA family (927, 1363, 1334, and 1474 amino acid residues in size). "In total, we identified 2,072 extracellular proteins, 89 of which displayed significant quantitative increases over time at 37°C. These 89 bona fide secreted proteins were sorted into 13 functional categories. Approximately half of the secreted proteins were predicted to possess transmembrane helixes. These proteins mainly include putative adhesins and leishmaniolysin-like metallopeptidases. The other half of the soluble proteins include several novel potential virulence factors, such as DNase II, pore-forming proteins, and β-amylases" (Štáfková *et al.* 2018).

Summary & Key Concepts

- *Giardia* is the most frequent waterborne etiologic agent; it is found on surfaces (such as soil or water) contaminated with feces.
- *Giardia* life cycle includes cysts and trophozoites.
- Common symptoms of giardiasis include diarrhea, dehydration and nausea/vomiting; a heavy infection may cause malabsorption and malnutrition.
- *Giardia* possesses a relatively small genome; the genome is enriched by LGT.
- *Giardia* utilizes RNAi to perform antigenic variation with VSPs.
- *Trichomonas* is the most abundant non-viral STD; it resides in the reproductive system only as trophozoites (no cysts).
- *Trichomonas* has a large genome; the genome is also enriched by LGT.
- *Trichomonas* does not have antigenic variation, but it possesses multiple BspA (*Bacteroides* surface protein A)-like proteins; BspA-like proteins bind to mammalian proteins for host-pathogen interactions.
- Both giardiasis and trichomoniasis can be treated with metronidazole.

References

Adl SM, Simpson AG, Lane CE, *et al*. The revised classification of eukaryotes. *J Eukaryot Microbiol* 2012;59(5):429–93. Erratum in: *J Eukaryot Microbiol* 2013;60(3):321.

Allain T, Fekete E, Buret AG. *Giardia* cysteine proteases: The teeth behind the smile. *Trends Parasitol* 2019;35(8):636–48.

Aquino MFK, Hinderfeld AS, Simoes-Barbosa A. *Trichomonas vaginalis*. *Trends Parasitol* 2020;36(7):646–7.

Aurrecoechea C, Brestelli J, Brunk BP, *et al*. GiardiaDB and TrichDB: Integrated genomic resources for the eukaryotic protist pathogens *Giardia lamblia* and *Trichomonas vaginalis*. *Nucleic Acids Res* 2009;37(Database issue):D526–30.

Bartelt LA, Sartor RB. Advances in understanding *Giardia*: Determinants and mechanisms of chronic sequelae. *F1000Prime Rep* 2015;7:62.

Benchimol M, Piva B, Campanati L, de Souza W. Visualization of the funis of *Giardia lamblia* by high-resolution field emission scanning electron microscopy — New insights. *J Struct Biol* 2004;147(2):102–15.

Bishop KM. A resistant case of familial nonsexual transmission of *Trichomonas*. *Cureus* 2020;12(7):e9246.

Bouchemal K, Bories C, Loiseau PM. Strategies for prevention and treatment of *Trichomonas vaginalis* infections. *Clin Microbiol Rev* 2017;30(3):811–25.

Bradic M, Warring SD, Tooley GE, *et al*. Genetic indicators of drug resistance in the highly repetitive genome of *Trichomonas vaginalis*. *Genome Biol Evol* 2017;9(6):1658–72.

Brown JR, Schwartz CL, Heumann JM, Dawson SC, Hoenger A. A detailed look at the cytoskeletal architecture of the *Giardia lamblia* ventral disc. *J Struct Biol* 2016;194(1):38–48.

Buret AG, Cacciò SM, Favennec L, Svärd S. Update on *Giardia*: Highlights from the seventh International *Giardia* and Cryptosporidium Conference. *Parasite* 2020;27:49.

Capewell P, Krumrie S, Katzer F, Alexander CL, Weir W. Molecular Epidemiology of *Giardia* Infections in the Genomic Era. *Trends Parasitol* 2021;37(2):142–53.

Carlton JM, Hirt RP, Silva JC, *et al*. Draft genome sequence of the sexually transmitted pathogen *Trichomonas vaginalis*. *Science* 2007;315(5809):207–12.

Cheon SH, Kim SR, Song HO, Ahn MH, Ryu JS. The dimension of *Trichomonas vaginalis* as measured by scanning electron microscopy. *Korean J Parasitol* 2013;51(2):243–6.

Corleto VD, Di Marino VP, Galli G, *et al*. Improving basic skills in celiac-like disease diagnosis: A case report. *BMC Gastroenterol*. 2018 Nov 3;18(1):162.

Cox FE (ed.). *The Welcome Trust Illustrated History of Tropical Diseases*. The Wellcome Trust, London, 1996.

Cox FE. History of human parasitology. *Clin Microbiol Rev* 2002;15(4):595–612.

Despommier DD, Gwadz RW, Hotez PJ, Knirsch CA. *Parasitic Diseases*, 7th ed. Parasite without Borders, Inc., NY, 2005.

Dessì D, Margarita V, Cocco AR, Marongiu A, Fiori PL, Rappelli P. *Trichomonas vaginalis* and *Mycoplasma hominis*: New tales of two old friends. *Parasitology* 2019;146(9):1150–5.

Dias-Lopes G, Saboia-Vahia L, Margotti ET, *et al*. Morphologic study of the effect of iron on pseudocyst formation in *Trichomonas vaginalis* and its interaction with human epithelial cells. *Mem Inst Oswaldo Cruz* 2017;112(10):664–73.

Dubourg A, Xia D, Winpenny JP, *et al*. *Giardia* secretome highlights secreted tenascins as a key component of pathogenesis. *Gigascience* 2018;7(3):1–13.

Dupont D, Gaucherand P, Wallon M. Fortuitous diagnosis of Trichomoniasis by PCR using panfungal primers. *Int J Infect Dis* 2020;90:234–36.

Escobedo AA, Acosta-Ballester G, Almirall P, *et al*. Potential sexual transmission of *Giardia* in an endemic region: A case series. *Infez Med* 2018;26(2):171–5.

Fettweis JM, Serrano MG, Huang B, *et al*. An emerging mycoplasma associated with trichomoniasis, vaginal infection and disease. *PLoS One* 2014 Oct 22;9(10):e110943.

Fong D, Calhoun DH, Hsieh WT, Lee B, Wells RD. Isolation of a cDNA clone for the human lysosomal proteinase cathepsin B. *Proc. Natl. Acad. Sci. USA* 1986;83:2909–13.

Gargantini PR, Serradell MDC, Ríos DN, Tenaglia AH, Luján HD. Antigenic variation in the intestinal parasite *Giardia lamblia*. *Curr Opin Microbiol* 2016;32:52–8.

Gutiérrez-Gutiérrez F, Palomo-Ligas L, Hernández-Hernández JM, *et al*. Curcumin alters the cytoskeleton and microtubule organization on trophozoites of *Giardia lamblia*. *Acta Trop* 2017 Aug;172:113–121.

Hamilton H, Pontiff KL, Bolton M, *et al*. *Trichomonas vaginalis* brain abscess in a neonate. *Clin Infect Dis* 2018;66(4):604–7.

Henien M, Nyirjesy P, Smith K. Metronidazole-Resistant Trichomoniasis: Beneficial pharmacodynamic relationship with high-dose oral tinidazole and vaginal paromomycin combination therapy. *Sex Transm Dis* 2019;46(1):e1–2.

Heyworth MF. Immunological aspects of *Giardia* infections. *Parasite* 2014;21:55.

Hirt RP, Sherrard J. *Trichomonas vaginalis* origins, molecular pathobiology and clinical considerations. *Curr Opin Infect Dis* 2015;28(1):72–9.

Hirt RP, Noel CJ, Sicheritz-Ponten T, Tachezy J, Fiori PL. *Trichomonas vaginalis* surface proteins: A view from the genome. *Trends Parasitol* 2007;23(11):540–7.

Hurník P, Žiak D, Dluhošová J, *et al*. Another case of coincidental *Giardia* infection and pancreatic cancer. *Parasitol Int* 2019;71:160–2.

Iza JA, Iza SN, Olivera MJ. Giardiasis: Report of a case refractory to treatment. *Infez Med* 2019;27(3):336–9.

Javed IN, Tajammal R, Ijaz SH, Ahmad N, Mahmood S. "Tear drops in the duodenum": Uncommon cause of iron deficiency anemia in adults. *Cureus* 2019;11(8):e5532.

Karanis P, Kourenti C, Smith H. Waterborne transmission of protozoan parasites: A worldwide review of outbreaks and lessons learnt. *J Water Health* 2007;5(1):1–38.

Kean BH, Mott KE, Russell AJ (eds.). *Tropical Medicine and Parasitology: Classic Investigations,* Volumes I and II, Cornell, 1978.

Leitsch D. Recent Advances in the *Trichomonas vaginalis* Field. *F1000Res* 2016;5. pii: *F1000* Faculty Rev-162.

Leitsch D. A review on metronidazole: An old warhorse in antimicrobial chemotherapy. *Parasitology* 2019;146(9):1167–78.

Lipoldová M. *Giardia* and Vilém Dušan Lambl. *PLoS Negl Trop Dis* 2014;8(5):e2686.

Ma S, Yan H, Shi W, You Y, Zhong ZD, Hu Y. *Giardia lamblia* mimicking acute graft versus host disease after allogeneic hematopoietic stem cell transplantation: A case report. *Medicine* (Baltimore) 2020;99(33):e21752.

Mehlhorn H. *Encyclopedia of Parasitology*. Springer-Verlag Berlin Heidelberg 2015.

Mitchell PD, Stern E, Tepper Y. Dysentery in the crusade kingdom of Jerusalem: An ELISA analysis of two medieval latrines in the city of Acre (Israel). *J Archaeological Sci* 2008;35:1849–53.

Morrison HG, McArthur AG, Gillin FD, *et al*. Genomic minimalism in the early diverging intestinal parasite *Giardia lamblia*. *Science* 2007;317(5846):1921–6.

Noel CJ, Diaz N, Sicheritz-Ponten T, *et al*. *Trichomonas vaginalis* vast BspA-like gene family: Evidence for functional diversity from structural organisation and transcriptomics. *BMC Genomics* 2010;11(1):99.

Prucca CG, Lujan HD. Antigenic variation in *Giardia lamblia*. *Cell Microbiol* 2009;11(12):1706–15.

Prucca CG, Rivero FD, Luján HD. Regulation of antigenic variation in *Giardia lamblia*. *Annu Rev Microbiol* 2011;65:611–30.

Riba A, Hassani K, Walker A, *et al*. Disturbed gut microbiota and bile homeostasis in *Giardia*-infected mice contributes to metabolic dysregulation and growth impairment. *Sci Transl Med* 2020;12(565):eaay7019.

Roberts LS, Janovy J Jr, Nadler S. *Foundations of Parasitology*, 9th ed. McGraw Hill, 2013.

Rowley J, Vander Hoorn S, Korenromp E, *et al*. Chlamydia, gonorrhoea, trichomoniasis and syphilis: Global prevalence and incidence estimates, 2016. *Bull World Health Organ* 2019;97(8):548–62.

Salakos E, Korb D, Morin C, Sibony O. A case of non-treated *Trichomonas vaginalis* infection and severe preterm labor with positive obstetrical outcome. *J Gynecol Obstet Hum Reprod* 2018;47(4):171–3.

Santos HJ, Makiuchi T, Nozaki T. Reinventing an organelle: The reduced mitochondrion in parasitic protists. *Trends Parasitol* 2018;34(12):1038–55.

Schwebke JR, Burgess D. Trichomoniasis. *Clin Microbiol Rev* 2004;17(4):794–803.

Serradell MC, Rupil LL, Martino RA, *et al.* Efficient oral vaccination by bioengineering virus-like particles with protozoan surfaceproteins. *Nat Commun* 2019;10(1):361.

Štáfková J, Rada P, Meloni D, *et al.* Dynamic secretome of *Trichomonas vaginalis*: Case study of β-amylases. *Mol Cell Proteomics* 2018;17(2):304–20.

Thorburn AL. Alfred François Donné, 1801–1878, Discoverer of *Trichomonas vaginalis* and of leukaemia. *Br J Vener Dis* 1974;50(5):377–80.

Torgerson PR, Devleesschauwer B, Praet N, *et al.* World Health Organization estimates of the global and regional disease burden of 11 foodborne parasitic diseases, 2010: A data synthesis. *PLoS Med* 2015;12(12):e1001920.

Tůmová P, Mazánek L, Lecová L, *et al.* A natural zoonotic giardiasis: Infection of a child via *Giardia* cysts in pet chinchilla droppings. *Parasitol Int* 2018;67(6):759–62.

Walochnik J, Duchene M. *Molecular Parasitology: Protozoan parasites and their molecules*. Springer, 2016.

Weisz F, Lalle M, Nohynkova E, Sannella AR, Dluhošová J, Cacciò SM. Testing the impact of Whole Genome Amplification on genome comparison using the polyploid flagellated *Giardia duodenalis* as a model. *Exp Parasitol* 2019;207:107776.

Widmer G, Carmena D, Kváč M, *et al.* Update on *Cryptosporidium* spp.: Highlights from the Seventh International *Giardia* and Cryptosporidium Conference. *Parasite* 2020;27:14.

Wiser MF. *Protozoa and Human Disease*. Garland, 2011.

Woehle C, Kusdian G, Radine C, Graur D, Landan G, Gould SB. The parasite *Trichomonas vaginalis* expresses thousands of pseudogenes and long non-coding RNAs independently from functional neighbouring genes. *BMC Genomics* 2014;15(1):906.

Xu F, Jerlström-Hultqvist J, Einarsson E, Astvaldsson A, Svärd SG, Andersson JO. The genome of *Spironucleus salmonicida* highlights a fish pathogen adapted to fluctuating environments. *PLoS Genet* 2014;10(2):e1004053.

Xu F, Jiménez-González A, Einarsson E, *et al.* The compact genome of *Giardia muris* reveals important steps in the evolution of intestinal protozoan parasites. *Microb Genom* 2020;6(8):mgen000402.

Zubácová Z, Cimbůrek Z, Tachezy J. Comparative analysis of trichomonad genome sizes and karyotypes. *Mol Biochem Parasitol* 2008;161(1):49–54.

7

Amoebiasis and Other Infections by Amoebae and Amoeboflagellates

7.1 Introductory Remarks

Amoebiasis is caused by parasitic protozoa exhibiting amoeboid movement, using pseudopodia (pseudopods; singular pseudopodium, pseudopod). Although not grouped with the neglected tropical diseases (NTDs), amoebiasis is an important disease. The NTDs malaria and schistosomiasis are the first and second leading causes of death, respectively, among parasitic infections wordwide; **amoebic dysentery** is considered to be the third. [Diarrhea is an increase in the frequency of stools and fluid in the stool; dysentery is blood and mucus in the stool, often accompanied by pain, fever and abdominal cramps.] "The estimations of the worldwide burden of amoebiasis by the WHO indicated that approximately **500 million** people were infected with the parasite and **10%** of these individuals had invasive amoebiasis" (Cui *et al.* 2019). The pathogen is the parasitic protozoan *Entamoeba histolytica*, a member of the supergroup Amoebozoa. Other members include the social amoeba/cellular slime mold *Dictyostelium discoideum*, a model organism for cell differentiation, and many free-living amoebae. Amoebic species are distributed worldwide; they live in a variety of aquatic and terrestrial niches (different habitats). There are species of amoebae that can become pathogenic if they gain access to the human body; this is known as **opportunistic** infections. The major amoebae are many *Acanthamoeba* species and *Balamuthia mandrillaris*. From another group the "Excavates," an important species is the amoeboflagellate *Naegleria fowleri*. In addition, single incidences of amoebae causing human encephalitis have been reported for *Sappinia diploidea* and *Paravahlkampfia francinae*. Genomic data for many strains of *E. histolytica* (from different geographical locations and associated with a variety of disease manifestations), plus other species, as well as related data (such as RNA sequencing) are available and updated in AmoebaDB.[1]

[1] https://amoebadb.org/amoeba/

7.2 *Entamoeba*

The current estimates of ***Entamoeba histolytica*** is 50 million cases of disease and 40,000–100,000 deaths annually (over **55,000 deaths** worldwide every year). Total infections may even be higher, at around 500 million as there are asymptomatic cases, as well as incomplete distinctions from the involvement of another species, ***Entamoeba dispar***, which is morphologically identical to *E. histolytica* in shape and size. [In contrast, the diseases caused by the pathogenic free-living amoeba lead to deaths in hundreds and thousands.]

Like giardiasis, amoebiasis utilizes the **fecal-oral route** for transmission. The very young, the pregnant, and the malnourished are more susceptible than other individuals. *Entamoeba* cysts from excreted stool can spread through the environment: soil and water, even fresh produce and unsanitary household conditions. In this sense, *Entamoeba* is considered a waterborne pathogen. Processes such as chemical and ultraviolet disinfection, filtration, flocculation, and sedimentation, have been used to remove amoebae from water sources (lagoons, wetlands).[2]

Entamoeba histolytica (ent means inner; amoeba means shape, change; histo means tissue; lytica means lysis) has a simple life cycle. The vegetative stage consists of the **trophozoite**: it feeds on bacteria and lives in the host's large intestine. The transmissible stage consists of the **cyst**: it allows survival outside the host and transmission to a new host. Encystment is self-stimulated by **catecholamine** secretion (an autocrine system). The morphology of trophozoite includes a nucleus with a central **endosome**, food vacuoles that may contain engulfed erythrocytes, plus ectoplasm and endoplasm (for the formation of lobose pseudopodia that are bulbous, short and blunt). *Entamoeba* has an unusual organelle known as the **mitosome** instead of classic mitochondrion. Graham Clark (London School of Hygiene and Tropical Medicine) discovered this organelle in 1999. The protozoan performs glycolysis, and stores extra energy sources as glycogen. The trophozoite also contains chromatoid bodies, that become the **chromatoid bars** of cysts; these are RNA-containing structures. A late cyst may have nuclei division from 1 to 4, and a mature cyst with 4 nuclei will yield 8 amoebae. *Entamoeba* cyst wall contains **chitin**, in contrast to that of *Acanthamoeba*, which contains **cellulose**. [Cellulose, common in plants, is a polymer of β-1,4-linked subunits of glucose; chitin, found in insects and fungi, is a polymer of β-1,4-linked subunits of N-acetyl-glucosamine.]

7.2.1 History

The history of parasitic diseases is closely related to the historical records of European imperialism. In 1828, Sir James Annesley published a book titled *Researches into the causes, nature and treatment of the more prevalent diseases of India, and of warm climates generally*. In

[2] https://www.waterpathogens.org/book/entamoeba-histolytica

this book, symptoms of **intestinal** and **hepatic amoebiasis** were accurately described for the first time, although the agent involved was not known.

Entamoeba histolytica was discovered in 1873, by Fedor Losch, when he was a lecturer at the Women's Medical College in St. Petersburg, Russia. He found amoeba in the stool of a 24-year-old farmer named J. Markow, who was suffering from bloody dysentery. Losch infected experimental dogs orally and rectally with amoeba-containing stools from the patient. He dissected the euthanized dogs and found ulcer in their colon mucosa. Later the patient died and he found a similar ulcer in the patient upon autopsy. Losch named the protozoan "'*Amoeba coli*,' after the site it was found." However, his interpretation was hesitant; he wrote: "The question remains whether the entire sickness was produced by the amoebae, or whether it resulted from other courses and the amoebae only reached the intestine later and sustained the disease." In 1903, at the Imperial Health Bureau of Berlin, the German zoologist Fritz Schaudinn described trophozoites and cysts of both *Entamoeba histolytica* and *E. coli*. Schaudinn died at the age of 35 of complications of self-inflicted amoebiasis (Kean *et al.* 1978; Cox 1996).

Using techniques of enzyme-linked immunosorbent assay (ELISA), *Entamoeba histolytica* (6 out of 8 samples) and *Giardia lamblia* (1 from 8) were found in excavated medieval latrines in the city of Acre, Israel (but none for *Cryptosporidium parvum*). The city of Acre was located on the coast of the eastern Mediterranean. From the crusades, in this 13th century Hospital of St. John latrine, in addition to evidence of parasitic protozoa, there was the presence of ova of intestinal worms, the whipworm *Trichuris*, the roundworm *Ascaris*, the tapeworm *Taenia* and the fish tapeworm *Diphyllobothrium*. This was the first demonstration of *Entamoeba* in the Middle East from archaeological samples (Mitchell *et al.* 2008). Piers Mitchell (Cambridge) and colleagues continued this work, the first archaeological study of the Ottoman Empire parasites in the early 1800's. Sediments from a latrine were analyzed in search of protozoan parasites and helminth eggs (infectious agents of dysentery). By examining the samples using light microscopy and ELISA kits, they found evidence for roundworm (*Ascaris lumbricoides*), whipworm (*Trichuris trichiura*), tapeworms (*Diphyllobothrium* sp. and *Taenia* sp.), lancet liver fluke (*Dicrocoelium dendriticum*, a cattle parasite), and the protozoa *Giardia lamblia* and *Entamoeba histolytica*. The diversity of parasitic species detected has led the investigators to consider the effects of Ottoman Period culture, diet, sanitation, and trade on the risk of parasitism in the Acre community (Eskew *et al.* 2019).

Whereas light microscopy and immunological assays are used in the studies mentioned above, molecular methods have also been useful in **paleoparasitology**, especially the polymerase chain reaction (PCR) (Côté and Le Bailly 2018). As an example, we described the archaeological research at the Pretos Novos cemetery (PNC), Rio de Janeiro, Brazil (1769–1830). The cemetery was used to bury those enslaved Africans who had died upon arrival (before being sold). PCR was applied using four molecular targets for *Ascaris* sp. (parasitic nematode) identification: 18S ribosomal DNA (18S rDNA), cytochrome b (*cytb*) (Loreille *et al.* 2001), NADH dehydrogenase subunit 1 (*nad1*), and cytochrome c oxidase subunit 1 (*cox1*). "*Ascaris* sp. *cytb* sequence was recovered in one individual. We emphasize that, even with the extensive degradation of PNC human remains and the process of curation of samples, it was possible to recover helminth ancient DNA (aDNA). The origin of PNC individuals confirms that these infections were brought to Brazil from western and central Africa during the colonial era" (Guedes *et al.* 2020). Please note that only one gene probe had worked; and there is always degradation in aDNA. [The mentioned human parasites will be discussed in later chapters.]

7.2.2 Life cycle

Please see Figure 7.1 for the life cycle, from CDC.[3]

The only species recognized as a human pathogen is *Entamoeba histolytica*. Many other non-pathogenic commensal species may also be present in the colon. They need to be distinguished from the pathogenic species during diagnosis. *E. histolytica* and related species can infect both humans and non-human primates. Please see Figure 7.2 for species distribution (Cui *et al.* 2019).

7.2.3 Pathology

There is a wide spectrum of pathology; only 10–20% of infections result in disease. Asymptomatic infection may be a result of **luminal amoebiasis**; a self-limiting colitis (inflammation) may lead to **invasive amoebiasis.** Trophozoites, the motile stage, move with the aid of pseudopodia, colonize the intestinal mucosa of the large intestine which leads to "flask-shaped" ulcers in the affected colonic region. Damage to the colon can be caused by neutrophils that respond to the infection. Contact with the host cells leads to parasite-induced death. Trophozoites take in erythrocytes (red blood cell, RBC) by phagocytosis (hematophagous); they invade the intestinal mucosal barrier and, via the bloodstream, disseminate to secondary sites including the liver, lung and brain, forming organ abscess. Thus, there are intestinal and **extraintestinal amoebiasis**.

Amoebic infections in a couple were reported in 2018. The 40-year-old woman, with no foreign travel history, had emergency surgery at the University College Hospital in London to remove a perforated appendix and returned 4 weeks later with bloody diarrhea, abdominal pain, and positive test for amoebiasis. The doctors found out that her partner had persistent diarrhea for 3 months after a trip to rural Argentina and Colombia. "Amoebiasis is the second most common cause of death from parasitic infection worldwide but is rarely seen in the UK without a history of travel to endemic areas. These cases demonstrate the spectrum of severity of amoebiasis, the importance of travel history (of both the patient and their sexual contacts) in raising the suspicion of amoebiasis, and the diagnostic usefulness of panprotozoal PCR and amoebic serology ..." (Wallis *et al.* 2018).

[3] https://www.cdc.gov/dpdx/amebiasis/index.html

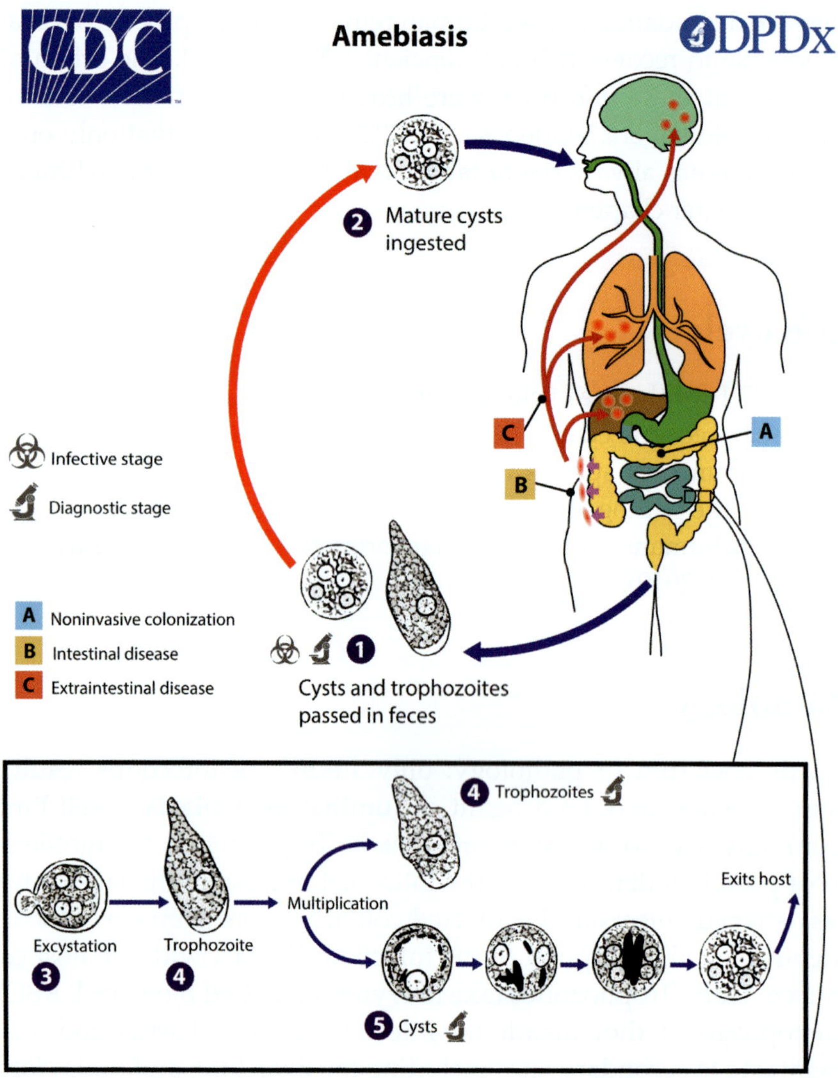

Fig. 7.1 ■ Life cycle of *Entamoeba histolytica*. Cysts and trophozoites are passed in feces ❶. Cysts are typically found in formed stool, whereas trophozoites are typically found in diarrheal stool. Infection with *Entamoeba histolytica* (and *E. dispar*) occurs via ingestion of mature cysts ❷ from fecally contaminated food, water, or hands. Exposure to infectious cysts and trophozoites in fecal matter during sexual contact may also occur. Excystation ❸ occurs in the small intestine and trophozoites ❹ are released, which migrate to the large intestine. Trophozoites may remain confined to the intestinal lumen (A: noninvasive infection) with individuals continuing to pass cysts in their stool (asymptomatic carriers). Trophozoites can invade the intestinal mucosa (B: intestinal disease), or blood vessels, reaching extraintestinal sites such as the liver, brain, and lungs (C: extraintestinal disease). Trophozoites multiply by binary fission and produce cysts ❺, and both stages are passed in the feces ❶. Cysts can survive days to weeks in the external environment and remain infectious in the environment due to the protection conferred by their walls. Trophozoites passed in the stool are rapidly destroyed once outside the body, and if ingested would not survive exposure to the gastric environment. Courtesy: CDC. Reproduced from https://www.cdc.gov/dpdx/amebiasis/index.html

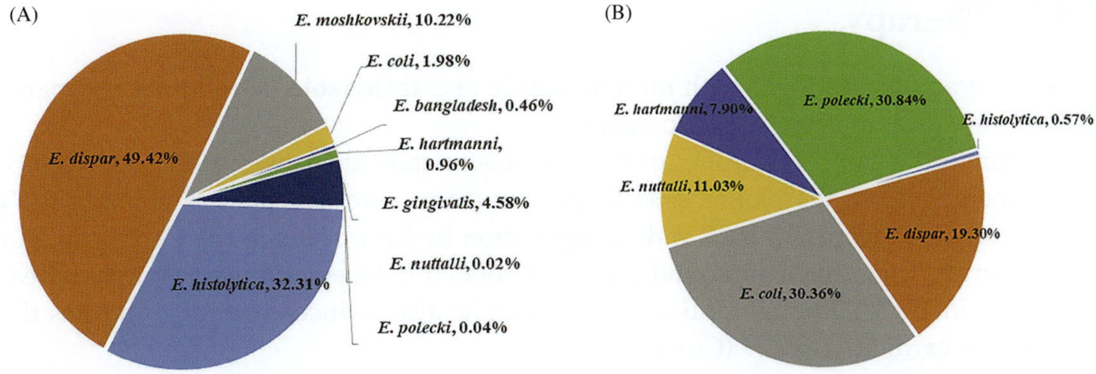

Fig. 7.2 ■ ***Entamoeba* species distribution in humans and non-human primates.** Distributions of *Entamoeba* species in humans and non-human primates. (A) *Entamoeba* species in humans; (B) *Entamoeba* species in non-human primates. Courtesy: Cui *et al. Infect Genet Evol* 2019;75:104018. Reproduced with permission from Elsevier.

The American writer Ernest Hemingway (1899-1961),[4] winner of the 1954 Nobel Prize in Literature, who wrote *The Old Man and the Sea* (1952),[5] had severe amebic dysentery during a safari trip in Africa with his wife Pauline Pfeiffer, in 1933. The amebic infection led to a prolapsed intestine and Hemingway had to be evacuated by airplane to Nairobi for treatment. This experience was later adapted in his short story: *The Snows of Kilimanjaro* (1938).[6]

Commensal species are also found. *E. histolytica* is morphologically similar to *E. dispar*, and while old literature may have confused the two, the latter does not engulf RBC and is non-pathogenic. Other species such as *E. coli*, *E. hartmanni*, and *E. moshkovskii* live in the colon. The commensal species ***Entamoeba gingivalis*** lives in the mouth and phagocytose bacteria, it is the only species with trophozoite stage but no cyst stage. Species can be identified by the size of trophozoites and cysts. Although there are no morphological or size differences between *E. histolytica* and *E. dispar*, molecular, biochemical and immunological differences allow establishment of the latter as a new species in 1993 (data from isoenzyme analyses).

7.2.4 Diagnosis

Stool examination is one diagnostic technique. Trophozoites predominate in liquid stool of diarrhea, and cysts in formed stool. Endoscopy, imaging, and serology, are also feasible.

---

[4] https://en.wikipedia.org/wiki/Ernest_Hemingway

[5] https://www.fadedpage.com/showbook.php?pid=20141070

[6] https://pdcrodas.webs.ull.es/naturalismo/HemingwayTheSnowsOfKilimanjaro.pdf

7.2.5 Therapy

Current therapy is treatment with **metronidazole** and **tinidazole**. Iodoquinol and paromomycin are used in asymptomatic carriers.

Similar to the case of quinine for malaria, historically there was the knowledge of roots ("ipecac") from the plant *Cephaelis ipecacuanha* to cure dysenteries ("bloody flu") from Portuguese records in 1625 and in application by Europeans in the Caribbean and Latin America. The active compound was later isolated to be **emetine** and shown to treat amoebiasis in 1912. Although anti-amoebic, emetine also induces vomiting and has the side effect of cardiomyopathy (Cox 1996).

7.2.6 Genome

The *Entamoeba histolytica* draft genome was published in 2005, as a collaboration between the Institute for Genome Research (TIGR, USA) and the Sanger Institute (UK), with a total of 9,938 predicted genes (Loftus *et al.* 2005). Subsequent updates and new assembly/reannotation led to 8,201 genes, but its genome assembly remains fragmented (Lorenzi *et al.* 2010). Current annotation from AmoebaDB suggests a total of **8,333** protein-coding genes for ***E. histolytica*** and **8,748** for ***E. dispar***. Genomic re-sequencing of 10 laboratory isolates suggests little nucleotide diversity in *E. histolytica*, even among lineages derived from widely separated geographical locations (Weedall *et al.* 2012). Initially, the chromosome number is unknown as mitosis occurs without condensation of chromosomes. Current data indicate *Entamoeba histolytica* has **14** chromosomes (by pulsed gel electrophoresis, Willhoeft and Tannich 1999).

The genome has a high AT content (approximately 75%). Surprisingly, telomerase genes are absent in the genome, and there is the absence of telomere-like repeats. [The lack of telomerase is also seen in the *Trichomonas vaginalis* genome.] There are unique features with respect to tRNA and rRNA organization. There are tandem repeated tRNA-containing arrays separated by repetitive intergenic DNA. Comprising almost 10% of the sequence reads, there are 25 types of long tandem array, each containing between 1 and 5 tRNA types per repeat unit. As tRNAs are exceptionally abundant (about 10 times of human genome), they may have some structural function. The genes for rRNA are extrachromosomal; they are located on large plasmids, at about 200 copies per haploid genome equivalent of the trophozoite.

Genes involving host-parasite interaction are abundant. Invasiveness is maintained by multiple copies of genes of the **lectin** protein that recognizes galactose and N-acetyl-D-galactosamine (31 genes) [killing by *Entamoeba histolytica* requires parasite adherence to host galactose- and N-acetyl-D-galactosamine-containing cell surface receptors], **cysteine proteinase** (CP, 10 genes) and **amoebapores** (pore forming amphipathic peptides, a total of 3 genes). The galactose/N-acetylgalactosamine (Gal/GalNAc)-specific lectin, the major adhesive factor of *E. histolytica*, binds to Gal and GalNAc, which are residues present in the intestinal mucins and enterocyte cell surface. The cysteine proteases, a major family of pathogenicity factors of *E. histolytica*, degrade many host proteins, including serum albumin, hemoglobin, collagen, fibronectin, colonic mucin, IgA, IgG, complement components, cytokines, and chemokines. The major proteinases are CP1, CP2, and CP5 for *E. histolytica*, but *E. dispar* lacks CP5. The CP5-overexpressing strains of amoebae are capable of destroying cell monolayers to cause liver abscess. In addition, the amoebae secrete the protein monocyte locomotion inhibitory factor (MLIF); it is an anti-inflammatory molecule.

From its genome, its limited biosynthetic capacities suggest that *Entamoeba* acquires essential molecules (amino acids, lipids, nucleotides, sugars) from both the host and the phagocytosed bacteria. Thus, it depends on the host and microbial nutrients for survival. Its unique organelle mitosome (also found in *Giardia*) has no DNA, and maybe an ancient or degenerate mitochondrion (a relic). It has **no glutathione** (found in mammals). The *Entamoeba histolytica* genome shows that it shares metabolic adaptation with those of *Giardia* and *Trichomonas*, via horizontal gene transfer (HGT) (borrowing bacterial detoxification systems). There is the reduction or elimination of most mitochondrial metabolic pathways, and the use of oxidative stress enzymes generally associated with anaerobic prokaryotes. It is an obligate fermenter. There are a total of 96 HGT genes. *Entamoeba* uses oxidative stress enzymes generally associated with anaerobic prokaryotes. Two examples are **flavoprotein A** and **rubrerythrin**. Flavoprotein A can detoxify nitric oxide (NO), which the host cells use to kill microbial pathogens, by changing it to nitrous oxide (N_2O). This mechanism is shared by *Trichomonas* and *Giardia*. Rubrerythrin can detoxify hydrogen peroxide (H_2O_2) and changes it to water (H_2O). This mechanism is also seen in *Trichomonas*.

7.2.7 Microbiota

Many organisms live in the colon besides *Entamoeba histolytica*. Colonic microbiota influences the parasitic protozoan, and vice versa. The amoeba perturbs the microbiome composition. There is alteration in the principal phyla of the host microbiota during disease: an increase in *Bifidobacterium* species accompanying a decrease in *Bacteroides*, *Campylobacter*, *Clostridia*, *Eubacterium*, and *Lactobacillus* species (Verma *et al.* 2012). Dysbiosis may result from the disruption of intestinal physiology by amoebic pathology and peristalsis, or *E. histolytica* directly induces dysbiosis through specific bacterial predation, exclusion, or modulation of the host immune response. Whether this is also true for asymptomatic protozoan infection is unknown. In addition, the microbiota may regulate the virulence of the parasitic protozoan. This is an area of current research interest.

7.2.8 Trogocytosis

Entamoeba histolytica kills colonic enterocytes by contact-dependent cytotoxicity (Ralston *et al.* 2014). This is the classic process of adherence, cytotoxicity, and ingestion, using the virulence factors discussed above. An unexpected discovery is **cell nibbing**: the trophozoites ingest pieces of intact living host cells by the process known as trogocytosis. Please see Figure 7.3 for trogocytosis (Ralston *et al.* 2014). The purpose for amoebic trogocytosis is to display human proteins (such as human leukocyte antigens, HLAs) on the amoeba's cell surface so as to prevent its lysis by human serum (Miller *et al.* 2019). Please see Figure 7.4 for a model of *Entamoeba* trogocytosis-mediated immune evasion (Miller *et al.* 2019).

7.3 Opportunistic Free-living Amoebae

Opportunistic amoebic infections are the results of human contact with free-living amoebae. These infections are caused by facultative, opportunistic, pathogenic amoebae. Species of importance are *Naegleria fowleri*, *Balamuthia mandrillaris*, and many *Acanthamoeba* species. Infections lead to encephalitis that can be fatal. *Naegleria* causes primary amoebic meningoencephalitis (**PAM**), *Balamuthia* and *Acanthamoeba* cause granulomatous amoebic encephalitis (**GAE**). In addition, *Acanthamoeba* species also cause amoebic keratitis (**AK**).

7.4 *Naegleria*

Free-living amoebae are commonly found in lakes, swimming pools, tap water, and heating and cooling units. *Naegleria* is thermophilic and prefers a warmer environment, 25–35°C (77–95°F), so it is found in hot springs, hot tubs, and heated swimming pools. There are over 30 species of *Naegleria*, but only ***Naegleria fowleri*** is pathogenic, as it causes acute and often fatal central nervous system (CNS) infection in healthy young adults. It has been nicknamed "**brain eating amoeba**." However, it is a rare disease, with only hundreds of cases on record to date. The US CDC record showed a total of 143 cases of PAM from 1962 to 2016. PAM has over 97% mortality. Worldwide there are about 440 reported cases, but only about a dozen patients have been treated successfully (Zysset-Burri *et al.* 2014; Bellini *et al.* 2018).

Individual cases have become news in USA. In 2013, a 12-year-old Arkansas girl, Kali Hardig, got infected after a July trip to the waterpark and was treated with miltefosine after 22 days in ICU (Linam *et al.* 2015). In 2016, a Florida teenager, 16-year-old Sebastian DeLeon was another PAM survivor. In 2016, an Ohio college student, 18-year-old Lauren Stitz, died of PAM after a trip with her church group to the US National Whitewater Center at Charlotte, North Carolina. The family sued and the lawsuit was settled in April 2019. A 29-year-old New Jersey surfer, Fabrizio Stabile, died of PAM in September 2018 after a trip to a Waco, Texas surf resort. His mother, Rita Stabile has filed a $ 1 million lawsuit against the BSR Surf Resort in April 2019. The case is still pending. A 13-year-old Florida boy, Tanner Lake Wall, died of PAM on August 2, 2020, after a family trip to a campground where he went swimming in a lake twice (July 24 and 25). He was initially misdiagnosed as having a strep throat, then tested positive for bacterial meningitis, and

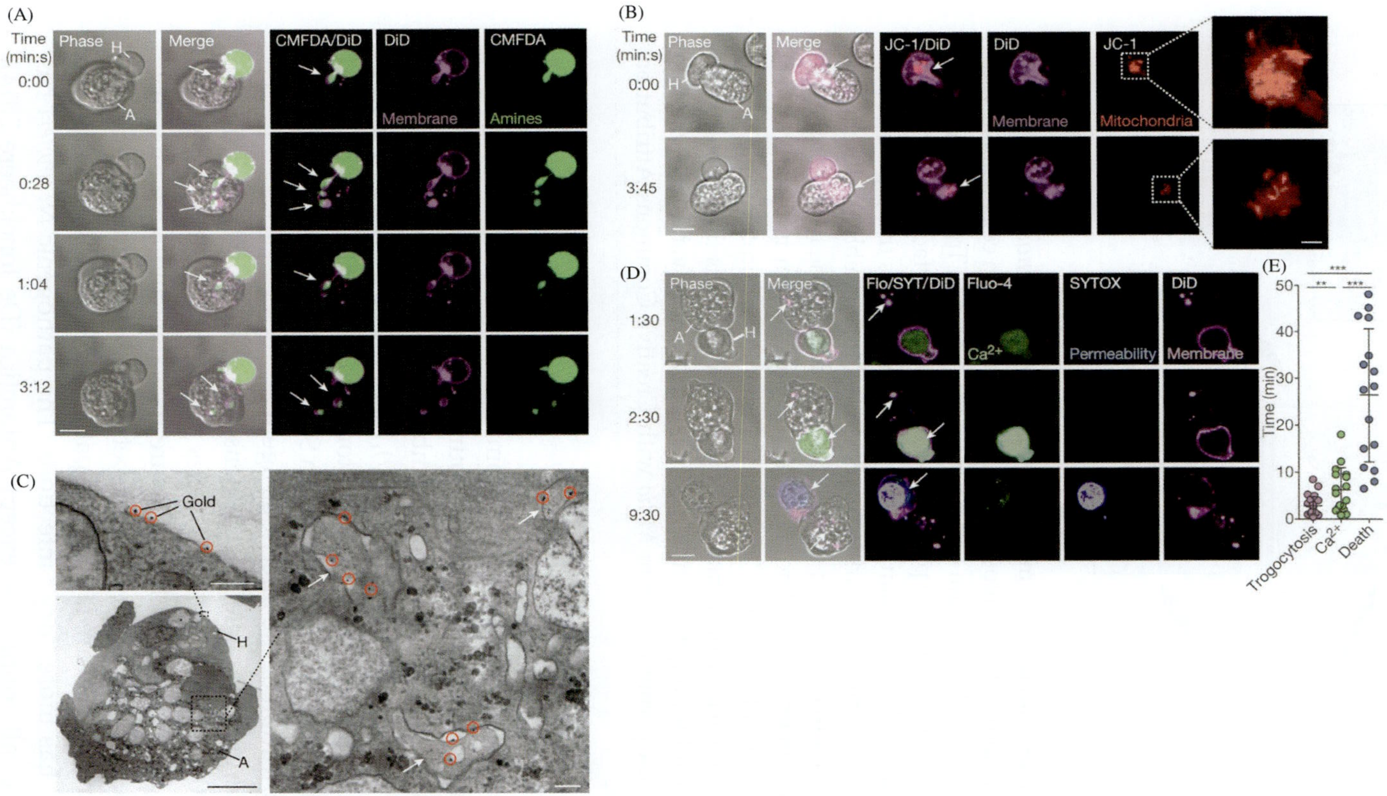

Fig. 7.3 ■ **Trogocytosis of *Entamoeba histolytica*.** Amoebae internalize human cell fragments, preceding human cell death. (A), DiD and CMFDA-labelled human Jurkat cells (H); an amoeba (A) internalizes human cell fragments (arrows) over time. Images are representative of three independent experiments. (B), DiD and JC-1-labelled human Jurkat cells; mitochondria (arrow) are ingested by the amoeba in an ingested fragment. Images are representative of six independent experiments. (C), Electron microscopy with gold-labelled human Jurkat cells. Inset (top left), gold-labelled human cell membrane (gold, circles). Inset (right), fragments (arrows) within the amoeba. Images are representative of two independent experiments. (D), DiD and Fluo-4-labelled human Jurkat cells; with SYTOX blue present during imaging. Arrows, amoebic trogocytosis (1:30), intracellular calcium concentration elevation (2:30) and membrane permeabilization (9:30). Images are representative of 15 independent experiments. (E), Timing in 60 cells from 15 independent experiments; shown are data points, means and standard deviations; P values from t-tests: *$P < 0.05$, **$P < 0.01$, ***$P < 0.001$. Scale bars, 10 μm (A, B, D), 2 μm (B, insets), 0.5 μm (C, top left, right) and 5 μm (C, bottom left). Courtesy: Ralston *et al.* *Nature* 2014;508:526–30. Reproduced with permission from Springer Nature.

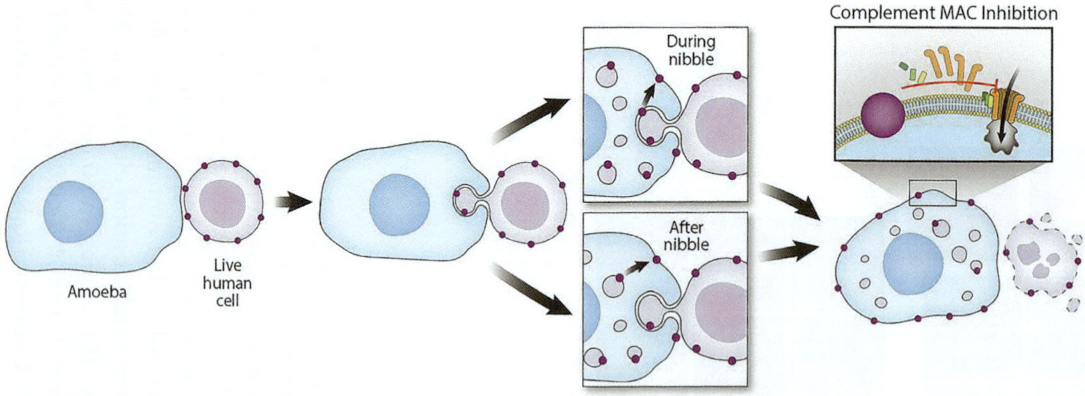

Fig. 7.4 ■ A model for trogocytosis-mediated immune evasion of *Entamoeba histolytica*. Proposed model of protection from serum lysis. Amoebae encounter live human cells while invading the intestine or disseminating in the bloodstream and perform trogocytosis. Trogocytosis leads to acquisition and display of human cell membrane proteins on the amoeba surface. One potential mechanism for the acquisition and display of human cell membrane proteins is through fusion of the amoebic and human cell plasma membranes during trogocytosis (during nibble). Human cell proteins might be directly transferred to the amoeba surface through membrane fusion at the site of trogocytosis without being first internalized. Another potential mechanism is through internalization of bites during trogocytosis (after nibble). The ingested membrane proteins might then be trafficked to the amoeba surface. Display of human cell membrane proteins then protects the amoebae from lysis in the blood by inhibiting the complement cascade. Courtesy: Miller *et al. MBio* 2019;10:e00068-19. Reproduced with permission from *MBio* with Creative Commons Attribution 4.0 (CC-BY) International License.

lastly had the presence of amoebae in drained fluid from his brain after showing brain swelling. In 2021, a case was released by the Tarrant County Public Health and the City of Arlington, Texas: the child was hospitalized on September 5 and died on September 11 (no further detail provided to protect the child's identity). The source was determined to be the splash pad of Don Misenhimer Park at Arlington, because CDC had detected *Naegleria* amoebae in water samples there (as reported on September 24). Most PAM cases are fatal without timely identification of the infectious agent.

Naegleria fowleri is an emerging parasite, in the sense that there is an increase in reported PAM cases since 2000. Among the PAM cases where the sources have been located, 93% are "wet" (314 cases out of 336 for exposure to water) and 6.5% are "dry" (cysts from soil or dust). Differences in epidemiology between the Indian subcontinent (ISC) and the southern states in the USA are found. The patient age range is greater in the ISC than in the USA, and ISC has more "dry" infections. The pathogenic *N. fowleri* has been reported to be present on all continents, except Antarctica (De Jonckheere 2014).

With ongoing climate change, the incidence of PAM and the geographic range of *N. fowleri* will spread poleward due to global warming (Maciver *et al.* 2020).

7.4.1 History

Historically, thermal spas were built by the Roman legions when they invaded England, now this location is the city of Bath. Evidence of *Naegleria* was found in such archaeological sites. *Naegleria* infection of humans was first described in 1965 by Malcolm Fowler in Adelaide Children's Hospital, South Australia (4 patients: a 9-year-old boy, two 8-year-old girls and a 28-year-old male). The disease was named primary amoebic meningoencephalitis (PAM), to differentiate from secondary invasions of the central nervous system (CNS) by *Entamoeba histolytica*. Patients die within 5–7 days and amoebae are found in cerebrospinal fluid (CSF), but cysts are not found. For *Naegleria fowleri*, the genus *Naegleria* is named after the French zoologist Mathieu Naegler, and the species is named after the Australian doctor Malcolm Fowler.

7.4.2 Life cycle

Please see Figure 7.5 for the life cycle, from CDC.[7]

Life cycle of *Naegleria fowleri* includes three stages: **trophozoite, cyst,** and **flagellate**. The trophozoite contains standard features of an amoeba, nucleus, mitochondria, contractile vacuole (osmoregulation, pumping water). Structures on the surface of trophozoites known as amoebastomes (**food cups**) are pesudopodial projections which enable the organism to ingest bacteria, fungi, and human tissue. Trophozoite replicates by **promitosis**; there is no disintegration of nuclear membrane during cell division. Under unfavorable conditions the trophozoite differentiates into temporary non-feeding flagellated form with two flagella. Hence, this protozoan is known as an **amoeboflagellate**. Please see Figure 7.6 for the three developmental forms of *Naegleria fowleri* by scanning electron microscopy (Piñero *et al.* 2019).

7.4.3 Pathology

When a child goes swimming during the warm weather in a lake with stagnant water, the amoeboflagellate trophozoites infect the human via the nose, from nasal mucosa, through olfactory nerve, to the brain. PAM starts with headache and fever, and ends with coma and death within a week.

---

[7] https://www.cdc.gov/dpdx/freelivingamebic/index.html

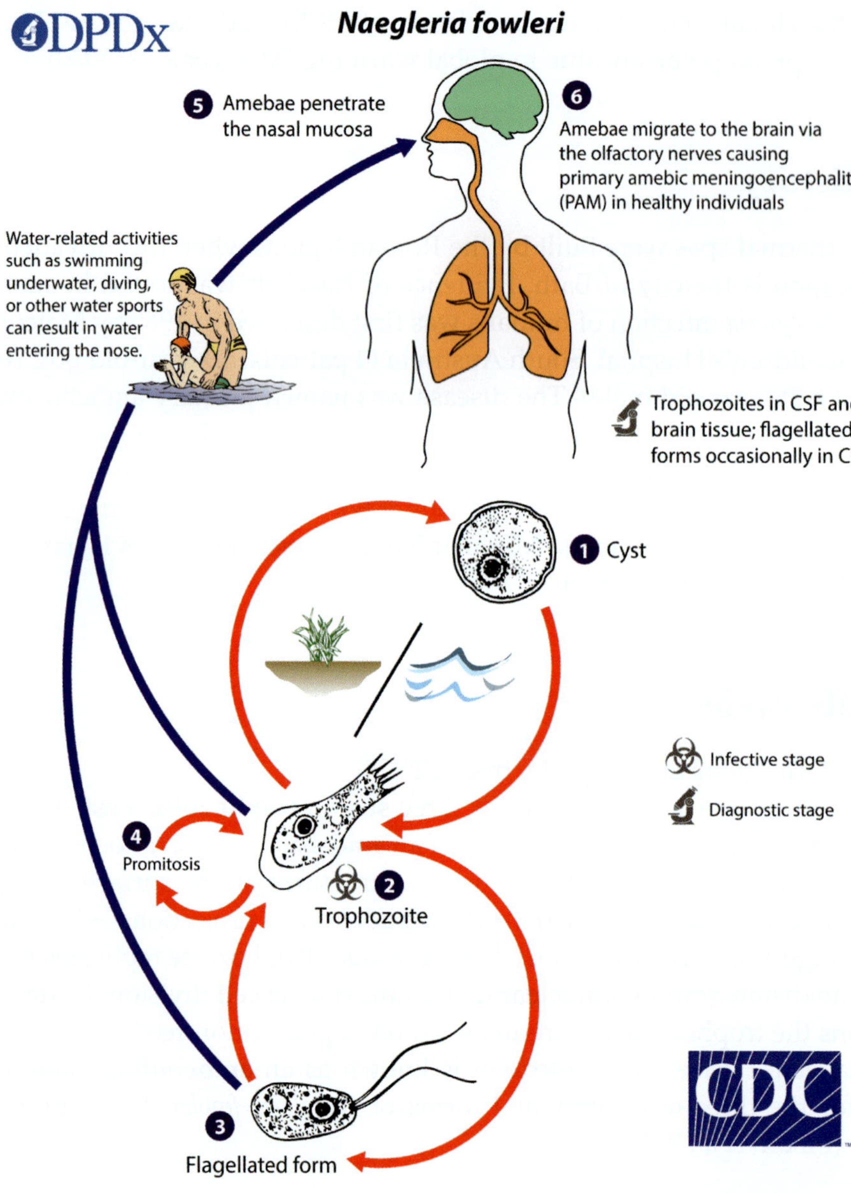

Fig. 7.5 ■ Life cycle of *Naegleria fowleri*. *Naegleria fowleri* has three stages in its life cycle: cysts ❶, trophozoites ❷, and flagellated forms ❸. The trophozoites replicate by promitosis (nuclear membrane remains intact) ❹. *N. fowleri* is found in fresh water, soil, thermal discharges of power plants, geothermal wells, and poorly-chlorinated recreational and tap water. Trophozoites can turn into temporary non-feeding flagellated forms which usually revert back to the trophozoite stage. Trophozoites infect humans or animals by penetrating the nasal mucosa, usually during swimming or sinus irrigation ❺, and migrating to the brain ❻ via the olfactory nerves causing primary amebic meningoencephalitis (PAM). *Naegleria fowleri* trophozoites are found in cerebrospinal fluid (CSF) and tissue, while flagellated forms are occasionally found in CSF. Cysts are not seen in brain tissue. Courtesy: CDC. Reproduced from https://www.cdc.gov/dpdx/freelivingamebic/index.html

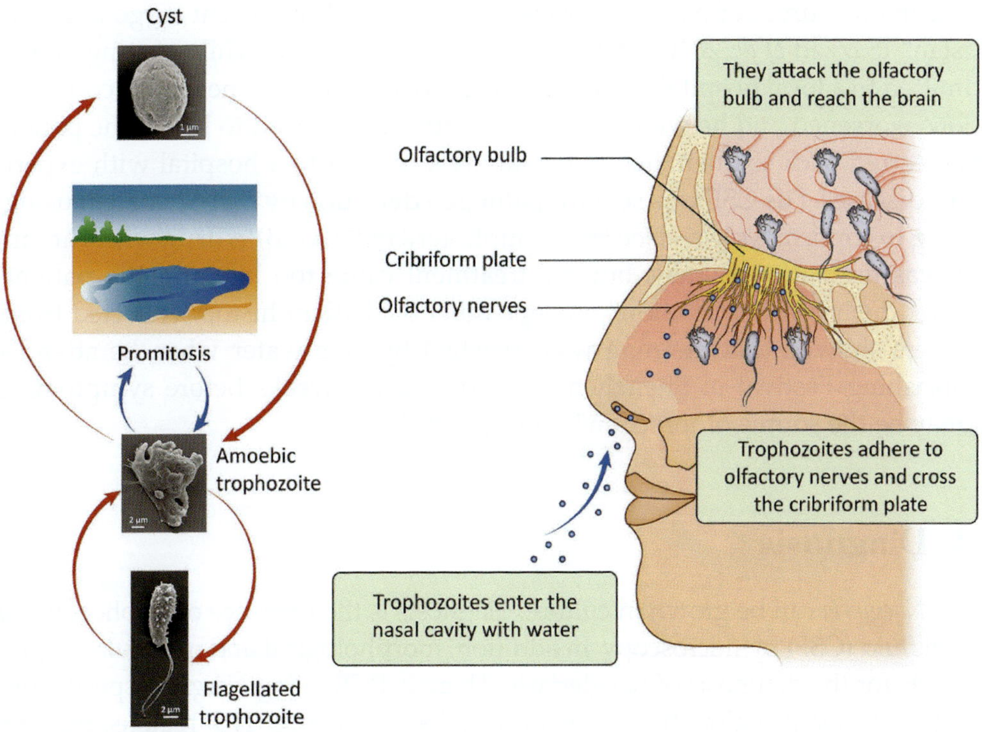

Fig. 7.6 ■ Developmental forms of *Naegleria fowleri* by scanning electron microscopy and its invasion pathway in humans. Courtesy: Piñero *et al. Trends Parasitol* 2019;35:848–9. Reproduced with permission from Elsevier.

In addition to contact *Naegleria* from swimming in lakes and water parks, the infection has been recorded from other sources. One example is the use of tap water in neti pots, killing 2 adults in Louisiana in 2011 (Yoder *et al.* 2012). In fact, *N. fowleri* has been isolated from both soils and different types of water bodies, including swimming pools, thermal waters, tap water, and lakes.

Individual cases of PAM have been reported in African and Asian countries. In Zambia, a 24-year-old male died of PAM 8 days after hospital admission, with his cerebral spinal fluid (CSF) indicating amoebae and species confirmed by PCR of ITS of the rDNA gene. "This case was detected during one of the hot months with spiking temperatures supporting observations that *N. fowleri* infections are associated with hot seasonality" (Chomba *et al.* 2017). In Bangladesh, a 15-year-old boy died of PAM 6 days after initial symptom onset (severe headache and fever on August 15, 2014, unconscious on August 17, at ICU for mechanical ventilation, died on August 21). Retrospective confirmation as PAM was done by CDC in 2017. "The patient's family members were contacted and asked about the patient's water exposures. The family reported that he prayed 5 times a day in a mosque and performed ablution (including nasal rinsing with water) in the same mosque. Ground water was transiently stored in an above-ground tank before being supplied through a pipe for ablution. Amoeba-contaminated ablution water appears to be one of the main sources of *N. fowleri* transmission behind the recent surge in PAM cases in Pakistan" (Sazzad *et al.* 2020). In China. A 42-year-old male, while visiting Hangzhou, was admitted to a local hospital on August 20, 2016 one day after headache complaint, his conditions worsened and he went into a coma (after transferred to ICU). The patient was later transferred back to Shenzhen at his family's request to a hospital with expertise in infectious diseases. His CSF was sent for pathogen detection by BGI-Shenzhen using NGS sequencing to confirm *Naegleria fowleri*. "Amphotericin B (AmB), a drug with anti-amoeba activity, was used immediately, but the treatment came too late and the patient died 2 days after the NGS confirmation" on September 3. "Patient history collected from family members showed that the man was splashed by lake water when he attended the Water-Splashing Festival in Shenzhen approximately 1 weeks before symptoms onset, which may be the source of infection" (Wang *et al.* 2018).

7.4.4 Diagnosis

Although *Naegleria* can be grown in culture, diagnosis is the presence of trophozoites in cerebrospinal fluid (CSF) by microscopy. In addition, morphological and molecular approaches are available for the diagnosis of naegleriasis. There is PCR using *Naegleria* specific primers, such as the 18S rDNA region, the internal transcribed sequence (ITS) regions, the 5.8S, and the 28S regions. As an example, in 2013, a real-time PCR assay showing positive result for *N. fowleri* was of critical importance for the successful treatment to save the life of Kali Hardig (Linam *et al.* 2015). The rapid development of the patients' clinical condition necessitates a prompt diagnosis. Without a timely diagnosis, the infection is aggressive and most PAMs are confirmed at autopsy (high mortality rate). Identification of the sources of *N. fowleri* is critical for prevention and diagnosis (Bellini *et al.* 2018).

7.4.5 Therapy

Therapy is amphotericin B in combination with other drugs (azithromycin, dexamethasone, fluconazole, miltefosine, rifampin). Miltefosine is also a drug for visceral leishmaniasis (Grace *et al.* 2015; Cooper *et al.* 2019).

"Drug repurposing is a powerful approach for drug discovery because it significantly improves the discovery time, reduces the amount of resources, and decreases costs required to advance lead candidate drugs of interest into the clinic. This is extremely helpful for neglected diseases including pathogenic free-living amoebae (**FLA**) where there is a need for new active therapies with limited budgets" (Rice *et al.* 2020). Christopher Rice (University of Georgia) and colleagues conducted a high throughput phenotypic screen of 12,000 compounds from the Calibr ReFRAME library to identify 58 nano- and 90 micro-molar inhibitors against *N. fowleri, A. castellanii* and *B. mandrillaris* (among them 113 shown for the first time targeting FLA). To treat PAM, rapid response is critical. A total of 19 compounds, all inhibiting *N. fowleri in vitro* within 24 hours, have been discovered (including the antifungal **fumagillin**, pneumonia drug solithromycin, topical antiseptic acriflavine, and histone deacetylase inhibitors quisinostat, pabinostat, pracinostat, dacinostat, and fimepinostat). They work much faster than any of the drugs currently used for chemotherapy. Thus, effective drugs may soon be available to treat pathogenic FLA infections (Rice *et al.* 2020).

7.4.6 Genome

The rDNA genes are located on a circular plasmid, with 4,000 copies in each cell. Based on internal transcribed spacers (ITSs), *Naegleria fowleri* can be divided into **8** different genotypes. *Naegleria* also contains group I introns, which means these are ribozymes with self-splicing capacity. Thus, the rDNA genes have **ribozyme** activity (De Jonckheere 2014).

The genome of *N. fowleri* was published in 2014 (Zysset-Burri *et al.* 2014). The protozoan has haploid genome size of 30 Mb, 35% GC content, and possesses **17,252** protein-coding genes (ORFs). Using proteomics and two-dimensional (2D) gels, comparisons from highly and weakly pathogenic strains revealed virulence factors (22 proteins), including heat shock protein 70 (**hsp70**) and actin. There are also pore-forming proteins, **naegleriapore A and B**. For the highly pathogenic strain, expression of the actin-binding protein **villin-1** is up-regulated.

With an aim to unravel pathways involved in the pathogenicity of PAM, genome of *N. fowleri*'s closest non-pathogenic relative, *N. lovaniensis* has been investigated (Liechti *et al.* 2018), showing 30 Mb DNA with 15,195 predicted genes. Comparison of gene families between the two and a third species previously sequenced, *N. gruberi*, show 8,114 common gene families and 323 unique to *N. fowleri*.

Molecular studies of PAM have moved from genes to proteins. In a comparison of membrane proteins of 3 *Naegleria* species, a 23-kDa protein (**Nf23**) of 229 amino acids was detected. The mRNA level of *nf23* was over-expressed 4-fold and 40,000-fold in *N. fowleri* compared with *N. lovaniensis* and *N. gruberi*, respectively. A 5-fold mRNA over-expression in *N. fowleri* trophozoites recovered from mouse brains compared with trophozoites axenically cultivated was also detected. Furthermore, the cytopathic effect on MDCK (Madin-Darby Canine Kidney) cells co-incubated with *N. fowleri* diminished in the presence of antibodies against Nf23. These findings suggest Nf23 may be involved in the virulence of *N. fowleri* (Flores-Huerta *et al.* 2020).

7.5 *Acanthamoeba*

Acanthamoeba species are ubiquitous with worldwide distribution. They are found in soil, fresh and brackish water, bottled mineral water, cooling towers of electric and nuclear power plants, heating and air conditioning units, humidifiers, Jacuzzi tubs, dialysis machines, dust in the air, swabs from nasopharyngeal mucosa of patients with respiratory complaints and from normal individuals, etc. *Acanthamoeba* can tolerate a wide range of osmolarity; this tolerance enables it to survive in distilled water, mammalian body fluids, and seawater. There are around 25 species of *Acanthamoeba* (based on morphology); about half can behave as human pathogens (as opportunistic infections) (Visvesvara *et al.* 2007).

Acanthamoebae are versatile. They feed on almost anything; they can live under both aerobic and anaerobic conditions, even with extreme situations of pH, salinity, and temperature. They are facultative protozoans, and normally do not need a host. However, when acanthamoebae accidentally come in contact to the human eye, lung, or skin, they can cause severe diseases. They are the causative agents of *Acanthamoeba* keratitis (AK), which is a sight-threatening infection of the eye. Coming in contact with immunocompromised patients, they are the causative agents of several disseminating infections that eventually lead to granulomatous amoebic encephalitis (GAE). AK occurs mainly in contact lens wearers. AK annual incidence is estimated as 1 to 10 cases per million inhabitants in industrialized countries, with low contact lens hygiene being the most important risk factor. In USA alone, there is an estimate of 5,000 cases. Early cases of GAE were found in AIDS patients, and there are about 400 cases of GAE documented worldwide (Walochnik and Duchene 2016).

7.5.1 History

Many species of *Acanthamoeba* are known. As an example, Aldo Castellani isolated one from a contamination in a yeast culture in 1930. This is now known as ***Acanthamoeba castellanii*** (Acantha means spine or thorn, referring to the tooth-like acanthopodium of this amoebae). [Axenic culture of *Acanthamoeba castellanii* is available; and cell biologists have used mass culture to study actin and cell motility. *Acanthamoeba* has made a contribution to biology.]

Historically, the first description of AK was in 1973, a South Texas ranger who had a history of trauma in his right eye, and both trophozoites and cysts were found. Via hematogenous dissemination *Acanthamoeba* can cause GAE. In 1948, Clyde Culbertson at Eli Lilly reported an injection of *Acanthamoeba* (found in contaminated cell culture) into mice and monkeys led to encephalitis. Its role for GAE in humans was later shown in AIDS patients. Thus, *Acanthamoeba* encephalitis is known to medicine before *Acanthamoeba* keratitis (Jiang *et al.* 2015).

7.5.2 Life cycle

Please see Figure 7.7 for the life cycle, from CDC.[7]

[7] https://www.cdc.gov/dpdx/freelivingamebic/index.html

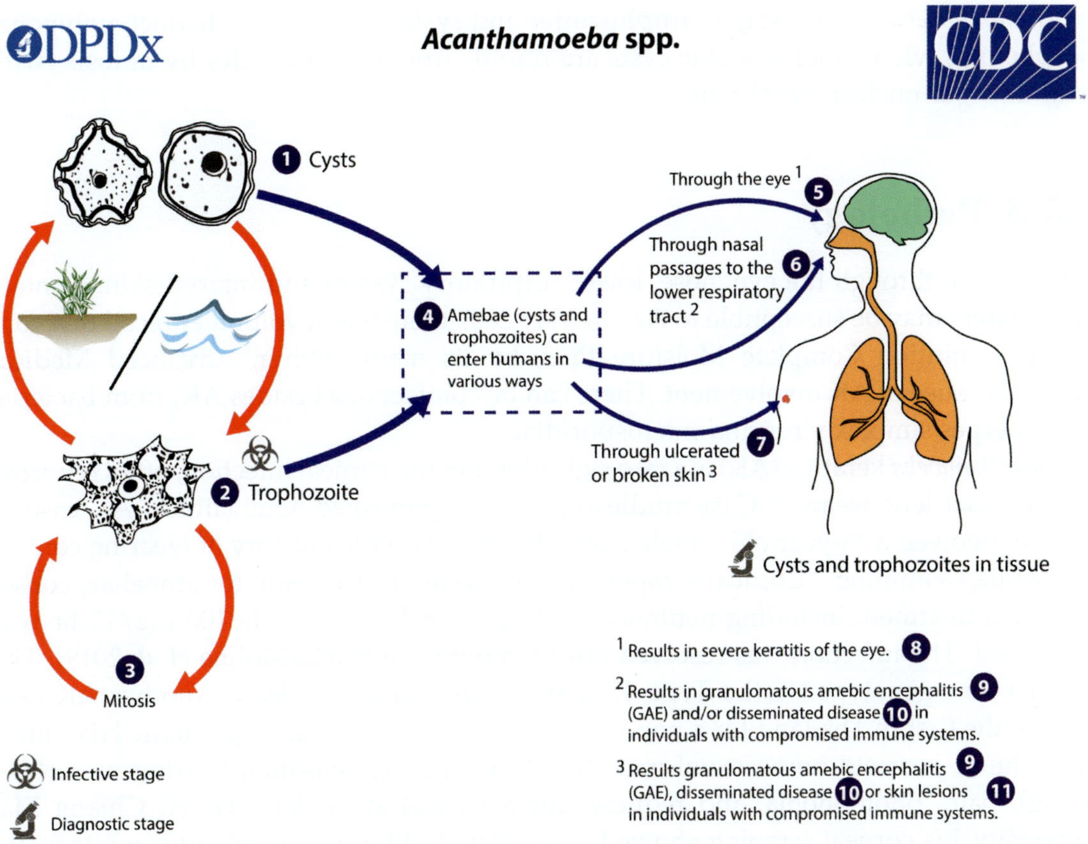

Fig. 7.7 ■ Life cycle of *Acanthamoeba* species. *Acanthamoeba* spp. are ubiquitous in the environment and have been found in a variety of sites, including soil; fresh, brackish, and sea water; field-grown vegetables; sewage; swimming pools; contact lens supplies; medicinal pools; dental treatment units; dialysis machines; heating, ventilating, and air conditioning systems; and tap water; mammalian cell cultures; and vegetables. *Acanthamoeba* has two stages; cysts ❶ and trophozoites ❷ in its life cycle and lacks a flagellate stage. The trophozoites replicate by mitosis (nuclear membrane does not remain intact) ❸. The trophozoites are the infective forms, although both cysts and trophozoites can enter the body ❹ through various means. Entry can occur through the eye ❺, the nasal passages to the lower respiratory tract ❻, or ulcerated or broken skin ❼. When *Acanthamoeba* spp. enters the eye it can cause severe keratitis in otherwise healthy individuals, particularly contact lens users ❽. When it enters the respiratory system or through the skin, it can invade the central nervous system by hematogenous dissemination causing granulomatous amebic encephalitis (GAE) ❾ or disseminated disease ❿, or skin lesions ⓫ in individuals with compromised immune systems. Both *Acanthamoeba* spp. cysts and trophozoites are found in tissue. Courtesy: CDC. Reproduced from https://www.cdc.gov/dpdx/freelivingamebic/index.html

Acanthamoeba has two stages, **trophozoites** and **cysts**. Cysts have a distinct, polygonal morphology, while other amoebic cysts are round. Trophozoite divides by mitosis (with breakdown of nuclear membrane).

7.5.3 Pathology

Entry can be through the eye, nose, lower respiratory system and injured skin. Contact lens wearers may be susceptible to AK. In May 2007 there was a volunteer recall of a contact lens solution Complete Moisture Plus, by its manufacturer, Advanced Medical Optics, because of AK involvement. There can be coinfections besides AK, from bacteria, fungi, herpes simplex virus and microsporidia.

Acanthamoeba keratitis (AK) is a rare sight-threatening corneal infection, often reported from contact lens wearers. Case studies have been published. One clinical AK case in Mexico involved a 38-year-old female from Mexico City with a history of wearing contact lens while swimming. "Corneal scrapes cultures were positive only for amoebae, consequently a treatment including netilmicin 0.3% and oral itraconazole 100 mg/12 hr was prescribed. The infection was resolved after 8 months" (Omaña-Molina *et al.* 2019). The amoeba was genotyped to be Type 4, alias *Acanthamoeba polyphaga*. Another AK case became the first in Thailand for a non-contact lens wearer with asymptomatic HIV infection. The 31-year-old homosexual male had foreign body sensation (during motorbike riding), pain, photophobia, and redness (for 3 weeks) at his left eye. At Chiang Mai University, his corneal scraping showed *Acanthamoeba*-like cysts (calcofluor white staining revealing bright blue cysts under fluorescent microscope), and cultured positive for amoebae in non-nutrient agar plate (monoxenic culture using heat-killed bacteria). *Acanthamoeba* species-specific PCR, followed by rDNA sequencing indicated the agent to be *Acanthamoeba* T4, the major genotype most frequently reported from clinical isolates. The patient was successfully treated (polyhexamethylene biguanide for 2 weeks) but had corneal scar (Tananuvat *et al.* 2019).

7.5.4 Diagnosis

Diagnosis involves microscopically identifying the amoebae from biopsy samples: CSF, lachrymal secretions, tissues. For GAE, diagnostic methods include CSF culture, histopathology, microscopy, neuroimaging, microscopy, molecular techniques, and serology. For proper patient management, early diagnosis is critical (Kalra *et al.* 2020).

7.5.5 Therapy

Treatment for AK uses topical eye drops containing biguanides, diamidines (propamidine), miconazole, propamidine and neosporin. A lengthy 6-month treatment may be needed to clear the infection. Proper care and cleaning of contact lens are advised for the prevention of AK. For GAE patients, although it takes a longer time to develop than PAM, most patients die. A definitive therapy is not yet available.

7.5.6 Genome

In 2013, the draft genome of *Acanthamoeba castellanii* was published (Clarke *et al.* 2013). The genome is 45 Mb in size and encodes 15,455 protein-coding genes (the number is 15,655 for this reference strain in AmoebaDB). The genes are compact but intron-rich, with an average of 6.2 introns per gene, among the highest known in eukaryotes. Large gene families involved in cell signaling and environmental sensing are present (such as protein kinases), including many for pattern recognition receptors (PRRs). Significantly, a large number of genes (450 genes) are acquired by later gene transfer (LTR), from aerobic, free-living bacteria. Acanthamoebae possess unusually broad biosynthetic and metabolic capabilities; they can synthesize most amino acids, cofactors, vitamins, and nucleotides de novo. Moreover, acanthamoebae can digest a wide range of nutrients. They possess cellulase (few protozoa do so) and alginate lyase (the only protozoans do so to date, via LGT, the enzyme is usually only found in bacteria and marine invertebrates). Acanthamoebae probably utilize alginate as a food source, breaking down biofilms and feeding on the enclosed bacteria. They also possess auxin-related genes; they are probably capable of exporting free auxin indole acetic acid (IAA) to influence the growth and development of plants. *Acanthamoeba* genome assemblies, from a geographically diverse range of species and strains, are available via AmoebaDB (Walochnik and Duchene 2016).

Based on their 18S rDNA sequences, *Acanthamoeba* species have been divided into 21 genotypes (different evolutionary lines or clades), and the number of genotypes is growing. Genotype T4 is the most abundant, as it is found in most habitats and is the most common genotype in human infections. Other frequently isolated genotypes are T3 and T11 from AK patients, and T1, T2, T5, T10, T12 and T18 for GAE (Siddiqui and Khan 2012; Kalra *et al.* 2020).

7.5.7 Reservoir

Acanthamoeba species serve as host for many bacteria, fungi and viruses. This is of clinical significance. Species of *Acanthamoeba* harbor many prokaryotes, including those that are highly pathogenic to humans. Examples include methicillin-resistant *Staphylococcus aureus* (MRSA), *Legionnella pneumophila, Mycobacterium avium, Vibrio cholera, Listeria monocytogenes, Helicobacter pylori, Escherichia coli* O157 and *Chlamydia*. A feature common in these prokaryotes that can develop within amoebae is that they are obligate or facultative parasites of human phagocytes, suggesting that pathogenesis of humans may have evolved from infection of the amoebae. Therefore, amoebae may play an essential role in the etiology of some human bacterial diseases. They serve as a training ground for potential human pathogens. *Acanthamoeba castellanii* has served as a host cell for the resurrection of a giant virus, pithovirus, from the Siberian permafrost (after 30,000 years in the frozen state, Legendre *et al.* 2014).

7.6 *Balamuthia*

Only one species, ***Balamuthia mandrillaris*** is pathogenic and an agent for GAE. Different from *Acanthamoeba, B. mandrillaris* encephalitis can occur in immunocompetent individuals. About 200 cases worldwide and 70 cases in the United States of *Balamuthia* infections are known.

7.6.1 History

A mandrill is a species of large baboons. The adult male mandrill has blue and red coloration in its face and sex organ. In 1986 a morphologically distinct amoeba was found upon autopsy in the brain of a pregnant female mandrill baboon who died of encephalitis at the San Diego Zoo Wild Animal Park. It was recognized as a new species, because an antibody had differentiated it from *Naegleria* and *Acanthamoeba* infected samples (using indirect immunofluorescence assay, IIF). In 1993 it was named *Balamuthia mandrillaris*, in honor of the late Professor William Balamuth (1914–1981), UC Berkeley, who studied many species of amoebae, and the mandrill from which it was first identified (Visvesvara *et al.* 1993).

7.6.2 Life cycle

Please see Figure 7.8 for the life cycle, from CDC.[7]

Balamuthia mandrillaris has a trophozoite and a cyst stage.

7.6.3 Pathology

Balamuthia mandrillaris is found in soil, and the route of initial infection is likely via the skin, but inhalation may also occur, resulting in an initial localized infection of the respiratory system with the potential for spread to the brain. GAE can occur in immunocompetent individuals. *Balamuthia* GAE is deadly, and patients die in weeks to months (versus days in PAM).

---

[7] https://www.cdc.gov/dpdx/freelivingamebic/index.html

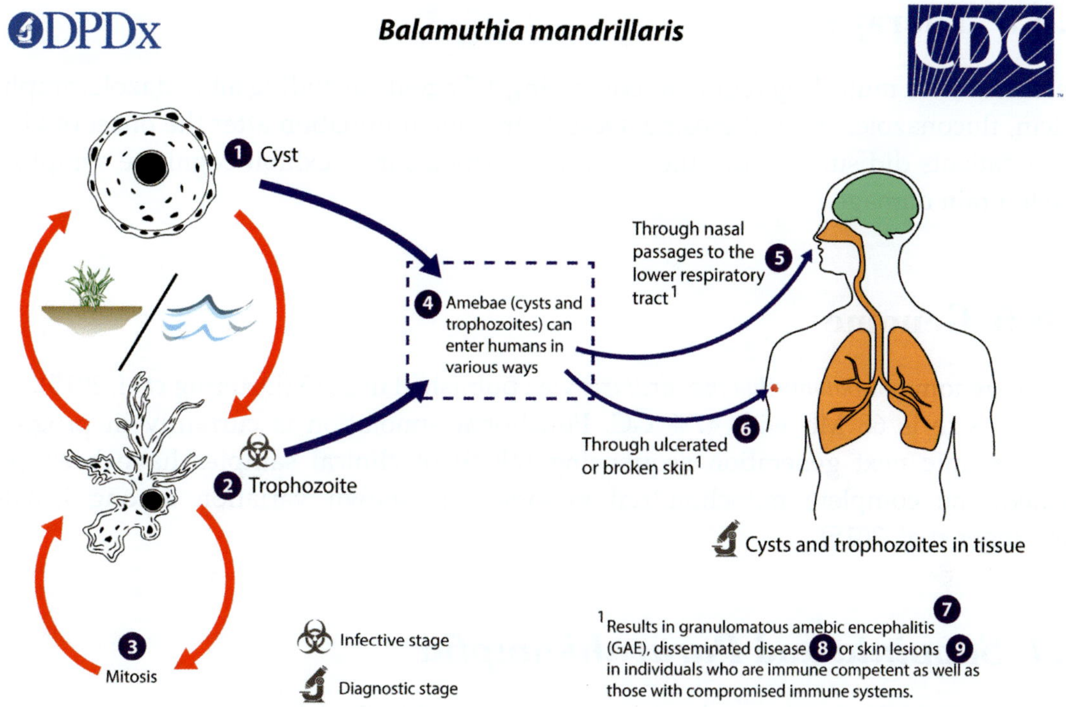

Fig. 7.8 ■ Life cycle of *Balamuthia mandrillaris*. *Balamuthia mandrillaris* has been isolated from soil and dust, and also from autopsy specimens of infected humans and animals. *B. mandrillaris* has two stages, cysts ❶ and trophozoites ❷ in its life cycle and lacks a flagellate stage. The trophozoites replicate by mitosis (nuclear membrane does not remain intact) ❸. The trophozoites are the infective forms, although both cysts and trophozoites gain entry into the body ❹ through various means. Entry can occur through the nasal passages to the lower respiratory tract ❺, or ulcerated or broken skin ❻. When *B. mandrillaris* enters the respiratory system or through the skin, it can invade the central nervous system by hematogenous dissemination causing granulomatous amebic encephalitis (GAE) ❼ or disseminated disease ❽, or skin lesions ❾. *B. mandrillaris* cysts and trophozoites are found in tissue; a few cases have been associated with solid organ transplantation from an infected donor. Courtesy: CDC. Reproduced from https://www.cdc.gov/dpdx/freelivingamebic/index.html

Fatal infections can occur via other routes. Improper nasal lavage by a 69-year-old woman with chronic nasal skin rash led to her death by *Balamuthia* brain infection (Piper *et al.* 2018). The first case of transplantation infection was reported in December 2009, 2 kidney transplant recipients were infected, via receiving kidney from an infected donor (however, the 2 recipients of other organs were not infected).

7.6.4 Diagnosis

Identify the protozoans in biopsy samples. Axenic culture of *B. mandrillaris* is available.

7.6.5 Therapy

Treatment with multidrug regimens containing 4-5 agents including albendazole, amphotericin, fluconazole, and miltefosine. Despite treatment initiation after the onset of GAE, some patients did survive, but the recovering patients may exhibit cognitive symptoms due to brain damage.

7.6.6 Genome

A draft genome of *Balamuthia mandrillaris* was published in 2015 (Detering *et al.* 2015). The genome size is 68 Mb with 47% GC. Functional annotation is currently in progress. Metagenomic next generation sequencing (NGS) of clinical samples have been performed, the complete mitochondrial genome has shown variation among isolates (Greninger *et al.* 2015).

7.7 *Sappinia* and *Paravahkampfia*

Sappinia diploidea is an amoeba that can be cultured in the lab with bacteria as its food source. It has a cyst and trophozoite stage. Interestingly, both trophozoite and cyst have 2 nuclei (hence *diploidea*). Only a single case is known, involving a 38-year-old male from a Texas farm, in 2001. The patient recovered after a multidrug treatment. The authors suggest that this protozoan may be less virulent than other pathogenic amoebae (Gelman *et al.* 2001).

Paravahlkampfia francinae is an amoeba isolated from the cerebrospinal fluid (CSF) of an 18-year-old male after swimming in a local pool and the Pacific Ocean and exhibiting signs of viral meningitis. It is classified as Vahlkampfiidae (nucleus persists through mitosis). In addition to the amoeba stage, it has a flagellate stage, with two flagella (thus, similar to *Naegleria*). Its cysts have bacterial endosymbionts. The patient recovered. The amoeba was co-cultured with mammalian cell culture. Intranasal inoculation of mice did not cause death, "indicating the amoeba is non-pathogenic" (Visvesvara *et al.* 2009). It was named francinae in honor of Francine Marciano-Cabral (Virginia Commonwealth University), who is an expert in the field of pathogenic free-living amoeba (Visvesvara *et al.* 2009).

Genomes for these two species are not yet available.

Summary & Key Concepts

- Amoebic dysentery is the third leading cause of death from parasitic diseases worldwide.
- Amoebiasis utilizes the fecal-oral route for transmission.
- *Entamoeba dispar* and *E. histolytica* are morphologically indistinguishable but they have molecular, biochemical and immunological differences.

- *E. gingivalis* is a commensal species that lives in the mouth and phagocytose bacteria. It is also the only species with only trophozoite stage and no cyst stage.
- *Naegleria fowleri* goes in through the nose and causes acute and often fatal central nervous system (CNS) infection known as primary amoebic meningoencephalitis (PAM).
- *Acanthamoeba* causes sight-threatening infections to the eyes; amoebic invasion of immunocompromised patients results in disseminating infections which can lead to granulomatous amoebic encephalitis (GAE).
- *Balamuthia mandrillaris* is another agent that cause GAE. It can cause encephalitis in immunocompetent individuals.

References

Bellini NK, Santos TM, da Silva MTA, Thiemann OH. The therapeutic strategies against *Naegleria fowleri*. *Exp Parasitol* 2018;187:1–11.

Ben Ayed L, Sabbahi S. *Entamoeba histolytica*. In: Rose JB, Jiménez-Cisneros B (eds.) Global Water Pathogen Project. http://www.waterpathogens.org (Fayer R, Jakubowski W (eds.) Part 3 *Protists*) www.waterpathogens.org/book/entamoeba-histolytica. Michigan State University, Lansing E, MI, UNESCO, 2017.

Chomba M, Mucheleng'anga LA, Fwoloshi S, Ngulube J, Mutengo MM. A case report: Primary amoebic meningoencephalitis in a young Zambian adult. *BMC Infect Dis* 2017;17(1):532.

Clarke M, Lohan AJ, Liu B, *et al*. Genome of *Acanthamoeba castellanii* highlights extensive lateral gene transfer and early evolution of tyrosine kinase signaling. *Genome Biol* 2013;14(2):R11.

Cooper AM, Aouthmany S, Shah K, Rega PP. Killer amoebas: Primary amoebic meningoencephalitis in a changing climate. *JAAPA* 2019;32(6):30–35.

Côté NM, Le Bailly M. Palaeoparasitology and palaeogenetics: Review and perspectives for the study of ancient human parasites. *Parasitology* 2018;145(5):656–64.

Cox FEG. *The Welcome Trust Illustrated History of Tropical Diseases* (The Wellcome Trust, London, 1996).

Cox FE. History of human parasitology. *Clin Microbiol Rev* 2002;15(4):595–612.

Cui Z, Li J, Chen Y, Zhang L. Molecular epidemiology, evolution, and phylogeny of *Entamoeba* spp. *Infect Genet Evol* 2019;75:104018.

Das K, Ganguly S. Evolutionary genomics and population structure of *Entamoeba histolytica*. *Comput Struct Biotechnol J* 2014;12(20–21):26–33.

De Jonckheere JF. What do we know by now about the genus *Naegleria*? *Exp Parasitol* 2014;145 Suppl:S2–9.

Detering H, Aebischer T, Dabrowski PW, *et al*. First draft genome sequence of *Balamuthia mandrillaris*, the causative agent of Amoebic Encephalitis. *Genome Announc* 2015;3(5). pii: e01013–15.

Eskew WH, Ledger ML, Lloyd A, Pyles G, Gosker J, Mitchell PD. Intestinal parasites in an Ottoman period latrine from Acre (Israel) dating to the early 1800s CE. *Korean J Parasitol* 2019;57(6): 575–80.

Farnon EC, Kokko KE, Budge PJ, *et al*. Transmission of *Balamuthia mandrillaris* by organ transplantation. *Clin Infect Dis* 2016;63(7):878–88.

Flores-Huerta N, Sánchez-Monroy V, Rodríguez MA, Serrano-Luna J, Shibayama M. A comparative study of the membrane proteins from *Naegleria* species: A 23-kDa protein participates in the virulence of Naegleria fowleri. *Eur J Protistol* 2020;72:125640.

Gelman BB, Rauf SJ, Nader R, *et al*. Amoebic encephalitis due to *Sappinia diploidea*. *JAMA* 2001;285(19):2450–1.

Grace E, Asbill S, Virga K. *Naegleria fowleri*: Pathogenesis, diagnosis, and treatment options. *Antimicrob Agents Chemother* 2015;59(11):6677–81.

Greninger AL, Messacar K, Dunnebacke T, *et al*. Clinical metagenomic identification of *Balamuthia mandrillaris* encephalitis and assembly of the draft genome: The continuing case for reference genome sequencing. *Genome Med* 2015;7:113.

Guedes L, Borba VH, Camacho M, Neto J, Dias O, Iñiguez AM. African helminth infection out of Africa: Paleoparasitological and paleogenetic investigations in Pretos Novos cemetery, Rio de Janeiro, Brazil (1769–1830). *Acta Trop* 2020;205:105399.

Jiang C, Sun X, Wang Z, Zhang Y. *Acanthamoeba* keratitis: Clinical characteristics and management. *Ocul Surf* 2015;13(2):164–8.

Kalra SK, Sharma P, Shyam K, Tejan N, Ghoshal U. *Acanthamoeba* and its pathogenic role in granulomatous amebic encephalitis. *Exp Parasitol* 2020;208:107788.

Kean BH, Mott KE, Russell AJ. *Tropical Medicine and Parasitology: Classic Investigations, Volumes I and II*. Cornell, 1978.

Król-Turmińska K, Olender A. Human infections caused by free-living amoebae. *Ann Agric Environ Med* 2017;24(2):254–60.

Legendre M, Bartoli J, Shmakova L, *et al*. Thirty-thousand-year-old distant relative of giant icosahedral DNA viruses with pandoravirusmorphology. *Proc Natl Acad Sci USA* 2014; 111(11):4274–9.

Liechti N, Schürch N, Bruggmann R, Wittwer M. The genome of *Naegleria lovaniensis*, the basis for a comparative approach to unravel pathogenicity factors of the human pathogenic amoeba *N. fowleri*. *BMC Genomics* 2018;19(1):654.

Linam WM, Ahmed M, Cope JR, *et al*. Successful treatment of an adolescent with *Naegleria fowleri* primary amebic meningoencephalitis. *Pediatrics* 2015;135(3):e744–8.

Loftus B, Anderson I, Davies R, *et al*. The genome of the protist parasite *Entamoeba histolytica*. *Nature* 2005;433(7028):865–8.

Loreille O, Roumat E, Verneau O, Bouchet F, Hänni C. Ancient DNA from *Ascaris*: extraction amplification and sequences from eggs collected in coprolites. *Int J Parasitol* 2001;31:1101–6.

Lorenzi HA, Puiu D, Miller JR, *et al*. New assembly, reannotation and analysis of the *Entamoeba histolytica* genome reveal new genomic features and protein content information. *PLoS Negl Trop Dis* 2010;4(6):e716.

Maciver SK, Piñero JE, Lorenzo-Morales J. Is *Naegleria fowleri* an Emerging Parasite? *Trends Parasitol* 2020;36(1):19–28.

Marie C, Petri WA Jr. Regulation of virulence of *Entamoeba histolytica*. *Annu Rev Microbiol* 2014;68:493–520.

Martínez-Castillo M, Cárdenas-Zúñiga R, Coronado-Velázquez D, Debnath A, Serrano-Luna J, Shibayama M. *Naegleria fowleri* after 50 years: Is it a neglected pathogen? *J Med Microbiol* 2016;65(9):885–96.

Miller HW, Suleiman RL, Ralston KS. Trogocytosis by *Entamoeba histolytica* mediates acquisition and display of human cell membrane proteins and evasion of lysis by human serum. *MBio* 2019;10(2)pii:e00068-19.

Mitchell PD, Stern E, Tepper Y. Dysentery in the crusader kingdom of Jerusalem: An ELISA analysis of two medieval latrines in the city of Acre (Israel). *Journal of Archaeological Science* 2008;35(7):1849–53.

Omaña-Molina M, Vanzzini-Zago V, Hernández-Martínez D, *et al*. *Acanthamoeba* keratitis in Mexico: Report of a clinical case and importance of sensitivity assays for a better outcome. *Exp Parasitol* 2019;196:22–7.

Piñero JE, Chávez-Munguía B, Omaña-Molina M, Lorenzo-Morales J. *Naegleria fowleri*. *Trends Parasitol* 2019;35(10):848–49.

Piper KJ, Foster H, Susanto D, Maree CL, Thornton SD, Cobbs CS. Fatal *Balamuthia mandrillaris* brain infection associated with improper nasal lavage. *Int J Infect Dis* 2018;77:18–22.

Ralston KS, Solga MD, Mackey-Lawrence NM, Somlata, Bhattacharya A, Petri WA Jr. Trogocytosis by *Entamoeba histolytica* contributes to cell killing and tissue invasion. *Nature* 2014;508(7497):526–30.

Rice CA, Colon BL, Chen E, Hull MV, Kyle DE. Discovery of repurposing drug candidates for the treatment of diseases caused by pathogenic free-living amoebae. *PLoS Negl Trop Dis* 2020;14(9):e0008353.

Sazzad HMS, Luby SP, Sejvar J, *et al*. A case of primary amebic meningoencephalitis caused by *Naegleria fowleri* in Bangladesh. *Parasitol Res* 2020;119(1):339–44.

Shehab KW, Aboul-Nasr K, Elliott SP. *Balamuthia mandrillaris* granulomatous amebic encephalitis with renal dissemination in a previously healthy child: Case report and review of the pediatric literature. *J Pediatric Infect Dis Soc* 2018;7(3):e163–8.

Shirley DT, Farr L, Watanabe K, Moonah S. A review of the global burden, new diagnostics, and current therapeutics for amebiasis. *Open Forum Infect Dis* 2018;5(7):ofy161.

Siddiqui R, Khan NA. Biology and pathogenesis of *Acanthamoeba*. *Parasit Vectors* 2012;5:6.

Skappak C, Akierman S, Belga S, *et al*. Invasive amoebiasis: A review of *Entamoeba* infections highlighted with case reports. *Can J Gastroenterol Hepatol* 2014;28(7):355–9.

Tananuvat N, Techajongjintana N, Somboon P, Wannasan A. The first *Acanthamoeba* keratitis case of non-contact lens wearer with HIV infection in Thailand. *Korean J Parasitol* 2019;57(5):505–11.

Tovar J, Fischer A, Clark CG. The mitosome, a novel organelle related to mitochondria in the amitochondrial parasite *Entamoeba histolytica*. *Mol Microbiol* 1999;32(5):1013–21.

Verma AK, Verma R, Ahuja V, Paul J. Real-time analysis of gut flora in *Entamoeba histolytica* infected patients of northern India. *BMC Microbiol* 2012;12:183.

Visvesvara GS, Moura H, Schuster FL. Pathogenic and opportunistic free-living amoebae: *Acanthamoeba* spp., *Balamuthia mandrillaris*, *Naegleria fowleri*, and *Sappinia diploidea*. *FEMS Immunol Med Microbiol* 2007;50(1):1–26.

Visvesvara GS, Schuster FL, Martinez AJ. *Balamuthia mandrillaris*, N. G., N. Sp., agent of amebic meningoencephalitis in humans and other animals. *J Eukaryot Microbiol* 1993;40(4):504–14.

Visvesvara GS, Martinez AJ, Schuster FL, *et al*. Leptomyxid ameba, a new agent of amebic meningoencephalitis in humans and animals. *J Clin Microbiol* 1990;28(12):2750–6.

Visvesvara GS, Sriram R, Qvarnstrom Y, *et al*. *Paravahlkampfia francinae* n. sp. masquerading as an agent of primary amoebic meningoencephalitis. *J Eukaryot Microbiol* 2009;56(4):357–66.

Wallis G, Curran L, Hearn P, Gothard P. An interesting pair of amoebic infections. *Lancet Infect Dis* 2018;18(1):121.

Walochnik J, Duchêne M. Eds. *Molecular Parasitology: Protozoan Parasites and their Molecules*, Springer, 2016.

Wang Q, Li J, Ji J, *et al*. A case of *Naegleria fowleri* related primary amoebic meningoencephalitis in China diagnosed by next-generation sequencing. *BMC Infect Dis* 2018;18(1):349.

Weedall GD, Clark CG, Koldkjaer P, *et al*. Genomic diversity of the human intestinal parasite *Entamoeba histolytica*. *Genome Biol* 2012;13(5):R38.

Willhoeft U, Tannich E. The electrophoretic karyotype of *Entamoeba histolytica*. *Mol Biochem Parasitol* 1999;99(1):41–53.

Wilson IW, Weedall GD, Hall N. Host-Parasite interactions in *Entamoeba histolytica* and *Entamoeba dispar*: What have we learned from their genomes? *Parasite Immunol* 2012;34(2–3):90–9.

Wiser MF. *Protozoa and Human Disease*, Garland, 2011.

Yoder JS, Straif-Bourgeois S, Roy SL, *et al*. Primary amebic meningoencephalitis deaths associated with sinus irrigation using contaminated tap water. *Clin Infect Dis* 2012;55(9):e79–85.

Zysset-Burri DC, Müller N, Beuret C, *et al*. Genome-wide identification of pathogenicity factors of the free-living amoeba *Naegleria fowleri*. *BMC Genomics* 2014;15:496.

8

Balantidiasis by a Ciliate and *Blastocystis* Infection by a Stramenopile

8.1 Introductory Remarks

Although both *Balantidium* and *Blastocystis* are within the same supergroup (SAR), the former is a ciliate and the latter a stramenopile. However, there are similarities between the two. They are the only species within the vast members of ciliates and stramenopiles that are agents of human infections. Both protozoa use the fecal–oral route for infection, both prefer the large intestine, and both are rarely fatal. Moreover, both protozoa have infected many individuals worldwide, but most are asymptomatic.

8.2 *Balantidium*

The supergroup SAR stands for Stramenopiles, Alveolata, and Rhizaria. Within the Alveolata is the group Ciliophora, the ciliates. *Balantidium* is a ciliate. In fact, *Balantidium* is the only species of ciliates that is pathogenic to humans. All ciliates, including *Paramecium* and *Balantidium*, have **nuclear dimorphism**: a macronucleus (for metabolic activities) and a micronucleus (for sexual reproduction, or conjugation). Being a ciliate, the protozoan is characteristically covered with rows and rows of cilia (for motility, swimming). It has a pointed anterior end with a depression named peristome ending in a cytostome ("cell mouth"); its back end shows a cytopyge ("cell anus"). *Balantidium* possesses hydrogenosomes, contractile vacuoles for osmoregulation (rare in parasitic protozoa as hosts usually maintain a constant environment), food particle vesicles, and mitochondrial-like bodies (**MLBs**). *Balantidium* is known as the **largest** parasitic protozoan infecting humans. It has a **trophozoite** and a **cyst** stage; the former has cilia and the

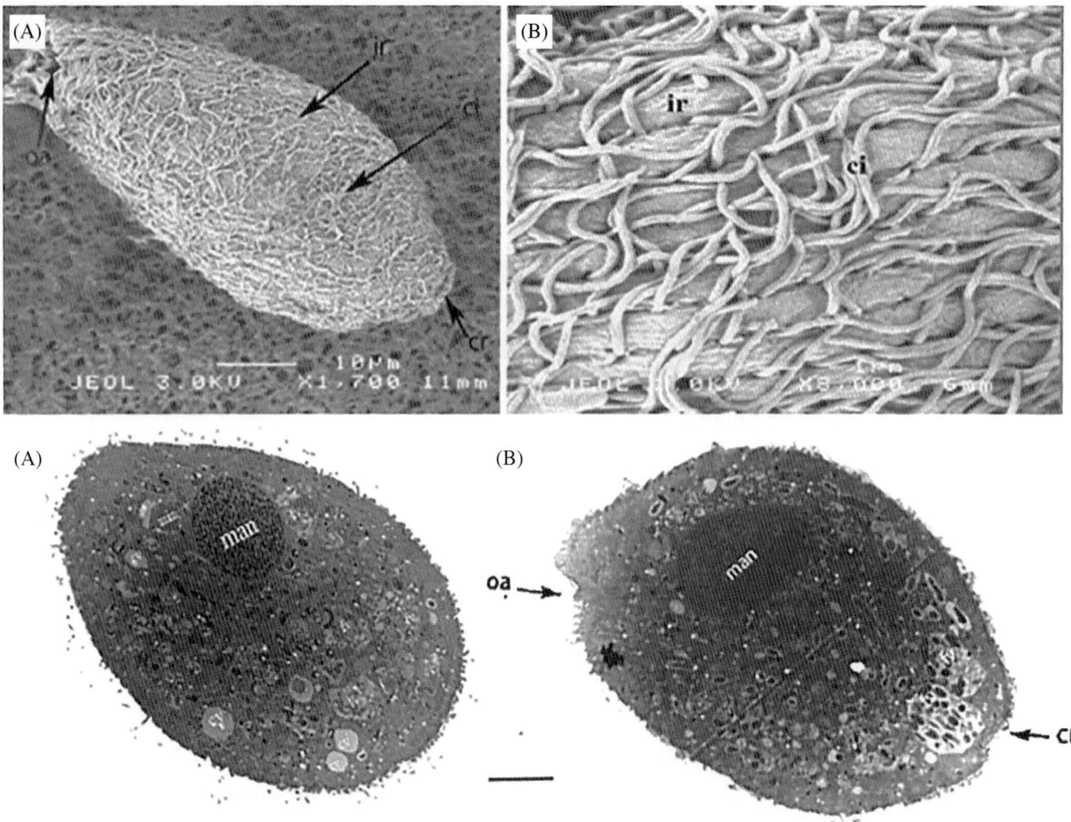

Fig. 8.1 ■ Scanning and transmission electron microscopic images of *Balantidium coli*. Upper panels: Scanning electron micrographs of the Philippine *B. coli* isolate. (A) General view showing the oral apparatus (*oa*) and the caudal region (*cr*). The interkinetal ridges (*ir*) along with its adjacent cilia (*ci*) are shown. *Bar*, 10 μm. (B) Magnified somatic cilia (*ci*) and interkinetal ridges (*ir*). *Bar*, 1 μm. Lower panels: Transmission electron micrographs of the Philippine *B. coli* isolate. (A) Longitudinal thin section showing the general aspect. The conspicuous macronucleus (*man*) and smaller micronucleus (*min*) are seen. Four contractile vacuoles (*cv*) and several food vacuoles (*fv*) are also observed. *Bar*, 6.25 μm. (B) Ultra-thin section showing the oral apparatus (*oa*) and caudal region (*cr*). The large macronucleus (*man*) is seen near the middle portion of the cell body. Micronucleus is no longer visible. *Bar*, 5.71 μm. Courtesy: Nilles-Bije M, Rivera W, *Parasitol Res* 2010;106:387–94. Reproduced with permission from Springer Nature.

latter a cyst wall. The trophozoite's size is 50–130 μm by 20–70 μm. The round cyst is 40–60 μm in diameter. Please see Figure 8.1 for scanning and transmission electron microscopic images of *Balantidium coli* (Nilles-Bije and Rivera 2010).

8.2.1 History

Unlike the opportunistic free-living amoebae (as discussed in Chapter 7), *Balantidium* has a long history. It was first described in 1857 in Stockholm, Sweden, in two patients with acute diarrhea. One patient recovered, the other died, and *Balantidium* was found to be a human pathogen. The Swedish medical doctor Pehr Henrik Malmsten reported these two clinical cases at Seraphim Hospital: a 38-year-old seaman Henrich B. suffering from recurrent diarrhea for 6 months survived, but a 35-year-old laborer's wife Christina Lindstrom died one week after a second admission to the hospital (9 months after her first episode of diarrhea). The same protozoan ("infusoria") was found in the stool of both patients by microscopic examination. Malmsten suggested, "Since these intestinal infusoria seem to be closer to the paramecium, perhaps they could be called *Paramecium (?) coli* for the time being" (Kean *et al.* 1978). The current name is *Balantidium coli* (Balanto means bag, coli refers to location). It is ironic that the first cases were seen in Sweden; balantidiasis is usually regarded as a disease of tropic and subtropic regions. In May and June 1971, an outbreak of balantidiasis was reported on the island of Truk in the western Pacific. After a typhoon, the residents were forced to use contaminated water in streams, resulting in 110 cases of balantidiasis, as well as increased infection from *Entamoeba* and *Ascaris* (Walzer *et al.* 1973).

8.2.2 Life cycle

Please see Figure 8.2 for the life cycle of *Balantidium coli*, from the CDC.[1]

Balantidium has a fecal–oral life cycle and a cyst is its infectious stage. Excystment leads to the trophozoite stage. Pigs may be reservoirs, but there is the question whether ***Balantidium coli*** and ***Balantidium suis*** are the same protozoan. It has been suggested that the former is larger in size than the latter, but different culture conditions can influence the size of this protozoan. It may be a single species that splits into two size variations. *Balatidium* species have been found in the intestines of crustaceans, insects (cockroaches), fish, amphibians (frogs, the giant Chinese salamander), birds, and mammals (rats, guinea pigs, camels, wild boars, primates, and humans) (Schuster and Ramirez-Avila 2008).

8.2.3 Pathology

Infections can be asymptomatic, and symptoms vary from mild diarrhea to **balantidyl dysentery** (balantidiasis, or balantidiosis). The most severe *Balantidium* infection causes weight loss, **tenesmus** (feeling the need to pass stool despite an empty colon), and bloody stools. In 2013, a case of balantidial liver abscess was found in a 48-year-old tailor in India (Kapur *et al.* 2016). In 2019, a case of *Balantidium coli*-caused dysentery was diagnosed in a 68-year-old male from Shanxi province presenting with a history of abdominal pain, tenesmus, and diarrhea with blood; he had worked as a pig farmer for 4 months. "*Balantidium coli* human infection predominantly occurs in tropical and subtropical regions in the world. Human case is extremely rare in China. ... Our case indicates possible occurrence of *Balantidium coli*-related disease in cooler climates" (Yu *et al.* 2020). As mentioned in the History section, this ciliate pathogen was first discovered in Stockholm, Sweden.

[1] https://www.cdc.gov/dpdx/balantidiasis/index.html

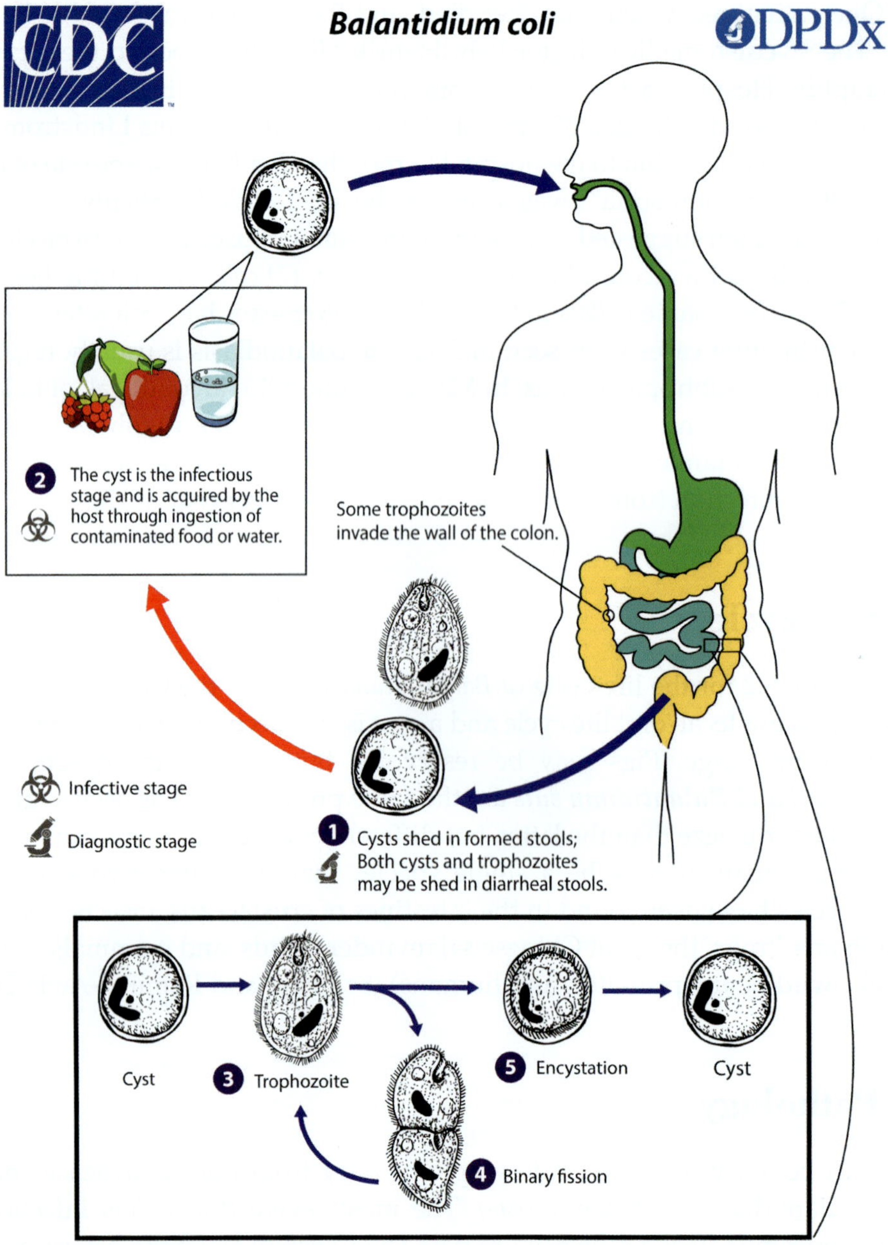

Fig. 8.2 ■ Life cycle of *Balantidium coli*. Cysts are the stage responsible for transmission of balantidiasis ❶. The host most often acquires the cyst through ingestion of contaminated food or water ❷. Following ingestion, excystation occurs in the small intestine, and the trophozoites colonize the large intestine ❸. The trophozoites reside in the lumen of the large intestine and appendix of humans and animals, where they replicate by binary fission, during which conjugation may occur ❹. Trophozoites undergo encystation to produce infective cysts ❺. Some trophozoites invade the wall of the colon and multiply, causing ulcerative pathology in the colon wall. Some return to the lumen and disintegrate. Mature cysts are passed with feces. Courtesy of the CDC. Reproduced from https://www.cdc.gov/dpdx/balantidiasis/index.html.

Humans ingest cysts, the transmission stage, via contaminated food or water. If the stomach acid is pH 5 or higher (a situation seen in malnourished persons with low stomach acid content), the cyst survives and excystment takes place in the small intestine, and then the trophozoite colonizes the large intestine. Some trophozoites may invade the colon wall. Trophozoites produce hyaluronidase that facilitates cell lysis and tissue invasion. Some trophozoites form cysts. Encystment is stimulated by the dehydration of feces. This feature is of epidemiological importance, because trophozoites can differentiate to cysts after leaving the host.

Pigs may serve as reservoir. Prevalence in pigs ranges from 20–100%, as shown in a Japanese study with 100% pigs infected. Infection is common in pig farmers and pig abattoir workers. In animals from pigs to guinea pigs, there is no pathogenesis, and most humans are asymptomatic (but can serve as carriers). Human prevalence ranges from 0.02–1%. High-prevalence areas include the Philippines, Papua New Guinea, Iran, and the Middle East. Less than **1,000** cases are diagnosed per year worldwide (Schuster and Ramirez-Avila 2008).

Although *Balantidium* infects pigs, other domestic animals can also be infected, although to a lesser extent. Arslan Ahmed (University of Veterinary and Animal Sciences, Lahore, Pakistan) and colleagues analyzed published data between 1989 and 2019 that listed the domestic animals: cattle and buffalo, sheep and goat, camel, horse and donkey, and pig. Thus, *Balantidium coli* is "an emerging protozoan pathogen of zoonotic significance" (Ahmed *et al.* 2020).

8.2.4 Diagnosis

Stool observation of live trophozoites is diagnostic, as first done by Malmsten in Sweden. *Balantidium coli* can be isolated and cultured under xenic conditions (from fecal samples), as shown in a study from 88 pigs and 116 monkeys (Barbosa *et al.* 2015). Xenic in vitro culture (XIVC) is defined as culture in the presence of an undefined bacterial flora.

8.2.5 Therapy

Typical therapy is **tetracycline** and **metronidazole**.

8.2.6 Genome

The *Balantidium* genome is not yet known. A study using small subunit ribosomal DNA (SSUrDNA) and internal transcribed spacer (ITS) sequencing, for different *Balantidium* isolates (a total of 49) from fecal samples of primates, pigs, and wild boars, has shown genetic diversity. The investigators have proposed a new genus ***Neobalantidium*** (for homeothermic or warm-blooded species) to substitute the *Balantidium* genus name (Pomajbilova *et al.* 2013). In this chapter, the more standard *Balantidium coli* is retained instead of the proposed name change.

8.3 *Blastocystis*

Blastocystis belongs to the Stramenopiles of the SAR supergroup. Stramenopiles are a diverse group; members include diatoms, water molds, brown algae (kelp), and many others. There are unicellular and multicellular forms, with both heterotrophic and photosynthetic feeding features. They are called Heterokonts, meaning "different flagella." The name Stramenopiles means "straw-haired" and refers to the three-part bristles on the front flagellum of the single-cell form; this feature is absent in the back flagellum. Although classified as a stramenopile, *Blastocystis* itself has no flagellum. Of interest is the fact that it is one of the most successful intestinal eukaryotes identified to date, being able to infect a wide range of host species and reside in the gut for years. Its taxonomic status was unclear for many years. At one time, it was thought to be a yeast, until small subunit ribosomal DNA (SSUrDNA) sequencing definitively identified it as stramenopile (Zierdt 1991; Silberman *et al.* 1996). *Blastocystis* is the eukaryotic microbe most frequently colonizing the human gut. Its prevalence is 30–60% in developing countries, and over 5% in industrialized countries. One study has found 100% infection in villages in Senegal. It is estimated that over **one billion** individuals are infected worldwide (Gentekaki *et al.* 2017). "*Blastocystis* is one of the most successful intestinal eukaryotes identified to date, being able to infect a wide range of host species. It may reside in the gut for years on end and appears to show remarkably little susceptibility to standard chemotherapeutic interventions..." (Stensvold and Clark 2016).

8.3.1 History

The *Blastocystis* protozoan was first described by Alexey Georgievich Alexeieff in 1911, who proposed the name *Blastocystis enterocola*. An extensive morphological description was given, and a life cycle was proposed. Later, the French parasitologist Emile Brumpt suggested the name ***Blastocystis hominis*** (Blastos means germ or vesicle, homo is human) because the organism was isolated from human fecal material, and this has become the name recognized in the literature. However, *Blastocystis* has been found in many organisms, from amphibians to birds and mammals (Stenzel and Boreham 1996; Denoeud *et al.* 2011). Genetic analysis based on SSUrDNA has shown at least **17** subtypes (**ST**), with ST1-9 seen in humans. Thus, *Blastocystis hominis* has been changed accordingly, to ***Blastocystis* species**, the term used in this chapter.

8.3.2 Life cycle

Please see Figure 8.3 for the life cycle of *Blastocystis* species, from the CDC.[2]

Blastocystis shows different morphologies: **cyst, amoeboid, granular,** and **vacuolar**. There are thin-walled and thick-walled cysts for different functions, responsible for auto-infection and transmission, respectively. The vacuolar form divides by binary fission (Stenzel and Boreham 1996; Tan 2004; Roberts *et al.* 2014). The complete life cycle is still under debate among investigators. *Blastocystis* species have unusual organelles (mitochondria-like organelle, **MLO**, or mitochondria-related organelle, **MRO**). Please see Figure 8.4 (Left panel) for *Blastocystis* cysts (Zaman *et al.* 1998) and Figure 8.4 (Right panel) for amoeboid and spherical forms by scanning electron microscopy (Tan *et al.* 2008). Based on ultrastructural analysis by transmission electron microscopy, *Blastocystis* has three modes of reproduction: binary fission, plasmotomy, and budding (Zhang *et al.* 2012). [Plasmotomy is a type of asexual reproduction in which a multinucleate protozoan cell divides into two or more multinucleate daughter cells without the occurrence of mitosis.] An axenic *Blastocystis* strain can be grown on agar in vitro (Tan *et al.* 2000). Different *Blastocystis* isolates show variations in their surface coat, which may influence pathogenic potential (Yason and Tan 2018).

8.3.3 Pathology

Blastocystis has been considered as a commensal organism and its infection is asymptomatic. This gastrointestinal (GI) protozoan parasite has been reported to cause non-specific GI symptoms including diarrhea, flatulence, abdominal pain, and nausea. It has even been associated with inflammatory bowel disease (**IBD**). There is debate about the pathogenicity of *Blastocystis* in humans. It can cause both gastro- and extra-intestinal diseases with persistent rashes. For example, a case of blastocystosis was reported in Mexico, where a 47-year-old female had extra-enteric blastocystosis with minimal cervicitis symptoms and her isolate was identified to belong to ST1 (Escutia-Guzman *et al.* 2020). *Blastocystis* may be transmitted by humans and by a number of animal hosts, including chickens, rats, and pigs.

A case of blastocystosis was documented in Italy (Angelici *et al.* 2018). A 41-year-old male had cramps, bloating, and watery diarrhea a few days after drinking water indicated as unpotable (from a fountain in a farm). His *Blastocystis* infection was typed as ST1 by restriction fragment length polymorphism-polymerase chain reaction (RFLP-PCR). Water from the fountain also tested positive for both *Blastocystis* and *Giardia lamblia*. The fountain was intended for watering livestock only; the nearby river was contaminated by animal feces. Interestingly, only a **probiotic** treatment based on *Saccharomyces boulardii* was administered to the patient and this apparently resolved his infection.

---

[2] https://www.cdc.gov/dpdx/blastocystis/index.html

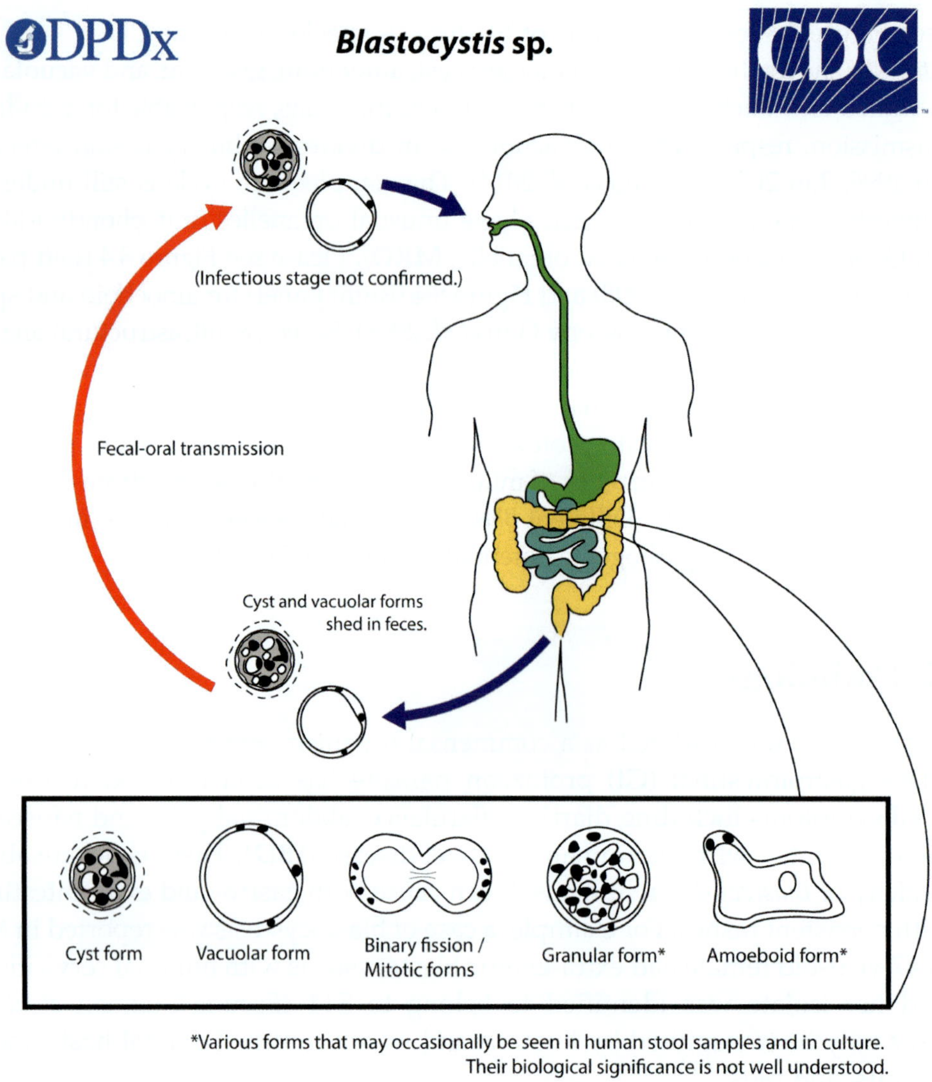

Fig. 8.3 ■ Life cycle of *Blastocystis* species. The life cycle of *Blastocystis* sp. is not yet understood, including the infectious stage and whether (and which of the) various morphologic forms of this polymorphic organism that have been identified in stool or culture constitute distinct biologic stages of the parasite in the intestinal tract of hosts. The cyst form (3–5 μm) is postulated to be an infectious stage, but not confirmed. The predominant form found in human stool specimens is referred to as the vacuolar (or central body) form and is of variable size (5–40 μm, occasionally much larger). Replication appears to occur via binary fission. Other morphologic forms (e.g., ameboid and granular forms) have also been noted in stool samples and/or culture; their biological role and eventual developmental fate require further investigation. Courtesy of the CDC. Reproduced from https://www.cdc.gov/dpdx/blastocystis/index.html.

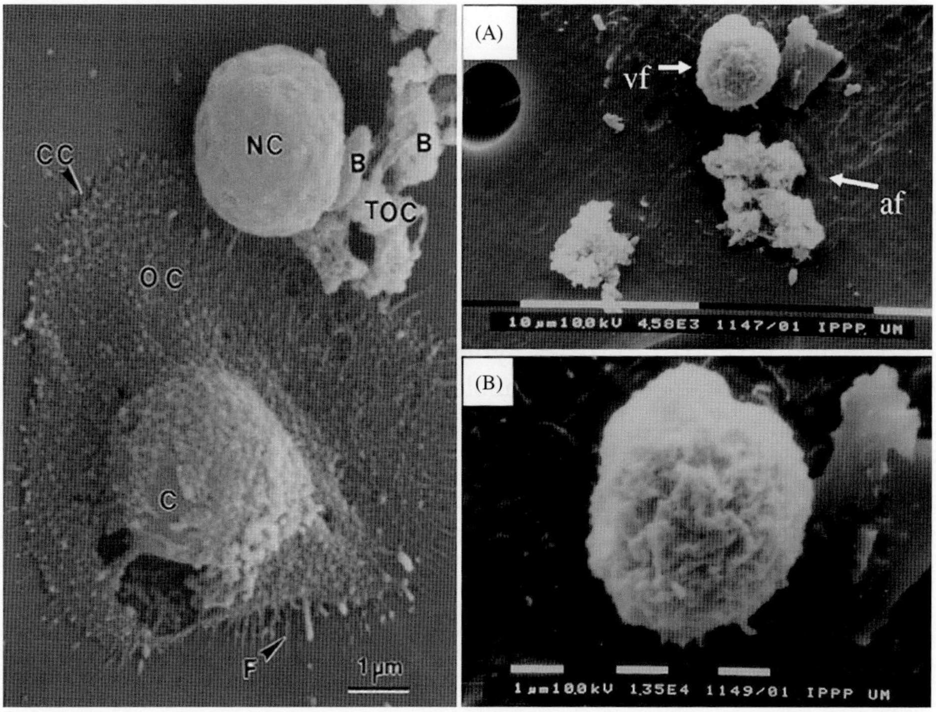

Fig. 8.4 ■ *Blastocystis* cysts, amoeboid and spherical forms under scanning electron microscopy. Left panel: *Blastocystis hominis* cysts (NC Naked cysts, OC outer coat, CC coated cyst, C cyst partially visible underneath the outer coat, F fimbria-like structure, B bacteria, TOC torn or fragmented outer coat). Right panel: Scanning electron micrographs of symptomatic *B. hominis* isolate (S1) grown in vitro. (A) Two types of parasite cells can be seen: (1) a spherical vacuolar form (vf) and (2) an irregularly shaped, amoeboid form (af) with a rough surface and projections. (B) Higher magnification of (A) showing a vacuolar form with a rough surface. Courtesy: (Left panel) Zaman *et al. Parasitol Res.* 1998;84:476–477; (Right panel) Tan *et al. Parasitol Res.* 2008;104:85–93. Reproduced with permission from Springer Nature.

Blastocystis infection may be linked to IBD; it may also be linked to colorectal cancer (**CRC**). In vitro, *Blastocystis* ST3 can elicit higher proliferation of colon cancer cell line. A case of colorectal cancer with *Blastocystis* ST3 was documented in a 35-year-old male taxi driver in India. "It is prudent to screen and treat *Blastocystis* on routine basis among IBD and CRC patients" (Padukone *et al.* 2017).

8.3.4 Diagnosis

Microscopic examination of stool samples for cysts is possible, as well as molecular assays such as the use of polymerase chain reaction (PCR).

8.3.5 Therapy

Metronidazole is the drug of choice, but **paromomycin** has also been used (Roberts *et al.* 2014). Two cases of metronidazole resistance in students, both frequent travelers, were documented in Malaysia (Rajamanikam *et al.* 2018). A 13-year-old boy from Denmark, residing in Malaysia, had a complaint of abdominal pains after a family vacation to Vietnam (in January 2017, to an area that had been flooded). A 30-year-old male, a student from Saudi Arabia studying in Malaysia for 2 years, had been suffering from chronic flatulence for 2 years. Both were found to be infected with *Blastocystis;* both showed increased parasite load and exacerbated symptoms upon treatment with the usual recommended dosage and regime of metronidazole (cyst count 5-fold higher than original cyst count prior to treatment). In both cases, the pathogen was shown to be ST3 by analysis of the 18S small subunit ribosomal RNA gene (SSUrDNA). The investigators had "previously demonstrated metronidazole resistance in vitro using a range of concentrations (unpublished observation). This suggests that it is highly possible that the parasite gained resistance towards metronidazole" (Rajamanikam *et al.* 2018).

8.3.6 Genome

As noted above, *Blastocystis hominis* has been changed to *Blastocystis* species, with 17 subtypes (ST1-17) based on small subunit rRNA genes (SSUrDNA). "STs are as divergent as species or even genera. Humans can host ST1–9 and 12; more than 90% of human *Blastocystis* strains belong to ST1–4" (Stensvold *et al.* 2020).

The draft genome of ST7, from a patient in Singapore, showed a total of **6,020** protein-coding genes, with evidence of horizontal gene transfer (HGT) for 133 candidate genes (Denoeud *et al.* 2011). In addition, its MRO genome is a circular DNA of 29 Kb, 80% AT-rich, and codes for 45 genes. The MRO has function in between that of classic mitochondria and hydrogenosomes. It performs lipid, cofactor, and vitamin biosynthesis (Makiuchi and Nozaki 2014; Santos *et al.* 2018). Thus, *Blastocystis* contains two genomes, from the nucleus and the MRO. ST7 was followed by a draft genome of ST4, with **5,713** protein-coding genes (Wawrzyniak *et al.* 2015). Soon after, Gentekaki *et al.* (2017) reported the draft genome of ST1, with **6,544** protein-coding genes. These three studies found extreme diversity among the *Blastocystis* genomes, but taken together these genomic studies suggest that the protozoan most likely can perform purine, pyrimidine, and thiamine syntheses. It can metabolize glucans, whereas other members of stramenopiles cannot.

Virulence factors are also suggested from the genome studies. ST7 shows 66 proteases; 18 are probably secreted. For both ST7 and ST1, cysteine proteases are the most abundant, including cathepsin B, which can degrade host IgA. ST7 also has three protease inhibitors, such as stefin, which can inhibit host cysteine proteases. These members are known as the secretome and degradomes (secreted and degradative proteins).

Horizontal gene transfer (**HGT**), also known as lateral gene transfer (**LGT**), serves the purpose of adapting the protozoan to the gut environment (Eme *et al.* 2017). There are 133

HGT genes for strain ST7. For strain ST1, there are **167** genes, corresponding to **74 transfer** events, with some cases to be followed by gene duplication. Gene duplication is also seen in ST7. Interestingly, while most HGT genes are of prokaryotic origin, about 20 HGT genes are from eukaryotes. Please see Figure 8.5 for *Blastocystis* HGT (Eme *et al.* 2017). The gene of beta-1,3-galactosyl transferase came from animals to *Blastocystis* in an HGT event and was subsequently duplicated several times. In humans, the gene is involved in surface antigen of epithelial cells of the digestive tract; this suggests that *Blastocystis* genome

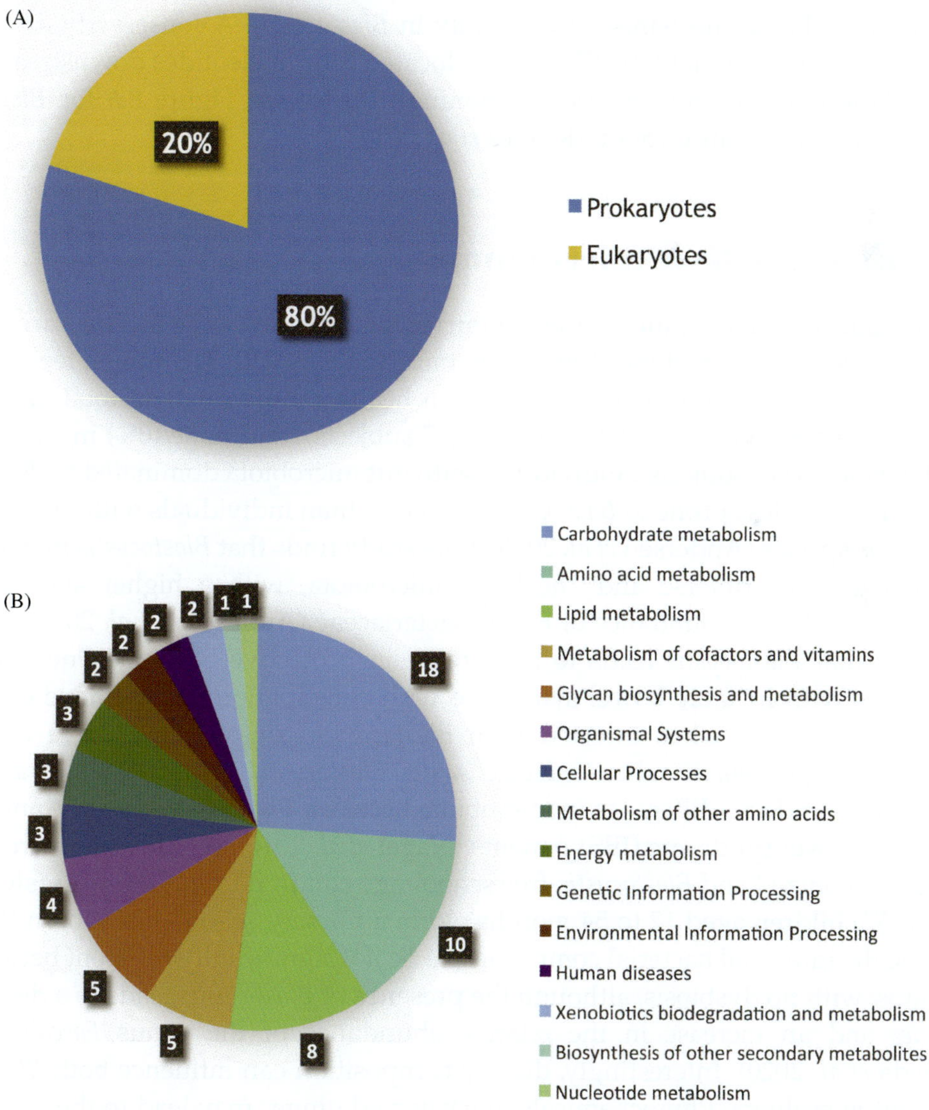

Fig. 8.5 ■ Lateral gene transfer in *Blastocystis*. Taxonomic Distribution of LGT Donors and Distribution of KEGG Annotations of LGT Candidates. LGT donors are shown in (A), and KEGG annotations of LGT candidates in (B). The numbers of LGT candidates in each KEGG category are shown in (B). Courtesy: Eme *et al. Curr Biol.* 2017;27:807–20. Reproduced with permission from Elsevier.

with this eukaryotic gene may serve the purpose of **molecular mimicry**. This prediction based on genomic analysis awaits experimental confirmation.

A novel way to create stop codons of nuclear genes has been discovered in *Blastocystis* (Klimes *et al.* 2014; Eme *et al.* 2017). In mammalian mitochondria, part of the termination codon UAA of some mRNAs is created by **polyadenylation**. This feature has been discovered in the processing of *Blastocystis* nuclear genes. Polyadenylation-mediated generation of functional termination codons for nuclear transcripts is a striking structural feature of *Blastocystis* STs that is unique among eukaryotic nuclear genomes. A full **26%** of the 6,544 protein-coding genes from ST1 have stop codons that are created at the mRNA level by a novel polyadenylation mechanism found only in *Blastocystis*. A conserved GU-rich element (with the common motif TGTTTGTT) is located four nucleotides downstream of the polyadenylation site (highly precise positioning). Please see Figure 8.6 for *Blastocystis* nuclear GTPase gene transcription (Klimes *et al.* 2014).

8.3.7 *Blastocystis* & microbiome

Blastocystis infection may influence the gut microbiota. However, the findings are variable and more work needs to be done. A metagenomics analysis with 316 human fecal samples has shown *Blastocystis* prevalence to be 20% in healthy individuals (a total of 236 subjects), 15% in ulcerative colitis (UC) patients (67 subjects), and none (0%) in Crohn's disease (CD) patients (13 subjects). Individuals with gut microbiota dominated by *Bacteroides* species were much less prone to *Blastocystis* infection than individuals with *Prevotella* and *Ruminococcus* species (Andersen *et al.* 2015). One study finds that *Blastocystis* may be associated with a more diverse and "healthy" microbiota, with a higher abundance of Clostridia and a lower abundance of Enterobacteriaceae (Auderbert *et al.* 2016). Another study finds that *Blastocystis* leads to a decrease in protective bacteria. One study has shown males with irritable bowel syndrome with constipation (IBS-C) have decreased *Bifidobacterium* species when infected with *Blastocystis*; control males have decreased *Faecalibacterium prausnitzii* when infected with *Blastocystis* (Nourrisson *et al.* 2016). A fourth study finds no difference in microbiota between *Blastocystis*-positive and -negative irritable bowel syndrome (IBS) patients (Nagel *et al.* 2016). A study on microbiota in *Blastocystis*-colonized and *Blastocystis*-free school-age children from Colombia (stool samples from 57 children aged 12 to 54 months old in a nursery school) has shown the composition of the intestinal bacterial community to be not significantly different between the two groups, with no dysbiosis, although the presence of *Blastocystis* leads to a decrease in *Bacteroides* and an increase in the relative abundance of the genus *Faecalibacterium* (Castañeda *et al.* 2020). Interestingly, dietary composition can influence both *Blastocystis* and the gut microbiota. Phytochemicals in garlic and ginger may lead to the eradication of *Blastocystis* (Lepczynska *et al.* 2017), and probiotic treatment with *Saccharomyces boular-*

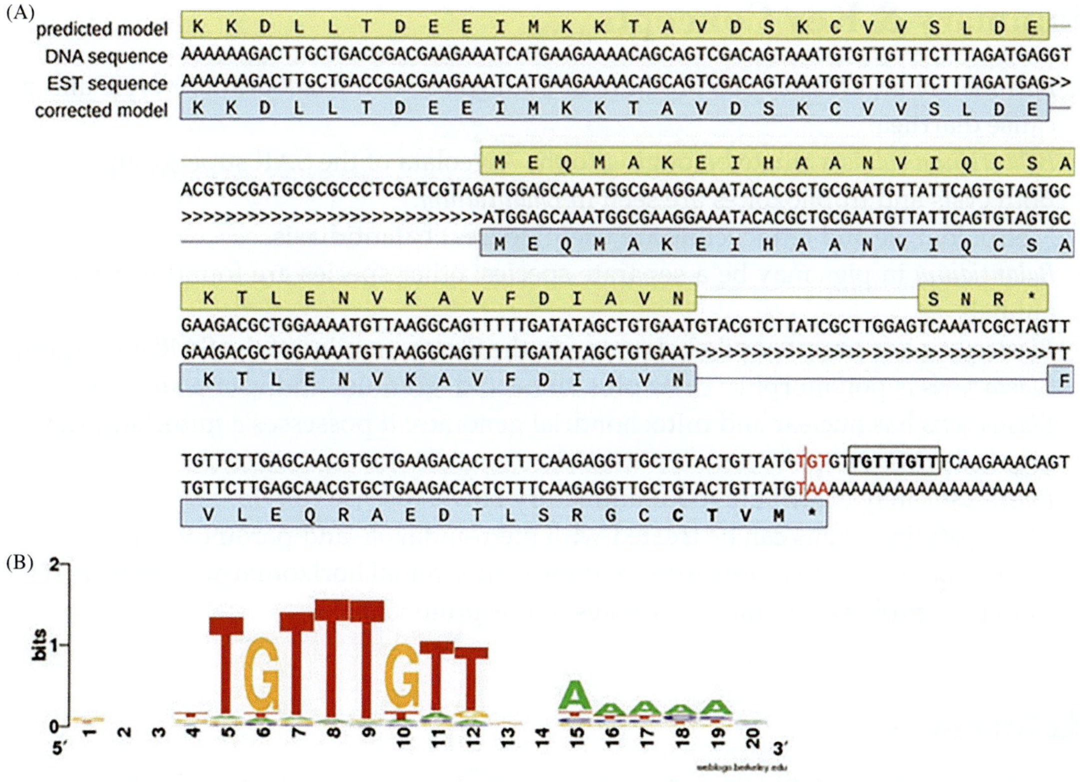

Fig. 8.6 ■ *Blastocystis* nuclear GTPase gene transcription. Polyadenylation-mediated creation of termination codons in *Blastocystis* sp. subtype 7. (A) An example of a gene from *Blastocystis* sp. subtype 7 with polyadenylation-dependent creation of a termination codon. The figure shows the 3′-end of a gene (FN668683.1, positions 539586–539266) encoding a GTPase of the RHO family, which is characterized by the presence of a C-terminal CXXX motif. Although the current prediction of the respective protein sequence (CBK24281.2) lacks the expected C-terminal motif, the protein sequence predicted by taking into account an EST sequence (FQ805196.1) does exhibit the motif (CTVM in bold). The termination codon in the EST sequence (TAA) created by polyadenylation is highlighted in red, the conserved polyadenylation motif (see the text) is boxed, introns are marked by the characters ">." The sequences displayed in the figure are defined above by their GenBank accession numbers. (B) A sequence logo for the conserved motif downstream from the polyadenylation site. The logo was created using WebLogo (Crooks *et al.*, 2004; http://weblogo.berkeley.edu/, last accessed July 15, 2014) on the basis of 2,419 individual sequences. Courtesy: Klimeš *et al. Genome Biol Evol.* 2014;6:1956–61. Reproduced with permission from *Genome Biol Evol.* with Creative Commons Attribution 3.0 (CC-BY) International License.

dii can alleviate *Blastocystis* infection-induced symptoms (as previously discussed, Angelici *et al.* 2018).

Summary & Key Concepts

- *Balantidium* and *Blastocystis* are human pathogens with fecal–oral life cycle and may cause diarrhea.
- *Balantidium coli* is a ciliate belonging to the Alveolata of the SAR supergroup.
- Both cysts and trophozoites are seen in *Balantidium*.
- Metronidazole and tetracycline are useful to treat balantidiasis.
- *Balantidium* in pigs may be a separate species; other species are found in a variety of animals
- *Blastocystis* is a stramenopile belonging to the Stramenopiles of the SAR supergroup.
- *Blastocystis* is polymorphic: cysts plus amoeboid, granular and vacuolar forms.
- *Blastocystis* has nuclear and mitochondrial genomes; it possesses a mitochondrion-like organelle (MLO).
- *Blastocystis* may contribute to inflammatory bowel disease (IBD).
- *Blastocystis* infections can be treated with metronidazole and paromomycin.
- From genomes of *Blastocystis* strains, there is substantial horizontal gene transfer (HGT) from both prokaryotes and eukaryotes to this protozoan.

References

Ahmed A, Ijaz M, Ayyub RM, *et al*. *Balantidium coli* in domestic animals: An emerging protozoan pathogen of zoonotic significance. *Acta Trop* 2020;203:105298.

Andersen LO, Bonde I, Nielsen HB, Stensvold CR. A retrospective metagenomics approach to studying *Blastocystis*. *FEMS Microbiol Ecol* 2015;91(7): fiv072.

Angelici MC, Nardis C, Scarpelli R, Ade P. *Blastocystis hominis* transmission by non-potable water: A case report in Italy. *New Microbiol* 2018;41(2):173–177.

Audebert C, Even G, Cian A, *et al*. Colonization with the enteric protozoa *Blastocystis* is associated with increased diversity of human gut bacterial microbiota. *Sci Rep* 2016;6:25255.

Barbosa Ada S, Bastos OM, Uchôa CM, *et al*. Isolation and maintenance of *Balantidium coli* (Malmsteim, 1857) culture from fecal samples of pigs and non-human primates. *Vet Parasitol* 2015;210(3–4):240–5.

Castañeda S, Muñoz M, Villamizar X, *et al*. Microbiota characterization in *Blastocystis*-colonized and *Blastocystis*-free school-age children from Colombia. *Parasit Vectors* 2020;13(1):521.

Denoeud F, Roussel M, Noel B, *et al*. Genome sequence of the stramenopile *Blastocystis*, a human anaerobic parasite. *Genome Biol* 2011;12(3):R29.

Eme L, Gentekaki E, Curtis B, Archibald JM, Roger AJ. Lateral gene transfer in the adaptation of the anaerobic parasite *Blastocystis* to the gut. *Curr Biol* 2017;27(6):807–20.

Escutia-Guzman Y, Martinez-Flores WA, Martinez-Ocaña J, *et al*. An unusual case of extra-enteric *Blastocystosis* in the Uterine Cervix. *Korean J Parasitol* 2020;58(5):571–6.

Gentekaki E, Curtis BA, Stairs CW, *et al*. Extreme genome diversity in the hyper-prevalent parasitic eukaryote *Blastocystis*. *PLoS Biol* 2017;15(9):e2003769.

Kapur P, Das AK, Kapur PR, Dudeja M. *Balantidium coli* liver abscess: First case report from India. *J Parasit Dis* 2016;40(1):138–40.

Kean BH, Mott KE, Russell AJ, editors. *Tropical Medicine and Parasitology: Classic Investigations*, volumes I and II (1978, Cornell).

Klimeš V, Gentekaki E, Roger AJ, Eliáš M. A large number of nuclear genes in the human parasite *Blastocystis* require mRNApolyadenylation to create functional termination codons. *Genome Biol Evol* 2014;6(8):1956–61.

Lepczyńska M, Białkowska J, Dzika E, Piskorz-Ogórek K, Korycińska J. *Blastocystis*: How do specific diets and human gut microbiota affect its development and pathogenicity? *Eur J Clin Microbiol Infect Dis* 2017;36(9):1531–40.

Makiuchi T, Nozaki T. Highly divergent mitochondrion-related organelles in anaerobic parasitic protozoa. *Biochimie* 2014;100:3–17.

Nagel R, Traub RJ, Allcock RJ, Kwan MM, Bielefeldt-Ohmann H. Comparison of faecal microbiota in *Blastocystis*-positive and *Blastocystis*-negative irritable bowel syndrome patients. *Microbiome* 2016;4(1):47.

Nilles-Bije ML, Rivera WL. Ultrastructural and molecular characterization of *Balantidium coli* isolated in the Philippines. *Parasitol Res* 2010;106(2):387–94.

Nourrisson C, Scanzi J, Pereira B, *et al*. *Blastocystis* is associated with decrease of fecal microbiota protective bacteria: Comparativeanalysis between patients with irritable bowel syndrome and control subjects. *PLoS One* 2014;9(11):e111868.

Padukone S, Mandal J, Parija SC. Severe *Blastocystis* subtype 3 infection in a patient with colorectal cancer. *Trop Parasitol* 2017;7(2):122–4.

Pomajbíková K, Oborník M, Horák A, *et al*. Novel insights into the genetic diversity of *Balantidium* and *Balantidium*-like cyst-forming ciliates. *PLoS Negl Trop Dis* 2013;7(3):e2140.

Rajamanikam A, Kumar S, Samudi C, Kudva M. Exacerbated symptoms in *Blastocystis sp*.-infected patients treated with metronidazole: Two case studies. *Parasitol Res* 2018;117(8):2585–90.

Roberts T, Stark D, Harkness J, Ellis J. Update on the pathogenic potential and treatment options for *Blastocystis sp*. *Gut Pathog* 2014;6:17.

Santos HJ, Makiuchi T, Nozaki T. Reinventing an Organelle: The reduced mitochondrion in parasitic protists. *Trends Parasitol* 2018;34(12):1038–55.

Schuster FL, Ramirez-Avila L. Current world status of *Balantidium coli*. *Clin Microbiol Rev* 2008;21(4):626–38.

Silberman JD, Sogin ML, Leipe DD, Clark CG. Human parasite finds taxonomic home. *Nature* 1996;380(6573):398.

Stenzel DJ, Boreham PF. *Blastocystis hominis* revisited. *Clin Microbiol Rev* 1996;9(4):563–84.

Stensvold CR, Clark CG. Current status of *Blastocystis*: A personal view. *Parasitol Int* 2016;65(6 Pt B):763–71.

Stensvold CR, Tan KSW, Clark CG. *Blastocystis*. *Trends Parasitol* 2020;36(3):315–6.

Tan KS. *Blastocystis* in humans and animals: New insights using modern methodologies. *Vet Parasitol* 2004;126(1–2):121–44.

Tan KS, Ng GC, Quek E, *et al*. *Blastocystis hominis*: A simplified, high-efficiency method for clonal growth on solid agar. *Exp Parasitol* 2000;96(1):9–15.

Tan TC, Suresh KG, Smith HV. Phenotypic and genotypic characterisation of *Blastocystis hominis* isolates implicates subtype 3 as a subtype with pathogenic potential. *Parasitol Res* 2008;104(1):85–93.

Walzer PD, Judson FN, Murphy KB, Healy GR, English DK, Schultz MG. Balantidiasis outbreak in Truk. *Am J Trop Med Hyg* 1973;22(1):33–41.

Wawrzyniak I, Courtine D, Osman M, *et al*. Draft genome sequence of the intestinal parasite *Blastocystis* subtype 4-isolate WR1. *Genom Data* 2015;4:22–3.

Yason JA, Tan KSW. Membrane surface features of *Blastocystis* subtypes. *Genes (Basel)* 2018;9(8):417.

Yu P, Rong J, Zhang Y, Du J. Dysentery caused by *Balantidium coli* in China. *Korean J Parasitol* 2020;58(1):47–9.

Zaman V, Howe J, Ng M. Scanning electron microscopy of *Blastocystis hominis* cysts. *Parasitol Res* 1998;84(6):476–7.

Zhang X, Zhang S, Qiao J, *et al*. Ultrastructural insights into morphology and reproductive mode of *Blastocystis hominis*. *Parasitol Res* 2012;110(3):1165–72.

Zierdt CH. *Blastocystis hominis* — past and future. *Clin Microbiol Rev* 1991;4(1):61–79.

9

Malaria by Apicomplexan Protozoa

9.1 Introductory Remarks

Throughout human history, malaria has been a major cause of mortality and morbidity. Today, malaria is the most important parasitic disease worldwide, in terms of numbers of affected people and mortality. According the World Malaria Report 2018 by the World Health Organization (WHO), there were an estimated **219 million** cases of malaria worldwide in 2017 (uncertainty range 203–262 million), with 92% in Africa (200 million), 5% in South East Asia, and 2% in Eastern Mediterranean. Malaria caused an annual estimate of **435,000** deaths globally, with 93% in Africa. Children aged under 5 years are the most vulnerable and accounted for 61% (266,000) of all malaria deaths worldwide. This figure means that one child dies every 2 minutes. In addition, there can be malaria-related anemia, a fatal condition if left untreated. Pregnant women and children aged under 5 years are most vulnerable for this anemia.[1] Please see Figure 9.1 for the relationship between age and malaria severity (White *et al.* 2014).

"Although global morbidity and mortality have decreased substantially, malaria, a parasite infection of red blood cells, still kills roughly 2,000 people per day, most of whom are children in Africa. Two factors largely account for these decreases; increased deployment of insecticide-treated bednets and increased availability of highly effective artemisinin combination treatments" (White *et al.* 2014). Whereas malaria is most important in sub-Saharan Africa, imported cases are found worldwide. A review of 100 cases seen at the George Washington University, Washington DC, USA (2000–2017) has shown 21 cases of severe malaria, including 10 with cerebral malaria. Most had *Plasmodium falciparum* (76%), after travel from sub-Saharan Africa (94%), had prior malaria experience (50%), but very low adherence to a prophylactic regimen (4%). "Timely diagnosis and recognition of severe illness are crucial; however, many US-based clinicians lack familiarity with this disease" (Akselrod *et al.* 2018).

[1] https://apps.who.int/iris/bitstream/handle/10665/275867/9789241565653-eng.pdf?sequence=1&isAllowed=y

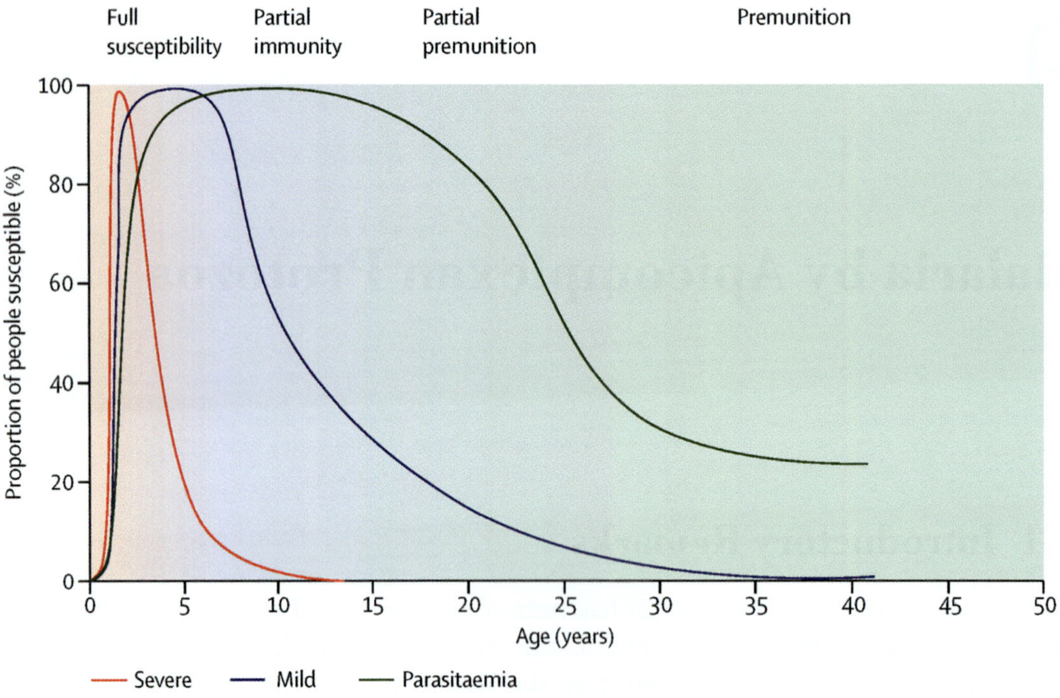

Fig. 9.1 ■ Age and malaria severity. Relation between age and malaria severity in an area of moderate transmission intensity. With repeated exposure protection is acquired, first against severe malaria, then against illness with malaria, and, much more slowly, against microscopy-detectable parasitemia. Courtesy: White *et al. Lancet* 2014;383:723–35. Reproduced with permission from Elsevier.

Malaria elimination is defined as: "interruption of local transmission (reduction to zero incidence of indigenous cases) of a specified malaria parasite species in a defined geographical area as a result of deliberate activities. Continued measures to prevent re-establishment of transmission are required" (Li *et al.* 2019). The World Health Organization (WHO) has developed a Malaria Elimination Certification Program. "The certification of malaria elimination in a country will require that local transmission is interrupted for all human malaria parasites" (Li *et al.* 2019). Examples of countries certified malaria-free by WHO are Spain (1964), United States (1970), Singapore (1982), Uzbekistan (2018), and China (2021).

Malaria is a vector-borne infectious disease. The carrier of the *Plasmodium* protozoans is the female *Anopheles* mosquito; hence, there are measures of vector control. Interventions that target the mosquitoes for reducing malaria transmission include long-lasting insecticidal nets (LLINs) and indoor residual spraying (IRS), when the insects feed on sleeping humans and rest inside their living quarters or livestock shelters. However, many malaria vector species show behavioral changes to avoid insecticides that they are fully susceptible to (by avoiding contact with treated surfaces, by only feeding on humans who are active and unprotected outdoors, by feeding only on animals instead of humans). This condition is known as residual malaria transmission, "defined as all forms of transmission that can persist after achieving full universal coverage with effective LLINs and/or IRS containing active ingredients to which local vector populations are fully susceptible. Residual transmission is sufficiently intense across most of the tropics to render malaria elimination infeasible without new or improved vector control methods" (Killeen 2014). Furthermore, it must be noted that mosquitoes can become insecticide-resistant, and insecticide applications need to address environmental concerns.

For a novel approach, ivermectin comes into the picture. "A roadmap for the development of ivermectin as a complementary vector control tool" was conceived and compiled by a group of experts led by Regina Rabinovich and Carlos Chaccour (Barcelona Institute for Global Health). The group has proposed mass drug administration (MDA) of ivermectin for malaria vector control. "Ivermectin reduces the life span of *Anopheles* mosquitoes that feed on treated humans and/or livestock, potentially decreasing malaria parasite transmission when administered at the community level" (The Ivermectin Roadmappers 2020). The group wanted "to make ivermectin available as a vector control tool by 2024 with a completely novel mechanism of action. The roadmap covers various aspects, which include 1) the definition of optimal dosage/regimens for ivermectin MDA in both humans and livestock, 2) the risk of resistance to the drug and environmental impact, 3) ethical issues, 4) political and community engagement, 5) translation of evidence into policy, and 6) operational aspects of large-scale deployment of the drug, all in the context of a drug given as a prevention tool acting at the community level" (The Ivermectin Roadmappers 2020).

Importance of the malaria parasites as human pathogens has led to many investigations by scientists and clinicians. Molecular studies have been done on the genomes of malaria parasites and related species. Current updates on genomic studies are available in PlasmoDB (database).[2] Findings are continually being published in scientific journals, including one that is dedicated to the disease: *Malaria Journal* (Springer), from 2002 to the present (open access by BMC under Springer Nature).[3]

In sum, malaria is the most important of the parasitic disease caused by species of protozoa. In the following we shall discuss current understanding of the disease, vaccine and treatments, molecular cell biology, as well as the long history of human encounter with this deadly parasitic disease.

9.2 *Plasmodium*

About 200 species of *Plasmodium* are known, infecting reptiles, birds and mammals. *Plasmodium* species are relatively host restricted, with only 4 species as true human parasites: *Plasmodium falciparum*, *P. vivax*, *P. ovale* and *P. malariae*. Common to monkeys, *P. knowlesi* can also be zoonotic to humans. The most severe is *P. falciparum*, also known

[2] https://plasmodb.org/plasmo/

[3] https://malariajournal.biomedcentral.com/

as malignant tertian malaria. *P. vivax* and *P. ovale* are benign tertian malaria, and *P. malariae* is quartan malaria. The tertian is derived from ancient Roman custom of counting the days of an event in sequence (day 1 is fever, day 2 is intervening day, day 3 is fever). The terms correspond to the duration of schizogony or fever, about 48 hours and 72 hours of synchrony. Consideration of global distribution of human malaria parasites, the species that is widely distributed and contributes to costly morbidity is *Plasmodium vivax*.

Malaria is an important parasitic protozoan disease caused by the apicomplexan protozoan *Plasmodium* species. The parasites are members of the supergroup SAR (Stramenopiles, Alveolata and Rhizaria), specifically, they belong to the A of SAR. A stands for Alveolata (referring to cortical alveoli, sacs or cavities underneath the cell surface). They further belong to the group Apicomplexa (a term coined by Norman D. Levine, University of Illinois Urbana in 1980, denoting the presence of **apical complex** as a unique structure). The apical complex consists of polar rings, rhoptries, micronemes. The latter two have secretory function. In addition, there are anterior and posterior polar rings, plus a cytostome. Organelles include a nucleus with nucleolus, a mitochondrion, Golgi and endo-membrane transport network, plus an organelle known as **apicoplast** (apicomplexan plastid). It is a vestigial plastid homologous to the chloroplast of algae and plants, derived from an ancient secondary endosymbiotic event when a progenitor parasite engulfed a red alga; this plastid relic has four membrane structure, it is found in almost all apicomplexans (Janouskovec *et al.* 2010; McFadden and Yeh 2017). Please see Figure 9.2 for apicoplast evolution (Chakraborty 2016) (*Vitrella brassicaformis* is a unicellular alga belonging to the eukaryotic supergroup Alveolata). Whereas a typical chloroplast is for photosynthesis, an apicoplast is essential for lipid biosynthesis. Please see Figure 9.3 for subcellular structures of a typical apicomplexan (Heintzelman 2015). Within the apical complex, some apicomplexan species possess a conoid, as found in *Toxoplasma*, whereas the conoid is absent in other species, including *Plasmodium*. In further classification, *Plasmodium* protozoa belong to the group known as Haemosporida.

The apicomplexan protozoa have a unique way of locomotion: they move by gliding. "This active process is based on the motility of the parasite, referred to as gliding, and is empowered by an actin/myosin motor. This motor is localized within the intermembrane space between the parasite's plasma membrane and inner membrane complex (**IMC**), an additional double-layer of membranes that is unique for these single cell organisms. The IMC provides stability to invasion competent stages of the parasite and functions as an anchor for the actin/myosin motor. While motility is achieved by the interaction of the myosin motor with actin filaments, myosin is linked to the IMC by a membrane-embedded multi-protein complex referred to as the **glideosome**" (Pazicky *et al.* 2020, citations in text deleted). Please see Figure 9.4 for a model of the glideosome (Pazicky *et al.* 2020). Available in the Protein Data Bank are over 75 structures of parasite receptors and glideosome proteins, inccluding adhesins, cytoskeletal proteins, bridging proteins, IMC, and motor proteins (Boucher & Bosch 2015). One example is the motor protein of *Plasmodium falciparum* 3D7: myosin A (6YCY). [4]

[4] https://www.rcsb.org/structure/6YCY

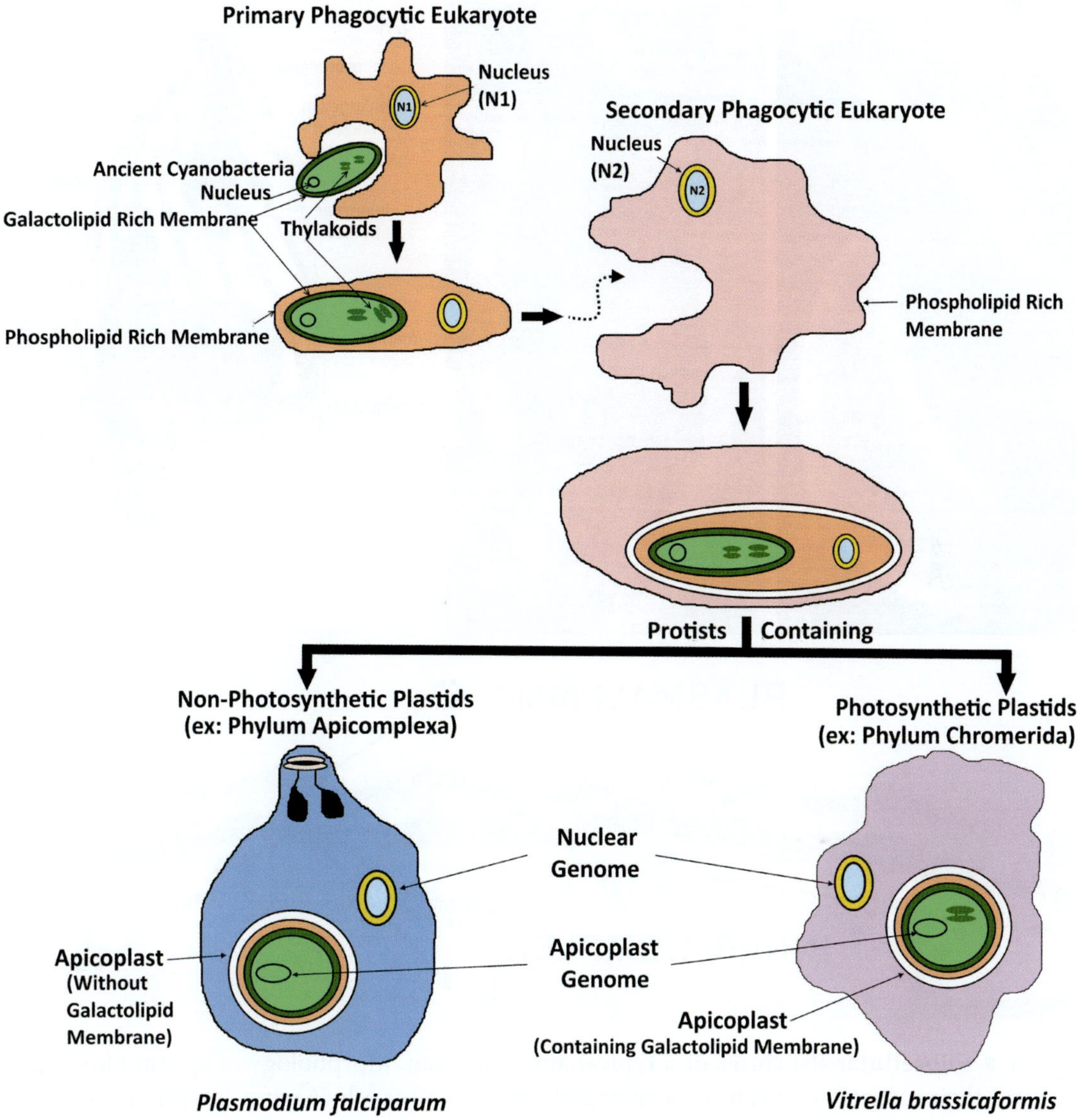

Fig. 9.2 ■ Apicoplast evolution. Schematic diagram illustrating the two sequential steps which led to the evolution of the apicoplast in related apicomplexan protists *Plasmodium falciparum* and *Vitrella brassicaformis*. A primary endosymbiotic plastid like the ones present in plants and algae evolved out of a phagocytized cyanobacteria. Secondary endosymbiotic plastids are a result of phagocytosis of a plastid containing primary eukaryote by a secondary eukaryotic cell. Secondary plastids have evolved in a way that either retained their photosynthetic activity (as in *Vitrella brassicaformis*) or lost it (as in *Plasmodium falciparum*). Courtesy: Chakraborty A, *Life Sci* 2016;158:104–10. Reproduced with permission from Elsevier.

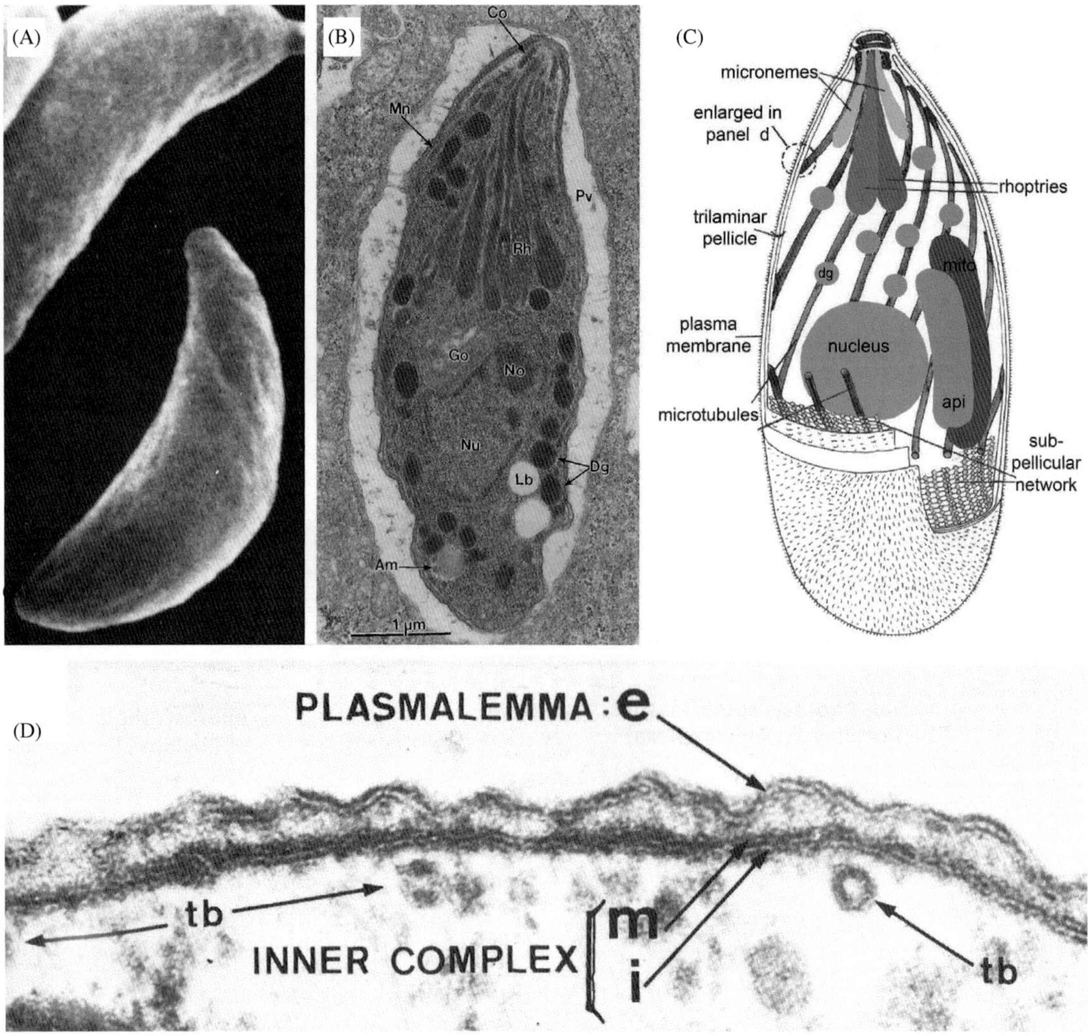

Fig. 9.3 ■ Subcellular structures of a typical apicomplexan. Morphology of apicomplexan parasites and their cortical architecture. Scanning electron micrograph (A) of a *Toxoplasma* tachyzoite, with the apical pole pointing upward. Transmission electron micrograph (B) of an intracellular *Toxoplasma* tachyzoite residing within a parasitophorous vacuole (Pv). The apical pole is at the top and the apical complex of organelles is evident. Schematic representation (C) of a prototypical apicomplexan zooite. Transmission electron micrograph (D) through the pellicle of an *Eimeria* sporozoite illustrating the plasma membrane and the subjacent inner membrane complex where the motor complex is anchored. Courtesy: Heintzelman M, *Semin Cell Dev Biol* 2015;46:135–42. Reproduced with permission from Elsevier.

9.3 History

Malaria has been associated with humans for a long period of time (Kean *et al.* 1978; Cox 1996; Esch 2007). Historically, there was a connection between swamps and fevers. Malaria is contracted by breathing in bad air (malum means bad, evil; aria means air).

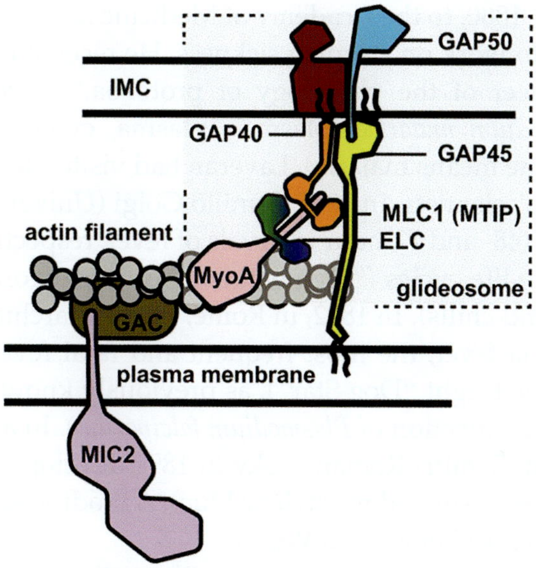

Fig. 9.4 ■ A model of the apicomplexan glideosome. Schematic representation of the current model of the glideosome and its localization in the *T. gondii* intermembrane space. Actin polymerization occurs between the plasma membrane (PM) and the inner membrane complex (IMC) whereas myosin A is part of the glideosome, which binds the essential light chains ELC and myosin light chain MLC1 (called myosin tail interacting protein, MTIP, in *Plasmodium spp.*). Myosin A and its light chains further interact with glideosome associated proteins GAP40, GAP45 and GAP50, which anchor the glideosome in the outer membrane of the inner membrane complex. On the other side, glideosome associated connector (GAC) facilitates the association of actin filaments with surface transmembrane proteins such as MIC2. Courtesy: Pazicky *et al. Commun Biol* 2020;3:568. Reproduced with permission from *Communications Biology* with Creative Commons Attribution 4.0 (CC-BY) International License.

Other names are marsh disease, swamp fever, paludism (paludisme means swamp). There were records of fevers in ancient Chinese texts and Egyptian papyri. Hippocrates differentiated tertian and quartan fevers, although he believed bile as the cause of fevers. It is likely that malaria was brought into the New World by Spaniards and African slaves.

Investigations of the malaria parasites were performed by many scientists and medical doctors, most notably in North Africa and India by Charles Louis Alfonse Laveran and Ronald Ross (for the first description of the parasite and for discovery of *Anopheles* mosquito as insect vector), respectively. As a French army physician, Laveran was interested in malaria. There was contemporary belief that malaria could be caused by bacterial pathogens from swamps. Working in Algeria, he observed, in fresh blood of patients pigments and clear bodies within erythrocytes, and he saw **exflagellation** (formation of male gametes). After finding 26 cases of parasite presence among 44 malaria patients, Laveran concluded: "Parasitic elements are found in the blood of patients who are ill with malaria. Up to now, these elements were thought to be pigmented leucocytes. The presence of these parasites in the blood probably is the principal cause of malaria." However, this report on November 23, 1880, to the Academy of Medicine in Paris, was not well received, and Laveran switched to work on sleeping sickness. He received the Nobel Prize in 1907 for "initiator and pioneer of the pathology of protozoa." Laveran's malaria parasite became today's *Plasmodium malariae* (plasm is plasma, cytoplasm and odium means resembling, like; malariae means malaria). Laveran had visited Italy where he had shared his findings with Italian scientists. In 1885 Camillo Golgi (University of Pavia) found tertian and quartan fevers (48- and 72-hour intervals of fever, respectively) as demonstration of synchrony of parasite life cycles ("segmentation" or schizogony) in relation to **paroxysms** (periodic fevers and chills). In 1892, in Rome, Ettore Marchiafava described the late summer-autumn malaria fever, the most frequent and fatal fever occurring during the ascendancy of Sirius (the bright "Dog Star"), as previously known to the ancient Greeks Homer and Hippocrates (infection of *Plasmodium falciparum*). In a quest to better observe the parasite, the Russian Dimitri Romanowsky in 1891 developed a staining method for blood smears (using dyes eosin and methylene blue). A modification of his method is still being used; other stains are Giemsa and Wright.

The discovery of the mosquito as a vector for *Plasmodium* was worked out by Ronald Ross. This finding was due to the intuition of Patrick Manson, who had previously discovered the mosquito as vector for filarial worms (elephantiasis). (Please see Chapter 18 for lymphatic filariasis.) Ross, born in India to a British general of the Indian army, was sent back to England for boarding school (at age 8) and medical education (St. Bartholomew's Hospital in London). Back to India in 1881, Ross joined the Indian Medical Service and became interested in malaria. In 1894, he visited Patrick Manson in his home in London, where Manson showed Ross slides with malaria parasites. When Ross returned to India, he was determined to prove the mosquito vector hypothesis. He was not an entomologist, and fed mosquitos to humans with fever, using species of *Culex* and *Aedes*, so the experiments did not work. He might have seen exflagellation but was unaware of its significance. In 1898, a young Canadian medical student, William George MacCallum, was able to find a related protozoan *Haemoproteus* in the blood of sparrows (5/80) and crows (16/21); he saw microgamete penetrating macrogamete and recognized this phenomenon as a sexual stage of development. This information was conveyed by Manson to Ross. Ross finally used the correct species, insects whose wings were dappled and had four dark spots, *Anopheles* mosquitoes. He observed cysts in mosquito stomachs in August 1897 after feeding in patients with crescent shaped bodies in the blood, and knew that female mosquitos are the definitive host of malaria parasite. But Ross was about to be transferred to another part of India to work on leishmaniasis (due to a kala azar outbreak). Manson intervened on his behalf, and Ross was sent to Calcutta, a malaria area. Locals refused to give him blood, so Ross had to switch focus from human to avian malaria, using *Culex* mosquito and sparrows. He followed exflagellation and fertilization in the insect gut, oocyst formation and sporogony, and migration of sporozoites to salivary glands. When he infected healthy sparrows with sporozoites, there was infection. Manson presented the findings on behalf of Ross at a meeting of the British Medical Association in Edinburgh on July 24, 1898. Ross received the Nobel Prize in 1902 for this malaria research.

Many scientists had participated in elucidation of the life cycle. Ronald Ross started with human malaria but ended in finding all parasitic stages in an avian malaria model, and demonstration of infection from mosquito derived sporozoites in healthy sparrows, in India. For the human malaria species *Plasmodium falciparum* (falc means sickle; parum means bearing) and its *Anopheles* mosquito vector, the life cycle was published by the Italian Giovanni Battista Grassi in 1898. Life cycles of *P. vivax* (vivax means vigorous) and *P. malariae* were later completed by the Italian Amico Bignami (Cook 2007).

Malaria life cycle discovery finally led to acrimony between Ross and Manson (Manson was only knighted but Ross both knighted and Nobel). Furthermore, the decision on Ross' Nobel Prize had led to discord between British and Italian scientists. Grassi had shown the *Anopheles* and *Plasmodium falciparum* life cycle. When it comes to human malaria, "birds don't count." Grassi published in November 1898 and briefly cited Ross at the very end. There is more to the historical record, and this included the German bacteriologist Robert Koch, of Koch's postulates fame in microbiology but without any experience in protozoa. Koch visited Rome and offered the Italians "a helping hand" (but probably contributing nothing). Grassi later sent Koch a Christmas present (his publication reprint). In 1902, when the Nobel committee was considering sharing prize between Grassi and Ross, Koch put in his authority/weight to insist that Grassi did not deserve the honor (and Ross became the sole recipient). "The dispute between Grassi and Ross about the priority of discovery has been interpreted as motivated by personal ambition, national pride, the desire for academic pre-eminence, and similar psychological and sociological explanations that have very little to do with science" (Capanna 2006). [Here we wish to add a modern case that has resulted with the 2020 Nobel prize in Chemistry to Jennifer Doudna and Emanuelle Charpentier. Similar to the history of malaria life cycle discovery, the CRISPR-Cas9 innovation also included regional and international competitions (between scientists at the University of California Berkeley and Broad Institute of Harvard-MIT within USA, and investigators from Spain, Lithuania, France, China, and elsewhere). For further reading, we recommend the exciting and entertaining nonfiction *The Code Breaker: Jennifer Doudna, Gene Editing, and the Future of the Human Race*, by Walter Isaacson, 2021 Simon & Schuster.]

However, the *Plasmodium* life cycle remained incomplete; researchers still did not know activities of the protozoan during its first 10 days inside the human body. There was an erroneous claim of sporozoite penetrating red blood cells by the German Fritz Schaudinn, discoverer of the bacterium *Treponama pallidum* as the pathogen of syphilis. Previously, exo-erythrocytic or tissue parasites had been observed in avian malaria. The initial, latent stage in the liver was detected in 1947, by Henry Shortt and Cyril Garnham at the London School of Hygiene and Tropical Medicine, via dissection of *Plasmodium cynomolgi*-infected monkey; they found the infected liver. Previously, in 1932, Robert Knowles and assistant surgeon Biraj Mohan Das Gupta reported experimental transmission of monkey malaria to 3 human volunteers (now *P. knowlesi*, after Knowles), thus establishing this species as a pathogen of the fifth human malaria. *P. knowlesi* is common in South East Asia where macaque monkeys (genus *Macaca*) are abundant.

Malaria has been shown to affect an Egyptian pharaoh. King Tut's tomb was discovered in 1922 by the British archaeologist Howard Carter. In 2010, a study was published on the death of the Egyptian King Tutankhamun (Hawass *et al.* 2010). The boy king was a cripple and investigators found *Plasmodium falciparum* in his mummified remains. Polymerase chain reaction (PCR) was used to detect parasite genes, including apical membrane antigen 1(*AMA1*), merozoite surface protein 1 (MSP1), and small subtelomeric variable open reading frame (*STEVOR*). The young pharaoh had malaria during his lifetime.

Malaria is no longer seen in the United States (not counting imported cases). However, it was found in states including New Jersey and Alabama until the recent past. The Tennessee Valley Authority (TVA) is an agency involved in overseeing dam constructions. In northern Alabama, TVA had conducted the most thorough experimental test on the effectiveness of mosquito-proof housing to reduce malaria transmission. TVA began the campaign to mosquito-proof all houses in 1939; the goal was accomplished within 7 years. "The results of their study show that mosquito-proofing virtually eradicated malaria from the area, with the decline occurring earlier in those zones in which mosquito-proofing was completed earlier" (Ewald *et al.* 1998).

9.4 Life Cycle

Please see Figure 9.5 for the life cycle of *Plasmodium* species, from CDC.[5]

The female mosquito is the definitive host; humans are the intermediate hosts. The sporogonic cycle is in the mosquito; both exo-erythrocytic (hepatic) and erythrocytic cycles are present in humans. Sporozoites from infected female *Anopheles* mosquito's bite enter the human body and migrate to the liver. In hepatocytes, sporozoites becomes schizonts that mature into merozoites. Different malaria parasite species differ somewhat in the life cycle in liver and in blood. In *P. falciparum* the hepatic stage takes 5 to 7 days and results in 40,000 merozoites. In *P. vivax* and *P. ovale*, there may be dormant stage known as **hypnozoites** (Flannery *et al.* 2019). Merozoites infect erythrocytes, from the ring stage, to trophozoites, digesting hemoglobin (leaving behind the malaria pigment derived from heme known as **hemozoin**), to schizonts, red blood cells rupture to release more merozoites (schizogony). This corresponds to the duration of schizogony or fever, about 48 hours and 72 hours of synchrony (depending on species). Whereas *P. falciparum* prefers erythrocytes, *P. vivax* and *P. ovale* preferentially invade reticulocytes (immature/developing blood cells). Usually only 1–2% of red blood cells are parasitized with *P. vivax* and *P. ovale* infections. Some parasites differentiate into sexual stages, gametocytes (gamogony). Blood stage parasites are responsible for the clinical symptoms. Please see Figure 9.6 for erythrocytic developmental stages of *Plasmodium falciparum* species as seen by scanning electron microscopy (Maier *et al.* 2019).

Schizogony is the production of merozoites asexually within infected erythrocytes. This process takes place in the human intermediate host. In vertebrates, host cell invasion

[5] https://www.cdc.gov/dpdx/malaria/index.html

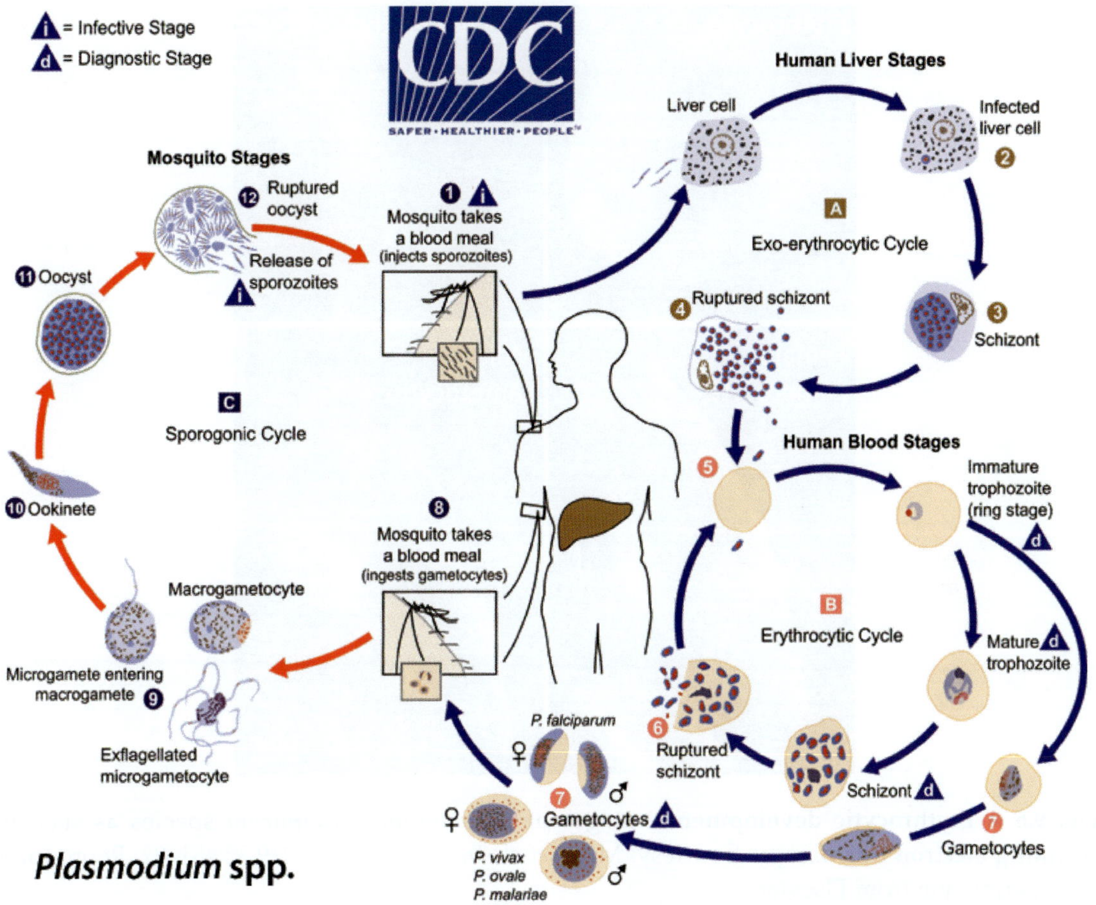

Fig. 9.5 ■ Life cycle of *Plasmodium* species. The malaria parasite life cycle involves two hosts. During a blood meal, a malaria-infected female *Anopheles* mosquito inoculates sporozoites into the human host (1). Sporozoites infect liver cells (2) and mature into schizonts (3), which rupture and release merozoites (4). (Of note, in *P. vivax* and *P. ovale* a dormant stage [hypnozoites] can persist in the liver and cause relapses by invading the bloodstream weeks, or even years later.) After this initial replication in the liver (exo-erythrocytic schizogony A), the parasites undergo asexual multiplication in the erythrocytes (erythrocytic schizogony B). Merozoites infect red blood cells (5). The ring stage trophozoites mature into schizonts, which rupture releasing merozoites (6). Some parasites differentiate into sexual erythrocytic stages (gametocytes) (7). Blood stage parasites are responsible for the clinical manifestations of the disease. The gametocytes, male (microgametocytes) and female (macrogametocytes), are ingested by an *Anopheles* mosquito during a blood meal (8). The parasites' multiplication in the mosquito is known as the sporogonic cycle C. While in the mosquito's stomach, the microgametes penetrate the macrogametes generating zygotes (9). The zygotes in turn become motile and elongated (ookinetes) (10) which invade the midgut wall of the mosquito where they develop into oocysts (11). The oocysts grow, rupture, and release sporozoites (12), which make their way to the mosquito's salivary glands. Inoculation of the sporozoites into a new human host perpetuates the malaria life cycle. Courtesy of CDC. Reproduced from https://www.cdc.gov/dpdx/malaria/index.html

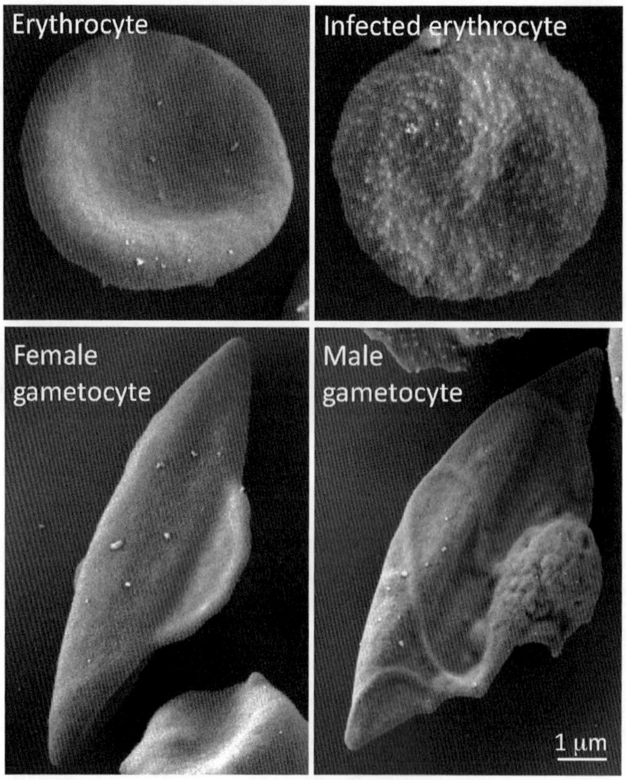

Fig. 9.6 ■ Erythrocytic developmental stages of *Plasmodium falciparum* species as seen by scanning electron microscopy. Courtesy: Maier *et al. Trends Parasitol* 2019;35:481–82. Reproduced with permission from Elsevier.

and egress are crucial steps for the protozoan's survival. Invasion occurs by invagination of the erythrocyte membrane; afterwards, the parasite resides in a parasitophorous vacuole within the host cell (now *Plasmodium*-infected erythrocyte). From within, the parasite controls host cell behavior by secreting proteins into the host cell cytoplasm, including ones that can be transported to the erythrocyte cell surface. Exposed parasite proteins at the host cell surface allow cytoadherence, a feature responsible for pathogenicity of malaria. Egress is initiated by rupture of the parasitophorous vacuole membrane, followed by disintegration of the erythrocyte membrane. Egress requires activation of the parasite's proteases, kinases, and membrane lytic enzymes.

Gamogony (the production of male and female gametes for sexual reproduction) and sporogony (the production of sporozoites for mosquito transmission to humans) occur in the insect definitive host. After entrance to female mosquitos, microgametes are formed by the process of exflagellation (with 6 to 8 nuclei). A microgamete fuses with a macrogamete to form a zygote. The zygote becomes elongated and motile, known as **ookinete**; it invades the midgut wall and develops into a round mature oocyst. Oocyst grows, matures, and releases sporozoites; sporozoites migrate to the salivary gland for the next infection. The *Anopheles* cycle takes 10–24 days.

9.5 Pathology

Fever/chill (paroxysm) is the major symptom, due to synchronous release of merozoites from infected erythrocytes. Malarial disease is caused by the direct effects of red-cell parasitization and destruction, and the host reaction. The release of cytokines following rupture of infected erythrocytes induces fever and the consequent chills and sweating associated with malaria. Different species induce fevers from mild to severe. Infected erythrocytes with *P. falciparum* become knobby, with the knob structure made up of parasite-coded histidine rich proteins. These cells adhere to endothelial cells of capillaries. Immunity to malaria takes time to build up, and both specific antibodies and anti-sporozoite antibodies can be detected, to control parasite load in populations in endemic regions. Malaria can also be responsible for a significant degree of anemia, often in populations already suffering from anemia due to other causes.

Danny A. Milner, Jr. (American Society for Clinical Pathology, Center for Global Health, Chicago, Illinois) wrote: "In the mosquito–human life cycle, the six species of malaria parasites infecting humans (*Plasmodium falciparum*, *Plasmodium vivax*, *Plasmodium ovale wallickeri*, *Plasmodium ovale curtisi*, *Plasmodium malariae*, and *Plasmodium knowlesi*) undergo 10 or more morphological states, replicate from single to 10,000+ cells, and vary in total population from one to many more than 10^6 organisms. In the human host, only a small number of these morphological stages lead to clinical disease and the vast majority of all malaria-infected patients in the world produce few (if any) symptoms in the human. Human clinical disease (e.g., fever, anemia, coma) is the result of the parasite preprogrammed biology in concert with the human pathophysiological response" (Milner 2018).

Malaria can be asymptomatic, a result after successful host immune response. There can be **uncomplicated malaria** or **severe malaria**. Uncomplicated malaria is easily treated with antimalarials specific to the parasite species. During each symptomatic episode, with proper compliance to treatment, the vast majority of patients easily clear the infection. For severe malaria, cerebral malaria (CM) is a major concern. The presentation of CM in children is different from that in adults (Moxon *et al.* 2020).

"Severe malaria cases might present with a range of disease syndromes including acute respiratory distress, metabolic acidosis, hypoglycemia, renal failure, anemia, pulmonary edema, cerebral malaria (CM) and placental malaria (PM) in pregnant women. Two main determinants of severe malaria have been identified: sequestration of parasitized red blood cells and strong proinflammatory responses" (Ioannidis *et al.* 2014). Cytokines such as tumor necrosis factor α (TNF α) and interleukin-1β (IL-1β) are involved, as well as chemokines (chemotactic cytokines).

Metabolic acidosis in severe malaria is caused by a combination of factors. *Plasmodium* species possess lactate dehydrogenase that makes lactic acid, leading to a decrease in pH. **Pulmonary edema** and acute respiratory distress syndrome (**ARDS**) are common feature of severe malaria, and somnolence and brain swelling may occur. Milner wrote: "direct central suppression of the respiratory centers leads to irregular breathing patterns in the setting of acidosis, which may contribute to the pH imbalance. Supportive therapy to protect the airway and more aggressively rebalance the pH may decrease mortality" (Milner 2018).

A very low blood glucose level may cause coma or death. Despite an increase in gluconeogenesis, **hypoglycemia** in severe malaria, including cerebral malaria, is still being detected and it is recommended to consider administering glucose in cases of cerebral malaria and pregnant females with malaria. "Fasting emerges as an important potential risk factor" (Thien *et al.* 2006).

Acute kidney injury (**AKI**) is common in adults with severe malaria. Reduced microcirculatory flow is a probable factor. Low blood pressure can cause kidney and liver failure, cardiovascular collapse, and spleen rupture. Thus, AKI is frequently associated with dysfunction of several other vital organs (potentially fatal). In most cases, acute kidney injury can be oliguria (low urine output, for adults, that is less than 400 mL daily). Early hemofiltration/dialysis substantially improves outcome.

Severe malarial anemia (**SMA**), found in young children in endemic areas, is associated with repeated infections by the malaria parasite. Accelerated splenic removal of mainly the unparasitized red blood cells and erythrocyte destruction at parasite schizogony are compounded by ineffective erythropoiesis. The termed "black water fever" has been used for the presence of hemoglobin in the urine of malaria patients as a result of extensive hemolysis (lysis of erythrocytes).

Cerebral malaria (**CM**) is a killer of infants and young children. It is the most devastating manifestation of severe *P. falciparum* infection. Children under the age of 5 are susceptible. They lack immunity to the pathogen, and there can be adverse effects due to immunopathology. A mouse model of CM has indicated that treatment of **rosiglitazone** (PPARγ ligand and diabetes medication) can increase murine survival. Thus, the host's immune response, if inappropriate or too much (immunopathology), can cause death. Potential use of rosiglitazone (adjunctive therapy) in children with severe malaria is being investigated (Varo *et al.* 2017).

Co-infection of the malaria parasite with other infectious agents can influence outcome. HIV will confer an increased susceptibility to symptomatic malaria; malaria will increase the survival of patients infected with the Ebola virus (Rosenke *et al.* 2016).

After recovery from malaria, there can be malaria **relapse** and **recrudescence**. Relapse is limited to *P. vivax* and *P. ovale* infections. Reactivation of their dormant hepatic hypnozoites leads to initiation of erythrocytic cycles and new attacks of malarial fever. Recrudescence is a sudden increase in parasite load from a persistent low level parasite population in the blood, i.e., from asymptomatic to symptomatic. Initially, parasites persist but the level of parasitemia is low, below the detection threshold and the infected individuals do not have fever. Then, parasitemia gradually increases to cross the fever threshold and new malarial attacks occur. Such attacks can appear within 8 weeks after the primary attack; the cause may be parasite antigenic variation and waning host immunity. Recrudescence has been observed in all human malaria.

After a patient is free from parasitemia, an unusual complication of malaria is post-malaria neurological syndrome (**PMNS**). Symptoms may include cerebellar ataxia and cerebellar ataxia, in rare cases, Guillain–Barre syndrome or neuropsychiatric disorder. Corticosteroids have been used as treatment. In India, a case of PMNS was documented in 2020. Following *Plasmodium falciparum* malaria, a 12-year-old girl had acute onset and isolated neuropsychiatric features, but showed normal neuroimaging. She had methylprednisolone pulse therapy and recovered completely. "This case report illustrates the need for creating awareness about this uncommon complication of malaria. In view of the uncommon complication, early diagnosis and prompt treatment might help in the early resolution of symptoms" (Panda *et al.* 2020).

Mixed-species malaria happens when an individual is infected by two (or more) species of *Plasmodium* parasites simultaneously. In clinical practice, such infections are often not detected by light microscopy (LM) or rapid diagnostic test because of the low number of parasites of one species. A case was documented of an 8-year-old girl (6 months after immigrating from Afghanistan to Switzerland) with a two-species mixed infection (*Plasmodium vivax* as the main species and *P. ovale* as the minor species). Among the 7-member family, 4 (aged 2, 8, 10, and 15 years) were admitted to the pediatric emergency ward. They all had a history of intermittent fever and malaise, with repeated fever attacks. LM of blood smear from the girl indicated probable mixed species and molecular techniques, including *Plasmodium* species–specific multiplex real-time PCR, provided confirmation. All 4 children were treated and recovered fully (artemether/lumefantrine, primaquine, chloroquine). "This is the first case report of a two-species mixed infection comprising both *P. vivax* and *P. ovale* confirmed by LM and different real-time PCR approaches" (Nguyen *et al.* 2020).

A suspected mixed-species infection turned out to be incorrect, as shown in a case in India (Acharya *et al.* 2020). A 5-year-old boy was admitted to the emergency ward with fever, chills, and rigor for 2 days. His Giemsa-stained blood smear showed the probable presence of both *Plasmodium vivax* and *P. falciparum*; even an ookinete was observed. The initial slide preparation had an inadvertent 6-hour delay after sample collection. When blood samples were recollected and smears prepared immediately, there was the absence of ookinetes. Three examiners independently reviewed the slides and excluded the presence of *P. falciparum* of any stage. "Blood sample transport and slide preparation should not be delayed in suspected cases of malaria" (Acharya *et al.* 2020).

Splenic rupture is a serious complication of malaria; the rupture is potentially fatal. Subcapsular hemorrhage of spleen can be a sign of impending splenic rupture. In a university hospital in Korea, 3 cases of vivax malaria and subcapsular hemorrhage were documented (Im *et al* 2019). Case 1, a 39-year-old male, without splenic rupture, was treated (chloroquine, primaquine) and the healing process took over 118 days (monitored by abdominal computed tomography, CT). Case 2, a 40-year-old male had splenic rupture, treated (chloroquine only), and he recovered (without surgery). Case 3, a 38-year-old male, with splenic rupture and hypotension, plus prior chemotherapy for B-cell lymphoma, was treated with splenic artery embolization. "The treatment plan of subcapsular hemorrhage should be determined carefully considering the vital signs, changes in hemoglobin, and bleeding tendency" (Im *et al.* 2019).

In endemic regions, co-infection between malaria and other parasitic diseases can occur. *Schistosoma haematobium* and *Plasmodium falciparum* co-infections are frequent in sub-Saharan Africa. In a study of 268 children in Benin during a malaria transmission season, the effect of trematode infection on antibody responses directed to *Plasmodium* merozoite antigens and on malaria susceptibility was investigated (Tokplonou *et al.* 2020). Children infected by *Schistosoma* had higher concentrations of IgG and lower *Plasmodium* densities than those uninfected by the trematode. Thus, *S. haematobium* infection modulates the host immune response directed to *P. falciparum* antigens.

9.6 Diagnosis

Microscopic examination is the gold standard: demonstration of malarial parasite in peripheral blood on thick and thin blood smears. Parasite detection and parasitic species determination (by microscopic examination) are possible with thin blood smears. However, the thick smear is more sensitive, so useful for parasite detection when there is low parasitemia (species identification is difficult in thick smear). Although molecular and serological rapid tests are available, for over a century the definitive diagnosis of malaria depends on the microscopic identification of parasites by Giemsa-stained blood smears. This procedure permits not only confirmation of the presence of the parasite, but makes possible the identification of the species of malaria and an indication of the level of parasitemia in the infected host. Species differentiation is possible by blood smear morphology. For *P. vivax* and *P. ovale*, there are Schuffner's dots, pinkish in the cytosol of infected cell. For *P. malariae*, there are Ziemann's dots; for *P. falciparum*, Maurer's dots or clefts.

9.7 Therapy

Many drugs are available to treat (or prevent) malaria. With the occurrence and our understanding of drug resistance in parasites, new drug combinations/formulations are still urgently needed, especially knowing the huge mortality and morbidity due to malaria (Tse *et al.* 2019).

The first known drug to treat malaria is **quinine**, which came from the bark of the cinchona tree of South America. Jesuit priests became aware of this remedy for fever used by indigenous Indian tribes. A story (probably fictitious) told by Sebastiano Bado in 1663 was about the wife of the fourth Count of Chinchon, Viceroy of Peru, who got a fever in Lima and was cured by the tree bark remedy, leading her to make this "Countess's powder" widely accessible to Lima's citizens with the fever. In 1742, Carl Linnaeus immortalized the countess and named the fever-bark tree *Cinchona* (misspelled from Chinchona). The remedy was brought from South America to Europe and Britain, known as "Jesuit's bark or powder." Chemists then isolated the active compounds. In 1820 the main alkaloid quinine was crystallized by French chemists, allowing more precise and standardized therapy for malarial fever (plus reducing the side effects, such as vomiting). Interestingly, a novel target for quinine towards *P. falciparum* has been shown to be **purine nucleoside phosphorylase**, using the technique cellular thermal shift assay coupled with mass spectrometry (MS-CETSA) (Dziekan *et al.* 2019). [We would like to introduce a summer cocktail here. The imperial drink, gin and tonic, was secret weapon of the British Empire, made with gin and quinine in tonic water, plus sugar and lime (to mask the bitterness of quinine, included as prophylactic against malaria). First drank by officers of the British army in India, gin and tonic has become a popular cocktail (now with less quinine, therefore less bitter).]

For continuous availability of "Jesuit's powder," the priests in Peru made sure to replace a seedling when a tree was chopped (sustainable tree culture). Later, the practice was abandoned when traders took over. Soon, the loss of bark led to the planting of cinchona trees elsewhere in the world, notably in plantations of Dutch East Indies (now Indonesia). During the Second World War, Japanese occupation of Indonesia forced the Allies to look for alternatives. Synthetic versions of quinine were made. The US army helped the development of **chloroquine** and **primaquine**. Primaquine is significant, because it can destroy the hypnozoites. Chloroquine accumulates in food vacuoles of the parasite. It raises pH of the food vacuole and also prevents the formation of hemozoin from hemoglobin digestion, heme is toxic to the parasite. Heavy chloroquine use led to resistant strains of the malaria parasites. Another drug, **mefloquine** became available in 1984. In 2018, **tafenoquine**, a single-dose 8-aminoquinoline antimalarial drug related to primaquine, was approved by US Food and Drug Administration (FDA) for radical cure of *P. vivax*. Both primaquine and tafenoquine can cause severe hemolytic anemia in people with glucose-6-phosphate dehydrogenase (G6PD) deficiency (Lacerda *et al.* 2019).

The folate acid pathway is another drug target, and **pyrimethamine** (PYR) became a drug for malaria. PYR was developed in the early 1950s by Gertrude Elion and George Hitchings (Wellcome Research Laboratory, New York; now Burroughs Wellcome, part of GlaxoSmithKline). PYR is currently sold under the trade name Daraprim. For this and other works, Elion and Hitchings, together with James Black, received the 1988 Nobel Prize in Physiology or Medicine for "their discoveries of important principles for drug treatment." Sulfadoxine was developed in the early 1960s, and the combination of PYR and sulfadoxine was approved for malaria in 1981 and is now sold under the trade name Fansidar. Both drugs are known to target the parasite's folate biosynthesis pathway, with sulfadoxine inhibiting dihydropteroate synthetase and PYR inhibiting dihydrofolate reductase.

Artemisinin is the Chinese traditional herbal medicine's contribution to malaria. The plant is *Artemisia annua*, annual wormwood, even found along the Potomac River in Washington DC, USA. In 1972 Tu Youyou found the active compound in *Artemisia annua* to be artemisinin (**qinghaosu** in Chinese). Tu was awarded the Nobel Prize in 2015 for "her discoveries concerning a novel therapy against malaria." (She got half; the rest went to discoverers of ivermectin, that story is presented in Chapter 17.) Analogs and derivatives of artemisinin have been synthesized: artesunate is water soluble, and artemether is lipid soluble. WHO suggests therapy of **ACTs** (artemisinin-based combination therapies) as an attempt to prevent parasite resistance to artemisinin. Artesunate, a semisynthetic artemisinin compound, and other artemisinin derivatives are used in combination with selected active antimalarial drugs per WHO recommendation. In addition, methods such as chemical modification and hybrid molecules combining artesunate chemically linked to another antimalarial compound, as well as novel delivery materials to enhance solubility and delivery of artesunate, have been employed (Adebayo *et al.* 2020).[6]

Artemisinin's mechanism of action has been widely debated. It is activated by heme to generate free radicals, which in turn damage proteins required for parasite survival. It binds heme and *Pf*ATP6 (ATPase 6 is a calcium pump/transporter) (Shandilya *et al.* 2013). In addition, artemisinin is an inhibitor of *P. falciparum* phosphatidylinositol-3-kinase (*Pf*PI3K). It is also associated with the up-regulation of unfolded protein response (UPR) pathway which may be linked to decreased parasite development.

Although recommended for combination therapy as an attempt to prevent drug resistance, resistance is already seen, starting in Cambodia, and is related to a particular gene known as *Kelch 13* (K13). Artemisinin resistance (delayed *P. falciparum* clearance following ACTs) is widespread across Southeast Asia but has not been reported in Africa until the finding of de novo emergence of *Pfkelch13*-mediated artemisinin resistance in Rwanda (Uwimana *et al.* 2020). Parasites with mutations in the propeller domains of *P. falciparum* K13 protein have enhanced *Pf*PI3K (phosphatidylinositol 3-kinase) levels that have been linked to delayed parasite clearance (Pasupureddy *et al.* 2019). One possible mechanism is that: mutations confer artemisinin resistance by reducing hemoglobin endocytosis, thus decreasing in hemoglobin-derived heme and reducing artemisinin activation to a level that will allow survival of the protozoan's early, ring stage in the erythrocyte (Xie *et al.* 2020).

A longer duration of treatment protocol (**temporizing**) of artemisinin may be a solution (Wang *et al.* 2019). Another approach is **triple artemisinin-based combination** therapies for malaria, to slow the spread of artemisinin and partner drug resistance in *Plasmodium falciparum* in the Greater Mekong Subregion (GMS). Triple artemisinin-based combination therapies combine artemisinin with two currently available partner drugs. "Their deployment beyond the GMS could delay or prevent the global emergence and spread of resistance to currently available drugs" (van der Pluijm *et al.* 2020).

Whereas artemisinin binds *Pf*ATP6, a molecule known as (+)-SJ733, made by the chemist Spencer Knapp (Rutgers University) and colleagues, targets *Pf*ATP4 (ATPase 4 is a sodium pump/transporter) (Jiménez-Díaz *et al.* 2014); the compound is currently undergoing clinical trial by Medicines for Malaria Venture (MMV).[7]

Novel approaches have been pursued for malaria therapy. Apicomplexans have the organelle apicoplast (derived from plastid). Apicoplast is absent in humans and should be an obvious drug target. Earlier studies have found delayed death, thus not practical,

[6] https://www.nobelprize.org/prizes/medicine/2015/advanced-information/

[7] https://www.mmv.org/

but later analyses have suggested that drugs can target the apicoplast and can still be effective (Biddau and Sheiner 2019). Recently, drug repurposing is posted as a potential way to treat malaria. In a study testing drugs approved for other diseases and illnesses to check their anti-malarial property, eight (out of 226) have been identified as potential drug candidates (Pazhayam *et al.* 2019). (The eight drugs are: azithromycin, pentamidine isethionate, auranofin, loperamide hydrochloride, amlodipine besylate, cyclosporin A, esomeprazole magnesium, and omeprazole.) Furthermore, feeding anti-malarial (a cytochrome *b* inhibitor atovaquone) to infected *Anopheles* mosquitos will prevent transmission of malaria (Paton *et al.* 2019).

Malaria therapy can aid other diseases as well. MMV has distilled over 25,000 compounds (that kill malaria parasites in vitro) into a group of 400 representative compounds, called the "Malaria Box." These compounds have been distributed for neglected tropical diseases (NTDs), cancer and other diseases (Van Voorhis *et al.* 2016). In cancer biology, for some cancers, there is the concept of oncofetal antigens, gene expression in inappropriate times. Cloning and analysis of the *Plasmodium falciparum* protein VAR2CSA has evolved to facilitate a specific and high-affinity binding of the infected erythrocytes to the placental syncytiotrophoblast. This targeting of oncofetal chondroitin sulfate has shown promise for novel cancer diagnostics and therapeutics (Agerbæk *et al.* 2019).

9.8 Genome

Studies on the genomes of the malaria parasites started with the *Plasmodium falciparum* 3D7 strain (Gardner *et al.* 2002), as a collaboration between The Institute of Genome Research (TIGR), Wellcome Trust Sanger Institute and others. The genome is a very **AT** rich (19.4% GC) genome of 23 Mb in size and codes for **5,268** genes, in 14 linear (haploid) chromosomes. The genome also includes two circular DNA, the **6 Kb** mitochondrial DNA for 3 protein-coding genes, and the **35 Kb** apicoplast *DNA* for 30 protein-coding genes. The scientists concluded: "The *P. falciparum*, *Anopheles gambiae* and *Homo sapiens* genome sequences have been completed in the past two years, and represent new starting points in the centuries-long search for solution to the malaria problem." Genome of the mosquito vector was also published in the same year (Holt *et al.* 2002). Current updates show *P. falciparum* 3D7 with **5,712** genes (5,640 protein-coding genes, 252 non-protein coding genes and 155 pseudogenes). For *P. falciparum*, technical advance allows direct whole-genome sequencing (WGS) from dried blood samples on filter papers, thus making possible sample acquisition from remote areas (Nag *et al.* 2018). After the *P. falciparum* draft genome, other *Plasmodium* genomes have become available: *P. vivax* (Carlton *et al.* 2008), *P. knowlesi* (Pain *et al.* 2008), *P. malariae* and *P. ovale curtisi* (Rutledge *et al.* 2017). *P. ovale* has been shown to be made up of two species (as non-recombining globally sympatric forms); the classic and variant *P. ovale* thus became ***Plasmodium ovale curtisi*** (honoring malaria researcher Christopher Curtis) and ***Plasmodium ovale wallikeri*** (honoring David Walliker) (Sutherland *et al.* 2010).

Among the various *Plasmodium* species infecting mammals, their genome organization is rather uniform. The genomes consist of **23-27 Mb** DNA in **14** chromosomes, and code for about **5,500 genes** organized in a highly syntenic manner. Additional genes are present as nonnuclear genomes of the organelles: mitochondria and apicoplasts. About 10% of the nuclear genome encodes for proteins that are targeted to the apicoplast. Almost 80% of the genes of human and rodent *Plasmodium* species are orthologous (Heussler *et al.* 2016). *Plasmodium* genomes are AT rich, the most AT rich (17.8% GC) is from *Plasmodium gallinaceum*, an infectious agent causing avian malaria (Videall 2018). Interestingly, the majority of *Plasmodium* genes encode for proteins with unknown function. Another important feature found in the different genomes is that coding sequences of proteins that are exported to the surface of host erythrocytes have evolved much faster than those that remain in the cytoplasm. It has been postulated that the accelerated evolution of exported proteins eventually resulted in the generation of gene families in *Plasmodium* parasites.

After the genomes, there are functional genomic, epigenomic, proteomic, metabolomic, and transcriptomic analyses (Kirchner *et al.* 2016; Bourgard *et al.* 2018; Garrido-Cardenas *et al.* 2019; Su *et al.* 2019). Karine G. Le Roch (University of California Riverside) and colleagues have investigated on the role of epigenetics and chromatin structure in transcriptional regulation of malaria parasites. Their 3-dimensional (3D) modeling of the *P. falciparum* genome has shown strong association between spatial genome organization and gene expression. Using the technology of chromosome conformation capture (**3C**) coupled with next generation sequencing (NGS), for the asexual erythrocytic cycle, the genome of the highly active trophozoite (nuclear radius 850 nm) stage adopts a more open chromatin structure with increase in chromosome intermingling, as compared to the ring (350 nm) or schizont (425 nm) stages (Ay *et al.* 2014). There are clustering of centromeres, telomeres, ribosomal DNA genes, as well as virulence genes (named VRSM, for var, rifin, stevor, and Pfmc-2tm genes). These families of hypervariable and highly amplified genes are located in the sub-telomeric regions, whereas in the central region, protected against instability, are the genes for the parasite's metabolic functions. Please see Figure 9.7 for 3D modeling of *Plasmodium* chromosomes (Ay *et al.* 2014). "Along with classical gene regulation by transcription factors (TFs), of which only one family, the AP2 TFs, has been described in the parasite genome, a large body of evidence points toward chromatin structure and epigenetic factors mediating the changes in gene expression associated with parasite life cycle stages. These attributes may be critically important for immune evasion, host cell invasion and development of the parasite in its two hosts, the human and the *Anopheles* vector. Thus, the factors involved in the maintenance and regulation of chromatin and epigenetic features represent potential targets for antimalarial drugs" (Abel and La Roch 2019). Please see Figure 9.8 for changes in nuclear structure and transcription in the *Plasmodium* life cycle (Abel and La Roch 2019).

Few master regulators of the *Plasmodium* life cycle are known, only one family of 27 apetala (AP2) domain-containing transcription factors. One of these, AP2-G, initiates sexual differentiation (Williamson 2022). A newly discovered transcription factor,

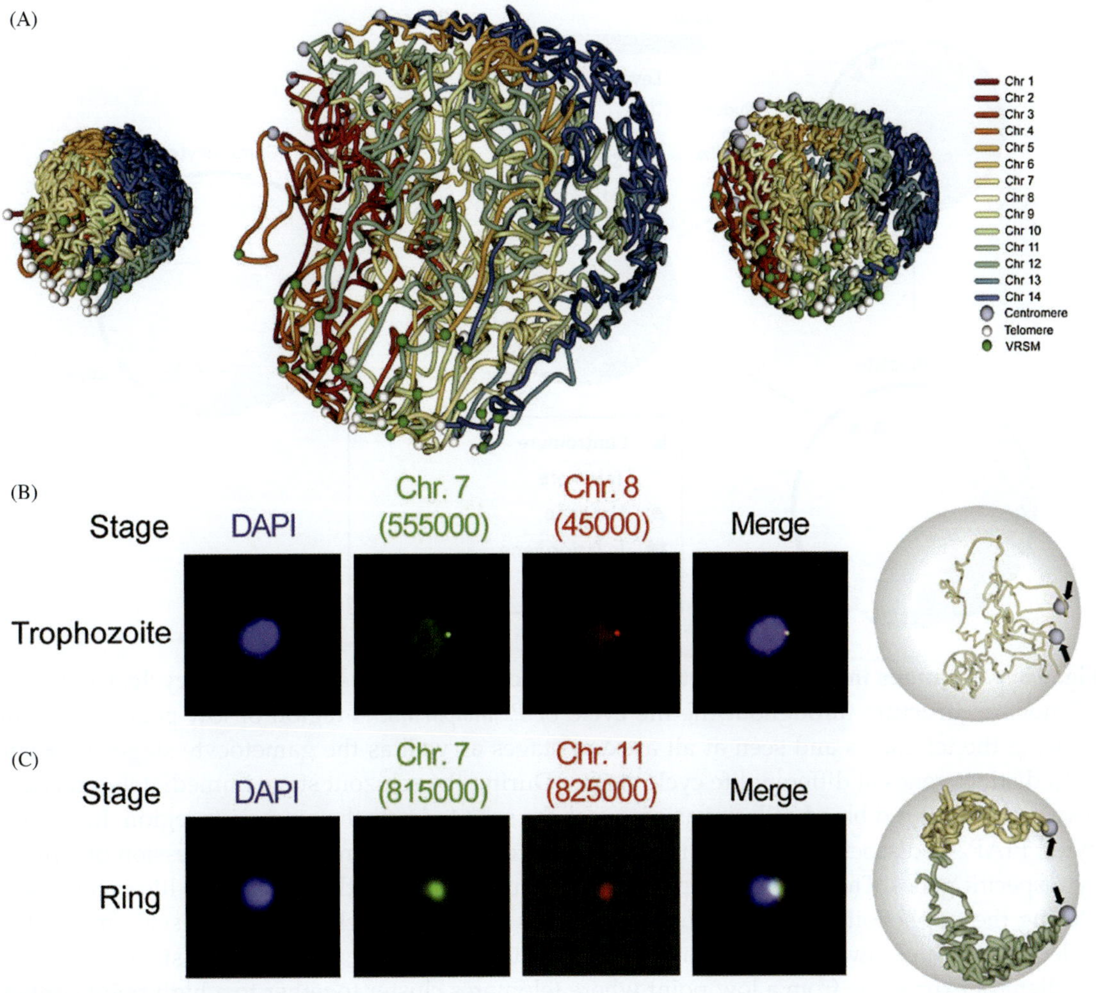

Fig. 9.7 ■ 3D modeling of *Plasmodium* chromosomes. 3D modeling and validation with DNA FISH. (A) 3D structures of all three stages. The nuclear radii used to model ring, trophozoite, and schizont stages were 350, 850, and 425 nm, respectively. Centromeres and telomeres are indicated with light-blue and white spheres, respectively. Midpoints of VRSM gene clusters are shown with green spheres. (B) Validation of colocalization between a pair of interchromosomal loci with VRSM genes (chr7: 550,000–560,000 that harbors internal VRSM genes and chr8: 40,000–50,000 that harbors subtelomeric VRSM genes) by DNA FISH (*left*) and by the three-dimensional model for the corresponding stage (*right*). The location of the loci in the 3D model is shown with light-blue spheres and indicated by black arrows. (C) Validation same as in *B* for a pair of interchromosomal loci that harbor no VRSM genes (chr7: 810,000–820,000 and chr11: 820,000–830,000). Courtesy: Ay *et al. Genome Res* 2014;24:974–88. Reproduced with permission from *Genome Research* with Creative Commons Attribution 4.0 (CC-BY) International License.

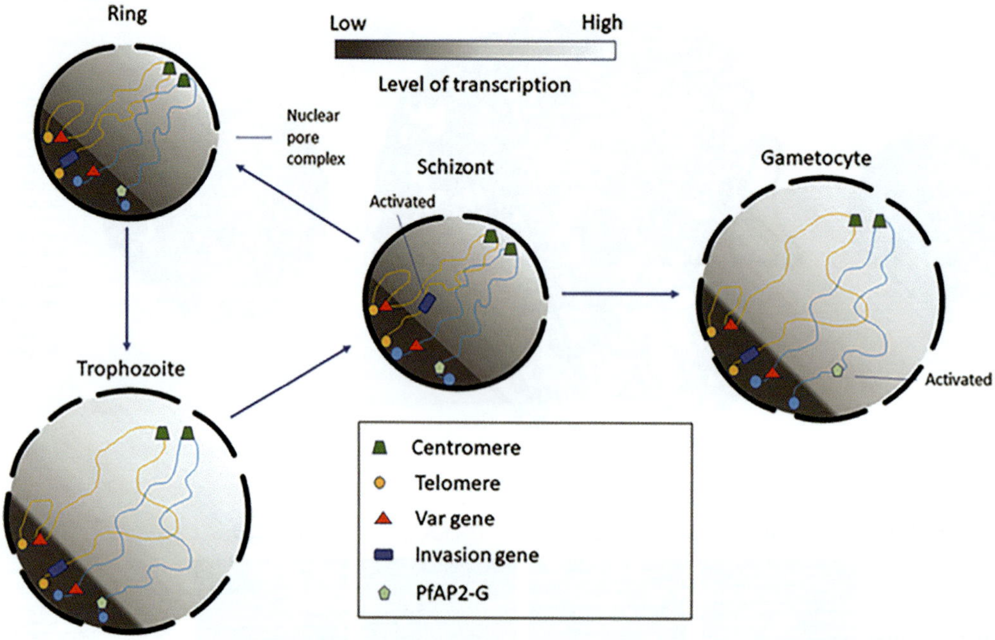

Fig. 9.8 ■ Changes in nuclear structure and transcription in *Plasmodium* life cycle. Changes in 3D nuclear structure throughout the life cycle of *P. falciparum*. A region of low gene expression, housing the telomeres and seen at all asexual stages as well as the gametocyte stage, associates with distinct genes at different life cycle stages. During the schizont stage immediately preceding invasion of new red blood cells, invasion genes are seen to leave the repressive region. In gametocytes, PfAP2-G dissociates from the region and becomes active, promoting expression of gametocyte-specific genes. The physical properties of the nucleus change throughout the life cycle as well. During the trophozoite stage, the nucleus enlarges and more nuclear pores are seen, most likely reflecting the high level transcriptional activity at this stage. The nucleus at all stages displays a gradient of expression from a low point where telomeres cluster together to a high point containing the centromeres. Courtesy: Abel S, Le Roch K, *Brief Funct Genomics* 2019;18:302–13. Reproduced with permission from Oxford University Press.

homeodomain protein 1 (HDP1), containing helix-loop-helix DNA binding motif, will further the gene expression for gamogony (including genes of inner membrane complex IMC) (Campelo Morillo *et al.* 2022).

9.9 Antigenic Variation

Like *Trypanosoma* and *Giardia*, *Plasmodium* exhibits antigenic variation. Antigenic variation, changes in surface molecules derived from the parasites and exposed on the plasma membrane of the *Plasmodium*-infected erythrocyte, at various times, is an elegant way for the pathogen to evade host immune response. As the malaria parasites multiply within red blood cells, parasite-derived proteins can be inserted into the erythrocyte host cell membrane, as parasite proteins on infected erythrocyte cell surface to be used to modulate host immune response. Antigenic variation of malaria was first found in the rodent species *Plasmodium berghei* in mice. It seems that the variant proteins differ in different species of the malaria parasite. As examples, for *P. vivax*, they are the *vir* (variant interspersed repeats) genes (346 copies) and for *P. knowlesi*, the *SICAvar* (variant schizont-infected cell agglutination) genes (107 copies). For *P. falciparum*, they are PfEMP1 (*Plasmodium falciparum* erythrocyte membrane protein 1). In the malaria parasite, antigenic variation is due to **epigenetic regulation** (Duraisingh and Skillman 2018). Current view of *Plasmodium falciparum* antigenic variation, the best-known case, is presented below.

Plasmodium falciparum possesses many multigene families whose proteins are expressed on the infected erythrocyte cell surfaces (Wahlgren *et al.* 2017). This means that infected erythrocyte surface contains the parasite-genome coded proteins. These proteins allow unique features of the infected red blood cell, including rosetting (forming a clump) and adherence to the microvasculature surface (may lead to the blocking of blood flow). The expression of parasite-derived proteins on its cell surface makes the infected erythrocyte "knobby." Please see Figure 9.9 for protein structures at the knob (Wahlgren *et al.* 2017). These variant surface antigens mediate the sequestration of infected erythrocytes in the microvasculature and block the blood flow when binding is excessive.

Binding is mediated by the adhesive proteins, including PfEMP1, *P. falciparum*-encoded repetitive interspersed families of polypeptides (RIFINs, 150 copies), and subtelomeric variant open reading frame (STEVOR, 30 copies). PfEMP1 members, encoded by multigene families, are responsible for antigenic variation and evasion of host immunity. The genome of *Plasmodium falciparum* possesses about **60 *var*** genes, coding for **PfEMP1**. In addition to gene abundance, gene expression levels can be modified by epigenetic means. Epigenetic mechanisms involved in antigenic variation include: transcription at the nuclear periphery, differential histone modulation (acetylation and methylation) patterns, and gene silencing via telomeric heterochromatin.

Analysis of the *var* genes show that PfEMP1 has different domains, the genes possess 2 exons and a conserved intron. Exon 1 possesses the polymorphic, variable extracellular portion that bind to different host molecules plus the transmembrane domain; exon 2 possesses a small intracellular portion for binding to other proteins forming knobs (for cytoadherence). Molecular studies have shown that at a single locus, expression of an antisense long non-coding RNA (**aslncRNA**) can open up the chromatin ending to allow transcription of that particular *var* gene, whereas the other genes are under heterochromatin silencing (by insulator-like DNA elements) (Scherf *et al.* 2008; Deitsch and Dzikowski 2017). Please see Figure 9.10 for PfEMP1 protein domains and antigenic variation (Deitsch and Dzikowski 2017).

Furthermore, there is allelic exclusion, at any one time only one *var* gene is expressed on the infected erythrocyte. The mutually exclusive expression of *var* genes ensures that the parasite exposes only a single PfEMP1 molecule to the immune system. Furthermore, recombination among the *var* genes is possible during the cell cycle, as seen in the divergence of *var* genes among different *P. falciparum* isolates. Although each parasite's genome

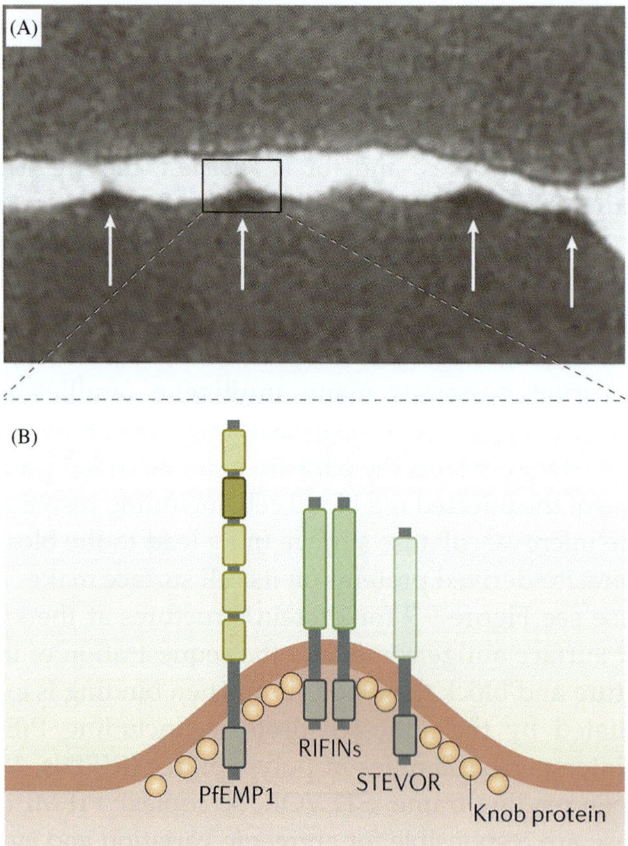

Fig. 9.9 ■ *Plasmodium falciparum*-coded proteins on cell surface of infected erythrocyte. (A) This transmission electron micrograph shows 'knobs' (arrows) on the surface of an erythrocyte that is infected with *Plasmodium falciparum*, in which fibrillar material is seen binding to uninfected red blood cells (RBCs) and holding the cells together. The fibrillar material may include serum proteins (such as immunoglobulin M (IgM), IgG, α2-macroglobulin and thrombospondin (TSP)), *P. falciparum* erythrocyte membrane protein 1 (PfEMP1) and other adhesins (*P. falciparum*-encoded repetitive interspersed families of polypeptides (RIFIN) and subtelomeric variant open reading frame (STEVOR)). (B) The variant surface antigen PfEMP1 proteins, which are the best-characterized adhesins of *P. falciparum*, and the RIFINs and STEVORs are encoded by the *var*, *rif* and *stevor* genes, respectively, and are exported from the parasitophorous vacuole to the erythrocyte surface. The knob protein (KP or KAHRP) makes up a sub-membraneous electron-dense structure that is important for an increased avidity of the pRBC for microvascular cells. Courtesy: Wahlgren *et al.* *Nat Rev Microbiol* 2017;15:479–91. Reproduced with permission from Springer Nature.

only possesses 60 *var* genes, the repertoire of different PfEMP1 variants in the total population of *P. falciparum* parasites can be huge. Claessens *et al.* (2014) wrote: "The high rate of *var* exon 1 recombination indicates that millions of new antigenic structures could potentially be generated each day in a single infected individual."

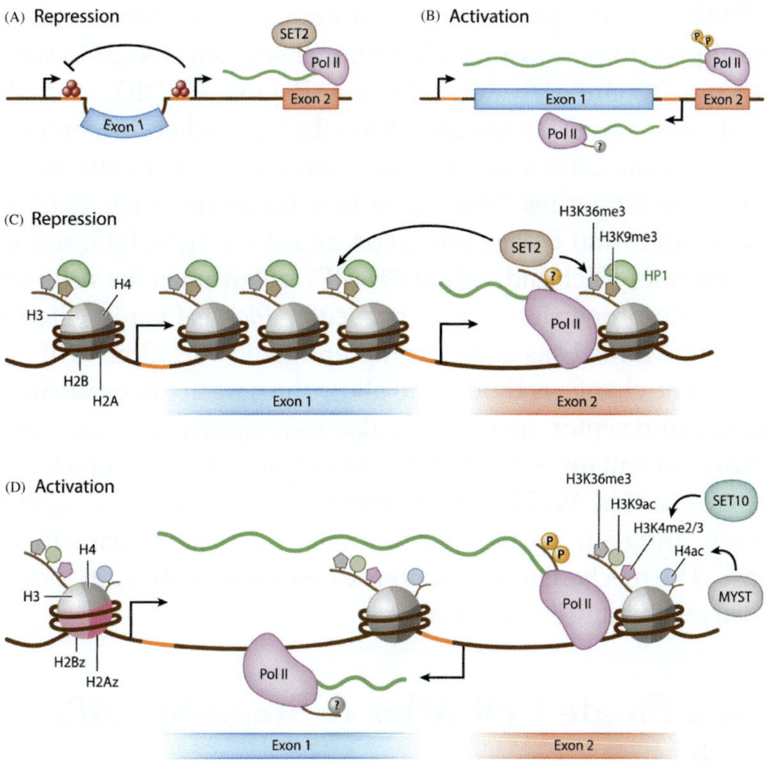

Fig. 9.10 ■ PfEMP1 protein domains and antigenic variation. var gene structure and elements of epigenetic transcriptional regulation. (A) The two-exon structure of each var gene is shown. In the repressed state, transcription by RNA polymerase II initiates from a promoter located within the intron, recruiting the histone modifier PfSET2 to the locus. Two pairing elements (orange) are bound by nuclear proteins (red spheres) and are proposed to facilitate interactions between the promoters, resulting in silencing of the upstream promoter. (B) In the active state, RNA polymerase II transcribes both an mRNA in the sense direction from the upstream promoter and a lncRNA in the antisense direction. The mRNA-transcribing polymerase has a phosphorylated C-terminal domain (CTD), whereas the status of the CTD of the antisense-transcribing polymerase is unknown. (C) Schematic representation of a silent var gene showing nucleosomes consisting of the histones H2A, H2B, H3, and H4 (gray spheres composed of four subunits). The posttranslational modifications H3K9me3 and H3K36me3 are also shown. Recruitment of PfSET2 through binding to the CTD of RNA polymerase II is shown, along with the binding of heterochromatin protein 1 (HP1) to the modified nucleosomes, resulting in condensed, transcriptionally inactive heterochromatin. (D) Schematic representation of an active var gene showing active transcription by RNA polymerase II of both mRNA and antisense lncRNA. Nucleosomes near the upstream promoter incorporate the alternative histones H2Bz (light pink) and H3Az (dark pink) and display the posttranslational modifications H3K9ac, H3K4me2/3, H3K36me3, and H4ac. The histone modifiers PfSET10 and PfMYST are recruited to the locus to transfer the modifications H3K4me2/3 and H4ac, respectively, although the mechanisms of recruitment are unknown. These histone modifications and the action of RNA polymerase II are proposed to perpetuate a more open chromatin structure. Abbreviations: Pol II, RNA polymerase II; SET, Su(var)3–9, Enhancer-of-zeste and Trithorax; MYST, moz, Ybf2/Sas2, Sas2, and Tip60. Courtesy: Deitsch K, Dzikowski R, *Annu Rev Microbiol* 2017;71:625–41. Reproduced with permission from Annual Reviews.

Different PfEMP1proteins possess different domains and hence show functional differences. A typical protein possesses an N-terminal segment (NTS) located at the amino terminus, different Cysteine-rich Inter-domain Region (CIDR), and different Duffy Binding-like (**DBL**) domains. This feature allows the infected erythrocytes to interact with endothelial cells, immune cells, extracellular matrix and other cells and molecules, via their specific adhesive properties (binding to host molecules such as α2-macroglobulin, CD36, complement 1q, E- and P-selectins, heparan sulfate, IgM, IgG, and ICAM, intercellular adhesion molecule). Each individual PfEMP1 determines the receptor binding specificities and antigenic properties of that particular *Plasmodium*-infected erythrocyte. A switch to a different PfEMP1, as seen during antigenic variation, will change receptor binding properties. The change is thought to allow the parasite to evade immune response of the host. Change in receptor specificities also influences organ tropism. For example, binding to chondroitin sulfate A (CSA) leads to sequestration of infected cells in a pregnant woman's placenta. The VAR2CSA protein mentioned above is a specific PfEMP1.

As seen above, antigenic variation is adopted by malaria parasites to evade host immune response. The mechanisms of actions differ somewhat from those used by other protozoa that also exhibit antigenic variation.

9.10 Malaria Single Cell Atlas & Stage-Specific Gene Expression

Genomics is followed by transcriptomics. Microarray studies give an average picture. In addition, there is the need to synchronize cells for the differentiated state under analysis. The technique of single cell transcriptomics will overcome these problems and has been applied to parasitology. A malaria cell atlas has been generated, for single parasite transcriptomes across the complete life cycle (Howick *et al.* 2019). The model mouse malaria was used in vivo (*Plasmodium berghei*) as well as the in vitro studies of the RBC intracellular stage that include the human pathogens *Plasmodium falciparum* and *P. malariae*. A total of 1,787 parasites were sorted and their transcriptomes characterized. Each developmental stage has been identified, and the data set can be used to check field isolates from human malaria. Please see Figure 9.11 for single cell RNA-seq results (Howick *et al.* 2019). The data set have been released via the interactive Malaria Cell Atlas website.[8]

As an introduction to this important publication, Elizabeth Winzeler (University of California San Diego) wrote: "This rich dataset can be used to find new therapeutic candidates as well as to better understand transcriptional control networks" (Winzeler 2019). This is her description of single cell RNA-sequencing: "**scRNA-seq** is a recent technological advance in which individual cells are captured using flow-sorting or microdroplets. RNA in these cells is then converted to DNA using a reverse transcriptase, and then the DNA is analyzed using next-generation sequencing methods. Advances in this pow-

[8] https://www.sanger.ac.uk/science/tools/mca/mca/

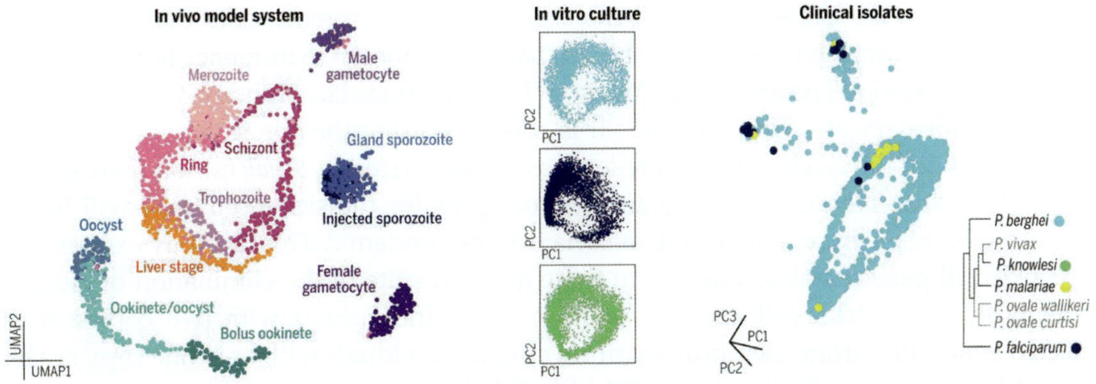

Fig. 9.11 ■ Malaria Cell Atlas. Single-cell RNA-seq references for the *Plasmodium* genus. Left: Single-cell transcriptomes from across the life cycle of *Plasmodium berghei* were profiled (including liver, blood, and mosquito life stages). Center: Deep exploration of blood-stage parasites captured transcriptomic diversity at single-cell resolution across three different *Plasmodium* species by droplet sequencing. Right: Such datasets can serve as references to understand wild parasites isolated from clinical samples. Courtesy: Howick *et al. Science* 2019;365:eaaw2619. Reproduced with permission from The American Association for the Advancement of Science.

erful technology have been driven by the availability of new instruments and methods that have led to vast reductions in the cost of DNA sequencing per base, as well as the development of powerful bioinformatic algorithms that can handle the large quantities of data produced from such studies."

9.11 Malaria & Human Genetics

Long association of malaria parasites and humans has led to changes in the host genome that can combat malaria. Humans possess genetic variations that can target malaria. The Duffy blood group (all humans possess another, the more well-known ABO blood group) has been used by *P. vivax* for invasion, thus 40% of West Africans are Duffy negative. The most severe malaria is caused by *P. falciparum*. Sickle cell anemia, glucose-6-phosphate dehydrogenase (G6PD) deficiency (favism), α-thalassemia, and ovalocytosis (aka hereditary elliptocytosis, common in Southeast Asia), have all been implicated as mediators of innate resistance against *P. falciparum* infection (Wambua *et al.* 2006). Mechanisms of other red blood cell (RBC) resistance to malaria have been investigated. For the Dantu blood group, this variant provides 74% protection against all forms of severe malaria in homozygous individuals. Dantu cells have a higher RBC tension than non-Dantu RBCs. There is a strong link between RBC tension and *P. falciparum* merozoite invasion, with a tension threshold above which invasion rarely occurs, as shown by video microscopy (Kariuki *et al.* 2020).

Mutations in the genes coding for the α and β globin proteins, ones that form hemoglobin (oxygen-carrying protein in the blood) have been shown to influence how people are affected by malaria. The most famous is **sickle cell anemia**. Anthony Clifford Allison (Radcliffe Infirmary at Oxford) wrote: "It is concluded that the abnormal erythrocytes of individuals with the sickle-cell trait are less easily parasitized by *P. falciparum* than are normal erythrocytes. Hence those who are heterozygous for the sickle-cell gene will have a selective advantage in regions where malaria is hyper-endemic. This fact may explain why the sickle-cell gene remains common in these areas in spite of the elimination of genes in patients dying of sickle-cell anemia" (Allison 1954). Individuals with two copies of the affected gene suffer from anemia and painful crises; individuals with only one copy are less susceptible to malaria. For blacks in USA, 1 in 5,000 is a carrier. This is due to hemoglobin S (HbS), the sixth residue of β hemoglobin chain has changed from glutamic acid to valine (Glu to Val, or E to V). In a murine cerebral malaria animal model, HbS confers host tolerance to *Plasmodium* infection through the inhibition of pathogenic CD8 T cells and the induction heme oxygenase-1 (HO-1). Ho-1 plays protective role in many immune-mediated inflammatory diseases. Its heme degradation product carbon monoxide (CO) prevents further accumulation of circulating heme to suppress the immunopathology of cerebral malaria (Ferreira *et al.* 2011). Free heme is cytotoxic; even the malaria parasite wants to get rid of free heme, by converting free heme to insoluble crystallized form known as hemozoin (aka malaria pigment). The sickle hemoglobin provides protection against malaria through induction of the expression of heme oxygenase-1, which prevents accumulation of circulating heme (Ferreira *et al.* 2011). In addition to HbS, there are HbC (β 6 Glu to Lys) and HbE (β 26 Glu to Lys), all can confer a survival advantage to malaria infections.

Frederic B. Piel (then, Oxford; now, Imperial College London) and colleagues noted: "More than 50 years ago, it was suggested that the gene responsible for this disorder could reach high frequencies because of resistance conferred against malaria by the heterozygous carrier state. This traditional example of balancing selection is known as the '**malaria hypothesis**'. However, the geographical relationship between the transmission intensity of malaria and associated HbS burden has never been formally investigated on a global scale" (Piel *et al.* 2010). The researchers investigated the geographical relationship between the transmission intensity of malaria and associated HbS burden on a global scale; they found geographical support for the malaria hypothesis, especially in Africa. Please see Figure 9.12 for HbS and malaria (Piel *et al.* 2010). The investigators also mentioned the increased disease burden for sickle cell anemia. The illness has additional symptoms, hence the name sickle cell disease (**SCD**) (Piet *et al.* 2017). On November 25, 2019, US FDA approved voxelotor for treatment of sickle cell anemia (brand name Oxbryta, by Global Blood Therapeutics at South San Francisco, CA). Voxelotor is an HbS polymerization inhibitor that reversibly binds to hemoglobin to stabilize the oxygenated hemoglobin state (Vichinsky *et al.* 2019). Therapy based on gene editing has been shown to work for SCD (Frangoul *et al.* 2020). BCL11A is a transcription factor that represses γ-globin expression and fetal hemoglobin in erythroid cells. Patient received autologous CD34+ cells edited with CRISPR-Cas9 targeting the *BCL11A* enhancer. The first patient

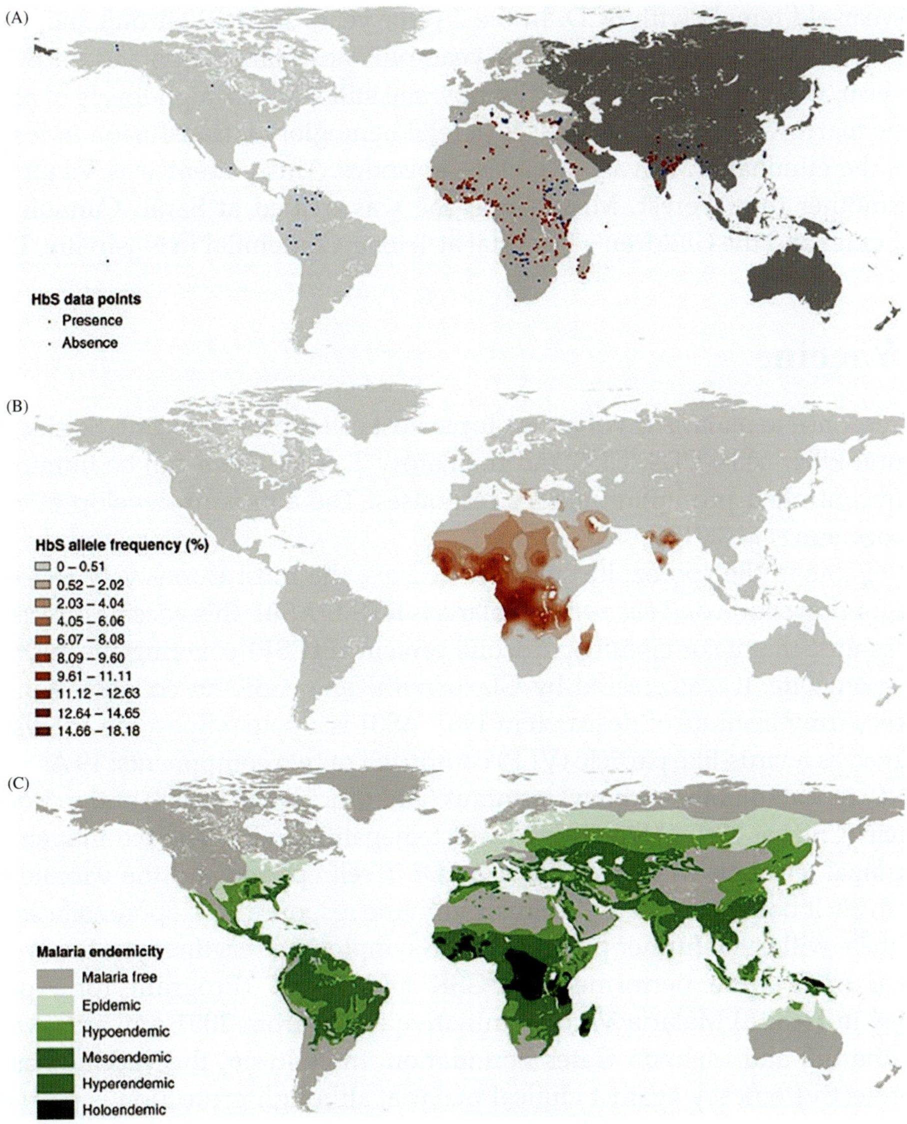

Fig. 9.12 ■ HbS and malaria. (A) Distribution of the data points. Red dots represent the presence and blue dots the absence of the *HbS* gene. The regional subdivisions were informed by Weatherall and Clegg, and are as follows: the Americas (light grey), Africa, including the western part of Saudi Arabia, and Europe (medium grey) and Asia (dark grey); (B) Raster map of HbS allele frequency (posterior median) generated by a Bayesian model-based geostatistical framework. The Jenks optimized classification method was used to define the classes; (C) The historical map of malaria endemicity was digitized from its source using the method outlined in Hay *et al.* The classes are defined by parasite rates (PR_{2-10}, the proportion of 2- up to 10-year olds with the parasite in their peripheral blood): malaria free, $PR_{2-10}=0$; epidemic, $PR_{2-10}=0$; hypoendemic, $PR_{2-10}<0.10$; mesoendemic, $PR_{2-10}\geq 0.10$ and <0.50; hyperendemic, $PR_{2-10}\geq 0.50$ and <0.75; holoendemic, $PR_{0-1}\geq 0.75$ (this class was measured in 0- up to 1-year olds). Courtesy: Piel *et al. Nat Commun* 2010;1:104. Reproduced with permission from Springer Nature.

was a 33-year-old female with SCD. In the 2 prior years she had chronic pain, averaged seven severe vaso-occlusive episodes per year, plus hospitalizations and 5 RBC transfusions per year. Over a year after gene therapy, she still showed high levels of allelic editing in bone marrow and blood, increases in fetal hemoglobin, transfusion independence, as well as the elimination of vaso-occlusive episodes. This patient was Victoria Gray, a wife and mother from Forest, Mississippi; she was treated at Sarah Cannon Research Institute Center and the Children's Hospital at TriStar Centennial in Nashville, Tennessee.

9.12 Vaccine

Immune response to malaria involves multiple host cell types, including B cells, dendritic cells, natural killer cells, CD4, CD8 and regulatory T cells. There can be immunopathology, via uncontrolled pro-inflammatory responses. The aim is to develop efficient vaccines (Moormann *et al.* 2019).

To date, among the sporozoite subunit vaccines, the most extensively tested vaccine candidate for prevention of *P. falciparum* malaria is **RTS,S/AS01**; this vaccine directs immune response against the major circumsporozoite protein (**PfCSP**) covering the surface of the infecting sporozoite. It was created by GlaxoSmithKline (GSK) in collaboration with the Walter Reed Army Institute of Research in 1987. AS01 is a potent liposome adjuvant. RTS,S was designed as a virus-like particle (VLP) comprised of two components: 19 Asn-Ala-Asn-Pro (NANP) repeats and the carboxyl terminus (amino acids 210 to 398) of the circumsporozoite protein (CSP has 37 NANP repeats) fused to hepatitis B virus surface antigen (HBsAg). The C-terminal terminus of CSP contains 2 CD4 T cell epitope and the vaccine has been designed to elicit both humoral and cellular immune response. The sporozoite stage is targeted, so there will be no further progress to the symptomatic erythrocytic life cycle stages.

Clinical trials were performed by GSK and PATH (Program for Appropriate Technology in Health) Malaria Vaccine Initiative (MVI) from 2001 onwards, with funding from the Bill and Melinda Gates Foundation. In children, the vaccine has demonstrated protective efficacy against clinical malaria, although protection is partial, wanes over time, and may be age-dependent (protection was lower in infants 6–12 weeks of age than in young children 5–17 months old). A phase III clinical trial of the RTS,S vaccine was completed with over 15,000 African infants and children, and pilot implementation studies are currently underway. The subunit vaccine was used in the field (for children under the age of 2, starting in Malawi and extending to Ghana and Kenya), although it is only partially effective (protecting 4 out of 10). In a phase IIIb trial with 709 children from Ghana, the RTS,S/AS01 vaccine has been shown to be active when co-administered with Vitamin A at 6 months, and with yellow fever and measles-rubella vaccines at 9 months of age, without immune response impairment to any vaccine antigen or negative safety effect (Asante *et al.* 2020).

In an announcement on October 6, 2021, the World Health Organization (WHO) is recommending widespread use of the RTS,S/AS01 malaria vaccine among children in sub-Saharan Africa and in other regions with moderate to high *P. falciparum* malaria transmission. WHO Director-General Tedros Ghebreyesus said: "This is a historic moment. The long-awaited malaria vaccine for children is a breakthrough for science, child health and malaria control. Using this vaccine on top of existing tools to prevent malaria could save tens of thousands of young lives each year."[9] Over 260,000 African children under the age of five die from malaria annually; now, "the world is about to get its first malaria vaccine, after a 35-year quest. ... Data from a pilot rollout involving more than 800,000 children in three countries convinced a panel of malaria and vaccine experts advising WHO that the vaccine, also called Mosquirix, is safe and effective" (Vogel 2021). The three African countries are Ghana, Kenya, and Malawi. However, "RTS'S is far from perfect: It requires four doses, only provides roughly 30% protection against severe malaria, and has a price tag that could be hard to afford" (Vogel 2021).

Because the RTS,S vaccine only yields partial protection to immunized children, other improved vaccines are being actively sought after. Traditionally, whole cells have been attenuated for use as vaccine candidates, as seen in many bacterial and viral diseases using inactivated pathogens. Instead of sporozoite subunit vaccine, the whole sporozoite has been modified for use as a potential vaccine. Earlier work involved irradiated sporozoites. Current works include genetic modifications. Deleting three genes of *P. falciparum* has yielded the PfGAP3KO sporozoites that are safe and immunogenic (Kublin *et al.* 2017). One such trial with whole sporozoites has begun in 2020, in Bioko, an island of Equatorial Guinea for 2,100 individuals (including children). The vaccine, called PfSPZ, can be injected intravenously. It is made from sporozoites, by the company Sanaria in Rockville, Maryland, by isolating sporozoites from farmed mosquitoes. PfSPZ is the only malaria vaccine claimed to have achieved 100% protection in laboratory trials with healthy volunteers. The endeavor is funded by Guinea's government and private energy companies (Olotu *et al.* 2018).

In addition to anti-sporozoite vaccines, there are other possibilities, such as anti-asexual blood stages and transmission-blocking vaccines. Current efforts to get better vaccines, with next-generation candidate vaccines using novel antigens, are ongoing (Laurens 2018; Draper *et al.* 2018).

There may be a bright future for malaria prevention (The Lancet Infectious Diseases Editorial 2021). Intervention using RTS,S/AS01 vaccine in combination with chemoprevention (sulfadoxine–pyrimethamine and amodiaquine) showed promising results in Mali and Burkina Faso. A different CSP-based vaccine (R21) with a different adjuvant (Matrix-M, MM) worked in low doses (also in Burkina Faso). A phase I clinical trial of a monoclonal antibody (CIS43LS) also showed protection against malaria in volunteers.

We end this discussion on malaria to bring forth the idea of elimination. "Enthusiasm for malaria elimination has resurfaced. This ambitious but laudable goal faces many challenges, including the worldwide economic downturn, difficulties in elimination of *vivax* malaria, development of pyrethroid resistance in some anopheline mosquitoes, and the

[9] https://www.who.int/news/item/06-10-2021-who-recommends-groundbreaking-malaria-vaccine-for-children-at-risk

emergence of artemisinin resistance in *Plasmodium falciparum* in southeast Asia" (White *et al.* 2014). Researchers and clinicians will continue to confront and tackle the adaptable malaria parasites and their mosquito vectors.

Summary & Key Concepts

- Malaria is the most important parasitic disease caused by protozoa, with estimated over 400,000 deaths annually, mostly of children in sub-Sahara Africa.
- The 4 species of human malaria parasites are *Plasmodium falciparum, P. vivax, P. ovale* and *P. malariae.*
- *Plasmodium* species infect humans first in the liver and then move to the blood, causing paroxysm, chills and fever.
- *Plasmodium* species complete sexual maturation in female *Anopheles* mosquitoes.
- Human genetic changes have been detected to fight malaria, with sickle cell trait being the best known.
- Drugs for malaria include chloroquine, mefloquine, artemisinin, and others; new ones are urgently in need because of drug resistance in the malaria parasites.
- The first malaria vaccine is RTS,S targeting *P. falciparum* sporozoites, others are currently in development.
- Single-cell RNA-seq atlas for *Plasmodium berghei* (murine malaria experimental model) has been constructed.

References

Abel S, Le Roch KG. The role of epigenetics and chromatin structure in transcriptional regulation in malaria parasites. *Brief Funct Genomics* 2019;18(5):302–13.

Acharya S, Ningombam A, Sarkar A. A suspected case of mixed infection of *Plasmodium vivax* with *Plasmodium falciparum*: A diagnostic conundrum due to pre-analytical error. *Am J Trop Med Hyg* 2020;103(5):1755.

Adebayo JO, Tijjani H, Adegunloye AP, Ishola AA, Balogun EA, Malomo SO. Enhancing the antimalarial activity of artesunate. *Parasitol Res* 2020;119(9):2749–64.

Agerbæk MØ, Bang-Christensen S, Salanti A. Fighting cancer using an oncofetal glycosaminoglycan-binding protein from malaria parasites. *Trends Parasitol* 2019;35(3):178–81.

Akselrod H, Swierzbinski MJ, Zheng Z, Keiser J, Parenti DM, Simon GL. Characteristics and severity of disease among 100 cases of imported malaria seen at a U.S. University Hospital, 2000–2017. *Am J Trop Med Hyg* 2018;99(6):1511–7.

Allison AC Protection afforded by sickle-cell trait against subtertian malareal infection. *Br Med J* 1954;1.(4857):290–4.

Asante KP, Ansong D, Kaali S, *et al*. Immunogenicity and safety of the RTS,S/AS01 malaria vaccine co-administered with measles, rubella and yellow fever vaccines in Ghanaian children: A phase IIIb, multi-center, non-inferiority, randomized, open, controlled trial. *Vaccine* 2020;38(18):3411–21.

Ay F, Bunnik EM, Varoquaux N, *et al.* Three-dimensional modeling of the *P. falciparum* genome during the erythrocytic cycle reveals a strong connection between genome architecture and gene expression. *Genome Res* 2014;24(6):974–88.

Bejon P, Lusingu J, Olotu A, *et al.* Efficacy of RTS,S/AS01E vaccine against malaria in children 5 to 17 months of age. *N Engl J Med* 2008;359(24):2521–32.

Biddau M, Sheiner L. Targeting the apicoplast in malaria. *Biochem Soc Trans* 2019;47(4):973–83.

Boucher LE, Bosch J. The apicomplexan glideosome and adhesins — Structures and function. *J Struct Biol* 2015;190(2):93–114.

Bourgard C, Albrecht L, Kayano ACAV, Sunnerhagen P, Costa FTM. *Plasmodium vivax* Biology: Insights provided by Genomics, Transcriptomics and Proteomics. *Front Cell Infect Microbiol* 2018;8:34.

Campelo Morillo RA, Tong X, Xie W, Abel S, Orchard LM, Daher W, Patel DJ, Llinás M, Le Roch KG, Kafsack BFC. The transcriptional regulator HDP1 controls expansion of the inner membrane complex during early sexual differentiation of malaria parasites. *Nat Microbiol.* 2022;7(2):289–299.

Capanna E. Grassi versus Ross: who solved the riddle of malaria? *Int Microbiol.* 2006;9(1):69–74.

Carlton JM, Adams JH, Silva JC, *et al.* Comparative genomics of the neglected human malaria parasite *Plasmodium vivax*. *Nature* 2008;455(7214):757–63.

Chakraborty A. Understanding the biology of the *Plasmodium falciparum* apicoplast; an excellent target for antimalarial drug development. *Life Sci* 2016;158:104–10.

Claessens A, Hamilton WL, Kekre M, *et al.* Generation of antigenic diversity in *Plasmodium falciparum* by structured rearrangement of Var genes during mitosis. *PLoS Genet* 2014;10(12):e1004812.

Cook GC. *Tropical Medicine: An illustrated history of the pioneers* (2007, Academic Press).

Cox FEG, editor. *The Welcome Trust Illustrated History of Tropical Diseases* (1996, The Wellcome Trust, London).

Deitsch KW, Dzikowski R. Variant gene expression and antigenic variation by malaria parasites. *Annu Rev Microbiol* 2017;71:625–41.

Draper SJ, Sack BK, King CR, *et al.* Malaria vaccines: Recent advances and new horizons. *Cell Host Microbe* 2018;24(1):43–56.

Duraisingh MT, Skillman KM. Epigenetic variation and regulation in malaria parasites. *Annu Rev Microbiol* 2018;72:355–75.

Dziekan JM, Yu H, Chen D, *et al.* Identifying purine nucleoside phosphorylase as the target of quinine using cellular thermalshift assay. *Sci Transl Med* 2019;11(473).

Esch GW. *Parasites and Infectious Diseases: Discoveries by Serendipity, and Otherwise* (2007, Cambridge).

Ewald PW, Sussman JB, Distler MT, *et al.* Evolutionary control of infectious disease: prospects for vectorborne and waterborne pathogens. *Mem Inst Oswaldo Cruz* 1998;93(5):567–76.

Ferreira A, Marguti I, Bechmann I, *et al.* Sickle hemoglobin confers tolerance to *Plasmodium* infection. *Cell* 2011;145(3):398–409.

Flannery EL, Markus MB, Vaughan AM. *Plasmodium vivax*. *Trends Parasitol* 2019;35(7):583–4.

Frangoul H, Altshuler D, Cappellini MD, *et al.* CRISPR-Cas9 gene editing for sickle cell disease and β-Thalassemia. *N Engl J Med* 2021;384:252–60.

Gardner MJ, Hall N, Fung E, *et al*. Genome sequence of the human malaria parasite *Plasmodium falciparum*. *Nature* 2002;419(6906):498–511.

Garrido-Cardenas JA, González-Cerón L, Manzano-Agugliaro F, Mesa-Valle C. *Plasmodium* genomics: An approach for learning about and ending human malaria. *Parasitol Res* 2019;118(1):1–27.

Hawass Z, Gad YZ, Ismail S, *et al*. Ancestry and pathology in King Tutankhamun's family. *JAMA* 2010;303(7):638–47.

Heintzelman MB. Gliding motility in apicomplexan parasites. *Semin Cell Dev Biol* 2015;46: 135–42.

Heussler V, Spielmann T, Frischknecht F, Gilberger T. *Plasmodium*. In: Walochnik J, Duchene M. editors, *Molecular Parasitology: Protozoan Parasites and their Molecules*, Springer, pp. 241–81, (2016, Springer).

Holt RA, Subramanian GM, Halpern A, *et al*. The genome sequence of the malaria mosquito *Anopheles gambiae*. *Science* 2002;298(5591):129–49.

Howick VM, Russell AJC, Andrews T, *et al*. The malaria cell Atlas: Single parasite transcriptomes across the complete *Plasmodium* life cycle. *Science* 2019;365(6455):eaaw2619.

Im JH, Chung MH, Durey A, *et al*. Subcapsular splenic hemorrhage in vivax malaria. *Korean J Parasitol* 2019;57(4):405–9.

Ioannidis LJ, Nie CQ, Hansen DS. The role of chemokines in severe malaria: More than meets the eye. *Parasitology* 2014;141(5):602–13.

Janouskovec J, Horák A, Oborník M, Lukes J, Keeling PJ. A common red algal origin of the apicomplexan, dinoflagellate, and heterokont plastids. *Proc Natl Acad Sci U S A* 2010;107(24):10949–54.

Jiménez-Díaz MB, Ebert D, Salinas Y, *et al*. (+)-**SJ733**, a clinical candidate for malaria that acts through ATP4 to induce rapid host-mediated clearance of *Plasmodium*. *Proc Natl Acad Sci USA* 2014;111(50):E5455–62.

Kariuki SN, Marin-Menendez A, Introini V, *et al*. Red blood cell tension protects against severe malaria in the Dantu blood group. *Nature* 2020;585(7826):579–83.

Kean BH, Mott KE, Russell AJ, editors. *Tropical Medicine and Parasitology: Classic Investigations*, volumes I and II (1978, Cornell).

Killeen GF. Characterizing, controlling and eliminating residual malaria transmission. *Malar J* 2014;13:330.

Kirchner S, Power BJ, Waters AP. Recent advances in malaria genomics and epigenomics. *Genome Med* 2016;8(1):92.

Kublin JG, Mikolajczak SA, Sack BK, Fishbaugher ME, Seilie A, Shelton L, VonGoedert T, Firat M, Magee S, Fritzen E, Betz W, Kain HS, Dankwa DA, Steel RW, Vaughan AM, Noah Sather D, Murphy SC, Kappe SH. Complete attenuation of genetically engineered *Plasmodium falciparum* sporozoites in human subjects. *Sci Transl Med* 2017;9(371):pii:eaad9099.

Lacerda MVG, Llanos-Cuentas A, Krudsood S, *et al*. Single-dose tafenoquine to prevent relapse of *Plasmodium vivax* Malaria. *N Engl J Med* 2019;380(3):215–28.

Laurens MB. The promise of a malaria vaccine-are we closer? *Annu Rev Microbiol* 2018;72:273–92.

Li XH, Kondrashin A, Greenwood B, Lindblade K, Loku Galappaththy G, Alonso P. A historical review of WHO certification of malaria elimination. *Trends Parasitol* 2019;35(2):163–71.

Maier AG, Matuschewski K, Zhang M, Rug M. *Plasmodium falciparum*. *Trends Parasitol* 2019;35(6):481–2.

Maxmen A. First proven malaria vaccine rolled out in Africa — but doubts linger. *Nature* 2019;569(7754):14–15.

McFadden GI, Yeh E. The apicoplast: Now you see it, now you don't. *Int J Parasitol* 2017; 47(2–3):137–44.

Milner DA, Jr. Malaria Pathogenesis. *Cold Spring Harb Perspect Med* 2018;8(1):a025569.

Moormann AM, Nixon CE, Forconi CS. Immune effector mechanisms in malaria: An update focusing on human immunity. *Parasite Immunol* 2019;41(8):e12628.

Moxon CA, Gibbins MP, McGuinness D, Milner DA Jr, Marti M. New insights into malaria pathogenesis. *Annu Rev Pathol* 2020;15:315–43.

Nag S, Kofoed PE, Ursing J, *et al.* Direct whole-genome sequencing of *Plasmodium falciparum* specimens from driederythrocyte spots. *Malar J* 2018;17(1):91.

Nguyen HTT, Romano F, Wampfler R, Mühlethaler K, Tannich E, Oberli A. Case report: Diagnostic challenges in the detection of a mixed *Plasmodium vivax/ovale* infection in a non-endemic setting. *Am J Trop Med Hyg* 2020;103(3):1085–7.

Olotu A, Urbano V, Hamad A, *et al.* Advancing global health through development and clinical trials partnerships: a randomized, placebo-controlled, double-blind assessment of safety, tolerability, and immunogenicity of PfSPZ Vaccine for malaria in healthy Equatoguinean men. *Am J Trop Med Hyg* 2018; 98(1):308–18.

Pain A, Böhme U, Berry AE, *et al.* The genome of the simian and human malaria parasite *Plasmodium knowlesi. Nature* 2008;455(7214):799–803.

Panda PK, Sharawat IK, Panda PK. Case report: An adolescent girl with isolated neuropsychiatric features and apparent post-malaria neurological syndrome. *Am J Trop Med Hyg* 2020;102(5):1030–2.

Pasupureddy R, Atul Seshadri S, Pande V, Dixit R, Pandey KC. Current scenario and future strategies to fight artemisinin resistance. *Parasitol Res* 2019;118(1):29–42.

Paton DG, Childs LM, Itoe MA, Holmdahl IE, Buckee CO, Catteruccia F. Exposing *Anopheles* mosquitoes to antimalarials blocks *Plasmodium* parasite transmission. *Nature* 2019;567(7747): 239–43.

Pazicky S, Dhamotharan K, Kaszuba K, *et al.* Structural role of essential light chains in the apicomplexan glideosome. *Commun Biol* 2020;3(1):568.

Pazhayam NM, Chhibber-Goel J, Sharma A. New leads for drug repurposing against malaria. *Drug Discov Today* 2019;24(1):263–71.

Piel FB, Steinberg MH, Rees DC. Sickle cell disease. *N Engl J Med* 2017;376(16):1561–73.

Piel FB, Patil AP, Howes RE, *et al.* Global distribution of the sickle cell gene and geographical confirmation of the malaria hypothesis. *Nat Commun* 2010;1:104.

Rosenke K, Adjemian J, Munster VJ, *et al. Plasmodium* parasitemia associated with increased survival in Ebola virus-infected patients. *Clin Infect Dis* 2016;63(8):1026–33.

Rutledge GG, Böhme U, Sanders M, *et al. Plasmodium malariae* and *P. ovale* genomes provide insights into malaria parasite evolution. *Nature* 2017;542(7639):101–4.

Scherf A, Lopez-Rubio JJ, Riviere L. Antigenic variation in *Plasmodium falciparum. Annu Rev Microbiol* 2008;62:445–70.

Shandilya A, Chacko S, Jayaram B, Ghosh I. A plausible mechanism for the antimalarial activity of artemisinin: A computational approach. *Sci Rep* 2013;3:2513.

Su XZ, Lane KD, Xia L, Sá JM, Wellems TE. *Plasmodium* genomics and genetics: New insights into malaria pathogenesis, drug resistance, epidemiology, and evolution. *Clin Microbiol Rev* 2019;32(4):pii:e00019–19.

Sutherland CJ, Tanomsing N, Nolder D, *et al.* Two nonrecombining sympatric forms of the human malaria parasite *Plasmodium ovale* occur globally. *J Infect Dis* 2010;201(10):1544–50.

The Ivermectin Roadmappers. A Roadmap for the development of Ivermectin as a complementary malaria vector control tool. *Am J Trop Med Hyg* 2020;102(2s):3–24.

The Lancet Infectious Diseases Editorial. A bright future for malaria prevention. *Lancet Infectious Diseases* 2021;21:1333.

Thien HV, Kager PA, Sauerwein HP. Hypoglycemia in falciparum malaria: Is fasting an unrecognized and insufficiently emphasized risk factor? *Trends Parasitol* 2006;22(9):410–5.

Tokplonou L, Nouatin O, Sonon P, *et al. Schistosoma haematobium* infection modulates *Plasmodium falciparum* parasite density and antimalarial antibody responses. *Parasite Immunol* 2020;42(4):e12702.

Tse EG, Korsik M, Todd MH. The past, present and future of anti-malarial medicines. *Malar J* 2019;18(1):93.

Uwimana A, Legrand E, Stokes BH, *et al.* Emergence and clonal expansion of in vitro artemisinin-resistant *Plasmodium falciparum* kelch13 R561H mutant parasites in Rwanda. *Nat Med* 2020;26(10):1602–8.

van der Pluijm RW, Amaratunga C, Dhorda M, Dondorp AM. Triple Artemisinin-based combination therapies for malaria — A new paradigm? *Trends Parasitol* 2020;S1471–4922(20):30254–3.

Van Voorhis WC, Adams JH, Adelfio R, *et al.* Open source drug discovery with the malaria box compound collection for neglected diseases and beyond. *PLoS Pathog* 2016;12(7):e1005763.

Varo R, Crowley VM, Sitoe A, *et al.* Safety and tolerability of adjunctive rosiglitazone treatment for children with uncomplicated malaria. *Malar J* 2017;16(1):215.

Vichinsky E, Hoppe CC, Ataga KI, *et al.* A phase 3 randomized trial of voxelotor in sickle cell disease. *N Engl J Med* 2019;381(6):509–19.

Videvall E. *Plasmodium* parasites of birds have the most AT-rich genes of eukaryotes. *Microb Genom* 2018;4(2).

Vogel G. WHO gives first malaria vaccine the green light. *Science*. 2021;374(6565):245–6.

Wahlgren M, Goel S, Akhouri RR. Variant surface antigens of *Plasmodium falciparum* and their roles in severe malaria. *Nat Rev Microbiol* 2017;15(8):479–91.

Wambua S, Mwangi TW, Kortok M, *et al.* The effect of alpha-thalassaemia on the incidence of malaria and other diseases in childrenliving on the coast of Kenya. *PLoS Med* 2006;3(5):e158.

Wang J, Xu C, Liao FL, *et al.* A Temporizing Solution to "Artemisinin Resistance". *N Engl J Med* 2019;380(22):2087–9.

White NJ, Pukrittayakamee S, Hien TT, *et al.* Malaria. *Lancet* 2014;383(9918):723–35.

Williamson KC. A new malaria gene regulator. *Nat Microbiol.* 2022;7(2):191–192.

Winzeler EA. A roadmap for malaria research. *Science* 2019;365(6455):753–4.

Xie SC, Ralph SA, Tilley L. K13, the Cytostome, and Artemisinin resistance. *Trends Parasitol* 2020;36(6):533–44.

10

Babesiosis, Toxoplasmosis, Cryptosporidiosis and Cyclosporiasis by Other Apicomplexans

10.1 Introductory Remarks

Together with *Plasmodium*, *Babesia*, *Toxoplasma*, *Cryptosporidium*, and *Cyclospora* are members of the apicomplexan protozoa. Apicomplexans belong to the Alveolata group, the 'A' of the SAR supergroup. (Please see Chapter 4 for a discussion of SAR and other supergroups in the classification of eukaryotes.) Both *Plasmodium* and *Babesia* are vector-borne human pathogens, via *Anopheles* mosquitoes and *Ixodes* ticks, respectively. Both organisms cause fevers. *Toxoplasma* is probably the most successful parasite, infecting a variety of animal species. The protozoan uses cats as definitive hosts (for sexual reproduction) and other vertebrates (including humans) as intermediate hosts (predator-prey cycle for *Toxoplasma*). All 3 protozoan parasites have **heteroxenous** life cycles, involving two (or more) hosts. In contrast, *Cryptosporidium* and *Cyclospora* possess **monoxenous** life cycles; they carry out the entire life cycle in a single host. Both protozoan parasites are food and water-borne pathogens; they cause diarrhea. These two are examples of monoxenous coccidians, a subgroup of apicomplexans possessing thick wall oocysts for secretion in the feces for transmission (fecal-oral route). Infections by these protozoa may be asymptomatic but can be severe, even potentially fatal in immunocompromised individuals. Although not classified as neglected tropical diseases (NTDs), their distribution is worldwide. Their genomes have been investigated, and updates are available in several databases: *Babesia* at PiroplasmaDB[1] *Toxoplasma* at ToxoDB[2] and *Cryptosporidium* at CryptoDB.[3]

[1] https://piroplasmadb.org/piro/app
[2] https://toxodb.org/toxo/
[3] https://cryptodb.org/cryptodb/

10.2 *Babesia*

Babesia belongs to the group **Piroplasmida** (meaning pear-shape); they are small parasites of ticks and mammals. Over 100 species have been identified in wild and domestic animals. *Babesia* species that infect livestock have significant economic impact worldwide; they are *Babesia bigemina, B. bovis,* and *B. divergens. Babesia microti* infects dogs, horses, deer and rodents. The proficiency of transmission and the worldwide distribution of tick vectors, makes *Babesia* the most common parasite of domestic animals. As an example, 1.2 billion cattle are at risk for bovine babesiosis, a major concern for the livestock industry. Humans are accidental hosts (Jalovecka *et al.* 2019). "Babesiosis, caused by piroplasmid protozoans in the genus *Babesia,* is arguably the most important vector-borne disease of livestock and companion animals and is growing in importance as a zoonosis" (Gray *et al.* 2019).

The majority of babesiosis cases worldwide are caused by ***Babesia microti***. The disease is endemic in the Northeastern and Midwestern regions of USA. There has been an increase from approximately 1,000 cases per year to 2,000 cases per year, and these figures are underestimates, due to asymptomatic infections, failure to report cases, and misdiagnoses. In Europe, approximately 50 cases of *Babesia divergens* have been described. Babesiosis has also been identified elsewhere in the world. In the United States, an increase in the population of white-tailed deer may be accountable for human infections by both *Babesia* and the spirochete bacterium *Borrelia burgdorferi* (agent for Lyme disease). Peter Krause (Yale) wrote: "Birds serve as reservoirs for *B. burgdorferi* but not *B. microti.* Thus, larval ticks may become infected with *B. burgdorferi* by feeding on birds and these infected larvae can be deposited hundreds of miles away where they molt to infected nymphs and establish a new site of infection. In contrast, *B. microti* can only spread when infected mice move to a new area, hence the saying that *B. burgdorferi* spreads on the wings of birds and *B. microti* on the backs of mice" (Krause 2019).

10.2.1 History

Babesiosis is due to the infectious agent *Babesia.* Initially, the parasitic protozoan was known as a cattle disease. In Bucharest, Romania, in 1888, the pathologist Victor Babes identified the intraerythrocytic parasite as the cause of fever and hemoglobinuria in cattle. He claimed he was able to transmit the disease to rabbits (*Babesia* named after Babes). In 1890, the southeastern United States had an outbreak of **Texas cattle fever** (aka Texas red water fever). In 1893, bacteriologist Theobold Smith (then at US Department of Agriculture, later to Harvard and Rockefeller) and veterinarian Frank Kilbourne found the agent to be *Babesia bigemina;* they also discovered the tick to be the vector. This was the first demonstration of a protozoan parasite transmission by an arthropod (leading to future identification of arthropod vectors for malaria, yellow fever, and other pathogens). Human *Babesia* infection was first reported in a splenectomized Croatian herdsman in 1957. The first US case in an immunocompetent person was identified on Nantucket

Island, Massachusetts, in 1969 ("Nantucket fever"). For *Babesia* species transmitted by ***Ixodes*** ticks, *B. microti* is common in the United States and *B. divergens* in Europe. [Paul de Kruif 1926 *Microbial Hunters* had a chapter on Theobald Smith.][4]

10.2.2 Life cycle

Please see Figure 10.1 for the life cycle, from CDC.[5]

The life cycle of *Babesia* comprises specific strategies originating in the adaptation to blood parasitism, and to the relatively complicated transmission by ticks. Tick bites transmit the sporozoites to the mammalian host, where the erythrocytes are infected, with asexual and sexual reproduction stages, merozoites and isogametes, respectively. Like other apicomplexans, *Babesia* has three phases: merogony, gamogony, and sporogony. Unlike malaria with a liver stage, *Babesia* sporozoite (known as **vermicle**) directly infects the red blood cell and divides to form four merozoites (known as **tetrad** or "Maltese cross form"). For gamogony, some protozoa become gamonts which are taken up by the tick. In the gut of the vector, the isogametes (known as **ray body** or Strahhenkorper) fertilize and develop into motile kinete that invades the hemocoel. Sporogony takes place in the salivary gland, where the sporoblast yields multiple sporozoites for the infection of mammals.

Kinetics of the invasion and egress processes of *Babesia divergens*, as observed by time-lapse video microscopy, have been investigated (Sevilla *et al.* 2018). Videos are available as supplement to the publication.[6]

Since the hard tick (including *Ixodes*) juvenile only feeds once per instar (a larval stage), *Babesia* persists through successive tick developmental stages. This is known as **transstadial** transmission, the transmission of *Babesia* between two or more tick instars (larva to nymph to adult). Another strategy, known as **transovarial** transmission, occurs when *Babesia* invades the ovary to allow for its spread from a single infected female tick to thousands of its offspring. This unusual feature is only seen in *Babesia bigemina* and related species. Mode of *Babesia* transmission has been incorporated in the *Babesia* phylogeny: (1) *Babesia sensu stricto* — the evolutionary lineage possessing transovarial transmission, aka the "true" *Babesia species*; (2) *Babesia sensu lato* — *Babesia* species of other evolutionary lineages where transovarial transmission is absent (Jalovecka *et al.* 2019).

10.2.3 Pathology

Clinical features of babesiosis vary from asymptomatic to life-threatening. Symptoms range from a mild flu-like illness to acute, severe, and sometimes fatal and fulminant disease. (Fulminant means severe and sudden in onset.) Manifestations include fever,

[4] https://lauriximenez.files.wordpress.com/2016/03/2-microbe-hunters-paul-de-kruif.pdf
[5] https://www.cdc.gov/dpdx/babesiosis/index.html
[6] https://www.nature.com/articles/s41598-018-32349-7

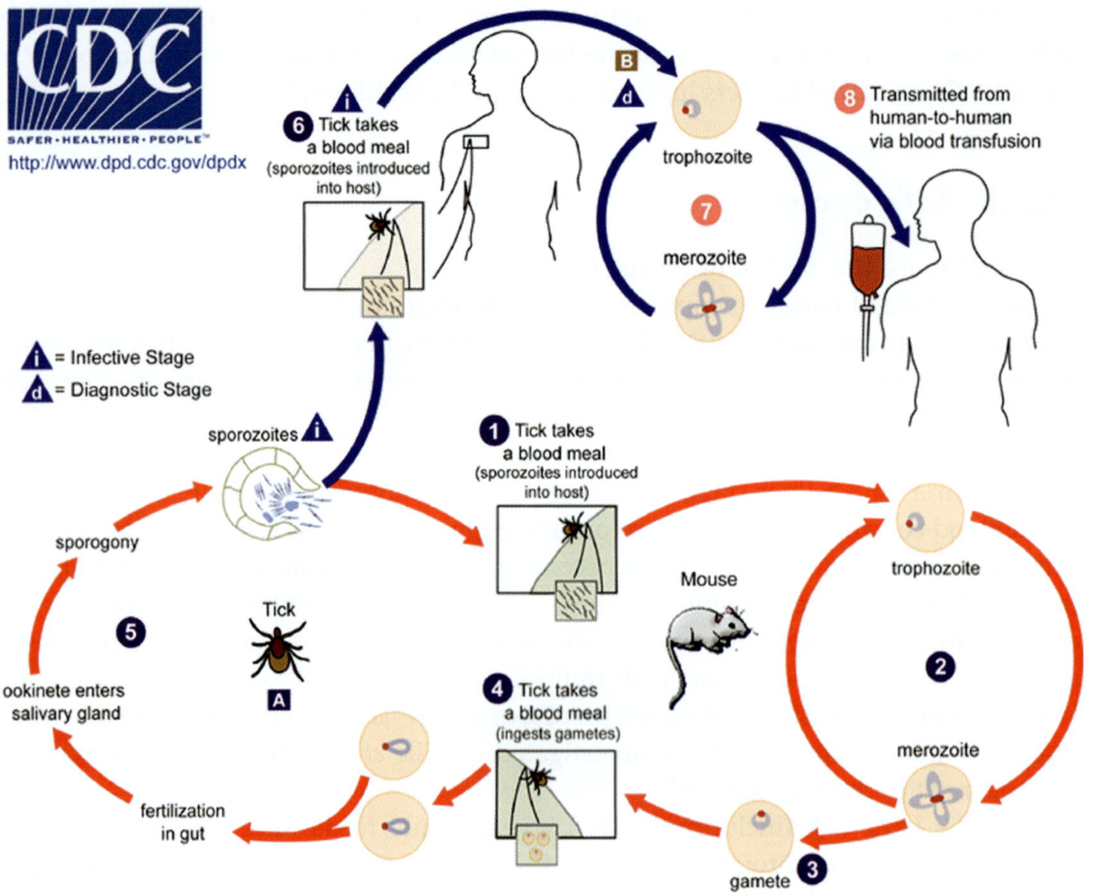

Fig. 10.1 ■ Life cycle of *Babesia* species. The *Babesia microti* life cycle involves two hosts, which includes a rodent, primarily the white-footed mouse, *Peromyscus leucopus*, and a tick in the genus, *Ixodes*. During a blood meal, a *Babesia*-infected tick introduces sporozoites into the mouse host ❶. Sporozoites enter erythrocytes and undergo asexual reproduction (budding) ❷. In the blood, some parasites differentiate into male and female gametes although these cannot be distinguished at the light microscope level ❸. The definitive host is the tick. Once ingested by an appropriate tick ❹, gametes unite and undergo a sporogonic cycle resulting in sporozoites ❺. Transovarial transmission (also known as vertical, or hereditary, transmission) has been documented for "large" *Babesia* spp. but not for the "small" babesiae, such as *B. microti* A. Humans enter the cycle when bitten by infected ticks. During a blood meal, a *Babesia*-infected tick introduces sporozoites into the human host ❻. Sporozoites enter erythrocytes B and undergo asexual replication (budding) ❼. Multiplication of the blood stage parasites is responsible for the clinical manifestations of the disease. Humans are, for all practical purposes, dead-end hosts and there is probably little, if any, subsequent transmission that occurs from ticks feeding on infected persons. However, human to human transmission is well recognized to occur through blood transfusions ❽. Courtesy of the CDC. Reproduced from https://www.cdc.gov/dpdx/babesiosis/index.html

chills, sweating, and hemolytic anemia. Babesiosis, caused by *Babesia microti* or *B. divergens*, is transmitted by Ixodid ticks. *Babesia divergens* infection causes acute babesiosis, and *B. microti* infection causes latent or chronic babesiosis. Immunocompromised and splenectomized patients are especially susceptible to babesiosis.

Babesiosis has been reported in Korea, with 9 imported and 1 endemic cases on record. Two imported babesioses documented the infection had previously occurred in the US (Kwon *et al.* 2018). Case 1 involved a 50-year-old female, a housewife with complaint of fever and abdominal pain. She was complicated by shock and splenic infarction, and initially mistaken as malaria; so she received hydroxychloroquine treatment. PCR for *Plasmodium* species failed to confirm malaria, but *Plasmodium*-like organisms in 1 erythrocyte showing Maltese cross forms in her blood smear slide conclusively diagnosed babesiosis. She was treated accordingly (atovaquone, proguanil, azithromycin). The patient had visited New Jersey, USA, 4 weeks prior to her symptoms, where she had gone to a forest and had noticed an erythematous lesion on her right proximal calf area after the trip (suspicious for a tick bite, though she did not recall getting bitten). Case 2 involved a 72-year-old woman without underlying disease except for a fever that had started 2 weeks before. She had visited Boston for 2 months. Her blood smear showed Maltese cross forms and confirmed babesiosis. She was treated first with atovaquone, proguanil, and azithromycin. However, fever persisted, and she developed pulmonary congestion. On diagnosis of severe babesiosis, she received quinine, clindamycin; red blood cell exchange was performed. As pulmonary congestion exacerbated, she was intubated due to respiratory failure. Doxycycline was added for possible coinfection with *Borrelia* or *Anaplasma* species. Her PCR for *B. microti* was positive, confirming the diagnosis of babesiosis. Her test for *Borrelia burgdorferi* was positive; she possessed IgG and IgM against the bacterial pathogen. Thus, the patient had co-infection of babesiosis and Lyme disease. "As the population traveling abroad increases every year, physicians should be aware of babesiosis which mimics malaria, co-infection with other diseases, and its complications" (Kwon *et al.* 2018).

10.2.4 Diagnosis

The microscopic examination of blood smears for the parasites can be a means of diagnosis (especially the diagnostic Maltese cross forms by tetrad *Babesia*).

10.2.5 Therapy

Treatment includes administration of clindamycin plus quinine, or atovaquone plus azithromycin (antimalarial and antibiotic).

10.2.6 Genome

Initially, only the genome of the cattle species, *Babesia bovis*, was known (Brayton *et al.* 2007). It causes tick-transmitted cattle disease (tick fever). *Babesia bovis* has 6 kb linear mitochondrial DNA, 33 kb apicoplast DNA, and 8.2 Mb nuclear DNA, containing 3,671 protein-coding genes. As shown in the genome, there is antigenic variation, with approximately 150 copies of the ves1α and β genes coding for variant erythrocyte surface antigen (**VESA**) protein, a heterodimer for cytoadhesion, sequestration and immune evasion. Segmental gene conversion is involved in gene expression. This expression of parasite encoded proteins on the erythrocyte surface is similar to those of the malaria parasite, another apicomplexan. Both variable (such as RAP-1, rhoptry-associated protein-1) and variant (such as VESA) gene families are found in the genome (Allred 2019).

Babesia microti possesses the smallest genome of apicomplexans (Cornillot *et al.* 2012 and 2013). *Babesia* has 4 chromosomes, **6.5 Mb** genome size for **3,513** genes, an 11 Kb circular mitochondrial genome, and a 29 Kb circular apicoplast DNA (current number is **3,685** for this reference strain in PiroplasmaDB). *B. divergens* has a 9.5 Mb gene size and **4,134** genes (current number is **4,187** for this reference strain in PiroplasmaDB) (Jackson *et al.* 2014). The current suggestions are to refer to *Babesia sensu stricto* (in a strict sense, true *Babesia*) for *B. bovis* and *B. bigemina*, and *Babesia sensu lato* (in a broad sense) for *B. microti* and *B. microti*-like species. *Babesia* is related to another group of cattle pathogens of the genus *Theileria*; ***Theileira parva*** causes East Coast fever in Africa.

Please see Figure 10.2 for genome sizes of parasitic protozoa (Suarez *et al.* 2018).

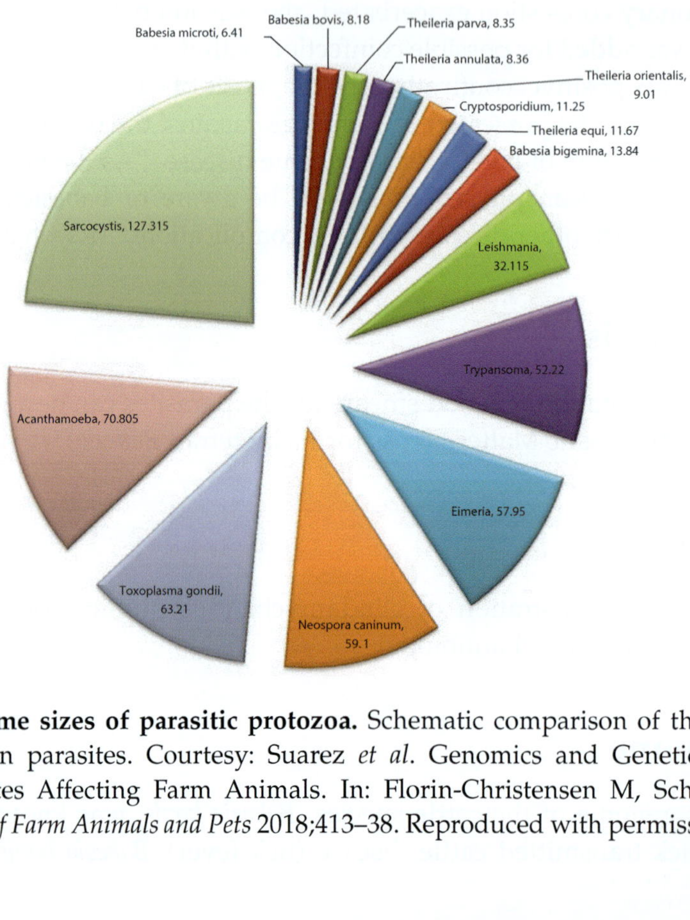

Fig. 10.2 ■ Genome sizes of parasitic protozoa. Schematic comparison of the genome sizes of selected protozoan parasites. Courtesy: Suarez *et al.* Genomics and Genetic Manipulation of Protozoan Parasites Affecting Farm Animals. In: Florin-Christensen M, Schnittger L. editors. *Parasitic Protozoa of Farm Animals and Pets* 2018;413–38. Reproduced with permission from Springer.

10.3 *Toxoplasma*

Toxoplasma is an obligate, intracellular parasite of warm-blooded vertebrates, including humans. Humans serve as a dead end intermediate host. In immunocompetent individuals, *Toxoplasma* infections are benign and mostly asymptomatic; in fetuses and immunocompromised individuals, *Toxoplasma* infections can be life-threatening. For fetuses, there is vertical (**transplacental**) transmission. Toxoplasmosis affects multiple organs including the brain and the eye. It can cause toxoplasmic encephalitis in immunocompromised patients, for example, as opportunistic infection in patients with AIDS. In 2016, a toxoplasmosis drug, Daraprim (pyrimethamine), became newsworthy and caught the attention of United States Congress on prescription drug prices, Martin Shkreli (aka "Pharma Bro") purchased the drug company Turing Pharmaceuticals and raised Daraprim price to $750 per pill (from the original price of $13.50 per pill).

Toxoplasma is credited to be the most **successful** parasite on earth. *Toxoplasma* infects all warm-blooded vertebrates: birds and mammals, including humans, sea otters, and beluga whales (in the Arctic). All of these vertebrates support the asexual reproduction of *Toxoplasma* and serve as its intermediate host. The main feature of *Toxoplasma* biology is its broad host range, and host cell range. Although local rates vary tremendously, it has an estimated prevalence of **30% worldwide**. On a global scale a third of the entire human population is infected with *Toxoplasma*. As the most common human parasite, *Toxoplasma* is found in 60–80% of older adults worldwide. "*Toxoplasma gondii is* a protozoan parasite that infects up to a third of the world's population" (Montoya and Liesenfeld 2004). "With its omnipresence and wide array of hosts, including all warm-blooded animals and some cold-blooded animal species, *Toxoplasma gondii* may be the most successful parasite on earth, estimated to infect up to one third of the global human population" (Djurković-Djaković *et al.* 2019).

Toxoplasma prevalence in cats is also known. The definitive host of *Toxoplasma gondii* is the cats (felids). Analysis of data from five decades (1967–2017) has yielded its prevalence (from serological data). The global *T. gondii* seroprevalence was estimated to be **35%** for domestic cats, and **59%** for wild cats, respectively (Montazeri *et al.* 2020).

10.3.1 History

The parasitic protozoan was first described in 1908 by Charles Nicolle and Louis Herbert Manceaux in a dead gundi (a desert rodent). At that time a cat was looming around the Pasteur Institute in Tunis. The French doctors noted "Reproduction is often by partition" and, due to its similarity to *Leishmania* and *Piroplasma*, "For the time being and as a provisory measure, we shall call the new protozoan *Leishmania gondii*." Independently, in 1908, the Italian doctor Alfonso Splendore found the same parasite in rabbits in Sao Paulo, Brazil, and wrote: "Morphologically, they are generally kidney-shaped with one end larger and more rounded than the other; a few are oval and seem to represent a form of primary division" (Kean *et al.* 1978). Historical records showed the first paper was presented on October 26 and the second October 29; therefore, priority of discovery is shared between these papers. In 1909 Nicolle and Manceaux realized the protozoan to be a new species and named it *Toxoplasma gondii* (toxo means arc or bow, plasma means life, gondi is the mammal gundi misspelled).

In 1923 at the Czech Children's Hospital in Prague, ophthalmologist Josef Janku described the first case of congenital toxoplasmosis, affecting both brain and eyes. In 1937 American neuropathologists Abner Wolf and David Cowen at Columbia University, along with pediatrician Beryl Paige at Babies' Hospital of Columbia Presbyterian Medical Center, described a case of congenital toxoplasmosis, from which an infant died at 31 days. Tissues from the cerebral cortex and cervical spinal cord were grounded in saline and inoculated to lab animals including infant mice, rats, rabbits, chicks, guinea pigs and even one rhesus monkey as "the first experimental transmission of a human toxoplasmosis to animals" (Kean *et al.* 1978). However, the sexual stage in cats was not discovered until the 1970s. In 1965 in Glasgow, William McPhee Hutchison showed the infectious agents were passed in cat feces. At that time the University of Strathclyde was new and no facility for dogs was available. He used a cat and at first kept it at home. (He originally thought *Toxoplasma* was transmitted together with a nematode worm, *Toxocara cati,* as the flagellate *Histomonas meleagridis* was known to transmit together with the nematode *Heterakis gallinae.*) Hutchison found cysts in cat feces. His finding was confirmed by other scientists in Germany, the Netherlands and the United States (Dubey 2008).

10.3.2 Life cycle

Please see Figure 10.3 for the life cycle, from CDC.[7]

For *Toxoplasma*, humans are the intermediate host, cats and related felines are the definitive hosts. *Toxoplasma* is an extremely successful parasitic protozoan, infecting multiple species and multiple cells and organs of the infected animal species. Its complex life cycle includes reproduction by asexual schizogony, sexual gamogony, and asexual sporogony. Initially as an unsporulated cyst, it matures into a cyst consisting of two sporocysts, with each sporocyst consisting of four sporozoites. The cyst is found in cat feces. In the cat intestine, the protozoa infect cells to form trophozoites, or make macro and microgametes (for sexual reproduction). Transplacental infection is possible, and bradyzoites grouped together as zoitocysts (tissue cysts) can be found in the fetal brain. A range of intermediate hosts include domestic and wild animals, birds and mammals. *Toxoplasma* invades macrophages and multiply as tachyzoites, which can inhibit phagosome-lysosome fusion. This is the tissue or **extra-intestinal** phase, seen in all intermediate hosts; the **enteric** or entero-epithelial phase is limited to the cat and other felines (Lourido 2019).

A **bradyzoite** is a sessile slow growing form (brady means slow). A **tachyzoite** grows and divides rapidly (tachy means fast). Tachyzoites stay as groups within the parasito-

[7] https://www.cdc.gov/dpdx/toxoplasmosis/index.html

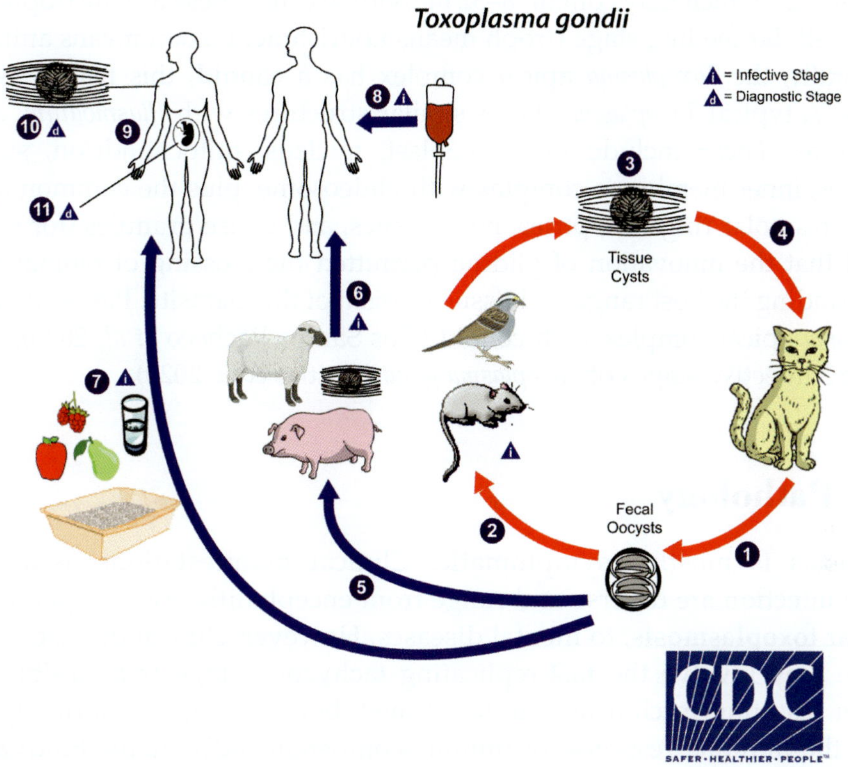

Fig. 10.3 ■ CDC Life cycle of *Toxoplasma gondii*. The only known definitive hosts for *Toxoplasma gondii* are members of family Felidae (domestic cats and their relatives). Unsporulated oocysts are shed in the cat's feces ❶. Although oocysts are usually only shed for 1–3 weeks, large numbers may be shed. Oocysts take 1–5 days to sporulate in the environment and become infective. Intermediate hosts in nature (including birds and rodents) become infected after ingesting soil, water or plant material contaminated with oocysts ❷. Oocysts transform into tachyzoites shortly after ingestion. These tachyzoites localize in neural and muscle tissue and develop into tissue cyst bradyzoites ❸. Cats become infected after consuming intermediate hosts harboring tissue cysts ❹. Cats may also become infected directly by ingestion of sporulated oocysts. Animals bred for human consumption and wild game may also become infected with tissue cysts after ingestion of sporulated oocysts in the environment ❺. Humans can become infected by any of several routes:

- Eating undercooked meat of animals harboring tissue cysts ❻.
- Consuming food or water contaminated with cat feces or by contaminated environmental samples (such as fecal-contaminated soil or changing the litter box of a pet cat) ❼.
- Blood transfusion or organ transplantation ❽.
- Transplacentally from mother to fetus ❾.

In the human host, the parasites form tissue cysts, most commonly in skeletal muscle, myocardium, brain, and eyes; these cysts may remain throughout the life of the host. Diagnosis is usually achieved by serology, although tissue cysts may be observed in stained biopsy specimens ❿. Diagnosis of congenital infections can be achieved by detecting *T. gondii* DNA in amniotic fluid using molecular methods such as PCR ⓫. Courtesy of the CDC. Reproduced from https://www.cdc.gov/dpdx/toxoplasmosis/index.html

phorous vacuole, which may contain 8–32 individual cells. These are the trophozoites, the active intracellular feeding stage (troph means nourishment, zoon means animal).

Structurally, the *Toxoplasma* apical complex has a **conoid**, this feature is absent in *Plasmodium*. A typical *Toxoplasma* shows similar structures with *Plasmodium*, as both are apicomplexans. These include the apicoplast, nucleus, mitochondrion, subpellicular microtubules, inner membrane complex with glideosome, plus the common apical complex structures polar rings, rhoptries, micronemes, and dense granules (for secretion). It is believed that the innovation of gliding permitted the crossing of biological barriers, greatly expanding the host range and tissue tropism of this parasite. Please see Figure 10.4 for *Toxoplasma* apical complex with conoid (Dos Santos Pacheco *et al.* 2020), and Figure 10.5 for the 3 infective stages of *Toxoplasma gondii* (Attias *et al.* 2020).

10.3.3 Pathology

Toxoplasmosis is mostly asymptomatic. Clinical manifestations associated with *Toxoplasma* infection are diverse and range from encephalitis, hydrocephalus, myocarditis, **ocular toxoplasmosis**, to mental diseases. However, clinical diseases are uncommon, since they involve the fast-replicating tachyzoite stage (responsible for tissue destruction resulting in clinical manifestations), but this stage is normally well controlled by the immune response of immunocompetent individuals. Bradyzoite infection is latent; it does not generate any clear clinical disease, but exceptions may occur. During immunosuppression, bradyzoites can convert back to the tachyzoite stage. During pregnancy, a primary infection can result in congenital infection of the fetus (where the absence of a mature immune system facilitates uncurbed tachyzoite replication). Severity of **congenital toxoplasmosis** depends on the timing of infection within the trimester. Please see Figure 10.6 for *Toxoplasm* infection and pregnancy, congenital toxoplasmosis (Borges *et al.* 2019).

Toxoplasma differentiation from fast replicating tachyzoites to metabolically inactive bradyzoites signals a transition from acute to chronic infection (with parasite persistence). The bradyzoites form tissue cysts and allow natural parasite transmission (among different intermediate hosts, or to the definitive host). The interconversion between bradyzoites and tachyzoites is known as **stage conversion**, which is key to the pathogenesis of toxoplasmosis (especially in the immunocompromised individual). The transition seems to be coupled to the cell cycle and regulated epigenetically. Benjamin Waldman (Massachusetts Institute of Technology) and colleagues have identified a master regulator of stage conversion using gene editing technology (Cas9-mediated screening). The gene has been named Bradyzoite-Formation Deficient 1 (BFD1); this master transcription factors contains zinc finger and Myb-like DNA binding domains, and binds to the promoters of many stage-specific genes. BFD1 mutants fail to differentiate and cannot form cysts in infected mice. "BFD1 provides a genetic switch to study and control *Toxoplasma* differentiation and will inform prevention and treatment of chronic infections" (Waldman *et al.* 2020).

(A)

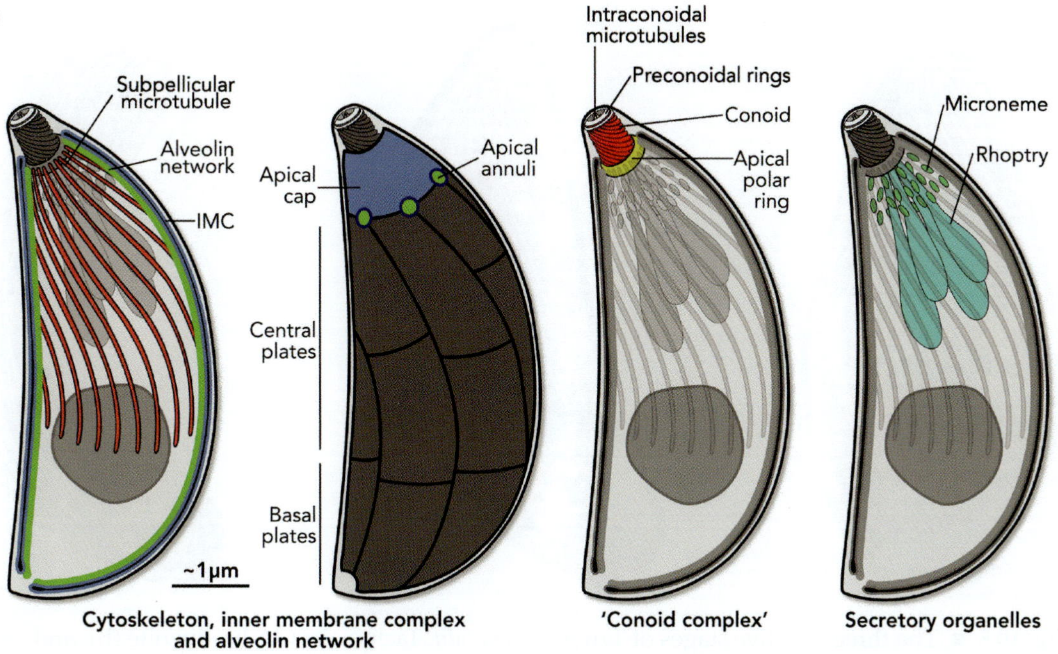

(B)

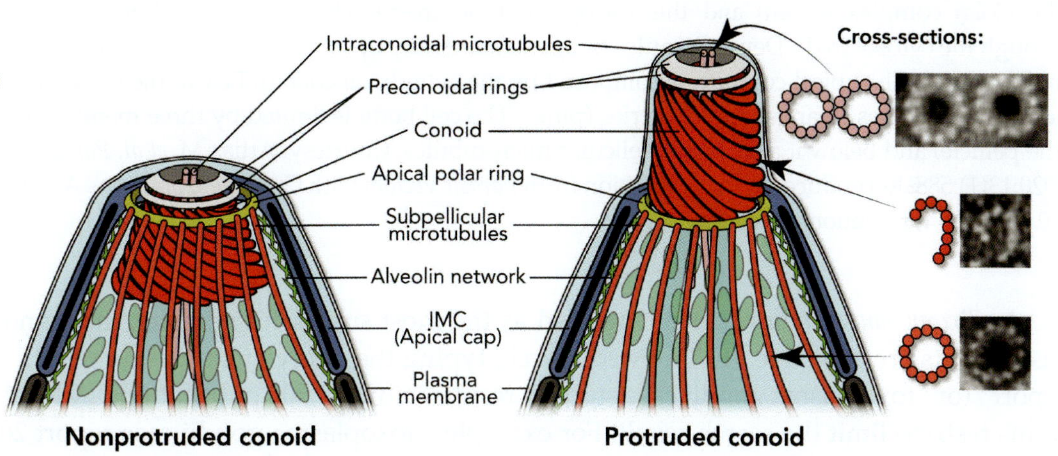

Fig. 10.4 ■ *Toxoplasma gondii* apical complex with conoid. (A) Structural and functional components of the apical complex: the cytoskeleton made of microtubules, alveolin network, and inner membrane complex (IMC), the 'conoid complex', and the secretory organelles. The different plates of the IMC are displayed on the second scheme, where the apical cap is at the top and the apical annuli are found at the level of the apical cap suture. (B) The apical complex is composed of three main tubulin-based structures: two intraconoidal microtubules, the conoid fibers of the conoid, and the subpellicular microtubules. The two intraconoidal microtubules and subpellicular microtubules are made of 13 protofilaments, as found in other organisms, while the tubulin fibers of the conoid are made of only nine protofilaments in a distinctive 'comma' cross-sectional shape. Courtesy: Dos Santos Pacheco *et al. Trends Parasitol* 2020;36:688–704. Reproduced with permission from Elsevier.

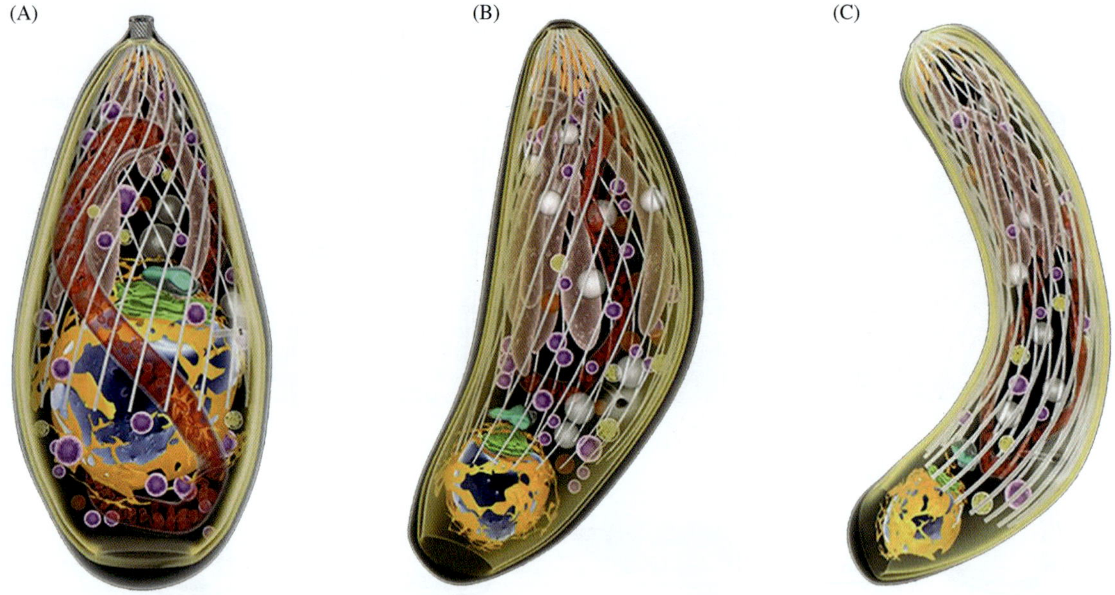

Fig. 10.5 ■ The three infective stages of *Toxoplasma gondii*. Tachyzoite (A), bradyzoite (B), and sporozoite (C). The nucleus (blue) is surrounded by the rough endoplasmic reticulum (yellow). Above it, The Golgi complex (green) and the apicoplast (blue-green). The single mitochondrion spreads through the cytosol (red). Dense granules (magenta) and amylopectin granules (white) are dispersed in the cytosol. The apical complex is composed by the cylindrical conoid. Below, the secretory organelles: micronemes (orange) and rhoptries (pink). The cell body is limited by three membrane units (the pellicle) and below it a set of subpelicular microtubules. Courtesy: Attias M. *et al. Parasit Vectors* 2020;13(1):588. Reproduced with permission from *Parasit Vectors* with Creative Commons Attribution 4.0 (CC-BY) International License.

As *Toxoplasma gondii* has been credited as the most successful parasite, thousands of case reports are available. [In PubMed search, typing the query "toxoplasma gondii case report" (or "toxoplasma gondii case study") results in over 1,500 publications. Additional terms restrict/limit the search result. For example, "toxoplasma gondii case report 2020" yields over 50, but "toxoplasma gondii case report 2020 ocular" yield only 15. Here we discuss the need to keep up with the literature (to your field of interest/research topic), so as to get rid of the scientific FOMO ('fear of missing out') feeling. Besides PubMed and Google Scholar websites, other free sources are available, such as visual literature mapping/recommendation websites Open Knowledge Maps (founded in 2015 by Peter Kraker in Austria) and Connected Papers (founded in 2019 by Eddie Smolyansky in Israel), and the "Spotify for papers" website ResearchRabbit (launched in 2021) (Matthews 2021).] Several case studies are provided below, to demonstrate the importance of toxoplasmosis in infectious diseases and clinical medicine.

Toxoplasmosis is a worldwide zoonosis. The disease can be severe in immunocompromised individuals. In HIV/AIDS patients, *Toxoplasma gondii* is a known cause of **encephalitis**,

Trimester of Maternal Acquisition	I	II	III
Incidence of Transmission	17%	25%	65%
Relative Severity of Congenital Disease	Severe	Intermediate	Mild or Asymptomatic
Consequences for fetus and disease manifestations in newborn clinical manifestations	 I - High risk of abortion, stillbirth or premature birth	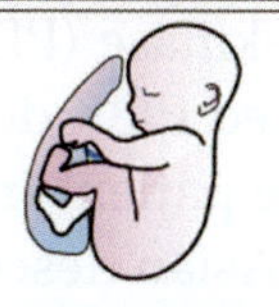 II - Intermediate risk of abortion, stillbirth, premature birth, blindness, chorioretinitis, mental retardation, neurological alterations or death	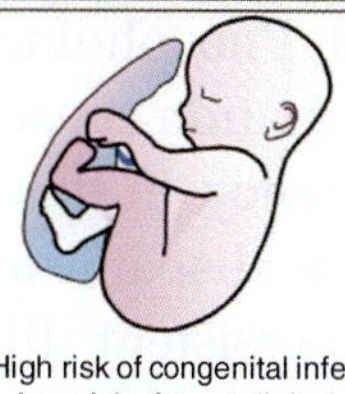 III - High risk of congenital infection. Low risk of overt clinical manifestations in newborn
CCL22	+↑	+↑	+↑
IL-12, IFN γ	+↑	+↑	+↑
IL-1 β	++ ↑	nd	nd
Granzyme A, C/EBP β	+↑	nd	nd
NKG2D	+↑	nd	nd
Th2 & Treg CD4 T cells	+↓	++↓	+++↓
Macrophage Activation	M1+↑, M2+↓	M1+↑, M2++↓	M1+↑, M2++↓
Tryptophan Degradation	+↑	+↑	+↑
Progesterone	+↓	++↓	+++↓
Estrogen	+↓	++↓	+++↓

Fig. 10.6 ■ *Toxoplasma* infection and pregnancy. Impact of *T. gondii* infection in pregnancy. Clinical consequences for the fetus and newborn and concomitant alteration to maternal immune mediators at the FMI and hormonal alterations (blue: relative levels during normal pregnancy; red arrows: effect of *T. gondii* infection on these levels during pregnancy and infection). nd: not described. Courtesy: Borges *et al. Parasite Immunol* 2019;41:e12606. Reproduced with permission from John Wiley and Sons.

and *Toxoplasma* pneumonitis is a manifestation of extracerebral toxoplasmosis that can be clinically indistinguishable from other opportunistic infections, such as *Pneumocystis jirovecii* pneumonia (**PJP**, a fungal infection, *Pneumocystis* was thought to be a protozoan at one time). In Illinois, USA, a case of *Toxoplasma* pneumonitis and disseminated toxoplasmosis was diagnosed by next-generation sequencing (NGS) and polymerase chain reaction (PCR) assessment in 2020. The 39-year-old male, an immigrant from the Democratic Republic of the Congo, had abdominal pain, cough, fatigue, fever (for 5 days), and vomiting; he was diagosed as HIV positive the year before. His blood sample was sent for NGS of microbial cell-free DNA (**cfDNA**) ("Karius Test") and showed positive result for *Toxoplasma gondii*. With the diagnosis, his AIDS medication (piperacillin-tazobactam) was discontinued and he was treated for toxoplasmosis (pyrimethamine, sulfadiazine). Later, he resumed antiretroviral therapy for HIV (bictegravir-emtricitabine-tenofovir alafenamide), and he recovered. "NGS can detect microbial cell-free DNA (cfDNA) circulating in the plasma of over 1,000 pathogens. ... Next-generation sequencing can help make a correct diagnosis and detect culture-negative opportunistic infections" (Roy *et al.* 2020).

Congenital toxoplasmosis is a concern in pregnancy of normal and immunodeficient mothers. The first case of disseminated and congenital toxoplasmosis in a mother and child who share a gene mutation in PIK3R1 was reported in USA (Karanovic *et al.* 2019). Phosphoinositide 3-kinase (PI3K) plays an integral role in lymphocyte function; its mutation causes activated PI3K delta syndrome (APDS), a form of primary immunodeficiency. In this case, the patient (mother), born to non-consanguineous healthy parents of Hispanic and East Asian descent, had recurrent sinopulmonary, otitis infections, and persistent diffuse lymphadenopathy since childhood and suffered from multiple episodes of herpes simplex oral infection and genital warts. At age 40, the patient was diagnosed with toxoplasmosis based on positive IgM serology results. This female had immigrated to Rhode Island, where she gave birth to a female baby at 37-week gestation. The child met the criteria for congenital toxoplasmosis and was treated (pyrimethamine, sulfadiazine, leucovorin). During the following year, the child had refractory seizures despite treatment (topiramate, levetiracetam, clonazepam), as well as progression of microcephaly.

There is ocular toxoplasmosis; there is congenital ocular toxoplasmosis. The first report of an immunocompetent individual with ocular toxoplasmosis and undetectable serum IgG and IgM was reported in Kansas, USA (Sigle *et al.* 2020). This 73-year-old immunocompetent female presented with a 2-year history of recurrent panuveitis and retinal necrosis not responsive to systemic antiviral therapy. "Aqueous fluid PCR testing is useful in suspected ocular toxoplasmosis in patients with vision-threatening lesions despite negative serology" (Sigle *et al.* 2020). The first case of North Carolina macular dystrophy (NCMD) in Australia has been documented (Tandon *et al.* 2019). It was originally misdiagnosed as congenital ocular toxoplasmosis. The 7-year-old boy was found to possess the previously reported single base substitution for NCMD on chromosome 6. "This case highlights the similarities between NCMD and more commonly recognized conditions, such as ocular toxoplasmosis, and raises the question; How many other cases are misdiagnosed as ocular toxoplasmosis?" (Tandon *et al.* 2019). At the opposite end, toxoplasmosis may be misdiagnosed as brain cancer. In Iowa, USA, a 71-year-old male's case of cerebral toxoplasmosis was presented as a solitary intracranial space-occupying lesion and considered as a primary brain malignancy based on brain imaging. This patient had received a combined kidney and pancreas transplant over 20 years ago. His brain biopsy led to the correct diagnosis of neurotoxoplasmosis (Patel and Swee 2020).

It has been reported that infection by *Toxoplasma* may be related to brain cancer (glioma). In an analysis of clinical samples (less than 400), a suggestive increase in glioma risk was observed among individuals infected with *Toxoplasma*, especially for those with high antibody titers specific to the sag-1 antigen. James Hodge (American Cancer Society, Atlanta, Georgia) and colleagues concluded: "Our findings provide the first prospective evidence of an association between *T. gondii* infection and risk of glioma. Further studies with larger case numbers are needed to confirm a potential etiologic role for *T. gondii* in glioma" (Hodge *et al.* 2021).

10.3.4 Diagnosis

Diagnosis is confirmed through observation of the parasite from tissue samples; serology and molecular techniques such as PCR (targeting region of the 18S rRNA gene) are available (Liu *et al.* 2015).

10.3.5 Therapy

Treatment for healthy individuals is unnecessary. Toxoplasmic encephalitis, probably due to reactivation of chronic infection, is the most common cause of intracerebral mass lesions in AIDS patients. The drug of choice is pyrimethamine (PYR). In addition, the combination of PYR with either sulfadiazine (SDZ) or sulfadoxine (SDX) for treatment of acute toxoplasmosis or uncomplicated malaria, respectively, has been used for decades. The drugs are inhibitors of critical enzymes in the folate pathway (dihydrofolate reductase, DHFR, by PYR and dihydropteroate synthetase, DHPS, by SDZ/SDX).

10.3.6 Genome

Toxoplasma gondii contains three genomes: nuclear, mitochondrial, and apicoplastic. The 6 kb linear mitochondrial genome contains only 3 protein-coding genes (the smallest mitochondrial genome known, similar to other apicomplexans), namely apo-cytochrome b (*cob*), cytochrome c oxidase I (*cox1*), and cytochrome c oxidase III (*cox3*), plus genes for rRNAs and internal repeats. However, to date, its localization in the mitochondrial organelle has not been formally proven. The 25 kb circular apicoplastic genome codes for 9-10 protein-coding genes; it is present in multiple copies (5-25). As one of the smallest known plastid genomes, the function of this organelle involves the synthesis of fatty acids and isoprenoids (Walochnik and Duchene 2016).

Like *Plasmodium*, *Toxoplasma* has 14 chromosomes (haploid in all asexual stages). Its genome size is 64 Mb and consists of **8,322** genes (current number is **8,920** for the *T. gondii* reference strain in ToxoDB) (Lau *et al.* 2016). Notably, the *Toxoplasma* surface is decorated with members of a large protein family, known as the **SRS** (SAG1-related sequence) family (SAG 1 stands for surface antigen 1, now known as SRS29B), with 122 members.

Genetically, three major strain types/genotypes of *Toxoplasma gondii* are known: type I, II, and III. A study of chicken isolates in Uganda found a type II and III hybrid strain, and close homology between African and North American isolates (Bontell *et al.* 2009). A new genotype, "type 12," was found in the sea otter (Webster *et al.* 2013).

The diverse host range and host cell type range of *Toxoplasma gondii* raise interest to try to find the possible reasons. One approach is to compare its genome with related species. A related apicomplexan, ***Neospora caninum***, has a limited host range, restricted to dogs and cattle (is becoming a leading cause of abortion in cattle). This comparison has shown similarities in gene expression between the two species, for SRS, microneme, dense granule, and rhoptry genes (Reid *et al.* 2012). One rhoptry gene, **ROP18** is active in *Toxoplasma* but is a pseudogene in *Neospora*. This rhoptry kinase phosphorylates host immunity-related GTPases (**IRGs**) and thus inhibits host interferon γ response that is important in innate immunity for pathogen clearance. ROP18 can thus be considered as a virulence factor.

There is the concept of Gene Expansion-Driven Diversification (GEDD), duplication of genes to perform novel functions. Again, comparison has been done between *Toxoplasma* and *Neospora* for the mitochondrial association factor 1 (**MAF1**), important for host mitochondrial association (HMA), for intimate association between the host mitochondria and the parasite-containing parasitophorous vacuole membrane (PVM). The copy number of MAF1 varies across strains and species. *Neospora* harbors 1 or 2 identical copies, while *Toxoplasma* has 6–10 copies depending on the strain type. MAF1 variants enhance *Toxoplasma* survival within the host cells. Thus, "Effector variation at tandem gene arrays in tissue-dwelling coccidia: who needs antigenic variation anyway?" (Blank and Boyle 2018).

10.3.7 Behavior modification

One interesting feature is the influence of *Toxoplasma* cysts in the brain on rodent behavior. This parasite-induced change in behavior of the intermediate host allows its sexual cycle to be completed in the intestine of the cat, its definitive host. *Toxoplasma*-infected rats become attracted to odors of the cat urine, as these odors activate the sexual arousal pathways in the rat brain (House *et al.* 2011). It is believed that bradyzoite cysts localized in the amygdala region of the brain, a site that responds to both predatory and sexual stimuli, hence the "fatal attraction." *Toxoplasma* infection also raises the brain dopamine levels, with the infected mice showing 15% higher than uninfected controls.

How about behavior in humans? Behavior modifications may exist in humans. Of the three genotypes, type I is fatal in mice, but types II and III are relatively avirulent and form cysts to establish chronic toxoplasmosis. The latter two types express higher tyrosine hydroxylase (a rate-limiting enzyme for dopamine synthesis) compared to type I. Infection with type II accounts for the majority of human cases (60–80%) in North America and Europe (Webster *et al.* 2013). *Toxoplasma* infections lead to multiple human behavioral changes. It "significantly increases the risk of having traffic accidents" (Gohardehi *et al.* 2018). Exposure to *Toxoplasma* has been suggested as a risk factor for **schizophrenia** and a range of other psychiatric disorders (Xiao *et al.* 2018). Therefore, we may need to "discuss *Toxoplasma* infection as a public health issue" (Tyebji *et al.* 2019).

10.3.8 Beyond cats

Toxoplasma can be transmitted transplacentally to cause severe outcomes (Fallahi *et al.* 2018). Pregnant moms are advised to avoid soiled cat litter. Along this line of thought, a British study has shown no association between cat ownership and psychotic symptoms of adolescents (ages 13 and 18) (Solmi *et al.* 2017). As noted before, cats are the definitive host of *Toxoplasma*. In 2019, the United States Department of Agriculture announced the closure of its *Toxoplasma* facility at the Animal Parasitic Diseases Laboratory in Beltsville, Maryland, due to pressure from animal rights groups claiming the activity as "USDA kitten cannibalism" and the research as "unnecessary and unjustifiable" (researchers commented "there is no laboratory in the world that produces *T. gondii* oocysts with the same efficiency"). Sexual reproduction of *Toxoplasma* has been shown to be possible in the lab mice (Martorelli Di Genova *et al.* 2019). The reason is the enzyme delta-6-desaturase (**D6D**). Cats are the only mammals that do not make D6D in their guts. They can still produce the enzyme in other organs, but they shut it off in their intestines. It is hypothesized that cats evolved in desert environments and this change would preserve their fatty acids. Indeed, linoleic acid makes up 25–46% of fatty acids in a cat's blood, but just 3–10% of those in a mouse's. This information is known to cat-food manufacturers and other researchers, but unaware by the Toxo community until the work of Laura Knoll (University of Wisconsin) and colleagues. *Toxoplasma* only has sex in cats because it depends on linoleic acid; cats are the only mammals that build up enough of the stuff. By feeding linoleic acid and using SC26196 (specific D6D inhibitor) sexual reproduction of *Toxoplasma* has been demonstrated in mice.

10.4 *Cryptosporidium*

Both cryptosporidiosis and cyclosporiasis cause diarrhea, the former is mostly waterborne (also fecal-oral and contact with cattle), and the latter, through consumption of fresh fruits and vegetables. Both are monoxenous coccidians, meaning that they complete their life cycle in a single host. A unique feature is seen in the invasion of *Cryptosporidium* sporozoites to the intestinal epithelial cells. The protozoan can induce the elongation and fusion of the microvilli located at the apical ends of intestinal epithelial cells. Then, it lives in this special **intracellular but extra-cytoplasmic** environment.

Among the *Cryptosporidium* species, they have different host specificity, invading reptiles (snakes, lizards), amphibians (toads), fish, birds, and mammals (rodents, rabbits, pigs, goats, cattle and humans). *Cryptosporidium hominis* is limited to humans. *Cryptosporidium parvum* and *Cryptosporidium meleagridis* have a wider host range and are known to infect both mammalian and avian species, including humans. *C. parvum* and *C. hominis* are listed as category B agents of **bioterrorism** in the United States, for water safety threats.

Cryptosporidium is a significant cause of gastrointestinal infections worldwide. After rotavirus, it is the second pathogen responsible for severe diarrhea in infants and toddlers; diarrhea accounts for 10.5% of the nearly 8 million deaths yearly of children under 5 (Striepen 2013). Globally, cryptosporidiosis is one of the commonest causes of mortality in children under 24 months old and may be associated with important long-term health effects (King *et al.* 2019).

10.4.1 History

From histological sections of the mouse intestine, Ernest Edward Tyzzer (Harvard) first described *Cryptosporidium* in 1907. He saw and sketched coccidial stages of sporozoites, oocysts, schizones, merozoites, microgamonts and macrogamonts; he wrote "Since no description of this organism has been found, the above name *Cryptosporidium muris* is offered." Although there was no sign of disease in mice, *Cryptosporidium meleagridis* was found to cause diarrhea in turkey in 1955. In 1976 human diarrhea due to cryptosporidiosis was first described in immunocompromised individuals (Cox 1996).

Cryptosporidium parvum and ***C. hominis*** are the major species infecting humans and cause outbreaks. (Crypto means hidden, sporos means spore or seed, referring to the absence of sporocysts, bodies found within mature oocysts of Coccidia which enclose sporozoites. Parvum means small, minute; hominis means humans.) Several outbreaks of cryptosporidiosis are known. In 1993, a severe outbreak occurred in Milwaukee, Wisconsin affecting 403,000 individuals with symptoms, over 4,000 hospitalized and over 50 cryptosporidiosis-related deaths; the cause was traced to Lake Michigan public water supply contaminated with oocysts (the thick wall cysts resistant to chlorination treatment of water) (Hoxie *et al.* 1997). Another outbreak occurred in 2013 in Baker City, Oregon, also associated with municipal drinking water, affecting 2,780 patients (chlorinated water was not filtered; there was cattle contamination at the watershed) (DeSilva *et al.* 2016). Although mostly water-borne, cryptosporidiosis can also be foodborne (Ryan *et al.* 2018). An outbreak involving fresh pre-cut salads occurred in May 2015 in England and Scotland with about 300 cases due to *C. parvum* (even traced to the particular strain: gp60 subtype IIaA15G2R1) (McKerr *et al.* 2015).

10.4.2 Life cycle

Please see Figure 10.7 for the life cycle *Cryptosporidium* species, from CDC.[8]

[8] https://www.cdc.gov/dpdx/cryptosporidiosis/index.html

Cryptosporidium completes its life cycle in a single host. It starts with the oocyst, each containing four sporozoites. Ingestion of oocysts leads to colonization of intestinal epithelial cells by the sporozoites. They induce microvilli to elongate and to fuse, forming a unique niche, intracellular but extracytoplasmic, for sexual and asexual growth (micro and macro gametocytes, merozoites, respectively). Two types of cysts are formed: thin wall oocytes for auto-infection and thick wall oocysts for excretion to feces (dissemination). Based on human volunteer studies, **10–83** oocysts for *C. hominis* and 10–1,000 oocysts for *C. parvum* are infectious doses (Ryan *et al.* 2014).

10.4.3 Pathology

Cryptosporidium infection causes watery diarrhea. Infection can be prolonged, with detrimental effects on the development of children. In immunocompromised individuals, cryptosporidiosis can result in life-threatening diarrhea plus malabsorption (occasionally even with multi-organ involvement). In a review and meta-analysis combining 161 studies totaling 51,123 AIDS patients, the overall prevalence of *Cryptosporidium* infection was **11.2%** (Ahmadpour *et al.* 2020). Current efforts are aimed at developing appropriate in vitro culture systems for life cycle studies and potential drug development (Bones *et al.* 2019).

Cryptosporidium species are common intracellular parasites responsible of severe diarrhea in T-cell immunocompromised patients. In France, the first case of cryptosporidiosis after drug treatment (fingolimod, for multiple sclerosis, MS) was reported in 2020. The 60-year-old female had fever and diarrhea; she also suffered from abdominal pain. For her MS, she had fingolimod (August 2017 to September 2018), around the time of occurrence of her first digestive symptoms. Her infection was shown to be positive for *Cryptosporidium* (by multiplex gastrointestinal parasite panel PCR). Further genotyping revealed IbA10G2 *C. hominis* infection. Because she had profound lymphopenia, fingolimod was stopped, and she was treated with nitazoxanide for cryptosporidiosis. Her diarrhea resolved, with no relapse. Therefore, "Physicians should be aware of this association and screen for *Cryptosporidium* in cases of diarrhea in patients treated with fingolimod" (Martinot *et al.* 2020).

In Cologne, Germany, a case of a patient who developed severe diarrhea shortly after an allogeneic hematopoietic stem cell transplantation (allo-HSCT, from her haplo-identical sibling, for relapsed T-lymphoblastic lymphoma) was reported in 2018. The 25-year-old female was diagnosed with *Cryptosporidium* enterocolitis; her colon biopsy showed the presence of *Cryptosporidium* oocysts. Following molecular confirmation of the diagnosis of cryptosporidiosis, she was treated (paromomycin, azithromycin) and recovered (Schiller *et al.* 2018).

In Alabama, USA, a case ultimately diagnosed as appendicitis secondary to *C. parvum* infection was reported in 2019. The 39-year-old female suffered from worsening abdomi-

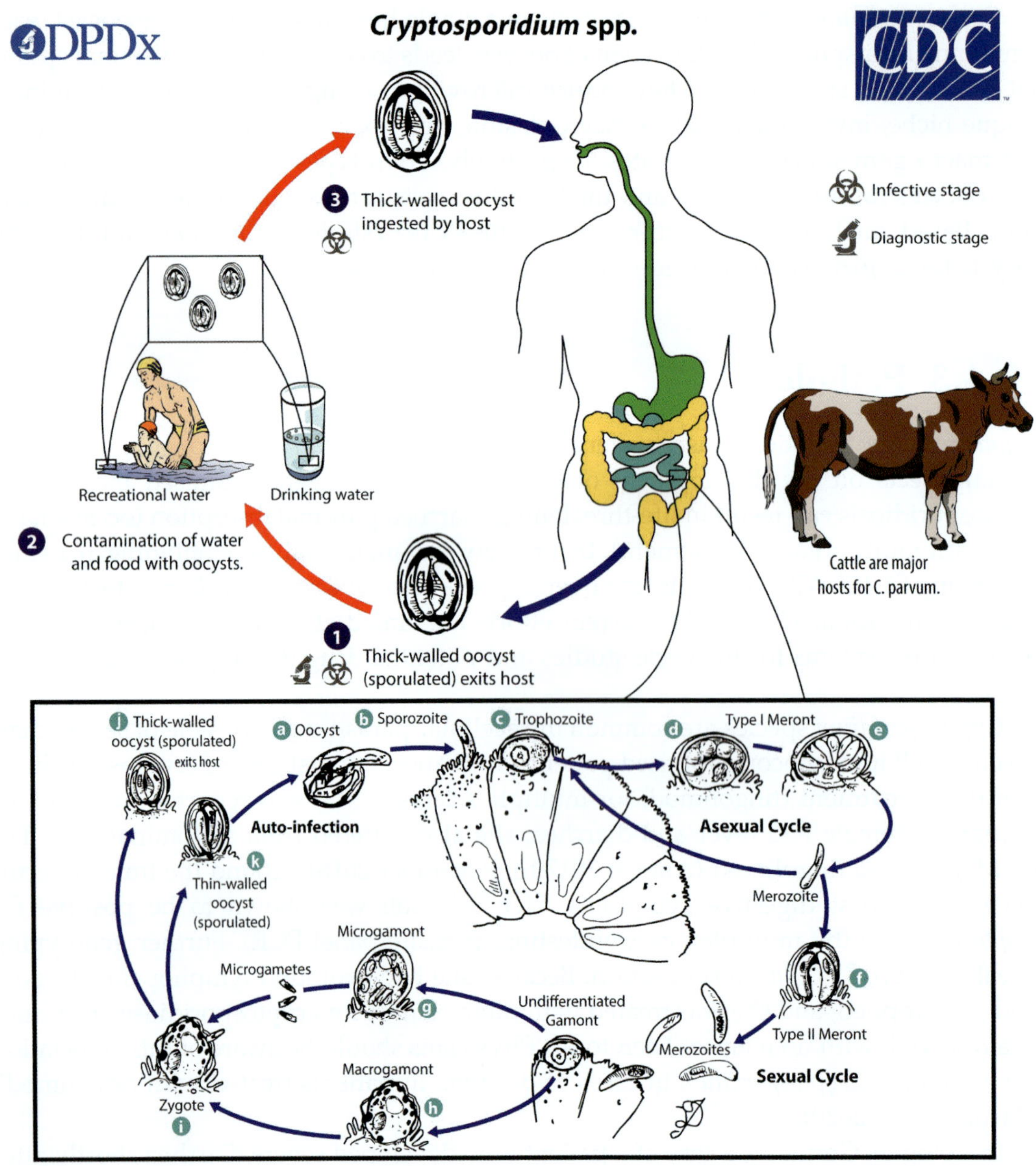

Fig. 10.7 ■ CDC Life cycle of *Cryptosporidium* species. Sporulated oocysts, containing 4 sporozoites, are excreted by the infected host through feces ❶ (and possibly other routes such as respiratory secretions). Transmission of *Cryptosporidium* spp. occurs mainly through ingestion of fecally contaminated water (e.g., drinking or recreational water) or food (e.g., raw milk) or following direct contact with infected animals or people ❷. Following ingestion (and possibly inhalation) by a suitable host ❸, excystation ⓐ occurs. The sporozoites are released and parasitize the epithelial cells (ⓑ, ⓒ) of the gastrointestinal tract (and possibly the respiratory tract). In these cells, usually within the brush border, the parasites undergo asexual multiplication (schizogony or merogony) (ⓓ, ⓔ, ⓕ) and then sexual multiplication (gametogony) producing microgamonts

nal pain plus diarrhea for one week. After negative results for *Clostridium difficile*, *Giardia lamblia* and *Cryptosporidium* of her stool samples, by abdominal CT, she was diagnosed with appendicitis and got appendectomy. The histological preparations showed clusters of small, basophilic spherical bodies - most consistent with *Cryptosporidium parvum* infection. Such diagnosis is exceedingly rare; only one previous case was known, in a 30-year-old male under similar situation in 1991 (Frankin *et al.* 2019).

10.4.4 Diagnosis

Microscopic examination for oocysts in fecal samples, with acid-fast stain. Serological and molecular diagnoses are also available.

10.4.5 Therapy

An effective therapy is still unavailable. For diarrhea, fluid and electrolyte replacement may be needed. **Nitazoxanide** has been used as treatment, by reducing the duration of illness in immunocompetent individuals. However, nitazoxanide cannot help the severely immunocompromised individuals such as HIV patients, and it only marginally effective in malnourished children. Novel targets, including kinases (calcium-dependent protein kinase 1, phosphatidylinositol-4-OH kinase), and cleavage and polyadenylation specificity factor 3 (AN7973), are currently being investigated by academic scientists and others (Choy and Huston 2020). Parasite tRNA synthetases (for Met, Lys, Phe) are potential drug targets. Based on the finding that **cladosporin** can inhibit lysyl-tRNA synthetase (KRS1) of the malaria parasite *Plasmodium falciparum*, a small molecule found after screening inhibits both the enzyme and *Cryptosporidium parvum* in a mouse model (Baragaña *et al.* 2019). For methionyl tRNA synthetase, the most potent compounds can inhibit target enzyme with *Ki* values in the low picomolar range. *Cryptosporidium* cells in culture can be inhibited with 50% effective concentrations as low as 7 nM, with 1,000-fold selectivity over mammalian cells (Buckner *et al.* 2019). These compounds are on the road as drugs targeting cryptosporidiosis.

Fig. 10.7 (figure on facing page) ■ (male) (g) and macrogamonts (female) (h). Upon fertilization of the macrogamonts by the microgametes ((i)) that rupture from the microgamont, oocysts develop and sporulate in the infected host. Zygotes give rise to two different types of oocysts (thick-walled and thin-walled). Thick-walled oocysts are excreted from the host into the environment (j), whereas thin-walled oocysts are involved in the internal autoinfective cycle and are not recovered from stools (k). Oocysts are infectious upon excretion, thus enabling direct and immediate fecal-oral transmission. Extracellular stages have been reported, but their relevance in the overall life cycle is unclear. Courtesy of the CDC. Reproduced from https://www.cdc.gov/dpdx/cryptosporidiosis/index.html

10.4.6 Genome

Genomes of *Cryptosporidium parvum* and *C. hominis* are known (Xu *et al.* 2004; Abrahamsen *et al.* 2004; Isaza *et al.* 2015). *Cryptosporidium* mainly uses glycolysis to generate ATP. It has limited biosynthetic capabilities but possesses an abundance of transporters. *Cryptosporidium* has eight chromosomes, 9.1 Mb genome size, and 3,745–3,941 genes (current number is **3,956** for ***C. hominis***, and **4,020** for ***C. parvum*** reference strains at the CryptoDB). Significantly, from genomic data, it lacks both mitochondrial and apicoplast genome (a feature different from other apicomplexans). "*C. parvum* has a minute genome (9.1 Mbp encoding 4,020 genes), lacks an apicoplast and mitochondrial DNA, has greatly reduced metabolic capabilities, and relies on host metabolism" (Blank and Boyle 2018). However, *Cryptosporidium* has mitochondrion-like organelle (**MLO**). It has been suggested that the acquisition of the prokaryotic type 1 fatty acid synthase (**FAS**) allows the loss of fatty acid synthesis by the apicoplast. *Cryptosporidium* possesses enzymes with similarity to plants and bacteria. It uses the sugar trehalose. Thus, trehalose metabolizing enzymes may be potential drug targets (trehalose-6-phosphate synthase/phosphatase).

Genomic studies on *Cryptosporidium parvum* and *C. hominis* have shown subfamilies and subtypes (Feng *et al.* 2018). Indeed, the IIaA15G2R1 subtype of *C. parvum* has been noted as hyper transmissible, a fitness marker for the parasitic protozoan. Further analyses on these genomes have shown DNA exchange between the two species, as well as a cryptic anthroponotic branch/clade subtype (IIc) of *Cryptosporidium parvum* (Nader *et al.* 2019). In Europe, the *C. hominis* subtype IbA10G2 is dominant and accounts for ~80% of human cases of *C. hominis* infections and responsible for almost all outbreaks (Widmer *et al.* 2020). Whereas most strains of *Cryptosporidium parvum* are zoonotic, *C. parvum* subtype IIc is almost certainly anthroponotic. IIc subtype is the major *Cryptosporidium* parasite among HIV-positive individuals, as well as people living in lower-income countries with poor sanitation (King *et al.* 2019).

10.5 *Cyclospora*

Cyclosporiasis is mostly foodborne and causes diarrhea. *Cyclospora* is a monoxenous coccidian with dissemination by infectious oocysts via water, soil, and unprocessed foods (fresh fruits and vegetables, ready-to-eat salads). The sporulated oocysts are small in size (8–10 μm), have low specific gravity but are highly infective; they survive for weeks and months in water and food (Giangaspero and Gasser 2019). *Cyclospora* has a worldwide distribution; outbreaks have been recorded in both developed and developing countries (Chacín-Bonilla 2010). *Cyclospora* is an emerging pathogen.

10.5.1 History

The first naming of the *Cyclospora* genus was made by Aime Schneider: a description of the protozoan in a millipede, in 1881. Actually, this was the only time *Cyclospora* was found in an invertebrate. A protozoan fitting this description was previously reported by T. Eimer in the intestine of a mole, in 1870 (without naming the organism); its life cycle in another mole was reported by Fritz Schaudinn, in 1902 (Lainson 2005). Since then, *Cyclospora* has been found in snakes, chickens, and mammals (including primates, such as monkeys and baboons); *Cyclospora* species show host specificity. In 1979, the novel coccidian parasite was identified as a human pathogen in Papua New Guinea (three clinical cases: a 14-month-old male child, a 2-year-old girl, and a 30-year-old female) (Ashford 1979). A reported case of *Cyclospora*-associated diarrhea in USA happened in Chicago, Illinois, in 1990, involving 21 individuals at a staff physicians' dormitory; the source was traced to tap water supply (Huang *et al.* 1995). As noted in this publication, *Cyclospora* was previously named Cyanobacteria (blue-green algae)-like bodies (CLB, also can be coccidian-like bodies). Ynes Ortega (University of Arizona, Tucson) named the human pathogen *Cyclospora cayetanensis* in 1993 (cyclo means round, spherical; sporos means spore, cayentanensis in honor of the scientist's alma mater, Peruvian University Cayetano Heredia at Lima, Peru, where it serves as a research base for field studies on the parasite) (Ortega *et al.* 1993). A large outbreak involving 1,645 cases covering 20 states and Washington DC in USA plus two provinces in Canada (Ontario and Quebec) in 1996 was traced to contaminated raspberries imported from Guatemala (Herwaldt and Ackers 1997).

Outbreaks of cyclosporiasis have been recorded at the CDC. Since the United States **MyPyramid** food guide suggests increase in intake of fresh fruits and vegetables, many outbreaks involve imported contaminated produces. Between May and October 2018, there were 2,299 confirmed cases of *Cyclospora* infections in USA (including 511 cases from consuming salads at McDonald's restaurants in the Midwest). In August 2014, 133 cases were traceable to imported cilantro from Puebla, Mexico. In the summer of 2013, 631 cases were traced to a salad mix (served at Olive Garden and Red Lobster restaurants, originally from Taylor Farms des Mexico). In the summer of 2020, from May 11 to July 24 there were cases from a multistate outbreak of *Cyclospora* infections linked to bagged salad mix containing carrots, red cabbage, and iceberg lettuce. As reported on September 23, 2020, a total of 701 people with laboratory-confirmed *Cyclospora* infections associated with this outbreak were reported from 14 states, ranging in age from 11 to 92 years (median age 57), 51% female, and 38 (5%) required hospitalization (but no deaths). Source of outbreak was traced to the Streamwood, Illinois Fresh Express production facility, the producer of the bagged salad mixes eaten by ill people.[9]

[9] https://www.cdc.gov/parasites/cyclosporiasis/outbreaks/2020/

As stated in a review on *Cyclospora*, "at least 54 countries have documented *C. cayetanensis* infections (involving 13,845 cases) up to December 2018. Of these countries, more than 13 have recorded cyclosporiasis outbreaks (including 6,557 cases). The overall *C. cayetanensis* prevalence in humans worldwide is **3.55%**" (Li *et al.* 2020B).

10.5.2 Life cycle

Please see Figure 10.8 for the life cycle, from CDC.[10]

Infection is via the fecal-oral route. The life cycle of *Cyclospora* starts with an unsporulated oocyte (thus differs from *Cryptosporidium*, another coccidian apicomplexan). It takes days for this sporulation process. In the mature oocyst, each oocyte consists of two sporocysts, and each sporocyst consists of two elongate sporozoites. Uptake of contaminated water, raspberries or basil carries the oocysts to the intestine, where the sporozoites invade intestinal epithelial cells (enterocytes) and complete asexual and sexual cycles within them as obligate intracellular parasites. Details of the developmental stages of *C. cayetanensis* in the gallbladder of a 33-year-old male with HIV have been described from light and transmission electron microscopic studies (Dubey *et al.* 2020). To date, the parasitic protozoan has not been cultured in the laboratory.

10.5.3 Pathology

Infection can be asymptomatic, or there can be diarrhea.

Cyclospora cayetanensis is the infectious agent for traveler's diarrhea. Whereas *Cyclospora* infections are found in inhabitants of endemic areas (in countries such as Guatemala, Haiti, Nepal, Peru), *Cyclospora* is also found in USA, Central America, Eastern Europe, and South Asia. In Europe, under 100 cases of *C. cayetanensis* infection were reported, almost all from individuals after traveling abroad. One such case was documented in Warsaw, Poland in November 2013. Three adult males developed acute traveler's diarrhea after a business trip to Indonesia. Among them, 2 were immunocompetent, and the third was a 35-year-old renal transplant recipient (after chronic glomerulonephritis in November 2010), who was having ongoing immunosuppressive treatment (tacrolimus, mycophenolic acid, deflazacort). All 3 had acute and prolonged diarrhea, but oocysts of *C. cayetanensis* were identified in fecal smears from only 2. PCR amplification of *Cyclospora* 18S rDNA confirmed the diagnosis, and 1 patient also had *Blastocystis hominis* co-infection. All 3 were successfully treated with trimethoprim–sulfamethoxazole (Bednarska *et al.* 2015).

Another case of renal transplant recipient whose *Cyclospora* infection/traveler's diarrhea resulted in acute kidney injury was documented in Yucatan, Mexico. A 35-year-old

[10] https://www.cdc.gov/dpdx/cyclosporiasis/index.html

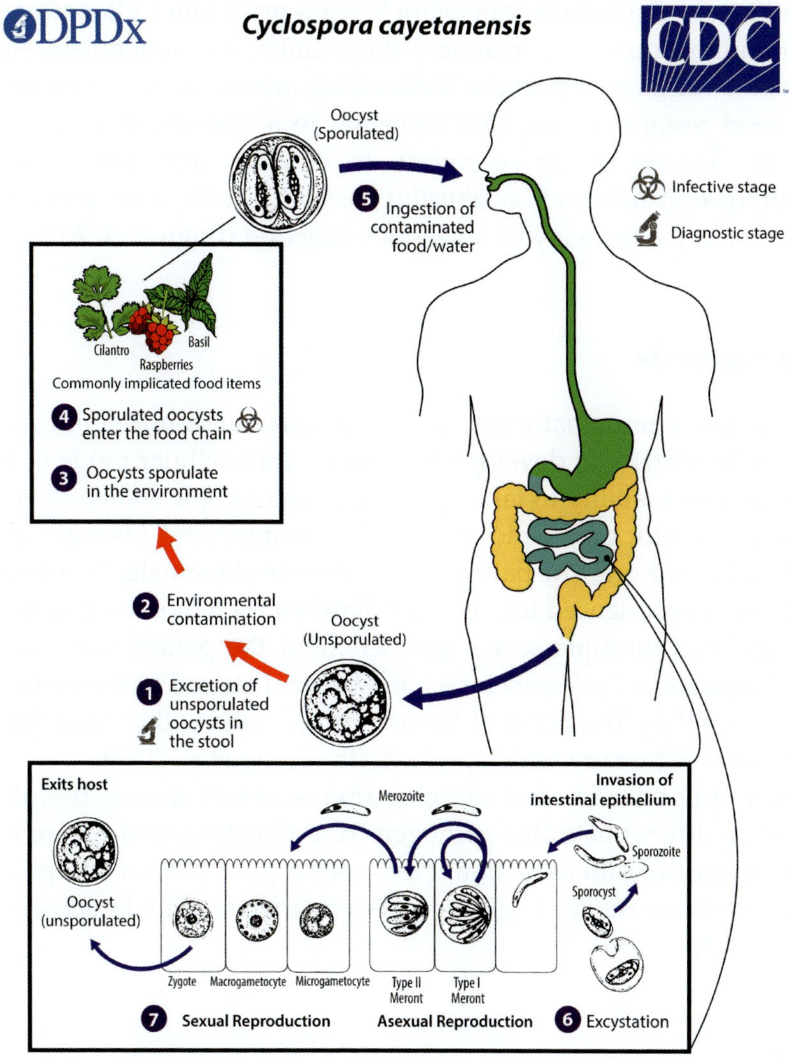

Fig. 10.8 ■ **CDC Life cycle of *Cyclospora cayetanensis*.** When freshly passed in stools, the oocyst is not infective ❶ (thus, direct fecal-oral transmission cannot occur; this differentiates *Cyclospora* from another important coccidian parasite, *Cryptosporidium*). In the environment ❷, sporulation occurs after days or weeks at temperatures between 22°C to 32°C, resulting in division of the sporont into two sporocysts, each containing two elongate sporozoites ❸. The sporulated oocysts can contaminate fresh produce and water ❹ which are then ingested ❺. The oocysts excyst in the gastrointestinal tract, freeing the sporozoites, which invade the epithelial cells of the small intestine ❻. Inside the cells they undergo asexual multiplication into type I and type II meronts. Merozoites from type I meronts likely remain in the asexual cycle, while merozoites from type II meronts undergo sexual development into macrogametocytes and microgametocytes upon invasion of another host cell. Fertilization occurs, and the zygote develops to an oocyst which is released from the host cell and shed in the stool ❼. Several aspects of intracellular replication and development are still unknown, and the potential mechanisms of contamination of food and water are still under investigation. Courtesy of the CDC. Reproduced from https://www.cdc.gov/dpdx/cyclosporiasis/index.html

male, who had received a kidney transplant 9 years prior (after idiopathic renal failure), was having immunosuppressive treatment (tacrolimus, mycophenolate, enalapril, prednisone). He took a business trip to the Netherlands where he ate green vegetables in an international food restaurant. So, after traveling to a non-endemic region, the patient developed acute kidney injury secondary to enteritis infection by *C. cayetanensis*. Treatment with ciprofloxacin and *Lactobacillus acidophilus* led to cure (absence of *Cyclospora* oocysts in stool) and the recovery of his kidney function (Lugo *et al.* 2021).

10.5.4 Diagnosis

"*Cyclospora* is an uncommon pathogen. The diagnosis of *Cyclospora* infection can be difficult because of its scarcity in developed countries, intracellular mode of life, small size of the parasite and its inability to take up routine microscopic stains. … Travel and food histories are important for the suspicion of *Cyclospora* infection" (Tsang *et al.* 2013). In this publication from Hong Kong, the patient was a 38-year-old female. Two weeks after a trip to Vietnam, she had experienced intermittent diarrhea for 6 months. It had been revealed that her husband had multiple sexual partners, and the patient was found to be HIV positive. Her diagnosis of *Cyclospora* infection was made based on the histological sample obtained by colonoscopy. Treatment of trimethoprim/sulfamethoxazole led to cure, after an initial unsuccessful therapy with ciprofloxacin (Tsang *et al.* 2013).

Examination of oocysts in stool samples after acid-fast stain is useful as diagnosis. There is a need to differentiate this pathogen from *Cryptosporidium*. Size measurements can be useful for species differentiation. Please see Figure 10.8 for morphology and size comparison of stool oocysts for *Cyclospora*, *Cryptosoridium*, and *Toxoplasma* (Soave 1996; Lindquist *et al.* 2003).

10.5.5 Therapy

Treatment is trimethoprim plus sulfamethoxazole (**TMP-SMX**). For patients who cannot tolerate TMP-SMX, the less effective **ciprofloxacin** can be used.

10.5.6 Genome

Cyclospora cayetanensis has three genomes: nuclear, mitochondrial and apicoplastic (Cinar *et al.* 2015; Cinar *et al.* 2016; Liu *et al.* 2016). Its mitochondrial genome is linear, 6.2 Mb in size, with three protein-coding genes (similar to other apicomplexans). Its apicoplast genome is circular, 34 Kb in size, with 29 protein-coding genes. Its nuclear genome, 44 Mb in size, with **7,457** genes (current number is **7,455** for this reference strain in the database, at ToxoDB). From the genome, *Cyclospora* shows a metabolism similar to other coccidians, and it possesses abundant transporters to get nutrients from its environment. Phylogenetic analysis shows a close relationship between *Cyclospora cayetanensis* and various *Eimera* species, some of which are coccidians of major veterinary importance.

The genome organization, metabolic capabilities, and potential invasion mechanism of *C. cayetanensis* are very similar to those of *Eimeria tenella* (Liu *et al.* 2016). It has gene families of secretory proteins: adhesins for host cell interaction, secreted/membrane-associated proteinases for processing rhoptry/microneme proteins and degrading host proteins, and secreted signaling proteins (kinases/phosphatases) for modulating host cell signaling pathways/immune responses for the promotion of parasite survival. It has been suggested that its relative lack of amino acid metabolic pathways has resulted in its reduced range of target hosts and tissues (as compared to *Toxoplasma*, for example). However, evidence of lateral gene transfer (LGT) is seen in 34 genes derived from bacterial, metazoan, fungal or viral origins, including ones for mannitol metabolism from fungi (also found in *Eimeria*).

10.6 Coccidia and Cancer

The major coccidian in chicken and turkey is *Eimeria tenella*. For chicken coccidiosis, a coccidiostat is the compound **salinomycin**, which can be put in chicken feed. Originally isolated from *Streptomyces albus*, salinomycin is an ionophore that binds potassium. Recent cancer biology research suggests the presence of cancer stem cells, ones that are resistant to standard chemotherapy and need novel compounds to target them. In a screening of molecules against human breast cancer stem cells, from 16,000 compounds, salinomycin was found to be active by scientists at the Massachusetts Institute of Technology (Gupta *et al.* 2009). Thus, potentially, a drug for chicken may be adapted for potential use to target human cancer stem cells (Dewangan *et al.* 2017).

10.7 Food and Waterborne Parasitic Diseases

Giardia, Cryptosporidium and *Cyclospora* are parasitic diseases from the intake of contaminated food and water. Resistant forms of these parasitic protozoa may be present in fresh produce, within the fruits and vegetables that we eat raw/uncooked. Timely diagnostic assays and microscopic observations are employed for their identification for samples from produce, water, stool. Apicomplexan oocysts can be differentiated by their size and morphology. [Please see Figure 10.9 for morphology and size comparison of oocysts of *Cyclospora, Cryptosporidium* and *Toxoplasma*, modified from Soave 1996.] Other parasitic protozoa found in fresh produce are *Entamoeba, Balantidium*, and *Blastocystis*. "Diarrheal diseases caused by intestinal protozoan parasites are a major food-borne public health problem across the world" (Li *et al.* 2020A). After presenting the parasitic protozoa, we shall continue with multicellular parasites, including flukes (*Paragonimus*), nematodes (*Trichinella*), and other helminths that are also transmitted to humans through contaminated food (Torgerson *et al.* 2015).

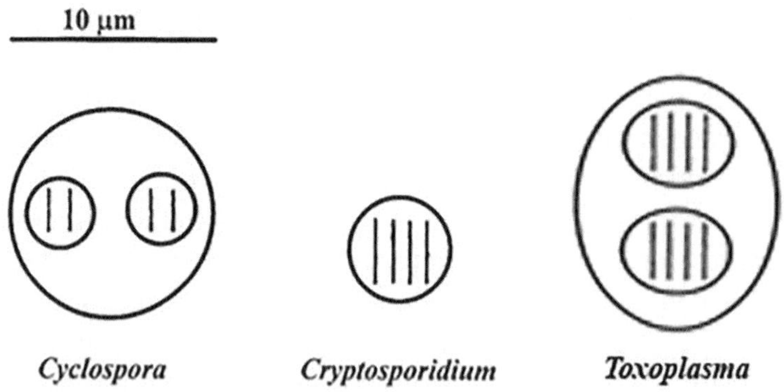

Variable	*Cyclospora*	*Cryptosporidium*	*Toxoplasma*
Oocyst size (µm)	8–10	4–6	10–13 X 9–11
No. of sporocysts	2	None	2
No. of sporozoites per sporocyst	2	4 per oocyst	4
Acid-fast staining	Variable	Yes	Yes
Ultraviolet autofluorescence	Blue-green	No	Yes
Auramine fluorescence	Weak	Bright	Bright

Fig. 10.9 ■ Morphology and size comparison of stool oocysts. Comparison of *Cyclospora*, *Cryptosporidium* and *Toxoplasma*. Modified from Soave. Courtesy: Soave R. *Clin Infect Dis* 1996;23:429–35. Used with permission from Oxford University Press.

Summary & Key Concepts

- *Babesia* and *Toxoplasma* have heteroxenous life cycles, involving two (or more) hosts, while *Cryptosporidium* and *Cyclospora* have monoxenous life cycles, carrying out the entire life cycle in a single host.
- Transmission of *Babesia* affects erythrocytes; the three stages there are merogony, gamogony, and sporogony.
- The worldwide distribution of tick vectors and the efficiency of transmission have made *Babesia* to become the most common parasite of domestic and wild animals.
- In immunocompetent hosts, *Toxoplasma* infections are benign and mostly asymptomatic; in fetuses and immunocompromised hosts, *Toxoplasma* infections can be life-threatening.
- *Toxoplasma* is credited to be the most successful parasite; it infects all warm-blooded vertebrates, birds, and mammals including humans (estimated at 30% global prevalence).
- Humans are the intermediate hosts of *Toxoplasma*; cats are the definitive hosts.
- With infection of *Toxoplasma*, the hosts may exhibit behavior modifications (dependent on the genotype of the parasite).

- Cryptosporidiosis causes diarrhea; it is mostly waterborne and transmitted via a fecal-oral route as well as contact with cattle.
- *Cyclospora*, an emerging pathogen with worldwide distribution, is mostly food and waterborne and infects via oocsyts in water, soil and unprocessed foods.
- Cyclosporiasis causes diarrhea, after the consumption of contaminated fruits and vegetables.

References

Abrahamsen MS, Templeton TJ, Enomoto S, *et al*. Complete genome sequence of the apicomplexan, *Cryptosporidium parvum*. *Science* 2004;304(5669):441–5.

Ahmadpour E, Safarpour H, Xiao L, *et al*. Cryptosporidiosis in HIV-positive patients and related risk factors: A systematic review and meta-analysis. *Parasite* 2020;27:27.

Al-Khedery B, Allred DR. Antigenic variation in *Babesia bovis* occurs through segmental gene conversion of the ves multigene family, within a bidirectional locus of active transcription. *Mol Microbiol* 2006;59(2):402–14.

Allred DR. Variable and variant protein multigene families in *Babesia bovis* persistence. *Pathogens* 2019;8(2):76.

Ashford RW. Occurrence of an undescribed coccidian in man in Papua New Guinea. *Ann Trop Med Parasitol* 1979;73:497–500.

Attias M, Teixeira DE, Benchimol M, Vommaro RC, Crepaldi PH, De Souza W. The life-cycle of *Toxoplasma gondii* reviewed using animations. *Parasit Vectors.* 2020;13(1):588.

Baragaña B, Forte B, Choi R, *et al*. Lysyl-tRNA synthetase as a drug target in malaria and cryptosporidiosis. *Proc Natl Acad Sci U S A* 2019;116(14):7015–20.

Bednarska M, Bajer A, Welc-Falęciak R, Pawełas A. *Cyclospora cayetanensis* infection in transplant traveller: A case report of outbreak. *Parasit Vectors* 2015;8:411.

Bhalchandra S, Cardenas D, Ward HD. Recent breakthroughs and ongoing limitations in *Cryptosporidium* research. *F1000Res* 2018;7:F1000 Faculty Rev-1380.

Blader IJ, Coleman BI, Chen CT, Gubbels MJ. Lytic cycle of *Toxoplasma gondii*: 15 Years Later. *Annu Rev Microbiol* 2015;69:463–85.

Blank ML, Boyle JP. Effector variation at tandem gene arrays in tissue-dwelling coccidia: Who needs antigenic variation anyway? *Curr Opin Microbiol* 2018;46:86–92.

Bones AJ, Jossé L, More C, Miller CN, Michaelis M, Tsaousis AD. Past and future trends of *Cryptosporidium* in vitro research. *Exp Parasitol* 2019;196:28–37.

Bontell IL, Hall N, Ashelford KE, *et al*. Whole genome sequencing of a natural recombinant *Toxoplasma gondii* strain reveals chromosome sorting and local allelic variants. *Genome Biol* 2009;10(5):R53.

Borges M, Magalhães Silva T, Brito C, Teixeira N, Roberts CW. How does toxoplasmosis affect the maternal-foetal immune interface and pregnancy? *Parasite Immunol* 2019;41(3):e12606.

Brayton KA, Lau AO, Herndon DR, *et al*. Genome sequence of *Babesia bovis* and comparative analysis of apicomplexan hemoprotozoa. *PLoS Pathog* 2007;3(10):1401–13.

Buckner FS, Ranade RM, Gillespie JR, *et al*. Optimization of methionyl tRNA-synthetase inhibitors for treatment of *Cryptosporidium* infection. *Antimicrob Agents Chemother* 2019;63(4):e02061–18.

Chacín-Bonilla L. Epidemiology of *Cyclospora cayetanensis*: A review focusing in endemic areas. Epidemiology of Cyclospora cayetanensis: A review focusing in endemic areas. *Acta Trop* 2010;115(3):181–93.

Choy RKM, Huston CD. Cryptosporidiosis should be designated as a tropical disease by the US Food and Drug Administration. *PLoS Negl Trop Dis* 2020;14(7):e0008252.

Cinar HN, Gopinath G, Jarvis K, Murphy HR. The complete mitochondrial genome of the food-borne parasitic pathogen *Cyclospora cayetanensis*. *PLoS One* 2015;10(6):e0128645.

Cinar HN, Qvarnstrom Y, Wei-Pridgeon Y, *et al*. Comparative sequence analysis of *Cyclospora cayetanensis* apicoplast genomes originatingfrom diverse geographical regions. *Parasit Vectors* 2016;9(1):611.

Cornillot E, Hadj-Kaddour K, Dassouli A, *et al*. Sequencing of the smallest Apicomplexan genome from the human pathogen *Babesia microti*. *Nucleic Acids Res* 2012;40(18):9102–14.

Cornillot E, Dassouli A, Garg A, *et al*. Whole genome mapping and re-organization of the nuclear and mitochondrial genomes of *Babesia microti* isolates. *PLoS One*. 2013;8(9):e72657.

Cox FEG, editor. *The Welcome Trust Illustrated History of Tropical Diseases* (1996, The Wellcome Trust, London).

Cuesta I, González LM, Estrada K, *et al*. High-quality draft genome sequence of *Babesia* divergens, the etiological agent of cattle and human *Babesiosis*. *Genome Announc* 2014;2(6):e01194–4.

DeSilva MB, Schafer S, Kendall Scott M, *et al*. Communitywide cryptosporidiosis outbreak associated with a surface water-supplied municipal water system — Baker City, Oregon, 2013. *Epidemiol Infect* 2016;144(2):274–84.

Dewangan J, Srivastava S, Rath SK. Salinomycin: A new paradigm in cancer therapy. *Tumour Biol* 2017;39(3):1010428317695035.

Djurković-Djaković O, Dupouy-Camet J, Van der Giessen J, Dubey JP. Toxoplasmosis: Overview from a one health perspective. *Food Waterborne Parasitol* 2019;15:e00054.

Dos Santos Pacheco N, Tosetti N, Koreny L, Waller RF, Soldati-Favre D. Evolution, composition, assembly, and function of the conoid in apicomplexa. *Trends Parasitol* 2020;36(8):688–704.

Dubey JP. The history of *Toxoplasma gondii* — the first 100 years. *J Eukaryot Microbiol* 2008;55(6):467–75.

Dubey JP, Almeria S, Mowery J, Fortes J. Endogenous developmental cycle of the human coccidian *Cyclospora cayetanensis*. *J Parasitol* 2020;106(2):295–307.

Dumaine JE, Tandel J, Striepen B. *Cryptosporidium parvum*. *Trends Parasitol* 2020;36(5):485–6.

Fallahi S, Rostami A, Nourollahpour Shiadeh M, Behniafar H, Paktinat S. An updated literature review on maternal-fetal and reproductive disorders of *Toxoplasma gondiiinfection*. *J Gynecol Obstet Hum Reprod* 2018;47(3):133–40.

Feng Y, Ryan UM, Xiao L. Genetic diversity and population structure of *Cryptosporidium*. *Trends Parasitol* 2018;34(11):997–1011.

Franklin H, Glosemeyer K, Hassoun A. *Cryptosporidium* infection in a case of appendicitis. *BMJ Case Rep* 2019;12(8):e230419.

Garg A, Stein A, Zhao W, *et al*. Sequence and annotation of the apicoplast genome of the human pathogen *Babesia microti*. *PLoS One* 2014;9(10):e107939.

Giangaspero A, Gasser RB. Human cyclosporiasis. *Lancet Infect Dis* 2019;19(7):e226–e236.

Gohardehi S, Sharif M, Sarvi S, *et al*. The potential risk of toxoplasmosis for traffic accidents: A systematic review and meta-analysis. *Exp Parasitol* 2018;191:19–24.

Gray JS, Estrada-Peña A, Zintl A. Vectors of *Babesiosis*. *Annu Rev Entomol* 2019;64:149–65.

Gupta PB, Onder TT, Jiang G, Tao K, Kuperwasser C, Weinberg RA, Lander ES. Identification of selective inhibitors of cancer stem cells by high-throughput screening. *Cell* 2009;138(4): 645–59.

Herwaldt BL. *Cyclospora cayetanensis*: A review, focusing on the outbreaks of cyclosporiasis in the 1990s. *Clin Infect Dis* 2000;31(4):1040–57.

Herwaldt BL, Ackers ML. An outbreak in 1996 of cyclosporiasis associated with imported raspberries. The Cyclospora Working Group. *N Engl J Med.* 1997;336(22):1548–56.

Hodge JM, Coghill AE, Kim Y, *et al. Toxoplasma gondii* infection and the risk of adult glioma in two prospective studies. *Int J Cancer* 2021.

House PK, Vyas A, Sapolsky R. Predator cat odors activate sexual arousal pathways in brains of *Toxoplasma gondii* infected rats. *PLoS One* 2011;6(8):e23277.

Hoxie NJ, Davis JP, Vergeront JM, Nashold RD, Blair KA. Cryptosporidiosis-associated mortality following a massive waterborne outbreak in Milwaukee, Wisconsin. *Am J Public Health* 1997;87(12):2032–5.

Huang P, Weber JT, Sosin DM, *et al*. The first reported outbreak of diarrheal illness associated with *Cyclospora* in the United States. *Ann Intern Med* 1995;123(6):409–14.

Isaza JP, Galván AL, Polanco V, *et al*. Revisiting the reference genomes of human pathogenic Cryptosporidium species: Reannotation of *C. parvum* Iowa and a new *C. hominis* reference. *Sci Rep* 2015;5:16324.

Jackson AP, Otto TD, Darby A, *et al*. The evolutionary dynamics of variant antigen genes in *Babesia* reveal a history of genomic innovation underlying host-parasite interaction. *Nucleic Acids Res* 2014;42(11):7113–31.

Jalovecka M, Sojka D, Ascencio M, Schnittger L. *Babesia* life cycle — When phylogeny meets biology. *Trends Parasitol* 2019;35(5):356–68.

Karanovic D, Michelow IC, Hayward AR, *et al*. Disseminated and congenital toxoplasmosis in a mother and child with activated PI3-Kinase delta syndrome Type 2 (APDS2): Case report and a literature review of *Toxoplasma* infections in primary immunodeficiencies. *Front Immunol* 2019;10:77.

Kean BH, Mott KE, Russell AJ, editors. *Tropical Medicine and Parasitology: Classic Investigations*, volumes I and II (1978, Cornell).

Khan A, Shaik JS, Grigg ME. Genomics and molecular epidemiology of *Cryptosporidium* species. *Acta Trop* 2018;184:1–14.

King P, Tyler KM, Hunter PR. Anthroponotic transmission of *Cryptosporidium parvum* predominates in countries with poorer sanitation: A systematic review and meta-analysis. *Parasit Vectors* 2019;12(1):16.

Krause PJ. Human babesiosis. *Int J Parasitol* 2019;49(2):165–74.

Kwon HY, Im JH, Park YK, Durey A, Lee JS, Baek JH. Two imported cases of babesiosis with complication or co-infection with Lyme disease in Republic of Korea. *Korean J Parasitol* 2018;56(6):609–13.

Lainson R. The genus Cyclospora (Apicomplexa: Eimeriidae), with a description of *Cyclospora schneideri* n.sp. in the snake *Anilius scytale* scytale (Aniliidae) from Amazonian Brazil—a review. *Mem Inst Oswaldo Cruz* 2005;100(2):103–10.

Lau YL, Lee WC, Gudimella R, *et al*. Deciphering the draft genome of *Toxoplasma gondii* RH Strain. *PLoS One* 2016;11(6):e0157901.

Li J, Wang Z, Karim MR, Zhang L. Detection of human intestinal protozoan parasites in vegetables and fruits: A review. *Parasit Vectors.* 2020A;13(1):380.

Li J, Wang R, Chen Y, Xiao L, Zhang L. *Cyclospora cayetanensis* infection in humans: biological characteristics, clinical features, epidemiology, detection method and treatment. *Parasitology* 2020B;147(2):160–70.

Lindquist HD, Bennett JW, Hester JD, Ware MW, Dubey JP, Everson WV. Autofluorescence of *Toxoplasma gondii* and related coccidian oocysts. *J Parasitol* 2003;89(4):865–7.

Liu Q, Wang ZD, Huang SY, Zhu XQ. Diagnosis of toxoplasmosis and typing of *Toxoplasma gondii*. *Parasit Vectors* 2015;8:292.

Liu S, Wang L, Zheng H, *et al*. Comparative genomics reveals *Cyclospora cayetanensis* possesses coccidia-like metabolismand invasion components but unique surface antigens. *BMC Genomics* 2016;17:316.

Lourido S. *Toxoplasma gondii*. *Trends Parasitol* 2019;35(11):944–5.

Lugo R, Angulo-Várguez F, Ávila-Nava A, *et al*. Acute kidney injury associated with intestinal infection by *Cyclospora cayetanensis* in a kidney transplant patient. A case report. *Parasitol Int* 2021;80:102212.

Martinot M, Abou-Bacar A, Lamothe M, *et al*. Cryptosporidiosis after treatment with fingolimod: A case report and pharmacovigilance review. *BMC Infect Dis* 2020;20(1):257.

Martorelli Di Genova B, Wilson SK, Dubey JP, Knoll LJ. Intestinal delta-6-desaturase activity determines host range for *Toxoplasma* sexual reproduction. *PLoS Biol* 2019;17(8):e3000364.

Matthews D. Keeping up with the literature. *Nature* 2021;597 (7874):141–2.

McKerr C, Adak GK, Nichols G, *et al*. An Outbreak of *Cryptosporidium parvum* across England & Scotland Associated with Consumption of Fresh Pre-Cut Salad Leaves, May 2012. *PLoS One* 2015 May;10(5):e0125955.

Montazeri M, Mikaeili Galeh T, Moosazadeh M, *et al*. The global serological prevalence of *Toxoplasma gondii* in felids during the last five decades (1967–2017): A systematic review and meta-analysis. *Parasit Vectors* 2020;13(1):82.

Montoya JG, Liesenfeld O. Toxoplasmosis. *Lancet* 2004;363(9425):1965–76.

Nader JL, Mathers TC, Ward BJ, *et al*. Evolutionary genomics of anthroponosis in *Cryptosporidium*. *Nat Microbiol* 2019;4(5):826–36.

Ortega YR, Sanchez R. Update on *Cyclospora cayetanensis*, a food-borne and waterborne parasite. *Clin Microbiol Rev* 2010;23(1):218–34.

Ortega YR, *et al*. *Cyclospora* species — a new protozoan pathogen of humans. *N Engl J Med* 1993;328 (18):1308–12.

Patel J, Swee M. Neurotoxoplasmosis mimicking primary brain malignancy. *IDCases* 2020;21:e00767.

Qvarnstrom Y, Wei-Pridgeon Y, Li W, *et al*. Draft genome sequences from *Cyclospora cayetanensis* oocysts purified from a human stool sample. *Genome Announc* 2015;3(6):e01324–15.

Reid AJ, Vermont SJ, Cotton JA, *et al*. Comparative genomics of the apicomplexan parasites *Toxoplasma gondii* and *Neospora caninum*: Coccidia differing in host range and transmission strategy. *PLoS Pathog* 2012;8(3):e1002567.

Roy M, Siddique N, Bathina B, Ahmad S. Rare presentation of *Toxoplasma* pneumonitis in the absence of neurological symptoms in an AIDS patient and use of next-generation sequencing for diagnosis. *Eur J Case Rep Intern Med* 2020;7(11):001862.

Ryan U, Fayer R, Xiao L. *Cryptosporidium* species in humans and animals: Current understanding and research needs. *Parasitology* 2014;141(13):1667–85.

Ryan U, Hijjawi N, Xiao L. Foodborne cryptosporidiosis. *Int J Parasitol* 2018;48(1):1–12.

Santos JM, Ferguson DJ, Blackman MJ, Soldati-Favre D Intramembrane cleavage of AMA1 triggers *Toxoplasma* to switch from an invasive to a replicative mode. *Science* 2011;331(6016):473–7.

Schiller J, Klein S, Engels M, *et al.* Case Report: A *Cryptosporidium* infection in a patient with relapsed T-lymphoblastic lymphoma undergoing allogeneic stem cell transplantation. *Eur J Haematol* 2018;100(4):383–5.

Sevilla E, González LM, Luque D, Gray J, Montero E. Kinetics of the invasion and egress processes of *Babesia divergens*, observed by time-lapse video microscopy. *Sci Rep* 2018;8(1):14116.

Sigle M, El Atrouni W, Ajlan RS. Seronegative ocular toxoplasma panuveitis in an immunocompetent patient. *Am J Ophthalmol Case Rep* 2020;19:100745.

Soave R. *Cyclospora*: An overview. *Clin Infect Dis* 1996;23(3):429–35; quiz 436–7.

Solmi F, Hayes JF, Lewis G, Kirkbride JB Curiosity killed the cat: No evidence of an association between cat ownership and psychotic symptoms at ages 13 and 18 years in a UK general population cohort. *Psychol Med* 2017;47(9):1659–67.

Striepen B. Parasitic infections: Time to tackle cryptosporidiosis. *Nature* 2013;503(7475):189–91.

Suarez CE, Alzan HF, Cooke BM. Genomics and genetic manipulation of protozoan parasites affecting farm animals. In: Florin-Christensen M, Schnittger L, editors. *Parasitic Protozoa of Farm Animals and Pets*, pp. 413–38 (2018, Springer).

Tandon M, Barnett C, Taranath D. Case report: North Carolina macular dystrophy misdiagnosed as congenital ocular toxoplasmosis. *Mol Vis* 2019;25:731–3.

Torgerson PR, Devleesschauwer B, Praet N, *et al.* World Health Organization estimates of the global and regional disease burden of 11 Foodborne parasitic diseases, 2010: A data synthesis. *PLoS Med* 2015;12(12):e1001920.

Tsang OT, Wong RW, Lam BH, Chan JM, Tsang KY, Leung WS. *Cyclospora* infection in a young woman with human immunodeficiency virus in Hong Kong: A case report. *BMC Res Notes* 2013;6:521.

Tyebji S, Seizova S, Hannan AJ, Tonkin CJ. Toxoplasmosis: A pathway to neuropsychiatric disorders. *Neurosci Biobehav Rev* 2019;96:72–92.

Vannier E, Krause PJ. Human babesiosis. *N Engl J Med* 2012;366(25):2397–407.

Waldman BS, Schwarz D, Wadsworth MH 2nd, Saeij JP, Shalek AK, Lourido S. Identification of a master regulator of differentiation in *Toxoplasma*. *Cell.* 2020;180(2):359–72.

Walochnik J, Duchene M. Eds, *Molecular Parasitology: Protozoan Parasites and their Molecules,* Springer, 2016.

Webster JP, Kaushik M, Bristow GC, McConkey GA. *Toxoplasma gondii* infection, from predation to schizophrenia: Can animal behaviour help usunderstand human behaviour? *J Exp Biol* 2013;216(Pt 1):99–112.

Widmer G, Köster PC, Carmena D. *Cryptosporidium hominis* infections in non-human animal species: Revisiting the concept of host specificity. *Int J Parasitol* 2020;50(4):253–62.

Xiao J, Prandovszky E, Kannan G, *et al. Toxoplasma gondii*: Biological parameters of the connection to Schizophrenia. *Schizophr Bull.* 2018;44(5):983–92.

Xu P, Widmer G, Wang Y, *et al.* The genome of *Cryptosporidium hominis*. *Nature.* 2004;431(7012):1107–12.

11

Introduction to Flukes (Trematodes)

11.1 Platyhelminthes

Human parasites include unicellular protozoa and multicellular helminths (worms). Based on the Adl classification, these worms belong to Opisthokonta, Metazoa (Adl *et al.* 2019). Based on the Ruggiero classification, under the kingdom Animalia, they belong to two phyla: **Platyhelminthes** and **Nematoda** (Ruggiero *et al.* 2015). Platyhelminthes (platy means flat, helminth means worm), the flatworms, can be free-living, commensal, or parasitic. Within the phylum Platyhelminthes, there is the subphylum Rhabditophora (rhadbito means rhabdite, phoros means bearer), as these species possess rhabdites, rod-like bodies that may function in adhesion, lubrication, and predator repellency. Members include many free-living forms in terrestrial and aquatic environments (both freshwater and marine), and used to be named Turbellaria (including species commensal to echinoderms and molluscs). Free-living species are carnivorous. One group, the planarians, are model organisms for developmental biologists because of their capacity for regeneration. Thomas Hunt Morgan, famous for fruit fly (*Drosophila*) genetics, observed that a planarian can regenerate from tissue fragments as small as 1/279th the size of an intact worm (Collins 2017). Regeneration is possible due to the presence of stem cells known as neoblasts; their presence has been extended from free-living to parasitic helminths (Collins *et al.* 2013). Within the subphylum Rhabditophora, based on both morphological and molecular data, there is the subclass known as **Neodermata** (neo means new, derma means skin). Members of Neodermata are all parasitic. Within the subclass, Neodermata has three infraclasses: Monogenea (mostly ectoparasites on skin and gill of fish), Cestoda (tapeworms) and Trematoda (flukes). The Neodermata subclass encompasses all major Platyhelminthes that parasitize vertebrates.

Members of Platyhelminthes are dorsoventrally flattened and bilaterally symmetrical (the left side the same as the right side). They possess three germ layers (ectoderm, endoderm, and mesoderm; triploblastic) but are acoelomates (lacking a body space other than the gut). They have an obvious anterior/head end. Their sizes vary from microscopic to 60 m long. Some flatworms serve as hosts for other flatworms. As an example, a parasitic cercaria may parasitize a planarian. In some parasitic species, they may either be oval/leaf-shaped (flukes) or extremely elongated (tapeworms).

11.2 Tegument & Other Structures

The outermost layer of the parasitic adult flatworm is the tegument (Halton 2004). It is syncytial (multi-nuclear), made up of proximal and distal cytoplasm. The distal cytoplasm, facing the environment, is the acellular layer, covered by glycocalyx and containing vesicles, secretory granules, and mitochondria. The distal cytoplasm is linked to the proximal cytoplasm via cytoplasmic bridges. The proximal cytoplasm, facing interior, consists of cytons (sub-tegumental cells), including nuclei, mitochondria, and Golgi. Spines may be present on the outside of the tegument. Please see Figure 11.1 for tegument of trematode (Mehlhorn 2016).

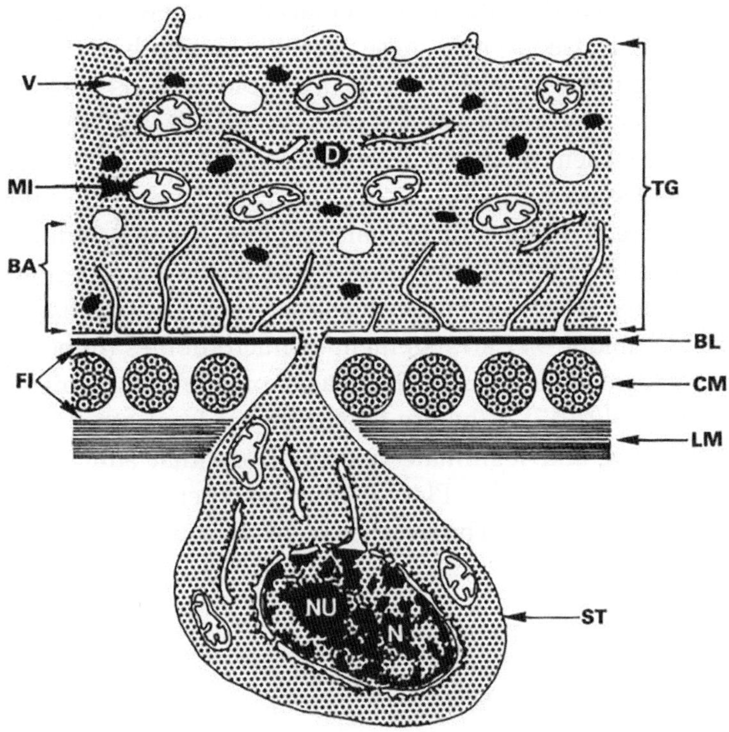

Fig. 11.1 ■ Tegument of trematode. Diagrammatic representation of the basic tegumental pattern in parasitic platyhelminths. In monogeneans different protrusions may occur, in digeneans additional infoldings or hooks are formed, whereas the surface of cestodes is endowed with microtriches. *BA*, basal labyrinth; *BL*, basal lamina; *CM*, circular muscles; *D*, dense bodies (may appear as disks); *FI*, fibrous layer; *LM*, longitudinal muscles; *MI*, mitochondrion; *N*, nucleus; *NU*, nucleolus; *ST*, subtegumental cell; *V*, vacuole. Courtesy: Mehlhorn H. *Encyclopedia of Parasitology*, 2016. Reproduced with permission from Springer Nature.

The tegument is important for the interactions between the worm and its environment. It allows diffusion and transport of materials between the worm and the host. As the adult parasitic worms have a relatively long lifespan, there must be ongoing repair and replacement of the tegument. This process is possible with the help of neoblasts, stem cells that are capable of replacing both the tegument and other cells/structures. Neoblasts can differential into ectodermal, mesodermal, and endodermal cells (Wendt and Collins 2016). For example, in the blood fluke *Schistosoma mansoni*, two DNA-binding zinc-finger proteins (*zfp*) regulate the differentiation of neoblasts towards tegumental cell structures (Wendt *et al.* 2018).

With an aim for vaccine candidates, components of the teguments have been investigated, especially for parasitic species, including the schistosomes and the sheep liver fluke *Fasciola hepatica*. Proteomes of the tegument include enzymes (acetylcholinesterase), transporters (for sugars, amino acids, multidrug resistance), ATPases, GTPases, and membrane structural proteins (annexins, tetraspanins) (Wilson *et al.* 2011).

The parasitic flatworms have lost the cilia on the surface (tegument), except in the larval stage. The larval ciliated epithelium is replaced by a new tegument, hence the term Neodermata (new skin) is used to note these parasitic helminths.

Underneath the tegument is muscle fibers, a simple nervous system with a brain, of the orthogonal or ladder type. Some species possess a digestive system ending as a blind tract, and an excretory system made up of flame cells.

Adult flatworms possess a fully functional and well-developed reproductive system. Almost all flatworms are hermaphrodites, male and female organs within the same adult. One major exception is the schistosomes, these blood flukes are dioecious; there are male and female adult worms. A typical flatworm sperm possesses two flagella, each with its axoneme exhibiting a unique **9+1** arrangement of microtubules (in both trematodes and cestodes). This differs from the normal flagellar axoneme arrangement of 9+2 (Levron *et al.* 2010; Bakhoum *et al.* 2017). Why are they different from other flagellar axonemes? The is a very interesting and legitimate question; one that still awaits a satisfactory answer. Please see Figure 11.2 for Platyhelminthes sperm by transmission electron microscopy (Bruňanská *et al.* 2020). The samples were taken from the tapeworm *Diplocotyle olrikii*, a parasite of amphipods.

11.3 Trematoda

Members of Trematoda are flukes. Another term used for trematodes is **Digenea** (di means double, genos means race). There is an **alternation of generations** between sexually-reproducing adults and asexually reproducing larval stages. The digenean trematodes have at least two hosts. The first immediate host is mostly a snail (gastropod mollusc). There may be a second and even a third immediate host. In the vertebrate

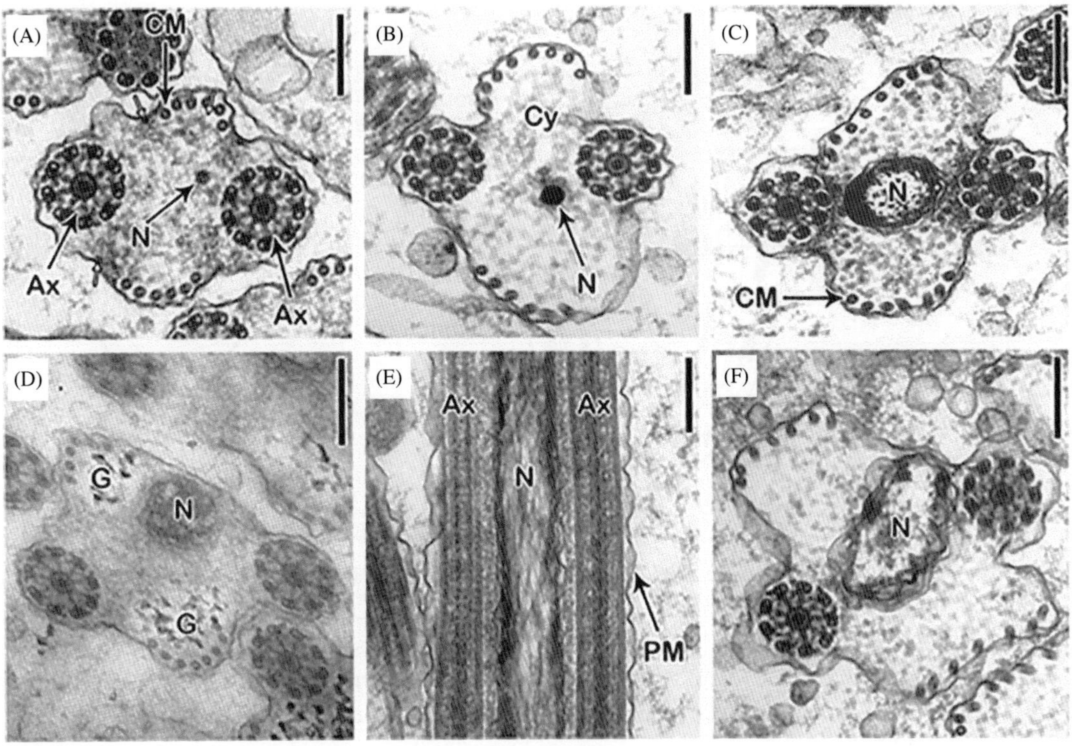

Fig. 11.2 ■ Platyhelminthes sperm. Ultrastructure of the middle nucleated (III) and posterior regions (IV and V) of the mature spermatozoa type I (with two 9 + '1' axonemes) in progenetic *D. olrikii.* (A) Cross-section through the proximal part of the nucleus in region III of the mature spermatozoa. Ax, axoneme; CM, cortical microtubules; N, nucleus; small arrows, attachment zones. Bar = 200 nm. (B), (C) Slightly enlarged profile of the nucleus (N) in serial cross-section. CM, cortical microtubules; Cy, cytoplasm. Bars = 200 nm. (D) Visualization of glycogen (G) using Thiéry method in cross-section of region III. N, nucleus. Bar = 200 nm. (E) Longitudinal section shows the nucleus (N) which is situated centrally between the two axonemes (Ax). PM, plasma membrane. Bar = 250 nm. (F) Cross section through the central part of region III of the mature spermatozoon. N, nucleus. Bar = 200 nm. Courtesy: Bruňanská *et al. Parasitol Res* 2020;119:177–87. Reproduced with permission from Springer Nature.

definitive host, nearly every organ of the body can be parasitized by a trematode. Trematode adults are primarily parasites of the vertebrate intestine, although species residing in other locations are also known. The digenean trematodes are among the most common and abundant parasitic worms, second only to the nematodes in distribution. There are almost **20,000** described species (Collins 2017). Although they occur in significant numbers in all classes of vertebrates (especially marine fish), they are surprisingly rare in cartilaginous fish (sharks and rays), where both cestodes and monogeneans are the dominant flatworms.

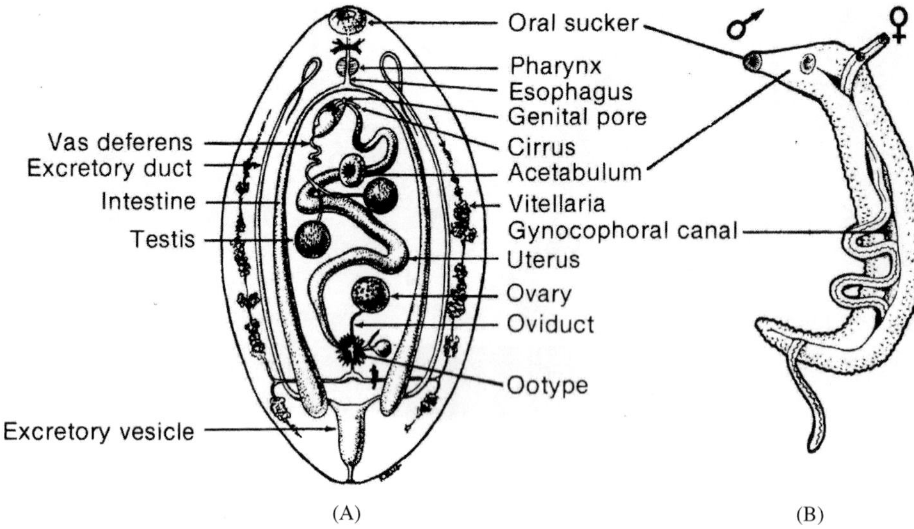

Fig. 11.3 ■ Typical Diagram of an adult trematode. Structure of flukes. (A) Hermaphroditic fluke. (B) Bisexual fluke. (Modified from Hunter GW, Swartzwelder JC, Clyde DF: A Manual of Tropical Medicine. 5th Ed. WB Saunders, Philadelphia, 1976, with permission.) Courtesy: Baron S. *Medical Microbiology*, 4th edition (1996). Reproduced from with permission from the Microbiology Department at the University of Texas Medical Branch Galveston and Scott Weaver.

Trematodes have at least two hosts. The first immediate host is mostly a mollusk, a snail (gastropod mollusc). There may be a second and even a third immediate host. In the vertebrate definitive host, nearly every organ of the body can be parasitized by a trematode. As adults they are primarily parasites of the intestine, but representatives are also found in fish under the scales, on the gills, in the swim bladder, in the body cavity, the urinary bladder, the gallbladder, in the muscles, connective tissue, ovary and in the circulatory system. In tetrapods, they may also be found in extra-intestinal sites including the circulatory system, lungs, esophagus, urinary bladder, liver, eye and ovary.

Among the digenean trematodes, there may be morphological variation, in the form and position of the suckers (for adhesion), the digestive tract and the reproductive system. A typical adult fluke possesses two suckers, the oral sucker and ventral sucker. Oral sucker and the mouth lead to the muscular pharynx and the digestive tract. The digestive tract consists of a branched blind gut (the mouth acts as an anus). The male and female reproductive systems occupy the central space and can be complex. The typical male organ may have two testes. The female organ may have ovary, oviduct and glands (Mehlis' gland, vitelline gland) to prepare the eggs for secretion via the genital pore. For metabolism, the adult flukes are facultative anaerobes. They use glucose and glycogen; glycolysis is the major pathway. Please see Figure 11.3 for typical trematode morphology (Castro 1996).[1]

[1] https://www.ncbi.nlm.nih.gov/books/NBK8282/

For the reproductive strategy of trematodes, there can be self-fertilization (they are hermaphrodites), as seen in the sheep liver fluke *Fasciola hepatica*. There can be cross-fertilization (between two hermaphrodites), as seen in the lung fluke *Paragonimus westermani* (the worms are found as two individuals sticking together within a capsule). For the dioecious species, there is fertilization between worms of the opposite sex, as seen in the blood fluke *Scistosoma mansoni* (the worms are found with the male worm holding the female worm via a special groove called gynaecophoric canal). In addition to sexual reproduction, there is asexual reproduction during the development of larval and juvenile stages in the trematode life cycle. (These species are discussed in Chapters 12 and 13.)

11.4 Life Cycles

For the digenean trematode, there is an alternation of sexual and asexual generations between hosts. The life cycle stages are: **egg, miracidium, sporocyst, redia, cercaria, metacercaria, juvenile, adult**. Variations to the general outline can occur. Depending on the individual species, some stages may be repeated and other stages skipped. A mother sporocyst may yield daughter sporocysts; a mother redia may yield daughter rediae. In other species, the stages of sporocyst and metacercaria may be absent. Thus, there is plasticity/flexibility in the life cycle stages of trematodes. The purpose of this complex life cycle is asexual expansion of individuals: **polyembryony**. As an example, one single miracidium of *Schistosoma mansoni* can give rise to 4,000 cercariae. Please see Figure 11.4 for trematode larval development (Mehlhorn 2016).

The fertilized egg is laid; within the egg, the embryo develops into a miracidium. The miracidium hatches from the egg (some eggs may possess an operculum to release the developed embryo within). Only miracidia have cilia on their epidermal plates, all other stages do not (hence the name Neodermata, new skin for the later stages). Cilia are necessary for the miracidium to swim to find its first intermediate host. The miracidium, a ciliated larva, is motile and short-lived (non-feeding stage); it possesses glands to secrete proteases and other materials for host penetration, as well as sensory and ganglion structures for appropriate response to the aquatic environment. Thus, it demonstrates active host-seeking activity. The miracidium swims to and then penetrates a molluscan intermediate host, where the larva sheds its ciliated outer layer to develop into a mother sporocyst. The parasitized snail host may undergo castration response to suit fluke larval development (no sex, only growth). Within the snail, the mother sporocyst, a simple sac, possesses no organs but consists of germ balls, since it absorbs nutrients via its body wall. The mother sporocyst produces a second intra-molluscan generation asexually, either multiple daughter sporocysts or rediae. Daughter sporocysts resemble the mother sporocyst, whereas the redia possesses a mouth, a pharynx, a short saccular gut, and germ balls within its body. In the case of both second intra-molluscan generation types, i.e., daughter sporocysts and rediae, there is followed by another round of asexual reproduction. Now, the progenies are usually cercariae, larvae of the generation that will ultimately become

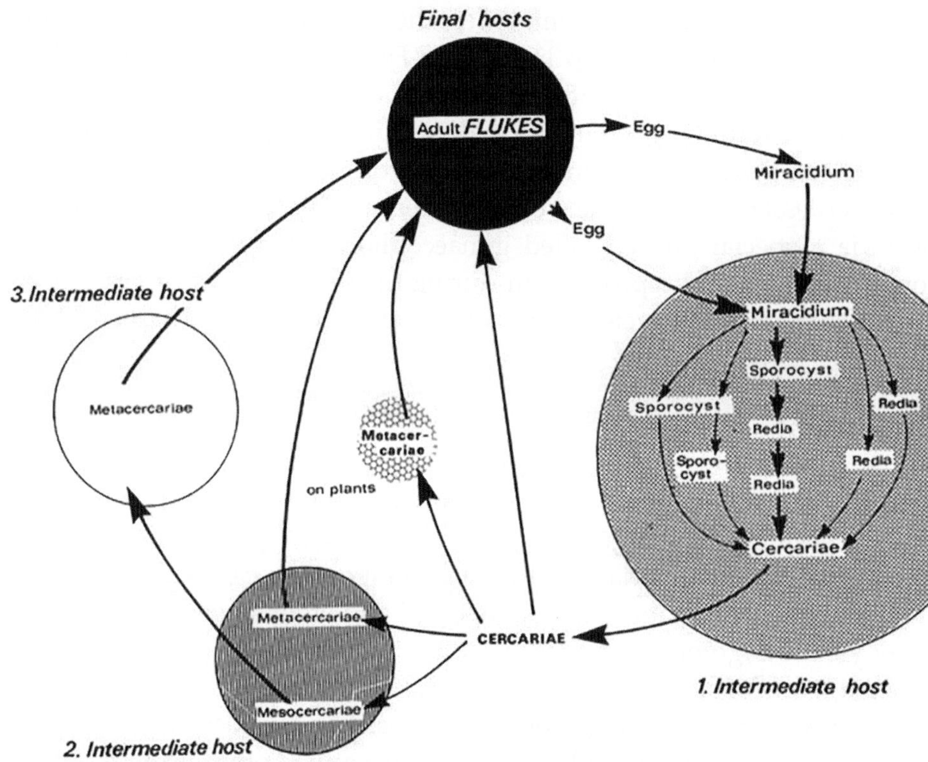

Fig. 11.4 ■ Trematode larval development. Some common pathways of digenean life cycles. (*1*) Egg-miracidium-redia-cercaria-metacercaria-adult worm (e.g., *Caecinola* sp.). (*2*) Egg-miracidium-redia I-redia II-cercaria-metacercaria-adult worm (e.g., *Stichorchis* sp.). (*3*) Egg-miracidium-sporocyst-redia-cercaria-metacercaria-adult worm (e.g., *Metorchis* sp.). (*4*) Egg-miracidium-sporocyst I-redia I-redia II-cercaria-metacercaria-adult worm (e.g., *Fasciola hepatica, Clonorchis sinensis*). (*5*) Egg-miracidium-sporocyst-cercaria-metacercaria-adult worm (e.g., Bucephaloidean species). (*6*) Egg-miracidium-sporocyst I-sporocyst II-cercaria-metacercaria-adult worm (e.g., *Dicrocoelium dendriticum, Prosthogonimus* sp.). (*7*) Egg-miracidium-sporocyst I-sporocyst II-cercaria-adult worm (e.g., *Schistosoma* sp.). (*8*) Egg-miracidium-sporocyst I-sporocyst II-cercaria-mesocercaria-metacercaria-adult worm (e.g., *Alaria* sp.). Courtesy: Mehlhorn H. *Encyclopedia of Parasitology*, 2016. Reproduced with permission from Springer Nature.

the sexually mature adults. The cercaria is usually a tailed form; it emerges actively from the mollusc. A typical cercaria contains the structures of an adult fluke, including two suckers, the blind gut, and a tail (can be simple, single end, or two-pronged fork end). Depending on the species, the cercaria searches for the second intermediate host or the definitive host. In some species, the cercaria is encased within a cyst to form the metacercaria (attached to aquatic plants, or on fish scales), waiting for the definitive host. Tails are lost once the cercariae find the hosts to become metacercariae or juvenile flukes. So, after emergence from the mollusc, the cercaria behaves in ways that are species-dependent. Activity of the cercaria finally leads to either active or passive infection of the vertebrate definitive host. Often, the vertebrate is infected by ingestion of a metacercaria associated with a second intermediate host. Thus, miracidium, cercaria, and metacercaria are infective stages. Sporocyst and redia are asexual reproductive stages. Asexual reproduction increases the number of individuals within the snail host. An interesting finding is the presence of a **caste system** in redia of some trematode species, ones that are not human parasites. A form of division of labor has been discovered: clonal rediae inside the snail intermediate host belong either to a large-bodied reproductive caste, or to a much smaller and morphologically distinct "soldier" caste which defends the colony against co-infecting trematodes (Poulin *et al.* 2019).

Morphology of trematodes can be viewed by scanning electron microscopy (SEM). Please see Figure 11.5 for life cycle of the trematodes (Collins 2017), and Figure 11.6 for adult *Schistosoma mansoni* (Buchter *et al.* 2018). Although schistosomes have female and male worms, most trematodes are hermaphrodites. Please see Figure 11.7 for adult *Fasciola hepatica* (Halferty *et al.* 2009) and Figure 11.8 for the larval forms: miracidium and cercaria (Bennett 2001). Please see Figure 11.9 for adult and metacercaria of *Metagonimus miyatai* (Chai *et al.* 1998). (These species will be discussed in the following two chapters).

Paleoparasitology has revealed a long history of association between the trematode parasite and its vertebrate host. Fossil site at Las Hoyas, Spain (dated to the early cretaceous age, 126–129 million years ago) has yielded fossilized feces/coprolites. In a study, parasite eggs were found in 2 out of 29 coprolites. These eggs showed morphologies belonging to trematodes and nematodes; they were discovered in an environment of lake-associated wetland ecosystem. "The cylindrical coprolite containing anisakid eggs was likely produced by a crocodylomorph as the parasite host, whereas the bump-headed lace coprolite indicates the role of a fish as an intermediary or definitive host of the trematodes and ascaridids. These trace and body fossils show that the Las Hoyas 126–129 Ma lacustrine ecosystem documents the early connection between basal Gonorynchiformes fish and digenetic trematodes" (Barrios-de Pedro *et al.* 2020). Please see Figure 11.10 for the hypothetical life history based on fossil egg finding (Barrios-de Pedro *et al.* 2020). (We shall discuss the nematodes later: *Ascaris* in Chapter 20 and *Anisakis* in Chapter 22.)

11.5 Evolution of Trematodes

The digenean trematodes have complex life cycles. How did these cycles evolve? Trematodes are typically parasites of vertebrates. From which stages are the parasites released into the environment to infect a mollusc? Within the mollusc, where multiple rounds of asexual replication may take place, from which stages are the parasites released to infect the next host? Which hosts are involved in the transmission, second intermediate hosts, or third intermediate? From which stages in the intermediate hosts are the parasites released to infect the vertebrate definitive hosts?

The types of host species have been investigated, using a database with information on over 1,000 species of digeneans for life-cycles, and over 5,000 species from fishes. A study on the distribution of digenean families in molluscs has shown their preferred association with gastropod molluscs, although host-switching has been found, to other

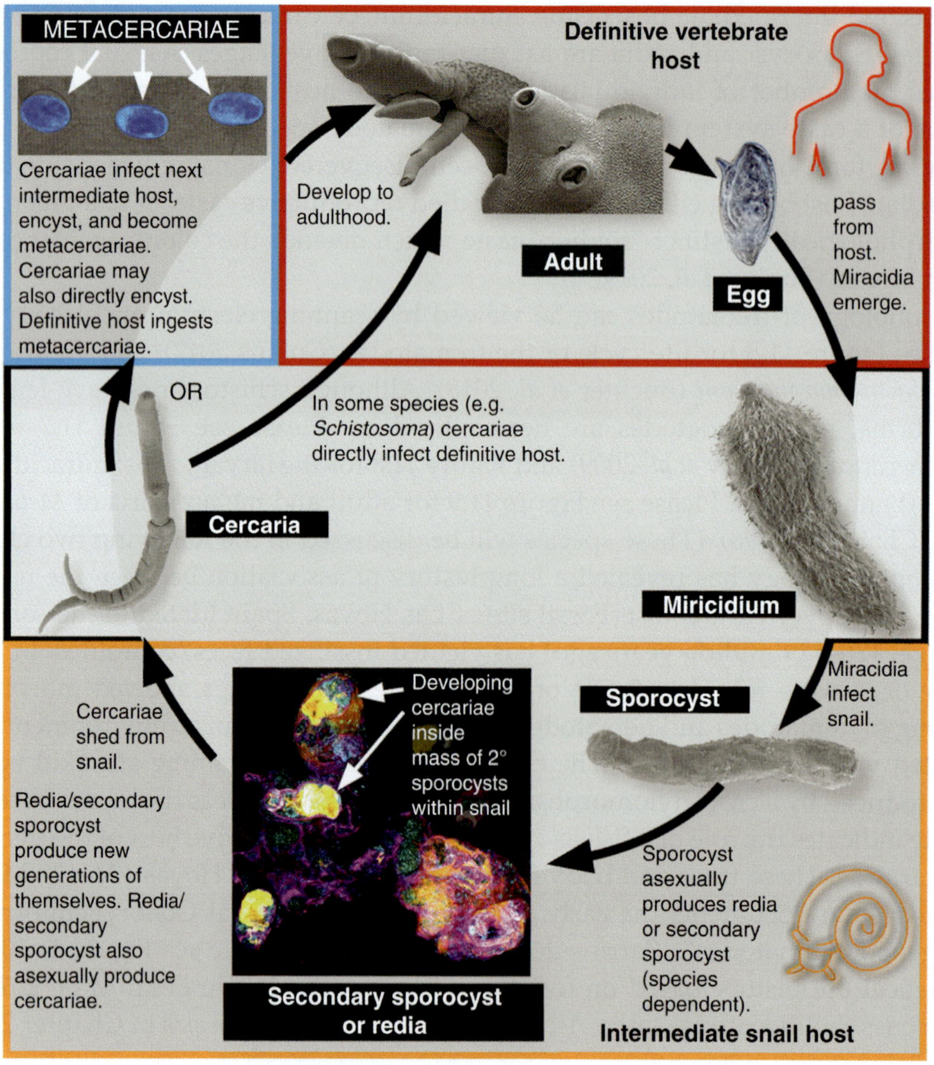

Fig. 11.5 ■ The complex lifecycles of digenetic trematodes. Miracidia emerge from eggs and infect a specific species of snail. Once inside the snail, miracidia transform into sporocysts. Specialized cells inside sporocysts, called germinal cells, undergo embryogenesis and produce either secondary (2°) sporocysts or redia, depending on the trematode species. Redia and 2° sporocysts are similar, except redia have the capacity to feed on the snail's tissues. Germinal cells inside 2° sporocysts/redia undergo new rounds of embryogenesis producing either cercariae or 2° sporocysts/redia. Usually cercariae can infect a second intermediate host and encyst as metacercariae, encyst as metacercariae on vegetation, or directly infect a definitive host. Images: metacercariae, *Apophallus* in coho salmon muscle (credit, M. Kent), adult *S. mansoni* (back) and *Fasciola hepatica* (front, credit, K. Hoffmann and A. Chakroborty), other stages are all *S. mansoni* (credit, J. Collins and A. Vieira). Courtesy: Collins J III. *Curr Biol* 2017;27:R252–6. Reproduced with permission from Elsevier.

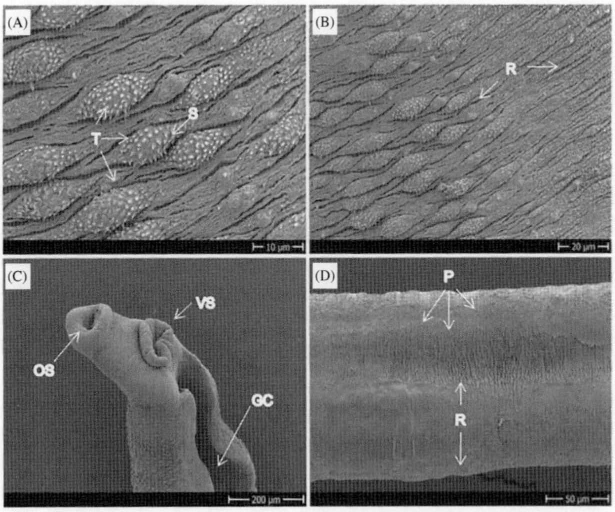

Fig. 11.6 ■ Morphology of adult *Schistosoma mansoni* by scanning electron microscopy. SEM images of *S. mansoni* control worms incubated with 1% DMSO. (A) Tubercles of dorsal mid-part of a male. (B) Lateral mid-part of a male showing the transition between the tubercles of the dorsal side to the spiny ridges of the ventral side of the body. (C) Head of a male showing the oral and ventral suckers and the gynaecophoric canal. (D) Mid-part of the body of a female showing the ridges and pores in a context of a smooth tegument. *Abbreviations*: GC, gynaecophoric canal; OS/VS, oral/ventral sucker; P, pores; R, ridges; S, spines; T, tubercles. *Scale-bars*: (A), 10 μm; (B), 20 μm; (C), 200 μm; (D), 50 μm. Courtesy: Buchter V. *Parasit Vectors* 2018;11:580. Reproduced with permission from *Parasit Vectors* with Creative Commons Attribution 4.0 (CC-BY) International License.

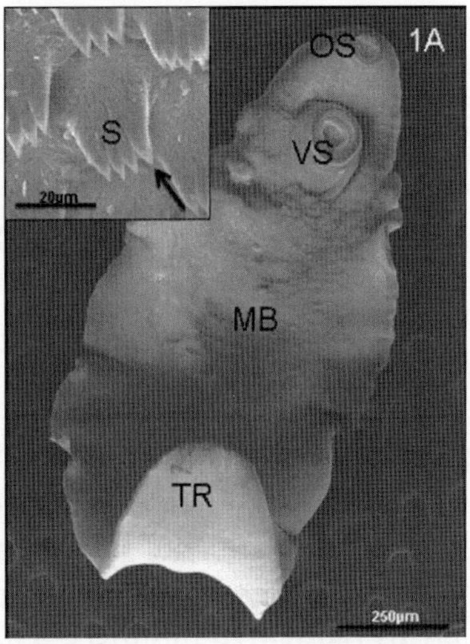

Fig. 11.7 ■ Morphology of adult *Fasciola hepatica* by scanning electron microscopy. Scanning electron micrographs (SEMs) of adult *Fasciola hepatica* incubated *in vitro* for 48 h. (1A) Control, incubated in NCTC culture medium. Low-power image, showing the oral sucker (OS), ventral sucker (VS), midbody region (MB) and tail region (TR). *Inset* shows spines (S) from the oral cone region, which bear distinct spinelets (arrow). Courtesy: Halferty *et al. Parasitology* 2009;136:1325–37. Reproduced with permission from Cambridge University Press.

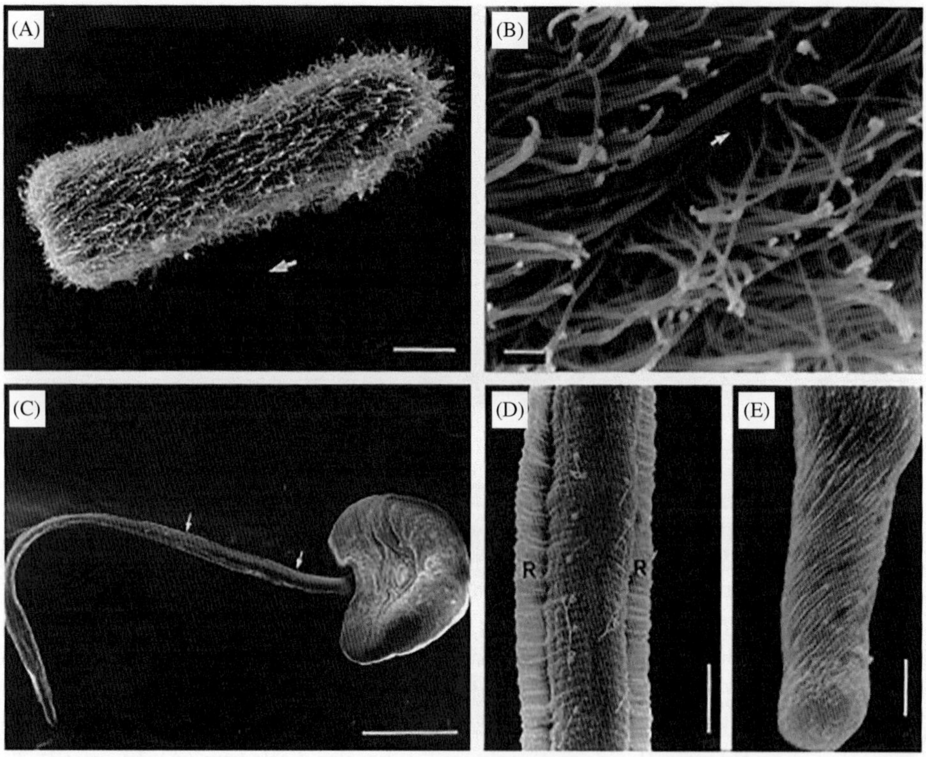

Fig. 11.8 ■ Morphology of miracidium and cercaria of *Fasciola hepatica* by scanning electron microscopy. Scanning electron micrographs of *Fasciola hepatica* miracidia (A and B) and cercariae (C, D and E). (A) Miracidium fixed while swimming in direction of the arrow. (B) High power region (from A) with cilia fixed in phases of dexioplectic metachronism. The direction of the power stroke of the metachronal wave is arrowed. (C) Cercaria: the tail has paired lateral ridges and a region between the arrows with many sensory endings. (D) Cercarial tail: (similar to region between arrows in C) with lateral ridges (R) and 8 μm cilia on the ventral surface. E. The terminal portion of the cercarial tail with a spiral surface pattern to the tegument. Courtesy: Bennett C. *J Helminthol* 2001;75:1–5. Reproduced with permission from Cambridge University Press.

intermediate hosts (bivalves, polychaetes, scaphopods). The digeneans seem to prefer teleosts (bony fish) as their vertebrates, although host-switching has been found to other definitive hosts, including agnathans (jawless fish) and chondrichthyans (cartilaginous fish). "The range of definitive hosts of digeneans is characteristically defined by eco-physiological similarity rather than phylogenetic relationship" (Cribb *et al.* 2001). This study suggests the digeneans first parasitized molluscs before adopting vertebrate hosts.

The digeneans, first evolved to parasitize molluscs, later began secondary colonization of vertebrates. Their most frequent intermediate hosts are gastropod molluscs; they have shown a high degree of species specificity to their intermediate hosts (Viney and Cable 2011). However, there can be other hypotheses on the evolution of the digenean life cycle. An alternative view is that: Neodermata as a whole adopted vertebrate parasitism,

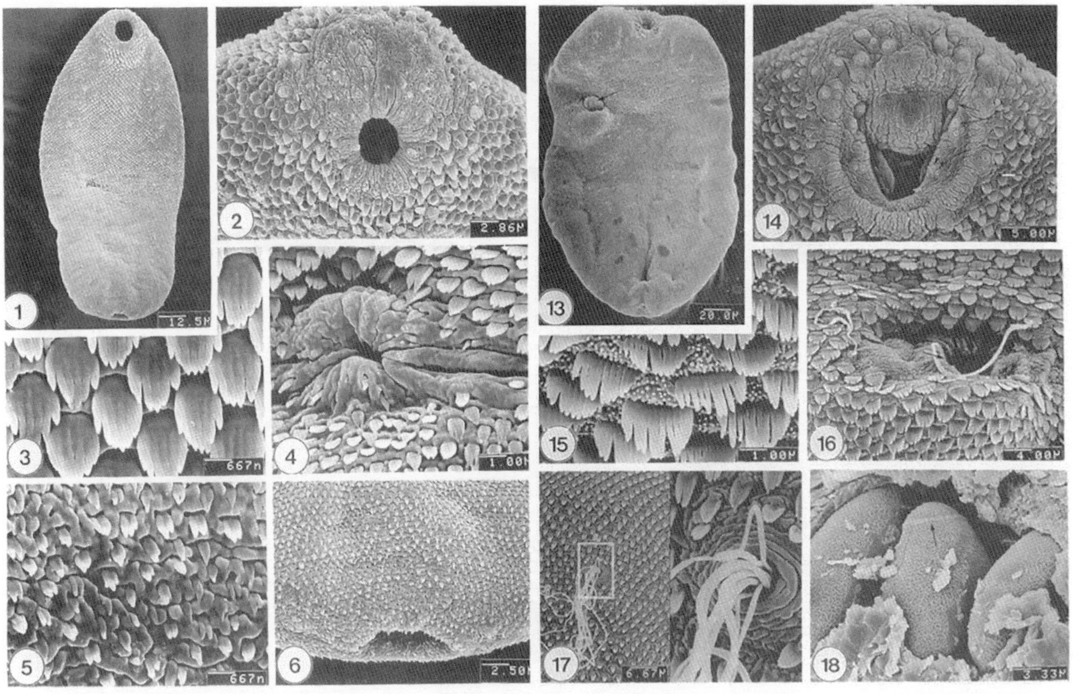

Fig. 11.9 ■ Morphology of adult and metacercaria of *Metagonimus miyatai* by scanning electron microscopy. No. 1–6. SEM view of metacercariae of *Metagonimus miyatai*. 1. Ventral view of an excysted metacercaria, showing oral, ventral suckers, and an excretory pore. 2. Tegument around the oral sucker. Note distribution of sensory papillae on the lip of the oral sucker. 3. Tegumental spines on the ventral surface between oral and ventral suckers. Digitations of spines are 5–7 pointed. 4. Tegument near the ventral sucker. Several uniciliated papillae are seen. 5. Tegument of the posterior ventral surface. Two- to three-pointed peg-like spines are seen. 6. Tegument around the excretory pore. Spines are sparsely distributed. No. 13–18. SEM view of 2- and 4-week-old adults of *Metagonimus miyatai*. 13. A whole worm, ventral view, showing prominent oral and ventral suckers, and the cirrus (arrow) protruding from the genital pore. 14. The oral sucker showing many sensory papillae and tegumental spines. The lip is equipped with seven type II papillae, and at inner side of the oral sucker one pair of large (arrows) and two pairs of small (arrow heads) type I papillae are seen on each side. 15. Tegumental spines between oral and ventral suckers. Spines are short but broad, having 10–11 pointed tips, and numerous knob-like projections are seen between spines. 16. Tegument near the ventral sucker, where two sperms are escaping from the genital pore (arrow). 17. Dorsal tegument around the Laurer's canal (left). Many sperms are seen entering into the canal, which is surrounded by several layers of sphincter-like structures (right). Tegumental spines are 5–6 pointed (right). 18. Three intrauterine eggs are seen after etching the middle portion of the dorsal surface, ovoid to ellipsoid in shape and showing a prominent operculum (arrow) and relatively smooth shell surface. Courtesy: Chai *et al. Korean J Parasitol* 1998;36:217–25. Reproduced with permission from *The Korean Journal of Parasitology* and Sung-Jong Hong.

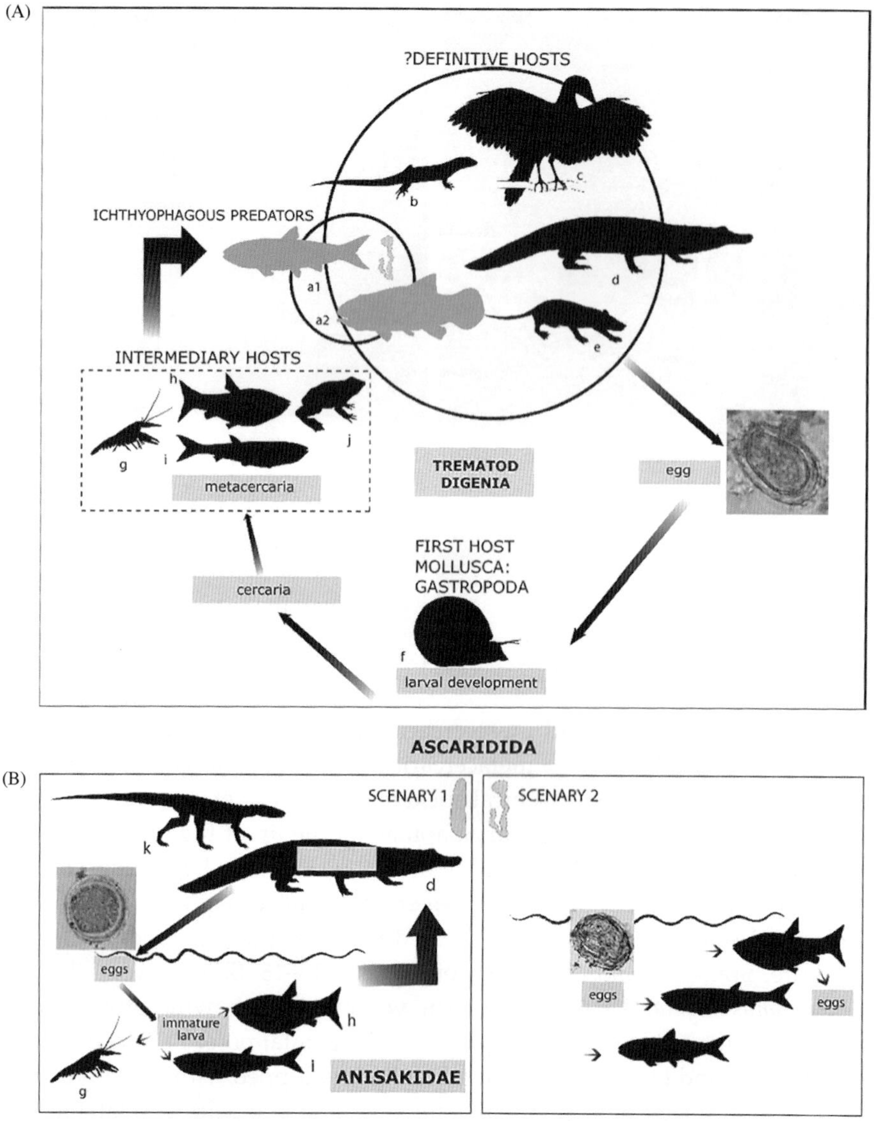

Fig. 11.10 ■ The hypothetical life history based on fossilized helminth eggs. Schematic draw of the hypothetical life-cycle of the parasites found in the lacustrine wetland of Las Hoyas (upper Barremian, Spain). (A) Digenea trematode. The grey silhouettes correspond to an adult teleost (a1) or to a young voracious amiiform (a2) that could produce the bump-headed lace coprolite. The putative definitive hosts are (b) the squamate *Meyasaurus*; (c) Enantiornithes; (d) neosuchian; (e) Gobiconodontidae mammals. The first host silhouette is (f) the pulmonated snail *Gyraulus* sp., whereas the intermediary hosts gather (g) decapods; (h) the Gonorynchiformes *Gordichthys* sp., and (i) *Rubiesichthys* sp.; and (j) the Salientia *Gracilibatrachus* sp. (B) Ascaridida. Scenario 1 depicts the cycle of Anisakidae, from the adult formed in crocodyliform whose eggs or immature larvae were swallowed by fish and crustaceans. Scenario 2 depicts two possible situations with ascaridid eggs: swallowed or defecated by a fish. Art work by Lara de la Cita (Scientific communicator, Department of Biology, UAM). This work is under a *CC BY-NC-ND* license. Courtesy: Barrios-de Pedro *et al. Sci Rep* 2020;10:18747. Reproduced with permission from Elsevier and Sandra Barrios-de Pedro.

and the Trematoda subsequently adopted parasitism of molluscs as intermediate hosts (Cribb *et al.* 2003).

In one scenario, the two host life cycle was original to the trematodes (plesiomorphic, or primitive, ancestral character state). The three host cycles have been developed from two host forms, and have been adapted repeatedly later. For the definitive hosts, the digenean trematodes are found in chondrichthyans, teleosts, and tetrapods. They are few in cartilaginous fish, and could be seen as host-switched from bony fishes or accidental infections (Cribb *et al.* 2003). For the complex life cycle of digenean trematodes, this is the idea of life cycle truncation or abbreviation ("short is sweet?"). Related to this view is **progenesis**: precocious development of the reproductive system leading to early sexual maturation in juvenile stages. The cercariae of *Schistosoma mansoni* invade humans and develop into adult blood flukes directly; this feat can be viewed as life cycle truncation (Poulin and Cribb 2002).

Phylogenetic relationship among the trematodes has been investigated, from early morphologies (presence or absence of a penetrating stylet in the cercariae) to current molecular biological studies (ribosomal RNA gene sequencing). Using complete small subunit ribosomal RNA gene (18S ssrDNA) and partial (D1–D3) large subunit ribosomal RNA gene (28S lsrDNA) sequences, the phylogeny of the Digenea was created using data of 163 digenean taxa representing 77 families, together with seven aspidogastrean outgroup taxa representing three families (Cribb *et al.* 2003). According to "a high-level classification of all living things" (Ruggiero *et al.* 2015), the Subclass Neodermata is within the Phylum Platyhelminthes; it contains three infraclasses, namely Cestoda, Monogenea, and Trematoda. The infraclass Trematoda contains four orders: **Aspidogastrida, Diplostomida, Plagiorchiida, Stichocotylida**. Please see Figure 11.11 for the phylogenetic tree of trematodes (Fraija-Fernández *et al.* 2015). Two branches are seen as Diplostomida and Plagiorchiida, including medially important species: *Schistosoma japonicum* within Diplostomida, and others (*Fasciola hepatica, Clonorchis sinensis, Opisthrochis viverrini, Metagonomus miyatai,* and *Paragonimus westernmani*) within Plagiorchiida. The color branches seen in the phylogeny tree indicate that at least for four times **host switch** had occurred: trematodes captured cetaceans (dolphins and whales) as their new hosts from old ones (marine fish and fish-eating birds/mammals) (Fraija-Fernández *et al.* 2015).

The "best molecular practice" for trematode taxonomy and systematic studies, as an attempt to help unify the field and provide a solid foundation to underpin future work, aims at "generating sequence data from all parasite species/host species/geographic location combinations and stress the importance of selecting two independently evolving loci (one ribosomal and one mitochondrial marker)" (Blasco-Costa *et al.* 2016). Trematode phylogeny was re-visited with more data: 1,077 digenean taxa allocated to 106 families for 28S and 419 taxa in 98 families for 18S. "Overall, the results were consistent with previous higher-level classification schemes, and most superfamilies and suborders were recovered as monophyletic assemblages" (Pérez-Ponce de León and Hernández-Mena

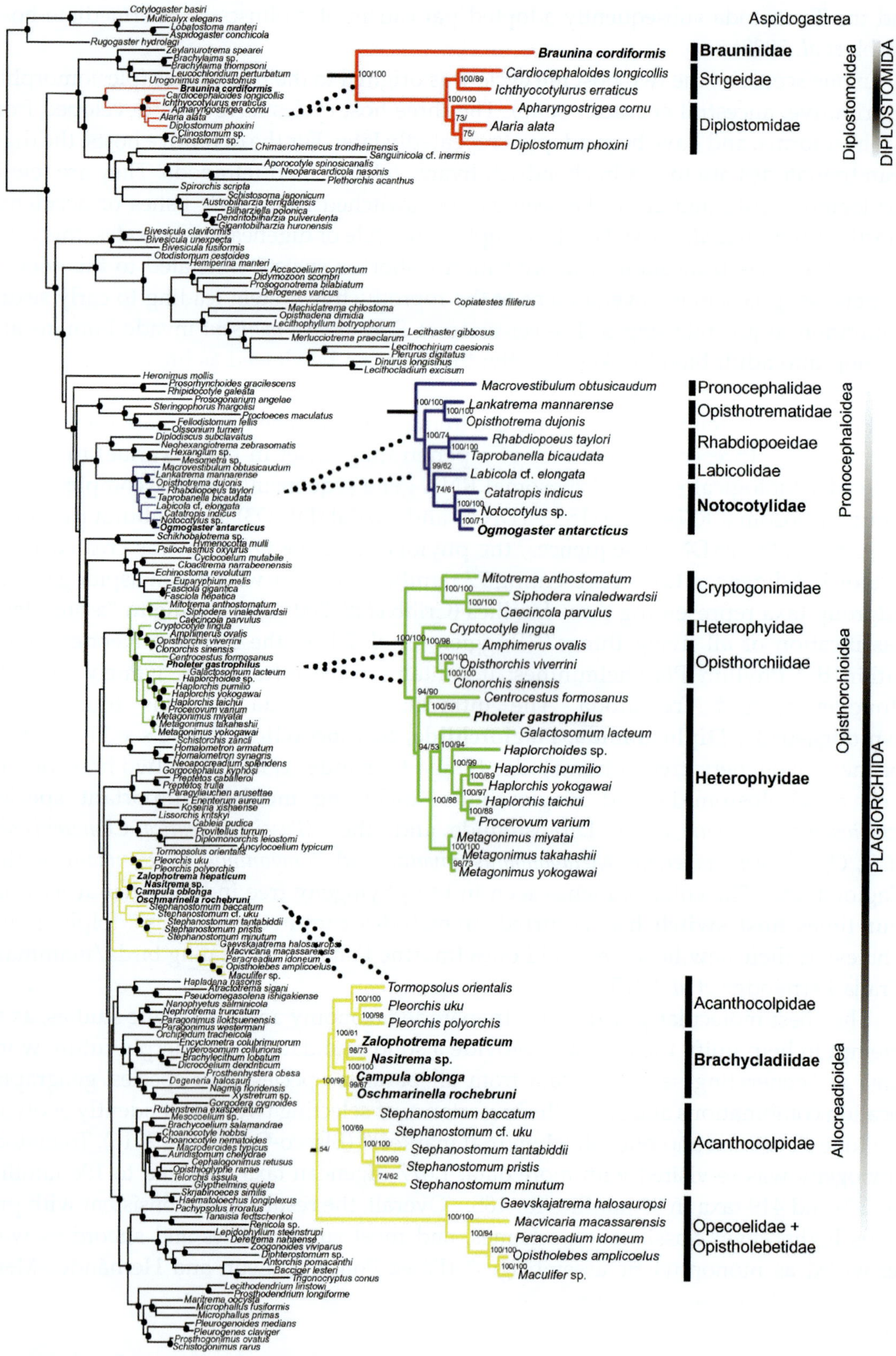
Aspidogastrea
Braunina cordiformis
Cardiocephaloides longicollis
Ichthyocotylurus erraticus
Apharyngostrigea cornu
Alaria alata
Diplostomum phoxini
Brauninidae
Strigeidae
Diplostomidae
Diplostomoidea
DIPLOSTOMIDA
Macrovestibulum obtusicaudum
Lankatrema mannarense
Opisthotrema dujonis
Rhabdiopoeus taylori
Taprobanella bicaudata
Labicola cf. elongata
Catatropis indicus
Notocotylus sp.
Ogmogaster antarcticus
Pronocephalidae
Opisthotrematidae
Rhabdiopoeidae
Labicolidae
Notocotylidae
Pronocephaloidea
Mitotrema anthostomatum
Siphodera vinaledwardsii
Caecincola parvulus
Cryptocotyle lingua
Amphimerus ovalis
Opisthorchis viverrini
Clonorchis sinensis
Centrocestus formosanus
Pholeter gastrophilus
Galactosomum lacteum
Haplorchoides sp.
Haplorchis pumilio
Haplorchis yokogawai
Haplorchis taichui
Procerovum varium
Metagonimus miyatai
Metagonimus takahashii
Metagonimus yokogawai
Cryptogonimidae
Heterophyidae
Opisthorchiidae
Heterophyidae
Opisthorchioidea
PLAGIORCHIIDA
Tormopsolus orientalis
Pleorchis uku
Pleorchis polyorchis
Zalophotrema hepaticum
Nasitrema sp.
Campula oblonga
Oschmarinella rochebruni
Stephanostomum baccatum
Stephanostomum cf. uku
Stephanostomum tantabiddii
Stephanostomum pristis
Stephanostomum minutum
Gaevskajatrema halosauropsi
Macvicaria macassarensis
Peracreadium idoneum
Opistholebes amplicoelus
Maculifer sp.
Acanthocolpidae
Brachycladiidae
Acanthocolpidae
Opecoelidae +
Opistholebetidae
Allocreadioidea

2019). The investigators indicated that future phylogeny will include whole mitochondrial DNA from next generation sequencing (NGS). We predict even more data will be generated to confirm and refine the phylogeny, with improved DNA sequencing methods such as the Nanopore technology.

11.6 Praziquantel (PZQ)

Trematodes infecting humans include blood flukes, intestinal flukes, and tissue flukes. To target these important human parasites, the aim is to develop prophylactic and therapeutic measures. Currently, vaccines are unavailable, but multiple drugs have been developed. Genomic NGS and proteomics (liquid chromatography-mass spectrometry, LC-MS) approach of the trematodes will lead to future applications (Haçariz and Sayers 2016). Databases of trematodes are freely accessible (Martin *et al.* 2015).[2]

One important drug for the digenean trematodes is praziquantel (PZQ) (da Silva *et al.* 2017; Vale *et al.* 2017). In chemical structure, PZQ is a pyrazino-isoquinoline derivative. In 1972, researchers at the German pharmaceutical companies E. Merck and Bayer A.G. selected PZQ (from over 400 analogs tested) as the drug to be commercialized for the treatment against schistosomiasis due to its characteristics of low toxicity, high efficacy, and tolerability. This is considered the most important development in the treatment of schistosomiasis. In 1977, the activity of PZQ against trematodes and cestodes was published. PZQ was first approved for veterinary treatment of schistosomiasis; then, its use was expanded to treat cestodes in humans. In 1983, Shin Poong Pharmaceutical Company in Korea, working with the government research institute Korea Advanced Institute of Science and Technology (KAIST) and a remarkably low investment of corporate funds (equivalent to US $14,000), succeeded in creating an innovative and cost-saving manufacturing process for the production of PZQ (Reich and Govindaraj 1998; Cioli *et al.* 2014). PZQ treatment results in contractile paralysis and tegument damage in the flatworms. Interestingly, PZQ treatment of the free-living

Fig. 11.11 (figure on facing page) ■ Trematode evolution. Bayesian inference of the small subunit and large subunit rDNA sequences from 177 species of the subclass Digenea. Bold letters indicate species, or group of species, parasitic in cetaceans. A closer view of each segment of the tree with digeneans of cetaceans is also shown. Classification of superfamilies and suborders follows Olson *et al.* (2003). Black circles in the general tree indicate nodal supports of Bayesian inference (posterior probabilities) ≥ 90% and maximum likelihood (bootstrap, n = 100) ≥ 80%. For the detailed trees, Bayesian inference (posterior probabilities) and maximum likelihood bootstrap for each node are shown as the first and second numbers, respectively. No bootstrap value means that the node was not resolved by maximum likelihood. Courtesy: Fraija-Fernández *et al. Int J Parasitol* 2015;45:167–73. Reproduced with permission from Elsevier.

[2] http://trematode.net/TN_frontpage.cgi

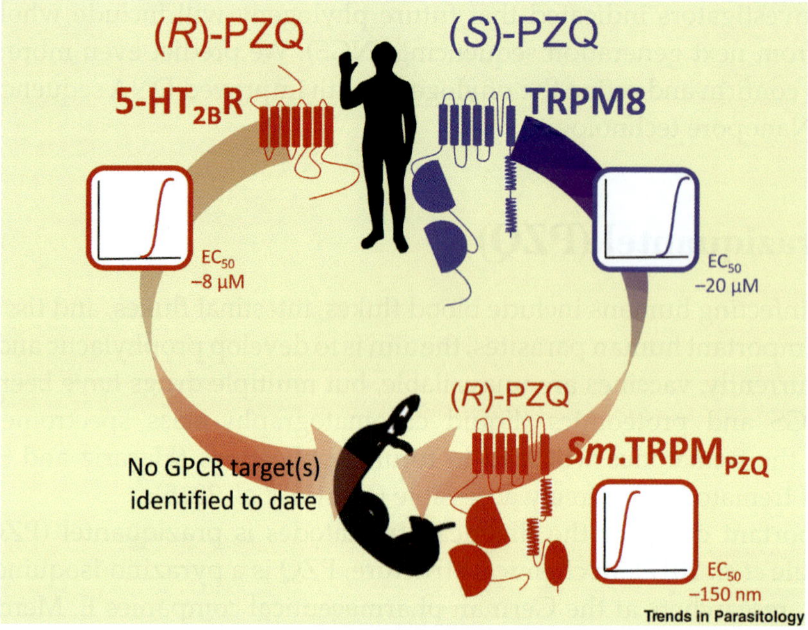

Fig. 11.12 ■ Targets for praziquantel (PZQ) in schistosomes and humans. Discovery of Host Targets for Praziquantel (PZQ) Refined the Search for Parasite Targets. Host targets for (*R*)-PZQ (red) and (*S*)-PZQ (blue) have been defined. These are a G-protein-coupled receptor (GPCR) [5-HT$_{2B}$R for (*R*)-PZQ and a transient receptor potential (TRP) channel (transient receptor potential melastatin; TRPM8) for (*S*)-PZQ]. Recently, using a homology-based search, a TRPM channel in *Schistosoma mansoni* (*Sm*.TRPM$_{PZQ}$) that is activated by (*R*)-PZQ in the nanomolar range has been identified. Additional target(s) for PZQ in parasitic flatworms may yet be found. PZQ sensitivity of each of these targets is schematically illustrated by dose–response curves, with EC$_{50}$s for activation by individual enantiomers. Courtesy: Park S, Marchant J. *Trends Parasitol* 2020;36:182–94. Reproduced with permission from Elsevier.

planarian has resulted in a worm with two heads (PZQ-evoked bipolarity) (Park and Marchant 2020).

To date, praziquantel (PZQ) is the only available anti-schistosomal drug. It is an excellent drug because of its low cost, efficacy, and safety. PZQ is active against all major forms of schistosomiasis (but less active against juvenile than adult flukes). PZQ has been distributed through mass drug administration (MDA) programs to millions of people every year (Cioli *et al.* 2014).

For PZQ treatment of schistosomiasis, variable cure rates among individuals have been noted. Many factors may be responsible for the reduced efficacy; there are host, parasite, and drug–related factors. Host PZQ metabolism contributes towards variable cure rates. Factors that may influence the levels of PZQ in systemic circulation include drug formulation (enantiomers) and brand, host liver health, host age, and genetic polymorphisms of liver enzymes involved in its metabolism as well as drug–drug interactions of co-administered drugs (Zdesenko and Mutapi 2020).

Given its massive and repeated use on large numbers of individuals via MDA, development of drug resistance is a major concern. Although there are cases of drug resistance, widespread resistance has not developed despite decades of use. This situation leads to the suggestion that PZQ acts on multiple targets of the parasite and may even act on the host.

Although PZQ has been used by millions of people for decades, the exact mechanisms of PZQ action are still unclear. After PZQ treatment, there is calcium influx in the worm, followed by worm muscle contraction and modifications of the worm surface (tegument alterations). This correlation between increased intracellular calcium and muscular contractions in schistosomes has been shown many years ago. However, how PZQ disrupts homeostasis in schistosomes still remains unknown. The overall effective steps are calcium influx, paralysis, and tegument disruption, but this may not be the whole picture.

Genomic studies have revealed an atypical schistosome β subunit of voltage-operated calcium channel (**VOCC**) as a molecular target of PZQ (Berriman *et al.* 2009). This calcium ion channel is a member of the transient receptor potential melastatin (**TRPM**) channel subfamily which is broadly expressed in PZQ-sensitive flatworms (Park and Marchant 2020). This calcium permeable transient receptor potential (TRP) channel in *Schistosoma mansoni,* named Sm.$TRPM_{PZQ}$, is the target of PZQ. It starts the deadly cascade in schistosomes, which is induced by the (R)-PZQ enantiomer that includes contemporaneous stereoselective activation of Sm.$TRPM_{PZQ}$-mediated calcium influx, disturbed calcium homeostasis, calcium-dependent spastic paralysis, and calcium and PZQ-dependent disruption of parasitic teguments. The tegument damages are irreversible. "As homologs of Sm.$TRPM_{PZQ}$ are also present in the other trematodes *S. japonicum, S. haematobium,* or *Clonorchis sinensis* and cestodes *Taenia solium, Echinococcus multilocularis,* or *Hymenolepis microstoma,* it is suggested that a similar deadly cascade will be operating generally in PZQ-sensitive parasites" (Harder 2020).

Furthermore, host actions may also be of assistance. Tegument disruption may activate the host immune response to the parasite. PZQ may act on a host protein, the G-protein-coupled receptor (GPCR) human 5-HT_{2B} receptor (5-Hydroxytryptamine receptor 2B, aka serotonin receptor 2B). The stimulated receptor leads to constriction of mesenteric vessels and ends in the displacement of the adult worms that live in the mesenteric vasculature. These findings suggest that PZQ acts on both the parasite and the host for its mechanisms of action (Day and Kimber 2018). Please see Figure 11.12 for PZQ targets in schistosomes and humans (Park and Marchant 2020).

Summary & Key Concepts

- Platyhelminthes are flatworms that may be free-living, commensal, or parasitic. They are acoelomates possessing three germ layers (ectoderm, endoderm, and mesoderm, triploblastic).
- The outermost layer of a parasitic adult flatworm is the tegument, which is important for the interaction of the worm to its environment. Underneath the tegument are muscle

fibers, a simple nervous system with a brain, a digestive system ending as a blind tract, and a simple excretory system.

- Tremadotas (also known as Digenea) are flukes. They are primarily parasites of the intestines.
- Trematodes have at least two hosts with the first immediate host mostly being a mollusc (gastropod).
- The digenean trematodes exhibit alternation of generations between sexually reproducing adults and asexually reproducing larval stages.
- The trematode life cycle stages include egg, miracidium, sporocyst, redia, cercaria, metacercaria, juvenile, and adult.
- Praziquantel (PZQ) is a pyrazino-isoquinoline derivative that is used for treatment against schistosomiasis due to its characteristics of low toxicity, high efficacy, and tolerability.

References

Adl SM, Bass D, Lane CE, *et al.* Revisions to the classification, nomenclature, and diversity of Eukaryotes. *J Eukaryot Microbiol* 2019;66(1):4–119.

Anderson TJC, Enabulele EE. *Schistosoma mansoni. Trends Parasitol* 2020;S1471–4922(20):30164–1.

Bakhoum AJS, Miquel J, Ndiaye PI, *et al.* Advances in spermatological characters in the Digenea: Review and proposal of spermatozoa models and their phylogenetic importance. *Adv Parasitol* 2017;98:111–65.

Barrios-de Pedro S, Osuna A, Buscalioni ÁD. Helminth eggs from early cretaceous faeces. *Sci Rep.* 2020;10(1):18747.

Bennett CE. *Fasciola hepatica*: Surfaces involved in movement of miracidia and cercariae. *J Helminthol* 2001;75(1):1–5.

Berriman M, Haas BJ, LoVerde PT, *et al.* The genome of the blood fluke *Schistosoma mansoni. Nature.* 2009;460(7253):352–8.

Blasco-Costa I, Cutmore SC, Miller TL, Nolan MJ. Molecular approaches to trematode systematics: 'Best practice' and implications for future study. *Syst Parasitol* 2016;93(3):295–306.

Bogitsh BJ, Carter CE, Oeltmann TN. *Human Parasitology*, 5th edition (2019, Elsevier).

Bruňanská M, Matoušková M, Jasinská R, Nebesářová J, Poddubnaya LG. Heteromorphism of sperm axonemes in a parasitic flatworm, progenetic *Diplocotyle olrikii* Krabbe, 1874 (Cestoda, Spathebothriidea). *Parasitol Res* 2020;119(1):177–87.

Buchter V, Hess J, Gasser G, Keiser J. Assessment of tegumental damage to *Schistosoma mansoni* and *S. haematobium* after *in vitro* exposure to ferrocenyl, ruthenocenyl and benzyl derivatives of oxamniquine using scanning electron microscopy. *Parasit Vectors* 2018;11(1):580.

Castro GA. Helminths: Structure, classification, growth, and development. In: Baron S, editor, *Medical Microbiology*, 4th edition (1996, Galveston (TX)): University of Texas Medical Branch at Galveston. https://www.ncbi.nlm.nih.gov/books/NBK8282/

Chai JY, Kang YJ, Choi SY, Guk SM, Yu JR, Lee SH. Surface ultrastructure of *Metagonimus miyatai* metacercariae and adults. *Korean J Parasitol* 1998;36(4):217–25.

Cioli D, Pica-Mattoccia L, Basso A, Guidi A. Schistosomiasis control: praziquantel forever? *Mol Biochem Parasitol* 2014;195(1):23–9.

Collins JJ. 3rd Platyhelminthes. *Curr Biol* 2017;27(7):R252–6.

Collins JJ. 3rd, Wang B, Lambrus BG, Tharp ME, Iyer H, Newmark PA. Adult somatic stem cells in the human parasite *Schistosoma mansoni*. *Nature* 2013;494(7438):476–9.

Cribb TH, Bray RA, Littlewood DT. The nature and evolution of the association among digeneans, molluscs and fishes. *Int J Parasitol*. 2001;31(9):997–1011.

Cribb TH, Bray RA, Olson PD, Littlewood DT. Life cycle evolution in the digenea: A new perspective from phylogeny. *Adv Parasitol* 2003;54:197–254.

da Silva VBR, Campos BRKL, de Oliveira JF, Decout JL, do Carmo Alves de Lima M. Medicinal chemistry of antischistosomal drugs: Praziquantel and oxamniquine. *Bioorg Med Chem* 2017;25(13):3259–77.

Day TA, Kimber MJ. Praziquantel interaction with mammalian targets in the spotlight. *Trends Parasitol* 2018;34(4):263–5.

Fraija-Fernández N, Olson PD, Crespo EA, Raga JA, Aznar FJ, Fernández M Independent host switching events by digenean parasites of cetaceans inferred from ribosomal DNA. *Int J Parasitol* 2015;45(2–3):167–73.

Haçarız O, Sayers GP. The omic approach to parasitic trematode research-A review of techniques and developments within the past 5 years. *Parasitol Res* 2016;115(7):2523–43.

Halferty L, O'Neill JF, Brennan GP, Keiser J, Fairweather I. Electron microscopical study to assess the *in vitro* effects of the synthetic trioxolane OZ78 against the liver fluke, *Fasciola hepatica*. *Parasitology* 2009;136(11):1325–37.

Halton DW. Microscopy and the helminth parasite. *Micron* 2004;35(5):361–90.

Halton DW. Nutritional adaptations to parasitism within the platyhelminthes. *Int J Parasitol* 1997;27(6):693–704.

Harder A. Activation of transient receptor potential channel Sm.(*Schistosoma mansoni*)$TRPM_{PZQ}$ by PZQ, enhanced Ca^{++} influx, spastic paralysis, and tegumental disrupture-the deadly cascade in parasitic schistosomes, other trematodes, and cestodes. *Parasitol Res* 2020;119(8):2371–82.

Levron C, Miquel J, Oros M, Scholz T. Spermatozoa of tapeworms (Platyhelminthes, Eucestoda): Advances in ultrastructural and phylogenetic studies. *Biol Rev Camb Philos Soc* 2010;85(3): 523–43.

Martin J, Rosa BA, Ozersky P, *et al.* Helminth.net: expansions to Nematode.net and an introduction to Trematode.net. *Nucleic Acids Res.* 2015;43(Database issue):D698–706.

McCusker P, McVeigh P, Rathinasamy V, *et al.* Stimulating neoblast-like cell proliferation in juvenile *Fasciola hepatica* supports growth and progression towards the adult phenotype *In Vitro*. *PLoS Negl Trop Dis* 2016;10(9):e0004994.

Mehlhorn H. *Encyclopedia of Parasitology* (2016, Springer).

Olson PD, Cribb TH, Tkach VV, Bray RA, Littlewood DT. Phylogeny and classification of the Digenea (Platyhelminthes: Trematoda). *Int J Parasitol* 2003;33(7):733–55.

Park SK, Marchant JS. The journey to discovering a flatworm target of praziquantel: A ong TRP. *Trends Parasitol* 2020;36(2):182–94.

Pérez-Ponce de León G, Hernández-Mena DI. Testing the higher-level phylogenetic classification of Digenea (Platyhelminthes, Trematoda) based on nuclear rDNA sequences before entering the age of the 'next-generation' Tree of Life. *J Helminthol* 2019;93(3):26076.

Poulin R, Cribb TH. Trematode life cycles: short is sweet? *Trends Parasitol* 2002;18(4):176–83.

Poulin R, Kamiya T, Lagrue C. Evolution, phylogenetic distribution and functional ecology of division of labour in trematodes. *Parasit Vectors* 2019;12(1):5.

Reich MR, Govindaraj R. Dilemmas in drug development for tropical diseases. Experiences with praziquantel. *Health Policy* 1998;44(1):1–18.

Roberts LS, Janovy J Jr., Nadler S. *Schmidt & Roberts Foundations of Parasitology*, 9th edition (2016, McGraw Hill).

Ruggiero MA, Gordon DP, Orrell TM, *et al.* A higher level classification of all living organisms. *PLoS One* 2015;10(4):e0119248. Erratum in: PLoS One 2015;10(6):e0130114.

Toledo R, Fried B, editors. *Digenetic Trematodes*, 2nd edition (2019, Springer).

Vale N, Gouveia MJ, Rinaldi G, *et al.* Praziquantel for Schistosomiasis: Single-drug metabolism revisited, mode of action, and resistance. *Antimicrob Agents Chemother* 2017;61(5):e02582–16.

Viney M, Cable J. Macroparasite life histories. *Curr Biol* 2011;21(18):R767–74.

Wendt GR, Collins JJ 3rd. Schistosomiasis as a disease of stem cells. *Curr Opin Genet Dev* 2016;40:95–102.

Wendt GR, Collins JN, Pei J, *et al.* Flatworm-specific transcriptional regulators promote the specification of tegumental progenitors in *Schistosoma mansoni*. *Elife* 2018;7:e33221.

Wilson RA, Wright JM, de Castro-Borges W, *et al.* Exploring the *Fasciola hepatica* tegument proteome. *Int J Parasitol* 2011;41(13–14):1347–59.

Zdesenko G, Mutapi F. Drug metabolism and pharmacokinetics of praziquantel: A review of variable drug exposure during schistosomiasis treatment in human hosts and experimental models. *PLoS Negl Trop Dis* 2020;14(9):e0008649.

12

Schistosomiasis (Snail Fever)

12.1 Introductory Remarks

Schistosomiasis, also known as **bilharzia** (or bilharziasis) and snail fever (the former due to its German discoverer, the latter for the different species of snails serving as its intermediate host), is caused by the fresh-water trematodes belonging to the genus *Schistosoma*. Among all neglected tropical diseases (NTDs), schistosomiasis is the second most important, in terms of prevalence and deaths (after malaria). A conservative estimate of cases for schistosomiasis is **230 million** worldwide, with annual deaths over **200,000** related to *Schistosoma* infections in Sub-Sahara Africa. Over 90% of schistosomiasis cases occur in Africa, with between 1 and 2 million in South America (Brazil) and the Middle East (Yemen), and another 1 million in Asia (China, Philippines and Southeast Asia).

In females with chronic *Schistosoma* infection, there is female genital schistosomiasis (**FGS**) resulting from egg deposition in the female reproductive tract (primarily by *S. haematobium*, less commonly by *S. mansoni*). FGS affects an estimated 20–56 million women worldwide, mostly in sub-Saharan Africa. FGS may be a potential risk factor for HIV-1 acquisition in these females, including a breach in the cervicovaginal barrier and vaginal inflammation (Sturt *et al.* 2020).

Over 220 million people worldwide were estimated to have active schistosomiasis in 2017, 90% of whom live on the African continent, but only 102 million were reported to have received treatment. Africa has an estimated 26 million people living with HIV in 2017. Relationships between the two epidemics have been investigated based on data from 1996 to 2018. Findings are: "(1) infection with *Schistosoma haematobium* increases the risk of HIV acquisition, (2) there is currently a lack of data on whether HIV infection increases the risk of *Schistosoma* acquisition, (3a) HIV coinfection was not an accelerating factor for adverse *Schistosoma* outcomes, (3b) schistosomiasis may be an important contributor to immune activation in HIV co-infected people, (4) praziquantel use in co-infected people may improve immune reconstitution on antiretroviral therapy for HIV, and (5) there is evidence that HIV infection reduces egg excretion in individuals infected with *Schistosoma mansoni*" (Furch *et al.* 2020).

Snail fever starts when infectious larval forms penetrate the skin of individuals that come in contact with infectious water environments, typically where freshwater snails reside. In this sense, schistosomiasis can be categorized as an infectious disease from a water-borne pathogen. As adults, these flatworms live in humans and feed on blood, hence they are known as blood flukes. There are two major forms of the disease: intestinal and urogenital schistosomiasis. The original classification of the schistosomes suggests three major species: ***Schistosoma haematobium*** (63% of cases) which is responsible for urinary and urogenital schistosomiasis; ***S. mansoni*** (35%) and ***S. japonicum*** (less than 1%) which are responsible for intestinal and hepatic schistosomiasis (Hotez 2013; Colley *et al.* 2014). Moreover, *S. haematobium* infection can be a virulence factor for bladder cancer.

Worldwide, schistosomiasis currently affects 78 countries, among which 58 are considered to be endemic, with a moderate-to-high transmission. For geographical distribution, *S. haematobium* is seen in Africa and the Middle East, plus Corsica (and France, due to African immigrants). *S. mansoni* is seen in Africa, the Middle East and the Americas (Brazil, Venezuela, Suriname, and the Caribbean, presumably brought over by the slave trade). *S. japonicum* is seen in China, Indonesia and the Philippines.

Further, for intestinal schistosomiasis, three additional minor species of limited distribution have been described. *Schistosoma mekongi* is seen in Cambodia and Laos (Limpanont *et al.* 2020). Another two species are seen in the rain forests of Central Africa: *Schistosoma intercalatum* in Congo, and *S. guineensis* in Guinea, Cameron, and Nigeria. A ribosomal DNA sequence analysis shows phylogenetic relatedness of the latter two species with *S. haematobium* (Webster *et al.* 2006).

Daniel Colley (University of Georgia) and colleagues established the Schistosomiasis Consortium for Operational Research and Evaluation (SCORE) program in 2008 to conduct operational research that would inform practices related to the control and elimination of schistosomiasis, with "an emphasis on openness and contributing to the development of a cohesive schistosomiasis control community, building linkages between researchers and national programs, and focusing on answering questions that will help Neglected Tropical Disease program managers" (Colley *et al.* 2020). Major efforts included large, multi-country field studies comparing multiple strategies for mass drug administration (MDA) with praziquantel, assessment of approaches to elimination, evaluation of a point-of-care assay for field mapping *Schistosoma mansoni*, and increasing the sensitivity of a laboratory-based diagnostic. SCORE was funded by the Bill & Melinda Gates Foundation, with an initial award of US$34 million, to support research that would provide evidence leading to improved means to reduce morbidity from schistosomiasis and to move toward elimination, with a focus on countries in Africa. From 2008 to 2019, SCORE engaged many stakeholders and sectors, with particular efforts to include endemic country neglected tropical disease program managers (Binder *et al.* 2020). SCORE is "Mission Accomplished" (Bergquist 2020). There were many schistosomiasis research and control programs before SCORE, and there will be many others in the future (Fenwick 2017).

12.2 History

Schistosomiasis the disease, or rather the symptoms, were known since antiquity. The trematode blood flukes were first reported by a German doctor (Theodor Bilharz) working in Egypt. The complete life cycle of the parasite in the intermediate host, the snail, was first completed by Japanese investigators who were familiar with the European research. A Scottish zoologist (Robert Thomson Leiper), who had visited Japan, completed the life cycle of the fluke species in Egypt.

12.2.1 Ancient knowledge

In ancient Egypt, it was believed that young males celebrated the arrival of manhood with the appearance of blood in their urine (**hematuria**), just like menstruation in young females. This phenomenon was later explained as caused by *Schistosoma haematobium* infections. In 1910, Marc Armand Ruffer found *S. haematobium* eggs in two Egyptian mummies dated 1250–1000 BC. This finding has signaled the dawn of the new field of paleoparasitology (Di Bella *et al.* 2018).

The concept of schistosomiasis as a disease is seen in ancient texts. In Biblical times, there was the event: the conquest of Jericho by Joshua (in the Book of Joshua). It was postulated that the curse Joshua had laid upon the city of Jericho was related to bombardment of the city with infected snails, resulting in schistosomiasis and the abandonment of Jericho (Hulse 1971). Today, after years of abandonment of the city and the removal of its snail habitats, Jericho is an agriculturally rich city of Jordan.

12.2.2 Modern understanding

The first European account of the trematode parasitic disease was from the French army surgeon A. J. Renoult, in 1798, during Napoleon's invasion of Egypt. He wrote, "A most stubborn hematuria manifested itself among the soldiers of the French Army.... The sickness gives sharp pains in the region of the bladder." The first report of the parasite was by the German doctor Theodor Bilharz in 1852. At the time Bilharz was working as an assistant to his former professor Wilhelm Griesinger, who had left Germany and went to Egypt to be the personal physician of the ruler of Egypt. At the recommendation from another professor Carl Theodor von Siebold, Bilharz was drawn to human helminths. During his dissections performed in Cairo, he came upon a delicate thread-like worm in the portal vein. He found a male worm first and later a female worm, as well as their eggs. Bilharz wrote: "… my portal vein worm … develop … into something more wonderful, a trematode with divided sex … The female was easily pulled out of the male's groove … The eggs are oval and are pointed at one end" (Kean *et al.* 1978).

In 1858, David Friedrich Weinland proposed the name *Schistosoma*, 3 months later Thomas Cobbold proposed *Bilharzia* (after Bilharz). The time gap meant the first name took priority; so, it is named *Schistosoma*, meaning split body, referring to the male worm's **gynecophoral canal** (a ventral longitudinal groove). [Think about the shape of a frankfurter/hotdog, with the male as the hotdog bun holding the long slender female hotdog sausage in between.] Eggs of *S. haematobium* contain terminal spines, but eggs with lateral spines were also seen. In 1902, after seeing a patient from the New World (38-year-old Englishman from Antigua) with "bilharzia ova from the alimentary canal, the spine is placed laterally," Patrick Manson suggested the possible presence of a second species. His colleague Louis Sambon at London School of Tropical Medicine named the species *S. mansoni* in his honor. Others disputed this new species, however, because the life cycle was not yet known at that time. (Genomic data have unequivocally shown as two species.)

Meanwhile, in Japan, the presence of a third species and its life cycle was completed before the Europeans working in North Africa. Referred to as Katayama disease, named after the affected location in Japan, the disease was found in humans, cattle and horses. The affected showed wasting, abdominal swelling, and rashes on the legs. Parasite eggs (ovoid, with no spine) were present in liver autopsies by Tokuho Majima in 1888. In 1904, Fujiro Katsurada found eggs and larvae like the *Schistosoma* previously published, round or a tiny vestigial spine. He studied 12 patients with symptoms of hepatosplenomegaly, diarrhea, anemia, and weight loss. He saw miracidia and found similar eggs and larvae in infected cats. Katsurada concluded; "I want to call the parasite that I discovered, and which belongs to the genus *Schistosoma*, '*Schistosoma haematobium japonicum*'." The link between Katayama disease and *S. japonicum* was independently reported in 1904 by Akira Fujinami (eggs and adults) and Kenji Kawanishi (eggs only) (Kean *et al.* 1978).

In 1909, Akira Fujinami and Hachitaro Nakamura showed conclusively that the infection route was through the skin (skin penetration): cattle in rice paddies were infected but not the cattle on dry land, nor cattle in rice paddies with their legs protected (legs both oiled and covered with waterproof bags). In 1913, Keinosuke Miyairi (a Japanese medical graduate sent to Germany for further study and returned to become a professor of Kyoto Imperial University) and Masatsugu Suzuki (a medical doctor and assistant to the professor) demonstrated that schistosome eggs harvested from an ox can be infective to the snail species (***Oncomelania*** for *S. japonicum*). Miracidia were observed to become sporocysts, and later split tail cercariae came out (in 32 days). However, they were unsuccessful in infecting mice with the lab bred cercariae. Field-caught snails were used instead, to demonstrate cercariae to vertebrate transmission in mice (one mouse was killed by its cage mate 3 weeks after infection, and the investigators found adult flukes after dissection of this mouse) (Esch 2007).

The life cycle of *S. haematobium* was later completed by Robert Leiper (who had visited Akira Fujinami in Japan), sent to Egypt by the British War Office because Lord Herbert Kitchener (Consul-General in Egypt) had concluded too many British soldiers had the disease. Leiper found cercariae in the snail of ***Bulinus*** species, he tested many animals and found adult worms in one rat and one mouse. Then, the experiment was repeated with mice, rats, and monkeys. The correct snail species was deemed important, the ones for *S. mansoni* are ***Biomphalaria*** species (*A Report to the War Officers on the Results of the Bilharzia Mission in Egypt*, 1915). It is believed in the evolution of trematodes, they might have started out as specific snail parasites and later took on additional hosts.

Schistosomiasis has also influenced history in modern China. In 1949, Chairman Mao Tse-tung of the People's Republic of China (China) had planned an amphibious attack on Taiwan (where the defeated Generalissimo Chiang Kai-shek of the Republic of China had fled to). As the People's Liberation Army (PLA) soldiers were trained in the Yangtze River, within weeks they had Katayama disease — extreme fatigue, muscle pains and coughing, infected by cercariae of *Schistosoma japonicum* from snails in the river. The attack was thus delayed. The United States Seventh Fleet arrived at the Strait of Formosa and saved the Republic of China (Taiwan). Later, in 1958, Mao had the "Great Leap Forward" campaign, with a scheme on getting rid of the snails (Hotez 2013).

Environmental changes influence the incidence of schistosomiasis. Dams are thought to increase schistosomiasis. However, surveys after the building of Aswan Dam in the Nile (in Egypt) had shown contradictory results (some demonstrating an increase and others indicating decline). "Perhaps the deleterious effects of the Dam were buffered by the national control programs launched by the government at the time" (Othman and Soliman 2015). For the new Three Gorges Dam in the Yangtze (in China), Li *et al.* (2017) reported that the snail population decreased after the dam, as assayed in the Dongting Lake area, with a corresponding reduction of schistosomiasis by 87% (between 2003 and 2015). The investigators concluded: "Risk of schistosomiasis transmission still exists in Dongting Lake area and long-term monitoring is required." It has been discussed that restoration of the native river snail-eating prawns may mitigate the increased risk of schistosomiasis due to dam constructions, as dams block prawn migration (Sokolow *et al.* 2017).

Whereas schistosomiasis is still prevalent in China, Japan has been declared *S. japonicum*-free since 1977. For control of this important parasitic disease, Wilson (2020) concluded with these sentences: "The eradication of schistosomiasis japonica in Japan shows that it can be done, even for a zoonotic parasite. However, it took 73 years from the identification of *S. japonicum* in 1904 to the last infected human detected in 1977 and many different measures plus economic development played a significant part in that success story," in his review on schistosomiasis titled "Schistosomiasis then and now: what has changed in the last 100 years?".

12.3 Life Cycle

Please see Figure 12.1 for life cycle of *Schistosoma* species, from CDC.[1]

The fresh-water snail is the intermediate host for schistosomiasis, with different snail species acting as hosts for different blood fluke species. The miracidium hatches from the egg; it seeks and enters the snail. Within the intermediate host, it develops into sporocyst

[1] https://www.cdc.gov/dpdx/schistosomiasis/index.html

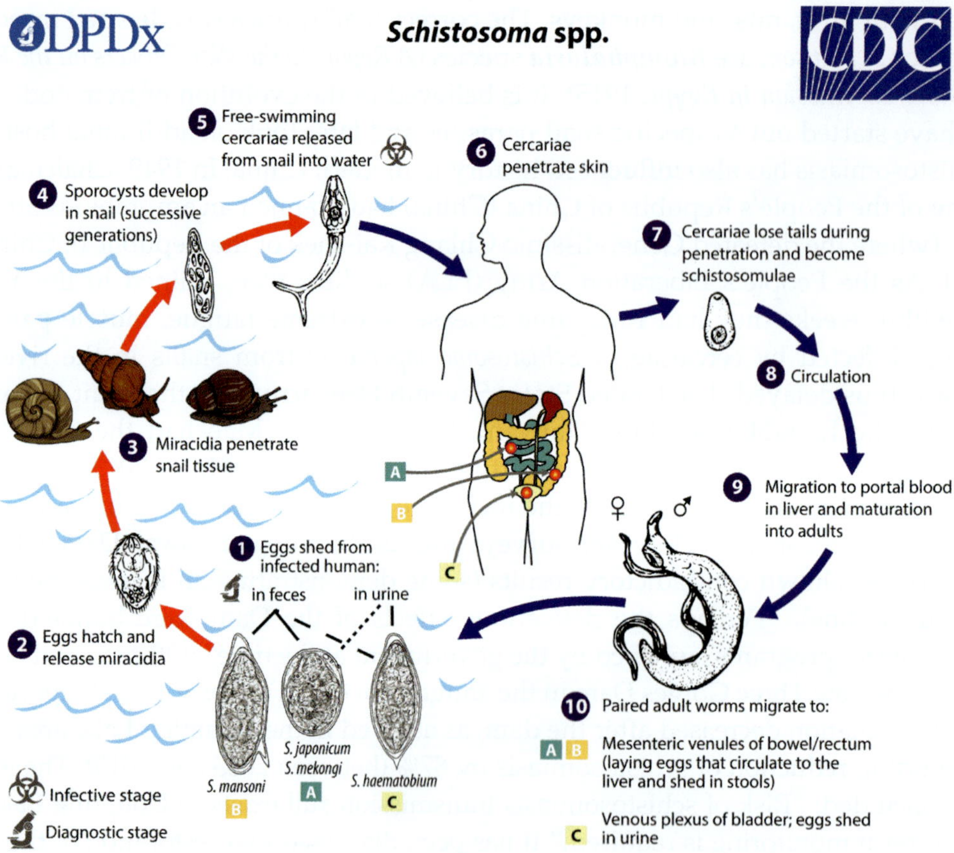

Fig. 12.1 ■ Life cycle of *Schistosoma* species. *Schistosoma* eggs are eliminated with feces or urine, depending on species ❶. Under appropriate conditions the eggs hatch and release miracidia ❷, which swim and penetrate specific snail intermediate hosts ❸. The stages in the snail include two generations of sporocysts ❹ and the production of cercariae ❺. Upon release from the snail, the infective cercariae swim, penetrate the skin of the human host ❻, and shed their forked tails, becoming schistosomulae ❼. The schistosomulae migrate via venous circulation to lungs, then to the heart, and then develop in the liver, exiting the liver via the portal vein system when mature, ❽ ❾. Male and female adult worms copulate and reside in the mesenteric venules, the location of which varies by species (with some exceptions) ❿ . For instance, *S. japonicum* is more frequently found in the superior mesenteric veins draining the small intestine A, and *S. mansoni* occurs more often in the inferior mesenteric veins draining the large intestine B. However, both species can occupy either location and are capable of moving between sites. *S. intercalatum* and *S. guineensis* also inhabit the inferior mesenteric plexus but lower in the bowel than *S. mansoni*. *S. haematobium* most often inhabitsin the vesicular and pelvic venous plexus of the bladder C, but it can also be found in the rectal venules. The females (size ranges from 7 to 28 mm, depending on species) deposit eggs in the small venules of the portal and perivesical systems. The eggs are moved progressively toward the lumen of the intestine (*S. mansoni*, *S. japonicum*, *S. mekongi*, *S. intercalatum/guineensis*) and of the bladder and ureters (*S. haematobium*), and are eliminated with feces or urine, respectively ❶. Courtesy of the CDC. Reproduced from https://www.cdc.gov/dpdx/schistosomiasis/index.html

for two generations (mother and daughter sporocysts, or primary and secondary sporocysts), and then into cercariae. The path is miracidium, to mother sporocyst, to daughter sporocyst, to cercaria, to schistosomulum (plural, schistosomula, juvenile form after losing its forked tail). This asexual reproduction increases the number of individuals: from a single miracidium, the result is 4,000 cercariae. A cercaria leaves the snail and swims to seek out the next host for entrance via skin penetration.

The three major human parasite blood flukes can be differentiated by egg spine morphology. Their sizes are also somewhat different: with *Schistosoma mansoni* adults being the smallest to 1.4 cm in length, *S. haematobium* somewhat bigger at 2 cm, and *S. japonicum*, the largest, at 2.6 cm (Brown and Neva 1983).

12.4 Pathology

The progression of schistosomiasis can be divided into three phases. The migratory phase is normally asymptomatic. The acute phase, known as Katayama fever, involves chills, fever, and fatigue, as immune responses to egg production. Schistosome eggs have been used to prepare **soluble egg antigen** (SEA). The chronic phase is the build-up of granulomas (immune cells surrounding the eggs) by the host. Immune response to eggs is the pathology (immunopathology). Sixty percent of eggs do not get excreted and cause pathology. An experimental study of murine liver fibrosis for *Schistosoma japonicum* has shown that co-treatment of praziquantel (anti-schistosome drug) with rosiglitazone (PPARγ ligand) will decrease liver damage. PPARγ is immunosuppressive, whereas NFκB is inflammatory (Chan *et al.* 2010). (Please see Chapter 3 for immunology of parasites.)

Adult male and female pairs are in close constant contact, with the female situated within the male's gynaecophoric canal, allowing copulation and egg production. Egg production rate is high, from 300 eggs per day for *S. mansoni* to 3,000 per day for *S. japonicum*. Adults also have long lifespans; a pair lives between 3 and 10 years (with extreme cases lasting 40 years). It seems the adults, as well as schistosomula juveniles, do not evoke major host immune responses. In fact, the adults use molecular mimicry to evade host immune response. They pick up host proteins onto their surface and also produce β2 microglobulin-like protein (a protein for recognition of self/non-self, gene product of the major histocompatibility complex, MHC).

Most blood flukes cause intestinal schistosomiasis: liver fibrosis, hepatomegaly, diarrhea, blood in the stool, portal hypertension, and even central nervous system (CNS) complications (the presence of eggs in the affected areas). Urinary schistosomiasis is caused by *Schistosoma haematobium*: urogenital tract fibrosis and renal failure. Furthermore, two additional severe medical concerns exist for individuals with infections by *S. haematobium*: bladder cancer and female genital schistosomiasis (FGS). Whereas most blood fluke adults live in the intestinal venules, *S. haematobium* adults live in the urinary venules. They become a risk factor for bladder cancer, rather a special type of bladder cancer. The most common bladder cancer is of the adenocarcinoma type, but the one related to the urinary blood fluke is of the **squamous cell carcinoma** type. It is believed to be related to the host inflammatory response and host cell proliferation after infection. For FGS, up to 75% of women with *S. haematobium* infection have eggs in their genitals. Eggs become granulomas and the female reproductive system develops lesions or "sandy patches" that are associated with genital bleeding, pain in intercourse, and infertility. One study in Zimbabwe has shown this increases the risk of HIV transmission 3-fold. Human schistosomiasis is thus an important infectious NTD.

Juvenile pork tapeworm infections lead to neurocysticercosis. (Please see Chapter 16 for this disease.) Similarly, schistosome infections lead to neuroschistosomiasis. Two rare cases of multiple schistosomiasis japonica cerebral granulomas were reported in China (Shen *et al.* 2020). A 61-year-old male who had worked as a fisherman in Yangtze River (until 4 years ago) with complaints of headache and weakness of right limbs, another 68-year-old male who used to swim in a local lake (until 2 years ago) with complaints of headache and dizziness for 2 weeks, both patients were from Anhui province. As no parasite eggs were detected in their stool but magnetic resonance revealed two intensive patchy lesions in the cerebral hemisphere with edema in both patients, they were misdiagnosed as brain cancer and were operated for tumor mass removal. Pathological examination confirmed schistosome diagnosis; the patients were administered praziquantel and dexamethasone. Both became symptom-free, without evidence of recurrence.

Schistosomiasis may act as a trigger in disease onset. A case of collapsing glomerulopathy (CG) associated with schistosomiasis and high-risk *APOL1* genotype (HRG) was reported in a 35-year-old black male in Brazil (Neves *et al.* 2020).

Human schistosomiasis is caused by three species of blood flukes: *Schistosoma hematobium*, *S. japonicum* and *S. mansoni*. The species can hybridize. Interspecific infection was reported in a 14-year-old male with hematuria from Ivory Coast (Côte d'Ivoire), with the presence of eggs (150 mm long, 62 mm wide) with a lateral spine (25 mm) in his urine but not in stool, and identified morphologically as *Schistosoma mansoni* (Depaquit *et al.* 2019). Sequencing of 28S-rDNA demonstrated the eggs to be a hybrid — the result of hybridization between a *S. hematobium* male and a *S. mansoni* female.

Besides the three human-invading *Schistosoma* species, many blood flukes invade other vertebrates, such as seagulls (the fluke is *Microbilharzia variglandis*). Their cercariae may infect humans who swim in lakes. Normal bird trematodes can infect humans by mistake. Commonly known as swimmer's itch due to penetration by cercariae into the skin (aka clam digger's itch), **cercarial dermatitis** can be found in New Jersey, USA.

12.5 Diagnosis

Detection of eggs in feces or urine is the definitive diagnosis, typically by classic microscopic examination. Morphology of eggs and the location of spines, allow for species identification: terminal spine for *S. haematobium*, lateral spine for S. *mansoni*, and none or vestigial spine for *S. japonicum*. Modern rapid serological and molecular assays are also available (Utzinger *et al.* 2015). For studying the distribution of FGS within schistosomiasis endemic areas, real-time PCR for the detection of *Schistosoma* DNA in gynecological samples is a valuable diagnostic tool (Pillay *et al.* 2020).

Diagnostic tests may be useful for screening purposes in the field. "Parasitology-based diagnostics cannot meet the demands of schistosomiasis detection. Most serology-based diagnostics have adequate sensitivity with low requirements, although it is prone to higher rates of cross-infection and false-positive results. At the same time, distinguishing current infection and previous infection after praziquantel administration using this method can be a challenge which hampers clinical diagnosis and treatment. A diagnosis based on nucleic acid testing shows high accuracy and can greatly reduce the number of false-positive results. However, the cost of a nucleic acid diagnosis is relatively high, and its operation process requires specific environmental conditions. As a result, it has not been used in the field. Each diagnostic method has its own merits, so combining two or three diagnostic methods could improve detection efficiency in the field. The serology-based diagnosis, due to its high sensitivity and low cost, could be used as the primary screening method. Then, parasitology-based diagnostic techniques or a nucleic acid test could be used on positive samples identified by the serologic diagnosis to reduce the false-positive rate" (Chen *et al.* 2021).

12.6 Therapy

Praziquantel (PZQ) is the first choice of drugs in treating schistosomiasis and is effective for all major species of blood flukes. Known as Biltricide and made by Bayer in the 1970s, PZQ increases calcium permeability by targeting voltage-gated calcium channels and leading to parasite paralysis. However, multiple targets may be involved and the exact mechanism is still unsure (Vale *et al.* 2017). A Korean company can mass-produce PZQ at low cost. A dose costs US$0.30 allowing mass treatment of school-age children in endemic areas (mass drug administration, MDA). Merck Soreno donated 250 million PZQ tablets annually for MDA (Mutapi *et al.* 2017). However, re-infection is common. "The clear and present danger is that the whole edifice of schistosome control is balanced on the monotherapy of praziquantel, and the development of drug resistance could topple that" (Wilson 2020). As a single drug there can be resistance, co-treatment of praziquantel with artemisinin (anti-malarial) or derivatives has been shown to be effective.

The drug **metrifonate** is effective for *S. haematobium*; it is an organophosphorus insecticide derivative. Metrifonate is an inhibitor of acetylcholinesterase, and has an unusual mode of action. In *S. haematobium*, it acts by paralyzing worms so that they release their hold and transit through the venous system to the lungs from where they cannot return to the bladder. This movement differs from *S. mansoni* and *S. japonicum*, which if paralyzed only travels as far as the liver and can then re-migrate back up the portal veins (Cioli *et al.* 1995).

The drug **oxamniquine (OXA)** is effective for *S. mansoni*. Molecular basis for OXA being specific for *S. mansoni* but not *S. haematobium* and *S. japonicum* has been investigated. OXA is a prodrug that needs activation, and the OXA-activating enzyme was identified and crystallized: *S. mansoni* sulfotransferase (SmSULT). Amino acid sequence comparison and protein structure analysis of SULTs from the three species indicate that structural differences, including the OXA contact residues, do not abrogate OXA binding in the active sites. "However, differences in sulfotransferase enzyme efficiency, variation in detoxification processes between species, and differences in sulfotransferase concentration remain possible explanations for species-specific resistance and may be interdependent in establishing OXA toxicity. Therefore, one answer to the question is that OXA kills *S. mansoni* but not *S. haematobium* or *S. japonicum* because it does not fit into the SULT binding pocket productively and does not get activated to a sufficiently toxic level" (Rugel *et al.* 2020). Another interesting point is on the potential resistance by *S. mansoni* to OXA. Chevalier *et al.* (2019) have provided evidence that alleles conferring resistance to OXA are widespread in natural parasite populations under minimal drug pressure and predate OXA deployment. The evidence was obtained by sequencing exomes of 204 *S. mansoni* parasites from West Africa, East Africa and the Middle East, and scoring variants in *SmSULT* and flanking regions. "Our results have important implications for both drug treatment policies and drug development efforts, and demonstrate the power of molecular surveillance approaches for guiding helminth control" (Chevalier *et al.* 2019).

Natural products, especially those compounds derived from medicinal plants including quinine and artemisinin, continue to save the lives of millions of people worldwide, but medicinal plants have been relatively under-explored as a source of anthelmintics. Wangchuk *et al.* (2016) have isolated 19 phytochemicals from two medicinal plants used in traditional medicine in Bhutan. They tested six compounds and found 2, the alkaloids isomyristicin and bergapten from the plant *Pleurospermum amabile*, to be active against *Schistosoma mansoni* (also the whipworm *Trichuris muris*). [We discuss whipworm in Chapter 20.] The schistosome worm surface was analyzed by scanning electron microscopy (SEM), using PZQ as a positive control. Please see Figure 12.2 for the results. Adult worms cultured in media only (with 1% DMSO in culture media as vehicle control) displayed normal physical appearance with numerous healthy tubercles and well-formed spines in the males, and clearly defined surface grooves with sensory papillae in the females. After treatment the worm surface/tegument was disturbed. The investigators noted that, despite their anthelmintic activity being significantly better than the untreated control group, the therapeutic effects of the alkaloids were markedly weaker than PZQ. However, unlike PZQ or mebendazole, the compounds have shown widespread anti-parasitic properties (for flukes and whipworms), especially against the infective schistosomulum stage of *S. mansoni*, a stage not that susceptible to PZQ. Thus, they will provide new scaffolds for broad-spectrum anthelmintic drug development.

12.7 Genome

Two schistosome genomes were published in July 2009 (Berriman *et al.* 2009; The Schistosoma japonicum Genome Sequencing and Functional Analysis Consortium 2009).

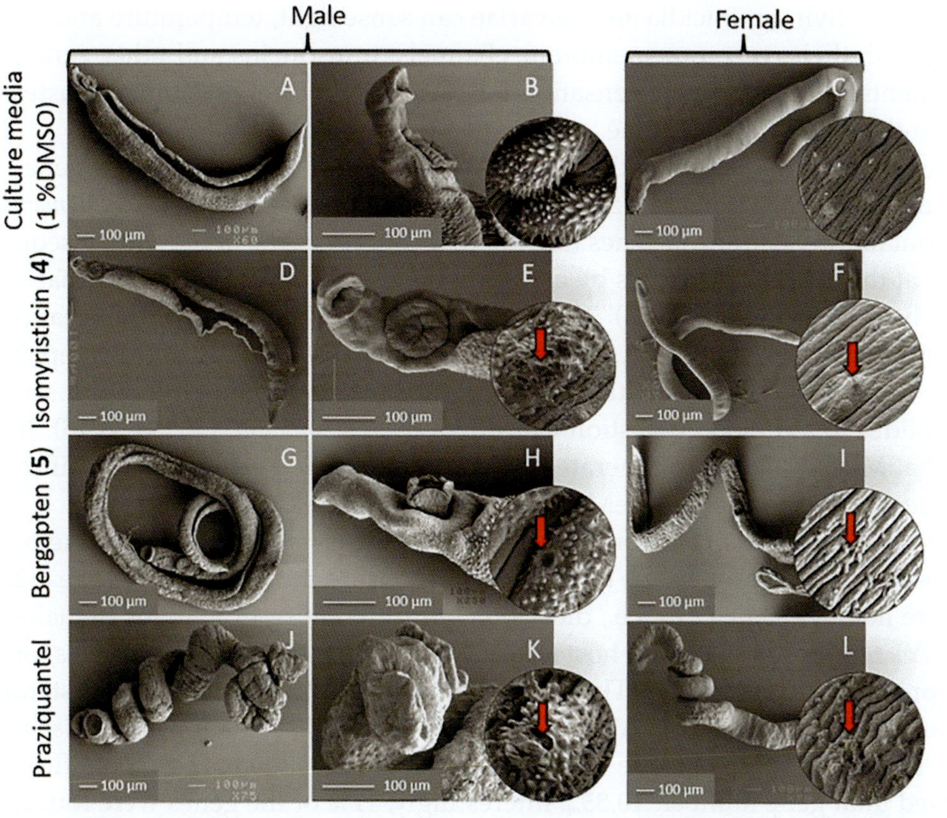

Fig. 12.2 ■ **Effects of compound treatment on surface morphology of *S. mansoni*.** Scanning electron micrographs showing the surface morphology of *S. mansoni* treated with solvent alone, isomyristicin, bergapten and praziquantel. The SEM photos represent different groups treated with the lowest dose concentration of 4 μg/mL (all inset photos are 1 μm). (A–C) Worms cultured in solvent alone (1% DMSO/culture media) displayed a relaxed (uncoiled) and healthy physical appearance. (D–F) Isomyristicin treated parasites displayed a partially damaged physical appearance including erosion of tubercles (E), loss of spines and cracks (marked with red arrow) in the dorsal surface of the tegument (E, inset photo) and damage to the sensory papillae in the female tegument (F, inset photo). (G–I) Bergapten-treated parasites displayed a coiled appearance with similar damage to the worm teguments including erosion of tubercles (H) and loss of spines and cracks (marked with red arrow) on the dorsal surface of the tegument (H, inset photo) and damage to the sensory papillae in the female tegument (I, inset photo). Similar patterns but with extensive morphological changes were seen in the praziquantel-treated parasites (J–L). Courtesy: Wangchuk *et al. Sci Rep* 2016;6:32101. Reproduced with permission from Springer Nature.

From these publications, *Schistosoma mansoni* possesses **11,809** and *S. japonicum* possesses **13,469** protein-coding genes. Forty percent of the genome is repetitive. Many protease genes (over 300) are found; over **100** belong to the **cysteine proteases** such as cathepsin B and related enzymes, for feeding and nutrition. A major egg antigen is leucine aminopeptidase (a potential anti-fluke vaccine); a cercarial elastase is active for tissue penetration. The free-living miracidia and cercariae can sense light, temperature and mechanical stimuli, with their receptors, membrane channels, transducins and other gene products. Components to recognize the sensation for salty, sour, sweet and umami tastes are also found in the blood fluke genome.

One outstanding feature is the discovery of 14 families of micro-exon genes (**MEGs**, family members vary from a single member to one with 23 members). "*S. mansoni* is notable in containing micro-exon genes (MEGs) that comprise 75% of the coding sequence, are flanked at the 5′ and 3′ extremes by conventional exons, and have lengths that are multiples of three bases (from 6 to 36)" (Berriman *et al.* 2009). MEGs allow the creation of protein variants via alternate RNA splicing; their transcripts are restricted to epithelia and glands (especially esophagus) that face the external environment, for the secretion of polypeptides to aid blood digestion (as shown in *S. japonicum*, Li *et al.* 2018). It must be noted that MEGs′ "ability to generate variant proteins could represent a significant obstacle to vaccine development" (DeMarco *et al.* 2020).

The blood fluke has **16** chromosomes: seven pairs of autosomes, and one pair of sex chromosomes. Schistosomes are dioecious. Females are the heterogametic sex (**ZW**), and males are homogametic (**ZZ**), i.e., dioecious but different from humans (females XX and males XY). Schistosomes exploit host nutrients and neuroendocrine hormones for growth, development and maturation. They cannot synthesize free fatty acids or sterols; these lipids are taken from the host. An improved genome of *S. mansoni* was published 3 years later (Protasio *et al.* 2012). The modified version has shown the blood fluke with a decreased total gene number: **10,852**. Interestingly, **11%** of the genes were found to demonstrate trans-splicing. Comparing cDNA sequencing (RNA-seq) from developmental stages (cercariae, 3 hours schistosomula, 24 hours schistosomula, and adults) show differences in transcriptomics. The genome of *S. haematobium* was published in the same year (Young *et al.* 2012). It possesses **13,073** protein-coding genes. There are excretory/secretory (**E/S**) proteins, similar to those of *S. mansoni*, as well as differences in transcription between male and female worms (musculature building in the male; nutrient and egg production in the female). Detailed transcriptomic analysis for male and female pairing and sexual maturation has shown the male produces biogenic amines such as dopamine and serotonin (by the enzyme aromatic L-amino acid decarboxylase, AADC) and the females possess allatostatin A receptor, for a type of hormonal regulation seen in insects and crustaceans (Wang *et al.* 2017).

A surprise finding came with the genome of the bovine blood fluke (Oey *et al.* 2019). The sequences of ***Schistosoma bovis*** (with 11,631 protein-coding genes) and *S. haematobium* are strikingly similar, at **97%** sequence identity. They share 98% of protein-coding genes, with an average sequence identity of 97.3% at the amino acid level. Such similarities allow **inter-species hybridization** between the ruminant and human pathogens and urge the consideration of zoonotic transmission. "The propensity for introgressive hybridization between the large number of animal and human schistosome species, is a future concern for schistosome adaptability" (Wilson 2020).

Current updates of the schistosome genome are available. With the retirement of the SchistoDB (Zerlotini *et al.* 2013), genomes are available in the WormBase ParaSite.[2] Genome analysis allows selection of potential drug targets. The schistosome voltage-gated calcium channel consists of four alpha and two beta subunits; a beta subunit has been implicated as the molecular target of praziquantel (PZQ). As the control of neglected tropical diseases (NTDs) depends on drug discovery from piggyback/tagalong or drug-repositioning, approved drugs were checked to target schistosome proteins. One example of a potential drug is disulfiram, currently for treatment of substance abuse and chronic alcoholism. Its molecular target is aldehyde dehydrogenase.

Proteomics accompanies genomics. One example is the proteomics and deep sequencing analysis of extracellular vesicles (**EV**) isolated from male and female adult worms of *S. japonicum* (Du *et al.* 2020). Data by shotgun liquid chromatography-tandem mass spectrometry (LC-MS/MS) identified a total of 558 proteins from male EVs and 894 proteins from female EVs (with 200 overlaps). EV marker proteins include actin, tubulin, heat shock protein (HSP) 70, glyceraldehyde 3-phosphate dehydrogenase (GAPDH), annexin, aldolase, and lactate dehydrogenase. RNA-sequencing analysis of a small RNA population associated with EVs identified 18 micro RNAs (miRNAs) enriched in male and female EVs. Among these, *miR-750* was specifically enriched in female EVs. Its inhibition by a miRNA inhibitor led to decreased egg production in female schistosomes cultured in vitro. Therefore, *miR-750* within female EV cargo may be involved in regulating ovary development and egg production in *S. japonicum* females (Du *et al.* 2020).

The schistosome genome allows cloning and expression of individual genes for functional analysis. One example is the structural, functional investigation of *Schistosoma mansoni* immunomodulatory molecule Sm16/SPO-1/SmSLP, a member of the trematode-specific helminth defense molecules (**HDMs**) (Shiels *et al.* 2020). Recombinant Sm16 was produced in *Pichia pastoris* as well as anti-Sm16 polyclonal antibodies by SM16 peptide-immunized rabbits. Structural analysis shows Sm16 consists predominantly of an amphipathic alpha-helix. It is highly expressed in the cercariae and eggs but not in adult worms, suggesting the molecule to be of importance not only during skin invasion but also in the pro-inflammatory response to eggs in the liver tissue. Sm16 inhibits TLR-3 and TLR-4 signaling in monocytes and the activation of macrophages in vitro. Analysis of the transcriptome of Sm16-stimulated macrophages in the presence or absence of LPS suggests that it mediates immunomodulatory activity via signaling pathways that are intricately involved in regulating cellular metabolism (fatty acid, cholesterol and glucose homeostasis) and central to inflammatory responses. A related molecule was isolated from the sheep liver fluke *Fasciola hepatica* and named FhHDM-1. It exhibits potent anti-inflammatory properties. FhHDM-1 can suppress leukocyte accumulation and ameliorate inflammatory disease in pre-clinical murine models of type 1 diabetes and multiple sclerosis. Sm16 and

---

[2] https://parasite.wormbase.org/index.html

FhHDM-1 are a family of trematode-specific small molecule HDM immune-modulators with immuno-biotherapeutic potentials (Shiels *et al.* 2020).

The availability of genomes of *Schistosoma* and other flatworms allows gene mining to study the tumor necrosis factor (TNF) receptors in these organisms. The TNF signaling pathway is involved in the regulation of many cellular processes, including apoptosis. Human TNF-α can affect the metabolism of *Schistosoma mansoni*. A total of 31 TNF receptors from 30 platyhelminth species have been identified; each platyhelminth displays a single TNF receptor. These receptors may be able to bind human TNF-α, leading to the hypothesis that an endogenous ligand was substituted by the host ligand in parasitic platyhelminths (host-parasite crosstalk). "The understanding of the molecular mechanism involved in evolutionary adaptation of parasites to the host signals is essential to enhance our knowledge that may help develop new approaches to combat the parasitic diseases" (Bertevello *et al.* 2020).

12.8 *Schistosoma* Stage-Specific Gene Expression and Single Cell Atlas

For *Schistosoma mansoni*, genomics analyses and molecular techniques have been adopted. Developing a functional tool kit for this organism includes the methodology for cell and stem cell biology, as well as functional genetic analysis (RNAi, transfection, and CRISPR) (Anderson and Duraisingh 2020; Anderson and Enabulele 2020). James Collins III (University of Texas Southwestern Medical School at Dallas) and colleagues performed large-scale RNA interference (RNAi) and published a single-cell atlas of *Schistosoma mansoni* (Wang *et al.* 2020; Wendt *et al.* 2020).

A large-scale RNAi study yields functional dissection and reveals novel druggable targets (Wang *et al.* 2020). Please see Figure 12.3 for the screening method. From the genome, appropriate dsRNAs were designed to target a set of genes expressed in adult male worms (enzymes, cell-surface receptors, ion channels for potential druggability). The adult worm pairs were harvested from infected mice; 5 pairs were placed under each RNAi treatment with dsRNA added at days 0, 2, 9, 16, and 23 for a 30-day in vitro experiment for worm morphological changes. The investigators examined 2,216 genes and identified 261 genes affecting parasite survival, tissue integrity, neuromuscular function, and stem cell maintenance. For functional genomics, they discovered a protein kinase pair (named SKT25 and TAO) that are essential for maintaining muscle-specific mRNA transcription. Loss of either one results in worm paralysis and death in the mammalian host. For potential clinical application, they found four Food and Drug Administration (FDA)-approved drugs with potential for drug repurposing to target schistosomiasis: simvastatin (HMG-CoA reductase), ixazomib (proteasome), panobinostat (histone deacetylase), and topotecan (topoisomerase). Thus, RNAi and similar approaches will lead to potential novel therapeutics. For now, the only major drug is PZQ for schistosomiasis.

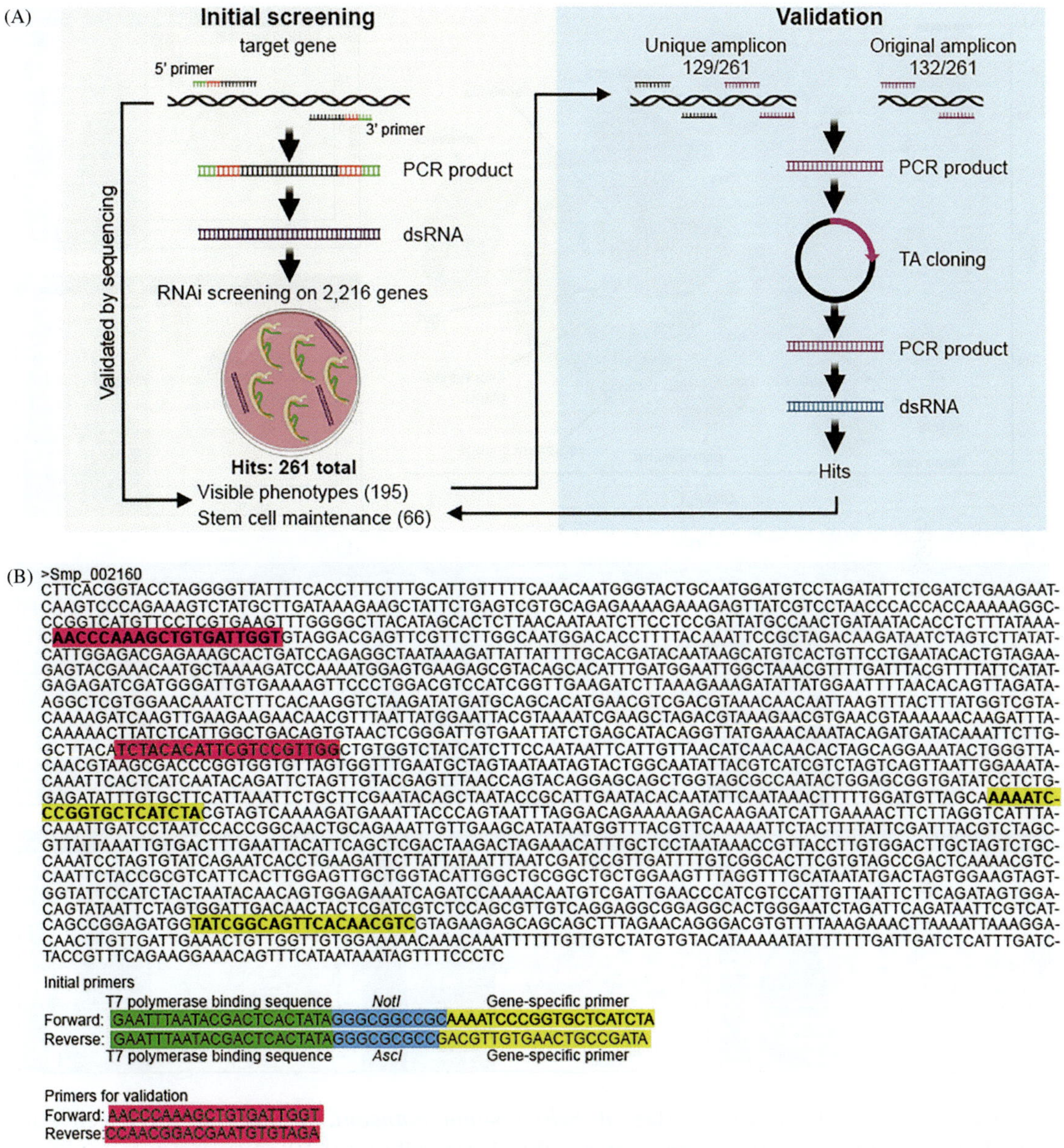

Fig. 12.3 ■ Large RNAi screening of *Schistosoma mansoni*. Large-scale RNAi screening in *S. mansoni*. (A) Pipeline for large-scale RNAi screening. (B) An example of strategy for a single gene from the initial RNAi screen and the subsequent validation. PCR primers for the initial screening were modified by adding sequences including restriction enzyme sites (NotI on forward primer, AscI on reverse primer) and a T7 polymerase promoter on both forward and reverse primers. To validate PCR product sequences we digested with NotI and the amplicon was sequenced with a T7 primer. To validate the initial screening results, in 129 cases we cloned a cDNA fragment that did not overlap with the initial amplicon. In 132 cases we assessed potential off-target effects by BLAST searching against the *S. mansoni* transcriptome. Courtesy: Wang *et al. Science* 2020;369:1649–53. Reproduced with permission from The American Association for the Advancement of Science.

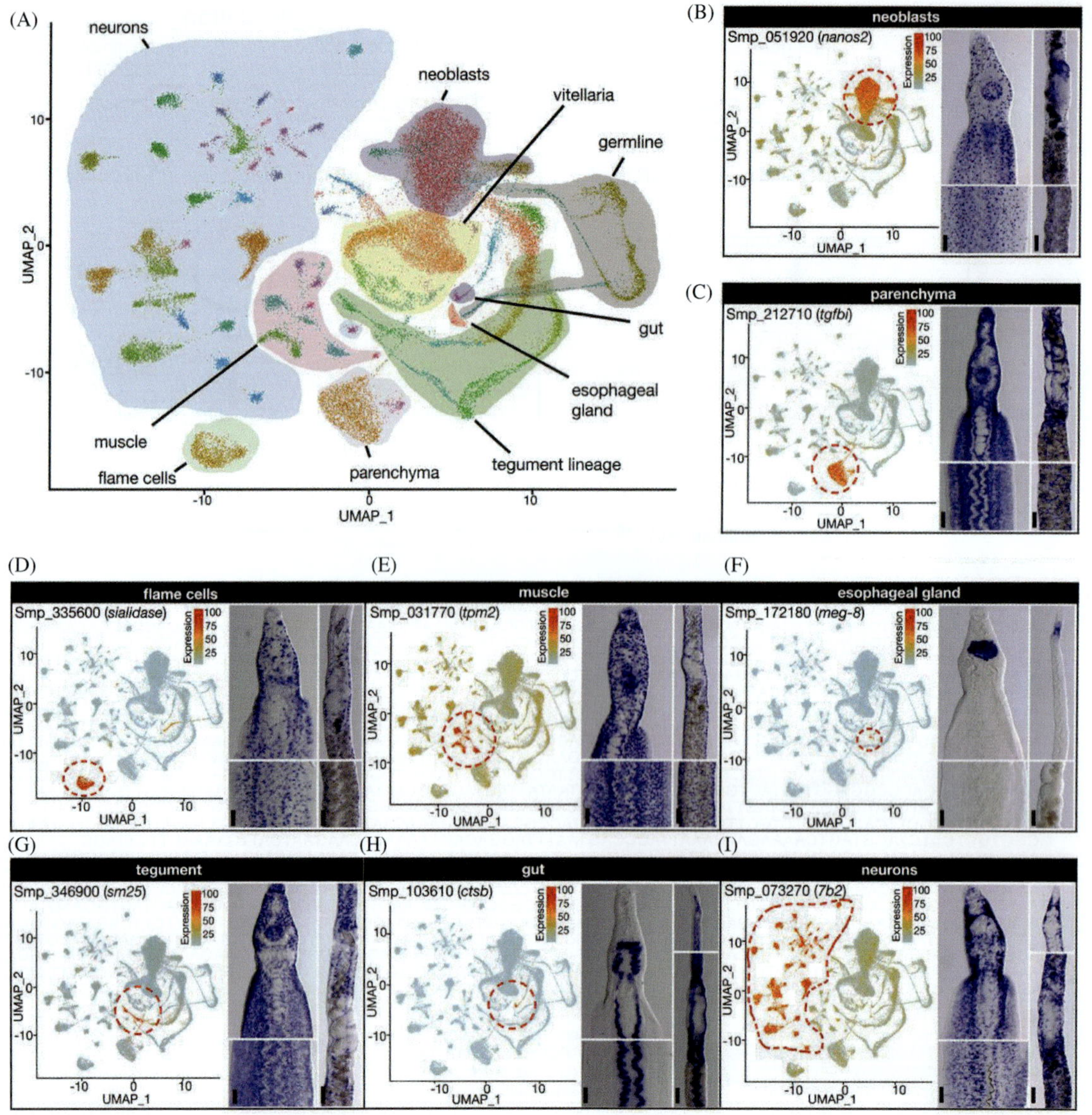

Fig. 12.4 ■ Single-cell RNA-seq atlas of *Schistosoma mansoni*. *S. mansoni* single-cell atlas. (A) UMAP plot of the 68 scRNA-seq clusters. (B to I) UMAP plot (left) and whole-mount in situ hybridization (WISH) of the indicated gene and its expression in the noted tissue in the head (middle, top) and body (middle, bottom) of a male and the ovary (right, top) [(B) to (E) and (G)] or the head (right, top) [(F), (H), and (I)] and vitellaria (right, bottom) of a mature female parasite. Scale bars are 100 μm. UMAP plots are colored by gene expression (blue is low, and red is high). The regions enclosed by red dashed lines indicate the location of the relevant clusters on the UMAP plot. Courtesy: Wendt *et al. Science* 2020;369:1644–9. Reproduced with permission from The American Association for the Advancement of Science.

Molecular insights into the organ systems and potential therapeutic targets may be provided by an analysis of single-cell RNA sequencing. *Schistosoma* cells were isolated from dissociated adult worms (using trypsin/EDTA) and selected with fluorescence-activated cell sorting (FACS) (tagging with the dye Hoechst 33342). FACS-selected cells were used to generate single-cell RNA sequencing (scRNA-seq) libraries (using the chromium controller from 10X Genomics). The investigators characterized a total of 43,642 cells and identified **68** distinct cell populations. Please see Figure 12.4 for *Schistosoma mansoni* **single-cell atlas** (Wendt *et al.* 2020). Among the cell populations are specialized stem cells that maintain the parasite's blood-digesting gut. The gene *hnf4,* coding for a zinc finger transcription factor, is required for gut maintenance, blood-feeding, and pathology in vivo. In an experiment of transplanting control and *hnf4*(RNAi) worms to mice for a 30-day experiment, worm recovery was the same between the two (except the RNAi knock-downed male worms were smaller in size). Interestingly, whereas the control host mice showed egg-induced granuloma in their livers, the experimental mice showed morphologically normal livers. The investigators commented: "These results show that hnf4 is at least indirectly required for parasite growth and egg-induced pathology *in vivo*. Together, these data suggest that hnf4, specifically, and gut homeostasis, generally, are potential therapeutic targets to blunt the pathology caused by adult parasites" (Wendt *et al.* 2020).

12.9 Stem Cells

The free-living flatworm, such as the planarian, is a famous model for studying regeneration by developmental biologists. Stem cells known as neoblasts are responsible for this activity (Reddien 2018). An atlas for the planarian *Schmidtea mediterranea* is available (Fincher *et al.* 2018).

Phillip Newmark (University of Illinois at Urbana-Champaign) and colleagues have found similar neoblast-like cells in *Schistosoma mansoni,* and even heterogeneity among the stem cells of different developmental stages (Collins *et al.* 2013; Wang *et al.* 2018). Adult worms of *S. mansoni* were treated with the thymidine analogue 5-ethynyl-29-deoxyuridine (EdU) to examine the distribution of S phase cells in the parasite and neoblast-like stem cells that were detected. These cells exhibit fibroblast growth factor receptor (SmfgfrA), suggesting fibroblast growth factor (**FGF**) receptor-mediated signaling pathway as essential for stem cell maintenance (Collins *et al.* 2013). It should be emphasized that adult schistosomes have a long lifespan, therefore somatic stem cells are important for repair and maintenance. "Schistosomes are nasty.… And despite aggressive immune responses by the infected host, the pathogens persist for 6–10 years on average, but sometimes for much longer" (Pearce 2013). Adult worms can regenerate damaged tissues after sublethal doses of the anti-schistosomal drug PZQ.

Whereas adult schistosome worms have sexual reproduction in humans, larval stages in the snail intermediate host have asexual reproduction. For survival between such disparate environments, there is remarkable developmental plasticity as manifested by five body plans deployed throughout the parasite's life cycle. The neoblast-like stem cells in *S. mansoni*

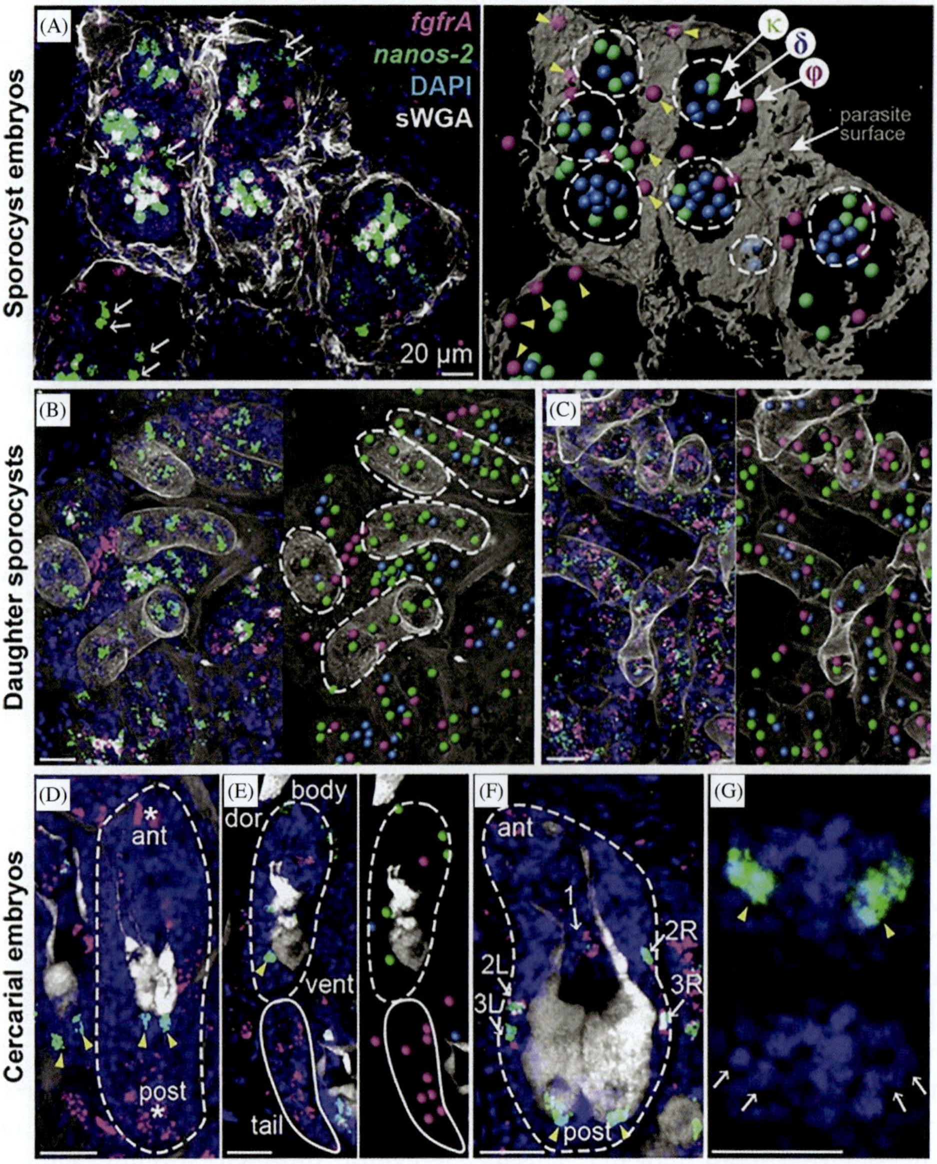

Fig. 12.5 ■ Neoblast-like stem cells in larval stages of *S. mansoni*. Stem cells exhibit class-specific spatial and temporal patterns during intramolluscan development. (A) FISH of *nanos-2* and *fgfrA* reveals spatial distributions of cell classes in a mother sporocyst containing daughter embryos (dashed circles), 10-days post-infection (dpi). sWGA (grey) labels the parasite surface (tegument). Arrows: extraembryonic κ-cells. Right: rendered image of that shown to the left. Spheres: cell centers; yellow arrowheads: φ-cells beneath the surface. (B) Mature daughter sporocysts contained in a mother sporocyst 15 dpi. Dashes outline the body surfaces of daughters. In daughters, κ-cells comprised 522 out of 592 counted stem cells in these daughters, while fewer δ-cells (61/592) and φ-cells (9/592) were observed. (C) Daughter sporocysts in snail ovotestis, 25 dpi. (D) Early cercarial embryo before the tail bud forms. φ-cells were found concentrated both anteriorly and posteriorly, where the mouth and tail bud form; only two κ-cells were detected

provide a source for such plasticity. They are found in different larval stages. Please see Figure 12.5 for neoblast-like stem cells in sample larval stages (sporocysts and cercariae) of *S. mansoni* (Wang *et al.* 2020). Different subsets of larvally derived stem cells are likely sources of adult stem cells and the germline. Thus, there exists stem cell heterogeneity. Please see Figure 12.6 for a model of stem cell hierarchy in *Schistosoma mansoni* (Wang *et al.* 2020).

Expanding from *Schistosoma mansoni*, Bikash Giri (Chinese Academy of Agricultural Sciences, Shanghai) and colleagues have identified orthologs of 11 neoblast-like stem cell transcription factors in *S. japonicum* using bioinformatics and confirmed them by polymerase chain reaction (PCR). In this study, the investigators also detected sex-based expression between male and female worms (Giri *et al.* 2018).

Schistosome stem cells may serve as a novel target of chemotherapy. Josina Kellershohn (Justus Liebig University, Giessen, Germany) and colleagues have shown that the harlequin ladybird beetle-derived compound, **harmonine**, significantly reduced the number of proliferating stem cells in testes, ovaries, reduced the number of proliferating parenchymal neoblasts, accompanying the down-regulated expression of stem cell markers (nanos-1, nanos-2) in harmonine-treated *S. mansoni* adult worms (by quantitative real-time PCR). In addition, harmonine also acted on worm acetylcholinesterase (AChE). Harmonine is the major defense alkaloid of the beetle; and alkaloids are widespread in bacteria, fungi, plants and animals. The investigators concluded with these remarks: "This is the first time to proof a direct effect of a defined insect-derived compound on schistosomes, and harmonine may serve as a basis for the development of new antischistosomal, or even broader antiparasitic compounds. This study highlights the potential of exploiting insects for the discovery of anthelmintics and motivates the screening of insect compound libraries for novel anthelmintic compounds in the future" (Kellershohn *et al.* 2019).

12.10 Vaccine

Vaccines would be ideal, and several are in progress. From the genome, leucine aminopeptidase (**LAP**) is found to be the major egg antigen. Previously, a recombinant sapo-

---

Fig. 12.5 (figure on facing page) ■ posterior to the two penetration glands. (E) Later development during cercarial embryogenesis. φ-cells were mostly located in the tails; the κ-cell pair were posterior to the glands. (F) Mature cercarial body in daughter sporocysts 30 dpi (dorsal view). 1: anterior midline cell; 2L, 2R: anterior lateral cells; 3L, 3R: posterior lateral cells. Arrowheads: κ-cells, asterisks: ϕ-cells, arrows: δ-cells. sWGA: penetration glands. Note that only the cercarial body is transmitted to the mammalian host, whereas tails are discarded outside of the host epidermis during penetration. (G) κ-cell clusters, magnified from (F), contain multiple cells each (single confocal section). Arrows: individual nuclei in κ-cell clusters. Scale bars: 20 μm. All images are maximum intensity projections from 30 μm tissue cryosections. Since animals are thicker than the sections, parasite surface and penetration glands were used to determine the orientation and position of the sections. Courtesy: Wang *et al. Elife* 2018;7:e35449. Reproduced with permission from *Elife* with Creative Commons Attribution 4.0 (CC-BY) International License.

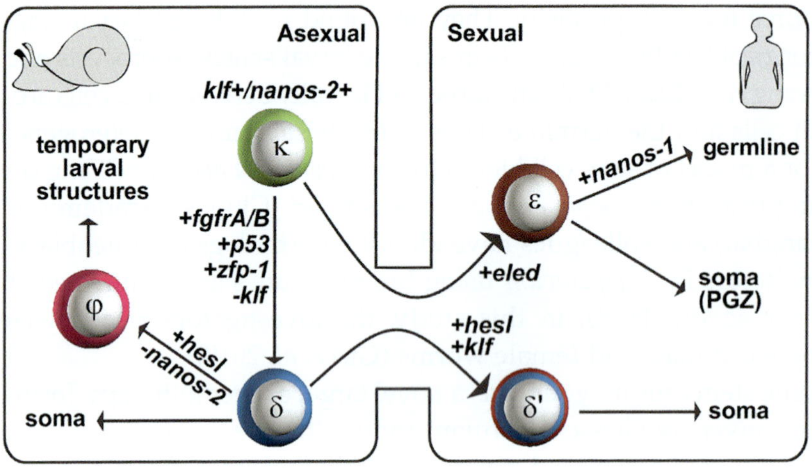

Fig. 12.6 ■ A model of stem cell heterogeneity of *Schistosoma mansoni*. A proposed model for the schistosome stem cell classes. κ-cells are at the top of the hierarchy, and express *nanos-2* and *klf*. Activation of several genes associated with somatic stem cell function in adults (*fgfrA/B; p53; zfp-1*) leads to the specification of δ-cells, which we propose serve to generate somatic tissues. Downregulation of *nanos-2* and activation of *hesl* in δ-cells leads to the formation of φ-cells, which are associated with many transitory larval structures, including the sporocyst epidermis (tegument) and the cercarial tail. Only a small number of κ and δ-cells is transmitted from the asexual to the sexual life-cycle stages. After entry into the mammalian host, activation of *hesl* in δ-cells leads to δ'-cells, which appear to serve as the source of the adult somatic stem cells. κ-cells downregulate *nanos-2* and activate expression of an intra-mammalian stage-specific transcript, *eled*, generating ε-cells, which are distributed in gonadal primordia and the posterior growth zone. During maturation, gonadal ε-cells subsequently activate germline-specific *nanos-1*, which commits ε-cells to germline fate. Courtesy: Wang *et al. Elife* 2018;7:e35449. Reproduced with permission from *Elife* with Creative Commons Attribution 4.0 (CC-BY) International License.

nin-like protein has been shown to work in rabbit models. Glutathione S-transferase (**GST**) is another potential vaccine, it differs from the human version and shows effect in experimental studies. Other targets include *S. mansoni* tegument apical membrane proteins, tetraspanin, cathepsin B, and *S. japonicum* paramyosin, triosephosphate isomerase, fatty acid-binding protein and thyroid hormone receptor (Tebeje *et al.* 2016). Phases I and II clinical trials for 3 *S. mansoni* proteins are ongoing or will start soon: calpain, fatty acid-binding protein, tetraspanin (Hotez *et al.* 2019). In addition, alternative approaches are available, such as irradiated cercariae.

12.11 Vector Control

Fresh-water snails can be controlled using molluscicide. One such compound is niclosamide, developed by Bayer (known as Bayluscide) in the 1960s. However, it may harm fish and other organisms. WHO has a field guide for its use: "Field use of molluscicides in schistosomiasis control programmes: an operational manual for programme managers" by WHO/Department of Control of Neglected Tropical Diseases[3] [We shall return to niclosamide when discussing tapeworms and human cancer.]

Biological controls include the introduction of snail-eating snails, crayfish and fish. Furthermore, there is ongoing interest in the use of phytochemicals (such as *Euphorbia milii* latex) to control aquatic snails (de Carvalho Augusto and Mello Silva 2018).

Snail control can complement preventive chemotherapy (PC) by reducing the risk of transmission from snails to humans. For reducing the global burden of schistosomiasis, it is time to bring back the "Old Fashioned" snail control, but with added features. Ideas for modernizing and scaling up snail control include spatiotemporal targeting, environmental diagnostics, better molluscicides, new technologies (e.g., gene drive), and "outside the box" strategies such as natural enemies, traps, and repellants (Sokolow *et al.* 2018).

Summary & Key Concepts

- Schistosomiasis is an important neglected tropical disease (NTD) with high prevalence in Africa, Asia and South America.
- The major blood fluke trematode species are *Schistosoma haematobium*, *S. japonicum* and *S. mansoni.*
- The intermediate host is the fresh-water snails; different snail species are hosts to different fluke species.
- There are 3 phases involved in the pathology of schistosomiasis: asymptomatic migratory phase, Katayama fever acute phase, and granuloma build-up chronic phase.
- *S. haematobium* infection is a risk factor for bladder cancer.
- Neoblast-like stem cells are present in the schistosomes.
- Praziquantel is the drug of choice for schistosomiasis.
- Metrifonae and oxamniquine also target *S. haematobium* and *S. mansoni*, respectively.
- Single-cell RNA-seq atlas for *Schistosoma mansoni* has been constructed.

References

Anderson TJC, Duraisingh MT. Transformative tools for parasitic flatworms. *Science* 2020;369(6511):1562–4.

Anderson TJC, Enabulele EE. *Schistosoma mansoni. Trends Parasitol* 2020;S1471–4922(20):30164–71.

Bergquist NR. Schistosomiasis consortium for operational research and evaluation: Mission accomplished. *Am J Trop Med Hyg* 2020;103(1_Suppl):1–4.

[3] https://apps.who.int/iris/bitstream/handle/10665/254641/9789241511995-eng.pdf;jsessionid=FEA4FB2CFA5D3285F7A30342D7FC3580?sequence=1

Berriman M, Haas BJ, LoVerde PT, *et al.* The genome of the blood fluke *Schistosoma mansoni*. *Nature* 2009;460(7253):352–8.

Bertevello CR, Russo BRA, Tahira AC, Lopes-Junior EH, DeMarco R, Oliveira KC. The evolution of TNF signaling in platyhelminths suggests the cooptation of TNF receptor in the host-parasite interplay. *Parasit Vectors* 2020;13(1):491.

Binder S, Campbell CH, Andros TS, *et al.* The schistosomiasis consortium for perational research and evaluation 2008–2020: Approaches, experiences, lessons, and recommendations. *Am J Trop Med Hyg* 2020;103(1_Suppl):114–24.

Brown HW, Neva FA. *Basic Clinical Parasitology*, 5th edition (1983, Appleton-Century-Croft, Norwalk, Connecticut).

Chan MM, Evans KW, Moore AR, Fong D. Peroxisome proliferator-activated receptor (PPAR): Balance for survival in parasitic infections. *J Biomed Biotechnol* 2010;2010:828951.

Chen C, Guo Q, Fu Z, *et al.* Reviews and advances in diagnostic research on *Schistosoma japonicum*. *Acta Trop* 2021;213:105743.

Chevalier FD, Le Clec'h W, McDew-White M, *et al.* Oxamniquine resistance alleles are widespread in Old World *Schistosoma mansoni* and predate drug deployment. *PLoS Pathog* 2019;15(10):e1007881.

Cioli D, Pica-Mattoccia L, Archer S. Antischistosomal drugs: past, present ... and future? *Pharmacol Ther* 1995;68(1):35–85.

Colley DG, Jacobson JA, Binder S. Schistosomiasis consortium for operational research and evaluation (SCORE): Its foundations, development, and evolution. *Am J Trop Med Hyg* 2020;103 (1_Suppl):5–13.

Colley DG, Bustinduy AL, Secor WE, King CH. Human schistosomiasis. *Lancet* 2014;383(9936): 2253–64.

Collins JJ 3rd, Wang B, Lambrus BG, Tharp ME, Iyer H, Newmark PA. Adult somatic stem cells in the human parasite *Schistosoma mansoni*. *Nature* 2013;494(7438):476–9.

Cox FEG, editor. *The Wellcome Trust Illustrated History of Tropical Diseases* (1996, The Wellcome Trust, London).

de Carvalho Augusto R, Mello Silva CC. Phytochemical molluscicides and schistosomiasis: What we Know and what we still need to learn. *Vet Sci* 2018;5(4):E94.

DeMarco R, Mathieson W, Manuel SJ, *et al.* Protein variation in blood-dwelling schistosome worms generated by differential splicing of micro-exon gene transcripts. *Genome Res* 2010;20(8):1112–21.

Depaquit J, Akhoundi M, Haouchine D, Mantelet S, Izri A. No limit in interspecific hybridization in schistosomes: observation from a case report. *Parasite* 2019;26:10.

Di Bella S, Riccardi N, Giacobbe DR, Luzzati R. History of schistosomiasis (bilharziasis) in humans: from Egyptian medical papyri to molecular biology on mummies. *Pathog Glob Health* 2018;112(5):268–73.

Du P, Giri BR, Liu J, Xia T, Grevelding CG, Cheng G. Proteomic and deep sequencing analysis of extracellular vesicles isolated from adult male and female *Schistosoma japonicum*. *PLoS Negl Trop Dis* 2020;14(9):e0008618.

Esch GW. *Parasites and Infectious Diseases: Discoveries by Serendipity, and Otherwise* (2007, Cambridge).

Fenwick A. Schistosomiasis research and control since the retirement of Sir Patrick Manson in 1914. *Trans R Soc Trop Med Hyg* 2017;111(5):191–8.

Fincher CT, Wurtzel O, de Hoog T, Kravarik KM, Reddien PW. Cell type transcriptome atlas for the planarian *Schmidtea mediterranea*. *Science* 2018;360(6391):eaaq1736.

Furch BD, Koethe JR, Kayamba V, Heimburger DC, Kelly P. Interactions of *Schistosoma* and HIV in sub-Saharan Africa: A systematic review. *Am J Trop Med Hyg* 2020;102(4):711–8.

Giri BR, Li H, Chen Y, *et al.* Preliminary evaluation of neoblast-like stem cell factor and transcript expression profiles in *Schistosoma japonicum*. *Acta Trop* 2018;187:57–64.

Hotez P. *Forgotten People, Forgotten Diseases: The Neglected Tropical Diseases and their Impact on Global Health and Development*, 2nd edition (2013, ASM Press).

Hotez PJ, Bottazzi ME, Bethony J, Diemert DD. Advancing the development of a human schistosomiasis vaccine. *Trends Parasitol* 2019;35(2):104–8.

Hulse EV. Joshua's curse and the abandonment of ancient Jericho: Schistosomiasis as a possible medical explanation. *Med Hist* 1971;15(4):376–86.

Kean BH, Mott KE, Russell AJ, editors. *Tropical Medicine and Parasitology. Classic Investigations*, Volume I and II (1978, Cornell, Ithaca).

Kellershohn J, Thomas L, Hahnel SR, *et al.* Insects in anthelminthics research: Lady beetle-derived harmonine affects survival, reproduction and stem cell proliferation of *Schistosoma mansoni*. *PLoS Negl Trop Dis* 2019;13(3):e0007240.

Li F, Ma S, Li Y, *et al.* Impact of the Three Gorges project on ecological environment changes and snail distribution in Dongting Lake area. *PLoS Negl Trop Dis* 2017;11(7):e0005661.

Li XH, DeMarco R, Neves LX, *et al.* Microexon gene transcriptional profiles and evolution provide insights into blood processing by the *Schistosoma japonicum* esophagus. *PLoS Negl Trop Dis* 2018;12(2):e0006235.

Limpanont Y, Phuphisut O, Reamtong O, *et al.* Recent advances in *Schistosoma mekongi* ecology, transcriptomics and proteomics of relevance to snail control. *Acta Trop* 2020;202:105244.

Mehlhorn H. *Human Parasites: Diagnosis, Treatment, Prevention* (2016, Springer).

Mutapi F, Maizels R, Fenwick A, Woolhouse M. Human schistosomiasis in the post mass drug administration era. *Lancet Infect Dis* 2017;17(2):e42–8.

Neves PD, Bridi RA, Ramalho JA, *et al.* *Schistosoma mansoni* infection as a trigger to collapsing glomerulopathy in a patient with high-risk APOL1 genotype. *PLoS Negl Trop Dis* 2020;14(10):e0008582.

Oey H, Zakrzewski M, Gravermann K, *et al.* Whole-genome sequence of the bovine blood fluke *Schistosoma bovis* supports interspecific hybridization with *S. haematobium*. *PLoS Pathog* 2019;15(1):e1007513.

Othman AA, Soliman RH. Schistosomiasis in Egypt: A never-ending story? *Acta Trop* 2015;148: 179–90.

Pearce EJ. Parasitology: Rejuvenation through stem cells. *Nature* 2013;494(7438):438–9.

Pillay P, Downs JA, Changalucha JM, *et al.* Detection of *Schistosoma* DNA in genital specimens and urine: A comparison between five female African study populations originating from *S. haematobium* and/or *S. mansoni* endemic areas. *Acta Trop* 2020;204:105363.

Protasio AV, Tsai IJ, Babbage A, *et al.* A systematically improved high quality genome and transcriptome of the human blood fluke *Schistosoma mansoni*. *PLoS Negl Trop Dis* 2012;6(1):e1455.

Reddien PW. The cellular and molecular basis for planarian regeneration. *Cell* 2018;175(2):327–45.

Rugel AR, Guzman MA, Taylor AB, *et al.* Why does oxamniquine kill *Schistosoma mansoni* and not *S. haematobium* and *S. japonicum*? *Int J Parasitol Drugs Drug Resist* 2020;13:8–15.

Shen J, Yuan L, Sun Y, *et al.* Case report: Multiple schistosomiasis japonica cerebral granulomas without gastrointestinal system involvement: Report of two cases and review of literature. *Am J Trop Med Hyg* 2020;102(6):1376–81.

Shiels J, Cwiklinski K, Alvarado R, *et al.* *Schistosoma mansoni* immunomodulatory molecule Sm16/SPO-1/SmSLP is a member of the trematode-specific helminth defence molecules (HDMs). *PLoS Negl Trop Dis* 2020;14(7):e0008470.

Sokolow SH, Jones IJ, Jocque M, *et al.* Nearly 400 million people are at higher risk of schistosomiasis because dams block the migration of snail-eating river prawns. *Philos Trans R Soc Lond B Biol Sci.* 2017; 372(1722):20160127.

Sokolow SH, Wood CL, Jones IJ, *et al.* To reduce the global burden of human schistosomiasis, use 'old fashioned' snail control. *Trends Parasitol* 2018;34(1):23–40.

Sturt AS, Webb EL, Francis SC, Hayes RJ, Bustinduy AL. Beyond the barrier: Female Genital Schistosomiasis as a potential risk factor for HIV-1 acquisition. *Acta Trop* 2020;209:105524.

Tebeje BM, Harvie M, You H, Loukas A, McManus DP. Schistosomiasis vaccines: Where do we stand? *Parasit Vectors* 2016;9(1):528.

The *Schistosoma japonicum* genome sequencing and functional analysis consortium the *Schistosoma japonicum* genome reveals features of host-parasite interplay. *Nature* 2009;460(7253):345–51.

Utzinger J, Becker SL, van Lieshout L, van Dam GJ, Knopp S. New diagnostic tools in schistosomiasis. *Clin Microbiol Infect* 2015;21(6):529–42.

Vale N, Gouveia MJ, Rinaldi G, *et al.* Praziquantel for schistosomiasis: Single-drug metabolism revisited, mode of action, and resistance. *Antimicrob Agents Chemother* 2017;61(5):e02582-16.

Wang B, Lee J, Li P, *et al.* Stem cell heterogeneity drives the parasitic life cycle of *Schistosoma mansoni. Elife* 2018;7:e35449.

Wang J, Paz C, Padalino G, *et al.* Large-scale RNAi screening uncovers therapeutic targets in the parasite *Schistosoma mansoni. Science* 2020;369(6511):1649–53.

Wang J, Yu Y, Shen H, *et al.* Dynamic transcriptomes identify biogenic amines and insect-like hormonal regulation for mediating reproduction in *Schistosoma japonicum. Nat Commun* 2017;8:14693.

Wangchuk P, Giacomin PR, Pearson MS, Smout MJ, Loukas A. Identification of lead chemotherapeutic agents from medicinal plants against blood flukes and whipworms. *Sci Rep* 2016;6:32101.

Webster BL, Southgate VR, Littlewood DT. A revision of the interrelationships of *Schistosoma* including the recently described *Schistosoma guineensis. Int J Parasitol* 2006;36(8):947–55.

Wendt G, Zhao L, Chen R, *et al.* A single-cell RNA-seq atlas of *Schistosoma mansoni* identifies a key regulator of blood feeding. *Science* 2020;369(6511):1644–9.

Wilson RA. Schistosomiasis then and now: what has changed in the last 100 years? *Parasitology* 2020;147(5):507–15.

Young ND, Jex AR, Li B, *et al.* Whole-genome sequence of *Schistosoma haematobium. Nat Genet* 2012;44(2):221–5.

Zerlotini A, Aguiar ER, Yu F, *et al.* SchistoDB: an updated genome resource for the three key schistosomes of humans. *Nucleic Acids Res* 2013;41(Database issue):D728–31.

13

Fascioliasis, Clonorchiasis, Opisthorchiasis and Paragonimiasis by Other Flukes

13.1 Introductory Remarks

Foodborne trematodiases are a group of neglected tropical diseases (NTDs), caused by the ingestion of parasitic flukes. These are zoonoses because the final definitive hosts are not humans. The natural final hosts of *Fasciola* are sheep, cattle, and other herbivores after eating contaminated aquatic vegetation. Fish-eating carnivores including cats and dogs are hosts of *Clonorchis* and *Opisthorchis*. The primary organ affected by these trematodes is the liver. Crustacean-eating carnivores, also including cats and dogs, are host to *Paragonimus*. The primary organ affected is the lung. Human consumption of fluke-contaminated vegetables may lead to fascioliasis, fluke-infected fish can lead to clonorchiasis or opisthorchiasis, and fluke-infected crustaceans (crabs and crayfish) can result in paragonimiasis.

Foodborne trematodes are hermaphrodites. They use various species of snails as intermediate hosts. It has been noted that trematodes are very successful parasites. They will invade many vertebrate species and, for each species, multiple organs can be sites for the parasites' residences. For each species, there is the migratory route within the host to reach the parasite's final destination. Parasites may use immunosuppression to combat host immunity, including their excretory/secretory (E/S) products for host-parasite interactions.

Fascioliasis is also an infection of veterinary significance for its effect on sheep and cattle, and their human handlers (occupational hazard). Clonorchiasis, opisthorchiasis, and paragonimiasis are effects of contaminated food. "The foodborne trematodiases refer to a cluster of zoonotic NTDs caused by trematodes, with transmission involving ingestion of contaminated plants, fishes, and crustaceans. Over **40 million** people are infected with foodborne trematodes and 750 million are at risk of infection" (Vale *et al.* 2020). One estimate for annual foodborne trematodiases is 200,000 new cases with over 7,000 deaths globally. For distribution, fascioliasis is a global disease; clonorchiasis and opisthorchiasis are restricted to Asia; paragonimiasis is seen in Asia, Africa and Latin America. There is a WHO foodborne trematodes website.[1]

13.2 *Fasciola*

Fasciola hepatica is the **sheep liver fluke**. Global estimation is around **17 million** individuals infected worldwide. Fascioliasis has been reported in over 50 countries. The intensity of human infection is always associated with animal husbandry (Mas-Coma *et al.* 2018). The sheep liver fluke is of veterinary importance; it is estimated that the global economic loss is in excess of US $3 billion annually. Human activities such as irrigation system management have a great impact on the transmission of fascioliasis as an emerging or reemerging disease in some regions (Sabourin *et al.* 2018).

13.2.1 History

Fasciola has a long history, probably due to its large size and its familiarity to sheep farmers (Kean *et al.* 1978). Its name, *Fasciola hepatica* (fasciola means small bandage, tape, hepatica means liver), was coined by Linnaeus in 1758, although he thought the worm to be a leech. Even before Linnaeus, the French monarch Charles V commissioned his best breeder to write a treatise on proper sheep management and wool production. So, in 1379, Jean de Brie described sheep liver rot; he was aware of the parasite in sheep liver which he described as "la dauve" (flounder/flatfish). "The good shepherd should be extremely careful in the months of March not to lead his animals to pasture in marsh regions. ... For there grows a very dangerous herb with a small round green leaf that is called la dauve... as soon as the sheep have tasted it and swallowed it ... la dauve ... adheres to and lives in the liver of the sheep ... The malady of la dauve can remain hidden for a year or more, but finally the sheep dies because la dauve destroyed the liver." (Kean *et al.* 1978) This first account suggests that *Fasciola* was familiar to shepherds, as large flatworms in the liver, and contaminated vegetation such as watercress were involved.

The discovery of the intermediate host is a fascinating story about competition between a young and an established scientist. The snail as an intermediate host was published in 1881, independently, by Algeron Phillips Thomas in Britain and Rudolf Leuckart in Germany. As a young demonstrator (lecturer) at Oxford, Thomas was awarded a grant from the Royal Society of Agriculture to study sheep liver rot, which was common in Britain at the time. His mentor, the professor of anatomy and physiology George Rolleston, suggested looking at slug as a possible host. The 23-year-old found snail

[1] https://www.who.int/foodborne_trematode_infections/en/

(today's genus *Lymnaea*) as the immediate host. Thomas was aware of Leuckart; he wrote: "The number of eggs produced by a single fluke is exceedingly large, and its fecundity has been under-rated. Leuckart has estimated that the oviduct can contain as many as 45,000 eggs. In one case I obtained 7,400,000 eggs from the gallbladder of a sheep suffering from the rot, and as the liver contained about 200 flukes, this gives these eggs an average of 37,000 to each fluke, and these eggs were found in the gallbladder alone; the liver must have contained at least as many more, and eggs have been passed copiously by the sheep for some months past. The number of eggs produced by a single fluke may be safely estimated at several hundred thousands." Unknown to Thomas, the eminent German parasitologist Rudolf Leuckart had found the same snail species and published 10 days before Thomas. Later, Thomas emigrated to New Zealand and led a successful career as a professor of biology and geology, and was also knighted for his educator role. Today, credit for discovering the snail as an intermediate host goes to both scientists. Sheep liver fluke has a worldwide distribution, and about 20 snail species are hosts in different places around the globe. This discovery is the beginning of the search for hosts of many other parasites. For fascioliasis, there was another finding. In 1892, Adolfo Lutz, a Brazilian medical doctor working at the Lepers' Hospital in Hawaii, found that ruminants got infected after eating vegetation containing encysted larvae, the metacercaria. He demonstrated infection using guinea pigs as his experimental animal. Studies of coprolites (fossil feces) have shown *Fasciola* was associated with humans for over 5,000 years in Europe (Kean *et al.* 1978).

13.2.2 Life cycle

Please see Figure 13.1 for the life cycle of *Fasciola hepatica*, from CDC.[2]

For fascioliasis, in addition to the trematode species *Fasciola hepatica* (common liver fluke/sheep liver fluke), there is another species *Fasciola gigantica* (large liver fluke). Adult sizes are: for *F. hepatica*, up to 30 mm by 15 mm; *F. gigantica*, up to 75 mm by 15 mm. It starts with fertilized, unembryonated eggs. The immature eggs need time to mature, to become embryonated in water (9–15 days). The miracidium has eyespots for positive phototaxis; it needs to find a snail host within 8 hours as it is non-feeding. Within the snail, there is asexual maturation into sporocyst, and redia 1 and 2 (two generations), followed by cercaria, which has a tail twice as long as its body. The cercaria finds a water plant and becomes the encysted metacercaria which waits for herbivore grazing. In humans, it takes 3–4 months for maturation to adults. There is a dramatic size increase from newly excysted juvenile (NEJ) to adult, 1,000-fold over 12 weeks. Adult liver fluke can survive for 11 years. Adult liver flukes secrete the amino acid proline, which stimulates the bile epithelial cells to divide, so the parasite farms its own food supply, making a cell lawn for grazing.

[2] https://www.cdc.gov/dpdx/fascioliasis/index.html

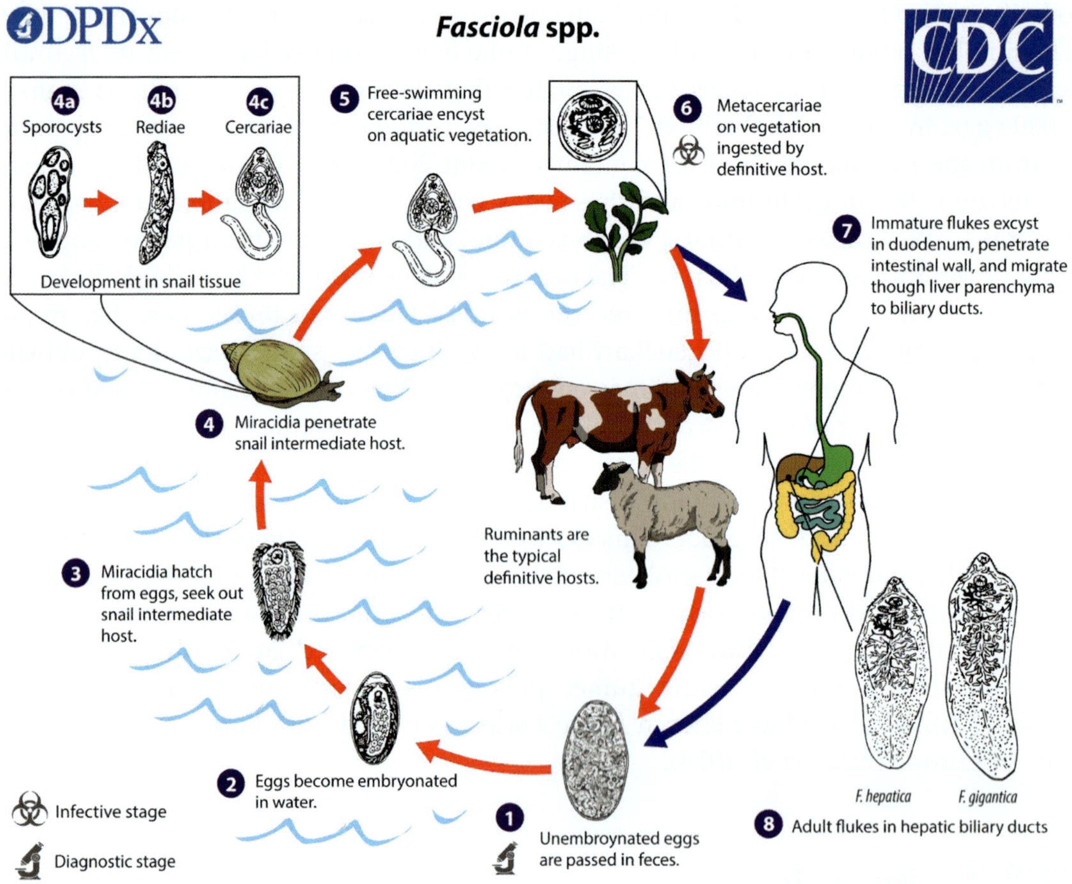

Fig. 13.1 ■ Life cycle of *Fasciola hepatica*. Immature eggs are discharged in the biliary ducts and passed in the stool ❶. Eggs become embryonated in freshwater over ~2 weeks ❷; embryonated eggs release miracidia ❸, which invade a suitable snail intermediate host ❹. In the snail, the parasites undergo several developmental stages (sporocysts 4a, rediae 4b, and cercariae 4c). The cercariae are released from the snail ❺ and encyst as metacercariae on aquatic vegetation or other substrates. Humans and other mammals become infected by ingesting metacercariae-contaminated vegetation (e.g., watercress) ❻. After ingestion, the metacercariae excyst in the duodenum ❼ and penetrate through the intestinal wall into the peritoneal cavity. The immature flukes then migrate through the liver parenchyma into biliary ducts, where they mature into adult flukes and produce eggs ❽. In humans, maturation from metacercariae into adult flukes usually takes about 3–4 months; development of *F. gigantica* may take somewhat longer than *F. hepatica*. Courtesy of the CDC. Reproduced from https://www.cdc.gov/dpdx/fascioliasis/index.html

13.2.3 Pathology

There are acute and chronic phases. After ingestion, the migration route is from the intestine to the liver parenchyma. Migrating metacercariae track through the liver, causing necrosis and fibrosis. The process leads to eosinophilia, allergic reactions, and tissue destruction.

Only a small number reaches the biliary tree and develops to sexual maturity. In the chronic phase, there can be inflammation and obstruction of the bile ducts and gallbladder.

In the Middle East and other regions, eating infected sheep liver raw/uncooked makes the adult flukes stay in the pharynx. The disease is known as halzoun, with coughing and hoarse voices. Another symptom is known as pseudofascioliasis (false fascioliasis), the presence of eggs in stools resulting from recent ingestion of infected liver containing liver fluke eggs.

The first molecular diagnosis of liver abscesses due to *Fasciola hepatica* acute infection imported from Vietnam to France has been documented (L'Ollivier *et al.* 2020). A 67-year-old female patient living in southeastern France was hospitalized in June 2018 after returning from her latest trip to Vietnam. She was born in Vietnam and would return home every 3 years to visit family over a 3-month period. She had fever, right abdominal pain, and major eosinophilia. Radiology showed multiple abscesses in the right lobe of her liver, and occlusive thrombosis of the right branch of the portal vein. Serology showed response to *Fasciola hepatica*; definitive diagnosis was established by polymerase chain reaction (PCR) and sequencing of *F. hepatica* ITS1 (internal transcribed spacer 1) region of the rRNA gene on her stool sample. The patient was successfully treated with rivaroxaban and triclabendazole.

Disseminated fascioliasis infection typically results in hepatobiliary disease, but extrahepatic manifestations are occasionally seen. A case report described a previously healthy 31-year-old Kurdish woman, from northern Iraq but migrated to Birmingham, UK and was admitted to hospital with a subarachnoid hemorrhage, eosinophilic meningitis, and lung and liver disease. A diagnosis of *Fasciola* infection was made based on strongly positive serology in blood and cerebrospinal fluid and the patient improved following treatment with triclabendazole and prednisolone (Hughes *et al.* 2020).

13.2.4 Diagnosis

Eggs can be detected in the feces, bile aspirates, or duodenal aspirates. These immature eggs are operculated (each egg possesses an operculum). An apopercular knob may also be seen (at the opposite end of the operculum). Imaging techniques (such as ultrasonography and CT) are also helpful in the diagnosis of fascioliasis.

13.2.5 Therapy

Fascioliasis is not responsive to praziquantel. **Triclabendazole** is the drug of choice for the treatment of infection with *Fasciola hepatica*. Its mechanism is targeting the tubulin and microtubule function (Gandhi *et al.* 2019). Triclabendazole has also been used in veterinary medicine; cases of drug resistance have been reported. Another drug is **bithionol**; its mechanism is possibly on oxidative phosphorylation and ATP production.

13.2.6 Genome

The genome of *Fasciola hepatica* has been published twice to date, from British and American isolates, respectively (Cwiklinski *et al.* 2015; McNulty *et al.* 2017). The sheep liver fluke has a large genome (**1.3/1.14 Gb**). The large size is a burden to DNA replication and the investigators cannot explain its existence. They said that the size cannot be explained by genome duplication or expansion of a single DNA repeat element. *Fasciola* genome size is three times that of *Schistosoma*; the large genome is a paradox. The non-coding sequences may be involved in gene regulation; the large genome size may be related to its complex life cycle. Comparative genome sequencing of many more platyhelminths may provide a more definitive answer in the future.

Foodborne trematodes retain more gene expression than blood flukes, whereas the tapeworms lost the most in metabolic pathway genes. Please see Figure 13.2 for a comparison table, from McNulty *et al.* (2017).

The liver fluke genome contains gene family expansion for tubulins and proteases. The British isolate shows horizontal gene transfer (HGT) from the ruminant hosts, namely the long interspersed element (**LINE**) of **BovB** repeats (with 67,000 copies). Such BovB transfer has previously been reported between ruminants and snakes. The American isolate has shown the presence of rickettsial endobacterium, ***Neorickettsia endobacterium*** (859,205 bp genome), associated with the liver fluke. *Fasciola hepatica* has **10** pairs of chromosomes; its genome codes for **14,642/15,740 genes.** RNA transcriptomics supports the estimated gene number. RNA transcriptomics has demonstrated differential gene expression between developmental stages, an example is the protease cathepsin L.

From omics studies, the excretory/secretory (E/S) proteins are important for host-parasite interaction (Cwiklinski and Dalton 2018). Adults also secrete extracellular vesicles (EV) that contain proteins, lipids and microRNAs (miRNAs). Two types (with different size ranges) are found, from the tegument surface and the gut. E/S or EV proteins may be potential targets for vaccines. Vaccines have been developed for animal use, but with low efficacy (only with some reduction in egg production and worm burden).

Stage-specific protein expression by *Fasciola hepatica* has been analyzed by high-performance liquid chromatography-tandem mass spectrometry (LC-MS/MS). The method has identified 629, 2,286, 2,254, and 2,192 proteins in metacercariae, juvenile (28 dpi, days post infection), immature (59 dpi), and adult flukes, respectively. These differentially expressed proteins (**DEPs**) are mainly involved in transport, localization, metabolism, enzyme regulation, protein folding and binding, and nucleoside and nucleotide binding. For this proteomics and bioinformatics study, the DEPs were submitted to the STRING database for protein–protein interaction analysis to generate a color-coded network representing different types of evidence for the associations between DEPs. STRING (Search Tool for the Retrieval of Interacting Genes/Proteins) is a biological database and web resource of known and predicted protein–protein interactions.[3] Please see Figure 13.3 for protein-protein interactions of stage-specific *Fasciola* proteins (Xu *et al.* 2020). The investigators concluded that their findings "provide a theoretical basis for vaccine development and establishing early diagnostic methods in the future" (Xu *et al.* 2020).

[3] https://string-db.org/

Not significantly reduced
Reduced
Strongly reduced

	Pathway ID	Food Borne Trematoda	Blood Fluke	Cestoda
General Metabolic Pathways				
Carbohydrate metabolism				
Pentose and glucuronate interconversions	ko00040	Reduced	Reduced	Reduced
Fructose and mannose metabolism	ko00051	Reduced	Reduced	Reduced
Galactose metabolism	ko00052	Reduced	Reduced	Reduced
Ascorbate and aldarate metabolism	ko00053	Reduced	Reduced	Strongly reduced
Propanoate metabolism	ko00640	Not significantly reduced	Reduced	Reduced
Butanoate metabolism	ko00650	Reduced	Strongly reduced	Strongly reduced
Lipid metabolism				
Fatty acid biosynthesis	ko00061	Reduced	Reduced	Reduced
Fatty acid elongation	ko00062	Not significantly reduced	Reduced	Reduced
Fatty acid degradation	ko00071	Not significantly reduced	Strongly reduced	Reduced
Synthesis and degradation of ketone bodies	ko00072	Reduced	Reduced	Reduced
Steroid biosynthesis	ko00100	Reduced	Reduced	Strongly reduced
Steroid hormone biosynthesis	ko00140	Reduced	Strongly reduced	Reduced
Arachidonic acid metabolism	ko00590	Reduced	Reduced	Reduced
Linoleic acid metabolism	ko00591	Reduced	Strongly reduced	Strongly reduced
alpha-Linolenic acid metabolism	ko00592	Not significantly reduced	Reduced	Reduced
Biosynthesis of unsaturated fatty acids	ko01040	Not significantly reduced	Reduced	Reduced
Nucleotide metabolism				
Purine metabolism	ko00230	Reduced	Reduced	Reduced
Amino acid metabolism				
Arginine biosynthesis	ko00220	Reduced	Reduced	Reduced
Alanine, aspartate and glutamate metabolism	ko00250	Reduced	Reduced	Reduced
Glycine, serine and threonine metabolism	ko00260	Reduced	Reduced	Reduced
Cysteine and methionine metabolism	ko00270	Reduced	Reduced	Reduced
Valine, leucine and isoleucine degradation	ko00280	Not significantly reduced	Strongly reduced	Strongly reduced
Arginine and proline metabolism	ko00330	Reduced	Reduced	Reduced
Histidine metabolism	ko00340	Reduced	Reduced	Reduced
Tyrosine metabolism	ko00350	Reduced	Reduced	Strongly reduced
Phenylalanine metabolism	ko00360	Strongly reduced	Strongly reduced	Strongly reduced
Tryptophan metabolism	ko00380	Reduced	Reduced	Reduced
Phenylalanine, tyrosine and tryptophan biosynthe	ko00400	Strongly reduced	Strongly reduced	Strongly reduced
Metabolism of other amino acids				
beta-Alanine metabolism	ko00410	Reduced	Strongly reduced	Reduced
Selenocompound metabolism	ko00450	Reduced	Reduced	Reduced
Metabolism of cofactors and vitamins				
Thiamine metabolism	ko00730	Reduced	Reduced	Strongly reduced
Riboflavin metabolism	ko00740	Reduced	Reduced	Strongly reduced
Vitamin B6 metabolism	ko00750	Reduced	Strongly reduced	Strongly reduced
Nicotinate and nicotinamide metabolism	ko00760	Reduced	Reduced	Reduced
Pantothenate and CoA biosynthesis	ko00770	Reduced	Reduced	Reduced
Biotin metabolism	ko00780	Reduced	Strongly reduced	Strongly reduced
Retinol metabolism	ko00830	Reduced	Reduced	Reduced
Xenobiotics biodegradation and metabolism				
Metabolism of xenobiotics by cytochrome P450	ko00980	Reduced	Reduced	Reduced
Drug metabolism - cytochrome P450	ko00982	Reduced	Reduced	Reduced
Genetic Information Processing				
Replication and repair				
Homologous recombination	ko03440	Reduced	Reduced	Reduced
Non-homologous end-joining	ko03450	Reduced	Reduced	Reduced
Environmental Information Processing				
Membrane transport				
ABC transporters	ko02010	Reduced	Reduced	Strongly reduced
Signal transduction				
NF-kappa B signaling pathway	ko04064	Reduced	Reduced	Reduced
TNF signaling pathway	ko04668	Reduced	Reduced	Reduced
Calcium signaling pathway	ko04020	Reduced	Reduced	Reduced
cAMP signaling pathway	ko04024	Reduced	Reduced	Reduced
Signaling molecules and interaction				
Neuroactive ligand-receptor interaction	ko04080	Reduced	Reduced	Reduced
Cellular Processes				
Transport and catabolism				
Peroxisome	ko04146	Reduced	Strongly reduced	Strongly reduced
Cellular community				
Gap junction	ko04540	Reduced	Reduced	Reduced

Fig. 13.2 (Figure on previous page) ■ Comparison of flatworm metabolic pathways. Metabolic pathway reduction in parasitic flatworms. The global number of proteins assigned to different metabolic pathway was compared between different parasitic flatworms, the free-living planaria and cattle predicted proteomes. Those pathways showing a significant reduction in the parasitic species in relation to those present in planaria are indicated (strongly reduced: less than 30% conservation; reduced: conservation between 30 and 80%; not significantly reduced: more than 80% conservation). While in general several pathways are reduced in all parasitic species, some pathways are differential between food borne trematodes (*F. hepatica*, *O. viverrini*, *C. sinensis*), blood flukes (*S. mansoni* and *S. japonicum*) and cestodes (*E. multilocularis*, *H. microstoma* and *T. solium*). Most notably some lipid metabolism and amino acid pathways (i.e. aliphatic amino acid degradation) are not reduced in FBT (green) while they are reduced in the other groups. In general, FBT seem to be less constrained than blood flukes, with cestodes being the most restricted metabolically. Courtesy: McNulty *et al. PLoS Genet* 2017;13:e1006537. Reproduced with permission from *PLoS Genetics* with Creative Commons Attribution 4.0 (CC-BY) International License.

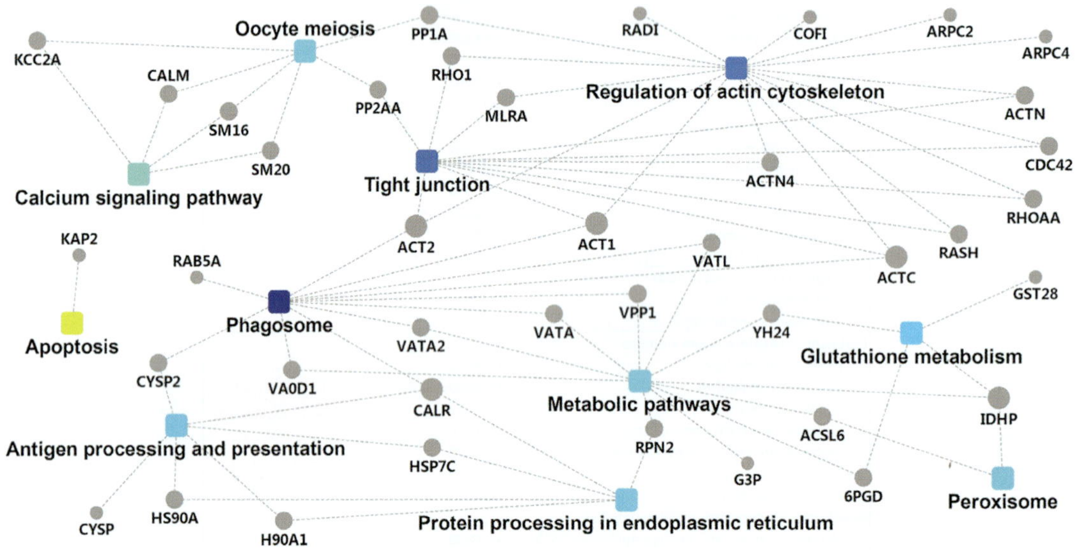

Fig. 13.3 ■ Protein–protein interactions of proteins of *Fasciola hepatica*. Protein–protein interactions of proteins in metacercariae, juvenile flukes 28dpi, immature flukes 59dpi, and adults. The dots are proteins, and the squares are pathways. Courtesy: Xu *et al. Parasitol Res* 2020;119:2837–50. Reproduced with permission from Springer Nature.

13.3 *Clonorchis*

Clonorchis sinensis is the **Chinese** or **oriental liver fluke** (Lai *et al.* 2016; Qian *et al.* 2016; Na *et al.* 2020). A person gets infected after consumption of raw/undercooked freshwater fish (such as carp) contaminated with metacercariae of the fluke. It is common in East and

Southeast Asia, with an estimate of 200 million people at risk, **15 million** infected, including 12 million in China (with expanding in prevalence). There was a study of New York City Chinese immigrants: 150 individuals showed a prevalence of 26% (Roberts *et al.* 2013). The fluke has long associations with humans, as their eggs were found in an excavated corpse of the West Han dynasty in China, 2,000 years ago.

Clonorchis sinensis, and related species, such as *Opisthorchis viverrini*, are known to be risk factors for a special type of cancer, the malignant cholangiocarcinoma (CCA). They are classified as group 1 carcinogens by the International Agency for Research on Cancer (IARC). "An estimated 12.5, 67.3 and 601 million people are currently at risk for infection with *O. felineus*, *O. viverrini* and *C. sinensis*, respectively" (Ershov *et al.* 2019). (This estimate of 601 million is higher than the 200 million just mentioned.)

13.3.1 History

In 1875, James McConnell, professor of pathology and resident physician of Calcutta Medical College, described a large number of flukes in the bile passage of a 20-year-old local Chinese carpenter who was brought to him in Calcutta in 1875. He concluded: "The Chinese ... are well known to be 'filthy feeders,' delighting in putting messes of half-raw fish....The sources from whence the larvae of such parasites may be derived are therefore not far to be sought." McConnell sent specimens to Thomas Spencer Cobbold, a famous contemporary helminthologist and the fluke recognized to be a new species and named *Distoma sinense* (di means two, stoma means mouth, referring to the two suckers of a fluke; sinense means China). Later, working in Cairo, Egypt in 1907, Arthur Looss examined the Chinese flukes and compared them with other flukes to create a new genus, *Clonorchis* (clon means branch, orchis means testes) for the **branched testes** of the hermaphrodite adult fluke. The liver fluke was described in patients from Hong Kong and Japan. Japanese scientists found snails and fish as intermediate hosts, and cats and dogs as animal reservoirs (including the contribution by Isao Ijima, 1887, a figure recognized as the father of Japanese parasitology) (Kean *et al.* 1978).

13.3.2 Life cycle

Please see Figure 13.4 for the life cycle of *Clonorchis sinensis*, from CDC.[4]

The life cycle goes from egg to miracidium that invades the snail, to sporocyst to redia to cercaria, that leaves the snail to the secondary intermediate host, a fish, where it differentiates into metacercaria until eaten by humans or cats and dogs. The egg has a lid/opening known as operculum (a feature absent in the schistosomes). The snail

[4] https://www.cdc.gov/dpdx/clonorchiasis/index.html

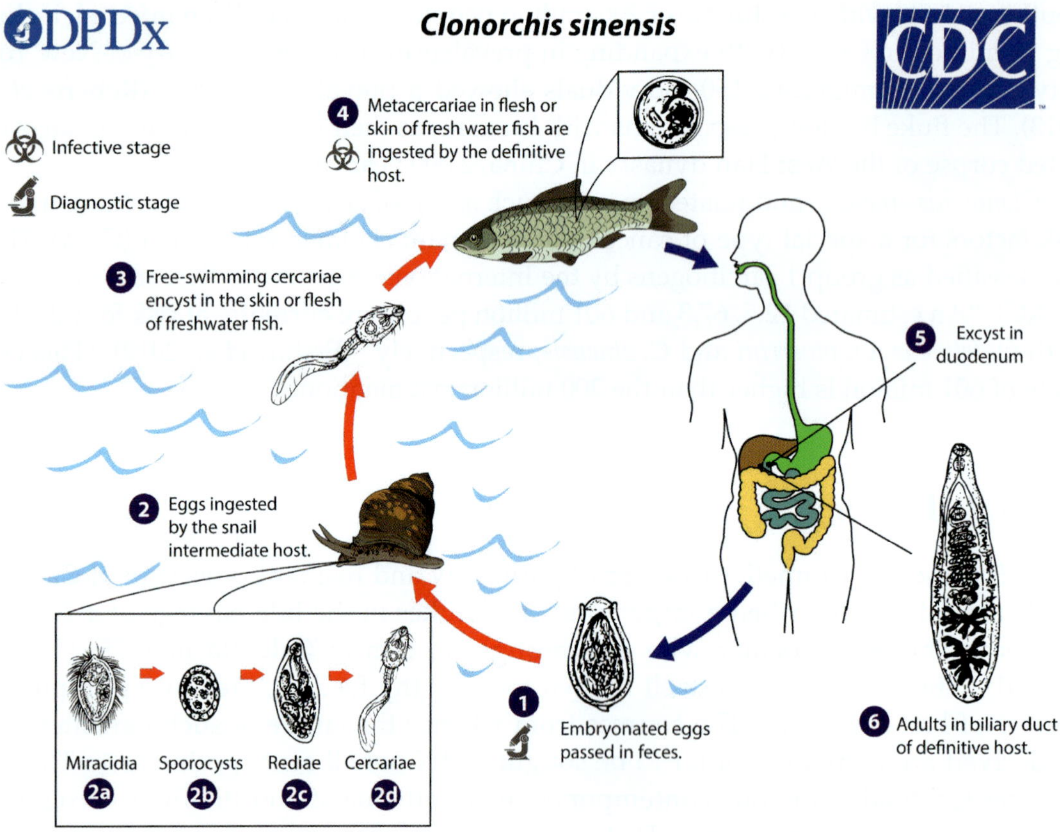

Fig. 13.4 ■ CDC Life cycle of *Clonorchis sinensis*. *Clonorchis sinensis* eggs are discharged in the biliary ducts and in the stool in an embryonated state ❶. Eggs are ingested by a suitable snail intermediate host ❷. Eggs release miracidia 2a, which go through several developmental stages (sporocysts 2b, rediae 2c, and cercariae 2d). The cercariae are released from the snail and, after a short period of free-swimming time in water, they come in contact and penetrate the flesh of freshwater fish, where they encyst as metacercariae ❸. Infection of humans occurs by ingestion of undercooked, salted, pickled, or smoked freshwater fish ❹. After ingestion, the metacercariae excyst in the duodenum ❺ and ascend the biliary tract through the ampulla of Vater ❻. Maturation takes approximately one month. The adult flukes (measuring 10–25 mm by 3–5 mm) reside in small and medium sized biliary ducts. Courtesy of the CDC. Reproduced from https://www.cdc.gov/dpdx/clonorchiasis/index.html

species vary from different regions. The adult size is 10–20 mm × 3–5 mm. The hermaphrodite produces 4,000 eggs per day. This liver fluke has a long lifespan; *Clonorchis* can live up to 25 years. Please see Figure 13.5 for an adult and an egg of *Clonorchis sinensis* (Na *et al.* 2020).

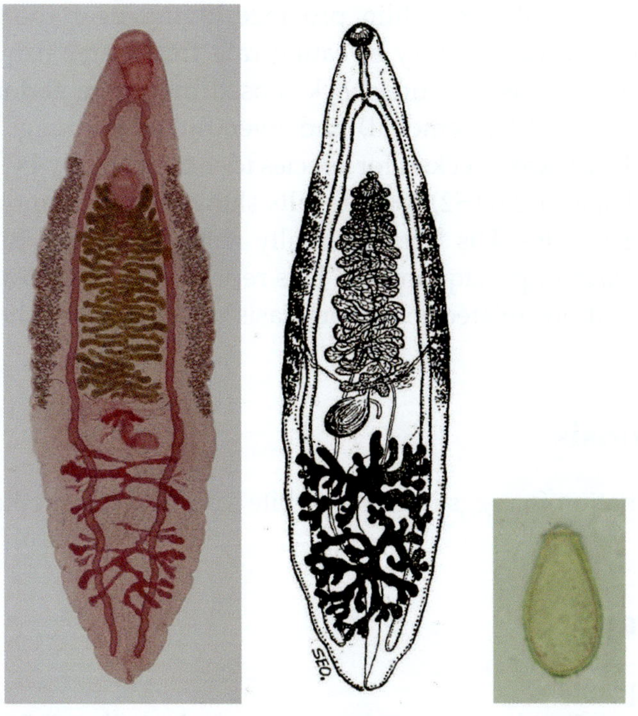

(A) (B) (C)

Fig. 13.5 ■ Adult and egg of *Clonorchis sinensis*. (A) An adult worm, unstained. (B) A drawing of an adult fluke (courtesy of Dr. J.-Y. Chai). (C) An egg. Courtesy: Na *et al. Acta Trop* 2019;203:105309. Reproduced with permission from Elsevier.

13.3.3 Pathology

Depending on the number of flukes in the liver, the intensity of symptoms differ. A light infection under 100 adults is usually accompanied by few clinical signs (abdominal discomfort and diarrhea). A patient with moderate infection (100–1,000 adults) may suffer similar but more pronounced symptoms (fever, chills, weight loss, abdominal distension). A patient with heavy infection (over 1,000 adults) can have acute pain, hepatomegaly, ascites, and hypertension. An autopsy had found over 6,000 adults in a single patient. Chronic infection leads to liver fibrosis and cancer (cholangiocarcinoma). The infected patient has eosinophilia and elevated IgE production, similar signs as in other helminth infections.

Clonorchiasis, a serious foodborne zoonosis, is often asymptomatic or shows only mild symptoms, which leads to delayed treatment. Chronic clonorchiasis can result in complications such as cholelithiasis, cholangitis, cholecystitis and cholangiocarcinoma. A case of acute shock caused by *Clonorchis sinensis* was documented in China (Wang *et al.*

2019). The 52-year-old male from Jilin province, living near the Songhua River (an endemic area) with a 20-year history of eating raw freshwater fish (during the annual summer fishing season), was in acute shock caused by severe abdominal pain. He had cholecystectomy (gall bladder removal) and liver flukes and eggs were found in the draining tube. Egg DNA was checked for species identification by PCR-sequencing of the internal transcribed spacer 2 (ITS2), with results showing 98% homology with *C. sinensis* China Heilongjiang isolates. His liver gradually restored normal function after anthelmintic therapy (30 days of praziquantel). "This report aims to increase awareness of the hazards and complications related to clonorchiasis" (Wang *et al.* 2019).

13.3.4 Diagnosis

Microscopic examination for eggs in feces (or bile samples) is a method of diagnosis.

13.3.5 Therapy

Treatment is praziquantel.

Another drug is tribendimidine (**TrBD**). We note here that TrBD was developed in China. "China was once a country plagued by parasitic diseases. At the beginning of the founding of the People's Republic of China, nearly 80% of the population suffered from parasitic diseases because of poverty and poor sanitary conditions. After nearly 70 years of development, China has made remarkable achievements in the prevention and control of parasitic diseases, and the prevalence of parasitic diseases has been greatly reduced. … China has independently developed tribendimidine (TrBD, a broad spectrum anthelminthic), and its anthelminthic spectrum has been comprehensively studied. It is active against almost 20 parasites, is especially superior to benzimidazoles against *Necator americanus*, and surpasses the effectiveness of praziquantel against *Clonorchis sinensis*." (Zhang *et al.* 2019)

13.3.6 Genome

The genome of *Clonorchis sinensis* has been published for two isolates. The draft genome was first published for the Chinese isolate (Wang *et al.* 2011; with revised version Huang *et al.* 2013) and then for the Korean isolate (Wang *et al.* 2018). The genome size is 516 Mb. Based on the transcriptional analysis, there are **13,688** protein-coding genes. The Chinese and Korean isolates have a karyotype of $2n$ = **56.** The Russian Far East parasite seems to possess a different karyotype, $2n = 14$; this suggests the possible presence of **cryptic species** (a situation also thought to be present in the related *Opisthorchis* parasite). Key genes for fatty acid synthesis are missing, because of its location the fluke can take in lipids from the bile. The parasite has about 300 excretory/secretory proteins (ESPs), including **granulin** (parasite-derived growth factor) which induces host cell proliferation, a feature that may be related to its cancer-causing capacity. Tissue-specific transcriptomes have been analyzed for sucker, muscle, ovary and testes. The Chinese and Korean isolates show regions of synteny with a 99% sequence identity. It has been noted that draft genomes yield challenges to the analysis of genetic variations among isolates.

The mitochondrial genome of *Clonorchis sinensis* has been re-investigated. Previous attempts have been incomplete because conventional techniques cannot reliably sequence repetitive regions. Long-read sequencing was used, with the MinION sequencing platform (Oxford Nanopore Technologies). The completed mitochondrial genome is **18,304 bp** in length and contains **12** protein-encoding genes, 2 rRNAs and 22 tRNAs, plus a non-coding region of 4,549 bp containing 6 tandem-repetitive units of 719–809 bp each (**R1 to R6**). The next steps would be to check for repeat length/sequence variation in this region (within and among individual worms, and among worm populations), and to look for its function (role in the regulation of replication and transcription, akin to the mitochondrial control region in mammals). "Although applied to *C. sinensis*, the technological approach established here should be broadly applicable to characterize complex tandem-repetitive or homo-polymeric regions in the mitochondrial genomes of a wide range of taxa" (Kinkar *et al.* 2020). Please see Figure 13.6 for mitochondrial genome of *Clonorchis sinensis* (Kinkar *et al.* 2020).

13.4 *Opisthorchis*

Two species of *Opisthorchis* infect humans: *Opisthorchis viverrini* and *O. felineus*. (Ogorodova *et al.* 2015). Both are flukes of cats and dogs, with humans as accidental definitive hosts (zoonosis). In 1892, flukes were found in the liver of nine patients in Siberia by Konstantin Winogradoff. The worms were found to be identical to those previously seen in cats and dogs and named *Distoma felineum* (feline means cat); today the species is *Opisthorchis felineus* (opis means behind and orchis means testes, for the location of testes in the posterior part of body). Originally found in a civet cat and named *Distoma viverrini* (viverrini means civet cat) in 1911, the fluke *O. viverrini* was first described in the autopsy of two dead prisoners in Chiang Mai, Thailand by Robert Thomson Leiper. In today's estimate, 10 million people in northern Thailand are infected with *O. viverrini*, and 16 million in the former Soviet Union with *O. felineus*. Local cuisine contributes to disease spread: the most common raw fish dish in Thailand is *koi pla*; it can be contaminated with metacercariae (Upatham and Vivyanant 2003). *Opisthorchis* species' life cycles are similar to that of *Clonorchis sinensis*, so it is not repeated here. The draft genome of ***Opisthorchis viverrini*** is known, with 635 Mb genome size and **16,379** protein-coding genes, plus 437 excretory/secretory proteins (ESPs) including granulins (Young *et al.* 2014; Gasser *et al.* 2017). The draft

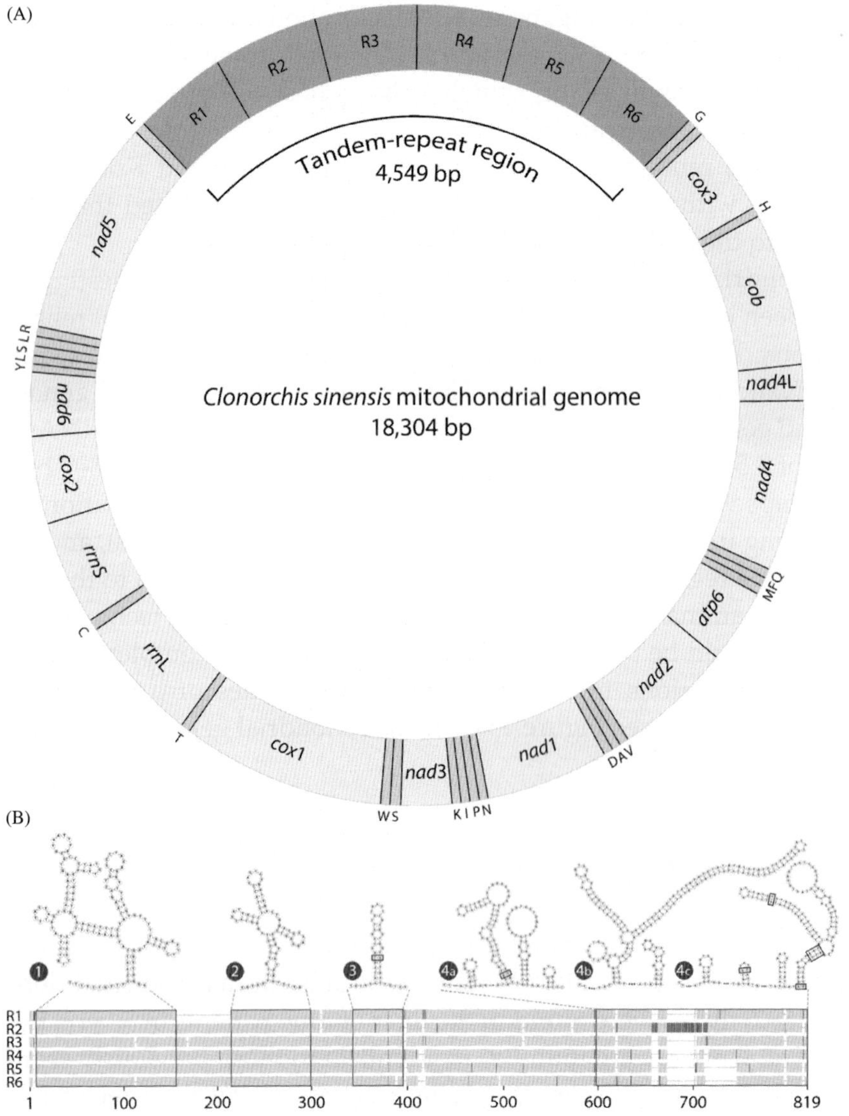

Fig. 13.6 ■ Mitochondrial DNA of *Clonorchis sinensis* including tandem repeats. Complete, annotated mitochondrial genome of *Clonorchis sinensis*. (A) Schematic representation of the mitochondrial genome, including the newly-identified tandem-repeat region (4,549 bp); the 12 protein-encoding genes, 2 rRNAs and 22 tRNAs (designated by their one-letter amino acid abbreviations) are in accord with a published reference mitochondrial genome available in GenBank (accession no. KY564177). The short non-coding region is between tRNA-Gly (G) and *cox*3. (B) A schematic alignment of the tandem-repeat units (R1 to R6; bottom), showing nucleotide identities (light grey) or differences (dark grey) and regions predicted to assume structures (boxed in black). Secondary structures predicted for individual repeat units are indicated above the alignment; mis-matches in stems are indicated (boxed). Positions 598 to 819 include a variable TA-rich region and was predicted to fold into three distinct structures (4a to 4c). Courtesy: Kinkar *et al. PLoS Negl Trop Dis* 2020;14:e0008552. Reproduced with permission from PLoS Neglected Tropical Diseases with Creative Commons Attribution 4.0 (CC-BY) International License.

genome of ***Opisthorchis felineus*** is known, with 684 Mb genome size and **21,036** protein-coding genes (Ershov *et al.* 2019).

Omics data may yield a new strategy for the control of opisthorchiasis. "As major progress continues in omics studies focused on *O. viverrini*-host interplays, many of the key molecules discovered has become potential candidates for the development of diagnostic biomarkers, vaccines, and drugs" (Prasopdee *et al.* 2019).

13.5 Liver Flukes and Cancer

From their genomes that express growth factors, this growth-inducing capacity of liver flukes, *Clonorchis sinensis* and *Opisthorchis viverrini* are risk factors for the malignant cholangiocarcinoma (**CCA**), a special bile duct cancer. The two species are classified as **group 1 carcinogens** by the International Agency for Research on Cancer (IARC) (IARC 2012). Chronic infections by these liver flukes can lead to host CCA. The flukes live for 15–20 years. They can cause mechanical damage, lead to host immune response and produce protein products that may affect carcinogenesis (Zheng *et al.* 2017).

Oxysterols are derivatives of cholesterol obtained by oxidation. They play a role in the regulation of cholesterol synthesis, transport, and efflux. Thus, they have a role in bile acid metabolism, in the conversion of cholesterol into bile acids (Crosignani *et al.* 2011). **Oxysterols** are produced by flukes such as *Opisthorchis viverrini.* "Oxysterols have been essentially described in animal model of opisthorchiasis and associated cholangiocarcinoma. Several oxysterol-like metabolites have been detected not only on developmental stages of *O. viverrini* and *O. felineus* but also on biofluids from experimentally infected hamsters as products of the activities of the liver flukes. These sterol derivatives are metabolized to active quinones that can modify host DNA. We have postulated that helminth parasite–associated sterols might induce tumor-like phenotypes in biliary epithelia, the cells of origin of liver fluke infection–associated cholangiocarcinoma, through the formation of DNA adducts, dysregulation of apoptosis, and other homeostatic pathways" (Vale *et al.* 2020).

13.6 Intestinal Trematodes

We have mentioned that trematodes are very successful parasites residing in different organs of their hosts. Instead of liver and bile ducts, some species prefer small intestines. We briefly discuss three species, with emphasis on adult sizes. *Heterophyes heterophyes* and *Metagonimus yokogawai* are tiny, with adult size at 1–2.5 mm × 0.3–0.75 mm. Differentiation between the two is a separate ventral sucker and genital sucker (gonotyl) in *Heterophyes* (two exits), and fused sucker displaced to the parasite's left side for *Metagonimus* (one exit). On the other end of the size scale, *Fasciolopsis buski* is the largest fluke infecting humans and pigs, its adult size can be 75 mm × 20 mm. One interesting finding is its limited lifespan, 1 year. As noted about cryptic species, analysis of mitochondrial and ribosomal DNA sequences has shown differences between Chinese/Vietnamese versus Indian isolates of *Fasciolopsis buski* (Ma *et al*. 2017).

13.7 *Paragonimus*

Paragonimus westermani is the **oriental lung fluke**. It has a broad host range with respect to both immediate and definitive hosts. *P. westermani* is found in China, Japan, Korea, Philippines and other countries. A total of 50 species have been described and seven can infect humans (some species are considered to be synonymous). Worldwide the prevalence is approximately **20 million**, with 300 million at risk. One estimate is approximately 1 million are infected annually. Humans acquire infection through the ingestion of raw, pickled or undercooked freshwater crustaceans, the parasite's second intermediate hosts, or consuming raw meat of wild boar or deer, its paratenic hosts. Regarding infection status, human paragonimiasis used to be highly endemic in Japan, Korea, China, Taiwan, and the Philippines, but its prevalence had drastically decreased in Korea and Japan by the 1980s. However, paragonimiasis is still highly endemic in some areas in the Philippines and China, and is re-emerging in Japan. Besides *P. westermani*, other species found in Asia are *P. heterotremus* and *P. skrjabini* (aka *P.s. miyazakii*) (Yoshida *et al*. 2019). Whereas *P. westermani*, widely found throughout the world, is presented as the model organism for foodborne lung flukes affecting humans, *P. kellicotti* is indigenous to the United States where it infects mink and opossum (zoonosis).

13.7.1 History

The discovery of *Paragonimus westermani* started with a dead tiger in the Amsterdam Zoo. The director, Professor C.F. Westerman, presented the dead animal to Coenraad Kerbert at the Zoological Laboratory. In 1878, Kerbert described flukes obtained from the lung of the dead tiger and wrote: "I feel justified… in introducing this unknown worm to the zoologists as *Distoma westermanni*." The new species was named in honor of Westerman; Kerbert would later followed Westerman's footsteps to become director of the Royal Zoological Society.

Patrick Manson, working in Formosa (today's Taiwan), found eggs in the sputum of a 35-year-old male named Tso-tong, in 1880. He noted **haemoptysis**, the coughing up of blood. Manson noticed that the eggs looked identical to those found in an autopsy of a Portuguese by B. S. Ringer, also in Formosa (with both adults and eggs). Specimens were sent to Cobbold who named the parasite *Distoma ringeri* (after Ringer). Manson had also speculated that snails could be the first intermediate host (at that time he had moved to Amoy, China; so he could not obtain eggs for further experiments). In 1899, Max Braun, professor of zoology at Konigsberg University, established the genus *Paragonimus* (para means side by side; gonimos means gonade; to denote having gonads side by side). In 1916, Japanese investigator Koan Nakagawa found snails as first and crabs as second intermediate hosts. In the same year, Harujiro Kobayashi also found snails and crayfish as hosts. The importance of paragonimiasis led to multiple studies to determine its life cycle (Kean *et al.* 1978; Cox 1996).

13.7.2 Life cycle

Please see Figure 13.7 for the life cycle of *Paragonimus westermani*, from CDC.[5]

The life cycle begins with egg developing to miracidium in water, miracidium invading snail to become sporocyst, redia 1 and 2 (two generations), to cercaria which is microcercous (short knobby tail) for crawling and attacking a crab, where it matures to metacercaria. Metacercaria infects all organs of the crab. Humans eat drunken crabs (or raw or undercooked) and get infected. Freshwater crabs are the most common intermediate host in the Far East. In the United States, *P. kellicotti* infection results from eating uncooked/undercooked crayfish. Humans can also be infected via paratenic hosts, such as the consumption of raw/undercooked game meat from deer and wild boar (Yoshida *et al.* 2019).

Ingested metacercaria excysts and moves from the intestine through the peritoneal cavity to the lung. Adult size is 7.5–12 mm × 4–6 mm. They are usually found in pairs of two, enclosed within a cyst in the lung, thus allowing cross-fertilization. Both diploid and triploid parasites are known, with triploid being more pathogenic. The triploid form produces eggs via parthenogenesis.

13.7.3 Pathology

Cough and recurrent hemoptysis are the most common clinical features. Patients may have chest pain, dyspnea (difficult breathing), fever, and chills. Bacterial superinfection may occur. An often-fatal clinical outcome results from extrapulmonary paragonimiasis, when the immature flukes migrate to tissues including the brain. Paragonimiasis can last up to 20 years.

Paragonimiasis is a parasitic disease caused by *Paragnonimus* species, with lung as the primary site, but extrapulmonary involvement can occur. Infection by *Paragonimus westermani* can lead to involvement of the central nervous system along with the liver, intestine, peritoneal cavity, retroperitoneum, and abdominal wall. Ectopic paragonimiasis raises a diagnostic challenge since it is uncommon and may be confused with malignancy or other inflammatory diseases. An ectopic paragonimiasis case was reported in Korea: the 45-year-old male had recurrent abdominal pain (three times for the previous 3 years) with his abdominal computed tomography (CT) revealing fluid collection/wall

[5] https://www.cdc.gov/dpdx/paragonimiasis/index.html

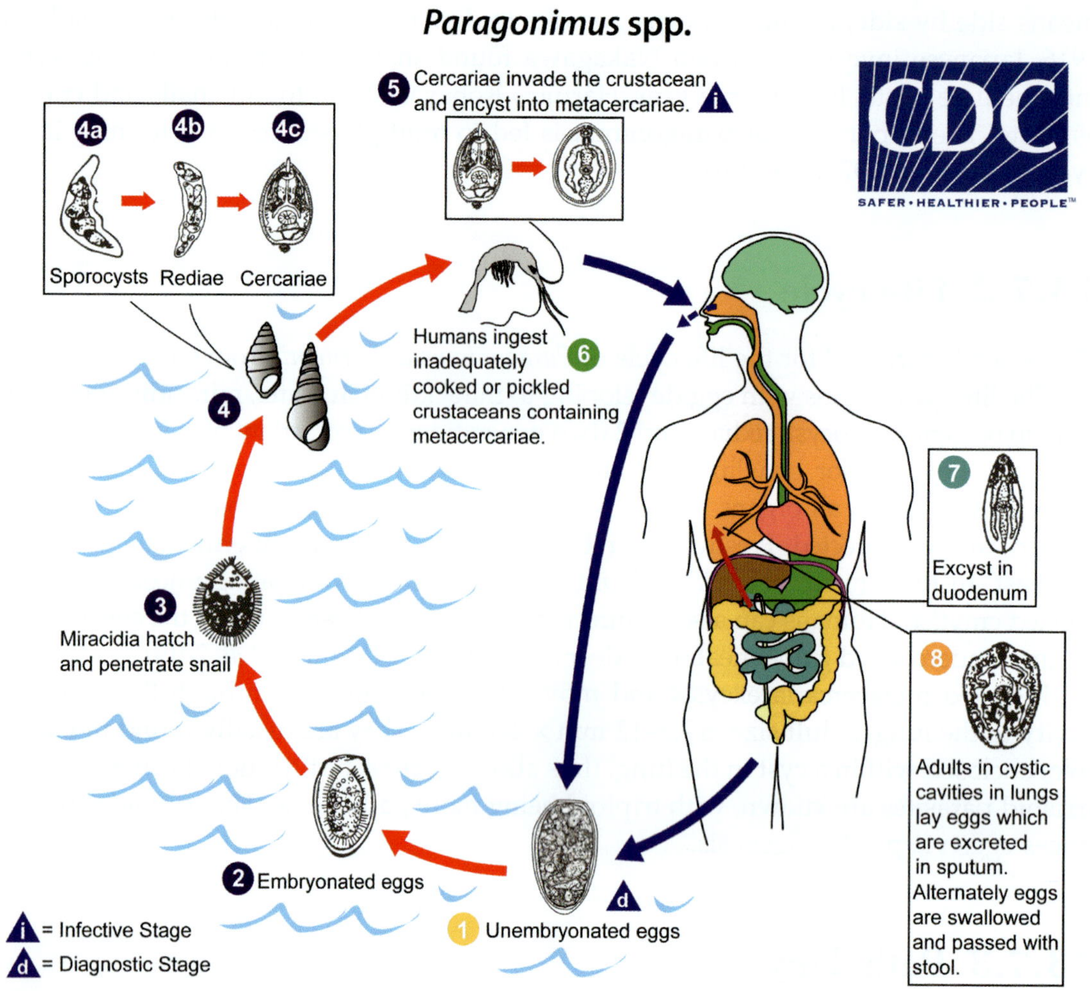

Fig. 13.7 ■ Life cycle of *Paragonimus westermani*. The eggs are excreted unembryonated in the sputum, or alternately they are swallowed and passed with stool 1. In the external environment, the eggs become embryonated 2, and miracidia hatch and seek the first intermediate host, a snail, and penetrate its soft tissues 3. Miracidia go through several developmental stages inside the snail 4: sporocysts 4a, rediae 4b, with the latter giving rise to many cercariae 4c, which emerge from the snail. The cercariae invade the second intermediate host, a crustacean such as a crab or crayfish, where they encyst and become metacercariae. This is the infective stage for the mammalian host 5. Human infection with *P. westermani* occurs by eating inadequately cooked or pickled crab or crayfish that harbor metacercariae of the parasite 6. The metacercariae excyst in the duodenum 7, penetrate through the intestinal wall into the peritoneal cavity, then through the abdominal wall and diaphragm into the lungs, where they become encapsulated and develop into adults 8. (7.5–12 mm by 4–6 mm). The worms can also reach other organs and tissues, such as the brain and striated muscles, respectively. However, when this takes place completion of the life cycles is not achieved, because the eggs laid cannot exit these sites. Time from infection to oviposition is 65–90 days. Infections may persist for 20 years in humans. Animals such as pigs, dogs, and a variety of feline species can also harbor *P. westermani*. Courtesy of the CDC. Reproduced from https://www.cdc.gov/dpdx/paragonimiasis/index.html

enhancement, therefore suggesting recurrent diverticulitis. However, his resected colon showed intact colon wall without evidence of diverticulitis but contained multiple parasite eggs and granulomas (70 μm with an operculum and relatively thick egg shell indicating *Paragonimus* species). The patient had enjoyed soy-marinated crabs; his antibody test by ELISA showed positive only to *P. westermani* but not *Clonorchis sinensis, Schistosoma haematobium*, cysteicercus, and *Anisakis* species. These data resulted in the definitive diagnosis as peritoneal paragonimiasis (Kim *et al.* 2017).

A case of group infection with *Paragonimus* in the Henan province, China was documented. Eleven got infected, with eosinophilia (11/11, 100%) and pulmonary manifestations including stethalgia (chest pain) and cough (7/11 or 63.6%) (Chen *et al.* 2020). An excursion with 51 participants (10 teachers and 41 students) from a primary school happened in May 2011, during which freshwater crabs were caught and 17 hikers had eaten raw or roasted freshwater crabs. Disease confirmation was delayed for more than a year because of misdiagnosis (five were thought to have tuberculosis and got 6-month anti-TB drug regimen with no benefit). Diagnosis of paragonimiasis was confirmed in July 2012 by PCR of ITS2 and COX1 sequencing; the fluke species was determined to be *Paragonimus skrjabini*. Among the 51, 12 (23.5%) were positive for *Paragonimus* antibodies. Among the 11 crabs caught at the infection site, six contained metacercariae. One patient presented with hemoptysis and eggs in respiratory secretions (the first time *P. skrjabini* eggs detected in the patient sputum from Henan province) (Chen *et al.* 2020).

Paragonimiasis may also be asymptomatic. A single case was found during mobile medical services provided by the Hospital for Tropical Diseases of Mahidol University between December 2013 and February 2014, among the villagers living in northern Thailand, on the Thai–Myanmar border, most of which were Thai and Karen farmers working in the fields and forests. From stool examination, about half had parasitic infections, with hookworm infection being the most common, followed by ascariasis, trichuriasis, and minute intestinal fluke infections. Protozoan parasites were less frequently detected than helminths, with mostly nonpathogenic species, and low incidence for *Entamoeba* spp, *Giardia*, and *Blastocystis*. During this coproparasitological examination, *Paragonimus* sp. eggs with golden brown color, symmetric oval-shape and operculated, were found in one fecal sample of a 72-year-old Karen female who did not have any symptoms. She admitted habitual consumption of semi-cooked or roasted waterfall crabs for several years. Using *cox*-1 PCR, the parasite was identified to be *Paragonimus heterotremus*. She was treated with praziquantel, those with helminth infections were treated with albendazole or mebendazole, and those with tapeworm infection with niclosamide (Kusolsuk *et al.* 2020).

13.7.4 Diagnosis

The definitive diagnosis of paragonimiasis is the detection of *Paragonimus* eggs in sputum or stool. Serological and molecular assays are also available (ELISA, PCR).

13.7.5 Therapy

Praziquantel is the drug of choice.

13.7.6 Genome

For *Paragonimus*, transcriptomes go ahead of genomes (McNulty *et al.* 2014; Li *et al.* 2016). The purpose of transcriptomics was to search for immunodominant parasite antigens. Metacercariae, isolated from infected crayfish, were fed to gerbils and the adult flukes were isolated from lung cysts for bulk RNA sequence analysis. For *Paragonimus kellicotti*, proteins such as **myoglobulin** and cysteine proteases are candidates for immunologic diagnosis. A subsequent analysis has compared the transcriptomes of *P. westermani* and *P. skrjabini*, using adult parasites from infected dogs (after infection with metacercariae, isolated from infected crabs collected in different regions in China). Transcriptomics confirm myoglobulin as a potential diagnostic candidate, showing both aerobic and anaerobic metabolism (but no fatty acid synthesis). A draft genome of *P. westermani* is available (Oey *et al.* 2019). It has a 1.1 Gb, a large genome size with over 45% repetitive DNA, and a predicted **12,852** protein-coding genes. Besides the nuclear genome, there is a circular mitochondrial genome of 20.6 Kb. The majority of proteins (80%) show homologs to those of the liver fluke *Opisthorchis viverrini*.

Summary & Key Concepts

- The primary organ affected by *Fasciola*, *Clonorchis* and *Opisthorchis* is the liver, and that by *Paragonimus* is the lung.
- The natural final hosts of *Fasciola* are sheep, cattle and other herbivores after eating contaminated aquatic vegetation, which makes the disease of veterinary importance.
- The natural final hosts of *Clonorchis* are fish-eating carnivores (including cats and dogs); humans get infection after consumption of raw or undercooked freshwater fish (such as carp) contaminated with the metacercariae of the fluke.
- *Opischorchis* is similar to *Clonorchis* in its life cycle and hosts. Only two species, *O. viverrini* and *O. felineus*, infect humans as accidental definitive hosts.
- *Clonorchis* and *Opischorchis* have been identified as risk factors for cancer, cholangiocarcinoma (CCA).
- Different species of *Paragonimus* infect a broad range of hosts.
- Praziquantel is used for the treatment of *Paragonimus*, *Clonorchis* and *Opischorchis* infections but not *Fasciola* infections. Triclabendazole and bithionol are used to treat *Fasciola* infections.

References

Chen WQ, Deng Y, Zhang YL, *et al.* A case of group infections with *Paraginimus* species in Henan, Central China. *Acta Trop* 2020;202:105111.

Cox FEG, editor. *The Welcome Trust Illustrated History of Tropical Diseases* (1996, Wellcome Trust, London).

Crosignani A, Zuin M, Allocca M, Del Puppo M. Oxysterols in bile acid metabolism. *Clin Chim Acta.* 2011;412(23-24):2037–45.

Cwiklinski K, Dalton JP. Advances in *Fasciola hepatica* research using 'omics' technologies. *Int J Parasitol* 2018;48(5):321–31.

Cwiklinski K, Dalton JP, Dufresne PJ, *et al.* The *Fasciola hepatica* genome: gene duplication and polymorphism reveals adaptation to the host environment and the capacity for rapid evolution. *Genome Biol* 2015;16:71.

Ershov NI, Mordvinov VA, Prokhortchouk EB, *et al.* New insights from *Opisthorchis felineus* genome: update on genomics of the epidemiologically important liver flukes. *BMC Genomics* 2019;20(1):399.

Gandhi P, Schmitt EK, Chen CW, Samantray S, Venishetty VK, Hughes D. Triclabendazole in the treatment of human fascioliasis: A review. *Trans R Soc Trop Med Hyg* 2019;113(12):797–804.

Gasser RB, Tan P, Teh BT, Wongkham S, Young ND. Genomics of worms, with an emphasis on *Opisthorchis viverrini* — Opportunities for fundamental discovery and biomedical outcomes. *Parasitol Int* 2017;66(4):341–5.

Huang Y, Chen W, Wang X, *et al.* The carcinogenic liver fluke, *Clonorchis sinensis*: New assembly, reannotation and analysis of the genome and characterization of tissue transcriptomes. *PLoS One* 2013;8(1):e54732.

Hughes G, Green CA, Street D, *et al.* Case Report: Subarachnoid hemorrhage and eosinophilic meningitis due to disseminated Fascioliasis. *Am J Trop Med Hyg* 2020;102(3):574–7.

IARC Monographs. *Biological Agents. Volume 100B. A review of human carcinogens.* IARC, Lyon, France, 2012.

Kean BH, Mott KE, Russell AJ, editors. *Tropical Medicine and Parasitology: Classic Investigations,* volumes I and II (1978, Cornell).

Kim MJ, Kim SH, Lee SO, *et al.* A case of ectopic peritoneal paragonimiasis mimicking diverticulitis or abdominal abscess. *Korean J Parasitol* 2017;55(3):313–7.

Kinkar L, Young ND, Sohn WM, Stroehlein AJ, Korhonen PK, Gasser RB. First record of a tandem-repeat region within the mitochondrial genome of *Clonorchis sinensis* using a long-read sequencing approach. *PLoS Negl Trop Dis* 2020;14(8):e0008552.

Kusolsuk T, Phuphisut O, Maipanich W, *et al.* Asymptomatic human paragonimiasis among the Karen people in Tak Province, Thailand: A case report. *Korean J Parasitol* 2020;58(1):57–60.

Lai DH, Hong XK, Su BX, *et al.* Current status of *Clonorchis sinensis* and clonorchiasis in China. *Trans R Soc Trop Med Hyg* 2016;110(1):21–7.

Li BW, McNulty SN, Rosa BA, *et al.* Conservation and diversification of the transcriptomes of adult *Paragonimus westermani* and *P. skrjabini*. *Parasit Vectors* 2016;9:497.

L'Ollivier C, Eldin C, Lambourg E, Brouqui P, Lagier JC. Case report: First molecular diagnosis of liver abscesses due to *Fasciola hepatica* acute infection imported from Vietnam. *Am J Trop Med Hyg* 2020;102(1):106–9.

Ma J, Sun MM, He JJ, *et al. Fasciolopsis buski* (Digenea: Fasciolidae) from China and India may represent distinct taxa based on mitochondrial and nuclear ribosomal DNA sequences. *Parasit Vectors* 2017;10(1):101.

Mas-Coma S, Bargues MD, Valero MA. Human fascioliasis infection sources, their diversity, incidence factors, analytical methods and prevention measures. *Parasitology* 2018;145(13):1665–99.

McNulty SN, Fischer PU, Townsend RR, Curtis KC, Weil GJ, Mitreva M. Systems biology studies of adult *Paragonimus* lung flukes facilitate the identification of immunodominant parasite antigens. *PLoS Negl Trop Dis* 2014;8(10):e3242.

McNulty SN, Tort JF, Rinaldi G, *et al*. Genomes of *Fasciola hepatica* from the Americas reveal colonization with *Neorickettsia endobacteria* related to the agents of potomac forse and fuman sennetsu fevers. *PLoS Genet* 2017;13(1):e1006537.

Na BK, Pak JH, Hong SJ. *Clonorchis sinensis* and clonorchiasis. *Acta Trop* 2020;203:105309.

Oey H, Zakrzewski M, Narain K, *et al.* Whole-genome sequence of the oriental lung fluke *Paragonimus westermani*. *Gigascience* 2019;8(1).

Ogorodova LM, Fedorova OS, Sripa B, *et al*. Opisthorchiasis: An overlooked danger. *PLoS Negl Trop Dis* 2015;9(4):e0003563.

Prasopdee S, Thitapakorn V, Sathavornmanee T, Tesana S. A comprehensive review of omics and host-parasite interplays studies, towards control of *Opisthorchis viverrini* infection for prevention of cholangiocarcinoma. *Acta Trop* 2019;196:76–82.

Roberts LS, Janovy J, Jr. Nadler S. *Schmidt & Roberts Foundations of Parasitology*, 9th ed., McGraw Hill, 2013.

Qian MB, Utzinger J, Keiser J, Zhou XN. Clonorchiasis. *Lancet* 2016;387(10020):800–10.

Sabourin E, Alda P, Vázquez A, Hurtrez-Boussès S, Vittecoq M. Impact of human activities on Fasciolosis transmission. *Trends Parasitol* 2018;34(10):891–903.

Upatham ES, Viyanant V. *Opisthorchis viverrini* and opisthorchiasis: A historical review and future perspective. *Acta Trop* 2003;88(3):171–6.

Vale N, Gouveia MJ, Gärtner F, Brindley PJ. Oxysterols of helminth parasites and pathogenesis of foodborne hepatic trematodiasis caused by *Opisthorchis* and *Fasciola* species. *Parasitol Res* 2020;119(5):1443–53.

Wang D, Korhonen PK, Gasser RB, Young ND. Improved genomic resources and new bioinformatic workflow for the carcinogenic parasite *Clonorchis sinensis*: Biotechnological implications. *Biotechnol Adv* 2018;36(4):894–904.

Wang N, Tang B, Hao Y, *et al.* Acute shock caused by *Clonorchis sinensis* infection: A case report. *BMC Infect Dis* 2019;19(1):1014.

Wang X, Chen W, Huang Y, *et al.* The draft genome of the carcinogenic human liver fluke *Clonorchis sinensis*. *Genome Biol* 2011;12(10):R107.

Xu J, Wu L, Sun Y, *et al.* Proteomics and bioinformatics analysis of *Fasciola hepatica* somatic proteome in different growth phases. *Parasitol Res* 2020;119(9):2837–50.

Yoshida A, Doanh PN, Maruyama H. *Paragonimus* and paragonimiasis in Asia: An update. *Acta Trop* 2019;199:105074.

Young ND, Nagarajan N, Lin SJ, *et al.* The *Opisthorchis viverrini* genome provides insights into life in the bile duct. *Nat Commun* 2014;5:4378.

Zhang H, Liu C, Zheng Q. Development and application of anthelminthic drugs in China. *Acta Trop* 2019;200:105181.

Zheng S, Zhu Y, Zhao Z, Wu Z, Okanurak K, Lv Z. Liver fluke infection and cholangiocarcinoma: A review. *Parasitol Res* 2017;116(1):11–19.

14

Introduction to Tapeworms (Cestodes)

14.1 Cestoda

Trematodes and cestodes (cestus means belt or girdle) are grouped under the phylum Platyhelminthes (flatworms). The two groups are members of Neodermata, ones with neodermis ("new skin," referring to their syncytial tegument) replacing the larval epidermis after host infection. This tegument innovation has made flatworms among the animal species with the most successful transitions into parasitism. Human tapeworms belong to the eucestodes (true tapeworms), composed of the bulk of the cestode species (Webb and Cabada 2017). Based on the Ruggiero classification, the infraclass Cestoda has a total of 16 orders, including two orders (Order **Cyclophyllidea** and Order **Diphyllobothriidea**), within which are many human parasites (Ruggiero *et al.* 2015). Cestoda has also been called Cestoidea.

Tapeworms are ribbon-shaped flatworms; they differ from trematodes in the lack of a mouth and digestive system. Tapeworms are remarkably adapted to parasitism: various attachment structures to hold on to the hosts, the hermaphroditic adult stage with serial repetition of reproductive systems (proglottids at different stages of maturation), complex life cycles (with two or more hosts), specialized larval stages designed for invasion of each host, and the total absence of a digestive system (absorbing nutrients and expelling waste via the tegument).

As an endoparasite, the adult tapeworm lives within the intestine of its vertebrate definitive host. Its body comprises the head (scolex), the neck, and the strobila (made up of proglottids). At the anterior head end, the scolex possesses specialized structures for attachment to the intestinal wall. The mature proglottids are bags (sacs) of fertilized eggs ready for dispersal at the posterior end. Please see Figure 14.1 for general cestode morphology (Andreassen 2010).

The scolices' unique morphological structures have been adopted as one method for the classification of tapeworms (scolices, plural; scolex, singular). The attachment organs can be in the form of grooves or suckers. The scolices may possess bothria, bothridia, or suckers.

The latter two are also known as acetabula. An acetabulum (plural acetabula) is a muscular organ; it is a membrane-bounded structure containing radial muscle fibers. Such configuration is absent in a bothrium (plural bothria), with the structure of a groove serving the function of a suction cup. A tapeworm may possess either **4 acetabula** or **2 bothria**, depending on the species. In addition to acetabula or bothria, other structures may be present in the head region. In some species, there is **rostellum**, a knob-like protrusion to enhance attachment. The rostellum may be decorated with hooks to further enhance attachment. Rostellum and hooks are found in many species of the cyclophyllidean tapeworms. An analysis of the hooks' amino acid composition has shown differences between the tapeworm subgroups and suggests the hooks may have evolved independently on multiple occasions (at least 6 times). The cyclophyllidean hooks are made with keratin-like proteins; the non-cyclophyllidean hooks have other proteins yet to be identified (Caira and Jensen 2014). In addition to attachment organs, the nervous (commissure and ganglia functioning as the brain) and osmoregulatory systems are also found in the tapeworm scolex.

The neck immediately follows the head (scolex). It is the region where new segments are being continually added. As the new segments mature, they are progressively displaced posteriorly, thus creating a developmental gradient (from the newest to the oldest, immature to mature). Therefore, the neck is the most metabolically active site of a tapeworm, with an abundance of stem cells (**neoblasts**). This unique feature differs from many other segmented animals; the latter normally generate new segments from growth zones located at their posterior sites.

The **strobila** (plural strobilae) is made up of successive **proglottids** or segments (some scientists think the term segment is a misnomer, as there may be issues with boundary and structure continuation). Within each proglottid is the presence of repetitive structures from all of the main body system: tegument containing periodical folds/grooves to delimit segments, muscular system consistently of transverse muscles plus the main longitudinal muscles running continuously through the proglottids, the excretory/osmoregulatory system with one transversal canal connecting the ventral longitudinal tubules, and the nervous system as stereotypical transverse ring commissures. Once a proglottid has been generated, its development becomes mostly autonomous. Thus, the strobila is a long series of sets of reproductive organs of both sexes, that is, a tapeworm possesses multiple genitalia. From the neck down, the proglottids go from immature, to mature, to gravid (male and female reproductive organs from non-functional, to functional, to segments with mostly fertilized eggs and developing embryos). In **apolysis**, gravid proglottids are detached from the worm and sent directly to the feces. In **anapolysis**, the eggs are released from the gravid proglottids and released to the feces. For tapeworms, massive reproductive output is possible because of the evolution of segmentation.

One estimate suggests a total of **6,000** species of tapeworms (Olson *et al.* 2012). Information on individual species and genera can be found at the Global Cestode Database (Caira and Jensen 2014).[1]

---

[1] https://tapeworms.uconn.edu/

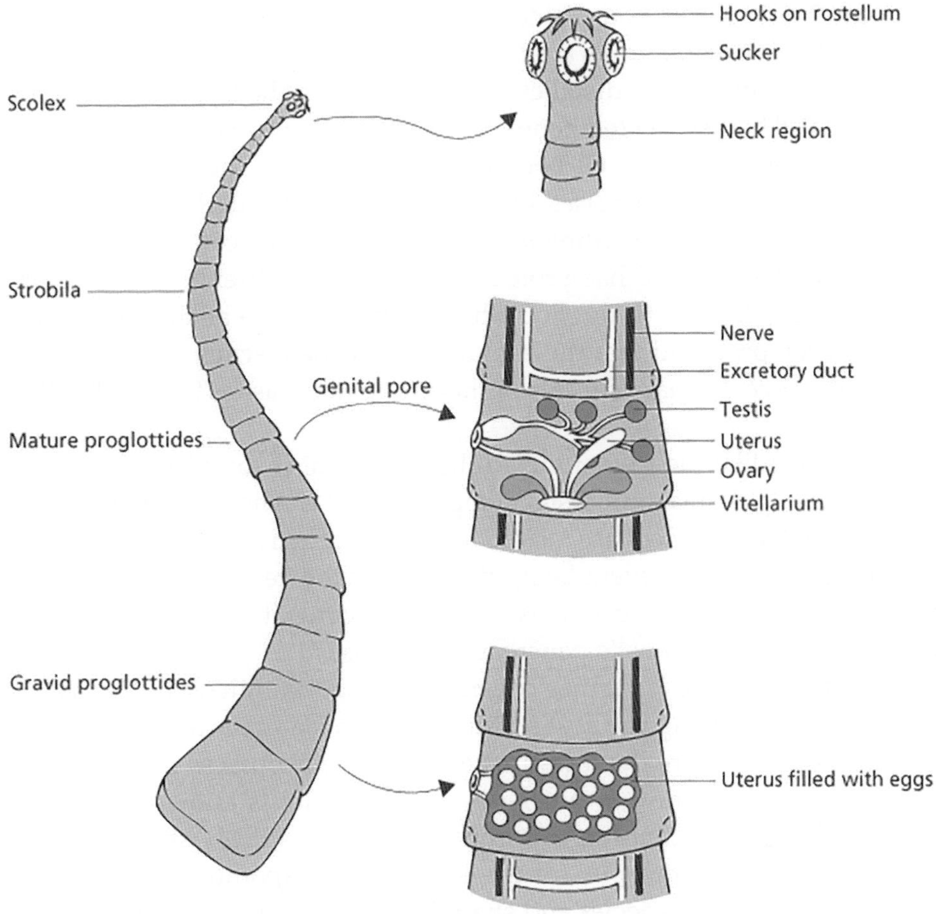

Fig. 14.1 ■ General cestode morphology. Courtesy: Andreassen J. Intestinal tapeworms. In: *Topley & Wilson's Microbiology and Microbial Infections* (2010, Wiley), Wiley Online Library. https://onlinelibrary.wiley.com/doi/abs/10.1002/9780470688618.taw0197 Reproduced with permission from John Wiley and Sons.

14.2 Tegument and Other Structures

Whereas the trematodes possess a blind gut, cestodes do not have a digestive system. Thus, the tapeworm has no gut. However, both adult trematodes and cestodes have a structure known as tegument on their surface. (Please see Figure 11.1 for trematode tegument.) The tapeworm tegument has an added feature, the novel structure named microtriches, with the purpose to increase surface area for nutrient absorption and waste disposal (Jones 1998; Bogitsh *et al.* 2019).

In a discussion on tapeworm evolutionary developmental biology (evo-devo), Uriel Koziol (Universidad de la República, Montevideo, Uruguay) had these comments on the tegument: "One of the most characteristic features of the Neodermata (which gives the group its name) is that their body is covered by a syncytial tegument, the neodermis, which replaces the larval epidermis after the infection of the first (or only) host. This syncytium consists of a continuous distal cytoplasm covering the body wall (the tegument), and of insunken cell bodies located beneath the body wall musculature, where the nuclei of the syncytium reside. These cell bodies are connected to the tegumental cytoplasm through thin cytoplasmatic processes that cross the outer muscle layers and the basal membrane that supports the tegument. The tegument protects the parasite from the immune system of the host, and has a role in the uptake of nutrients (especially in the case of cestodes, which lack a gut throughout the life cycle) and in anchoring the parasite to the host. It has been proposed that the evolution of the neodermis was an important factor in the immense evolutionary success of this group of parasites" (Koziol 2017, citations in text deleted here).

In summary, just like the trematode adults, tegument is found in the cestodes, with cell bodies (**cytons**), proximal and distal cytoplasm, and a syncytial outer layer. The high levels of ATPase in the tegument are related to its need of active transport. These enzymes may also help the worm to prevent being digested by the vertebrate host. [Niclosamide, an inhibitor of worm ATPase, is useful as a tapeworm drug; it causes disintegration of the adult worm by action of the host's pancreatic hydrolases.]

The tapeworm's surface is further covered with special microvilli, so as to increase the surface area for absorbing the host's nutrients. This feature is analogous to the mammalian small intestine, where the intestinal epithelial cells possess microvilli to increase the surface area for absorption of nutrients. The structure is known as the **microthrix** (plural mircrotriches). A scanning electron microscopy (SEM) study has confirmed microtriches to be a **synapomorphy** for the cestodes. (Synapomorphy refers to a characteristic present in an ancient species and shared exclusively by its evolutionary descendants.) After three International Workshops on Cestode Systematics in Storrs, Connecticut, USA in 2002, České Budějovice, the Czech Republic in 2005, and Smolenice, Slovakia in 2008, there is now a unified terminology for cestode microtriches. "The following terms were endorsed for the components of individual microtriches: The distal, electron-dense portion is the *cap*, the proximal more electron-lucent region is the *base*. These two elements are separated from one another by the *baseplate*. The base is composed of, among other elements, *microfilaments*. The cap is composed of *cap tubules*. The electron-lucent central portion of the base is referred to as the *core*. The core may be surrounded by an electron-dense *tunic*. The entire microthrix is bounded by a *plasma membrane*, the external layer of which is referred to as the *glycocalyx*. Two distinct sizes of microtriches are recognized: those ≤200 nm in basal width, termed *filitriches*, and those >200 nm in basal width, termed *spinitriches*" (Chervy 2009). Please see Figure 14.2 for components of microtriches by transmission electron microscopy (TEM), and Figure 14.3 for classification of microtriches based on images from SEM (Chevry 2009). Concerning microtriches, Caira and Jensen (2014) wrote: "Happily, cestodologists have now reached a consensus regarding a standardized terminology for the various forms of these unique tegumental extensions, distinguishing a small type, referred to as a filithrix, from a large type,

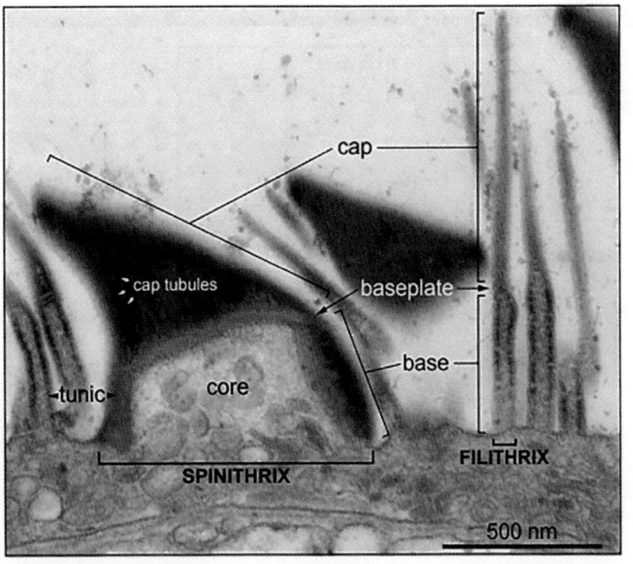

Fig. 14.2 ■ Components of microtriches. Standardized terminology proposed for components of microtriches (filitriches and spinitriches). TEM through proximal surface of bothridium of *Calliobothrium* cf. *verticillatum* (Rudolphi, 1819). Note: base microfilaments and glycocalyx not shown. Courtesy: Chervy L. *Folia Parasitol (Praha)* 2009;56:199–230. Reproduced with permission from *Folia Parasitologica* and Tomas Scholz.

referred to as a spinithrix. In total, **3** forms of **filitriches** and **25** forms of **spinitriches** are recognized."

Microtriches are surface features unique and ubiquitous among cestodes. They form the outermost layer of the cestode tegument. Within the tegument, there are special structures known as calcareous corpuscles. These are composed of calcium and magnesium carbonates, and organized as concentric rings with double envelopes. The exact function is unknown but probably serves for buffering and replenishment of inorganic ions. Beyond the tegument there is the parenchyma, cellular tissue lying in a fluid-filled space between the body wall and the organs of this acoelomate flatworm.

14.3 Life Cycles

Human tapeworms are members of Eucestoda (true tapeworms). They have hexacanth larvae (six hooks). For tapeworm species that infect humans, two types of life cycle development are the pseudophyllidean and the cyclophyllidean patterns. The aquatic life cycle goes from **egg** to **coracidium** (with cilia for swimming), to **procercoid**, to **plerocercoid**, and then to **adult**. The terrestrial life cycle goes from the egg to an **oncosphere,** which goes either to **cysticercus, cysticercoid,** or **hydatid cyst** (depending on the species), as well as to some other forms.

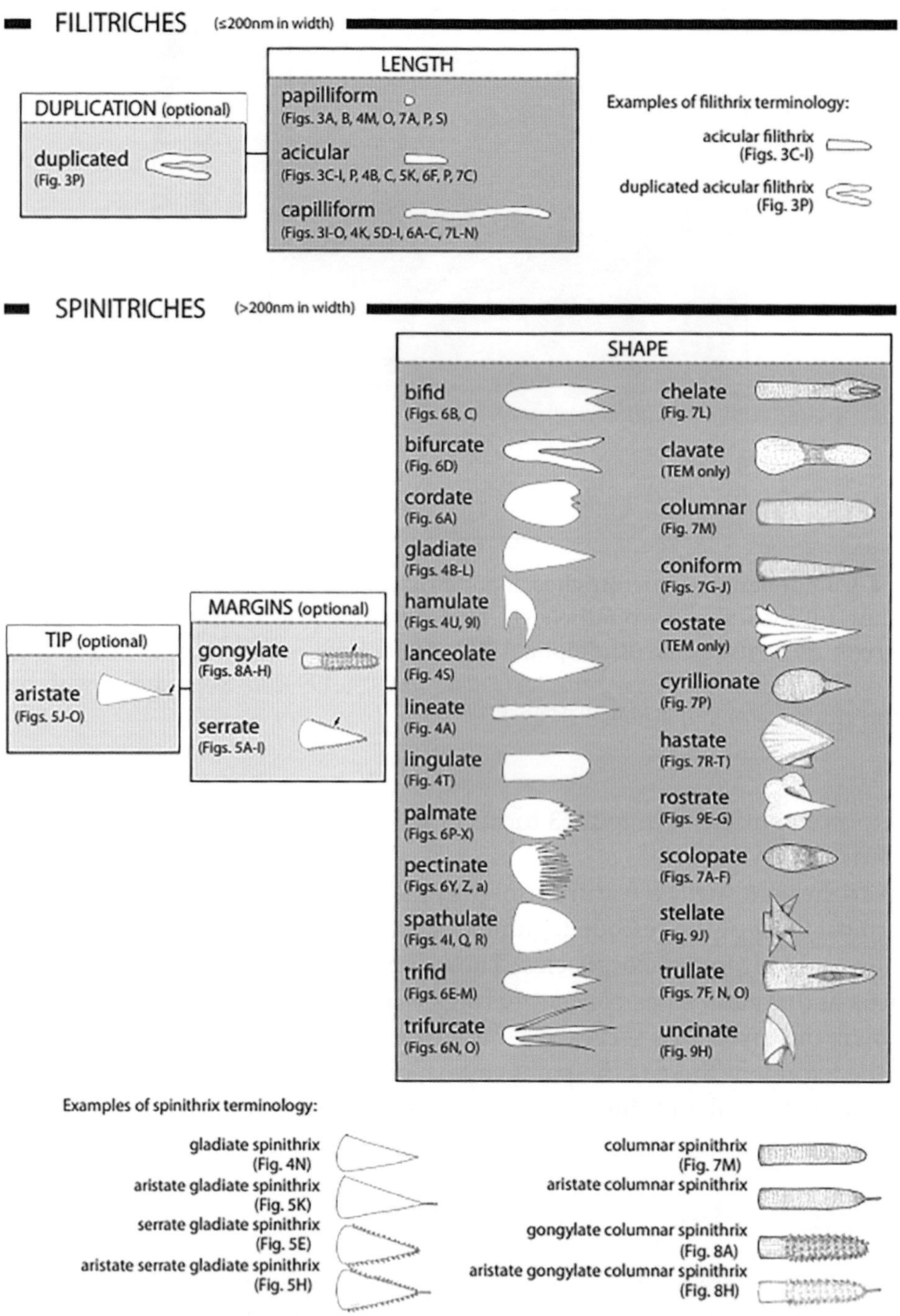

Fig. 14.3 ■ Classification of microtriches based on images from scanning electron microscopy. Schematic representation of terms proposed to describe filithrix (upper panel) and spinithrix (lower panel) forms. Dark grey boxes indicate mandatory descriptors; lighter grey boxes indicate those used only when applicable. Courtesy: Chervy L. *Folia Parasitol (Praha)* 2009;56:199–230. Reproduced with permission from *Folia Parasitologica* and Tomas Scholz.

Achieving by the same approach as consensus terminology for tapeworm microtriches, cestodologists gathered for the Fifth International Workshop on Cestode Systematics and Phylogeny at the Institute of Parasitology, Biology Centre, Academy of Sciences of the Czech Republic (in the city Ceske Budejovice, Czechia) in 2005 to establish a uniform terminology for embryonic envelopes and associated developmental stages of tapeworms. "A consensus was reached for standardized definitions of the oncosphere, hexacanth, coracidium, embryonic envelopes, outer envelope, inner envelope, embryophore, vitelline capsule, shell, and outer coat. All of these are defined as components of the embryo or its vitellocyte-derived or uterine-derived coatings" (Conn and Swiderski 2008).

"Glossary of Terms

Standard terms: Consensus was reached by all participants in the International Workshop on the following 10 definitions, thus standardizing these terms.

Hexacanth — a six-hooked larva derived from micromeres, which is the definitive product of embryogenesis of a cestode, and that invades the first or sole intermediate host.

Oncosphere — a hexacanth enclosed by one or two embryonic envelopes.

Coracidium — a hexacanth enclosed only by a ciliated inner envelope that provides a mechanism for free swimming.

Embryonic envelopes — the two syncytial envelopes derived from blastomeres and completely enclosing developmental stages from the late cleavage embryo through the fully formed hexacanth larva.

Outer envelope — the outermost embryonic envelope, derived from macromeres and enclosing all other embryonic and larval components. This envelope generally undergoes apoptosis early in embryonic development, and prior to final morphogenesis of the hexacanth.

Inner envelope — the innermost embryonic envelope, derived from mesomeres and enclosing micromeres and ultimately the hexacanth. This envelope generally persists throughout embryonic and larval development, and thus may be considered part of the fully formed larva.

Embryophore — name applied both to the full ciliated inner envelope of a coracidium, and to a specialized intracellular proteinaceous lamina produced within the inner envelope of a cestode with a non-swimming oncosphere. (Note: some authorities prefer to distinguish the motile inner envelope of a coracidium by referring to it as a "ciliated embryophore".)

Vitelline capsule — a thin proteinaceous layer that forms from coalescence of material released by exocytosis from one or more vitellocytes near the time of fertilization, and that quickly encloses the vitellocyte(s) along with a single oocyte and a single sperm. Depending on the species, this layer may or may not persist through embryogenesis.

Shell — sclerotin proteinaceous material that is secreted by vitellocytes and is deposited on the inner surface of the vitelline capsule prior to hardening by a polyphenol/quinone tanning process. This occurs in cestode species that have a large number of vitellocytes per oocyte (i.e., polylecithal). The hardened shell typically encloses the oncosphere outside the host.

Outer coat — proteinaceous or other material that is secreted by the oviduct and/or uterus and is deposited on the outer surface of the vitelline capsule in some cestode species that have one or few vitellocytes per oocyte (i.e., oligolecithal)" (Conn and Swiderski 2008).

In addition, diagrammatic representations of developing tapeworm eggs are provided in the publication. Please see Figures 14.4A and 14.4B for mature oncospheres of pseudophyllidean and cyclophyllidean cestodes, respectively (Conn and Swiderski 2008).

Actual images of tapeworm development are visualized by light microscopy. For aquatic tapeworms, please see Figure 14.5A for coracidium of *Spirometra* sp. from Malaysia (copepod to hamster to cat) (Kavana *et al.* 2014) and Figure 14.5B for procercoid of *Schistocephalus solidus* (copepod to fish to bird) by light microscopy (Jakobsen *et al.* 2012). Please see Figure 14.6 for plerocercoid of *Dibothriocephalus latus* (syn. *Diphyllobothrium latum*) by SEM showing variations in microtriches (Barčák *et al.* 2019).

For terrestrial tapeworms, please see Figure 14.7A & B for *Taenia asiatica* egg by SEM and Figure 14.7C for *Taenia* egg sketch (Galán-Puchades *et al.* 2016), and Figure 14.8 for oncosphere and postoncospheral forms of *Taenia solium* by SEM (Chile *et al.* 2016). Please see Figure 14.9A for the ultrastructure of the *Echinococcus multilocularis* egg by TEM and Figure 14.9B for egg envelope sketch (Świderski *et al.* 2017). In vitro postoncosphere development for *Taenia saginata* has been established, please see Figure 14.10 for scolex development after 189 days in culture (Palma *et al.* 2019).

Life cycles of cestodes exhibit diversity; many species have shown variations in their developmental strategies. However, invariable aspects of the life cycles have been established for a generalized life cycle scheme (with all the main transitions). The adult lives in the intestine of a vertebrate definitive host (with few exceptions). It is (almost always) a hermaphrodite (thus generating zygotes by sexual reproduction). Further embryonic development ends in a small larval form (for environmental release). The larva infects an intermediate host (typically an invertebrate, but can be a vertebrate), where it undergoes metamorphosis to the next stage, the **metacestode**. The metacestode is considered either a larval form or a juvenile, because it already possesses a body plan like the adult (with a scolex and the general organization of primary tissues and systems). Eventually, it is ingested by the definitive host (together with the intermediate host), where it develops into the adult stage to complete the life cycle. In aquatic tapeworm species, the metacestodes often transit through one or more intermediate hosts, where further growth/development may occur.

From the fertilized eggs, proliferating cells develop into the larva proper (usually called "**hexacanth** larva" with the presence of 6 larval hooks, in 3 pairs) together with

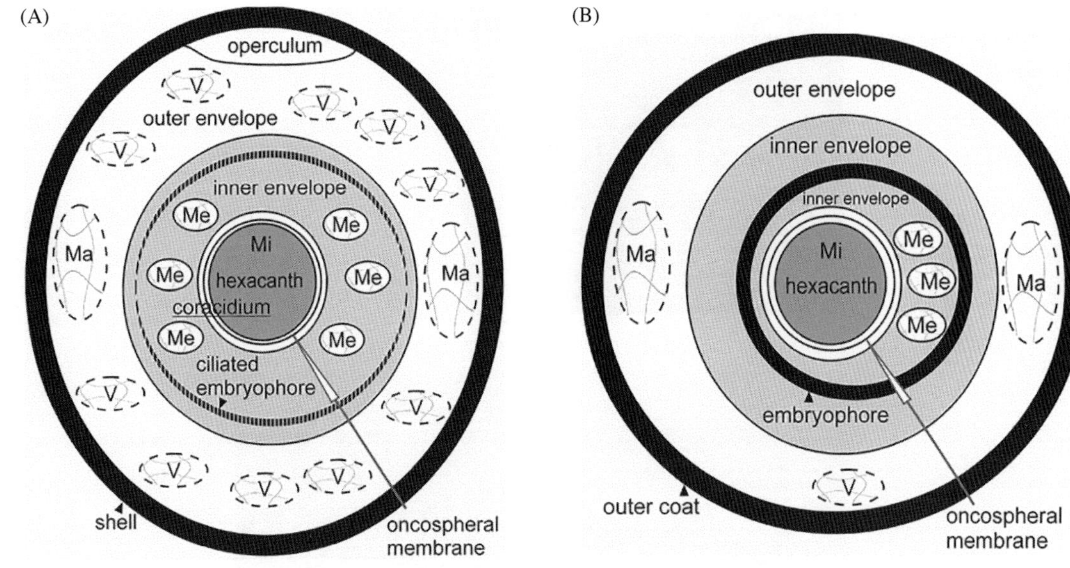

Fig. 14.4 ■ Mature oncosphere of (A) pseudophyllidean and (B) cyclophyllidean cestodes. (A) Diagrammatic representation of a fully formed oncosphere of a cestode with polylecithal eggs and a ciliated embryophore (e.g., Diphyllobothriidea, some Bothriocephalidea). The vitelline capsule, formed by secretions of numerous vitellocytes (V) at fertilisation, becomes coated internally by shell precursors secreted from vitellocyte vesicles, and the vitellocytes have deteriorated. These species have a suture at one end of the shell, forming an operculum. The syncytial outer envelope derived from macromeres (Ma), including all organelles, has deteriorated by apoptosis. The syncytial inner envelope derived from numerous mesomeres (Me) remains active, becoming a ciliated embryophore that, together with the enclosed hexacanth, constitute a coracidium, which will swim actively after emerging from the surrounding outer envelope remnant and shell, through the operculum. The oncospheral membrane has formed by membrane delamination between the inner envelope and hexacanth. The hexacanth, which is derived from micromeres (Mi) and is the only part that will invade the next host after it ingests the coracidium, is now fully formed. The exact number of formative blastomeres of each type, and the number of cells making up the final hexacanth, varies between species. **(B)** Diagrammatic representation of a fully formed oncosphere of a cestode with oligolecithal eggs and belonging to the order Cyclophyllidea. The vitelline capsule, formed by secretions of 1–2 vitellocytes (V) at fertilization, disappears altogether in some species, thickens in others, or becomes covered externally by uterine secretions to form the outer coat in others; the outer coat varies greatly in thickness between species. The syncytial outer envelope derived from macromeres (Ma), including all organelles, has deteriorated by apoptosis. The syncytial inner envelope derived from mesomeres (Me) remains active, forming the embryophore as an intracellular proteinaceous lamina. The oncospheral membrane has formed by membrane delamination between the inner envelope and hexacanth. The hexacanth, which is derived from micromeres (Mi) and is the only part that will invade the next host, is now fully formed. The exact number of formative blastomeres of each type, and the number of cells making up the final hexacanth, varies between species. Courtesy: Conn D, Swiderski Z. *Folia Parasitol (Praha)* 2008;55:42–52. Reproduced with permission from *Folia Parasitologica* and Tomas Scholz.

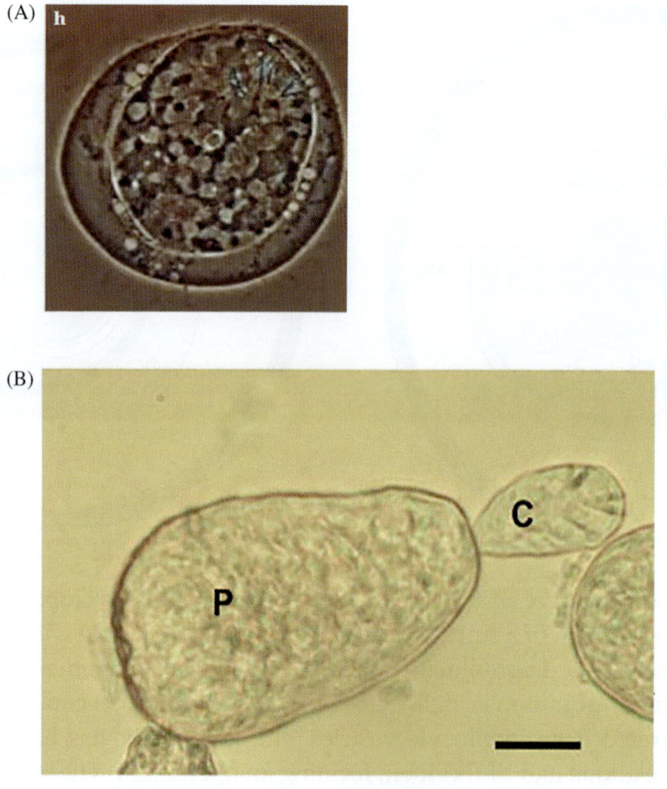

Fig. 14.5 ■ **(A) Coracidium of *Spirometra* sp. from Malaysia.** h: Hatched coracidium, 3 pairs of hooks are obvious under light microscope. Courtesy: Kavana *et al.*, 2014, *Trop Biomed*. 31, 487–495. Reproduced with permission from *Tropical Biomedicine*, Stephen Ambu, and Chandrawathani Panchadcharam. **(B) Procercoid of *Schistocephalus solidus*.** A fully developed procercoid (P) bred for 33 days in the culture. The cercomer (C) seems to be fully separated from the body (bar = 10 μm). Courtesy: Jakobsen *et al. Exp Parasitol* 2012;130:267–73. Reproduced with permission from Elsevier.

syncytial coverings that segregate from the early embryo (the inner and outer envelopes). In the aquatic tapeworm lineages including Diphyllobothriidea, the inner envelope may be ciliated (the ciliated form is named **coracidium**). In terrestrial tapeworm species, the larval form is known as the **oncosphere**, consisting of a hexacanth (with penetration glands and 6 larval hooks) plus envelopes covering the hexacanth that will be discarded during the infection. The oncosphere can only infect the intermediate host passively, i.e. the host must ingest the oncosphere. The oncosphere is composed of very few cells (less than 200); it could be evolutionarily derived from a more complex larva by extensive reduction of the larval body plan. An oncosphere develops into larval and juvenile forms or metacestodes. There are active studies on tapeworm life cycle developments, as well as searches for unknown intermediate hosts. For example, the postoncospheral (PO) form of *Taenia solium*, an intermediate form between oncosphere and cysticercus, has been

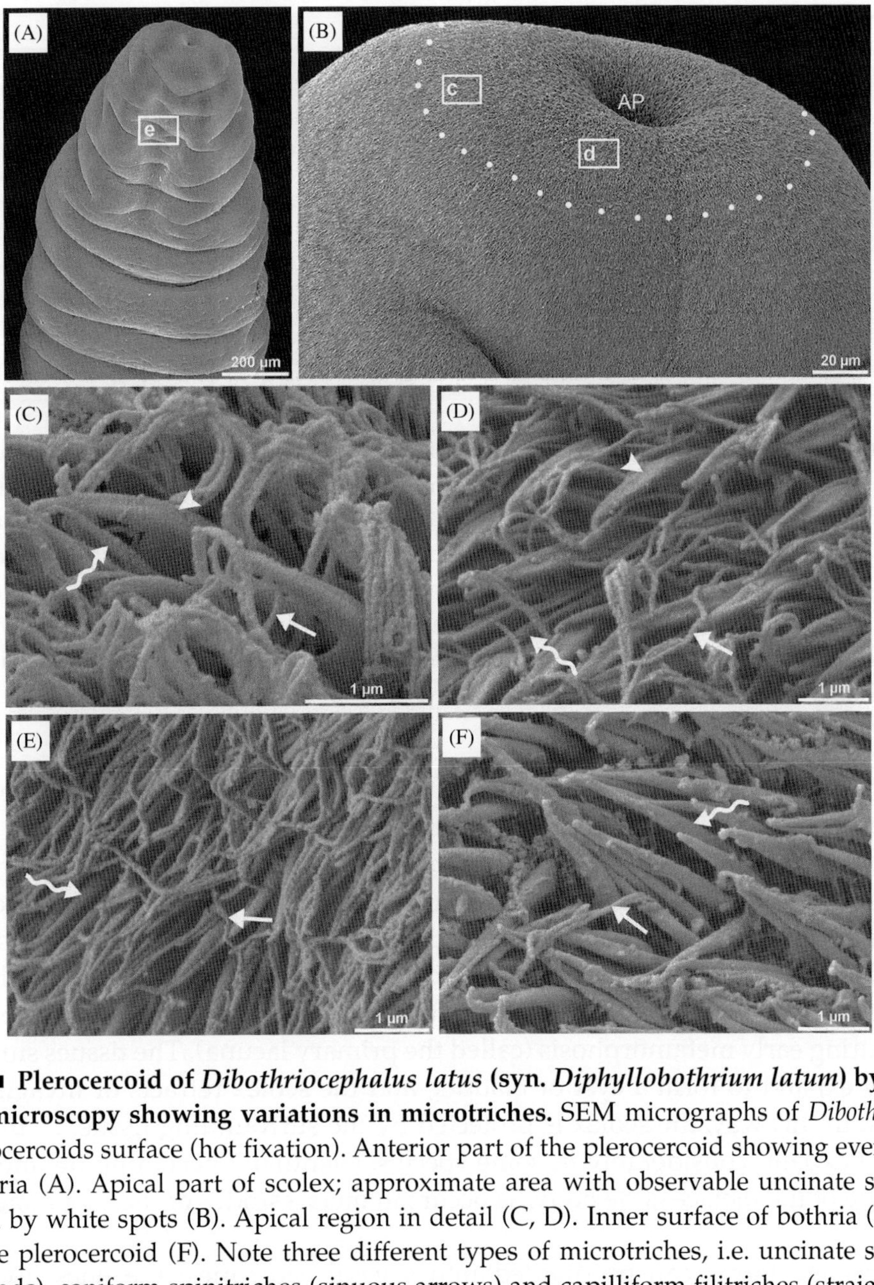

Fig. 14.6 ■ Plerocercoid of *Dibothriocephalus latus* (syn. *Diphyllobothrium latum*) by scanning electron microscopy showing variations in microtriches. SEM micrographs of *Dibothriocephalus latus* plerocercoids surface (hot fixation). Anterior part of the plerocercoid showing everted scolex with bothria (A). Apical part of scolex; approximate area with observable uncinate spinitriches demarked by white spots (B). Apical region in detail (C, D). Inner surface of bothria (E). Middle part of the plerocercoid (F). Note three different types of microtriches, i.e. uncinate spinitriches (arrow heads), coniform spinitriches (sinuous arrows) and capilliform filitriches (straight arrows) (A–F). *Abbreviation*: AP, apical pore. Courtesy: Barčák *et al. Parasit Vectors* 2019;12:408. Reproduced with permission from *Parasites & Vectors* with Creative Commons Attribution 4.0 (CC-BY) International License.

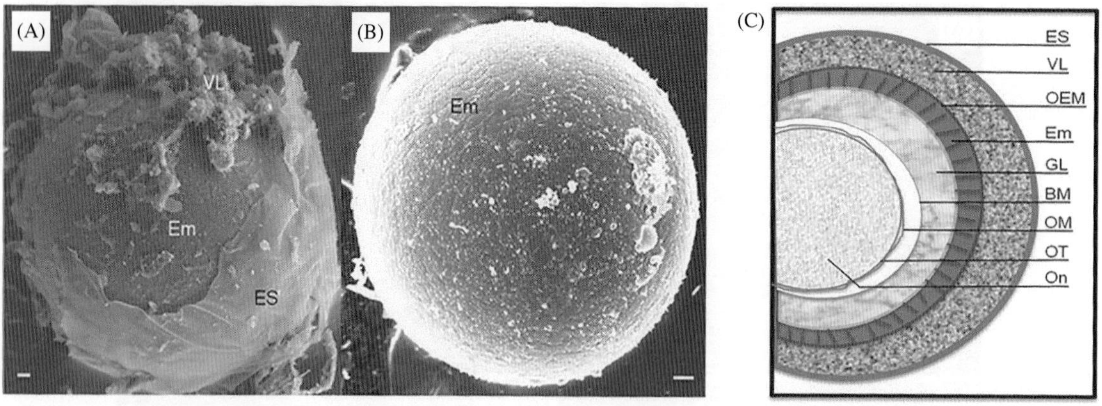

Fig. 14.7 ■ *Taenia* egg. (A) SEM image of an immature egg of *T. asiatica* showing remains of the egg shell and the vitelline layer adhered to the embryophore. (B) SEM image of an embryophore without its most external layers. (*Scale bars* for (A) 1 μm and for (B) 2 μm.) (C) Drawing of the general morphology of a *Taenia* egg with the different envelopes which surround the oncosphere. *ES* egg shell, *VL* vitelline layer, *OEM* outer embryonic membrane, *Em* embryophore, *GL* granular layer, *BM* basal membrane, *OM* oncospheral membrane, *OT* oncospheral tegument, *On* oncosphere. Courtesy: Galán-Puchades *et al. Parasitol Res* 2016;115:3649–55. Reproduced with permission from Springer Nature.

investigated for 60 days in vitro, in a co-culture system using HCT-8 human intestine cells as a feeder layer, as shown in Figure 14.8 (Chile *et al.* 2016).

Among different cestode lineages, morphological and developmental diversity are found for the metacestode stage. These variations indicate adaptation of metacestodes to their targeted intermediate or definitive hosts. Many human infections are caused by the cyclophyllidean group of tapeworms. "One derived developmental character that can be found in most cyclophyllideans is the formation of a cavity within the developing metacestode during early metamorphosis (called the primary lacuna). The tissues surrounding this cavity expand to form a cyst or bladder, and the scolex retracts or invaginates into this cavity. In this way, the scolex is protected by the surrounding tissue. … the bladder tissue may expand considerably in some species, eventually becoming the most prominent feature of the metacestode body, as occurs in metacestodes of the Taeniidae" (Koziol 2017).

Metacestode forms can be divided into several categories; the ones involving in human parasitic tapeworms are discussed here. The **cysticercus** is a single invaginated scolex situated on the germinal membrane which encloses a fluid-filled space (known as a bladder). Examples are *Taenia saginata* and *Taenia solium*. The **cysticercoid** is a solid bodied structure including a single invaginated scolex. An example is *Hymenolepsis nana*. In contrast, the **hydatid** is a cyst of fluid-filled space housing multiple developing tapeworm larvae. The cyst is a thin germinal layer surrounded by a laminated layer (acellular, with polysaccharides from materials secreted from the germinal layer tegument). Inside the

Fig. 14.8 ■ Oncosphere and postoncospheral forms of *Taenia solium* by scanning electron microscopy. Scanning electron micrographs of *T. solium* postoncospheral forms. (A) *T. solium* activated oncosphere showing elongated microvilli. (B) 15 day postoncospheral forms showing the protuberance at one end of the body. (C) Close-up of the tegument of 30 day postoncospheral form showing microtriches. (D) 30 day postoncospheral form showing vesicles. Courtesy: Chile *et al.* *PLoS Negl Trop Dis* 2016;10:e0004396. Reproduced with permission from *PLoS Neglected Tropical Diseases* with Creative Commons Attribution 4.0 (CC-BY) International License.

cyst are the brood capsules. Protoscolices (singular protoscolex) are formed by budding within the brood capsules. With a single cyst, thousands, even millions, of protoscolices can be found. The unilocular hydatid is a single defined cyst. An example is *Echinococcus granulosus*. The multilocular hydatid is a cyst that lacks a defined shape and develops through the host tissue. An example is *Echinococcus multilocularis*. As a single protoscolex

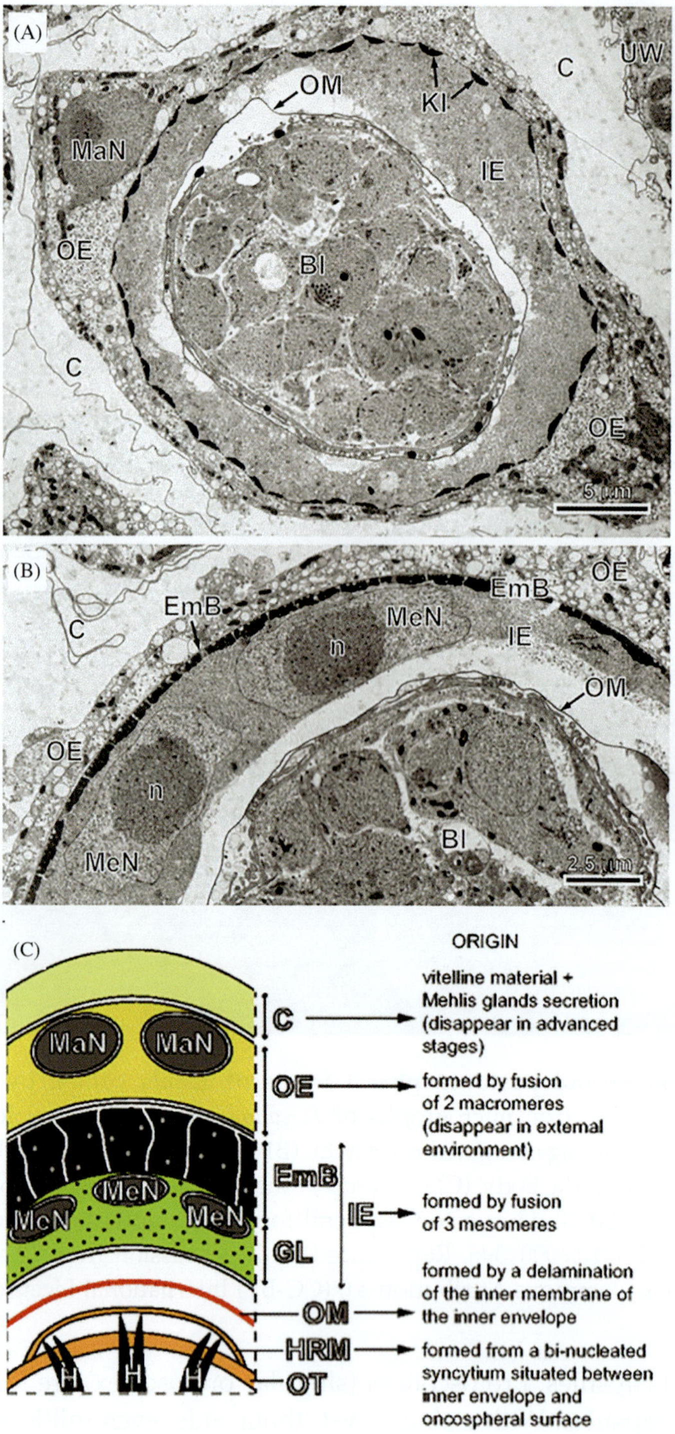
(A)
OM
KI
C
UW
MaN
IE
OE
Bl
C
OE
5 µm
(B)
EmB
OE
C
MeN
n
IE
OM
OE
n
Bl
MeN
2.5 µm
(C)
ORIGIN
MaN
MaN
C
vitelline material + Mehlis glands secretion (disappear in advanced stages)
OE
formed by fusion of 2 macromeres (disappear in external environment)
EmB
MeN
MeN
MeN
IE
formed by fusion of 3 mesomeres
GL
formed by a delamination of the inner membrane of the inner envelope
OM
HRM
formed from a bi-nucleated syncytium situated between inner envelope and oncospheral surface
H
H
H
OT

will develop into a tapeworm, asexual reproduction is present in the tapeworm species with hydatid cysts during life cycle development. Please see Figure 14.11 for the main types of metacestodes (Koziol 2017). There are other types of cestode larvae and metacestodes. "Based on a review of the literature, the key characters differentiating the types of larval cestodes are the presence of a primary lacuna and the invagination/retraction of the scolex. The presence of a cercomer and of a bladder-like enlargement of the larval cestode were considered to be useful secondary characteristics" (Chevry 2002). [Individual species of tapeworms are discussed in Chapter 15 and Chapter 16.]

A dedicated cestode life cycle database is available (Lefebvre *et al.* 2009).[2]

14.4 Evolution of Cestodes

The majority of adult cestodes parasitize vertebrates. The following steps can be one scenario of tapeworm evolution. An ancestral free-living, bottom-dwelling marine form evolved adhesive organs. First, it became attached as an ectoparasite to a bottom-dwelling vertebrate. Next, the ectoparasitic form migrated internally to the gut and became an endoparasite — the tapeworm (Bogitsh *et al.* 2019).

A diverse spectrum of tapeworm species infects elasmobranchs (sharks and rays). There are 977 species, covering 201 genera and 9 orders. Many tapeworm species are

Fig. 14.9 (figure on facing page) ■ *Echinococcus* egg. (A, B) The ultrastructure of the *Echinococcus multilocularis* egg by transmission electron microscopy. Ultrastructure of *Echinococcus multilocularis* eggs in the middle and more advanced preoncospheral phase of the embryonic development. (A) Median cross section through the entire egg in the middle phase of preoncospheral development. Note the (1) presence of four embryonic envelopes (vitelline capsule, outer envelope, inner envelope and oncospheral membrane), undergoing differentiation into oncospheral or egg envelopes, (2) presence of a large nucleus of macromere in the outer envelope, (3) presence of a discontinuous layer of flat embryophoric islands of keratin-like protein adjacent to the outer membrane of the inner envelope and (4) evident detachment of the oncospheral membrane from the inner surface of the inner envelope which participated in its formation. (B) Part of the embryo showing a thin layer of embryophoric blocks and two large flattened mesomere nuclei with prominent electron-dense nucleoli situated in the deeper granular sub-layer of the inner envelope. *Bl* blastomere, *C* vitelline capsule, *EmB* embryophoric blocks of keratin-like protein, *IE* inner envelope, *KI* keratin-like protein islands, *MaN* macromere nucleus, *MeN* mesomere nucleus, *n* nucleolus, *OE* outer envelope, *OM* oncospheral membrane, *UW* uterine wall. **(C) Egg envelope sketch.** Schematic diagram recapitulating our data on egg envelope ultrastructure with notes on the origin of different layers. *C* vitelline capsule, *EmB* embryophoric blocks of keratin-like protein, *GL* granular layer of embryophore, *H* oncospheral hooks, *HRM* hook region membrane, *IE* inner envelope, *MaN* macromere nucleus, *MeN* mesomere nucleus, *OE* outer envelope, *OM* oncospheral membrane, *OT* oncospheral tegument. Courtesy: Świderski *et al. Parasitol Res* 2017;116:1963–71. Reproduced with permission from *Parasitology Research* with Creative Commons Attribution 4.0 (CC-BY) International License.

[2] http://clcdb.myspecies.info/

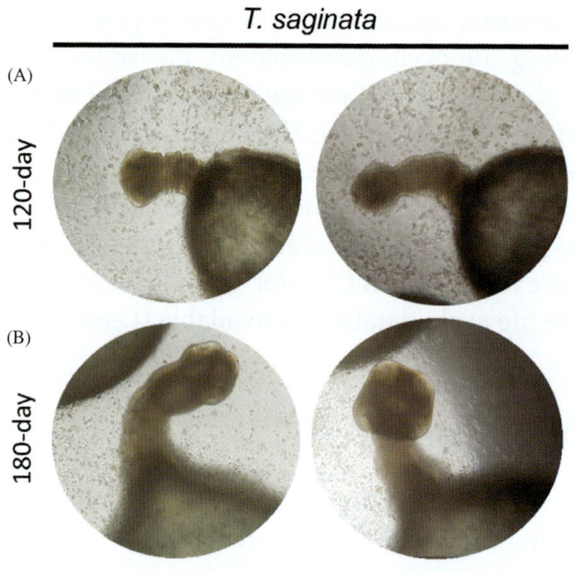

Fig. 14.10 ■ *Taenia saginata* scolex development. Light microphotography of *T. saginata* postoncospheral form at 120 and 180 days of culture in INT-407 cells. At 120 days of culture a pre-scolex-like structure appears (A) and at 180 days of culture, a scolex appears (B). Magnification 100x. Courtesy: Palma *et al. PLoS Negl Trop Dis* 2019;13:e0007261. Reproduced with permission from *PLoS Neglected Tropical Diseases* with Creative Commons Attribution 4.0 (CC-BY) International License.

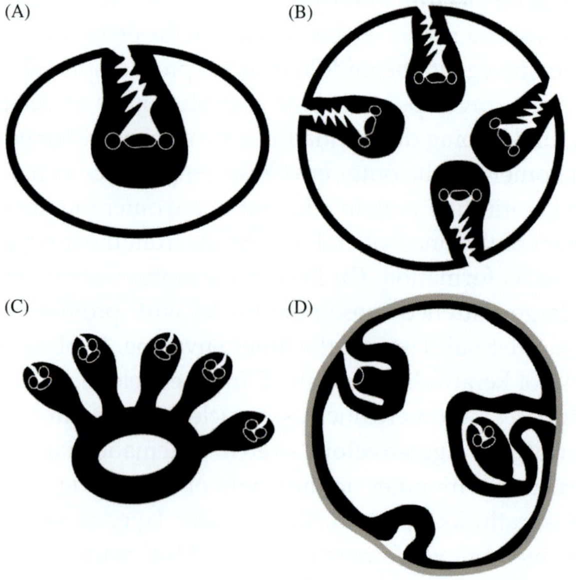

Fig. 14.11 ■ Main types of metacestodes. Diagram showing some of the main types of metacestodes found in the Taeniidae. (A) Cysticercus. (B) Coenurus. (C) Polycephalic. (D) Hydatid (the laminated layer is represented in light grey). Courtesy: Koziol U. *Exp Parasitol* 2007;180:84–100. Reproduced with permission from Elsevier.

specific to their host species of cartilaginous fish (elasmobranchs). Both the host fish and the tapeworm parasites are organisms of the marine environment. However, some elasmobranchs can enter estuarine waters, and several groups, independently, have adapted to the freshwater environment. From phylogenetic analyses, after the tapeworms had parasitized the elasmobranchs, they became the source of essentially all acetabulate taxa that would parasitize the freshwater and terrestrial hosts. Furthermore, it appears to be a rare event — it might have happened only two times (twice). Terrestrial tapeworm species infecting humans belong to the order Cyclophyllidea; this group (clade) "containing … the remarkably speciose Cyclophyllidea. This clade is often referred to as the 'terrestrial clade' because the majority of its members parasitize terrestrial birds, mammals, and snakes, with only a few hosted by marine birds and mammals, and freshwater fishes" (Caira and Jensen 2014). Please see Figure 14.12 for cestode evolution (Caira *et al.* 2014).

The aquatic bothrial tapeworms possessing the ciliated coracidia (singular, coracidium) diverged earlier from the later acetabular species. In a study of tapeworm phylogeny, with 30 species, including sequences of their large and small nuclear ribosomal RNA subunits, large subunit mitochondrial ribosomal RNA, and cytochrome c oxidase subunit I (cox1), it was concluded that humans have been acquired as accidental hosts 4 times across the various members of the diphyllobothriidean tapeworms (Waeschenbach *et al.* 2017).

Cyclophyllidean tapeworms are terrestrial; they use birds and mammals as definitive hosts. A case of host switch has been found in Africa. The cyclophyllean tapeworm made a switch from bird to fish. "Tapeworms (Cestoda) of the order Cyclophyllidea include over 3,000 species of intestinal parasites of tetrapods, especially birds and mammals including humans. However, adults of cyclophyllideans have never been found in bony fishes, even though hundreds of thousands of these hosts have been examined for parasites globally over more than 250 years. In the present paper, we report on a unique example of host switching of a tapeworm from birds to teleost fish in Africa. A new genus, Ichthyolepis (Cyclophyllidea: Dilepididae), is erected to accommodate ***Ichthyolepis africana*** n. sp., which is the first cyclophyllidean tapeworm that sexually matures in teleost fishes. The new species parasitizes several freshwater elephantfishes (Mormyriformes: Mormyridae). … All fish hosts of the new tapeworm are bottom feeders, live in muddy biotopes and are insectivorous, which indicates that its intermediate hosts may be insect larvae" (Scholz *et al.* 2020). Please see Figure 14.13 for this amazing species by SEM (Scholz *et al.* 2020).

14.5 Niclosamide

Although human tapeworm infections are less prevalent than ones from trematodes (especially *Schistosoma* species), "their enormous reproductive output and potential for metastatic growth can produce severe pathological consequences" (Olson *et al.* 2012). In immunocompromised patients, there can be lethal invasive metastatic larval disease (ces-

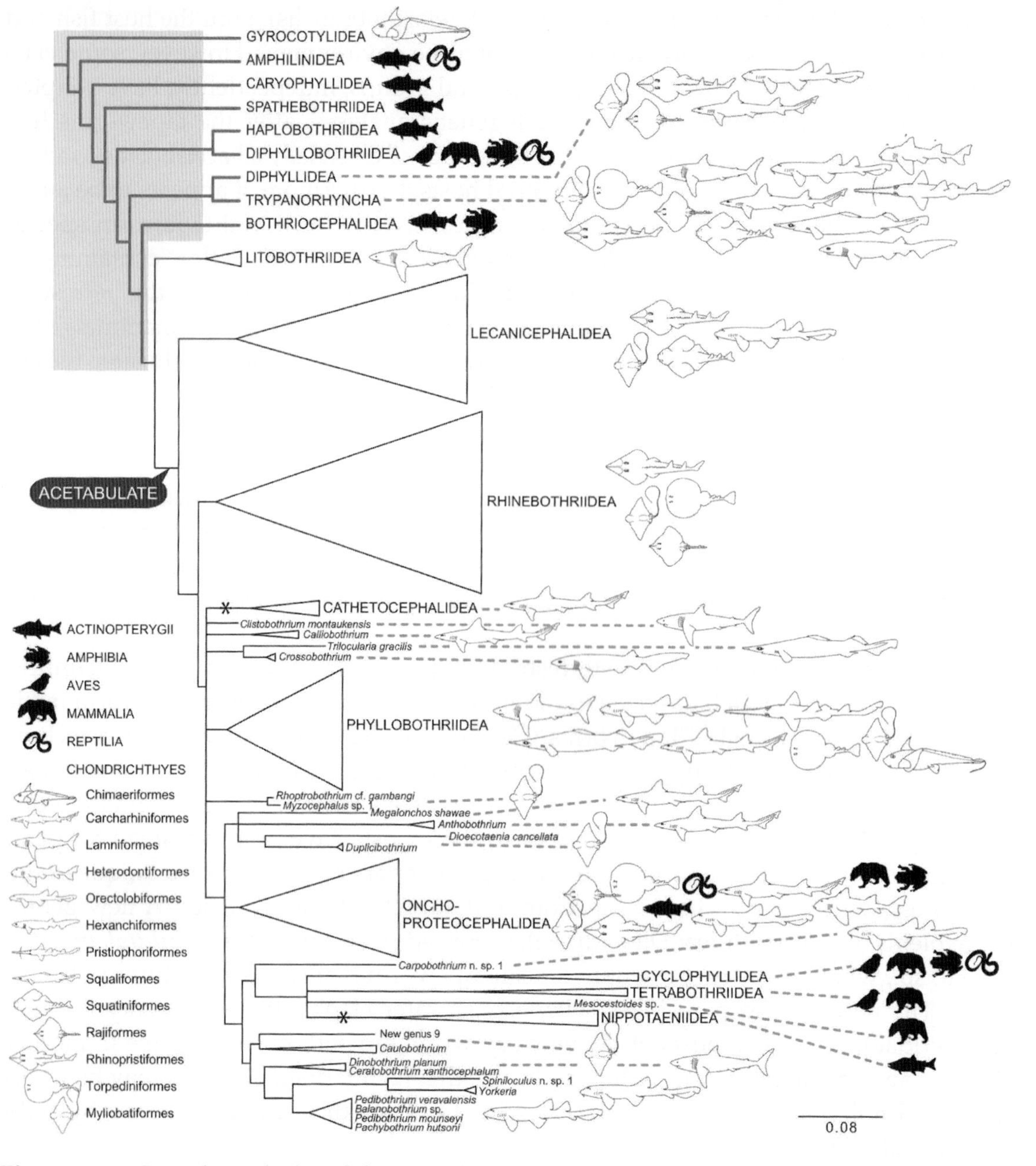

Fig. 14.12 ■ Cestode evolution. Schematic diagram of phylogenetic tree (with outgroups). Major vertebrate host groups are indicated. Nodes which were supported by <0.95 Bayesian posterior probability and/or <75% Maximum Likelihood bootstrap support were collapsed. Asterisks indicate loss of acetabulae. Branch length scale bar indicates number of substitutions per site. Courtesy: Caira *et al. Int J Parasitol* 2014;44:55–73. Reproduced with permission from Elsevier.

Fig. 14.13 ■ *Ichthyolepis africana* n. sp. by scanning electron microscopy. *Ichthyolepis africana* gen. et sp. n. from *Marcusenius macrolepidotus* (type host), South Africa (A–C) and *Marcusenius senegalensis*, Senegal (D–J). (A, B) Sublateral view of the scolex and everted rostellum with 40 hooks in two rows, respectively; (C) rostellum with everted hooks; (D–G) frontal and apical views of the scolex and its surface (outer rim of suckers and sucker cavity) with acicular filitriches; scanning electron micrographs; (H–J) eggs in distilled water (courtesy of J. Mariaux). Courtesy: Scholz *et al.* *Int J Parasitol* 2020;50:561–8. Reproduced with permission from Elsevier.

todiasis) (2 cases reported to date) (Olson *et al.* 2003) and tapeworm cell malignant transformation in one AIDS patient (Muehlenbachs *et al.* 2015); both were due to *Hymenolepis nana*. It has been remarked that: "The challenges of inhibiting cancer tumors and metacestodes (particularly those of *E. multilocularis*) with drugs are in some ways similar; both show uncontrolled proliferation, invasion and metastasis, and are difficult to kill without causing damage to the surrounding tissue. Therefore, metacestodes may be vulnerable to similar strategies as cancer; suppression of mitosis, induction of apoptosis and prevention of DNA replication" (Tsai *et al.* 2013).

Therapeutic drugs for tapeworms include **niclosamide** and **praziquantel**. Niclosamide is an inhibitor of worm ATPase. It causes the disintegration of adult worms by digestion in the presence of pancreatic enzymes. Besides tapeworms, niclosamide is active against bacteria and viruses, including *Helicobacter pylori* and SARS-CoV, respectively (Chen *et al.* 2018; Tharmalingam *et al.* 2018). It may play a role in several metabolic diseases, such as inflammatory airway disease (Cabrita *et al.* 2019), diabetes, rheumatoid arthritis, and others (Chen *et al.* 2018). In the field of cancer, niclosamide has been shown to target cancer stem cells (CSCs), the cells that putatively maintain the cancer state. Niclosamide can block multiple CSC signaling pathways, such as NF-κB, Notch, STAT3, and Wnt. In a screening for repurposed drugs targeting CSCs, investigators from Taiwan selected niclosamide from a chemical library containing 1,258 drugs to demonstrate its effect in the inhibition of human breast and ovarian cancer stem cells (Yo *et al.* 2012; Wang *et al.* 2013; Chan *et al.* 2018).

Historically, niclosamide was discovered in the Bayer Company in 1953. Originally developed as a molluscicide and named Bayluscide, it was marketed in 1959 to destroy gastropod snails, the intermediate host of blood flukes (trematodes). In 1960, Bayer scientists discovered its activity against tapeworms. Named Yomesan, niclosamide was marketed in 1962 for human use. Approved by the US Food and Drug Administration (FDA) for use in humans to treat tapeworm infection in 1982, niclosamide is included in the World Health Organization's list of essential medicines, although its exact mechanisms of action still have not been delineated. However, it has been reported to involve the uncoupling of oxidative phosphorylation. Niclosamide is a multifunctional drug that can inhibit/regulate multiple signaling pathways and biological processes. Hence, there is repurposing of niclosamide from tapeworm-targeting to other diseases and disorders (Chen *et al.* 2018; Fong *et al.* 2021).

Summary & Key Concepts

- Trematodes possess a blind gut; cestodes have no digestive system.
- Tapeworms are remarkably adapted to parasitism: attachment structures, hermaphroditic adult stage with serial repetition of reproductive systems, complex life cycles usually with two or more hosts, and specialized larval stages designed for invasion of each host.
- The body of a tapeworm is composed of the head (scolex), the neck, and the strobila (made up of proglottids).
- Just like the trematode adults, tegument is found in the cestodes, with cytons, proximal and distal cytoplasm. The syncytial outer layer is covered with microtriches to increase surface area for nutrient absorption.
- Human tapeworms include ones with either the pseudophyllidean or the

cyclophyllidean patterns of life cycle development.

- The aquatic tapeworm develops from an egg to coracidium, to procercoid, to plerocercoid, and then to adult.
- The terrestrial tapeworm develops from oncosphere to metacestodes (including cysticercus, cysticercoid, or hydatid cyst, depending on the species).
- Therapeutic drugs for tapeworms include niclosamide and praziquantel. Niclosamide has been shown to inhibit cancer stem cell signaling pathways.

References

Andreassen J. Intestinal tapeworms. In: *Topley & Wilson's Microbiology and Microbial Infections* (2010, Wiley). Wiley Online Library. https://onlinelibrary.wiley.com/doi/abs/10.1002/9780470688618.taw0197

Barčák D, Yoneva A, Sehadová H, Oros M, Gustinelli A, Kuchta R. Complex insight on microanatomy of larval "human broad tapeworm" *Dibothriocephalus latus* (Cestoda: Diphyllobothriidea). *Parasit Vectors* 2019;12(1):408.

Bogitsh BJ, Carter CE, Oeltmann TN. *Human Parasitology*, 5th edition (2019, Elsevier).

Cabrita I, Benedetto R, Schreiber R, Kunzelmann K. Niclosamide repurposed for the treatment of inflammatory airway disease. *JCI Insight* 2019;4(15):128414.

Caira JN, Jensen K. A digest of elasmobranch tapeworms. *J Parasitol* 2014;100(4):373–91.

Caira JN, Jensen K, Waeschenbach A, Olson PD, Littlewood DT. Orders out of chaos — Molecular phylogenetics reveals the complexity of shark and stingray tapeworm relationships. *Int J Parasitol* 2014;44(1):55–73.

Chan MM, Chen R, Fong D. Targeting cancer stem cells with dietary phytochemical — Repositioned drug combinations. *Cancer Lett* 2018;433:53–64.

Chen W, Mook RA Jr, Premont RT, Wang J. Niclosamide: Beyond an antihelminthic drug. *Cell Signal* 2018;41:89–96.

Chervy L. The terminology of larval cestodes or metacestodes. *Syst Parasitol* 2002;52(1):1–33.

Chervy L. Unified terminology for cestode microtriches: A proposal from the International Workshops on Cestode Systematics in 2002–2008. *Folia Parasitol (Praha)*. 2009;56(3):199–230.

Chile N, Clark T, Arana Y, *et al.* In Vitro Study of *Taenia solium* Postoncospheral Form. *PLoS Negl Trop Dis* 2016;10(2):e0004396.

Conn DB, Swiderski Z. A standardised terminology of the embryonic envelopes and associated developmental stages of tapeworms (Platyhelminthes: Cestoda). *Folia Parasitol (Praha)*. 2008;55(1):42–52.

Fong D, Christensen CT, Chan MM. Targeting cancer stem cells with repurposed drugs to improve current therapies. *Recent Pat Anticancer Drug Discov*. 2021;16(2):136–60.

Galán-Puchades MT, Yang Y, Marcilla A, *et al.* First ultrastructural data on the human tapeworm *Taenia asiatica* eggs by scanning and transmission electron microscopy (SEM, TEM). *Parasitol Res* 2016;115(9):3649–55.

Gunn A, Pitt SJ. *Parasitology. An Integrated Approach.* (2012, Wiley-Blackwell).

Jakobsen PJ, Scharsack JP, Hammerschmidt K, Deines P, Kalbe M, Milinski M. In vitro transition of *Schistocephalus solidus* (Cestoda) from coracidium to procercoid and from procercoid to plerocercoid. *Exp Parasitol* 2012;130(3):267–73.

Jones MK. Structure and diversity of cestode epithelia. *Int J Parasitol* 1998;28(6):913–23.

Kavana NJ, Lim L HS, Ambu S. The life-cycle of *Spirometra* species from Peninsular Malaysia. *Trop Biomed* 2014;31(3):487–95.

Koziol U. Evolutionary developmental biology (evo-devo) of cestodes. *Exp Parasitol* 2017;180: 84–100.

Lefebvre F, Georgiev BB, Bray RA, Littlewood DTJ. Developing a dedicated cestode life cycle database: Lessons from the hymenolepidids. *Helminthologia* 2009;46(1):21–27.

Muehlenbachs A, Bhatnagar J, Agudelo CA, *et al.* Malignant Transformation of *Hymenolepis nana* in a Human Host. *N Engl J Med* 2015;373(19):1845–52.

Olson PD, Zarowiecki M, Kiss F, Brehm K. Cestode genomics — Progress and prospects for advancing basic and applied aspects of flatworm biology. *Parasite Immunol* 2012;34(2–3): 130–50.

Olson PD, Yoder K, Fajardo L-G LF, Marty AM, van de Pas S, Olivier C, Relman DA. Lethal invasive cestodiasis in immunosuppressed patients. *J Infect Dis.* 2003;187(12):1962–6.

Palma S, Chile N, Carmen-Orozco RP, *et al.* In vitro model of postoncosphere development, and in vivo infection abilities of *Taenia solium* and *Taenia saginata*. *PLoS Negl Trop Dis* 2019;13(3):e0007261.

Roberts LS, Janovy J Jr., Nadler S. *Schmidt & Roberts Foundations of Parasitology*, 9th edition (2013, McGraw Hill).

Ruggiero MA, Gordon DP, Orrell TM, *et al.* A higher level classification of all living organisms. *PLoS One* 2015;10(4):e0119248. Erratum in: PLoS One 2015;10(6):e0130114.

Scholz T, Tavakol S, Luus-Powell WJ. First adult cyclophyllidean tapeworm (Cestoda) from teleost fishes: Host switching beyond tetrapods in Africa. *Int J Parasitol* 2020;50(8):561–8.

Świderski Z, Miquel J, Azzouz-Maache S, Pétavy AF. Origin, differentiation and functional ultrastructure of egg envelopes in the cestode *Echinococcus multilocularis* Leuckart, 1863 (Cyclophyllidea: Taeniidae). *Parasitol Res* 2017;116(7):1963–71.

Tharmalingam N, Port J, Castillo D, Mylonakis E. Repurposing the anthelmintic drug niclosamide to combat *Helicobacter pylori*. *Sci Rep* 2018;8(1):3701.

Tsai IJ, Zarowiecki M, Holroyd N, *et al.* The genomes of four tapeworm species reveal adaptations to parasitism. *Nature* 2013;496(7443):57–63.

Verastegui M, Gilman RH, Arana Y, *et al. Taenia solium* oncosphere adhesion to intestinal epithelial and Chinese hamster ovary cells in vitro. *Infect Immun* 2007;75(11):5158–66.

Waeschenbach A, Brabec J, Scholz T, Littlewood DTJ, Kuchta R. The catholic taste of broad tapeworms — multiple routes to human infection. *Int J Parasitol* 2017;47(13):831–43.

Wang YC, Chao TK, Chang CC, *et al.* Drug screening identifies niclosamide as an inhibitor of breast cancer stem-like cells. *PLoS One.* 2013;8(9):e74538.

Webb C, Cabada MM. Intestinal cestodes. *Curr Opin Infect Dis* 2017;30(5):504–10.

Yo YT, Lin YW, Wang YC, *et al.* Growth inhibition of ovarian tumor-initiating cells by niclosamide. *Mol Cancer Ther*. 2012;11(8):1703–12.

15

Taeniasis, Diphyllobothriasis and Hymenolepiasis by Adult Tapeworms

15.1 Introductory Remarks

Tapeworms are the flatworms known as cestodes. As human parasites, they can be intestinal (mostly adults) and extra-intestinal (mostly juveniles). Clinically, with respect to symptoms, adult tapeworm infections are less severe than juvenile infections. Adults cause taeniasis; juveniles cause cysticercosis. Both taeniasis and cysticercosis are included as neglected tropical diseases (NTDs), with an estimated 12 million incidences and 28,000 annual deaths (including the deadly neurocysticercosis).[1]

Here, we use the term **taeniasis**. However, the term **taeniosis** is also used. It seems that veterinary parasitology prefers –iosis and medical parasitology retains –iasis. There are suggestions to unify terminology to be similar to naming bacterial and fungal diseases (Kassai 2006).

Both terrestrial and aquatic tapeworms can infect humans. The more famous species are ***Taenia saginata*** (beef tapeworm, larval cysticerci in cattle muscle) and ***Taenia solium*** (pork tapeworm, laeval cysticerci in pig muscle). It has been suggested that beef and pork tapeworms are misnomers because the definitive hosts are humans where the hermaphroditic flatworms reach sexual maturation, while the juvenile cysticerci live in muscles of cattle and pigs. Another species is ***Taenia asiatica*** (larval cysticerci in pig liver). "This third species exhibits a *T. saginata*-like morphology, but a *T. solium*-like life cycle" (Galán-Puchades and Fuentes 2013). *T. asiatica* has become the most neglected human *Taenia* with the possibility of cysticercosis. "Although these parasites have a worldwide distribution, the overwhelming burden is felt by communities in low- and middle-income countries. This is particularly true for *T. solium*, whereby infection of the central nervous system with the larval stage of the parasite (neurocysticercosis) is a major cause of acquired epilepsy in low-resource settings" (Okello and Thomas 2017).

[1] https://www.who.int/news-room/fact-sheets/detail/taeniasis-cysticercosis

In humans, *Taenia solium* is the cause of both adult and juvenile infections. (Human cysticercosis, from ingestion of *T. solium* eggs, will be discussed in the next chapter, Chapter 16, together with other juvenile tapeworm infections.) Adult tapeworm infections in humans happen after the ingestion of juveniles through contaminated beef or pork. The terrestrial tapeworm ***Hymenolepsis nana*** is probably the most common tapeworm of humans, with worldwide distribution. It even allows **autoinfection**, bypassing the flour beetle, the intermediate host. Consumption of contaminated fish causes infection of the aquatic tapeworm ***Diphylobothrium latum***, aka broad tapeworm, and several other related species.

For *Taenia solium*, ingestion of eggs causes porcine cysticercosis (PCC) and human cysticercosis (HCC). Human ingestion of undercooked PCC-contaminated pork leads to taeniasis. Both anthelmintic treatment and vaccination of pigs are available for short-term control. For sustaining, long-term control, health education is a necessity. "Lack of knowledge is an acknowledged barrier for control. ... Different health education approaches have been tested; including the use of informational movies, street plays, songs, interactive discussions, leaflets, posters, banners, trained teachers and software programs" (Vaernewyck *et al.* 2020). Maria Vang Johansen (University of Copenhagen, Denmark) and colleagues have developed an evidence-based educational software program, *The Vicious Worm*, targeting lay persons, professionals, and policy makers (Johansen *et al.* 2014).[2] PCC and HCC are found in East African countries, where over 50 million people speak Swahili. Hence, a Swahili version is available since this is the most common spoken language (Trevisan *et al.* 2017). Applications of the program have been successful. One example is seen in educational workshops and follow-ups with pork supply chain workers in Zambia (47 in workshops; 43 in follow-up sessions); the investigators concluded: "educational interventions with '*The Vicious Worm*' could be considered for integrated *T. solium* control programs in sub-Saharan Africa, especially if the educational content is further simplified and clarified" (Vaernewyck *et al.* 2020).

15.2 Taenia

Taeniasis is caused by *Taenia saginata* (taenia means tape; saginata means strong), *T. asiatica* (asiatica means Asia), and *T. solium* (solus means only, alone). Humans are the only definitive hosts. Although approximately 100 million people are thought to be infected annually with *Taenia* (Song *et al.* 2019), in most instances the infection is asymptomatic. Adults are large, up to 25 m, average 2–7 m for pork and under 5 m for beef tapeworm. Adults may cause mild abdominal symptoms, but juveniles of *T. solium* cause cysticercosis, and, among different forms, the worst is neurocysticercosis, with juvenile tapeworm invasion of the brain. In an epidemiological study on taeniasis in the Middle East and Africa, 18 out of 21 countries have human taeniasis (most likely due to the beef tape-

[2] https://theviciousworm.be/

worm, as pork is prohibited due to religious reason). For bovine cysticercosis, the frequency is 0.1–20% from meat inspection records in Egypt and Israel (Saratsis *et al.* 2019).

15.2.1 History

Historical records of tapeworms are abundant because of their large size. Cysticerci of *Taenia solium* and hydatid cysts of the dog tapeworm *Echinococcus granulosus* were known since ancient times. Aristotle (384–322 BC) mentioned measly pork (measly means measles, spotty), as well as pig diseases with bladders the size of hailstones. In 1857 the German Friedrich Kuchmeister, who had studied both ministry and medicine (son of a Protestant minister), commented that infections with cysticerci were not found in Jews and Moslems, whose religious beliefs forbid pork consumption. In 1992, four unrelated cases of neurocysticercosis were reported among the Orthodox Jewish community in New York City. The cause was traced to the intake of *Taenia solium* eggs passed from their domestic employees, who were recent immigrants of Latin America (Schantz *et al.* 1992).

Tapeworms are large and therefore conspicuous. In 1683, Edward Tyson saw scolex and reported on tapeworms from humans, dogs and other animals. In 1782, a German pastor Johann August Ephraim Goeze described similarities between scolices of the tapeworms in humans and those in cysts in the muscle of pigs (intermediate host). This was proved in 1855 by Friedrich Kuchmeister in a controversial experiment. Under his direction, the attending doctor fed pork contaminated with cysticerci of *Taenia solium* to a criminal condemned to death (some last meal). A total of 75 pieces of cysticerci were fed by hiding them in soups and in sausage. After execution, immature tapeworms were recovered in the small intestine at autopsy. Kuchenmeister used the term *Cysticercus cellulosae* for the larval form and *Taenia solium hominis* for the adult form. He wrote: "…briefly look at the results obtained by this experiment, the following is established: (1) that the *C. cellulosae* is the scolex of the *T. solium hominis*; (2) that the mode of infection with *T. solium* is exactly the same as with all other originating from bladder worms and probably like that of most of the Taeniae; (3) that we, therefore, infect ourselves with *T. solium* since cysticercus is transmitted by those foods which we eat raw…" (Kean *et al.* 1978).

In 1934, Kozen Yoshino of Okinawa published six research papers on *T. solium* for his doctoral thesis, including one on four volunteers (number 4 was Yoshino himself). As retold by Akira Ito (Asahikawa Medical University, Asahikawa, Japan) and colleagues, this human experimental infections with the pig tapeworms is "an experiment never to be repeated" (Ito *et al.* 2020). Yoshino (34-year-old) swallowed 3 cystercerci (isolated from a pig) on June 16, 1931 and was treated with anthelmintic on September 8, 1932 (the 451th day post-infection) resulting in the release of two tapeworms (one 223 cm long with 883 proglottids, the other 218 cm with 874 proglottids). In this case, the prepatent period was 72 days: the day with the first appearance of gravid proglottids (GPs) in feces. The number of GPs appearing in each bowel movement was tracked daily for 371 days afterwards, together with the number of bowel movements each day. GPs were observed on 275 of the 284 days.

There was a decline in the number of GPs over the observation period. GPs were observed on 97% of all days on which defecation occurred, they were present on 87% of days in the last month of infection. The cumulative number of GPs for a month in the first, sixth and 12th months of infection was 334, 174 and 126, respectively. Yoshino concluded: "Healthy patients who harbored two or three tapeworms had light stomach dysfunction (unstable dejection, stomach pain, etc.) during the early stage of infection."

The year 2019 was the 70th anniversary of the People's Republic of China (founded in 1949). President Xi Jinping has promoted his Belt and Road Initiative, a global development strategy involving infrastructure development and investments in countries and organizations. Included in this effort is the Silk Road Economic Belt and the 21st century Maritime Silk Road, for countries in Asia, Europe, Africa, and the Middle East. Historically, the Silk Road was prominent in the Han Dynasty (202 BCE to CE 220) for travelers between China and the Mediterranean. Besides cultural exchange, the Silk Road has been blamed for the spread of infectious diseases between East Asia, the Middle East, and Europe. In a study of relay station latrines in the town of Dunhuang, archaeologists found hygiene sticks, made with wood or bamboo, containing feces, and feces containing parasite eggs, including ones from *Taenia* (*T. asiatica*, *solium*, or *saginata*), Chinese liver fluke (*Clonorchis sinensis*), roundworm (*Ascaris lumbricoides*), and whipworm (*Trichuris trichiura*) (Yeh *et al.* 2016). As the Chinese liver fluke is abundant in well-water areas in southern or eastern China, travelers from these areas went to the layover stations for trade or official business. (We discuss roundworm and whipworm in Chapter 20.)

15.2.2 Life cycle

Please see Figure 15.1 for life cycle of *Taenia* species, from CDC.[3]

The pork and beef tapeworms can be differentiated by the morphology of their heads and gravid proglottids. In the scolex of *Taenia solium*, there is rostellum (a bulging) and a ring of hooks, this feature is absent in *Taenia saginata*. For the lateral branches that house eggs in gravid proglottids (GPs), *T. solium* has 7–12 branches, while *T. saginata* has over 12. Tapeworms have long lifespan. A typical *T. solium* can live as long as 25 years.

Please see Figure 15.2 for an illustration of the 3 human tapeworm species: *Taenia saginata*, *T. asiatica* and *T. solium* (Mendlovic *et al.* 2021).

15.2.3 Pathology

Human taeniasis is generally asymptomatic. The adult stage beef and pork tapeworms show minimal effect on the infected human host. Tapeworm carriers may suffer some distress from observing proglottids in their feces, especially those of *T. saginata* that are motile.

[3] https://www.cdc.gov/dpdx/taeniasis/index.html

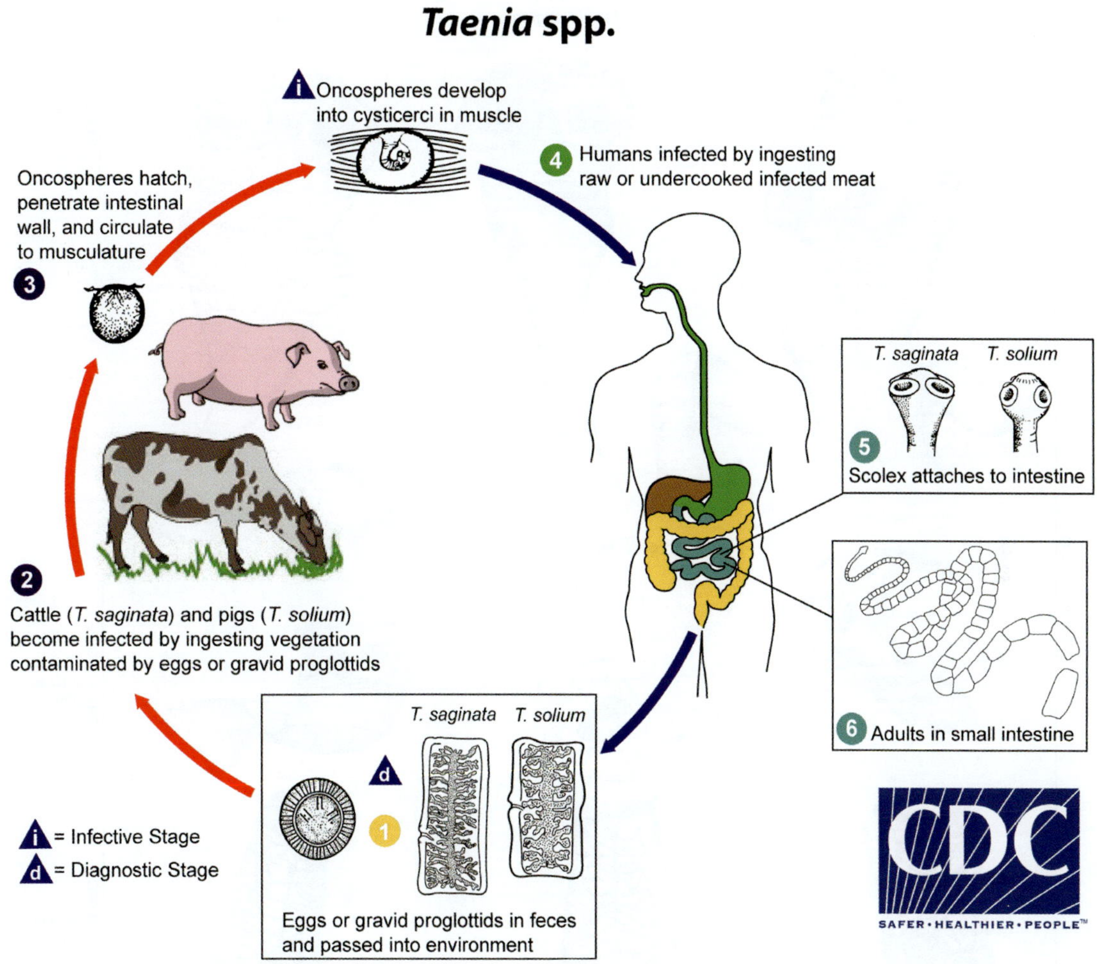

Fig. 15.1 ■ Life cycle of *Taenia* species. Taeniasis is the infection of humans with the adult tapeworm of *Taenia saginata*, *T. solium* or *T. asiatica*. Humans are the only definitive hosts for these three species. Eggs or gravid proglottids are passed with feces ❶; the eggs can survive for days to months in the environment. Cattle (*T. saginata*) and pigs (*T. solium* and *T. asiatica*) become infected by ingesting vegetation contaminated with eggs or gravid proglottids ❷. In the animal's intestine, the oncospheres hatch ❸, invade the intestinal wall, and migrate to the striated muscles, where they develop into cysticerci. A cysticercus can survive for several years in the animal. Humans become infected by ingesting raw or undercooked infected meat ❹. In the human intestine, the cysticercus develops over 2 months into an adult tapeworm, which can survive for years. The adult tapeworms attach to the small intestine by their scolex ❺ and reside in the small intestine ❻. Length of adult worms is usually 5 m or less for *T. saginata* (however it may reach up to 25 m) and 2–7 m for *T. solium*. The adults produce proglottids which mature, become gravid, detach from the tapeworm, and migrate to the anus or are passed in the stool (approximately 6 per day). *T. saginata* adults usually have 1,000 to 2,000 proglottids, while *T. solium* adults have an average of 1,000 proglottids. The eggs contained in the gravid proglottids are released after the proglottids are passed with the feces. *T. saginata* may produce up to 100,000 and *T. solium* may produce 50,000 eggs per proglottid respectively. Courtesy of the CDC. Reproduced from https://www.cdc.gov/dpdx/taeniasis/index.html

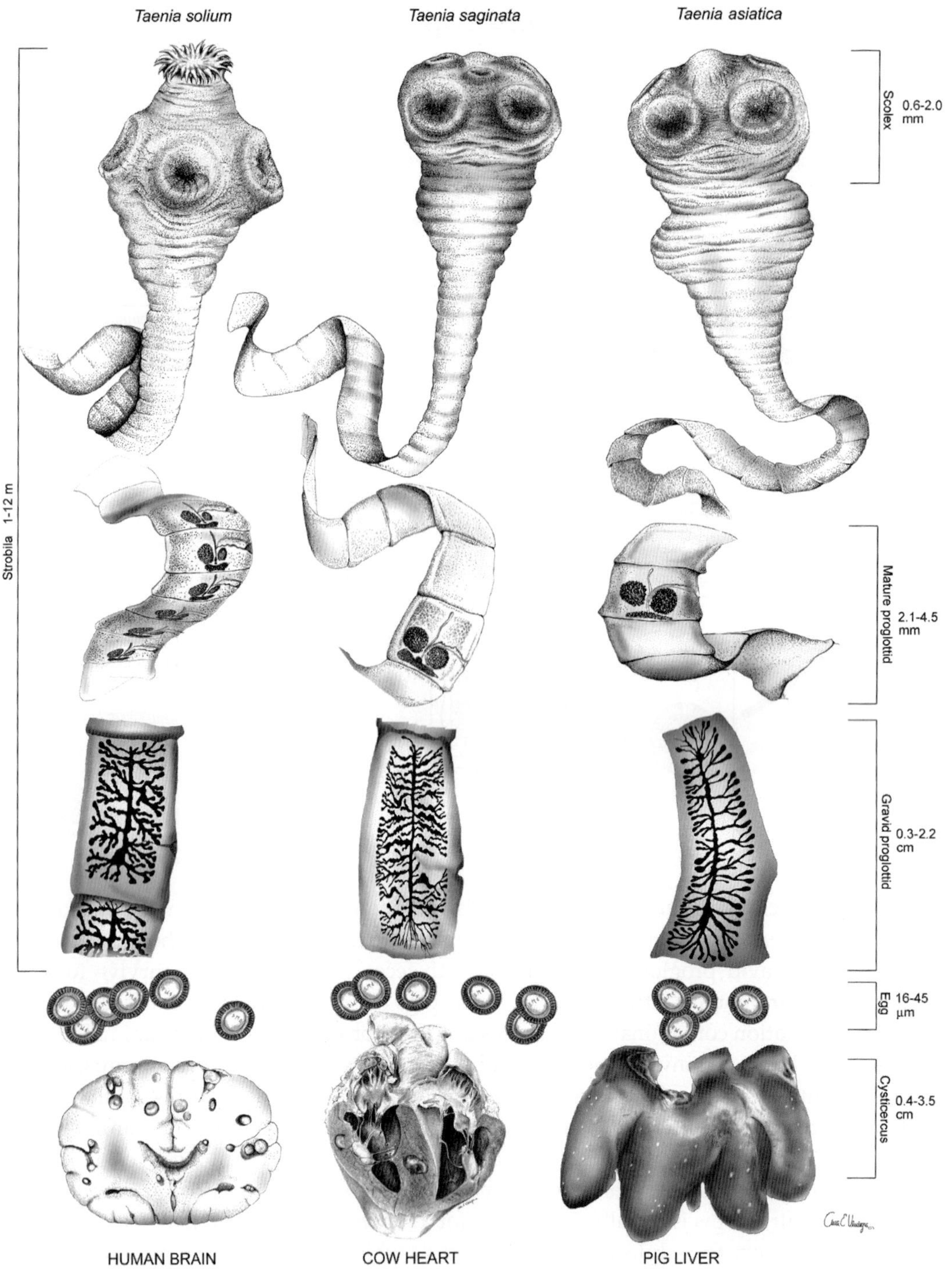

Fig. 15.2 ■ An illustration of the three tapeworm species: *Taenia saginata, T. asiatica,* and *T. solium*. Diagram showing the three tapeworm species found in humans. Morphological features and size ranges of the different parasite stages of the life cycle are shown. Source: Flisser *et al.* 2004. Portrait of human tapeworms. J. Parasitol. 90, 914–916, Allen Press Publishing Services. Courtesy: Mendlovic *et al. Res Vet Sci* 2021;134:69–77. Reproduced with permission from Elsevier.

Humans get taeniasis after ingestion of the metacestode larval stage, the cysticerci of *T. saginata* in beef or *T. solium* in pork. Ingestion of *T. solium* eggs, however, leads to their further development to cysticerci which can establish in the central nervous system (CNS) as neurocysticercosis (**NCC**). NCC is a major cause of neurological morbidity in the world and its prevalence may be on the rise recently as a result of immigration, travel, and commerce (Symeonidou *et al.* 2018). (It must be stressed here that juvenile pork tapeworms cause major disease in infected humans, especially NCC that leads to epilepsy. Please see Chapter 16. It is interesting that only the pork tapeworm does this. Why do other tapeworm species not show this detrimental effect on infected humans? This is an interesting question, one that we still do not have a satisfactory answer.)

For taeniasis case study, two reports from *The Korean Journal of Parasitology* are discussed here. Between October 2015 to August 2018, a total of 10 cases of tapeworm infection were reported (Song *et al.* 2019). All 10 patients had noticed whitish yellow tapeworm segments in their underwear or feces (7 females and 3 males, ages 23 to 74), including 3 with complaint of perianal itching. They were from provinces (Daegu and Gyeongbuk) with culinary tradition of raw beef consumption. Gravid proglottids (GPs)

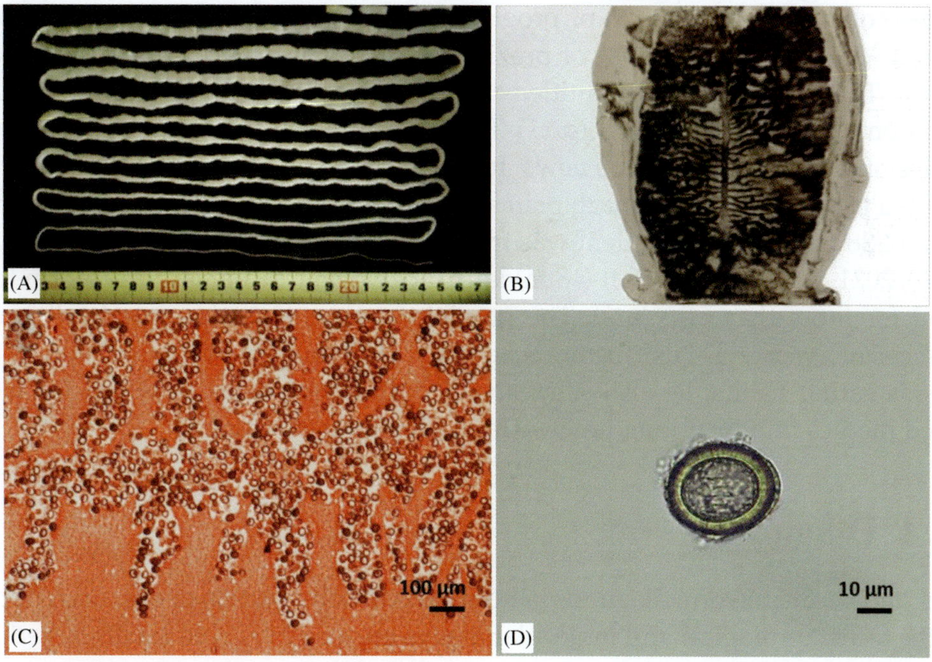

Fig. 15.3 ■ Strobila and egg of *Taenia saginata*. Strobila and eggs of *Taenia saginata*. (A) Whole strobila without the scolex, approximately 2.7 m in length. (B) The gravid proglottid shows the lateral uterine branches (India ink injection). (C) Longitudinal section of a gravid proglottid shows the uterine branches filled with eggs (H & E stain). (D) An egg smeared from a gravid proglottid. Courtesy: Song *et al. Korean J Parasitol* 2019;57:417–22. Reproduced with permission from *The Korean Journal of Parasitology*, Sung-Jong Hong, and Youn-Kyoung Goo.

from these patients showed 15–20 lateral uterine branches, and PCR-Ale I restriction digest-agarose gel electrophoresis of internal transcribed spacer 1 (ITS1) DNA portion confirmed the species to be *Taenia saginata* (PCR-restriction fragment length polymorphism, RFLP). Sequences of ITS1 and cytochrome c oxidase subunit 1 (*cox1*) showed higher homology to *T. saginata* than to *T. asiatica* and *T. solium*. "As taeniasis is one of the important parasitic diseases in humans, it is necessary to maintain hygienic conditions during livestock farming to avoid public health concerns" (Song *et al.* 2019). Please see Figure 15.3 for strobila and egg of Taenia saginata (Song *et al.* 2019).

A case of *Taenia asiatica* was documented in Korea. "A 42-year-old man was admitted to a hospital due to daily spontaneous discharge of small pieces of mobile white flat objects. Those were seen during defecation or found on the panty early in the morning" (Kim and Chung 2017). This condition had continued for a year, despite his use of drugs such as albendazole with no relief. Because he had chronic hepatiis B during childhood, he was advised by his grandmother to eat raw pig liver to enhance his liver function, and he did (ate raw pig liver regularly, but seldom ate beef). His tapeworm infection was detected by small bowel series radiology (an X-ray examination of the small intestine that uses a special form of X-ray called fluoroscopy after oral ingestion of the contrast material barium) and colonoscopy. There was a moving tapeworm from the terminal ileum to the ascending colon; a total of 12 cm of proglottids was removed from the patient. He was prescribed with a single oral dose of praziquantel, and had no recurrence in follow-ups for 5 years. The tapeworm was identified as *T. asiatica* by mitochondrial DNA sequencing of cytochrome c oxidase subunit 1 (*cox1*) (Kim and Chung 2017).

A case of taeniasis has become news. In Nong Khai province, Thailand, a 67-year-old man visited the hospital for stomach pain and flatulence. His stool sample had shown the presence of 28 eggs, and the patient was treated with niclosamide. On the following day, March 20, 2021, he excreted a 59 ft (18 m) long tapeworm (the biggest tapeworm found in Thailand for more than 50 years). The possible cause was eating raw beef containing *Taenia saginata* cysticerci. His doctor, Schawanya Rattanapitoon advised the patient to change his eating habits; he also suggested family members to be tested for taeniasis. "Shocked medics find 59 ft long tapeworm in Thai man's bottom".[4]

15.2.4 Diagnosis

The pork and beef tapeworm diagnosis in humans is the observation of eggs and/or proglottids in the feces. Serological and molecular assays are also available (as discussed above).

15.2.5 Therapy

The drugs for tapeworms are praziquantel and niclosamide.

[4] https://www.dailymail.co.uk/news/article-9397203/Thai-man-excretes-59-FOOT-tapeworm-doctors-visit-extreme-flatulence.html

15.2.6 Genome

Genomes of *T. solium, T. saginata,* and *T. asiatica* have been published (Tsai *et al.* 2013; Wang *et al.* 2016). Tapeworms possess 9 pairs of chromosomes (diploid $2n$ = **18**). Genome size is 131 Mb (*T. solium*), 168 Mb (*T. asiatica*), and 169 Mb (*T. saginata*). The tapeworm genome contains about 10% repetitive DNA (lower than flukes). Protein-coding gene number is **11,902 (*T. solium*), 13,323 (*T. asiatica*)** and **13,161 (*T. saginata*)**. Speciation history was postulated as the ancient humans first acquired the tapeworm from bovids in Africa and transmitted the tapeworm to suids in Asia for *T. saginata* and *T. asiatica* evolution. *T. asiatica* and *T. saginata* are genetically related sister species that are not completely reproductively isolated from each other. Current evidence indicates that most *T. asiatica* adult worms are hybrid-derived descendants (Ito *et al.* 2019).

Expansion and reduction in gene families are found in the tapeworm genome. On one end, there is an extreme reduction of homeobox (**Hox**) genes; these genes are important for body plan and pattern formation. On the other end, there is an expansion of detoxification genes, such as heat shock protein 70 (**Hsp 70**). Tapeworms cannot synthesize lipids, so lipid uptake genes are abundant. For adaptive evolution, genes are expressed for tegument maintenance (cytoskeletal proteins, glycosyltransferases) and internal homeostasis regulation (carbonic anhydrase).

15.3 *Diphyllobothrium*

For aquatic tapeworms, the major human infection is due to ***Diphyllobothrium latum*** (di means two, phyllo means leaf, bothros means slit or depression; latus means large). It is commonly known as the broad tapeworm or fish tapeworm. *Diphyllobothrium latum* is the largest (longest) tapeworm infecting humans. *Diphyllobothrium latum* is being renamed: now known as ***Dibothriocephalus latus***.

A more recently characterized aquatic tapeworm infection, from *D. nihonkaiense* found in North American salmon, may be related to the increase in consumption of sushi and sashimi (Kuchta *et al.* 2017). Infected raw or undercooked fish leads to infection. An epidemiological study has shown a total of 825 cases of *D. nihonkaiense* infection in Japan between 2001 and 2016 (Ikuno *et al.* 2018).

Another species infecting humans is the Pacific broad tapeworm *Adenocephalus pacificus* (aka *Diphyllobothrium pacificum*). This is the causative agent of the third most common fish-borne cestodosis among humans, with about 1,000 cases reported in South America (Peru, Chile, and Ecuador) (Kuchta *et al.* 2015).

In their review on this topic, Tomaš Scholz (Institute of Parasitology, Biology Centre of the Czech Academy of Sciences) and colleagues wrote: "Tapeworms of the family Diphyllobothriidae, commonly known as broad tapeworms, are predominantly large-bodied parasites of wildlife capable of infecting humans as their natural or accidental host" (Scholz *et al.* 2019).

15.3.1 History

The broad tapeworm was named by Linnaeus in 1751. In 1917, Swiss zoologists Constantin Janicki and Felix Rosen described the procercoid stage as well as the complete life cycle; they published "the life cycle of *Dibothriocephalus latus L.*" (current renaming is thus the revival of its old name for *Diphyllobothrium latum*) (Kean *et al.* 1978).

For readers interested to know more about the history of tapeworms and people, we recommend *New Guinea Tapeworms and Jewish Grandmothers: Tales of Parasites and People* (1981) by Robert S. Desowitz (1926–2008), professor of parasitology at the University of Hawaii.

15.3.2 Life cycle

Please see Figure 15.4 for the life cycle of *Diphyllobothrium* species, from CDC.[5]

Diphylobothrium latum is known as the fish tapeworm or the broad tapeworm. It is the largest tapeworm of humans, as long as 10 m because of anapolysis, retaining gravid proglottids (3000 proglottids total). It is classified into the order of Pseudophyllidea (scolex with 2 bothria), while the other tapeworms presented here are grouped into the order of Cyclophyllidea (scolex normally with 4 suckers). Immature eggs are released in water, where development takes place to the stage known as a coracidium (the process takes 8 days to several weeks). This is taken in by a copepod (*Cyclops*) where it develops into a procercoid larva. Eaten by a small fish the procercoid larva develops into a **plerocercoid** larva (also known as a **sparganum**). A minnow may be eaten by a trout which then may be eaten undercooked by humans leading to the ingestion of the larva. Once it is eaten by the human, the plerocercoid larva develops into an adult tapeworm. An adult aquatic tapeworm may survive up to 10 years in the human host.

There is a particularly interesting aspect of this fish tapeworm's life cycle. A swimming coracidium (plural, coracidia) infects a copepod; within the crustacean it develops into a procercoid. Procercoids can influence copepod (host) behavior. Parasite induced trophic transmission (**PITT**) is the ecological term. Infection changes the behavior, or physiology, or morphology of the intermediate host to facilitate transmission to the next host. We have mentioned previously that *Toxoplasma* in the rat brain may change the rodent's behavior. Here, copepods' motility may be impaired so they become easier prey for the fish (the next intermediate host). Experimentally, the infection of copepods by a young tapeworm makes the hosts less active than uninfected control, thus less likely to be eaten by a fish. If two tapeworms infect the same copepod host, when they are ready to move to the next host (a fish), that copepod (with two tapeworms) is more active than the copepod infected with only a single tapeworm.

[5]https://www.cdc.gov/dpdx/diphyllobothriasis/index.html

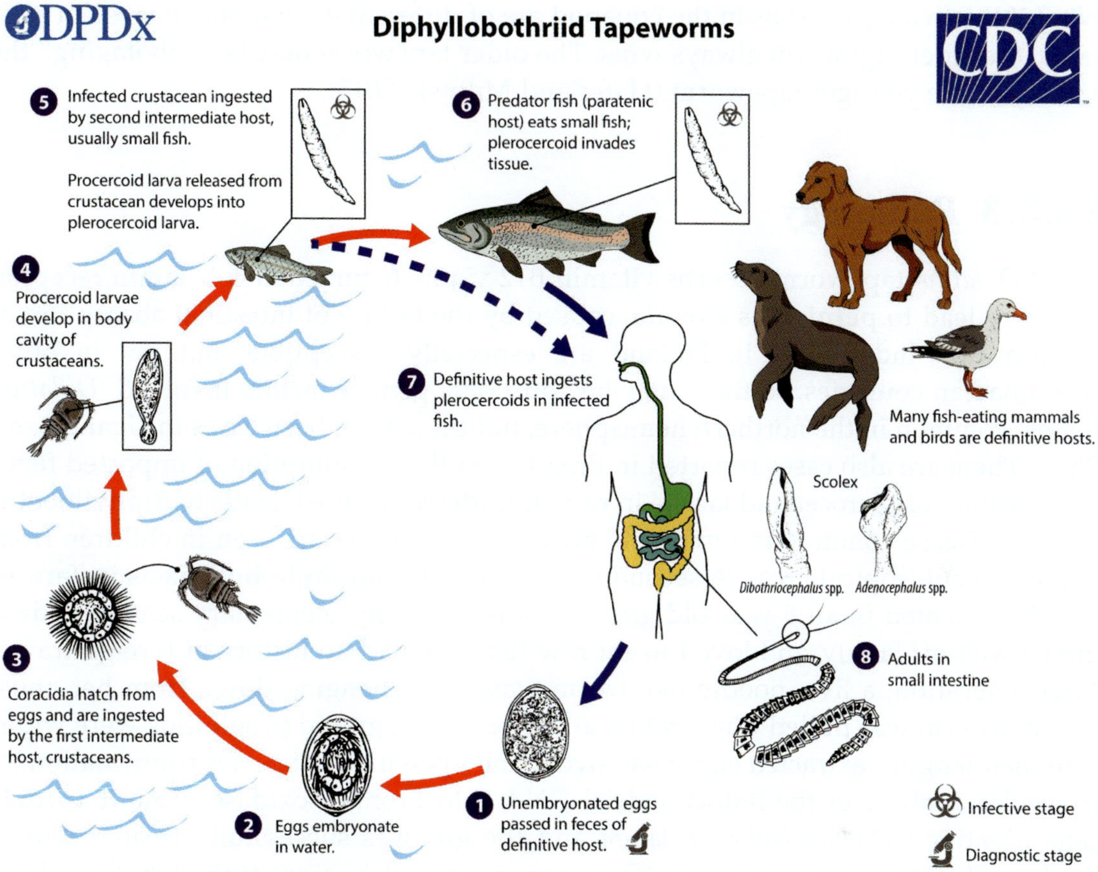

Fig. 15.4 ■ Life cycle of *Diphyllobothrium latum*. Eggs are passed unembryonated in feces ❶. Under appropriate conditions, the eggs mature (approximately 18–20 days) ❷ and yield oncospheres which develop into coracidia ❸. After ingestion by a suitable crustacean (first intermediate host) the coracidia develop into procercoid larvae ❹. Procercoid larvae are released from the crustacean upon predation by the second intermediate host (usually a small fish) and migrate into the deeper tissues where they develop into plerocercoid larvae (spargana), the infectious stage for the definitive host ❺. Because humans do not generally eat these small fish species raw, the second intermediate host probably does not represent an important source of human infection. However, these small second intermediate hosts can be eaten by larger predator species that then serve as paratenic hosts ❻. In this case, the plerocercoid migrates to the musculature of the larger predator fish; humans (and other definitive host species) acquire the parasite via consumption of undercooked paratenic host fish ❼. In the definitive host, the plerocercoid develops into adult tapeworm in the small intestine. Adult diphyllobothriids attach to the intestinal mucosa by means of two bilateral groves (bothria) of their scolex ❽. The adults can reach more than 10 m in length, with more than 3,000 proglottids. Immature eggs are discharged from the proglottids (up to 1,000,000 eggs per day per worm) and are passed in the feces. Eggs appear in the feces 5–6 weeks after infection. Courtesy of the CDC. Reproduced from https://www.cdc.gov/dpdx/diphyllobothriasis/index.html

What if the two tapeworms in the copepod are of different development ages? In such cases, the older tapeworm always wins. The older tapeworm may be "sabotaging" the activity of the younger tapeworm (Hafer and Milinski 2015).

15.3.3 Pathology

Adult *D. latum* tapeworm absorbs vitamin B12 via its tegumental cobalamin receptor. This may lead to **pernicious anemia**, caused by the failure of intestinal absorption of vitamin B12. Individuals in Finland are especially susceptible, but not in other Scandinavian countries, so there may be additional genetic factors involved. *D. latum* is most common in the northern hemisphere, but there have been cases in Uganda and Chile. There are also cases reported in Brazil from the consumption of imported fish.

Ingestion of plerocercoid larvae in raw or undercooked fish leads to diphyllobothriasis, a disease common in temperate areas, but rare cases are seen in children from tropical or subtropical areas. A second case of **pediatric diphyllobothriasis** in Taiwan was documented in an 8-year-old girl. She was a healthy, elementary school student from a well-off family, and loved to eat raw fish. She had no history of foreign travel. After defecation, a live, noodle-like worm was found hanging down from her anus. The tapeworm was pulled (the strobila at 260 cm long); gravid proglottids were wider than their lengths; extracted eggs were ovoid and operculated. Species confirmation by molecular analysis of the mitochondrial DNA cytochrome *c* oxidase subunit 1 (*cox1*) gene identified *Diphyllobothrium latum* and the girl was successfully treated with a single oral dose of praziquantel. "The reemergence of human diphyllobothriasis in non-endemic countries is probably due to prevalent habit of eating imported raw fish from endemic areas" (An *et al.* 2017).

Diphyllobothriasis has been documented in China: 4 cases of the fish tapeworm, *Diphyllobothrium nihonkaiense,* identified by morphological and molecular criteria (*cox1*). (1) A 43-year-old female, from Heilongjiang province, expelled several worm fragments in her feces. She had consumed raw/undercooked salmon often while working in Russia in 2012. (2) A 40-year-old male with no foreign travel history, liked eating raw/undercooked salmon and had consumed nearly 1 kg of raw salmon in a Japanese restaurant in Shanghai in March 20215. He passed proglottids in his feces 2 months later, and expelled a tapeworm (3.2 m long) after a decoction of pumpkin seed and betel nut. (3) A 42-year-old Chinese man, living in Canada, ate a lot of raw/undercooked salmon and other sea fish, and expelled fragments of a flat white worm in his feces in January 2016 when visiting relatives in Shanghai. (4) A healthy 36-year-old man from Shanghai expelled worm fragments in his feces since October 2015. He liked raw/undercooked fish, including salmon and trout. "The main reason for *D. nihonkaiense* infection is that the salmon has become an increasingly important commodity globally, and the salmon trade has increased markedly due to rapid advances in international and domestic transport systems. This results in an increase in the occurrence of diphyllobothriasis as an emerging parasitic disease in regions where it previously did not exist" (Cai *et al*. 2017).

15.3.4 Diagnosis

Diagnosis is observation of fish tapeworm eggs and/or gravid proglottids (GPs) containing eggs in feces.

15.3.5 Therapy

Diphyllobothriasis can be treated with praziquantel or niclosamide.

15.3.6 Genome

Diphyllobothrium latum has a larger genome, 531 Mb, than *Taenia* species. It possesses 18 chromosomes (2*n*) like the other tapeworms; it has **19,966** genes (International Helminth Genomes Consortium 2019).

15.4 *Hymenolepsis*

Only two *Hymenolepsis* species infect humans: *Hymenolepsis nana* (hymen means thin skin, lepis means scale, nanus means dwarf) and *H. diminuta*. *H. nana* is known as the **dwarf tapeworm** of mice and humans, adult size 7–50 mm, with 200 proglottids. Proglottid is broad (4X) rather than long. It is unique among tapeworms is the sense that an intermediate host may be omitted (optional). Autoinfection can carry on without the flour beetle (*Tribolium*) or another arthropod host, and this can increase parasite load in the infected human. A related species is *H. diminuta* (diminuta means small) a rat tapeworm that can parasitize humans (20–40 cm).

15.4.1 History

Hymenolepsis nana was first described by Theodore Bilharz in 1852. Bilharz also described *Schistosoma hematobium* and the disease was named bilharzia after him. (Please see Chapter 12 for Bilharz and his discovery of the schistosomiasis parasite.) Bilharz wrote: "The first incision into the intestine from the cadaver of a boy who died of meningitis disclosed immediately large numbers of a small tapeworm. The worm was a fully developed *Taenia* with broad segments; it was the width of a sewing thread and a length of hardly 10 mm … inhabited only a limited portion of the ileum" (Kean *et al*. 1978).

15.4.2 Life cycle

Please see Figure 15.5 for the life cycle of *Hymenolepsis nana*, from CDC.[6]

Hymenolepis nana is the most common cestode infection in humans and has worldwide distribution. *H. diminuta* is a rat tapeworm that can also infect humans. It needs two hosts including the flour beetle. The life cycle is similar to *H. nana*, except there is no autoinfection.

For the life cycle, the eggs from stool are taken by fleas and beetles, where the hexacanth (six hooks) larva or oncosphere develops into a **cysticercoid**. After ingestion by humans or rodents, the oncosphere develops into **cercocystis** which then develops into an adult worm in the small intestine, by evagination of the scolex. Adult worms live for 4–6 weeks, but internal autoinfection can persist for years. Via its autoinfection capacity, the tapeworm species can increase its number in the infected human host.

Jesús Alonso Panti-May (Universidad Autónoma de Yucatán, Mexico) and colleagues (2020) reviewed the rat tapeworm *Hymenolepis diminuta*, which is a zoonotic cestode parasitizing the small intestine of rodents (definitive hosts). Humans can accidentally enter into the life cycle of this tapeworm via the ingestion of infected insects (intermediate hosts) containing cestode cysticercoids in their body cavity. There were 1,561 cases of human infections reported from 1810 to 2018. With over 500 cases reported since 2000, this tapeworm continues to present a potential risk to public health. Its prevalence reported in recent parasitological surveys has been low, ranging from 0.002 to 8.222% (Panti-May *et al.* 2020).

15.4.3 Pathology

Most cases are asymptomatic. Heavy infection of *H. nana* leads to diarrhea.

15.4.4 Diagnosis

It is diagnosed by the observation of eggs in feces. However, in cases of light infections, repeated examinations and concentration techniques may be necessary.

15.4.5 Therapy

Treatment for hymenolepiasis is praziquantel.

15.4.6 Genome

The gene number is **13,777** for *H. nana* and **11,271** for *H. diminuta* (International Helminth Genomes Consortium 2019).

---

[6] https://www.cdc.gov/dpdx/hymenolepiasis/index.html

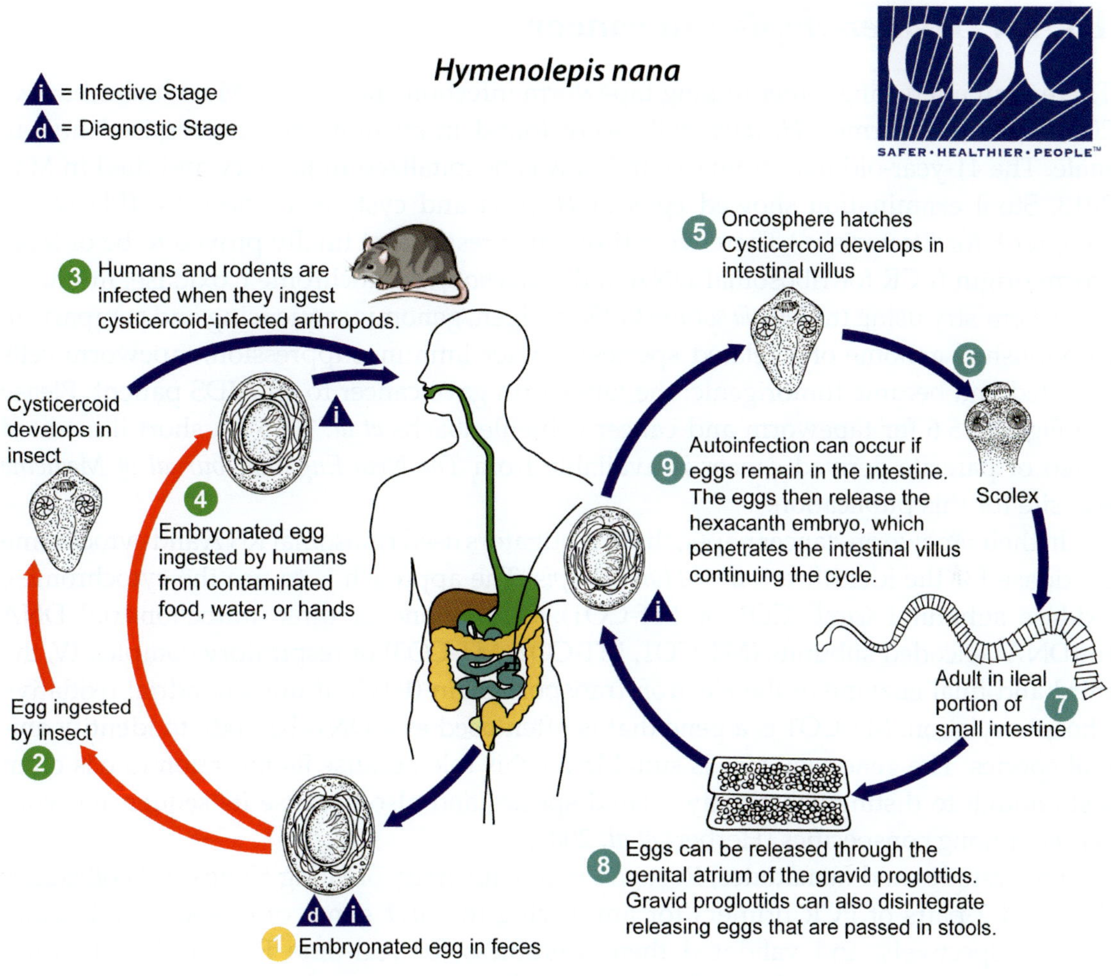

Fig. 15.5 ■ Life cycle of *Hymenolepis nana*. Eggs of *Hymenolepis nana* are immediately infective when passed with the stool and cannot survive more than 10 days in the external environment (1). When eggs are ingested by an arthropod intermediate host (2) (various species of beetles and fleas may serve as intermediate hosts), they develop into cysticercoids, which can infect humans or rodents upon ingestion (3) and develop into adults in the small intestine. A morphologically identical variant, *H. nana* var. *fraterna*, infects rodents and uses arthropods as intermediate hosts. When eggs are ingested (4) (in contaminated food or water or from hands contaminated with feces), the oncospheres contained in the eggs are released. The oncospheres (hexacanth larvae) penetrate the intestinal villus and develop into cysticercoid larvae (5). Upon rupture of the villus, the cysticercoids return to the intestinal lumen, evaginate their scoleces (6), attach to the intestinal mucosa and develop into adults that reside in the ileal portion of the small intestine producing gravid proglottids (7). Eggs are passed in the stool when released from proglottids through its genital atrium or when proglottids disintegrate in the small intestine (8). An alternate mode of infection consists of internal autoinfection, where the eggs release their hexacanth embryo, which penetrates the villus continuing the infective cycle without passage through the external environment (9). The life span of adult worms is 4–6 weeks, but internal autoinfection allows the infection to persist for years. Courtesy of the CDC. Reproduced from https://www.cdc.gov/dpdx/hymenolepiasis/index.html

15.4.7 *Hymenolepis* and cancer

There is an interesting paper linking tapeworm infection and cancer (Muehlenbachs *et al.* 2015). The transformed *H. nana* cells were found in an immunocompromised human male. The 41-year-old man from Columbia was hospitalized in January and died in May 2013. Stool examination showed eggs of *H. nana* and cysts of *Blastocystis*. (Please see Chapter 8 for *Blastocystis*.) There were tiny cells present that finally proved to be of tapeworm origin (PCR for ribosomal DNA and *Hymenolepis* cytochrome c oxidase; immunohistochemistry using the *Taenia solium* GP50 antigen, genomic sequencing and comparison to published genome of a related species). Under immunosuppression, tapeworm cells mutated and became tumorigenic: the tapeworm gave cancer to an AIDS patient. Please see Figure 15.6 for tapeworm and cancer (Muehlenbachs *et al.* 2015). A short illustrated video of parasite-derived cancer is available from *The New England Journal of Medicine* website for this publication.[7]

In their tapeworm-cancer paper, the investigators used ribosomal RNA and cytochrome c oxidase for the identification of *Hymenolepis*. The approach is to use the cytochrome c oxidase subunit I (*cox1*, CO1 or MT-CO1). CO1 is one of three mitochondrial DNA (mtDNA) encoded subunits (MT-CO1, MT-CO2, MT-CO3) of respiratory complex IV, the third and final enzyme of the electron transport chain (ETC) of mitochondrial oxidative phosphorylation. MT-CO1 is a gene that is often used as a DNA barcode to identify animal species. The gene sequence is suitable for this role because its mutation rate is often fast enough to distinguish closely related species and also because its sequence is conserved among conspecifics (Herbert *et al.* 2003).

For cestodes and nematodes, Rosana Poon (University of Hong Kong) and colleagues designed 2 pairs of PCR primers for amplifying the *cox1* genes of cestodes and nematodes, respectively, and validated their usefulness for real-time PCR and sequencing identification using clinical samples with cestodes and nematodes collected from a variety of animals and humans in 7 countries in Asia, Europe and Africa. Conserved sequences of 26 bp and 28 bp for cestodes and those of 22 bp and 22 bp for nematodes were chosen for designing 2 pairs of degenerate primers for cestodes (pan_cestode_cox1_82F 5′-TGGGTTATTGTTTGCTATGTTTTCWA-3′ and pan_cestode_cox1_209R 5′-CCCTATTATCATAGTAACMGAACTAAA-3′) and nematodes (pan_nematode_cox1_692F 5′-TGTCTTTACCWGTTTTRGCTGG-3′ and pan_nematode_cox1_835R 5′-CCGAAAGCAGGYAAAATHARAA-3′) respectively. The degenerate probes used for cestodes and nematodes were pan_cestode_cox1_143P (5′-HEX-ATGTTTACGGTTGGGT TRGATGTKAAG-3IABkFQ-3′) and pan_nematode_cox1_795P (5′-LC610-TCARCATTTRT TTTGRTTTTTTGGTCATCC-BBQ-3′), respectively. These "pancestode" or "pan-nematode" PCR primers allow real time PCR and sequencing for species identification of ces-

[7] https://www.nejm.org/doi/10.1056/NEJMoa1505892?url_ver=Z39.88-2003&rfr_id=ori:rid:crossref.org&rfr_dat=cr_pub%20%200pubmed

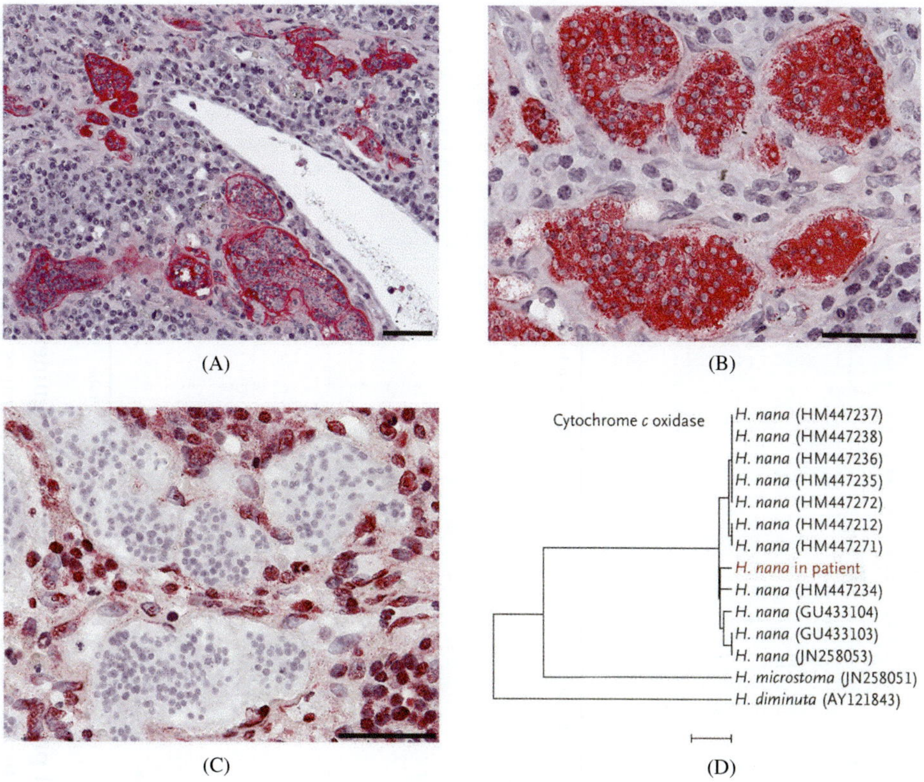

Fig. 15.6 ■ Tapeworm and cancer. Confirmation of *H. nana* Infection. Proliferative cells are labeled by means of immunohistochemical staining with the use of a cross-reactive polyclonal antiserum against *Taenia solium* GP50 antigens, shown in Panel A, and in situ hybridization with the use of a cestode 18S ribosomal DNA probe, shown in Panel B, with an absence of proliferative-cell labeling on in situ hybridization with a human Alu probe, which labels the surrounding human cells, shown in Panel C. Scale bars in Panels A, B, and C correspond to 50 μm. Panel D shows a phylogenetic analysis of the 391-bp *H. nana CO1* nucleotide sequence in the patient (KT362138), together with all available *H. nana* sequences; the scale bar corresponds to a genetic distance of 0.02 substitutions per site. Courtesy: Muehlenbachs *et al. N Engl J Med* 2015;373:1845–52. Reproduced with permission from Massachusetts Medical Society.

todes and nematodes (Poon *et al.* 2017). Please see Figure 15.7 for sequence alignment and primer locations (Poon *et al.* 2017).

Akira Itoa (Asahikawa Medical University) and colleagues have reviewed "Taeniasis and cysticercosis in Asia" and stated: "Taeniasis is an important parasitic condition in Asia, especially since all three human-infecting *Taenia* spp., *Taenia solium, Taenia saginata,* and *Taenia asiatica* are found in this region. These three species are believed to be sympatrically distributed, with the largest disease burden found in remote and rural areas where people raise pigs and cattle in a traditional manner" (Ito *et al.* 2019). In Asian countries, "Lifestyle choices, such as the consumption of undercooked meat, are important in

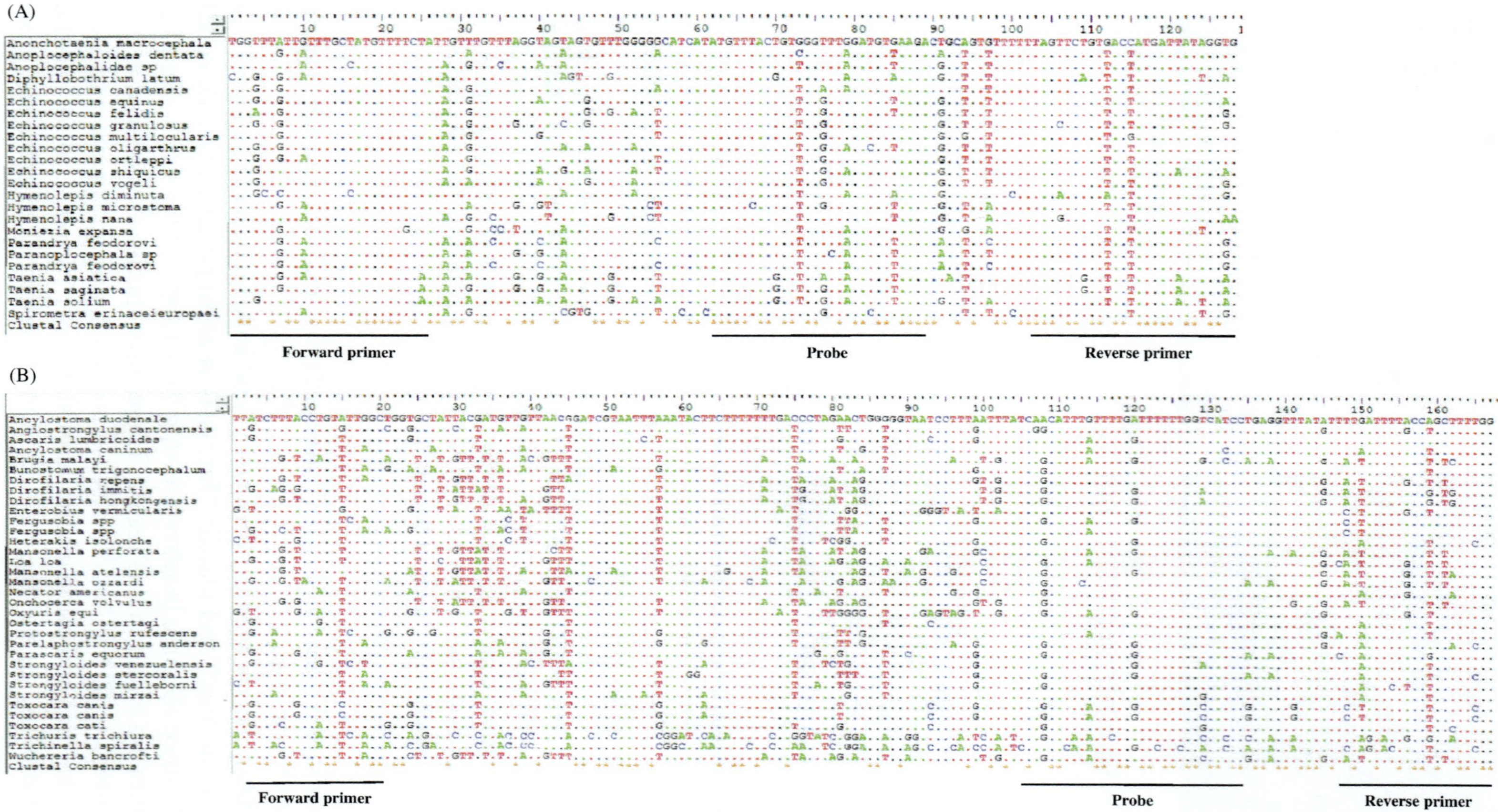

Fig. 15.7 ■ Cestode and nematode cox1 sequence alignment and primer locations. Multiple alignment of *cox1* gene sequences of selected cestodes (Panel A) and nematodes (Panel B) in GenBank for design of real-time PCR primers and probes. Courtesy: Poon *et al. Diagn Microbiol Infect Dis* 2017;89:185–90. Reproduced with permission from Elsevier.

maintaining the life cycles of these parasites. In addition, poor hygiene and sanitation, in highly endemic areas, make disease control difficult, resulting in the need for sustainable education programs" (Ito *et al.* 2019). "In many Asian countries where both pork and beef are consumed without religious barriers, pork tends to be the more commonly eaten meat. Pigs are popular livestock to raise due to their high fecundity and the relatively low cost of feeding" (Ito *et al.* 2019). Please see Figure 15.8 for close relationship between pigs and humans in Asia (Ito *et al.* 2019). Note that the Chinese words for house and bride both show a pig living under the roof.

Education programs to teach parasitic worms such as *Taenia solium* have shown promising results. One example is using *The Vicious Worm* to teach health and agricultural professionals in Tanzania (Lauridsen *et al.* 2019) and primary school students in Zambia

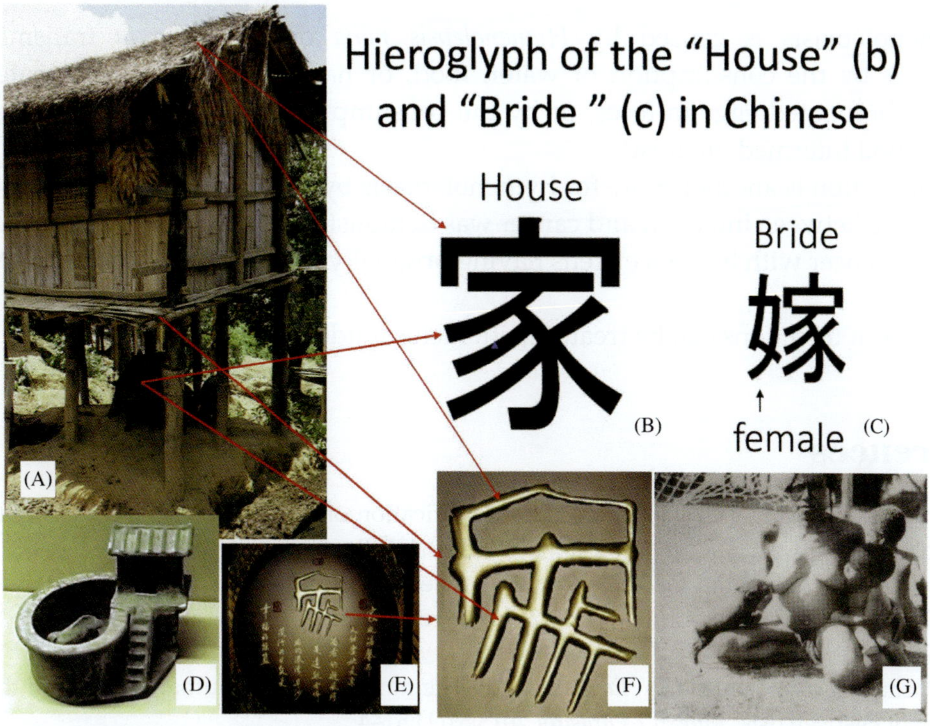

Fig. 15.8 ■ Close relationship between pigs and humans in Asia. Humans and pigs living together. Typical house in rural Southeast Asia (A). Chinese hieroglyphic characters for the words "house" (depicting a pig under a roof) (B) and "bride" (depicting a woman carrying a house on her back) (C). Funeral statue of a pig toilet (=toilet with pigsty) (China, Eastern Han dynasty 25–220 AD) (from Wikipedia) (Carr, 2017) (D). Former character of "house" showing a pig under the floor of a house (E, F). Photograph of a Chimbu woman from the Eastern Highlands of Papua New Guinea, photographed in 1939 suckling a pig; from The Ian Skinner Collection (G). Courtesy: Ito *et al. Acta Trop* 2019;198:105075. Reproduced with permission from Elsevier.

(Hobbs *et al.* 2019). This resource has been introduced in the beginning of this chapter to show its effectiveness in educating pork supply chain workers in Zambia.[2]

Summary & Key Concepts

- Tapeworms are cestodes; both adults and juveniles from terrestrial and aquatic environments can infect humans.
- Taeniasis is caused by *Taenia saginata, Taenia solium,* or *Taenia asiática* transmitted to humans by the consumption of raw or undercooked meat.
- Diphyllobothriasis is caused by *Diphyllobothrium latum, D. nihonkaiense,* or *Adenocephalus pacificus* transmitted to humans by the ingestion of larvae present in raw or undercooked fish.
- Hymenolepiasis is caused by *Hymenolepsis nana* or *H. diminuta* transmitted to humans by the consumption of water, food, or hands that are contaminated with the embryonated eggs in feces, or by the consumption of infected flour beetles (the arthropod intermediate host).
- Autoinfection is another route for hymenolepiasis by *Hymenolepsis nana.*
- A linking between infection and cancer was demonstrated in an AIDS patient who had died of cancer with his cancer cells having originally from the tapeworm *Hymenolepsis nana.*
- Tapeworm infections can be treated with niclosamide or praziquantel.

References

An YC, Sung CC, Wang CC, *et al.* Molecular identification of *Diphyllobothrium latum* from a pediatric case in Taiwan. *Korean J Parasitol* 2017;55(4):425–8.

Cai YC, Chen SH, Yamasaki H, *et al.* Four human cases of *Diphyllobothrium nihonkaiense* (Eucestoda: Diphyllobothriidae) in China with a brief review of Chinese cases. *Korean J Parasitol* 2017;55(3):319–25.

Galán-Puchades MT, Fuentes MV *Taenia asiatica*: The most neglected human *Taenia* and the possibility of cysticercosis. *Korean J Parasitol* 2013;51(1):51–4.

Hafer N, Milinski M. When parasites disagree: evidence for parasite-induced sabotage of host manipulation. *Evolution* 2015;69(3):611–20.

Hebert PD, Ratnasingham S, deWaard JR. Barcoding animal life: Cytochrome c oxidase subunit 1 divergences among closely related species. *Proc Biol Sci* 2003;270(Suppl 1):S96–9.

Hobbs EC, Mwape KE, Devleesschauwer B, *et al.* Effects of 'The Vicious Worm' educational tool on *Taenia solium* knowledge retention in Zambian primary school students after one year. *PLoS Negl Trop Dis* 2019;13(5):e0007336.

Ikuno H, Akao S, Yamasaki H. Epidemiology of *Diphyllobothrium nihonkaiense* Diphyllobothriasis, Japan, 2001–2016. *Emerg Infect Dis* 2018;24(8):1428–34.

International Helminth Genomes Consortium. Comparative genomics of the major parasitic worms. *Nat Genet*. 2019;51(1):163–74.

Ito A, Saito M, Donadeu M, Lightowlers MW. Kozen Yoshino's experimental infections with *Taenia solium* tapeworms: An experiment never to be repeated. *Acta Trop* 2020;205:105378.

Ito A, Li T, Wandra T, *et al*. Taeniasis and cysticercosis in Asia: A review with emphasis on molecular approaches and local lifestyles. *Acta Trop* 2019;198:105075.

Johansen MV, Trevisan C, Braae UC, *et al*. The Vicious Worm: A computer-based Taenia solium education tool. *Trends Parasitol*. 2014;30(8):372–4.

Kassai T. Nomenclature for parasitic diseases: cohabitation with inconsistency for how long and why? *Vet Parasitol* 2006;138(3-4):169–78.

Kean BH, Mott KE, Russell AJ, editors. *Tropical Medicine and Parasitology: Classic Investigations*, volume I and II (1978, Cornell, Ithaca).

Kim HU, Chung YB. A case of *Taenia asiatica* infection diagnosed by colonoscopy. *Korean J Parasitol* 2017;55(1):65–69.

Kuchta R, Serrano-Martínez ME, Scholz T. Pacific broad tapeworm *Adenocephalus pacificus* as a causative agent of globally reemerging diphyllobothriosis. *Emerg Infect Dis* 2015;21(10): 1697–703.

Kuchta R, Oros M, Ferguson J, Scholz T. *Diphyllobothrium nihonkaiense* tapeworm larvae in Salmon from North America. *Emerg Infect Dis*. 2017;23(2):351–3.

Lauridsen S, Braae UC, Ngowi HA, Johansen MV. Impacts of using the electronic-health education program 'The Vicious Worm' for prevention of *Taenia solium*. *Acta Trop* 2019;193:18–22.

Mehlhorn H. *Human Parasites* (2016, Springer).

Mendlovic F, Fleury A, Flisser A. Zoonotic *Taenia* infections with focus on cysticercosis due to *Taenia solium* in swine and humans. *Res Vet Sci* 2021;134:69–77.

Muehlenbachs A, Bhatnagar J, Agudelo CA, *et al*. Malignant transformation of *Hymenolepis nana* in a human host. *N Engl J Med* 2015;373(19):1845–52.

Okello AL, Thomas LF. Human taeniasis: Current insights into prevention and management strategies in endemic countries. *Risk Manag Healthc Policy* 2017;10:107–16.

Panti-May JA, Rodríguez-Vivas RI, García-Prieto L, Servián A, Costa F. Worldwide overview of human infections with *Hymenolepis diminuta*. *Parasitol Res* 2020;119(7):1997–2004.

Poon RWS, Tam EWT, Lau SKP, *et al*. Molecular identification of cestodes and nematodes by cox1 gene real-time PCR and sequencing. *Diagn Microbiol Infect Dis* 2017;89(3):185–90.

Saratsis A, Sotiraki S, Braae UC, *et al*. Epidemiology of *Taenia saginata* taeniosis/cysticercosis: A systematic review of the distribution in the Middle East and North Africa. *Parasit Vectors* 2019;12(1):113.

Schantz PM, Moore AC, Muñoz JL, *et al*. Neurocysticercosis in an Orthodox Jewish community in New York City. *N Engl J Med*. 1992;327(10):692–5.

Scholz T, Kuchta R, Brabec J. Broad tapeworms (Diphyllobothriidae), parasites of wildlife and humans: Recent progress and future challenges. *Int J Parasitol Parasites Wildl* 2019 Apr 1;9:359–69.

Song SM, Yun HS, VanBik D, *et al*. Ten Cases of *Taenia saginata* infection confirmed by analysis of the internal transcribed spacer 1 rDNA region in the Republic of Korea. *Korean J Parasitol* 2019;57(4):417–22.

Symeonidou I, Arsenopoulos K, Tzilves D, Soba B, Gabriël S, Papadopoulos E. Human taeniasis/cysticercosis: A potentially emerging parasitic disease in Europe. *Ann Gastroenterol* 2018;31(4):406–12.

Trevisan C, Fèvre EM, Owiny M, Ngere I, Vang Johansen M. Minyoo Matata. The Vicious Worm — A *Taenia solium* computer-based health-education tool — in Swahili. *Trends Parasitol.* 2017;33(10):746–8.

Tsai IJ, Zarowiecki M, Holroyd N, *et al.* The genomes of four tapeworm species reveal adaptations to parasitism. *Nature* 2013;496(7443):57–63.

Vaernewyck V, Mwape KE, Mubanga C, Devleesschauwer B, Gabriël S, Trevisan C. Effects of 'The Vicious Worm' educational software on *Taenia solium* knowledge among key pork supply chain workers in Zambia. *PLoS Negl Trop Dis* 2020;14(10):e0008790.

Wang S, Wang S, Luo Y, *et al.* Comparative genomics reveals adaptive evolution of Asian tapeworm in switching to a new intermediate host. *Nat Commun* 2016;7:12845.

Yeh H, Mao R, Wang H, Qi, W., & Mitchell, P. 2016. Early evidence for travel with infectious diseases along the Silk Road: Intestinal parasites from 2000 year-old personal hygiene sticks in a latrine at Xuanquanzhi Relay Station in China. *J Archaeol Sci Rep* 2016;9:758–64.

16

Juvenile Tapeworm Infections

16.1 Introductory Remarks

Adult tapeworms are intestinal parasites and do not cause major damage to the human host. Among the adult intestinal tapeworms, only the pork tapeworm *Taenia solium* can cause very serious consequences because when their eggs are taken up, they eventually develop into juvenile tapeworms (metacestodes) within the human body. Other juvenile tapeworms that infect humans mature in different animal species as their normal definitive hosts; infected humans become dead end intermediate hosts. Juvenile tapeworm infections of humans lead to cysticercosis, hydatidosis and sparganosis.

16.2 Cysticercosis by *Taenia solium*

Taenia solium metacestodes causes cysticercosis. The most severe is neurocysticercosis (NCC), a leading cause of epilepsy in children and young adults after cysticerci infection in their brains. NCC has been found in United States cities near the border of Mexico, including Los Angeles, San Diego, Phoenix, El Paso, San Antonio and Houston. It is especially common in Hispanic population where a family member typically harbors an adult *Taenia solium*.

In their review on the pork tapeworm, Isaia Symeonidou (Aristotle University of Thessaloniki, Greece) and colleagues wrote: "Humans can become infected with *T. solium* (pork tapeworm) after consumption of raw or insufficiently cooked pork meat harboring the larval stage of this tapeworm, which subsequently develops to the adult stage in the human small intestine … Additionally, *T. solium* infection in humans can occur through the accidental ingestion of the eggs of this parasite (fecal-oral route), in a similar way to the mode of infection of the intermediate hosts. In the latter case, infection with *T. solium* can result in the formation of cysticerci (larval stage) in the human body, which are of major importance when located in the central nervous system (neurocysticercosis, NCC). Human NCC is the most common parasitic disease of the central nervous system and constitutes a major concern in endemic regions of Latin America, India, Asia, Africa and Eastern Europe. NCC accounts for about 50,000 deaths per year and is currently considered to be the most common cause of acquired epilepsy in the developing world, with an estimated 2 million people being affected. Unfortunately, more cases are being reported in Europe nowadays, mostly as a result of migration. *T. solium* is the most important foodborne parasite globally" (Symeonidou *et al.* 2018, citations in the quote deleted). As an example, a total of 751 NCC cases were reported from 1985–2011 in different countries of Western Europe, with particular epidemic situations in Portugal and Spain (Symeonidou *et al.* 2018).

16.2.1 History

Aristotle (384–322 BC) recorded measly pork (measly means measles, spotty) and porcine diseases with bladders the size of hailstones. This condition was known as the bladder worm disease. The bladder worm is the **cysticercus** (plural, cysticerci), which is the metacestode of *Taenia solium*. Before the knowledge that the bladder worms are larvae of the adult pork tapeworm, the term *Cysticercus cellulosae* was used as the infecting organism.

16.2.2 Life cycle

Please see Figure 16.1 for *Taenia solium* cysticercosis, from CDC.[1]

Humans get cysticercosis via ingestion of eggs from the pork tapeworm. Thus, it is via the fecal-oral route. This route is different from ingestion of undercooked pork contaminated with cysticerci, the pathway leading to intestinal maturation to adult pork tapeworms.

Cysticercosis can be caused by inadvertant ingestion of eggs, contaminated food, or autoinfection. The proglottids are carried into stomach by reverse peristalsis. Oncospheres, after hatching in the intestine, invade the intestinal wall and migrate to various regions of the body. They develop into cystercerci in places such as skeletal muscles, brain, and other parts of the body. This is a slow process; it may take 5–10 years for development.

Mouse models of tapeworm infection are available, with the severe combined immunodeficiency (SCID) mice. Investigators have found cysticerci in the rodents after *Taenia* infection, and hydatid cysts after *Echinococcus* infection (Nakaya *et al.* 2006). These animal models allow studies of developmental biology, drug efficacy, and host specificity in cysticercosis and echinococcosis.

16.2.3 Pathology

Disease symptom is due to dead or dying worms that result in host immune response. NCC is the most severe, and brain imaging can detect the infection. NCC is the leading

[1] https://www.cdc.gov/dpdx/cysticercosis/index.html

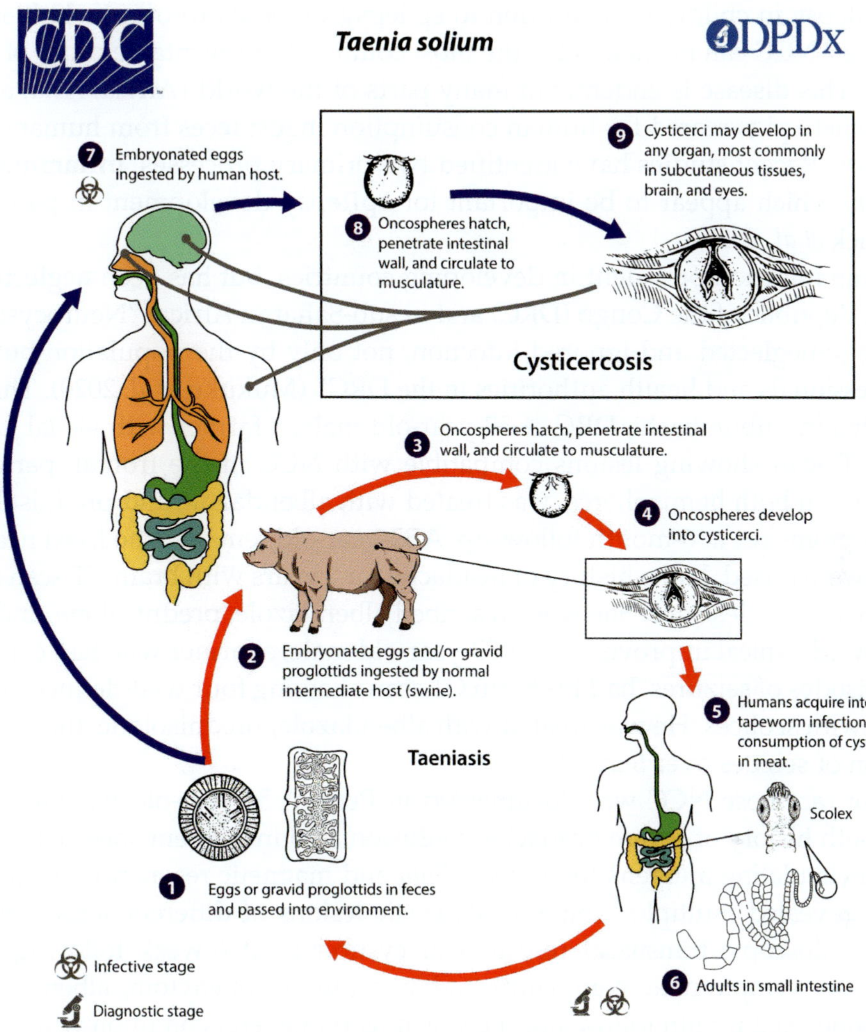

Fig. 16.1 ■ ***Taenia solium* Cysticercosis. Cysticercosis** is an infection of both humans and pigs with the larval stages of the parasitic cestode, *Taenia solium*. This infection is caused by ingestion of eggs shed in the feces of a human tapeworm carrier ❶. These eggs are immediately infectious and do not require a developmental period outside the host. Pigs and humans become infected by ingesting eggs or gravid proglottids ❷, ❼. Humans are usually exposed to eggs by ingestion of food/water contaminated with feces containing these eggs or proglottids or by person-to-person spread. Tapeworm carriers can also infect themselves through fecal-oral transmission (e.g. caused by poor hand hygiene). Once eggs or proglottids are ingested, oncospheres hatch in the intestine ❸, ❽ invade the intestinal wall, enter the bloodstream, and migrate to multiple tissues and organs where they mature into cysticerci over 60–70 days ❹, ❾. Some cystercerci will migrate to the central nervous system, causing serious sequelae (neurocysticercosis). This differs from **taeniasis**, which is an intestinal infection with the adult tapeworm. Humans acquire intestinal infections with *T. solium* after eating undercooked pork containing cysticerci ❺. Cysts evaginate and attach to the small intestine by their scolices. Adult tapeworms develop to maturity and may reside in the small intestine for years ❻. Courtesy of the CDC. Reproduced from https://www.cdc.gov/dpdx/cysticercosis/index.html

cause of epilepsy in children. In addition to epilepsy, other symptoms include headache and blindness. NCC can be fatal yet is the most commonly preventable cause of epilepsy worldwide. This disease is endemic in many parts of the world (Africa, Asia, and Latin America), where pigs reared for human consumption ingest feces from humans infected with *T. solium*. Recent studies have identified two primary processes, **inflammation** and **calcification**, which appear to be important for **epilepsy** development in patients with NCC (Herrick *et al.* 2020).

NCC is an infection prevalent in developing countries, but has been neglected in the Democratic Republic of the Congo (DRC) and in sub-Saharan Africa. "Neurocysticercosis is a pathology-neglected and ignored infection, not only by the population but also by health professionals and health authorities in the DRC" (Mukuku *et al.* 2020). Three cases were reported in Lubumbashi, DRC. A 53-year-old male, a farmer with visual hallucinations and CT scan showing lesions compatible with NCC in the frontal, parietal, and occipital lobes in both hemispheres, was treated with albendazole and prednisolone and became symptom-free at 6-month follow-up. A 32-year-old female, who lived near a farm where pigs were raised, had a history of headache for 2 years with brain CT scan showing multiple small cystic lesisons. She was prescribed albendazole, prednisolone, and ibuprofen and showed clinical improvement. A 33-year-old male, a farmer who had experienced multiple episodes of seizures, had his brain CT scan showing four well-defined parenchymal lesions with scolices. He was treated with albendazole, prednisolone, that resulted in the cessation of seizues over 6 months.

A case of racemose NCC was documented in Peru. A 53-year-old woman presented with a 3-month history of severe headache, confusion, and incoherent speech, had saturating levels of circulating antigens for *Taenia solium* and magnetic resonance imaging (MRI) of her head revealed multiple conglomerate cystic lesions of different sizes. The patient underwent endoscopic transnasal resection of cysticerci. At 6-week follow-up, she no longer had any symptomatic complaints and was put on phenytoin, albendazole, and dexamethasone. At 2-month follow-up, she was in good general condition with slight dizziness and complaint of mild intermittent headaches attributed to stress (Yang *et al.* 2020).

An interesting case of autochthonous NCC was documented in Australia. A 25-year-old female who had always lived in Australia, had never traveled overseas to a country endemic for *T. solium*, showed worsening visual symptoms in association with headache and previously diagnosed as a migraine with visual aura. NCC was diagnosed after MRI showing cysts in brain and surgically removed material demonstrated *T. solium* mitochondrial cytochrome oxidase subunit 1 of Asian genotype by polymerase chain reaction (PCR). The female worked as a barista at a local café located in greater Melbourne where the second most common country of birth after Australia is India at 5.9%, and over 10% of residents were born in Asia. The investigators thus proposed: "the patient had inadvertently ingested eggs of *T. solium* released from a tapeworm carrier who had traveled to, or originated from, an endemic country" (Forster *et al.* 2020).

In the human females, the pouch of Douglas is a small area between the uterus and the rectum. In Germany, there was a case on the molecular identification of larval *Taenia martis* infection in the pouch of Douglas. The 24-year-old female underwent surgery for endometriosis, after presented to her gynecologist with chronic lower abdominal pain and dysmenorrhea in October 2019. One of her biopsy specimens revealed structures suggestive of a parasitic infection. PCR sequencing of cestode cytochrome c oxidase subunit 1 (cox1) revealed 100% nucleotide similarity with the marten tapeworm (*Taenia martis*). A survey for helminth infections in carnivores of southern Germany demonstrated that 36% of stone martens were infected with this species of tapeworm. The patient, a final year teacher trainee, lived in a small town in Bavaria and used to eat unwashed strawberries from the garden of her aunt who lived nearby. In addition, she used to pet her aunt's dog and she herself had a free-roaming cat. "It can be anticipated that human infections are due to ingestion of uncooked food, for example, vegetables or lettuce, contaminated with infective parasite ova from marten feces" (Müller *et al.* 2020).

16.2.4 Diagnosis

Imaging techniques are used in diagnosis. Brain imaging techniques have been successful in detecting NCC. NCC can be confirmed by immunoblotting (western blot) for the presence of *Taenia solium* antigen in serum and/or cerebrospinal fluid (CSF).

16.2.5 Therapy

Treatment includes the prescription of anti-inflammatory drugs along with albendazole and praziquantel (Mendlovic *et al.* 2021).

16.3 Hydatidosis by *Echinococcus*

Juvenile tapeworms of *Echinococcus* (Echino means hedgehog or spiky; coccus means spherical) cause **cystic echinococcosis** or hydatidosis (hydatid disease) in humans. *Echinococcus* is among the smallest tapeworms. Adult worms often range in size from 2 to 8 mm and have a scolex and three proglottids. Two species that normally infect carnivores that give juvenile tapeworm infections to humans are ***Echinococcus granulosus*** and ***E. multilocularis*** (granulosis means granular; multilocularis means within multiple vacuoles). The hydatid cysts are fluid-filled space containing many mother and daughter **pseudoscolices** (or pseudoscoleces; pseudoscolex, singular; inverted scolices) that have potential to develop into adults and hence is often known as brood chamber. It has been estimated that about **3 million** people are infected with *Echinococcus granulosus*. As sheep and goats are susceptible to *Echinococcus granulosus*, up to US $2 billion are lost annually in the livestock industry due to this tapeworm. For humans, cystic hydatid disease is a zoonosis associated with poverty and poor hygiene practices, particularly in livestock-raising communities.

16.3.1 History

Records of massive cysts seen in slaughtered animals have been found in texts of ancient Babylon, Greece, and Rome. Hippocrates was the first to describe cysts in patients more than 2,400 years ago. The biology of tapeworms was investigated by various Europeans. In 1782, a German pastor Johann Goeze described protoscolices in sheep liver. In 1853, a German zoology professor, Carl von Siebold described adult worms in dogs and also demonstrated that cysts from sheep, when fed to dogs, gave rise to adult tapeworms and it took 22 days for them to reach adulthood. It is also worthy to note that Theodor Bilharz, who discovered schistosomes, was a student of von Siebold. In 1863, Bernhard Naunyn fed the contents of hydatid cysts from a human infection to dogs, and recovered adult tapeworms in dogs, thus linking echinococcosis between animal and human infections (zoonosis). In 1901, a French professor of medicine Felix Deve, who used rabbits in experiments, suggested this therapy: "We believe that the only prophylaxis for secondary post-operative echinococcosis would be to kill the infective *Echinococcus* parasites in the cyst by a taeniacide injection before opening the sac widely" (Kean *et al.* 1978).

16.3.2 Life cycle

Please see Figure 16.2 for life cycle of *Echinococcus granulosus*, from CDC.[2] Please see Figure 16.3A for *E. multilocularis* (Casulli *et al.* 2019a) and Figure 16.3B for *E. granulosus* (Casulli *et al.* 2019b).

Echinococcus granulosus matures in the dog and its normal intermediate host is the sheep. In humans, ingestion of eggs leads to oncosphere migration via circulation to various locations, including the liver and the lung, where they have space to occupy. This disease is named cystic echinococcosis (**CE**), with the development of thick-walled hydatid cysts that enlarge gradually, producing protoscolices and daughter cysts that fill the cyst interior. A hydatid cyst has an ability to develop bidirectionally, either into an adult worm in the dog intestine, or into a secondary cyst in the intermediate host (such as human and sheep). The trigger is bile acids, the higher concentration in the dog induces adult development.

Echinococcus multilocularis matures in the fox and its intermediate host is a rodent, such as the vole. In humans, ingestion of eggs leads to oncosphere migration via circulation to various locations, including the liver and the lung, where they have space to occupy. This disease is named alveolar echinococcosis (**AE**), with the development of multi-chambered ("multilocular"), thin-walled (alveolar) hydatid cysts that proliferate by successive outward budding, with each cyst containing numerous **protoscolices** (or **protoscoleces**).

A third type, named neotropical echinococcosis (**NE**), is cause by ***Echinococcus vogeli*** or ***E. oligarthra***, with geographic distribution of the *Echinococcus* species involved residing in the tropical areas of the New World (Vuitton *et al.* 2020).

---

[2] https://www.cdc.gov/dpdx/echinococcosis/index.html

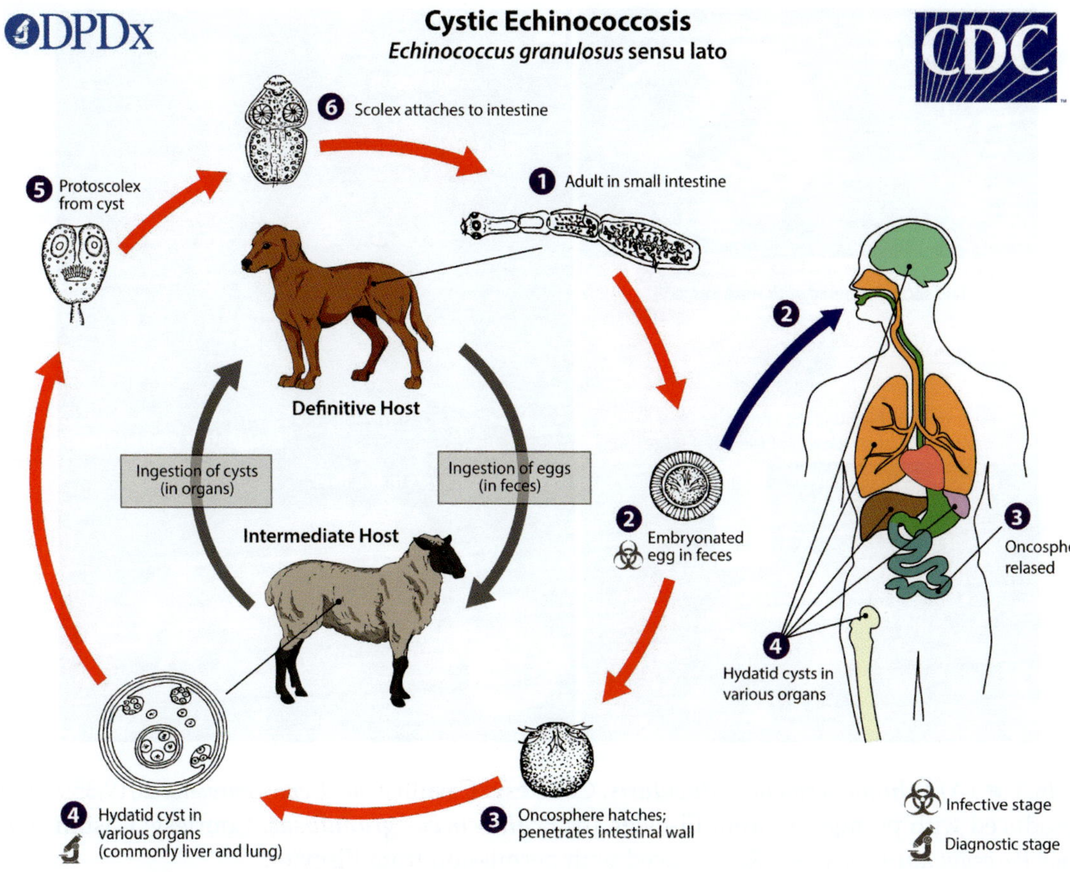

Fig. 16.2 ■ Life cycle of *Echinococcus granulosus*. The adult *Echinococcus granulosus* (sensu lato) (2–7 mm long) ❶ resides in the small intestine of the definitive host. Gravid proglottids release eggs ❷ that are passed in the feces, and are immediately infectious. After ingestion by a suitable intermediate host, eggs hatch in the small intestine and release six-hooked oncospheres ❸ that penetrate the intestinal wall and migrate through the circulatory system into various organs, especially the liver and lungs. In these organs, the oncosphere develops into a thick-walled hydatid cyst ❹ that enlarges gradually, producing protoscolices and daughter cysts that fill the cyst interior. The definitive host becomes infected by ingesting the cyst-containing organs of the infected intermediate host. After ingestion, the protoscolices ❺ evaginate, attach to the intestinal mucosa ❻, and develop into adult stages ❶ in 32–80 days. Humans are aberrant intermediate hosts, and become infected by ingesting eggs ❷. Oncospheres are released in the intestine ❸, and hydatid cysts develop in a variety of organs ❹. If cysts rupture, the liberated protoscolices may create secondary cysts in other sites within the body (secondary echinococcosis). Courtesy of the CDC. Reproduced from https://www.cdc.gov/dpdx/echinococcosis/index.html

Dominique A. Vuitton (National French Reference Centre for Echinococcosis, University Bourgogne Franche-Comté, Besançon, France) and colleagues gave these recommendations: "Echinococcoses require the involvement of specialists from nearly all disciplines; standardization of the terminology used in the field is thus crucial. To harmonize echinococcosis terminology on sound scientific and linguistic grounds, the World

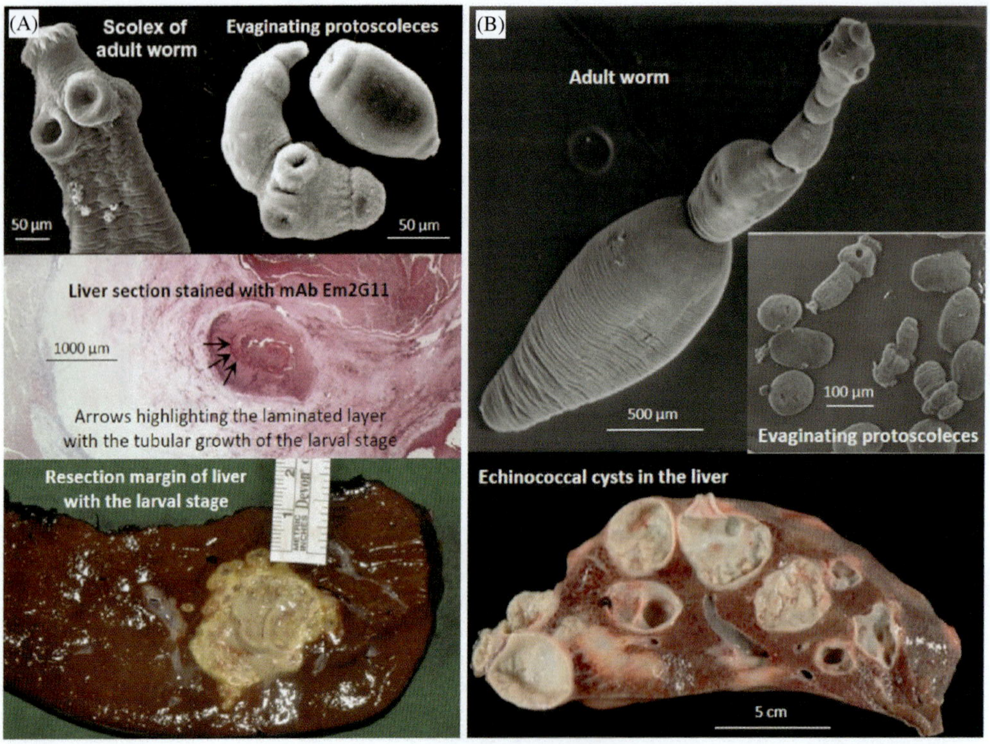

Fig. 16.3 ■ (A) ***Echinococcus multilocularis.*** Courtesy: Casulli *et al. Trends Parasitol* 2019;35:738–9. Reproduced with permission from Elsevier. (B) ***Echinococcus granulosus.*** Courtesy: Casulli *et al. Trends Parasitol* 2019;35:663–4. Reproduced with permission from Elsevier.

Association of Echinococcosis launched a Formal Consensus process.... The main achievements of this process were: (1) an update of the current nomenclature of *Echinococcus* spp.; (2) an agreement on three names of diseases due to *Echinococcus* spp.: CE, AE and NE, and the exclusion of all other names; (3) an agreement on the restricted use of the adjective 'hydatid' to refer to the cyst and fluid due to *E. granulosus sensu lato*; and (4) an agreement on a standardized description of the surgical operations for CE, according to the 'Approach, cyst Opening, Resection, and Completeness' (AORC) framework. In addition, 95 'approved' and 60 'rejected' terms were listed" (Vuitton *et al.* 2020). Illustrations are also provided. Please see Figure 16.4 for *Echinococcus* egg and oncosphere, and Figure 16.5 for *Echinococcus* metacestode (Vuitton *et al.* 2020).

16.3.3 Pathology

Echinococcus granulosus infections often remain asymptomatic for years until the cysts grow large enough to cause symptoms in the affected organs. *Echinococcus multilocularis* mainly affects the liver. It is also slow growing and can lead to abdominal pain and biliary obstruction.

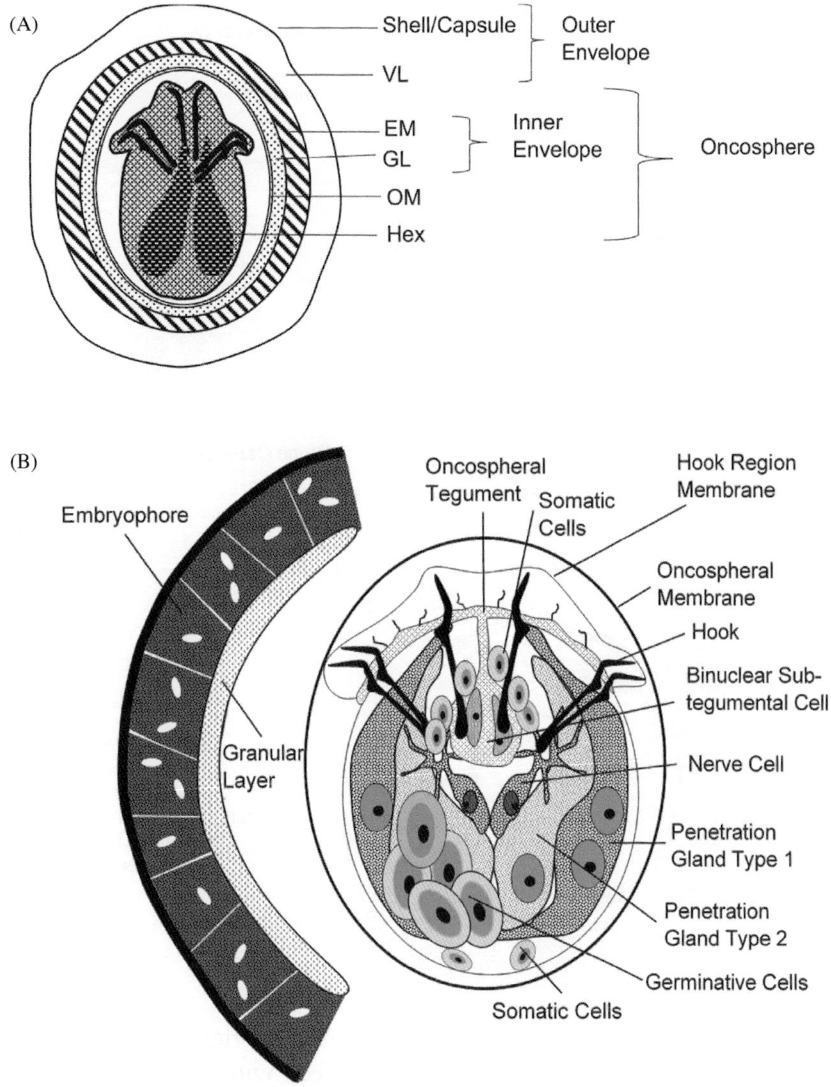

Fig. 16.4 ■ ***Echinococcus* egg and oncosphere.** General description of the egg and oncosphere of *Echinococcus* spp, according to Jabbar *et al.*, 2010. (A) Schematic diagram of an oncosphere illustrating the structure and bilateral symmetry in the pattern of hooks and cellular organization of the hexacanth embryo. VL: vitelline layer; EM: embryophore; GL: granular layer; OM: oncospheral membrane; Hex: hexacanth embryo. (B) Cellular organization of the oncosphere. Oncospheres are approximately 25 × 30 μm. Courtesy: Vuitton *et al. Parasite* 2019;27:41. Reproduced with permission from *Parasite* with Creative Commons Attribution 4.0 (CC-BY) International License.

Hydatid cysts are slow growing. They increase in size at the rate of 1–5 cm per year. There may be calcification at 5–10-year post-infection, usually occurs when the protoscolices begin to die. An average fertile primary cyst may contain up to **2 million** protoscolices. There may be links – the protoscolices and the brood capsules may be attached to the wall layer with pedicels (small stalks), as shown in Figure 16.5. While cysts in sheep and rodents

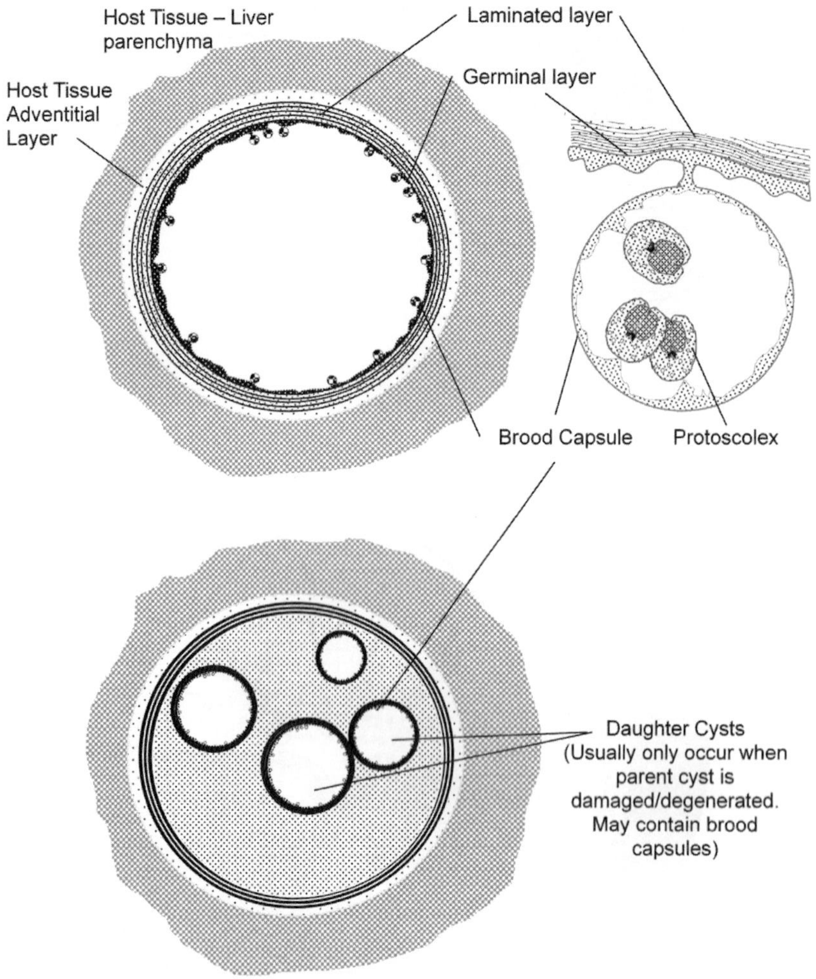

Fig. 16.5 ■ *Echinococcus* metacestode. General description of the metacestode of *Echinococcus* spp. Courtesy: Vuitton *et al. Parasite* 2019;27:41. Reproduced with permission from *Parasite* with Creative Commons Attribution 4.0 (CC-BY) International License.

eaten by dogs and foxes develop into adult tapeworms, those in humans are at dead end. There can be cyst ruptures that lead to dissemination of protoscolices and the release of cyst fluid can cause host immune response and in some cases even anaphylactic shock. Hydatid cysts have long survival time period. A human case has shown a latent period of 53 years.

Cystic echinococcosis (CE) is a global parasitic zoonosis for which ultrasound is the gold standard for diagnosis. The WHO-Informal Working Group on Echinococcosis (WHO-IWGE) for the treatment of human echinococcosis has provided a consensus on diagnosis, treatment and follow-up for both CE and AE. Enrico Brunetti (University of Pavia and WHO Collaborating Center for Clinical Management of Cystic Echinococcosis, Pavia, Italy) and colleagues wrote: "For CE, consensus has been obtained on an image-based, stage-specific approach, which is helpful for choosing one of the following options: (1) percutaneous treatment, (2) surgery, (3) anti-infective drug treatment or (4) watch and wait. Clinical decision-making depends also on setting specific aspects. The usage of an imaging-based classification system is highly recommended. For AE, early diagnosis and radical (tumour-like) surgery followed by anti-infective prophylaxis with albendazole remains one of the key elements. However, most patients with AE are diagnosed at a later stage, when radical surgery (distance of larval to liver tissue of >2 cm) cannot be achieved. The backbone of AE treatment remains the continuous medical treatment with albendazole, and if necessary, individualized interventional measures. With this approach, the prognosis can be improved for the majority of patients with AE" (Brunetti *et al.* 2010). An analysis on the progress towards adoption of the WHO ultrasound classification of CE has shown adoption of the new classification takes time and varies regionally (Mirabile *et al.* 2019).

Several cases of echinococcosis are provided here. The liver, lungs, and spleen are sites accounting for 90% of hydatid cysts. Two cases of unusual location of hydatid cysts were documented in Romania. (1) A 67-year-old female who had pulmonary tuberculosis was hospitalized for persistent pain in the hip joint. Although the clinical diagnosis was tuberculosis of the joint, there was the presence of specific acellular membranes indicating a hydatid cyst of the synovial membrane. The mass was surgically removed and then she had albendazole treatment for 3 months, with no recurrences at 5 years after diagnosis. (2) The case was an intramural hydatid incidentally discovered at autopsy, in the left heart ventricle of a 52-year-old male, hospitalized for aneurysm and brain hemorrhage. Despite surgical removal of the hematoma for brain decompression, he died 20 days after surgery (Gurzu *et al.* 2017).

A case of AE occurring in the hilar bile duct was documented in China (Yang *et al.* 2019). A 58-year-old Han Chinese woman from Qinghai province was admitted to hospital after complaints of epigastric pain (for 3 months), she was misdiagnosed as cholangiocarcinoma and had an operation to remove the tumor. Pathological examination of surgical specimens turned out to be hilar bile duct AE. Microscopically, alveolar cysts of varying sizes were observed scattering in bile duct epithelial tissues, with surrounding granulation and fibrous tissues.

An imported case of disseminated echinococcosis was documented in Korea. A frequent traveler (business trips to Kazakhstan, Russia, China in 2001–2007), the 53-year-old male was first diagnosed with a large liver cyst by ultrasound in 2011. He did not follow up until 2017, at that time he had cough, dizziness, and dysarthria; cystic lesions were found in his brain, liver, and lungs. He had multiple surgeries but inadequate treatment (a short duration of albendazole) before visiting Seoul University Hospital in August 2018, where his symptoms were definitively diagnosed with echinococcosis (by imaging and serology); he had prolonged albendazole treatment and showed a gradual recovery. "A high index of suspicion is warranted to early diagnose echinococcosis in a patient with a travel history to endemic areas of echinococcosis" (Shin *et al.* 2019).

16.3.4 Diagnosis

Ultrasound and other imaging techniques are used in the diagnosis of echinococcosis. Serological assays are available to confirm the infection. (Neuroimaging studies include magnetic resonance imaging, MRI, and non-contrast computed tomography, CT, scan of the brain, plus confirmation by immunoblots.) Because hydatid cysts derived microRNA (miRNA) such as egr-miR-71 and egr-let-7 are detectable in the human plasma, such molecules may be feasible to serve as novel biomarkers for early diagnosis and monitoring of hydatidosis (Alizadeh *et al.* 2020).

16.3.5 Therapy

Hydatid cysts grow slowly but can attain a size of 5 cm or larger. For earlier single cysts, the technique of puncture, aspiration, injection and re-aspiration (**PAIR**) is warranted, using 95% alcohol in order to kill protoscolices together with drugs such as albendazole (Velasco-Tirado *et al.* 2018). Surgery is also suggested for the removal of cysts but may not be 100% effective.

AE can be cured by radical surgery. However, many patients are no longer candidates for radical surgery due to late diagnosis. Infection in these cases is managed by life-long albendazole therapy (Casulli *et al.* 2019a). The management of CE envisages four clinical options, guided by cyst-stage classification as seen in imaging: surgery, percutaneous treatments, antiparasitic treatment with albendazole, and watch and wait (active surveillance by imaging) (Casulli *et al.* 2019b).

16.3.6 Genome

Echinococcus multilocularis, *E. granulosus* and *T. solium*, together with a model species *Hymenolepis microstoma*, were the first tapeworm species with their genomes published by scientists at the Wellcome Trust Sanger Institute and their collaborators (Tsai *et al.* 2013). Predicted gene numbers are **10,345** and **10,231** for *Echinococcus multilocularis* and *E. granulosus*, respectively. Transcriptomics analysis shows **13%** of trans-splicing transcripts for *Echinococcus multilocularis*, with **308** putative poly-cistrons (coding 2–4 genes). Promising drug targets for tapeworms include tubulin (albendazole), voltage-dependent calcium channel (praziquatel), thioredoxin glutathione reductase, fatty acid amide hydralase, cathepsin B, and others. There is expansion of gene families (heat shock protein 70) and contraction of gene families (homeobox proteins). Based on the four tapeworm genomes and those of other flatworms, an evolution scheme has been proposed. Please see Figure 16.6 for tapeworm evolution (Tsai *et al.* 2013).

Independently, Chinese and Australian scientists have also published the genome of *Echinococcus granulosus* (Zheng *et al.* 2013). The tapeworm possesses nine pairs of chromosomes, 151.6 Mb of DNA and codes for 11,325 protein-coding genes. Gene families such as hsp 70 and antigen B are confirmed to be *E. granulosus*-specific. An enzyme, **prenylcysteine oxidase**, that degrades prenylated proteins, has been suggested as a novel drug target. In addition, seven genes of **EG95** have been identified. EG95 recombinant vaccine may protect sheep from ovine cystic echinococcus, as demonstrated in an 8-year pilot field trial in Argentina (Larrieu *et al.* 2019).

Transcriptomics of *Echinococcus granulosus* has been reported (Fan *et al.* 2020). The protoscoleces in the encystation process were analyzed by high-throughput RNA sequencing. A total of 32,401 transcripts and 14,903 cDNAs revealed stage-specific and differently expressed genes, with up-regulation of genes involved in signaling pathways (kinases, putative G-protein coupled receptor), antioxidants (thioredoxin, glutathione peroxidase), collagen, and, intriguingly, the vasopressin-regulated water reabsorption metabolic pathway. These molecules may play important roles in the transport of proteins, carbohydrates, and other molecules.

Currently, *Echinococcus granulosus* has been divided into **10** different genotypes: G1 to G10. From mitochondrial phylogenetic analyses, *Echinococcus granulosus sensu lato* ("in a broad sense") species complex has become: *Echinococcus granulosus sensu stricto* ("in a narrow sense" G1/ G2/G3), *Echinococcus equinus* (G4), *Echinococcus ortleppi* (G5), *Echinococcus canadensis* (G6/ G7/G8/G10) and *Echinococcus felidis*. From worldwide case reports, the most prevalent species are **77% *Echinococcus granulosus sensu stricto*** and 22% *Echinococcus canadensis* (Maldonado *et al.* 2017).

Argentinian and Brazilian scientists published the genome of *Echinococcus canadensis* (G7) (Maldonado *et al.* 2017). The genome size is 115 Mb and it codes for **11,449** genes, with 8% repetitive DNA. Gene structure and organization are conserved between *Echinococcus granulosus* (G1), *Echinococcus canadensis* (G7) and *Echinococcus multilocularis*, with 95% synteny. In addition, variations seen as single nucleotide polymorphisms (SNPs) are more abundant between G7 and G1 than between G7 and *Echinococcus multilocularis*. From the G7 genome, proteins absent or highly divergent in humans have been proposed as drug targets. Examples include the antigen B (tapeworm antigen) and vacuolar proton ATPase G subunit (for transport).

Similarities between tapeworms and human cancers have been noted by the investigators who reported the first four tapeworm genomes. Tsai *et al.* (2013) wrote: "The challenges of inhibiting cancer tumors and metacestodes (particularly those of *E. multilocularis*) with drugs are in some ways similar; both show uncontrolled proliferation, invasion and metastasis, and are difficult to kill without causing damage to the surrounding tissue. Therefore, metacestodes may be vulnerable to similar strategies as cancer; suppression of mitosis, induction of apoptosis and prevention of DNA replication. In fact, the anthelminthic medicines niclosamide, mebendazole and albendazole have already been shown to inhibit cancer growth." **Niclosamide**, which is useful for tapeworm infections, has multiple effects, including antiviral activity due to its function as a proton carrier (Jurgeit *et al.* 2012). Niclosamide is also found to be active against ovarian cancer cells in experimental models. We have proposed combination of repurposed drugs (including

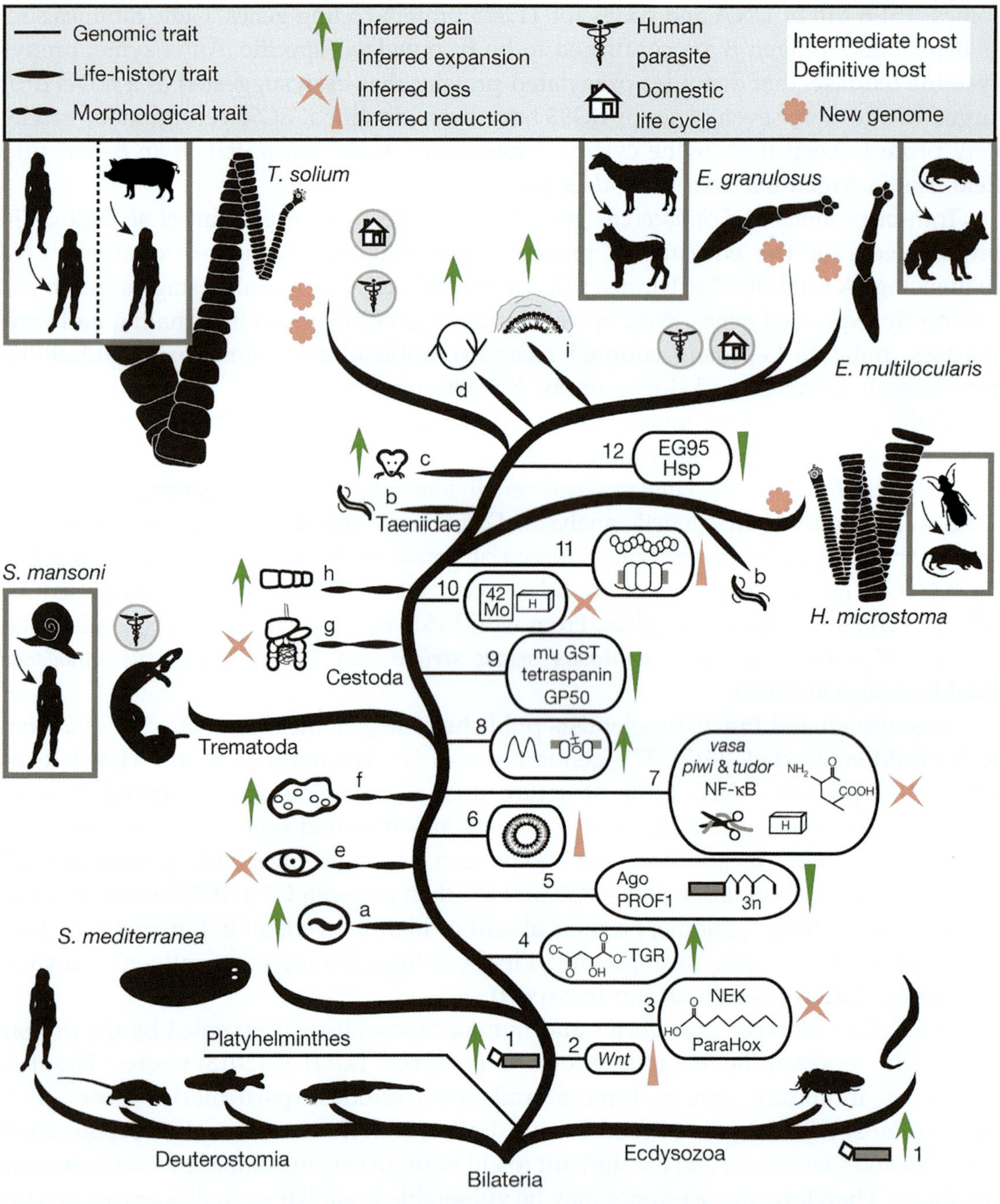

Fig. 16.6 ■ Evolution of tapeworm parasitism. Phylogeny of the main branches of Bilateria; Ecdysozoa (including fruitflies and nematodes), Deuterostomia (including lancelet, zebrafish, mice and humans), and Lophotrochozoans (including Platyhelminthes (flatworms). The gains and losses of life-cycle traits for these parasitic flatworms include the evolution of endoparasitism (A), passive transmission between hosts (B), acquisition of vertebrate intermediate host (C), ability to proliferate asexually in intermediate host (D). Morphological traits that have evolved include the

niclosamide) and dietary phytochemicals (including curcumin) to target cancer stem cells as a novel approach for cancer chemotherapy (Chan *et al.* 2018).

16.4 Sparganosis by *Spirometra*

Sparganosis is human infection caused by the plerocercoid larvae of aquatic tapeworms. Many tapeworms with metacestode stages are known to be present for various host species, but their complete life cycles are yet to be investigated. The plerocercoid larva stage used to have its own genus known as *Sparganum*. Infection by such metacestode is known as sparganosis. Once these are found to be the larval stages, the genus name was deleted but the disease name remains the same. A common species that causes sparganosis in US is ***Spirometra mansonoides***. The species that causes sparganosis in Europe and Asia is ***Spirometra erinaceieuropaei***. Clinical cases of sparganosis are relatively rare, with estimates of 300 cases worldwide between 1953 and 2003, and over 1,000 cases in China from 1882 to 2010 (Bennett *et al.* 2014).

16.4.1 History

Patrick Mansion first described *Spirometra* infections from China in 1882. The first human sparganosis was reported by an American parasitologist Charles Wardell Stiles from Florida in 1908.[3]

Fig. 16.6 (figure on facing page) ■ loss of eye cups (E), gain of neodermatan syncytial epithelia (F), loss of gut (G), segmentation of body plan (H), and changes in the laminated layer (to contain specialized apomucins; (I). Gains and losses of genomic traits include spliced-leader *trans*-splicing (1), loss of *Wnt* genes (2), loss of NEK kinases, fatty acid biosynthesis and ParaHox genes (3), anaerobic metabolic ability through the malate dismutation/rodhoquinone pathway, merger of *glutaredoxin* and *thioredoxin reductase* to *thioredoxin glutathione reductase* (TGR) (4), evolution of tapeworm- and fluke-specific Argonaute (Ago) family, micro exon genes (MEGs) and PROF1 GPCRs (5), loss of peroxisomal genes (6), and complete loss of *vasa*, *tudor* and *piwi* genes, NF-κB pathway, loss of 24 homeobox gene families (indicated by 'H'), metabolic proteases and amino acid biosynthesis (7). In tapeworms, gains and losses of genomic traits include innovation of bimodal intron distribution and novel fatty acid transporters (8), expansion of mu-class glutathione *S*-transferases, GP50 antigens and tetraspanins (9), loss of the molybdopterin biosynthesis pathway, loss of 10 homeobox gene families (10), fewer GPCRs and fewer neuropeptides encoded by each protopeptide (11), and expansion of heat shock proteins (Hsp) and species-specific antigens (12). Courtesy: Tsai *et al.* *Nature* 2013;496:57–63. Reproduced with permission from Springer Nature.

[3] https://en.wikipedia.org/wiki/Sparganosis

16.4.2 Life cycle

Please see Figure 16.7 for life cycle of *Spirometra sp.*, from CDC.[4]

The definitive hosts for the many species of *Spirometra* are birds, felines, canines and other carnivores. Adult tapeworms of *Spirometra mansonoides* live in intestines of cats and dogs.

Experimentally, the complete life cycle of *Spirometra erinaceieuropaei* has been established using three species as hosts: copepod (first intermediate host), mouse (second intermediate host) and dog (final definitive host) (Okino *et al.* 2017). Plerocercoids isolated from snakes were shown to be the correct species by sequencing the mitochondrial cytochrome oxidase subunit 1 gene, and fed to mice. A plerocercoid from mice was then administered orally to a dog, and dog feces containing eggs were found 40 days after inoculation. Collected eggs were maintained for over a week, cold-shocked to induce coracidia formation, and incubated with the copepod *Cyclops*. Infected copepods were then fed to mice by lavage. After one month plerocercoids were isolated from mice and fed to dog. By repeating the process for 5 times, a clone was generated and named *Spirometra erinaceieuropaei* Kawasaki triploid ($3n$ = **27**), after the institution Kawasaki Medical School.

16.4.3 Pathology

Human sparganosis is a zoonotic disease caused by infection and migration of the plerocercoid of *Spirometra* spp. Although the disease is found worldwide, it is common in China, Japan, and countries in Southeast Asia. Sparganosis is the result of drinking contaminated beverages or the consumption of infected raw meat (including fish, frog, snakes). Humans can also acquire sparganosis by drinking water contaminated with infected copepods. After intake, the procercoid larvae develop into plerocercoid larvae (aka sparganum). Sparganosis can occur after consumption of an under-cooked meat of second intermediate or paratenic host containing plerocercoids. Some cultures favor the use of poultice, meat of snakes, frogs or other species for soothing purpose, and the plerocercoids can migrate into human skin. For invasion and migration by the plerocercoid, a cysteine protease is critically involved. Purified from the plerocercoid larvae of *Spirometra erinaceieuropaei*, it is known as **Se23kCP** yielding a mature enzyme composed of 216 amino acids and showing a high sequence similarity with cathepsin L. Since Se23kCP induces host tissue invasion and migration, it might be an essential molecule for sparganosis onset and progression (Tsubokawa *et al.* 2017).

The migrating spargana (plural of sparganum) can cause different symptoms depending on their final destination in the human host. The disease sparganosis mostly involves subcutaneous fat (in limbs, genitourinary tract, and the abdomen). In rare cases, sparga-

[4]https://www.cdc.gov/dpdx/sparganosis/index.html

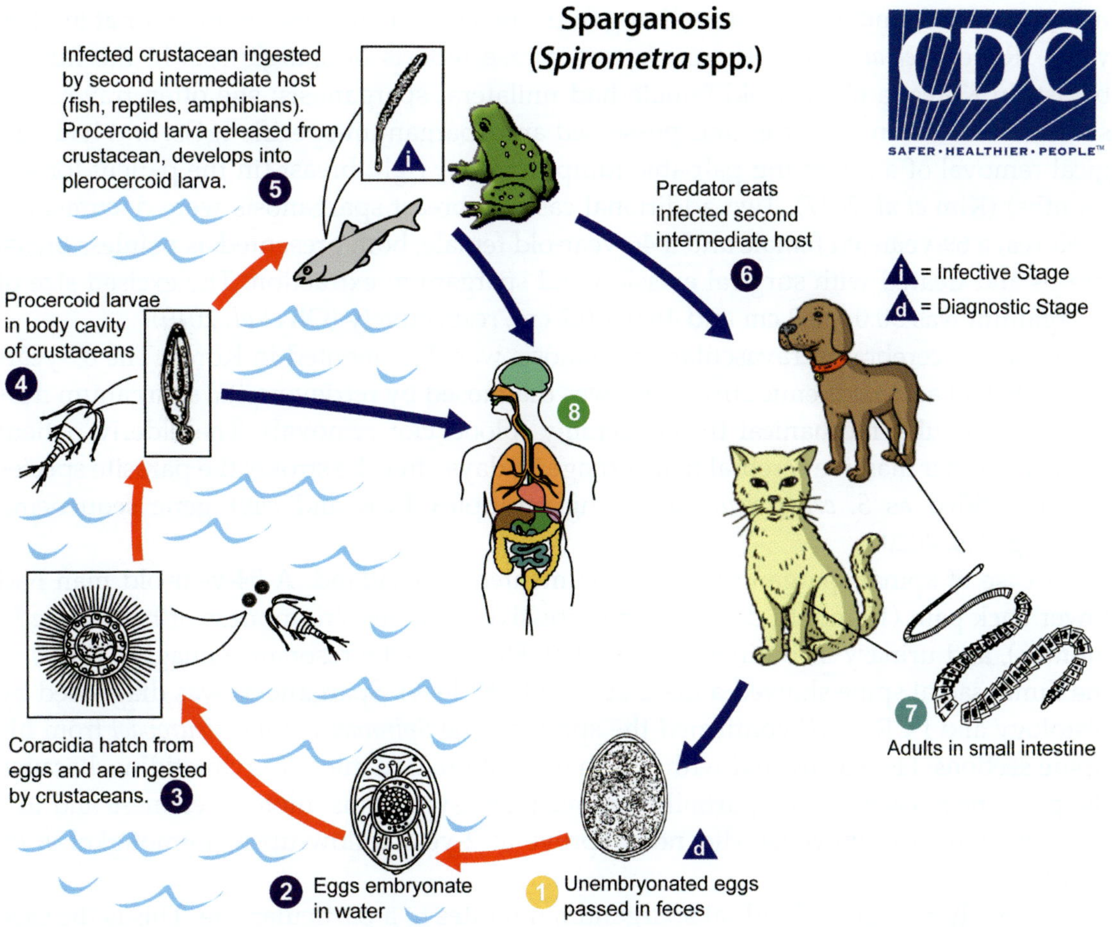

Fig. 16.7 ■ **Life cycle of *Spirometra species*.** Adult members of the genus *Spirometra* live in the intestines of dogs and cats 7. Eggs are shed in feces 1 and embryonate in the environment 2. Eggs hatch in water and release coracidia 3, which are ingested by copepods. The coracidia develop into procercoid larvae in the copepod intermediate host 4. Second intermediate hosts, including fish, reptiles and amphibians, ingest infected copepods and acquire procercoid larvae. The procercoid larvae develop into plerocercoid larvae in the second intermediate host 5. The cycle is completed when a predator (dog or cat) eats an infected second intermediate host 6. Humans cannot serve as definitive hosts for *Spirometra* spp., but serve as paratenic or second intermediate hosts 8 and develop sparganosis. Humans acquire sparganosis by either drinking water contaminated with infected copepods or consuming the flesh of an under-cooked second intermediate or paratenic host. Spargana can live up to 20 years in the human host. Courtesy of the CDC. Reproduced from https://www.cdc.gov/dpdx/sparganosis/index.html

nosis affects the breast (2% of total cases). Migration through the subcutaneous tissues is usually painless. However, if the sparganum settles in the brain or spine, there can be neurological symptoms (seizure, headache, plus abnormal skin sensations including numbness or tingling). Spargana can live up to 20 years in the human host. A paper published in 1975 found a sparganum living in the breast of a Japanese woman for at least 30 years (Roberts *et al.* 2013). There are recent case reports of sparganosis in the human breast. In Korea, a 62-year-old female had unilateral sparganosis; she often traveled to southeastern Asian countries and possessed anti-sparganum-specific IgGs, and had surgical removal of a migrating palpable lump from her right breast (in the patient for 4–5 months) (Kim *et al.* 2017). Two additional cases of breast sparganosis were documented in Korea, a 69-year-old female and a 46-year-old female, both presented as painless breast lumps and treated with surgical excision and sparganum extraction. The excised size of sparganum was 30.0 × 0.3 cm and 16.0 × 0.2 cm, respectively (Oh *et al.* 2019).

A case of cerebral intravascular sparganosis was documented in Korea. The 89-year-old male had acute ischemic stroke and was diagnosed by retrieving the sparganum during endovascular mechanical thrombectomy (blood clot removal). The elderly patient died of another massive cerebral hemorrhage 15 days after the stroke; the parasite species was identified as *S. erinaceieuropaei* using multiplex PCR and *cox*1 gene sequencing (Hwang *et al.* 2020).

A case of spinal sparganosis was documented in Thailand. A 54-year-old man had lower back pain (10-month duration), progressive weakness/numbness of his left leg (4 months), and urinary incontinence (3 weeks). His magnetic resonance imaging (MRI) of the lumbosacral spine showed a mass at the T12-S1 level. Sparganosis was diagnosed by histology and PCR (*cox1*) confirmed the species to be *Spirometra erinaceieuropaei* from his tissue sections. He was treated with a high dose of praziquantel plus cimetidine, because the parasitic mass was only partially removed. His symptoms, motor weakness and urinary incontinence, however, did not improve at 2-year follow-up (Chotmongkol *et al.* 2020).

Normally a single individual sparganum migrates to a particular site. This is the case for most of the *Spirometra* species metacestodes. One pseudophyllidean tapeworm species, named ***Sparganum proliferum***, can proliferate within the lesion, resulting in many plerocercoids at the same site. Proliferative sparganosis is one of the most bizarre and mysterious parasitic diseases ever described. Taisei Kikuchi and Haruhiko Maruyama (University of Miyazaki) did a literature search for the last 115 years since the first case in 1943. Proliferative sparganosis is divided into two disease types, cutaneous and internal proliferative. Only 10 internal and 8 cutaneous cases were reported in a century. They wrote: "One of the major riddles about *S. proliferum* is its life cycle. Nobody has ever discovered the definitive host for this enigmatic tapeworm. With regard to this point, it is puzzling that dogs and cats cannot be the definitive hosts" (Kikuchi and Maruyama 2020). The complete life cycle of this enigmatic tapeworm awaits discovery.

16.4.4 Diagnosis

Diagnosis is recovery of the sparganum from the affected tissue. Imaging techniques have been helpful in diagnosing sparganosis.

16.4.5 Therapy

Surgical removal of the sparganum is the method of choice.

16.4.6 Genome

The genome of ***Spirometra erinaceieuropaei*** has been characterized by scientists at the Wellcome Trust Sanger Institute at Cambridge, from the biopsy of a person who had a migrating brain lesion (Bennett *et al.* 2014). The patient was a 50-year-old man of Chinese ethnicity and had been visiting his homeland on occasion. He was admitted for headache, seizures, memory impairment and progressive right-side pain. MRI of his brain revealed right side lesion. A series of images over 4 years showed lesion movement. A neurosurgical biopsy was done, and the DNA was isolated from formalin-fixed paraffin embedded worm (cox1 for species identification) and its genome analysis was completed using a small amount of worm DNA (0.048 μg). From the sample it is shown that *S. erinaceieuropaei* maintains a huge genome, **1.26 Gb** in size. Scientists are baffled by this large size, but one explanation is the presence of **46%** repetitive DNA. The predicted gene number is 39,856 (most likely an over-estimate due to fragmented gene assembly). Current drugs albendazole and praziquantel probably would not work for *Spirometra*. For benzimidazole resistance, 24 out of 26 β tubulin transcripts (as expressed sequence tags, ESTs) show resistant amino acid residue at the putative target site. Gene families are present, including ones for **titin** (the largest known natural protein), HSP 70, antigen B and EG 95. From the genome, putative drug targets are proposed, which include thioredoxin glutathione reductase, fatty acid amide hydrolase, cysteine protease cathepsin B, and others, the same targets as *Taenia* and *Echinococcus*. In addition, the gene encoding for plerocercoid growth factor (PGF) has been identified (thus confirming previous reports).

16.4.7 Plerocercoid growth factor

One interesting finding in the aquatic tapeworm metacestodes is their effects on host metabolism. Infected rodents with plerocercoids show accelerated body growth, due to **PGF**. PGF interacts with growth hormone receptor and mimics the action of growth hormone by acting like the growth hormone agonist. Unexpectedly, when the gene was cloned, the protein turned out to be a cysteine proteinase (**CP**) (Phares 1996). CP degrades collagen for worm movement and also degrades immunoglobulins to modulate inflammation. Thus, proteinase and their inhibitors aid in parasite digestion and migration, they also have activities against host immune response in host-parasite interactions. Please see Figure 16.8 for the large size of *Spirometra mansonoides*-infected rats (Mueller 1974). [The experiment was performed in hypophysectomized animals. Hypophysectomy is the surgical removal of the hypophysis (pituitary gland).]

Fig. 16.8 ■ Effect of *Spirometra mansoides* on rat growth. Hypophysectomized rats of the same initial lot, operated at 90 g. The only difference is the two larger rats received 20 larval scoleces of *S. mansonoides* approximately 1 month after the operation. They are now seen 6 months later. The experimental animals outweigh the controls by a factor of 3 or 4X. Courtesy: Mueller J. *J Parasitol* 1974;60:3–14. Reproduced with permission from Allen Press Inc.

Summary & Key Concepts

- Juvenile tapeworm infecting humans cause diseases cysticercosis, hydatidosis and sparganosis.
- Cysticercosis is caused by ingestion of eggs of the pork tapeworm *Taenia solium*, with the developing larvae present in various part of the human body.
- Neurocysticercosis (NCC) is the most common cause of epilepsy worldwide.
- Hydatidosis, aka echinococcosis, is caused by hydatid cysts containing fluid and a multitude of developing larvae known as protoscolices from the tapeworm *Echinococcus* species, whose normal definitive hosts are dogs and foxes.
- Sparganosis is caused by juvenile tapeworms of cats and dogs living in the human body, including the brain.

- Metacestodes or juvenile tapeworm share characteristics, such as invasion and metastasis, with human cancers; the tapeworm drug niclosamide has been shown to target human cancer stem cells.

References

Alizadeh Z, Mahami-Oskouei M, Spotin A, *et al.* Parasite-derived microRNAs in plasma as novel promising biomarkers for the early detection of hydatid cyst infection and post-surgery follow-up. *Acta Trop.* 2020;202:105255.

Bennett HM, Mok HP, Gkrania-Klotsas E, *et al.* The genome of the sparganosis tapeworm *Spirometra erinaceieuropaei* isolated from the biopsy of a migrating brain lesion. *Genome Biol* 2014;15(11):510.

Brunetti E, Kern P, Vuitton DA, *et al.* Expert consensus for the diagnosis and treatment of cystic and alveolar echinococcosis in humans. *Acta Trop* 2010;114(1):1–16.

Casulli A, Barth TFE, Tamarozzi F. *Echinococcus multilocularis*. *Trends Parasitol* 2019a;35(9):738–9.

Casulli A, Siles-Lucas M, Tamarozzi F. *Echinococcus granulosus* sensu lato. *Trends Parasitol* 2019b;35(8):663–4.

Chan MM, Chen R, Fong D. Targeting cancer stem cells with dietary phytochemical — Repositioned drug combinations. *Cancer Lett* 2018;433:53–64.

Chotmongkol V, Phuttharak W, Jingjit K, *et al.* Case report: Sparganosis of the Cauda Equina: Case report and literature review. *Am J Trop Med Hyg* 2020.

Cox FE. History of human parasitology. *Clin Microbiol Rev* 2002;15(4):595–612.

Fan J, Wu H, Li K, *et al.* Transcriptomic features of *Echinococcus granulosus* protoscolex during the encystation process. *Korean J Parasitol* 2020;58(3):287–99.

Forster D, Ko DK, Koehler AV, *et al.* Case report: Neurocysticercosis acquired in Australia. *Am J Trop Med Hyg* 2020.

Gurzu S, Beleaua MA, Egyed-Zsigmond E, Jung I. Unusual location of hydatid cysts: Report of two cases in the heart and hip joint of romanian patients. *Korean J Parasitol* 2017;55(4):429–31.

Herrick JA, Bustos JA, Clapham P, *et al.* Unique characteristics of epilepsy development in neurocysticercosis. *Am J Trop Med Hyg* 2020;103(2):639–45.

Hwang YH, Son W, Kim YW, *et al.* A retrieved Sparganum of *Spirometra erinaceieuropaei* from a Korean Man during mechanical thrombectomy. *Korean J Parasitol* 2020;58(3):309–13.

International Helminth Genomes Consortium. Comparative genomics of the major parasitic worms. *Nat Genet* 2019;51(1):163–74.

Jurgeit A, McDowell R, Moese S, Meldrum E, Schwendener R, Greber UF. Niclosamide is a proton carrier and targets acidic endosomes with broad antiviral effects. *PLoS Pathog* 2012;8(10): e1002976.

Kean BH, Mott KE, Russell AJ, Editors. *Tropical Medicine and Parasitology: Classic Investigations,* volume I and II (1978, Cornell, Ithaca).

Kikuchi T, Maruyama H. Human proliferative sparganosis update. *Parasitol Int* 2020;75:102036.

Kim HS, Shin MS, Kim CJ, *et al.* Sparganosis of the unilateral breast: A case report. *Korean J Parasitol* 2017;55(4):421–4.

Larrieu E, Mujica G, Araya D, *et al.* Pilot field trial of the EG95 vaccine against ovine cystic echinococcosis in Rio Negro, Argentina: 8 years of work. *Acta Trop* 2019;191:1–7.

Maldonado LL, Assis J, Araújo FM, *et al.* The *Echinococcus canadensis* (G7) genome: A key knowledge of parasitic platyhelminth human diseases. *BMC Genomics* 2017;18(1):204.

Mehlhorn H. *Human Parasites* (2016, Springer).

Mendlovic F, Fleury A, Flisser A. Zoonotic *Taenia* infections with focus on cysticercosis due to *Taenia solium* in swine and humans. *Res Vet Sci* 2021;134:69–77.

Mirabile E, Solomon N, Fields PJ, Macpherson CNL. Progress towards international adoption of the World Health Organization ultrasound classification of cystic echinococcosis. *Acta Trop* 2019;189:6–9.

Mueller JF. The biology of *Spirometra*. *J Parasitol* 1974;60(1):3–14.

Mukuku O, Sánchez SS, Bugeme M, Garcia HH. Case report: Three cases of neurocysticercosis in Central Africa. *Am J Trop Med Hyg* 2020;103(5):1955–7.

Müller A, Förch G, Zustin J, Muntau B, Schuldt G, Tappe D. Case report: Molecular identification of larval *Taenia martis* infection in the Pouch of Douglas. *Am J Trop Med Hyg* 2020;103(6):2315–7.

Nakaya K, Mamuti W, Xiao N, *et al.* Usefulness of severe combined immunodeficiency (scid) and inbred mice for studies of cysticercosis and echinococcosis. *Parasitol Int* 2006;55(Suppl):S91–7.

Oh MY, Kim KE, Kim MJ, *et al.* Breast sparganosis presenting with a painless breast lump: Report of two cases. *Korean J Parasitol* 2019;57(2):179–84.

Okino T, Ushirogawa H, Matoba K, Nishimatsu SI, Saito M. Establishment of the complete life cycle of *Spirometra* (Cestoda: Diphyllobothriidae) in the laboratory using a newly isolated triploid clone. *Parasitol Int* 2017;66(2):116–8.

Phares K. An unusual host-parasite relationship: the growth hormone-like factor from plerocercoids of spirometrid tapeworms. *Int J Parasitol* 1996;26(6):575–88.

Roberts LS, Janovy J Jr, Nadler S. *Foundations of Parasitology*, 9th ed. McGraw Hill, 2013.

Shin DH, Jo HC, Kim JH, *et al.* An mported case of disseminated echinococcosis in Korea. *Korean J Parasitol* 2019;57(4):429–34. doi: 10.3347/kjp.2019.57.4.429. Epub 2019 Aug 31.

Symeonidou I, Arsenopoulos K, Tzilves D, Soba B, Gabriël S, Papadopoulos E. Human taeniasis/cysticercosis: A potentially emerging parasitic disease in Europe. *Ann Gastroenterol* 2018;31(4):406–12.

Tsai IJ, Zarowiecki M, Holroyd N, *et al.* The genomes of four tapeworm species reveal adaptations to parasitism. *Nature* 2013;496(7443):57–63.

Tsubokawa D, Hatta T, Maeda H, *et al.* A cysteine protease from *Spirometra erinaceieuropaei* plerocercoid is a critical factor for host tissue invasion and migration. *Acta Trop.* 2017;167:99–107.

Velasco-Tirado V, Alonso-Sardón M, Lopez-Bernus A, *et al.* Medical treatment of cystic echinococcosis: Systematic review and meta-analysis. *BMC Infect Dis* 2018;18(1):306.

Vuitton DA, McManus DP, Rogan MT, *et al.* International consensus on terminology to be used in the field of echinococcoses. *Parasite* 2020;27:41.

Wen H, Vuitton L, Tuxun T, *et al.* Echinococcosis: Advances in the 21st Century. *Clin Microbiol Rev* 2019;32(2):e00075-18.

Yang J, Zhao Z, Li S, *et al.* A case of Alveolar echinococcosis occurring in the hilar bile duct. *Korean J Parasitol* 2019;57(5):517–20.

Yang SY, Lines WW, Vásquez CM, For The Cysticercosis Working Group In Perú Racemose neurocysticercosis. *Am J Trop Med Hyg* 2020;102(4):703–4.

Zheng H, Zhang W, Zhang L, *et al.* The genome of the hydatid tapeworm *Echinococcus granulosus*. *Nat Genet* 2013;45(10):1168–75.

17

Introduction to Nematodes

17.1 Nematoda

Human parasites include protozoa and helminths. In 1758, Carl Linnaeus classified the roundworms as members of Vermes, along with other worms and worm-like animals. Based on the Adl classification, all the worms belong to Metazoa, under Opisthokonta (Adl *et al.* 2019). Based on Ruggiero classification, under the kingdom Animalia, the worms belong to two phyla: Platyhelminthes and Nematoda (Ruggiero *et al.* 2015). After presenting human parasites including flukes and tapeworms, we conclude the worms with the nematodes. Nematodes are roundworms that belong to the phylum Nematoda (nema means thread). True to their name, nematodes generally have bodies that are long, narrow and threadlike, but not segmented as seen in earthworms.

Nematodes are the most abundant multicellular animals on earth. They occupy a variety of niches: terrestrial (soil), aquatic (fresh water, marine), and parasitic. Nematodes live on or in plants; nematodes live on or in animals (including humans). Thus, they can be free-living, predatory, or parasitic. The scientific study of these worms is known as **nematology**.

Nathan Cobb, "the father of nematology in the United States," wrote: "In short, if all the matter in the universe except the nematodes were swept away, our world would still be dimly recognizable, and if, as disembodied spirits, we could then investigate it, we should find its mountains, hills, vales, rivers, lakes, and oceans represented by a film of nematodes. The location of towns would be decipherable since, for every massing of human beings, there would be a corresponding massing of certain nematodes. Trees would still stand in ghostly rows representing our streets and highways. The location of the various plants and animals would still be decipherable, and, had we sufficient knowledge, in many cases, even their species could be determined by an examination of their erstwhile nematode parasites," (1914 *Yearbook of the United States Department of Agriculture*).

Nematodes live literally everywhere. They are the most abundant and speciose extant group of metazoans (Roberts *et al.* 2013; Viney 2018). Up to 9 billion nematodes per acre can be found in a good farmland. A total of 1,074 nematodes representing 236 species, were counted in 6.7 mL of coastal mud. In marine sediments, up to 95% of the organisms present can be nematodes; nematodes are the majority of benthic invertebrate biomass (as members of the **meiofauna** or meiobenthos). Free-living nematodes feed on bacteria, fungi or detritus. Some are predators. As members of the biosphere, nematodes in turn can be food for other species, such as nematode-eating fungi (the carnivorous nematophageous fungi). As an example, Alessandro Maciel (Universidade Federal de Vicosa/ Federal University of Viçosa) and colleagues demonstrated the destruction of *Ancylostoma* L3 larvae by the nematophagous fungus *Duddingtonia flagrans* using scanning electron microscopy (Maciel *et al.* 2009). This hookworm L3 larva is the infective stage that will penetrate the human skin. Different species of nematodes are parasites of plants and animals (both invertebrates and vertebrates).

In phylogenetic and classification studies, Nematoda is a sister group to Nematomorpha (including Gordian worms, such as African hairworm *Paragordius obamai*). Both phyla are close relatives to the Panarthropoda, which include the phyla Arthropoda (insects), Onychophora (velvet worms) and Tardigrada (tardigrades). All these phyla also come under the group known as Ecdysozoa (a superphylum) (Kiontke and Fitch 2013).

To biologists today, the best known nematode is the free-living ***Caenorhabditis elegans***, a model organism for genetic and biomedical research. The worm feeds on bacteria (a lawn of *Escherichia coli* in a petri plate). It is small in size (1 mm adult length) and has a short life cycle (3 days from fertilized egg to adult). Moreover, *C. elegans* is transparent throughout the life cycle; thus, changes at the cellular level are observable under light microscopy. Cell lineages of this free-living nematode are known, from 558 nuclei in the hatching larva to 959 nuclei in the hermaphroditic adult (excluding cells of the germline). The adult nervous system consists of only 302 cell nuclei (after apoptosis along the way). *C. elegans* is the first metazoan with a sequenced genome (before the human genome). The use of this model organism has led to 3 Nobel prizes in diverse research areas: programmed cell death (2002), RNA interference (2006), and development of the green fluorescent protein (GFP) as a marker for gene expression (2008).

Compared to their free-living cousins, parasitic nematodes generally are larger in size, presumably due to the constant internal environment of their hosts. As an example, for the roundworm *Ascaris lumbricoides*, adult females are 20–35 cm in length (smaller adult males are 15–30 cm). The largest nematodes are parasites of whales (cetaceans). The species living within the placenta of the sperm whale is known as *Placentanema gigantissma*. The female worm can reach up to 8.4 m long, and the smaller male 3.75 m in length. Another species that infect pigmy sperm whale is *Crassicauda magna*; their adult sizes are over 3 m (Keenan-Bateman *et al.* 2018).

In occupying a variety of niches, nematodes exhibit an amazing biodiversity. Around 23,000 to **30,000** species of nematodes have been described. The actual, total number of species is estimated to be over 1 million. As noted above, nematodes differ widely in body size (from 0.2 mm to over 6 m). They also differ in feeding structures and cuticular decorations. With respect to human endeavors, nematode species can be plant and animal parasites. As such, they inflict substantial damage on humans and their agricultural products. Approximately 8–15% of crop losses are attributed to nematodes worldwide, at a cost of $80 billion (Kiontke and Fitch 2013). Hence, there is the field of nematology.

Information on *Caenorhabditis elegans*, is available at WormBase.[1] Information on parasitic nematodes are available at Helminth.net[2] (Martin *et al.* 2015) and WormBase ParaSite.[3]

17.2 Cuticle and Other Structures

Whereas tegument is the outer surface of flukes and tapeworms, cuticle is the outer surface of nematodes or roundworms. The cuticle covers the entire external surface, as well as the buccal cavity, esophagus, rectum, vagina, cloaca, and excretory pore. Different ways have been used to describe the cuticular structure. Cuticle is composed of layers. From the environmental side to the internal side (outermost to innermost), the layers are **epicuticle, exocuticle, mesocuticle,** and **endocuticle,** followed by **basal lamina**, and **hypodermis**. Cuticle is acellular; the cellular hypodermis secretes materials for the formation of cuticle. (Since hypodermis is the first cellular layer, some scientists refer this layer as epidermis.) Another way is to divide the cuticle into 4 parts: a **triple-layered epicuticle** at the external surface, a **cortical zone**, a **median zone**, and a **basal zone**. Instead of layer, the term zone is preferred because zones are closely apposed and their boundaries are often difficult to define. Comparing the two ways to look at the cuticle, epicuticle is the same in both, exocuticle is the cortical zone, mesocuticle is the median zone, and endocuticle is the basal zone. Biochemically, the cuticle is composed of 3 groups of molecules: (1) structural components – **collagen** is the most abundant, plus the non-collagenous **cuticulin** (aka cuticlin); (2) soluble proteins – enzymes (collagen metabolism); and (3) low molecular weight components – lipids. Cuticle structures may be useful for phylogenetic studies. It has been suggested that several structural elements of the cuticle may have arisen independently several times within the Nematoda (Decraemer *et al.* 2003). Since the cuticle serves multiple functions, including body movement, shape maintenance, and protection of the organism, it is a complex structure. Please see Figure 17.1 for nematode cuticle ultrastructure under transmission electron microcopy (TEM). Cuticular structures are similar between free-living and parasitic species (Page 2001; Page *et al.* 2014).

Nematodes, covered with cuticle, have one-way guts (with front-end mouth and back-end anus). They are **dioecious**. Normally, females are larger than males. Please see Figure 17.2 for generalized nematode structure, and Figure 17.3 and Figure 17.4 for scanning electron micrographs showing the anterior and posterior ends of select nematodes, respectively (all from Mehlhorn 2016). The nematode body plan is basically a tube within a tube: the gonad and gut are surrounded by the body wall, which is made up of cuticle,

[1] https://wormbase.org//#012-34-5
[2] http://www.helminth.net
[3] https://parasite.wormbase.org/index.html

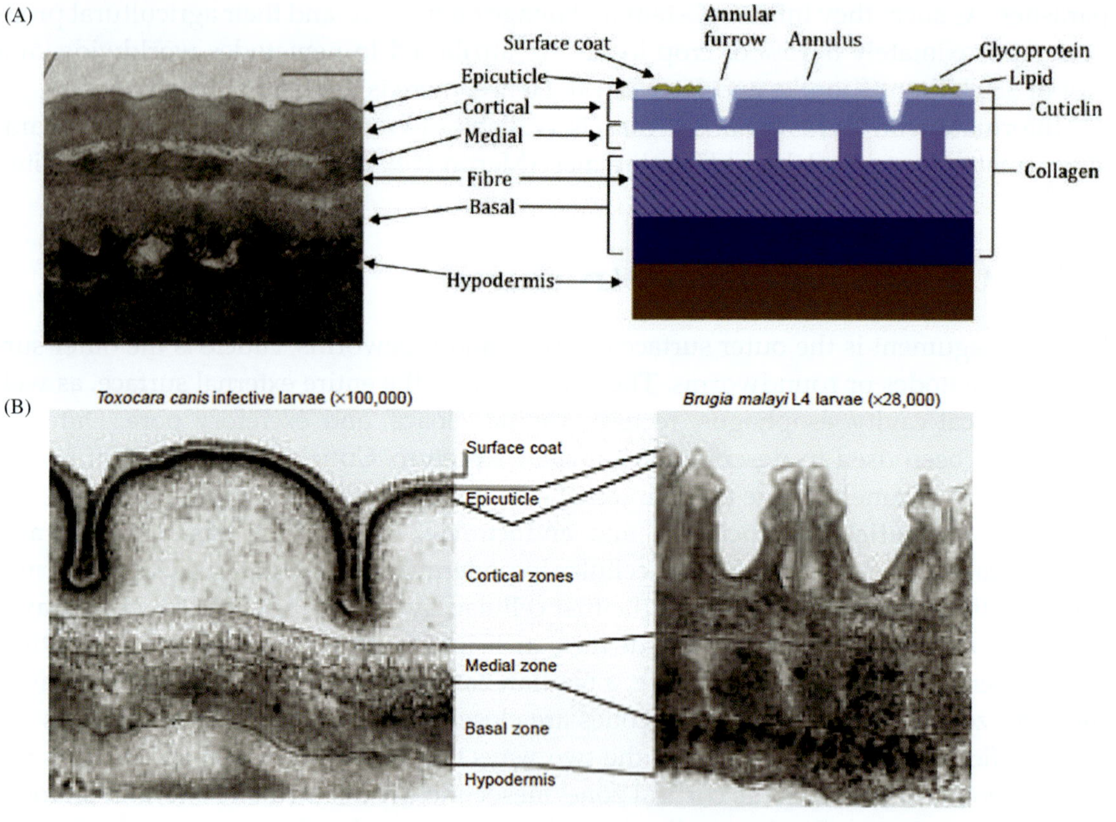

Fig. 17.1 ■ Nematode cuticle structure by transmission electron microscopy (TEM), from free-living and parasitic species. (A) ***Caenorhabditis elegans.*** The organization and structure of the *C. elegans* cuticle. Left image is a transmission electron micrograph (TEM) depicting a longitudinal cross-section of the adult cuticle. Right panel is a cartoon depiction highlighting the distinct structural layers and their composition. With the exception of the epicuticle and surface coat, collagens are present in all major layers. Cuticlins are restricted to the cortical layer. The epicuticle contains lipids and is covered by a glycoprotein-rich coat (scale bar 1 μm). Courtesy: Page *et al. Int J Parasitol Drugs Drug Resist* 2014;4:133–41. Reproduced with permission from Elsevier. (B) ***Toxocara canis*** and ***Brugia malayi.*** Transmission electron micrographs of parasitic nematode cuticles in transverse section. The structurally distinct layers and the underlying hypodermal syncytia are indicated. Nematodes depicted are the infective larval stage of the canid parasite *Toxocara canis* and the fourth larval stage of the human filarial parasite *Brugia malayi*. Courtesy: Page A. In: Kennedy M, Harnett W, editors. *Parasitic Nematodes*, pp. 167–93 (2001). Reproduced with permission from CABI (Commonwealth Agricultural Bureaux International).

epidermis, and muscles. A pressurized, fluid-filled cavity known as a pseudocoel (aka pseudocoelom) is located between the inner and outer tubes. The body fluid is the hemolymph. The somatic musculature, the pseudocoel with hemolymph, and the cuticle function together as a **hydrostatic skeleton** to allow the nematode S-shaped motion. Roundworms rely on tough body wall and pressurized body cavity as an antagonist for

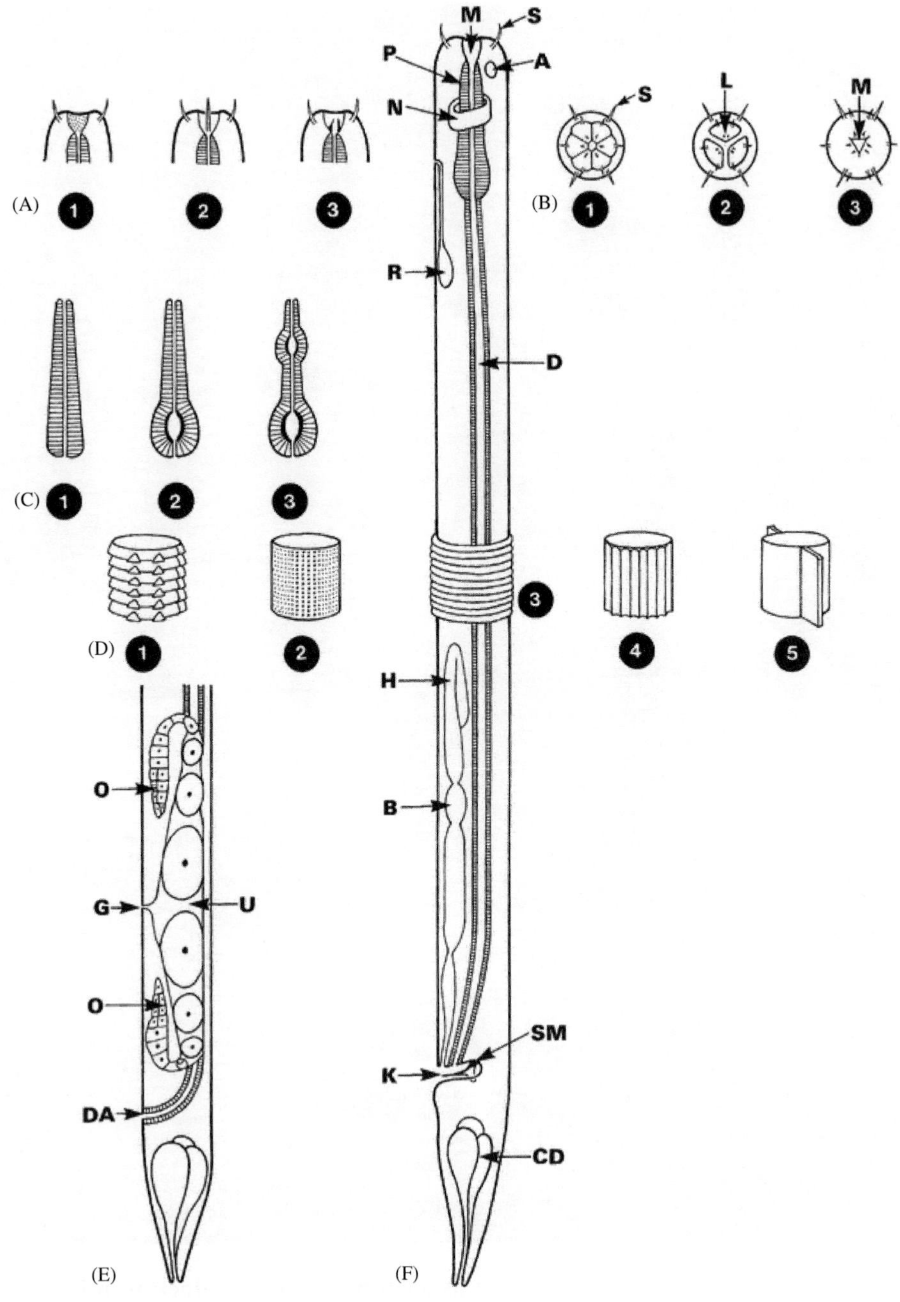

Fig. 17.2 ■ General nematode morphology. Diagrammatic representation of the organization of nematodes. (A) Mouth: (*1*) unarmed, (2) with stylet; (*3*) with teeth. (B) Lips: (*1*) = 6 lips, (*2*) = 3 lips, (*3*) = without lips. (C) Pharynx: (*1*) undivided, (*2*) with bulbus, (*3*) with two bulbi. (D) Cuticular stripings: type 5 shows alae. (E) Posterior ends of females. The intestine runs below the sexual system in the midregion. (F) Males. *A* amphid, *B* seminal vesicula, *CD* caudal glands, *DA* anus, *G* genital opening (vulva), *H* testis, *K* cloaca, *L* lip, *M* mouth, *N* nerve ring, *O* ovary, *P* pharynx, *R* renette, *S* seta, *SM* spiculum, *U* uterus. Courtesy: Mehlhorn H, editor. *Encyclopedia of Parasitology* (2016). Reproduced with permission from Springer Nature.

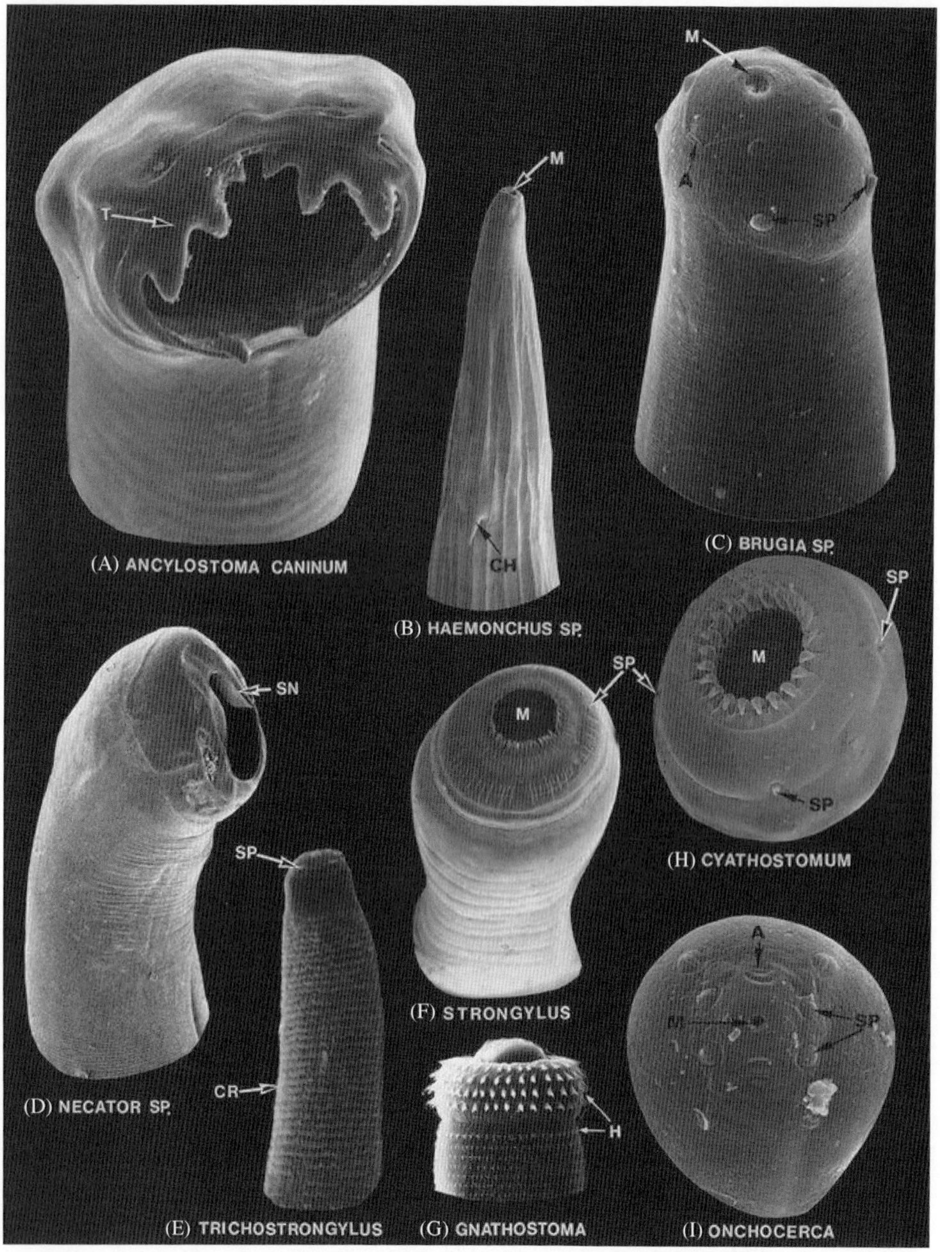

Fig. 17.3 ■ Anterior ends of select nematodes as seen by scanning electron microscopy. (A–I) SEMs of cuticular peculiarities along the anterior pole of some genera of nematodes (G by courtesy of Professor Dr. Ishii, Japan). *A* amphid, *CH* large cuticular hook, *CR* cuticular rings, *H* small cuticular hooks, *M* mouth, *SP* sensory papillae, *T* tooth with hooks. Courtesy: Mehlhorn H, editor. *Encyclopedia of Parasitology* (2016). Reproduced with permission from Springer Nature.

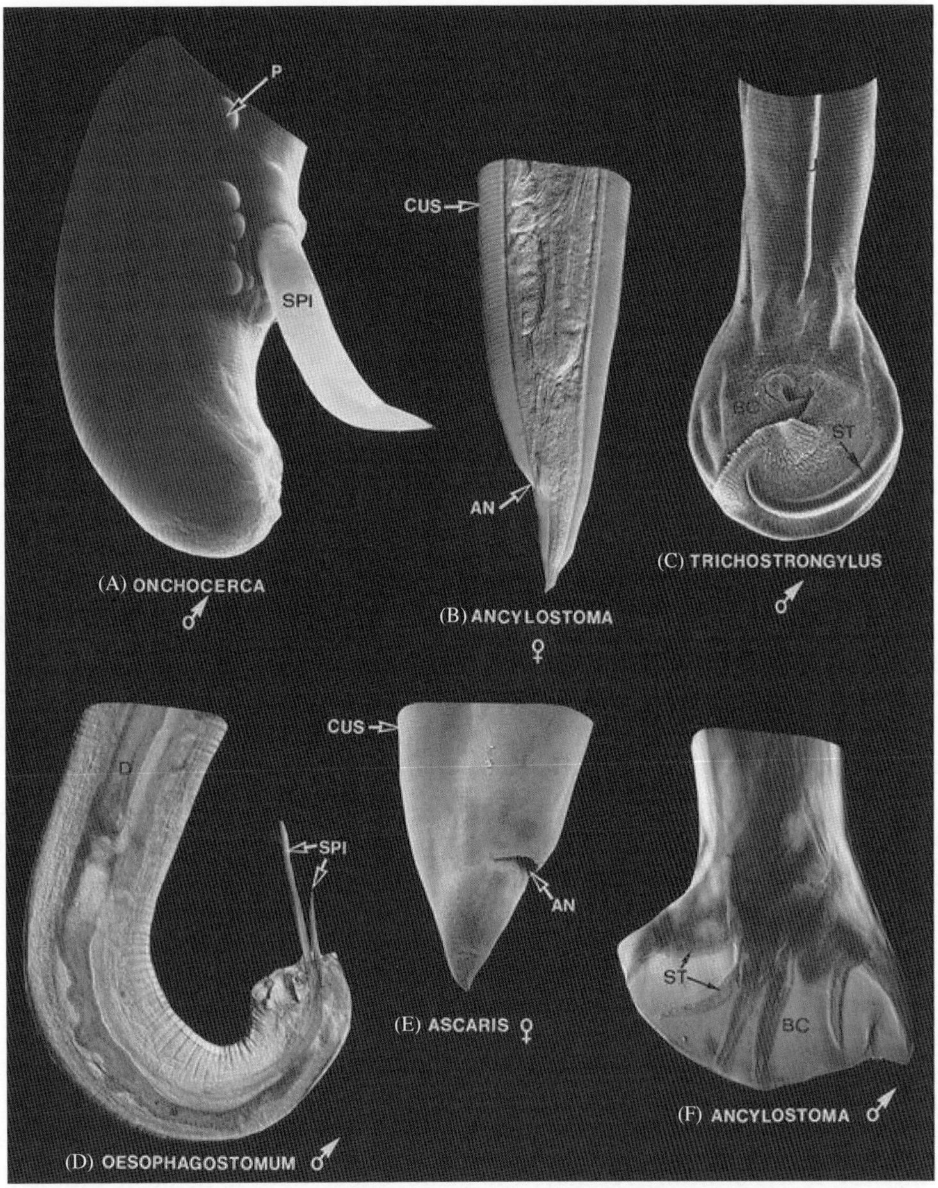

Fig. 17.4 ■ Posterior ends of select nematodes as seen by scanning electron microscopy. SEMs of the posterior ends of nematodes. *AN* anus, *BC* bursa copulatrix, *CUS* striation of the cuticle, *P* papillae, *SP* speculum. Courtesy: Mehlhorn H, editor. *Encyclopedia of Parasitology* (2016). Reproduced with permission from Springer Nature.

muscle action, as they only have longitudinal muscles. The hydrostatic pressure is very high in the nematode, as compared to other invertebrates that also use hydrostatic skeleton (such as the earthworm). A study with the roundworm *Ascaris lumbricoides* found the pressure at 69 mm Hg average in worms collected from a slaughterhouse but increased to 118 nm Hg when kept *in vitro* for 20 hours (even to a maximum of 210 mm Hg) (Harpur 1964).

Some nematodes (such as *Ascaris*) possess ring-like anatomical structure. The feature is known as **annulation**. However, nematodes are not segmented animals. Nematodes lack circulatory and respiratory systems, but have digestive, reproductive, nervous, and excretory systems (Basyoni and Rizk 2016). The digestive system includes foregut, midgut, and hindgut. The foregut contains the muscular structure, named bulbs, to propel food. This is the triradiate pharynx (esophagus), a myoepithelial structure that serves the function of sucking and swallowing (Nielsen 2013). The hindgut ends in anus in the female, but ends in **cloaca** in the male (also receiving sperms). Nematodes have two main nerve centers: **circumesophageal commissure** (nerve ring) and the **rectal commissure**. They use chemosensory and mechanosensory neurons embedded in the cuticle to orient and respond to a wide range of environmental stimuli. They possess chemo and mechanoreceptors. Labile and cephalic papillae (mechanoreceptors) and amphids (chemoreceptor) are found in the mouth region. In the back region, there are phasmids (chemoreceptor) and caudal papillae in the males (for copulation). In reproduction, the females normally are **didelphic**, possessing 2 cylindrical ovaries and uteri. Males mostly have a single testis, and possess **copulatory spicules** for mating.

An interesting finding refers to the nematode sperm. Whereas human sperms possess one flagellum, flatworm sperms possess two flagella, roundworm sperms possess none; they are amoeboid in motility, via pseudopod extension. Members of the Nematoda phylum all have motile amoeboid spermatozoa. These male gametes possess membranous organelles that can be used to fuse to the plasma membrane during motility. The spermatozoon undergoes morphological and physiological changes: membrane rearrangement, pseudopodium-like projection (spike) extension, confinement of organelles into the cell body, together with a pH gradient formation from the tip to the base of the pseudopod (Fraire-Zamora and Cardullo 2010).

For protozoan species such as *Entamoeba* and *Dictyostelium*, amoeboid locomotion involves microfilament protein actin and motor protein myosin. In nematodes, a special protein is used for amoeboid locomotion. The nematode sperm possesses major sperm protein (**MSP**), a 14 kDa molecule completely unrelated to actin. MSP forms nonpolar fibers/higher-order structures to drive pseudopod protrusion and cell locomotion, via MSP protein assembly/disassembly. Motility of *Ascaris* spermatozoa has been analyzed. Like actin, MSP is dynamically regulated to achieve locomotion; its basic unit is the MSP dimer. In the pseudopod, polymerization of MSP occurs at the leading edge, and fiber rearrangement/and disassembly (for recycling) occurs at the rear (for retraction) (Bottino *et al.* 2002; Ellis and Stanfield 2014). Please see Figure 17.5 for nematode sperm morphology (Roberts and King 1991). Thus, nematode sperms differ in their motility from sperms of many other animals.

17.3 Life Cycles

All nematodes go through 4 larval stages. At the end of each larval stage, a new cuticle is synthesized and the old one is molted off. After each molt the larval worm gets bigger.

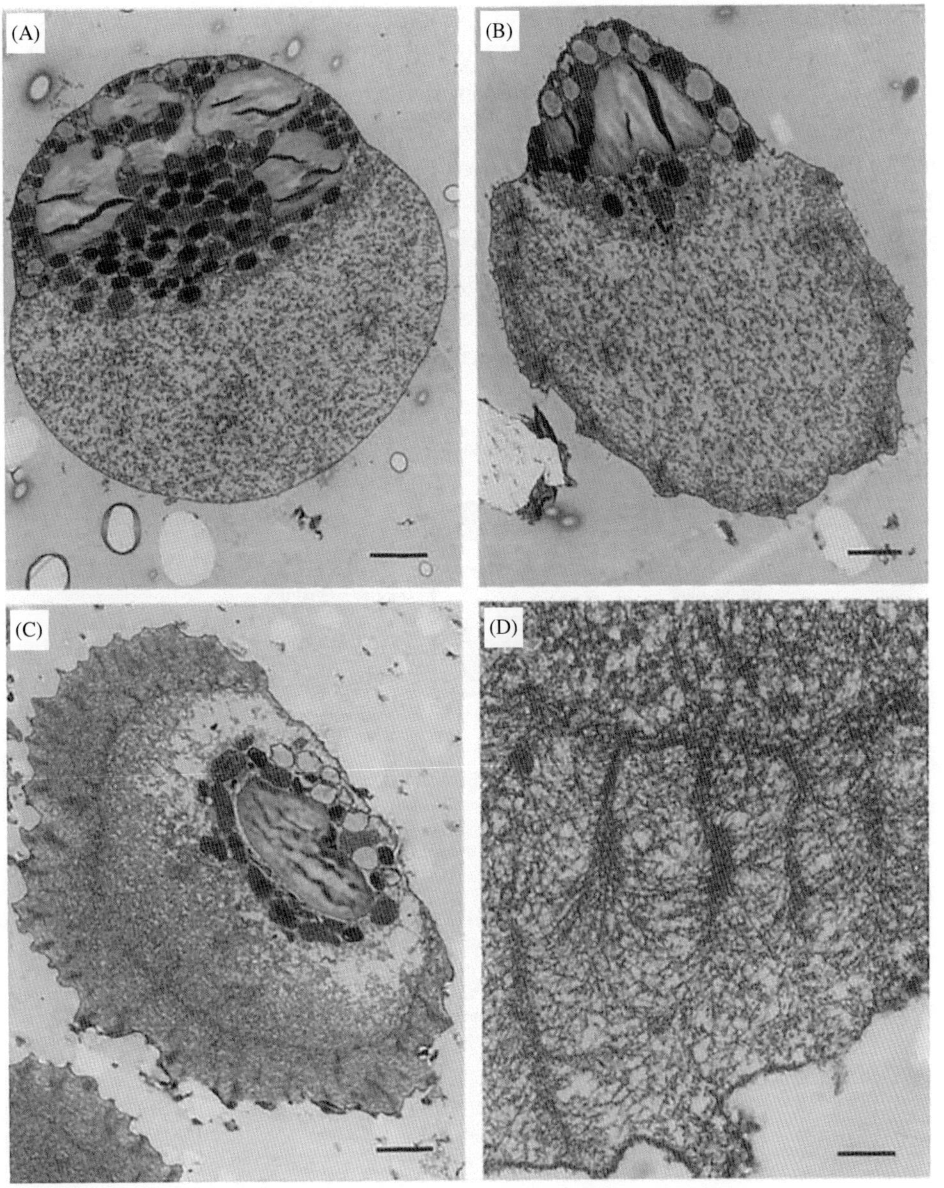

Fig. 17.5 ■ Transmission electron micrographs of *Ascaris suum* sperms. Electron micrographs of thin sections of spermatozoa fixed at selected stages of cytoskeletal reassembly after acid-induced disassembly. (A) Fixed in the presence of 20 mM acetate, the rounded pseudopod contains no fiber complexes. (B) Fixed 5 sec after acid removal; reconstruction of the fiber complexes has begun at the periphery. (C) Fixed 20 sec after acid removal; the radial array is clearly visible at the proximal end of the reforming fiber complexes. (D) Higher magnification of a cell at about the same stage **of** reassembly as that shown in c showing the filamentous composition of the radial array and the organization of the fiber complexes. Filaments emerge laterally from a central core in each complex. Bars in A–C = 2 pm; bar in D = 500 nm. Courtesy: Roberts T, King K. *Cell Motil Cytoskeleton* 1991;20:228–41. Reproduced with permission from John Wiley and Sons.

The four stages are named **L1, L2, L3** and **L4**. The process of molting permits the worm to increase in size. (Think the cuisine: Maryland blue crab in season, available as tasty "soft shell crabs" in the eastern US. Molting is also present in crustaceans and arthropods, as their exoskeleton is also a barrier to size increase. We shall discuss arthropods in Chapter 23.) Please see Figure 17.6 for the life cycle of *C. elegans* and note the size increase (WormBase)[4]

The same molt stages (L1 to L4) are present in parasitic nematodes. The L3 form is infective (to humans and other host species), hence it is named infective L3 (**iL3**). L1 is also known as the **rhabditiform**, and L3, **filariform**. (Some investigators prefer **J1, J2, J3,** and **J4,** with J for juvenile.) In some species, a pre-larval or pre-L1 form known as

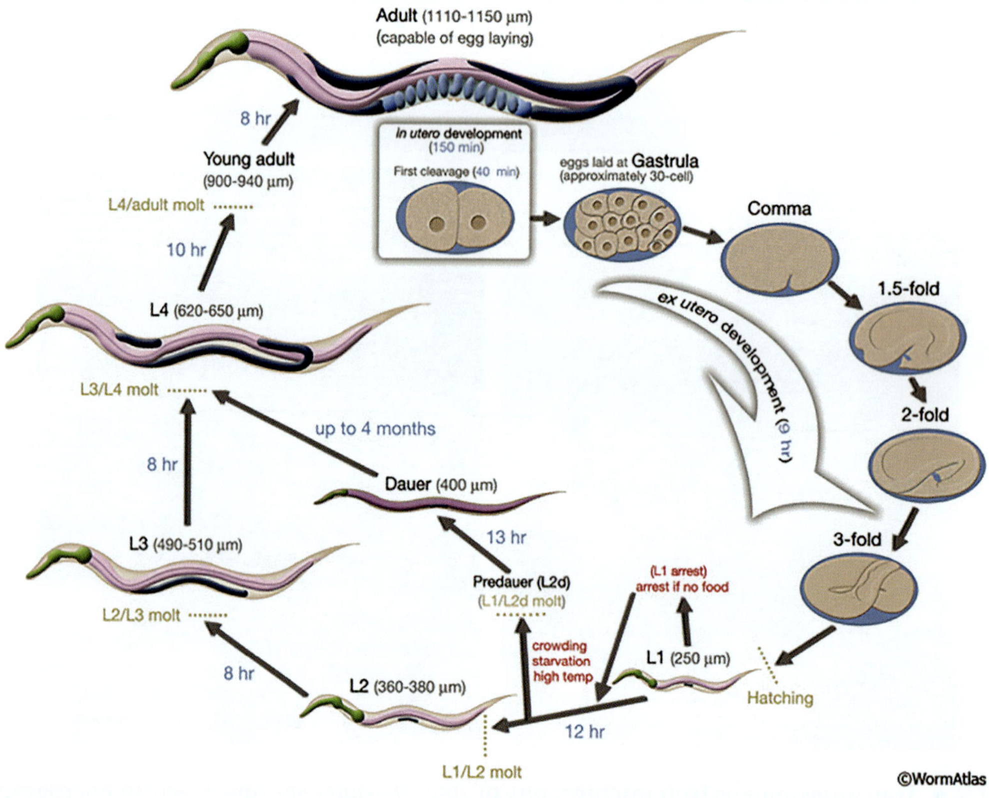

Fig. 17.6 ■ Life cycle of *Caenorhabditis elegans*. Life cycle of *C. elegans* at 22°C. 0 min is fertilization. Numbers in blue along the arrows indicate the length of time the animal spends at a certain stage. First cleavage occurs at about 40 min. post-fertilization. Eggs are laid outside at about 150 min. post-fertilization and during the gastrula stage. The length of the animal at each stage is marked next to the stage name in micrometers (µm). Courtesy of the Wormatlas. Reproduced with permission from Wormatlas (wormatlas.org) and Zeynep Altun-Gultekin. https://www.wormatlas.org/hermaphrodite/introduction/mainframe.htm

[4] https://www.wormatlas.org/hermaphrodite/introduction/Introframeset.html

microfilaria (microfilariae plural) is present, that may possess a protective sheath on the outer surface. Whether these advanced embryos are protected with a cover known as a sheath is species-dependent. Furthermore, the free-living *Caenorhabditis elegans* possesses a specialized dispersal/survival alternative third larval stage, known as the **dauer** larva, to withstand adverse conditions. The dauer larva does not age and it does not feed. It may be an evolutionary precursor to the infective juveniles (iL3) of parasitic nematodes. Please note the size of adult *C. elegans*, about 1 mm (1110 to 1150 µm). Parasitism, with its constancy in environment, has resulted in a huge increase in size: an adult female roundworm *Ascaris lumbricoides* is about 30 cm (20 to 35 cm) in length.

The animal hosts of parasitic nematodes are vertebrates and arthropods. Some species have complex life cycles that involve alternating generations of parasitic and free-living life styles (facultative parasite, such as *Strongyloides stercoralis*). Some species show switches between hosts (such as *Wucherichia bancrofti*, the intermediate host is a mosquito, the definitive host is a human). Some species participate in migrations through different tissues of their vertebrate host (such as *Ascaris lumbricoides*). [*Strongyloides* will be discussed in Chapter 21, *Wucherichia* in Chapter 18, and *Ascaris* in Chapter 20.]

During larval development of many parasitic nematodes, the iL3 stage is an environmental infective larval stage. The iL3 must get to a host. The phenomenon is **host seeking**; many sensory cues are used by an iL3 in search of its host. The iL3 exhibits complex behavior, involving multiple sensory modalities, for gustation, humidity sensation, olfaction, and thermosensation (Gang and Hallem 2016). Thermoregulation is a necessity because there are temperature differences among the soil, the insect, and the mammalian host for the parasitic nematodes. The role of heat shock protein (such as **HSP 90**), heat shock factor, and other molecules are important in this transition (Devaney 2006). Only after the iL3 has successfully completed its infection, can the parasitic life cycle continue. In soil-transmitted helminths (STHs), the iL3 forms demonstrate behavioral responses to host-emitted sensory cues (such as the respiratory byproduct carbon dioxide). Molecular and cellular mechanisms that mediate these responses are being investigated (such as enzyme production for skin penetration). As STHs are important human pathogens and the iL3s are waiting for humans in the soil, the situation becomes "terror in the dirt" (Bryant and Hallem 2018).

17.4 Evolution of Nematodes

One phylogenetic study uses sequences from the nuclear small subunit ribosomal RNA gene (nSSU), as it combines features of conservation and change that are informative over deep timescales. With this approach five major clades (**I, II, III, IV,** and **V**) have been identified in the phylum Nematoda. Parasitism arose independently multiple times. There were 3 origins of plant parasitism, 10 origins of parasitism of a wide range of non-vertebrates and 5 origins of vertebrate parasitism (Blaxter *et al.* 1998). The classification still stands when additional genes and proteins are analyzed, in a later study of 81 worm genomes (International Helminths Genome Consortium 2019). Please see Figure 17.7 for nematode evolution (Blaxter 2011).

For the origin of nematodes, one hypothesis suggests that Nematoda had a marine origin. Clade II, Enoplia, includes the most common nematodes in marine sediments, free-living and feeding on diatoms and marine algae. Some Enoplia members are found in brackish/fresh water and on land (including plant parasites). Clade I, Dorylaimia, includes freshwater or terrestrial nematodes (with major groups of plant and animal parasites, such as the human parasites *Trichinella spiralis* and *Trichiuris trichura*). The Chromadoria includes a large number of marine groups, plus a major terrestrial radiation (including animal and plant parasites). The phylogeny indicates that terrestrial taxa appear to have arisen from marine ancestors. A majority of Chromadoria is named Rhabditida, and is further divided into clades III, IV and V. Clade III, Spirurina, are all parasites, mostly of vertebrates (including the majority of human parasitic worms such as *Ascaris, Anisakis, Enterobius, Brugia, Dracunculus, Loa*). Clade IV, Tylenchina, include the mammal-parasitic parasites (including the human parasite *Strongyloides stercoralis*) that are related to the entomopathogenic worm species. One model suggests the mammalian worms represented host capture by an ancestral terrestrial, entomopathogenic or entomoparasitic species, and subsequent radiation into new host groups. Clade V, Rhabditina, include the famous *Caenorhabditis elegans* and the human parasites *Ancylostoma* and *Angiostrongylus* (Blaxter and Koutsovoulos 2015). [Individual human parasitic nematodes are discussed in Chapters 18 to 22.]

Overall, nematodes are abundant, diverse, and include many parasitic species. Molecular phylogenetic analyses have shown that parasitism of plants and animals has arisen multiple times independently. Ancient DNA analysis has shown early association of nematode parasites to Pleistocene mammals. Molecular study (cox 1, cytochrome oxidase 1 PCR) of puma coprolite from Argentina showed the presence of the parasite *Toxascaris* dated 16,573–17,002 years BP, as "the oldest molecular parasite record worldwide" (Petrigh *et al.* 2019).

Although different parasitic nematodes have group-specific adaptations to parasitism, a common theme is their comparative expansion of genes and gene families. Major protein groups include the genes coding for proteases, protease inhibitors, and sperm coat proteins (SCP). In addition, parasitic nematodes secrete molecules to interact with the hosts. The secretome will be useful as potential targets for treatment, as well as to see how the nematodes are adapted to their parasitic lifestyle (Viney 2018).

17.5 Ivermectin

Major therapeutic drugs for roundworms include **benzimidazoles** (albendazole, mebendazole) and **ivermectin**. Ivermectin is a broad spectrum anthelmintic, acaricide and insecticide. It is "rightly accorded the title of 'wonder drug'" (Geary 2005).

The discovery of ivermectin is an interesting story (Esch 2007; Campbell 2020). A collaboration was set up between Merck and the Kitasato Institute (now Kitasato University)

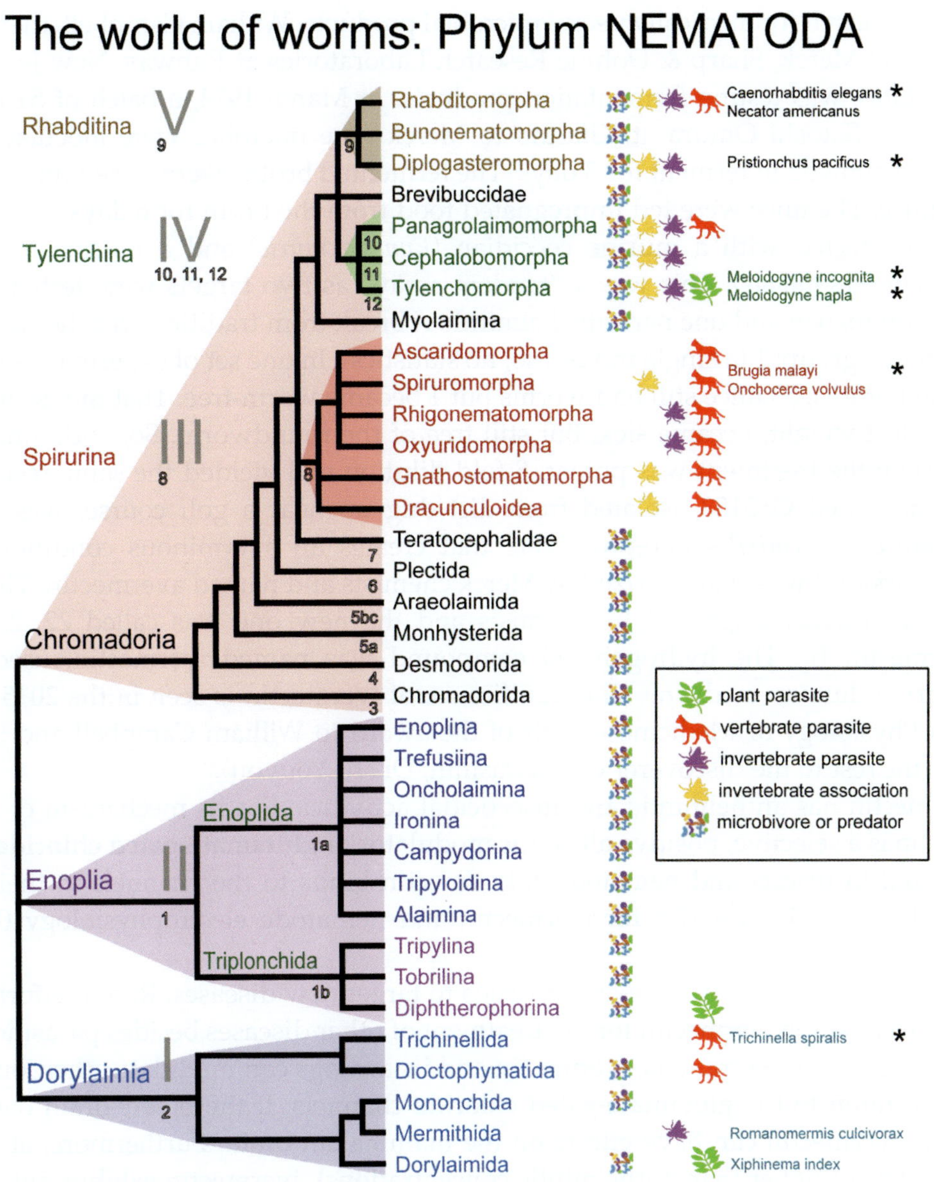

Fig. 17.7 ■ Nematode evolution. The relationships of the Nematoda. This phylogeny is based on molecular phylogenetic analyses utilising the small subunit ribosomal RNA gene. The systematic names given by De Ley and Blaxter are given, as is the "clade" naming convention introduced by Blaxter *et al.* in 1998. More recently, Helder and colleagues have introduced a numerical clade name scheme: this is given in outlined letters below the relevant branches. Feeding mode, and animal and plant parasitic and vector associations, are indicated by small icons, and representative species are named for some groups. Species with a sequenced genome are indicated by an asterisk. Courtesy: Blaxter M. *PLoS Biol* 2011;9(4):e1001050. Erratum in: *PLoS Biol* 2011;9(4). Reproduced with permission from *PLoS Biology* with Creative Commons Attribution 4.0 (CC-BY) International License.

in Tokyo to search for medically useful microbial products. William Campbell, then a new researcher at Merck, Sharp & Dohme Research Laboratories at Rahway, New Jersey, the United States, was testing fermentation products. In March 1974, a batch of 54 isolates was sent by Satoshi Omura at Kitasato to Merck. The microbes were inoculated into broths and allowed to ferment for 3 days. The fermented broths were mixed into the feed for lab mice. The mice were fed impregnated food from the broth for 6 days. These mice had been infected with a murine coccidian (*Eimeria muris*) and a murine nematode (*Nematospiroides dubius*). This was a "tandem assay" as two targets were tested — one parasitic protozoan and one parasitic helminth. A break from tradition was the size of the experimental group: 1 (a single mouse, so, no statistics). In one set of experiments with 54 fermented broths, 53 mice still had worms but 1 became worm-free. That mouse had lost appetite, lost weight, became sick, but still free of the roundworm. So, additional mice were tested; the treatment was potent, 8-fold dilution still yielded the same result. The bacterium, coded OS3153, isolated from dirt dug up near a golf course, was named ***Streptomyces avermitilis*** (streptomycete that creates an averminous condition). The active compound was characterized by Merck chemists and named avermectin. The compound was further improved by chemists and the new one was called 22, 23-**dihydroavermectin** B_1. The hydrogenated compound was named ivermectin, used from veterinary to human medicine. The significance of ivermectin is seen in the 2015 Nobel Prize in Physiology or Medicine — half of the award to William Campbell and Satoshi Omura (the rest to the discoverer of artemisinin, Dr. Tu Youyou).[5]

Ivermectin has anthelmintic and insecticidal activities. For its mechanism of action, ivermectin is a selective, positive allosteric modulator of **glutamate-gated chloride channels** (found in insects and nematodes); ivermectin binds to the channels in their lipid phase. Please see Figure 17.8 for ivermectin and nematode electrophysiology (Martin *et al.* 2020).

Drug repurposing is using existing drugs to target new diseases. Recent efforts have sought to reposition ivermectin for the treatment of other diseases besides parasitic infections. At higher concentrations, ivermectin and its analogs can modulate other ion channels in addition to the glutamate-gated chloride channels. If the blood–brain barrier is impaired, ivermectin can have effects on the mammalian brain. Furthermore, at higher concentrations (higher than anthelmintic concentrations), ivermectin exhibits anticancer, antimalarial, antimetabolic, and antiviral effects in tissue culture (Martin *et al.* 2020).

Ivermectin belongs to the group macrocyclic lactone (ML). These molecules, probably, are the most important class of anthelmintics, since they can control both ectoparasites and nematode parasites infecting us (humans), our pets (companion animals), and our livestock (a source of meat for most of us). A major concern is the development of resistance to these compounds by the parasites. There is suspected resistance to ivermectin in humans for the nematode *Onchocerca volvulus*. Another ML currently being introduced is **moxidectin** (MOX) (Prichard and Geary 2019).

[5]https://www.nobelprize.org/prizes/medicine/2015/advanced-information/

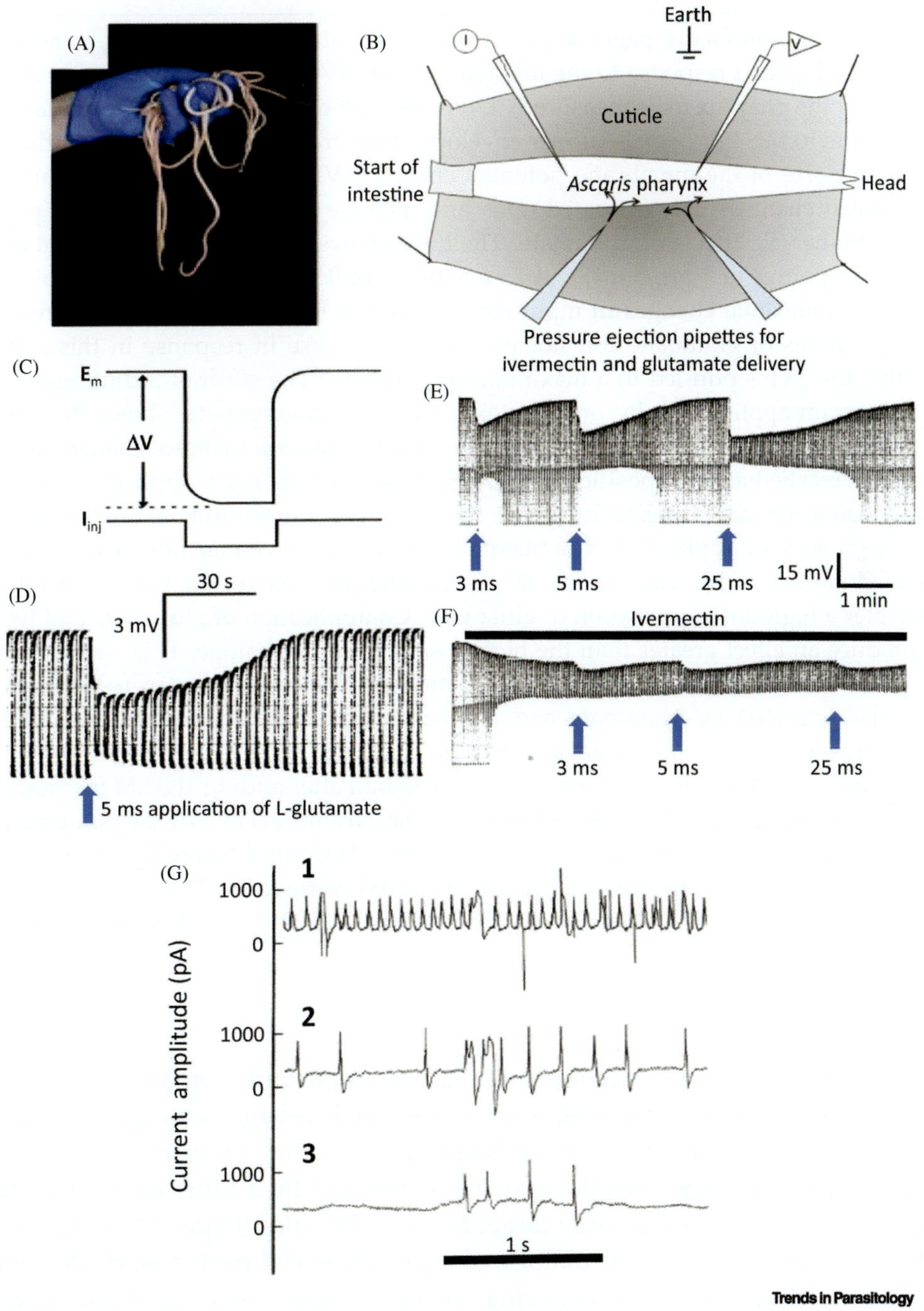

Fig. 17.8 ■ Ivermectin and nematode electrophysiology. Electrophysiologic Effects of Ivermectin in Parasitic Nematodes. (A) *Ascaris suum* is a large nematode that is tractable for electrophysiologic recordings. (B) A diagram of the dissected *A. suum* pharynx. Two glass micropipettes are placed in the pharynx, one for injecting rectangular current pulses (I) and one for recording the membrane potential (V). Two 'puffing' microelectrodes are used to apply, separately, glutamate or ivermectin at different time intervals. (C) Higher time resolution recording showing the injection of a hyper

Fig. 17.8 (figure on non-facing page) ■ polarizing rectangular current pulse (I_{inj}) and the membrane potential (E_m) and response to the injected current (ΔV) allowing the input conductance (= 1/resistance) of the pharynx to be measured. (D) A 5 ms puff of 0.5 M glutamate produces a hyperpolarization due to the entry of Cl^- (upper envelope of the trace) and a reduction in the width of the trace as the size of the membrane potential change (ΔV) is reduced as the glutamate-gated chloride (GluCl) channels, one activated open and increase the conductance of the pharyngeal muscle membrane. (E) Effects of glutamate. The trace shows the membrane potential and input conductance responses to 3 ms, 5 ms, and 25 ms 'puffs' of 0.5 M glutamate from a micropipette, which produces maximal changes in input conductance of 16 μS, 33 μS, and 60 μS, respectively. Longer applications of glutamate did not produce an increase in response in this experiment, showing that the 25 ms puff led to a maximum response. (F) The effect of a continuous 'puff' of 100 μM ivermectin applied also by pressure ejection from a micropipette shows that ivermectin mimics the effect of glutamate but has a slower onset. Once the conductance change produced by the ivermectin reached a stable position of 32.7 μS, glutamate was again applied in the same controlled way using the same application times; this produced a maximum conductance change of 28 μS with a 25 ms puff application. The maximum conductance change obtained with the coapplication of glutamate and ivermectin was 60 μS, virtually the same conductance (cf. 60 μS) change produced after a high-dose application of glutamate. Co-application of glutamate and ivermectin did not produce an effect greater than the high dose of glutamate alone. This was interpreted as indicating that these two substances activate the same ion channel. If there were two separate ion channels, one activated by glutamate and another activated by ivermectin, then these high concentrations would have produced an additive response. (G) Electropharyngeograms from *Trichostrongylus colubriformis* before, 5 min after, and 15 min after adding 100 nM ivermectin to the bath (from [106]). A patch-pipette was used to record the currents elicited by the pumping pharynx by sucking the head of the worm into the patch-pipette. (1) Control recording before application of 100 nM ivermectin; (2) 5 min after application of 100 nM ivermectin; (3) 15 min after application of 100 nM ivermectin. Courtesy: Martin *et al. Trends Parasitol* 2021;37:48–64. Reproduced with permission from Elsevier.

There is always a growing interest in new drugs for parasitic nematodes. One area is to look for enzymes involved in molting (such as the cuticle collagen enzymes). Different collagens are used for different larval stages. Molts are obligatory. There are cuticle-associated proteases of various classes (metallo, cysteine, serine and their inhibitors). Thus, the area of collagen metabolism is a potential target for anthelmintics (Page *et al.* 2014). As previously discussed on the molecular biology of trypanosomatid protozoa, mRNA synthesis involves spliced leader and trans-splicing. Whereas these steps are absent in humans, spliced leader trans-splicing are present in nematodes. Thus, here is another area for anthelmintics and anti-trypanosomatids. The compound **sinfungin** has been shown to inhibit spliced leader trans-splicing in a screening using *Caenorhabditis elegans* as a model (Pandarakalam *et al.* 2019).

Summary & Key Concepts

- Nematodes are ubiquitous, diverse, and abundant.
- Nematodes may have marine origins; some are parasitic to both plants and animals.
- Larval stages mature and molt to increase size, from L1 to L2 to L3 to L4 forms.
- L3 forms are infective to humans, known as iL3.
- Adults are a tube within a tube structure, but males and females have structural differences.
- Ivermectin is the drug of choice for parasitic nematodes (and for other diseases).

References

Adl SM, Bass D, Lane CE, *et al.* Revisions to the classification, nomenclature, and diversity of Eukaryotes. *J Eukaryot Microbiol* 2019;66(1):4–119.

Basyoni MM, Rizk EM. Nematodes ultrastructure: Complex systems and processes. *J Parasit Dis* 2016;40(4):1130–40.

Blaxter M. Nematodes: The worm and its relatives. *PLoS Biol* 2011;9(4):e1001050. Erratum in: *PLoS Biol* 2011;9(4).

Blaxter M, Koutsovoulos G. The evolution of parasitism in Nematoda. *Parasitology* 2015;142(Suppl1):S26–39.

Blaxter ML, De Ley P, Garey JR, *et al.* A molecular evolutionary framework for the phylum Nematoda. *Nature* 1998;392(6671):71–5.

Bogitsh BJ, Carter CE, Oeltmann TN. *Human Parasitology*, 5th edition (2019, Elsevier).

Bottino D, Mogilner A, Roberts T, Stewart M, Oster G. How nematode sperm crawl. *J Cell Sci* 2002;115(Pt 2):367–84.

Bryant AS, Hallem EA. Terror in the dirt: Sensory determinants of host seeking in soil-transmitted mammalian-parasitic nematodes. *Int J Parasitol Drugs Drug Resist* 2018;8(3):496–510.

Campbell WC. *Catching the Worm.* (2020, Royal Irish Academy).

Decraemer W, Karanastasi E, Brown D, Backeljau T. Review of the ultrastructure of the nematode body cuticle and its phylogenetic interpretation. *Biol Rev Camb Philos Soc* 2003;78(3):465–510.

Devaney E. Thermoregulation in the life cycle of nematodes. *Int J Parasitol* 2006;36(6):641–9.

Ellis RE, Stanfield GM. The regulation of spermatogenesis and sperm function in nematodes. *Semin Cell Dev Biol* 2014;29:17–30.

Esch GW. *Parasites and Infectious Disease* (2007, Cambridge).

Fraire-Zamora JJ, Cardullo RA. The physiological acquisition of amoeboid motility in nematode sperm: Is the tail the only thing the sperm lost? *Mol Reprod Dev* 2010;77(9):739–50.

Gang SS, Hallem EA. Mechanisms of host seeking by parasitic nematodes. *Mol Biochem Parasitol* 2016;208(1):23–32.

Geary TG. Ivermectin 20 years on: Maturation of a wonder drug. *Trends Parasitol* 2005;21(11):530–2.

Gunn A, Pitt SJ. *Parasitology. An Integrated Approach.* (2012, Wiley-Blackwell).

Harpur RP. Maintenance of *Ascaris lumbricoides in vitro.* 3. Changes in the hydrostatic skeleton. *Comp Biochem Physiol* 1964;13:71–85.

International Helminth Genomes Consortium. Comparative genomics of the major parasitic worms. *Nat Genet* 2019;51(1):163–74.

Keenan-Bateman TF, McLellan WA, Costidis AM, *et al.* Habitat use pattern of the giant parasitic nematode *Crassicauda magna* within the pygmy sperm whale Kogia breviceps. *Dis Aquat Organ* 2018;127(3):163–75.

Kiontke K, Fitch DH. Nematodes. *Curr Biol* 2013;23(19):R862–4.

Maciel AS, Araújo JV, Campos AK, Benjamin LA, Freitas LG. Scanning electron microscopy of *Ancylostoma spp.* dog infective larvae captured and destroyed by the nematophagous fungus *Duddingtonia flagrans*. *Micron* 2009;40(4):463–70.

Martin J, Rosa BA, Ozersky P, *et al.* Helminth.net: Expansions to Nematode.net and an introduction to Trematode.net. *Nucleic Acids Res* 2015;43(Database issue):D698–706.

Martin RJ, Robertson AP, Choudhary S. Ivermectin: An anthelmintic, an insecticide, and much more. *Trends Parasitol* 2021;37(1):48–64.

Mehlhorn H, editor. *Encyclopedia of Parasitology* (2016, Springer).

Nielsen C. The triradiate sucking pharynx in animal phylogeny. *Invertebr Biol* 2013;132(1): 1–13.

Page AP. The nematode cuticle: Synthesis, modification and mutants. In: Kennedy MW, Harnett W, editors. *Parasitic Nematodes*, pp. 167–93 (2001, CABI (Commonwealth Agricultural Bureaux International)).

Page AP, Stepek G, Winter AD, Pertab D. Enzymology of the nematode cuticle: A potential drug target? *Int J Parasitol Drugs Drug Resist* 2014;4(2):133–41.

Pandarakalam GC, Speake M, McElroy S, *et al.* A high-throughput screen for the identification of compounds that inhibit nematode gene expression by targeting spliced leader trans-splicing. *Int J Parasitol Drugs Drug Resist* 2019;10:28–37.

Petrigh RS, Martínez JG, Mondini M, Fugassa MH. Ancient parasitic DNA reveals *Toxascaris leonina* presence in Final Pleistocene of South America. *Parasitology* 2019;146(10):1284–8.

Prichard RK, Geary TG. Perspectives on the utility of moxidectin for the control of parasitic nematodes inhe face of developing anthelmintic resistance. *Int J Parasitol Drugs Drug Resist* 2019;10:69–83.

Roberts LS, Janovy J Jr., Nadler S. *Schmidt & Roberts Foundations of Parasitology*, 9th edition (2013, McGraw Hill).

Roberts TM, King KL. Centripetal flow and directed reassembly of the major sperm protein (MSP) cytoskeleton in the amoeboid sperm of the nematode, *Ascaris suum*. *Cell Motil Cytoskeleton* 1991;20(3):228–41.

Ruggiero MA, Gordon DP, Orrell TM, *et al.* A higher level classification of all living organisms. *PLoS One* 2015;10(4):e0119248. Erratum in: *PLoS One* 2015;10(6):e0130114.

Viney M. The genomic basis of nematode parasitism. *Brief Funct Genomics* 2018;17(1):8–14.

18

Lymphatic Filariasis (Elephantiasis)

18.1 Introductory Remarks

Lympatic filariasis (**LF**) is a neglected tropical disease (NTD). Its most severe clinical form is commonly known as elephantiasis, and patients suffer with grotesque swellings of the limbs, breasts, and genitals. Please see Figure 18.1 for photograph of elephantiasis patients, from the World Health Organization (WHO).[1] Physical deformity can lead to social stigma/society outcast. Actually, **elephantiasis** is a misnomer ("look like an elephant" differs from "caused by an elephant," as in -iasis). In our discussion on parasitic nematodes, we put lymphatic filariasis first, for several reasons. The adult roundworms live in the lymphatics and reproduce many larval forms known as microfilariae. Its life cycle requires transmission via an insect vector. Patrick Manson discovered mosquito as the vector during his stay in China; he was honored as the father of tropical medicine. One filarial species, *Brugia malayi*, became the first parasite whose genome was investigated (Ghedin *et al.* 2007). A total of three species can infect humans. The major species is ***Wuchereria bancrofti***, accounting for 90% of LF (widely distributed in the tropics, especially South Asia, Africa, Pacific islands). The other two are ***Brugia malayi*** (Southeast Asia) and ***B. timori*** (Indonesia). The importance of this parasite can be seen in the dedicated research journal: *Filaria Journal* (but now no more. In 2008, a merger between *Filaria Journal* and *Kinetoplastid Biology* formed *Parasites & Vectors*, published by BioMed Central). In supermarkets in USA, iodized salt (45 mg iodine/kg NaCl) is available for providing this micronutrient to prevent goiter and other diseases. Similarly, it has been shown that addition of the compound diethylcarbamazine (**DEC**) to table salt can control LF (Taylor *et al.* 2010).

The prevalence of LF indicates over 120 million people were infected in 2000 (WHO data), and 36 million suffered from chronic disease manifestations: pain, severe disability and social stigma. Current estimate is **100 million** infected, and 886 million in 52 countries are at risk. In 2000, WHO launched the Global Programme to Eliminate Lymphatic

[1] https://www.who.int/health-topics/lymphatic-filariasis#tab=tab_3

Fig. 18.1 ■ Photos of elephantiasis patients. Courtesy of the WHO. Reproduced from https://www.who.int/lymphatic_filariasis/disease/en/

Filariasis (GPELF). The program uses preventive chemotherapy in mass drug administration (**MDA**). Over 7.1 billion MDA treatments have been delivered to date and 554 million people no longer need MDA due to success in tackling the disease. MDA programs to eliminate LF in western Africa use the anthelminthics ivermectin plus albendazole. As seen in Côte d'Ivoire (Ivory Coast), community-wide MDA to eliminate LF and onchocerciasis has additional beneficial effect of reducing STH infections. An annual MDA regimen seems to be an efficient strategy for controlling hookworm infection in endemic areas with low and moderate infection prevalence (Loukouri *et al.* 2020).

18.2 History

Symptoms of elephantiasis were recognized since ancient times. Statue of the Egyptian Pharaoh Mentuhotep II from about 2000 BC had swollen limbs, suggesting that he could have elephantiasis. In India, lymphatic filariasis became known as "the curse of St. Thomas," as recorded by the Dutch explorer Jan Huygen van Linschoten who had visited Goa in 1588–1592. Descendants of those who killed St. Thomas "are accursed by God, which is that they are all borne with one of their legs and one foot from the knee downwards as thick as an elephant's leg" (Gordon *et al.* 2018).

Whereas physical deformities due to LF were known since ancient times, actual studies on the filarial parasites started in the 19th century. The larval microfilariae were seen in urine by Otto Wucherer (his German father was a merchant moving to Bahia in Brazil, but Wucherer received medical education in Germany) in Brazil in 1866. In 1872 the Scottish physician Timothy Lewis, working in Calcutta (today's Kolkata, in India), confirmed the finding of microfilariae in urine and in blood. The British physician John Bancroft described adult worms from Australia: "The worm is about the thickness of a human hair, and is from three to four inches long.... My first specimen I got on December 21, 1876 in a lymphatic abscess of the arm." The preeminent British helminthologist Thomas Spencer Cobbold named the species *Filaria bancrofti* in his honor.

In 1877, Patrick Manson elucidated life cycle of the microfilarial worm to pinpoint mosquito as the vector while working in China. He was aware of transmission by copepods for the guinea worm *Dracunculus medinensis* by Fedchenko (see the following chapter, this knowledge also led Manson astray when he tried to demonstrate that infection was caused by drinking contaminated water). Working in Amoy, south China, he found microfilariae in blood of infected humans and dogs. In his medical report titled *Further observations on Filaria sanguinis hominis* for the China Imperial Maritime Customs, Manson wrote: "The degree in which the general population of this district is affected with *Filaria sanguinis hominis*, Number examined: 670, Filaria found in: 62; Percentage: 9.21; Proportion, 1 in 10.8." In hypothesizing that these filariae might be transmitted by blood sucking insects, his comment was: "The mosquito found to be the nurse." Manson fed mosquitoes on the blood of his gardener (named Hinlo), who was infected, and found developing stages in these mosquitoes. "I procured mosquitoes that had fed on the patient Hinlo's blood and examined the expressed contents of their abdomen from day to day with the microscope ... the haematozoon which entered the mosquito a simple structureless animal, left it, after passing through a series of highly interesting metamorphoses, much increased in size...." Manson thought that the parasites escaped from the mosquito into water. Actual mode of transmission was shown by Manson's assistant George Carmichael Low who demonstrated the presence of microfilariae in the mouthparts of mosquitoes in 1900 (using infected mosquitoes from Australia, provided by Thomas Bancroft, son of John Bancroft).

In 1879 Patrick Manson reported "the periodicity observed by the embryo of *Filaria bancrofti* in the blood." Manson had two assistants; one worked days and the other evenings and nights, who were told to check the microfilariae from patients' blood samples daily. He noted the numbers were numerous from the evening worker but few from the day worker. So Manson ordered blood samples to be taken every 4 hours for one patient (Oah, Case 53, with elephantiasis). For over 2 weeks (between June 16 and July 1, 1879), the numbers of microfilariae were determined from one drop of blood taken from a finger. For 8 AM, 12 Noon, and 4 PM the numbers were mostly 0, sometimes 1 (one time 2). The numbers for 8 PM, 12 Midnight and 4 AM showed numerous microfilariae, 10s, 20s, and higher (one time 105 at 8 PM and 89 at 12 Midnight). This became known as **nocturnal periodicity**: microfilariae enter peripheral blood vessels at the time of female mosquito bites (for better transmission). "The nocturnal habits of *Filaria sanguinis hominis* are adapted to the nocturnal habits of the mosquito, its intermediary host, and is only another of the many wonderful instances of adaptation so constantly met with in nature." Manson wondered where did the microfilariae go? Later, one patient committed suicide (poisoning himself at 8.30 AM on February 19, 1897). Upon autopsy, 16 adult female and 1 male worm were found in his lymphatics, as well as many microfilariae present in various tissue sample slides, with the most abundant number in the lung (Kean *et al.* 1978; Cox 1996).

Patrick Manson (1844–1922) is widely regarded as the father of tropical medicine. Born in Aberdeenshire, Scotland, at the age of 14 he went to work as an ironworks apprentice. Illness prevented him from this career; he studied medicine at the University of Aberdeen. He joined the Chinese Imperial Maritime Customs Service and worked in Amoy (Xiamen). Manson established vector-borne disease (mosquito and *Wuchereria bancrofti*) and recorded nocturnal periodicity of microfilariae. He later moved to Hong Kong and helped to establish the Hong Kong College of Medicine (in 1887, today The University of Hong Kong, HKU) and became its first dean. Back in England he suggested two species of *Schistosoma*. His inspiration led to the founding of London School of Tropical Medicine in 1898. In 1907, Manson was the first president of the Society of Tropical Medicine and Hygiene (now the Royal Society of Tropical Medicine and Hygiene) (To and Yuen 2012; Barrett et al. 2015; Cox 1996 and 2017).[2] Manson's textbook of tropical medicine is still being updated and available today. Please see Figure 18.2 for Sir Patrick Manson, investigator of tropical diseases, in an oil painting by Harry Herman Salomon after a photograph, at Wellcome Trust.[3]

For LF, there was fierce competition for priority of discovery. Various names given to the parasite led to confusion. In 1921, the major species became *Wuchereria bancrofti* (after the physicians Wucherer and Bancroft). A different species with different microfilaria morphology was found in Indonesia in 1927, and Steffen Brug in Netherlands named the species *Wuchereria malayi*. Today it is *Brugia malayi* (after Brug and location of species). Another species, first named *Wuchereria pahangi*, infects humans, monkeys, cats and dogs in Malaysia. Today this is the zoonotic species ***Brugia pahangi***. Another species causes LF in the island of Timor in Southeast Asia. This becomes *Brugia timori*. American soldiers participated in the Second World War in the Pacific acquired LF. Following 25 veterans for 16 years after returning from Samoa and Bora Bora, there were pain and swelling in the genital areas but luckily no symptoms of elephantiasis, attributed to "relatively short exposure and absence of reinfection" (Trent 1963).

18.3 Life Cycle

Please see Figure 18.3 for the life cycle, from CDC.[4]

The life cycle of *Wuchereria bancrofti* and *Brugia malayi* are similar, so only one is shown. For the 2 nematode species, different species of mosquitoes are involved in

[2] https://www.nms.ac.uk/media/1160948/scottish-encounter-booklet-2015-glasgow.pdf

[3] https://wellcomecollection.org/works/r5x8wnvt

[4] https://www.cdc.gov/dpdx/lymphaticfilariasis/index.html

Fig. 18.2 ■ Sir Patrick Manson (1844–1922), invesigator of tropical diseases, oil painting by Harry Herman Salomon (1860–1936) after a photograph. Painting: oil on canvas; canvas 104.5 × 74 cm. Commissioned by Henry S. Wellcome for his Gallery of Portraits.

transmission. Adult worms live in the lymphatics and the females are ovoviviparous to give live larval forms known as microfilariae. The blood microfilariae have an outer protective layer, known as a **sheath**. As discovered by Patrick Manson, the microfilariae show nocturnal periodicity, most active in peripheral blood at night (10 PM to 2 AM), otherwise they are located in the lung. By altering the sleep-wake cycle it has been shown to be possible to reverse the periodicity. One variant of the parasite in the south Pacific exhibits diurnal periodicity, to coincide with the feeding habit of the local mosquito species. The adults live for 5–8 years (up to 15 years) and microfilariae can survive for 18 months.

Please see Figure 18.4 for *Brugia malaya* microfilariae by light microscopy (CDC)[4] and Figure 18.5 for their exsheathment at the mosquito gut by scanning electron microscopy (Intakhan *et al.* 2014).

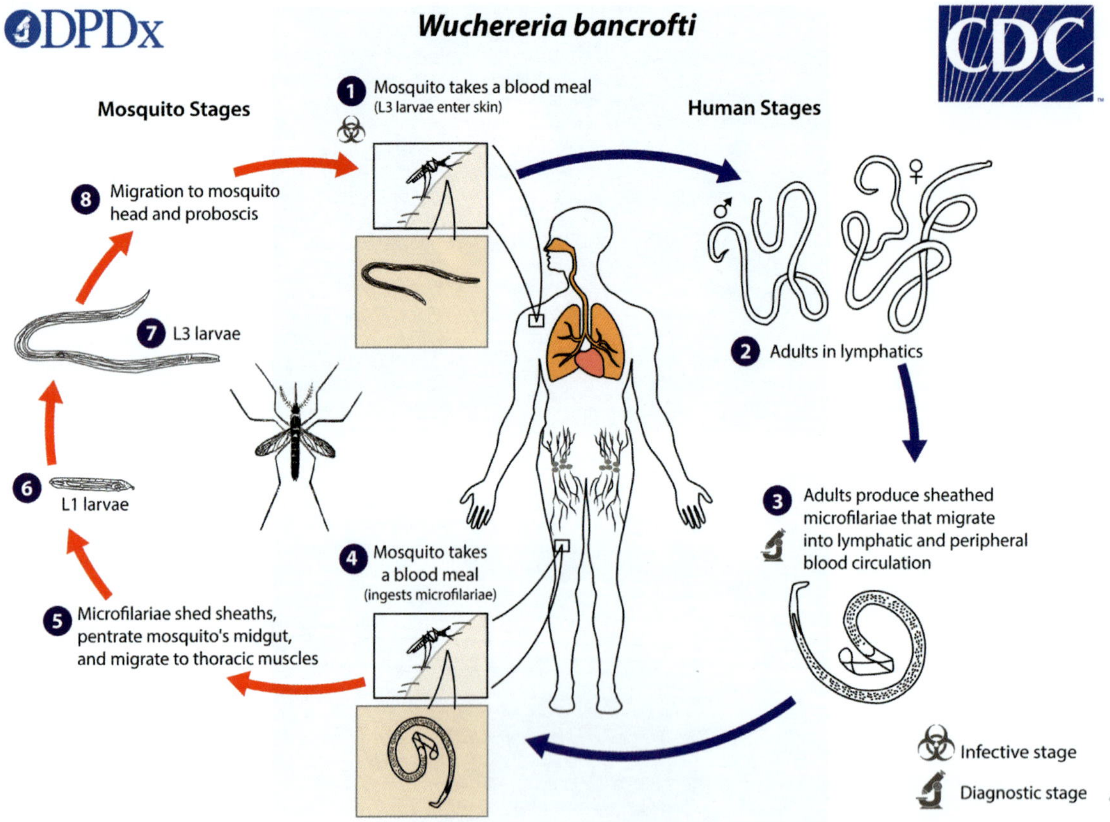

Fig. 18.3 ■ Life cycle of *Wuchereria bancrofti*. During a blood meal, an infected mosquito introduces third-stage filarial larvae onto the skin of the human host, where they penetrate into the bite wound ❶. They develop in adults that commonly reside in the lymphatics ❷. The female worms measure 80–100 mm in length and 0.24–0.30 mm in diameter, while the males measure about 40 mm by 1 mm. Adults produce microfilariae measuring 244–296 μm by 7.5–10 μm, which are sheathed and have nocturnal periodicity, except the South Pacific microfilariae which have the absence of marked periodicity. The microfilariae migrate into lymph and blood channels moving actively through lymph and blood ❸. A mosquito ingests the microfilariae during a blood meal ❹. After ingestion, the microfilariae lose their sheaths and some of them work their way through the wall of the proventriculus and cardiac portion of the mosquito's midgut and reach the thoracic muscles ❺. There the microfilariae develop into first-stage ❻ larvae and subsequently into third-stage infective larvae ❼. The third-stage infective larvae migrate through the hemocoel to the mosquito's prosbocis ❽ and can infect another human when the mosquito takes a blood meal ❶. Courtesy of the CDC. Reproduced from https://www.cdc.gov/dpdx/lymphaticfilariasis/index.html

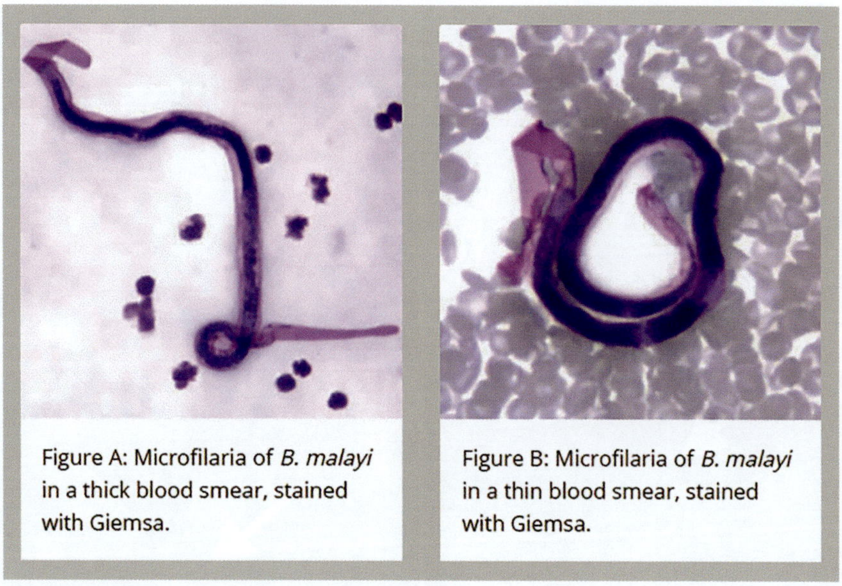

Figure A: Microfilaria of *B. malayi* in a thick blood smear, stained with Giemsa.

Figure B: Microfilaria of *B. malayi* in a thin blood smear, stained with Giemsa.

Fig. 18.4 ■ *Brugia malayi* microfilariae by light microscopy. Microfilariae of *Brugia malayi* are sheathed and in stained blood smears measure 175–230 μm. In 2% formalin they are longer, measuring 240–300 μm. The tail is tapered, with a significant gap between the terminal and subterminal nuclei. Microfilaria circulate in the blood. Courtesy of the CDC. Reproduced from https://www.cdc.gov/dpdx/lymphaticfilariasis/index.html

18.4 Pathology

"Lymphatic filariasis, one of the most debilitating diseases associated with the lymphatic system, affects over a hundred million people worldwide and manifests itself in a variety of severe clinical pathologies. The filarial parasites specifically target the lymphatics and impair lymph flow, which is critical for the normal functions of the lymphatic system in maintenance of body fluid balance and physiological interstitial fluid transport. The resultant contractile dysfunction of the lymphatics causes fluid accumulation and lymphedema, one of the major pathologies associated with filarial infection" (Chakraborty *et al.* 2012).

In addition, there is tropical pulmonary eosinophilia syndrome associated with chronic infections by *W. bancrofti* and *B. malayi*. Symptoms include eosinophilia, eosinophilic pulmonary infiltrate, wheezing, chest pain, and bloody sputum.

The living worms seem to be immunosuppressive to the human host. Since they live in the lymphatic system, immune evasion may also be involved. However, dead and dying worms, and calcification of worms, lead to host immune response. Another aspect concerns the obligate, endosymbiont bacterial species *Wolbachia* of LF. There is a strong host immune response to the bacteria after death of the worms. Infection of the filariae may be initially asymptomatic but later develop into the severe, disfiguring elephantiasis.

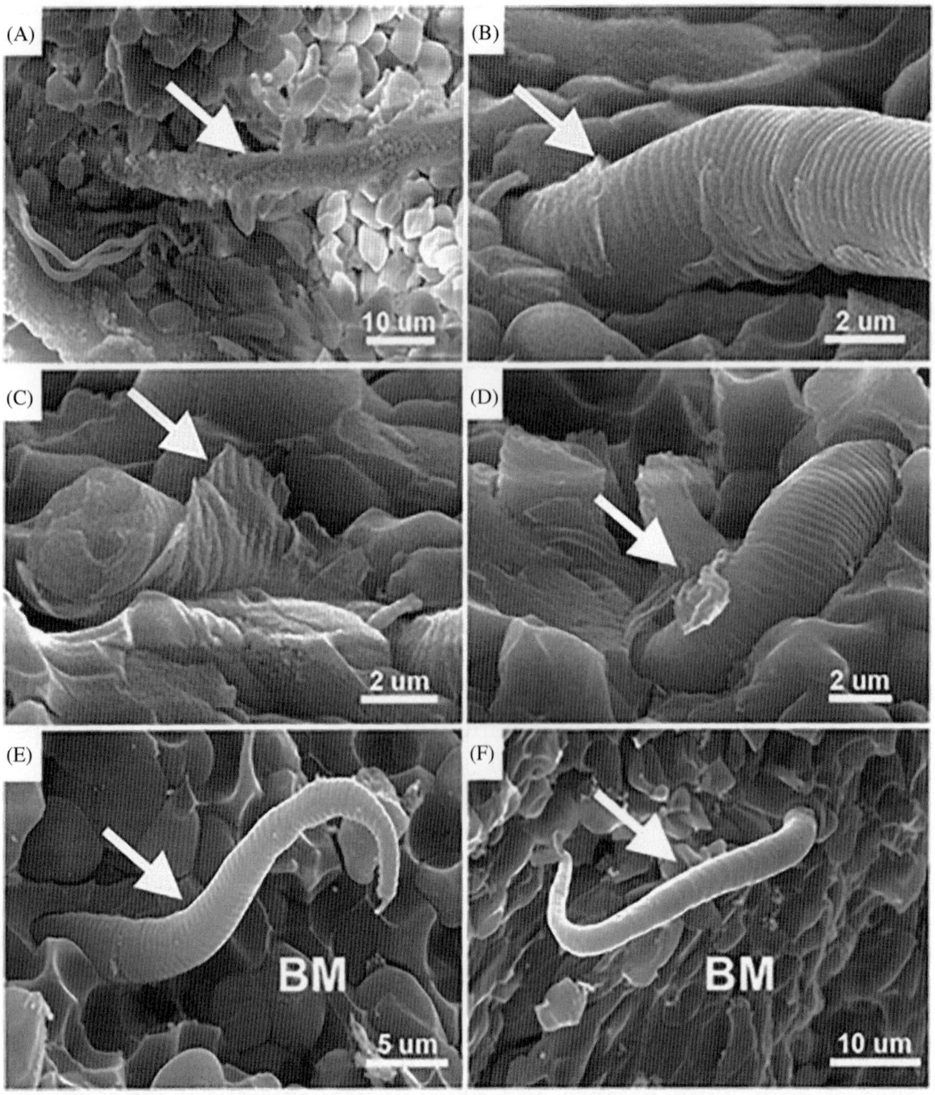

Fig. 18.5 ■ Exsheathment of *Brugia malaya* microfilariae at the mosquito gut by scanning electron microscopy. SEM micrographs of abdominal midguts showing the exsheathment of filariae. (A) Representative image of a sheathed microfilariae (*arrow*) surrounded by small particles in the midgut lumen observed in a midgut dissected at 1-h post-infected blood meal (PIBM). (B–D) Representative examples of maceration of the sheaths (*arrows*) of microfilariae in midguts dissected at 3-h PIBM. (E–F) Representative examples of exsheathed microfilariae (*arrows*) inside the blood meal (*BM*) in the midgut dissected at 3-h PIBM. Courtesy: Intakhan *et al. Parasitol Res* 2014;113:4141–9. Reproduced with permission from Springer Nature.

There can be blockage of the lymphatic system, and lymph fluid can enter urine, making it milky white in color (**chyluria**). There is inflammation of the lymphatics as a result of infection (**lymphangitis**), as well as dilation of the lymphatic vessels. There is hydrocele, fluid accumulation in scrotum in males. Lymphatic obstruction ends in lymphoedemas, in which body tissues become enlarged such as in the legs and arms, and features "like an elephant." Secondary infections from bacteria and yeasts can happen in elephantiasis.

Both *Wuchereria bancrofti* and *Brugia malayi* are lymphatic nematodes, with the latter accounting for approximately 10% of LF cases worldwide. *Brugia malayi* is endemic in South and Southeast Asia, including southern Thailand. Extra-lymphatic presentation of *B. malayi* is rare. One such case was documented in a 70-year-old woman from central Thailand presented with an erythematous periorbital nodule at the left medial canthal area that had persisted for 2 weeks. She had surgery for nodule removal. During the surgery, a thin-walled cyst was found attached to the anteronasal orbital rim of the left eye. Inside the cyst was a coiled nematode, approximately 9.5 cm long by 1 mm in size. It was a viable, sexually mature filarial adult; species identification was *Brugia malayi* by histology and PCR sequencing of the partial mitochondrial 12S rRNA gene. "This is the first case report of *B. malayi* presenting with a periorbital nodule that has occurred in a disease non-endemic area of Thailand with possibly a zoonotic origin" (Nunthanid *et al.* 2020). The old lady, previously healthy, had a domestic pet dog at home. In Thailand, the mosquito genera *Aedes*, *Anopheles*, and *Mansonia*, all transmit brugian filariasis. *B. malayi* has natural animal reservoirs besides humans, including cats, dogs, monkeys, and pangolins (Nunthanid *et al.* 2020).

18.5 Diagnosis

Microscopic observation of microfilariae in blood samples gives definitive diagnosis. Ultrasound (using high-frequency sound waves to create images inside the body) can be used to detect the presence of adult worms in the lymphatics. A recent development is rapid point-of-care test (POCT) diagnostic, which is LF immunochromatographic card test (ICT), the first rapid antigen test detecting *W. bancrofti* circulating filarial antigen (CFA) using an antifilarial monoclonal antibody (AD12.1) that is easy-to-use, more sensitive than microfilaria light microscopy and can be used at any time of the day (Kelly-Hope *et al.* 2018).

18.6 Therapy

The drug of choice is diethylcarbamazine (DEC). It was first discovered in 1947. The parasitologist Frank Hawking, working in Brazil, had proposed the addition of DEC in table salt as a means to control LF. (The parasitologist had a famous son, the theoretical physicist and cosmologist Stephen Hawking, 1942–2018, author of *A Brief History of Time* and sufferer of amyotrophic lateral sclerosis, ALS). The idea was tested in Shandong province in China in 1976, by administering DEC-medicated salt to 40,000 people for 6 months. There was a reduction of LF, as shown by the number of microfilariae in their blood. Thus, the LF life cycle was discovered in China, and LF was first eliminated in China. The fortification approach was repeated elsewhere and led to elimination or near elimination in Taiwan, Japan, Brazil, and Tanzania.

DEC is active against microfilariae (less so for adults). It interacts with the arachidonic acid pathway, such as cyclooxygenase (COX1) leading to prostaglandin synthesis. Treatment of pathway inhibitors (dexamethasone or indomethacin) would decrease DEC effects on the microfilariae. Inducible nitric oxide synthase (iNOS) is also essential for the rapid sequestration of microfilariae by DEC, because mice without the iNOS gene (knock-out mice) showed no effect with DEC treatment. DEC administration to BALB/c mice results in a rapid reduction in circulating microfilariae within 5 min. Microfilarial level recovers after 24 hours and return to pretreatment level 2 weeks later (suggesting that sequestration and parasite killing are independent events) (McGarry *et al.* 2005).

Other drugs for LF are ivermectin and albendazole. **Surgery** can be done for elephantiasis. As the historical record of LF had shown, in 1877, Patrick Manson operated on 237 patients with elephantiasis and "removed over a ton of this redundant blubbery tissue in 61 cases" including one street vendor "who spread a cloth over his gross deformity and used it as a table to sell his goods" and, after successful treatment, "instead of showing gratitude to his benefactor he tried to sue him for compensation for loss of his livelihood. Such is human nature." This account was from the biography of Patrick Manson by his son-in-law Philip Manson-Bahr (who adopted the name Manson from Philip Bahr after marrying Patrick's daughter and becoming editor of the Manson tropical medicine text book).

New guidelines for LF recommend triple drug therapy using a combination of ivermectin, DEC, and albendazole (**IDA**) (Kelly-Hope *et al.* 2018).

18.7 Genome

Brugia malayi is the first filarial nematode with genome published in 2007 (Ghedin *et al.* 2007). The worm was chosen because it is the only filaria that can be maintained in small laboratory animals. It possesses **5** chromosomes, with **XY** sex chromosomes. With 90 Mb in size, it has **11,515** protein-coding genes. There is the presence of operons: A total of **838** potential operons containing ~1,800 genes (16% of the total; 2–5 genes per operon). Additional genes of interest include parasite derived macrophage migration inhibition factor (MIF) and transforming growth factor *beta* (TGF β); these molecules may influence host immune response.

The filarial worm *Brugia malayi* has **3** genomes: nuclear, mitochondrial, and ensymbiont bacterial. A mutualistic relationship with the endosymbiont *Wolbachia* is seen. The worm cannot make heme but the bacterium can. Genes involved in molting and collagen metabolism have been proposed as potential drug targets. As an example, the collagen prolyl 4-hydroxylase (**C-P4H**) enzymes are essential for development in *B. malayi*. Unique features of these essential enzymes may be exploited in future control mechanisms (Winter *et al.* 2013). In addition, drugs targeting the bacteria are also useful for LF. The *Wolbachia* bacterial genome is about 1.1 to 1.4 Mb in size and codes for about **800** genes (Fenn and Blaxter 2006).

The first published parasitic nematode genome was followed by the genome of ***Brugia pahangi*** by Malaysian scientists (Lau *et al.* 2015). This zoonotic species has 85 Mb in size and has **9,678** protein-coding genes. There is sequence similarity between *Brugia malayi* and *B. pahangi*. A population genomics study was performed for *Wuchereria bancrofti* by sequencing a total of 13 L3 larvae in mosquitoes from three patients (Small *et al.* 2016). In the genome, a total of 73,922 single nucleotide polymorphisms (SNPs) were detected, as well as evidence of polyandrous mating (one female mates with multiple males), reported for the first time for this parasite. As shown in the WormBase ParaSite, the worm has **11,068** protein-coding genes.[5]

With the availability of *Brugia* and other filarial genomes, there is "Mining filarial genomes for diagnostic and therapeutic targets" (Bennuru *et al.* 2018), because the global efforts for eliminating filarial infections by MDA programs may require additional tools (safe macrofilaricidal drugs, vaccines, and diagnostic biomarkers). There are transcriptomics and metabolomics. For post-genomic protein and nucleic acid based biomarkers, there are stage-specific protein markers (from excretory/secretory, E/P proteins) for the infective iL3 stage, and plasma-derived microRNAs (miRNAs) as diagnostic markers. Metabolomic approaches have identified urine-derived N-acetyltyramine-O-b-glucuronide (NATOG) as a potential biomarker for the filarial worm *Onchocerca volvulus* (Bennuru *et al.* 2018).

Availability of genomes leads to transcriptomes and proteomes. Potential novel targets may be found, as well as candidate for vaccines. Screening of available or approved drugs leads to drug repurposing. There is interest in the application of "omics" towards the elimination of human filariasis, including LF (Lustigman *et al.* 2017).

Elodie Ghedin (now at New York University) was the first author in the published genome of *Brugia malayi* in 2007 (then at the University of Pittsburgh, Ghedin *et al.* 2007). She and colleagues were the first to study in detail the developmentally regulated gene promoters of this filarial worm (Grote *et al.* 2020), with the use of a novel motif prediction pipeline, Emotif Alpha, that integrates 10 different motif discovery algorithms, multiple statistical tests, and a comparative analysis of conserved elements between the filarial worms *Brugia malayi* and *Onchocerca volvulus*, and the free-living nematode *Caenorhabditis elegans*. With this computational method they have identified motifs that correspond to transcription factor (TF) binding sites in the *Brugia* genome. In this study they put emphasis on stage-specific TF binding motifs in *B. malayi* that are potentially involved in the L3–L4 molt, a stage important for the establishment of infection in the mammalian host. They used RNA-seq to profile transcription at different time points during the molt, collecting samples from the infective L3 (from mosquitoes), L3 Day 6, and L3 Day 9 worms

[5] https://parasite.wormbase.org/Wuchereria_bancrofti_prjna275548/Info/Index/

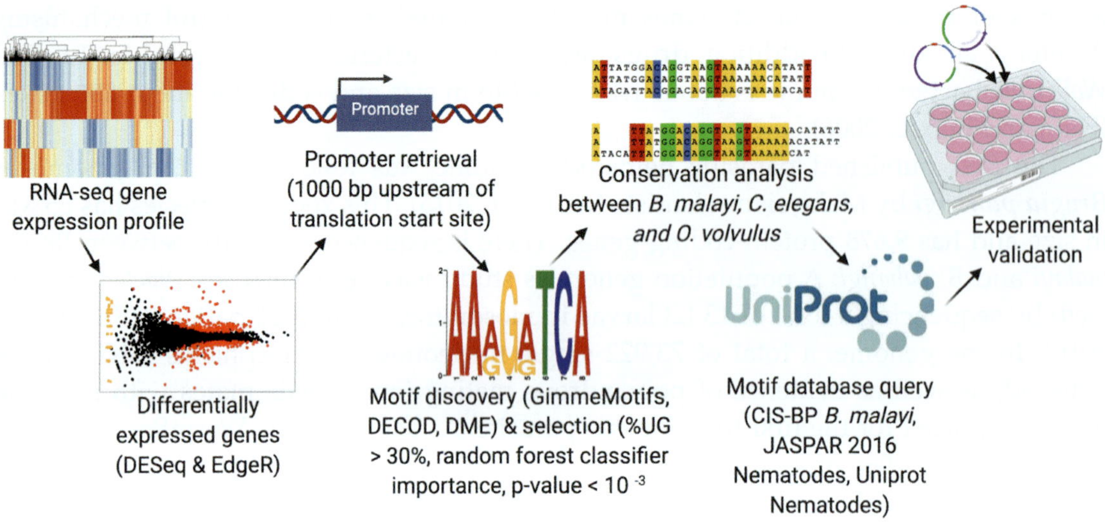

Fig. 18.6 ■ Workflow for *Brugia* promoter motifs identification. The six main steps for motif discovery were: (1) generation of an RNA-seq profile; (2) determination of up-regulated genes for every pairwise comparison using DESeq2 (FDR <0.01) and EdgeR (adjusted *p*-value <0.01); (3) promoter retrieval: 1000 bp upstream of the translation start site; (4) ensemble motif discovery using GimmeMotifs (Homer, AMD, BioProspector, MDmodule, MEME, Weeder, GADEM, and Improbizer), DECOD, DME, and selection of enriched motifs: %UG > 30% and random forest classifier feature importance and over-representation p-value $< 10^{-3}$; (5) TFBS conservation analysis between *B. malayi*, *C. elegans*, and *O. volvulus*; and (6) motif database query: CIS-BP *B. malayi*, JASPAR 2016 Nematodes, Uniprot Nematodes. Finally, a subset of those identified motifs were experimentally validated. Courtesy: Grote *et al. PLoS Negl Trop Dis* 2020;14:e0008275. Reproduced with permission from *PLoS Neglected Tropical Diseases* with Creative Commons Attribution 4.0 (CC-BY) International License.

recovered from infected gerbils. "In total, 2.36 billion reads were generated, with 1.38 billion reads mapping to the *B. malayi* genome. ... Of the **11,841** *B. malayi* gene models, 87.6% were expressed in at least one stage of the L3 to L4 molt" (Grote *et al.* 2020) Please note an increase in gene numbers, the previous number was 11,515 (Ghedin *et al.* 2007). Computational analysis of the transcripts led to a final of 12 motifs. Please see Figure 18.6 for their work flow and Figure 18.7 for the promoter motifs of *Brugia malaya* (Grote *et al.* 2020). They discovered a total of **12** promoter motifs located around 1 kb before the genes; they then validated 2 using DNA transfection (with both normal and mutant promoters plus the firefly luciferase reporter in a piggyBac vector for chromosomal integration). They also found the corresponding TFs that recognize these motifs and searched for genes active at L3 to L4 molt. As examples, Motif M1.4 is found in the promoter region of Bm2270, a predicted metalloprotease significantly up-regulated in L3 D9 worms; Motif M5 is found in the promoter region of Bm1938, a predicted serpin, a serine protease inhibitor, significantly up-regulated in the iL3 larvae. Protease and protease inhibitors are important players in the worm molting process. Among the dozen motifs, two motifs and

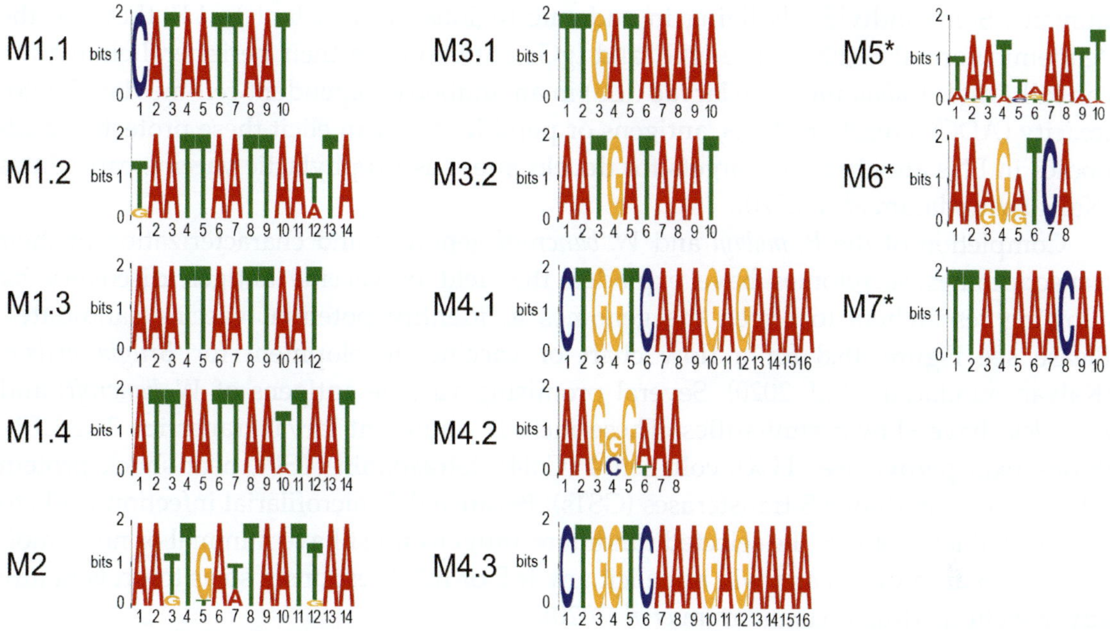

Fig. 18.7 ■ Promoter motifs of *Brugia malayi*. Logos of enriched promoters motifs over the L3–L4 molt. Motifs found to be enriched (p-value < 10^{-3}) in the upstream elements of up-regulated genes between different stages of molting and to be conserved in either *C. elegans* or *O. volvulus*. The * denotes the three motifs that have been validated experimentally. Note that M7 was included in the experimental validation because it passed 4 out of 5 filters, including the foreground coverage filter, the random forest filter, the known motif filter, and the conservation filter. However, it was not included in the 12 reported motifs due to its non-significant p-value. Courtesy: Grote *et al. PLoS Negl Trop Dis* 2020;14:e0008275. Reproduced with permission from *PLoS Neglected Tropical Diseases* with Creative Commons Attribution 4.0 (CC-BY) International License.

their cognate TFs appear to be related to the insect ecdysone response: zfh-2, the transcription factor predicted to bind four identified motifs (M1.1, M1.2, M1.3, and M1.4), is a common cofactor implicated in ecdysone signaling in *Drosophila melanogaster*; blimp-1, the transcription factor predicted to bind 3 identified motifs (M4.1, M4.2, and M4.3), is an ecdysone-inducible repressor that is essential for the prepupal development in the fruit fly. The investigators concluded: "This analysis provided biological insight into the development of the parasite as well as the identification of novel drug targets" (Grote *et al.* 2020).

18.8 Vaccine

The current control strategy against LF is effective but the progress is slow. Vaccines have been successfully used for over two centuries to control, eliminate, and eradicate infectious diseases. Studies have suggested the existence of protective immunity against LF in humans. Some individuals living in endemic regions are resistant to LF; they are the "endemic normals" (ENs). The IgG1 and IgG3 antibodies in their peripheral circulation can kill *Brugia malayi* infective larvae (iL3) in an antibody-dependent cell-mediated cytotoxicity (ADCC) reaction. Thus, antigens or peptides that can elicit these protective antibodies in ENs are attractive targets for development as prophylactic vaccine candidates (Kalyanasundaram *et al.* 2020).

Completion of the *B. malayi* and *W. bancrofti* genomes and characterization of their transcriptomes/secretomes have exploded the field of vaccine antigen discovery by allowing researchers to screen the genomes to identify potential vaccine candidates. Please see Figure 18.8 for a flow chart of vaccine development for *Brugia malaya* (Kalyanasundaram *et al.* 2020). Several promising vaccine antigens of *W. bancrofti* and *B. malayi* have shown similarities. These include abundant larval transcript 2 (ALT2), thioredoxin peroxidase (TPX), collagen 4 (Col4), tetraspanin (TSP), heat shock protein (HSP), and glutathione S-transferases (GSTs). Because iL3 microfilarial infection leads to an elevated level of IgE, the selected candidate antigens must have minimal or no homology to human proteins and will not elicit any IgE or IgG4 responses so as to prevent any adverse effects (Kalyanasundaram *et al.* 2020).

Vaccine design can be monovalent (such as GST alone), bivalent (HSP plus ALT2, TPX plus ALT2), or multivalent (multiantigen peptide, **MAP**). Preclinical animal models include jirds, mice, and Rhesus monkeys. Once available, such a prophylactic vaccine against LF will benefit millions of people at risk.

"A prophylactic vaccine, combined with targeted chemotherapy, is critically required for eliminating LF worldwide" (Kalyanasundaram *et al.* 2020).

18.9 Novel Drugs and Targets

For the filarial species with the obligate endosymbiont, targeting *Wolbachia* is another strategy. The macrolide veterinary antibiotic, **tylosin A,** and its analogs have potential as agents for LF (as compared to doxycycline). Pre-clinical experiments using mice have shown efficacy, with ABBV-4083 developed by AbbVie in Chicago (Taylor *et al.* 2019; von Geldern *et al.* 2019).

One potential drug target is trehalose-6-phosphate phosphatase (**TPP**). It is a key enzyme in the biosynthesis of trehalose. Trehalose is an essential disaccharide for many pathogens including the filarial parasites. It is neither required nor synthesized by mammalian cells. Its silencing leads to impaired *Brugia malayi* embryogenesis in experimental animal models (the rodent, Persian jirds) (Kushwaha *et al.* 2012). TPP is a target for LF, as well as other nematodes and bacteria such as *Mycobacterium* (Cross *et al.* 2017).

In drug repurposing, screening of approved drugs has shown that **auranofin**, a gold-salt compound for treatment of rheumatoid arthritis in use for 25 years, is active against LF and onchocerciasis (Bulman *et al.* 2015). The drug's likely target is thioredoxin reductase (TrxR). Actually, auranofin is also active against other parasitic protozoa, including

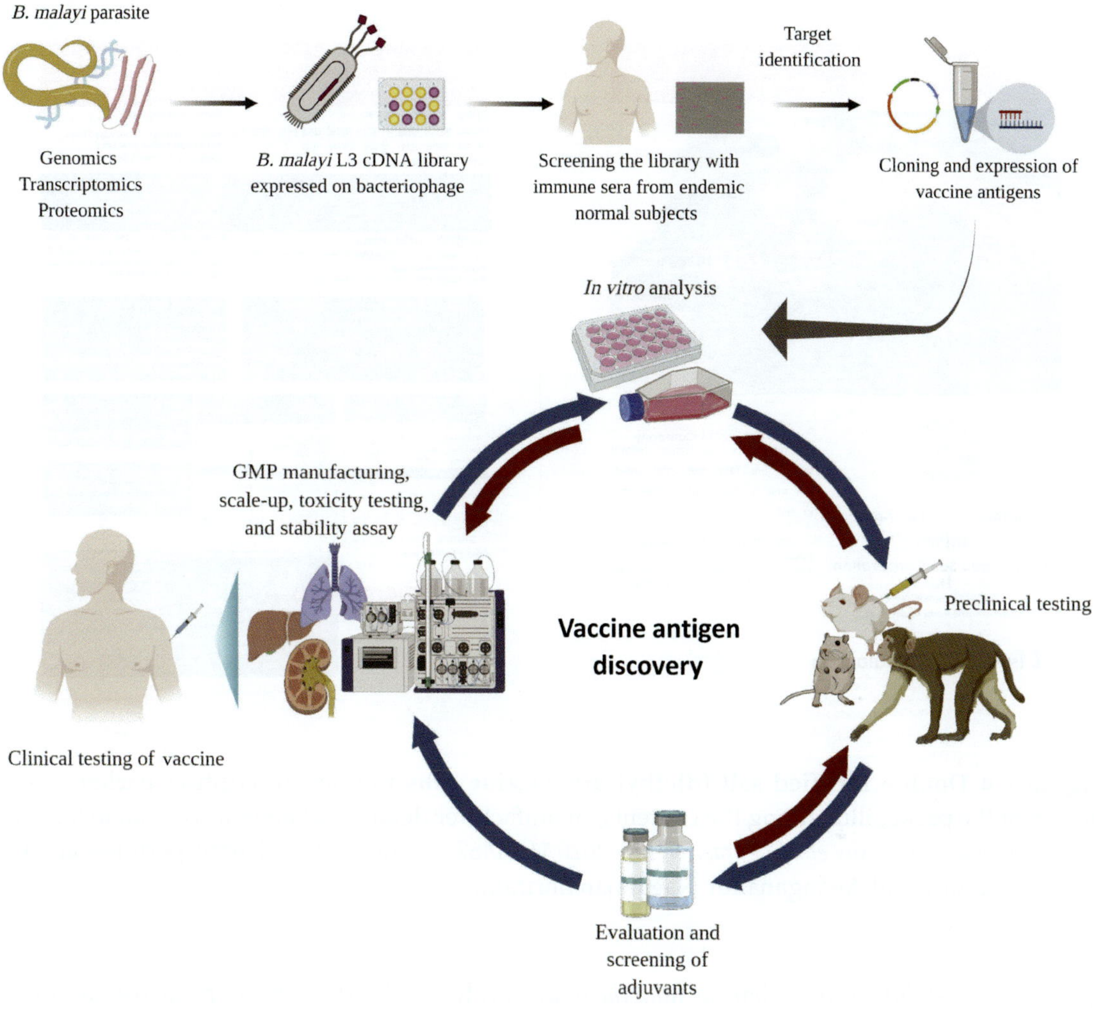

Fig. 18.8 ■ Flow chart of vaccine development for ***Brugia malaya*****.** Vaccine antigen discovery pipeline for developing a prophylactic vaccine for lymphatic filariasis (LF). The completion of the genome project — identification of the transcriptome and secretome of the *Brugia malayi* and *Wuchereria bancrofti* parasites — gave a tremendous boost to the identification of target vaccine candidate antigens for LF. It is now well established that, in the endemic area, certain subjects ('endemic normals' — ENs) carry protective antibodies against LF in their peripheral blood and remain uninfected. Recent advances in genomic screening have enabled us to screen the genome of LF parasites with the immune sera from EN subjects and identify antigens that are specifically recognized by the protective antibodies. Using a bioinformatics approach, the target antigens are then identified, cloned, expressed, and evaluated for their vaccine potential using *in vitro* assays. Promising candidates among these, along with suitable adjuvants, are then tested in various experimental animal models for their preclinical vaccine efficacy. The most promising vaccine candidates are then chosen for good manufacturing practice (GMP) manufacturing, scale-up production, and toxicity and stability testing, before being developed for clinical testing in humans. The figure was created with BioRender.com. Courtesy: Kalyanasundaram *et al. Trends Parasitol* 2020;36:195–205. Reproduced with permission from Elsevier.

Fig. 18.9 ■ Double fortified salt (diethylcarbamazine plus iodine) description packet. Cover design of the packet illustrating the contents, manufacturer details and benefits of double fortified salt. Courtesy: Shriram *et al. Parasitol Res* 2020;119:1467–83. Reproduced with permission from Springer Nature and Ananganallur Nagarajan Shriram.

Entamoeba histolytica and *Giardia lamblia* (Capparelli *et al.* 2016). Screening for developmental inhibitors of filarial parasites has identified **closantel** (a known anthelmintic for veterinary use) that acts like a proton ionophore, and targets L3-expressed chitinase (Bennuru *et al.* 2018). We look to the day when these compounds are approved as antifilaria drugs.

We conclude the chapter by returning to Frank Hawking's idea of adding DEC to table salt for LF control. As seen in Andaman and Nicobar Islands, India, elimination of diurnally sub-periodic *Wuchereria bancrofti* has been hastened by mass DEC-fortified salt as a supplementary intervention to MDA (albendazole). The investigators did a two-arm community-based study: one arm (12 villages, population 2,936) received double fortified salt along with annual MDA of DEC plus albendazole (DEC-salt + MDA-arm), and another (14 villages; population 4,840) received MDA under the National Filaria Elimination Programme. Please see Figure 18.9 for double fortified salt description packet (Shriram *et al.* 2020). A total of 21 metric tons of free-flow DEC salt manufactured by Tamil Nadu Salt Corporation, India, was distributed for 1 year. Community microfilariae prevalence reduced from 2.27% to 0.14% in the DEC-salt-arm, versus from 1.26% to 0.74% in the MDA-arm (Shriram *et al.* 2020). Thus, MDA of DEC plus albendazole shows better elimination together with daily use of DEC-fortified table salt.

Summary & Key Concepts

- Lymphatic filariasis (LF), aka elephantiasis, is a stigmatizing NTD.
- The major species is *Wuchereria bancraofti*; others are *Brugia malayi* and *B. timori*.
- *Wolbachia* is the endosymbiont bacterium of the filariae.
- The developmental stages are microfilariae (18 months) and the adults (5–8 years).
- Adults are immunosuppressive and live in the lymphatic system.
- Dead worms and endosymbionts induce immune response, leading to lymphatic obstruction, fluid accumulation and physical deformity.
- Microfilariae show periodicity to coincide with the vector mosquito species.
- DEC is a drug that has been supplemented in table salt for disease prevention.
- DEC, ivermectin, and albendazole are effective drugs, as well as surgery.
- *Brugia malayi* is the first human parasite whose genome is known (published in 2007).
- Genome sequencing has shown genes related to how the nematode silences the immune response of the host, as well as potential drug targets such as trehalose pathway enzymes.
- Novel drugs being tested include auranofin (drug repurposing from rheumatoid arthritis), and derivatives of tylosin A (to target bacterial endosymbiont).

References

Barrett MP, Innes EA, Cox FEG. *The Scottish Encounter with Tropical Diseases*, Wellcome Trust, Glasgow, 2015.

Bennuru S, O'Connell EM, Drame PM, Nutman TB. Mining filarial genomes for diagnostic and therapeutic targets. *Trends Parasitol* 2018;34(1):80–90.

Bulman CA, Bidlow CM, Lustigman S, *et al.* Repurposing auranofin as a lead candidate for treatment of lymphatic filariasis and onchocerciasis. *PLoS Negl Trop Dis* 2015;9(2):e0003534.

Capparelli EV, Bricker-Ford R, Rogers MJ, McKerrow JH, Reed SL. Phase I Clinical trial results of auranofin, a novel antiparasitic agent. *Antimicrob Agents Chemother* 2016;61(1):e01947-16.

Chakraborty S, Gurusamy M, Zawieja DC, Muthuchamy M. Lymphatic filariasis: perspectives on lymphatic remodeling and contractile dysfunction in filarial disease pathogenesis. *Microcirculation.* 2013;20(5):349–64.

Cox FEG, Ed. *The Wellcome Trust Illustrated History of Tropical Diseases*, The Wellcome Trust, London, 1996.

Cox FEG. The Golden Age of parasitology-1875–1925: The Scottish contributions. *Parasitology* 2017;144(12):1567–81.

Cross M, Lepage R, Rajan S, *et al.* Probing function and structure of trehalose-6-phosphate phosphatases from pathogenic organisms suggests distinct molecular groupings. *FASEB J* 2017;31(3):920–6.

Fenn K, Blaxter M. *Wolbachia* genomes: Revealing the biology of parasitism and mutualism. *Trends Parasitol* 2006;22(2):60–5.

Ghedin E, Wang S, Spiro D, *et al.* Draft genome of the filarial nematode parasite *Brugia malayi*. *Science* 2007;317(5845):1756–60.

Gordon CA, Jones MK, McManus DP. The history of Bancroftian lymphatic filariasis in Australasia and Oceania: Is there a threat of re-occurrence in Mainland Australia? *Trop Med Infect Dis.* 2018;3(2):58.

Grote A, Li Y, Liu C, *et al.* Prediction pipeline for discovery of regulatory motifs associated with *Brugia malayi* molting. *PLoS Negl Trop Dis* 2020;14(6):e0008275.

Intakhan N, Jariyapan N, Sor-Suwan S, *et al.* Exsheathment and midgut invasion of nocturnally subperiodic *Brugia malayi* microfilariae in a refractory vector, *Aedes aegypti* (Thailand strain). *Parasitol Res* 2014;113(11):4141–9.

Kalyanasundaram R, Khatri V, Chauhan N. Advances in vaccine development for human lymphatic filariasis. *Trends Parasitol* 2020;36(2):195–205.

Kean BH, Mott KE, Russell AJ, editors. *Tropical Medicine and Parasitology: Classic Investigations*, volume I and II (1978, Cornell, Ithaca).

Kelly-Hope LA, Blundell HJ, Macfarlane CL, Molyneux DH. Innovative surveillance strategies to support the elimination of filariasis in Africa. *Trends Parasitol* 2018;34(8):694–711.

Kushwaha S, Singh PK, Shahab M, Pathak M, Bhattacharya SM. In vitro silencing of *Brugia malayi* trehalose-6-phosphate phosphatase impairs embryogenesis and in vivo development of infective larvae in jirds. *PLoS Negl Trop Dis* 2012;6(8):e1770.

Lau YL, Lee WC, Xia J, *et al.* Draft genome of *Brugia pahangi*: High similarity between *B. pahangi* and *B. malayi*. *Parasit Vectors* 2015;8:451.

Loukouri A, Méité A, Koudou BG, *et al.* Impact of annual and semi-annual mass drug administration for lymphatic filariasis and onchocerciasis on hookworm infection in Côte d'Ivoire. *PLoS Negl Trop Dis* 2020;14(9):e0008642.

Lustigman S, Grote A, Ghedin E. The role of 'omics' in the quest to eliminate human filariasis. *PLoS Negl Trop Dis* 2017;11(4):e0005464.

McGarry HF, Plant LD, Taylor MJ. Diethylcarbamazine activity against *Brugia malayi* microfilariae is dependent on inducible nitric-oxide synthase and the cyclooxygenase pathway. *Filaria J* 2005;4:4.

Nunthanid P, Roongruanchai K, Wongkamchai S, Sarasombath PT. Case report: Periorbital filariasis caused by *Brugia malayi*. *Am J Trop Med Hyg* 2020;103(6):2336–8.

Shriram AN, Premkumar A, Krishnamoorthy K, *et al.* Elimination of diurnally sub-periodic *Wuchereria bancrofti* in Andaman and Nicobar Islands, India, using mass DEC-fortified salt as a supplementary intervention to MDA. *Parasitol Res* 2020;119(5):1467–83.

Small ST, Reimer LJ, Tisch DJ, *et al.* Population genomics of the filarial nematode parasite *Wuchereria bancrofti* from mosquitoes. *Mol Ecol* 2016;25(7):1465–77.

Taylor MJ, Hoerauf A, Bockarie M. Lymphatic filariasis and onchocerciasis. *Lancet* 2010;376(9747):1175–85.

Taylor MJ, von Geldern TW, Ford L, *et al.* Preclinical development of an oral anti-*Wolbachia* macrolide drug for the treatment of lymphatic filariasis and onchocerciasis. *Sci Transl Med* 2019;11(483):eaau2086.

To KKW, Yuen KY. In memory of Patrick Manson, founding father of tropical medicine and the discovery of vector-borne infections. *Emerg Microbes & Infect* 2012;1:e31.

Trent SC. Reevaluation of World War II veterans with filariasis acquired in the South Pacific. *Am J Trop Med Hyg* 1963;12:877–87.

von Geldern TW, Morton HE, Clark RF, *et al.* Discovery of ABBV-4083, a novel analog of Tylosin A that has potent anti-*Wolbachia* and anti-filarial activity. *PLoS Negl Trop Dis* 2019;13(2):e0007159.

Winter AD, McCormack G, Myllyharju J, Page AP. Prolyl 4-hydroxlase activity is essential for development and cuticle formation in the human infective parasitic nematode *Brugia malayi*. *J Biol Chem* 2013;288(3):1750–61.

19

Loiasis (African Eye Worm), Onchocerciasis (River Blindness) and Dracunculiasis (Guinea Worm)

19.1 Introductory Remarks

Lymphatic filariasis (elephantiasis), discussed in Chapter 18, is a neglected tropical disease (NTD). The designation of NTD has been given to onchocerciasis (river blindness) too. Similar to the agents of lymphatic filariasis, both *Loa loa* and *Onchocerca volvulus* are classified as filarial worms, because the adults produce microfilariae. However, loiasis (African eye worm) is not prioritized as NTD (Whittaker *et al.* 2018). A related species is *Dracunculus medinensis*, although it is not a filarial worm. Dracunculiasis (Guinea worm) is a parasitic disease that is close to be eradicated. The bacterial endosymbiont *Wolbachia* is present in all species that cause lymphatic filariasis. However, among the three species, only *Onchocerca volvulus* carries *Wolbachia*. Both *Loa loa* and *Dracunculiasis medinensis* are *Wolbachia*-free (Foster *et al.* 2014). Thus, the role of bacterial endosymbiont in the parasitic worms needs further clarification.

The filariae and other nematodes have small genomes relative to other multicellular eukaryotes. Rory Post (Natural History Museum, London) has suggested that "An understanding of the nature of the chromosomes of the filariae is expected to greatly assist the future interpretation of genome data" (Post 2005). Furthermore, relationship among the filarial species can be seen through an investigation of their chromosomes. Evolution of chromosome number has been detected in their karyotypes (Post 2005). Initially the karyotype, as seen in *Loa loa,* was composed of five pairs of autosomes and X chromosome (males are **XO** and females are **XX**). Chromosome fusion and changes led to the karyotype to be four pairs of autosomes plus XY (males are **XY** and females are XX), as seen in *Brugia* and *Wuchereria* species. Further chromosome fusion, as seen in *Onchocerca volvulus*, the karyotypes became three pairs of autosomes plus XY. Please see Figure 19.1 for karyotype evolution (after Post 2005).

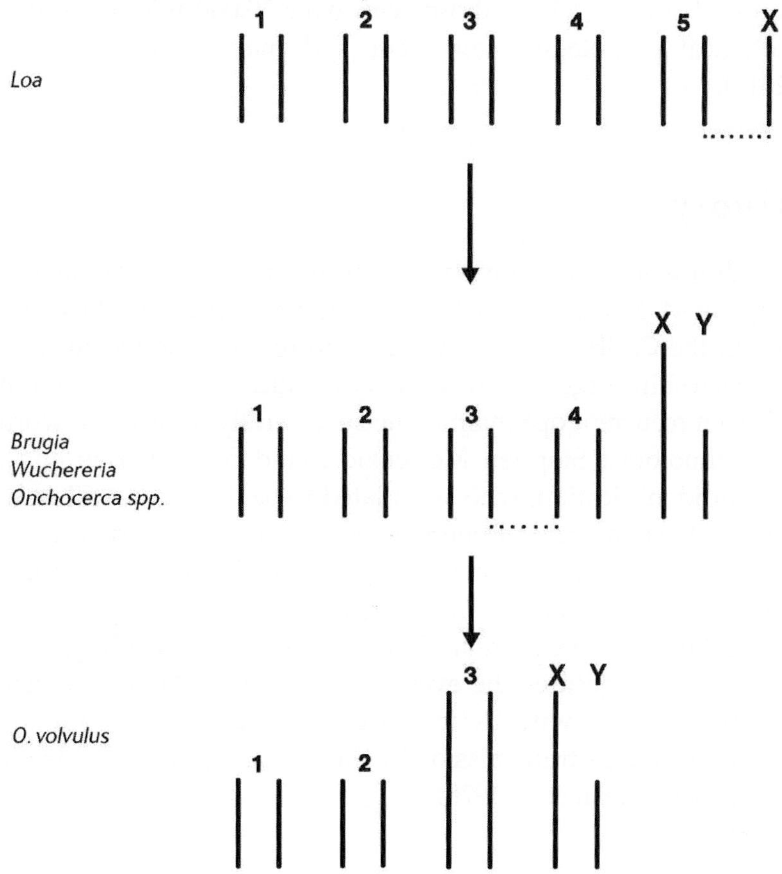

Fig. 19.1 ■ **Filaria worm karyotype evolution.** Modified from "The chromosomes of the Filariae" by Post R. *Filaria J* 2005;4:10.

Filariases are vector-borne diseases. Female mosquitoes (many species) carry the agent for elephantiasis. Female deerflies carry the agent for loiasis. Female black flies carry the agent for river blindness. The study of these insects are part of medical entomology. For Guinea worm disease, their larval stages are carried by copepods (intermediate host).

19.2 *Loa*

Loa loa (an African name originating from Angola) is the **eye worm of Africa**, and loiasis is restricted to Africa. Loiasis (tropical eye worm disease) affects 13–**15 million** individuals in Central Africa (Ndzeshang *et al.* 2020). An estimate of 30 million people is at risk of this NTD. In an effort to combat river blindness in the region, mass drug administration (MDA) of ivermectin has been implemented (see next section). For individuals having heavy infection of *Loa loa*, such as those with over 30,000 microfilariae per ml blood, adverse neurological pathologies can occur and may even be fatal (Metzger and Mordmüller 2014).

19.2.1 History

For *Loa loa*, the adult worms can move across the eye under the conjunctiva. In 1770, the French ship surgeon M. Mongin described a worm passing across the eye of a woman in Santo Domingo in the Caribbean; he attempted to remove the worm (unsuccessful). In 1778, another French ship surgeon Francois Guyot noticed that slaves in transit from West Africa suffered from recurrent ophthalmia; he successfully removed a worm from one of them. The ophthalmologist Stephen McKenzie found microfilariae and sent them to Patrick Manson for identification, who speculated to be the larvae of *Loa loa*. In 1895, the Scottish physician Douglas Argyll-Robertson removed adult worms (named *Filaria loa*) from under the conjunctiva in a woman (32-year-old Miss J.H — had lived in the Old Calabar region of West Africa for 8 years, the region is part of today's Nigeria). Swellings in arms and faces from the infection are known as **Calabar swelling**, as such infection manifests in many places besides the eyes. In 1910 Patrick Manson suggested that the swellings might be associated with *Loa* infections. In 1912, British helminthologist Robert Thomas Leiper discovered its transmission by the day biting fly (alias deer fly, mango fly, or tabanid fly) *Chrysops* (Kean *et al.* 1978).

19.2.2 Life cycle

Please see Figure 19.2 for the life cycle, from CDC.[1]

Life cycle of *Loa loa* starts from an infected insect vector (*Chrysops*) biting humans. Life expectancy of an adult worm is about 9 years, but individuals can live as long as 15–20 years. Females measure up to 60 mm in length and males are much smaller at 32 mm. Female worms produce eggs that develop into microfilariae, about 250–300 μm in length. A single female can release an average of 10,000–22,000 microfilaria per day, and more than 100,000 parasites per mL blood have been recorded in an infected individual. These microfilariae have a protective layer on their surface; they are thus known as sheathed. During the day microfilariae are in circulation in peripheral blood, and at night in the lungs (**diurnal periodicity** to accompany feeding habit of the insect vector). The fly ingests microfilariae during blood meal. Microfilariae loose sheath, migrate to thoracic muscles of the fly and molt to L3 larvae, the infective stage (iL3). In another blood meal, larvae enter the human skin bite wound, develop into adults and live in subcutaneous tissues. Humans are the definitive hosts.

[1] https://www.cdc.gov/dpdx/loiasis/index.html

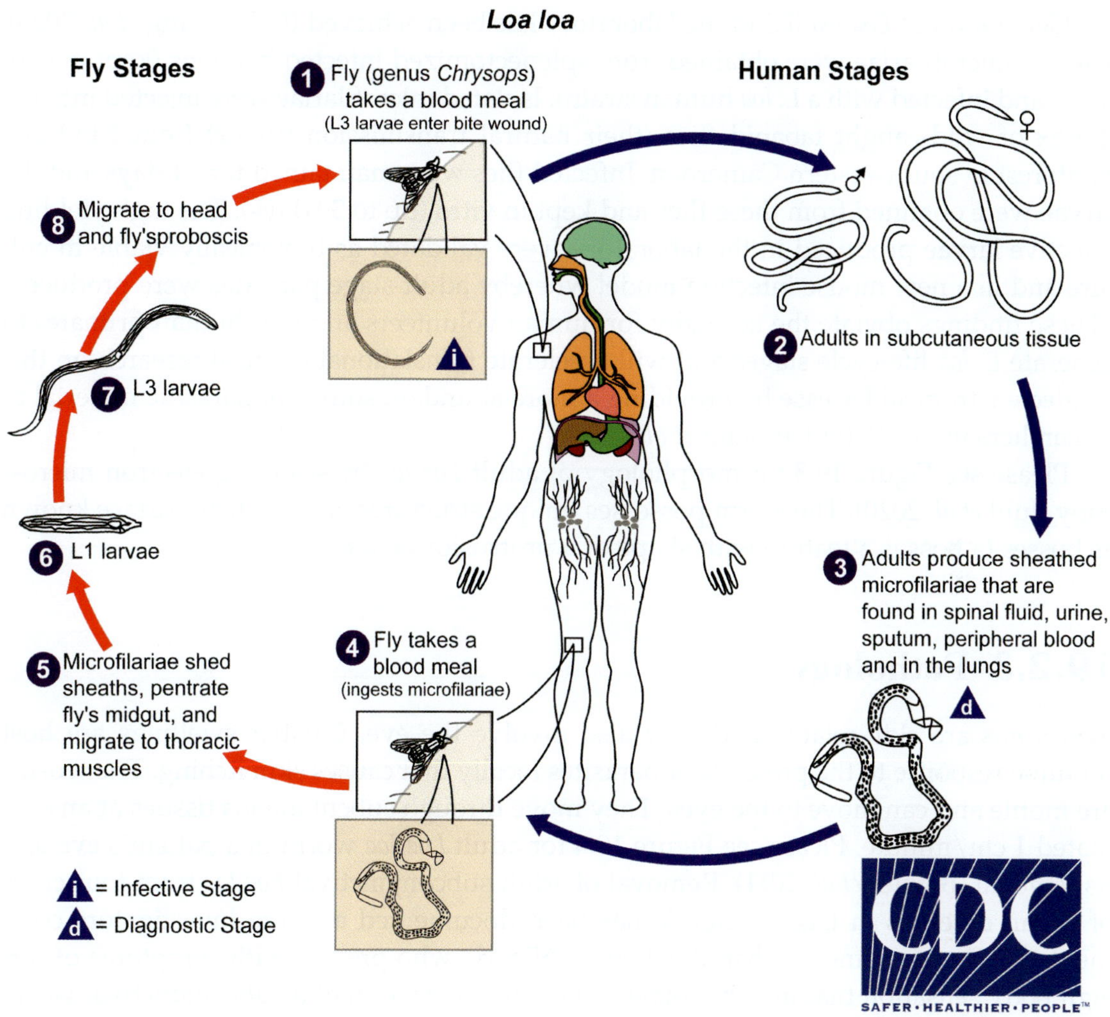

Fig. 19.2 ■ Life cycle of *Loa loa*. The vector for *Loa loa* filariasis are flies from two species of the genus *Chrysops*, *C. silacea* and *C. dimidiata*. During a blood meal, an infected fly (genus *Chrysops*, day-biting flies) introduces third-stage filarial larvae onto the skin of the human host, where they penetrate into the bite wound ❶. The larvae develop into adults that commonly reside in subcutaneous tissue ❷. The female worms measure 40–70 mm in length and 0.5 mm in diameter, while the males measure 30–34 mm in length and 0.35–0.43 mm in diameter. Adults produce microfilariae measuring 250–300 μm by 6–8 μm, which are sheathed and have diurnal periodicity. Microfilariae have been recovered from spinal fluids, urine, and sputum. During the day they are found in peripheral blood, but during the noncirculation phase, they are found in the lungs ❸. The fly ingests microfilariae during a blood meal ❹. After ingestion, the microfilariae lose their sheaths and migrate from the fly's midgut through the hemocoel to the thoracic muscles of the arthropod ❺. There the microfilariae develop into first-stage larvae ❻ and subsequently into third-stage infective larvae ❼. The third-stage infective larvae migrate to the fly's proboscis ❽ and can infect another human when the fly takes a blood meal ❶. Courtesy of the CDC. Reproduced from https://www.cdc.gov/dpdx/loiasis/index.html

Generation of *Loa loa* iL3 in the laboratory has been achieved (Ndzeshang *et al.* 2020). The *Loa* microfilariae were obtained from splenectomized infected baboons (kept in captivity and infected with a *L. loa* human strain). Isolated microfilariae were injected into the thorax of wild-caught tabanid flies (their natural transmission vector) from Kindongi rainforest in southwestern Cameroon. Infected flies were maintained for 14 days and iL3 larvae were obtained from these flies and kept in vitro (up to 30 days). The high yielding infective larvae produced in the laboratory were validated as biologically viable in culture and in a new mouse infection model whereby adult-stage parasites were produced. "These findings obviate the necessity for human volunteers and non-human primates to generate *L. loa* life-cycle stages and will accelerate translational medical research on this Neglected Tropical Disease by providing a more abundant source of parasitic material to researchers in need" (Ndzeshang *et al.* 2020).

Please see Figure 19.3 for morphology of adult *Loa loa* by scanning electron microscopy (Juul *et al.* 2020). The worm possesses unique structures on its cuticle surface known as bosses (a boss is a feature with shape of a protrusion/knob).

19.2.3 Pathology

Symptoms are skin-related and may also involve the eye. Calabar swellings are host immune response to the presence of parasites locally that causes skin itching. The worms are motile and can move to the eyes. They move through subcutaneous tissues at an estimated 1 cm/minute. Please see Figure 19.4 for adult *Loa loa* worm in a patient's eye and its removal (Bowler *et al.* 2011). Removal of adult subconjunctival *Loa loa* from four cases of urban dwellers in Lagos, Nigeria has been documented and the investigators commented: "There are more urban dwellers in Nigeria who present with symptoms of foreign body sensation that may be related to the manifestation of a subconjunctival worm and are not recognized. This is because the emphasis on this disease has erstwhile been on the rural, village dwellers and not on urban dwellers. Eye care practitioners working in urban centers need to be aware of the possibility of this presentation, and be ready to remove any subconjunctival worm when it presents" (Okonkwo *et al.* 2018).

A case of *Loa loa* worm infection (loiasis) was documented in Germany (Boden *et al.* 2019). A 15-year-old girl from Cameroon had lived in Germany for 5 years. She visited an ophthalmological center after having witnessed a worm migrating through her eye, and reporting transient abdominal pain and mild itching in the preceding weeks. An adult *Loa loa* worm was extracted from her left eye; her blood smear microscopy demonstrated microfilaraemia of approximately 2,000 microfilariae per mL blood. She recovered after treatment with oral diethylcarbamazine (DEC).

Next to Germany is France, where another case was reported (Mouri *et al.* 2019). This was the first documented use of flow cytometry as a method to count microfilaraemia in peripheral blood from a patient with *L. loa* infection. A 61-year-old male from Cameroon

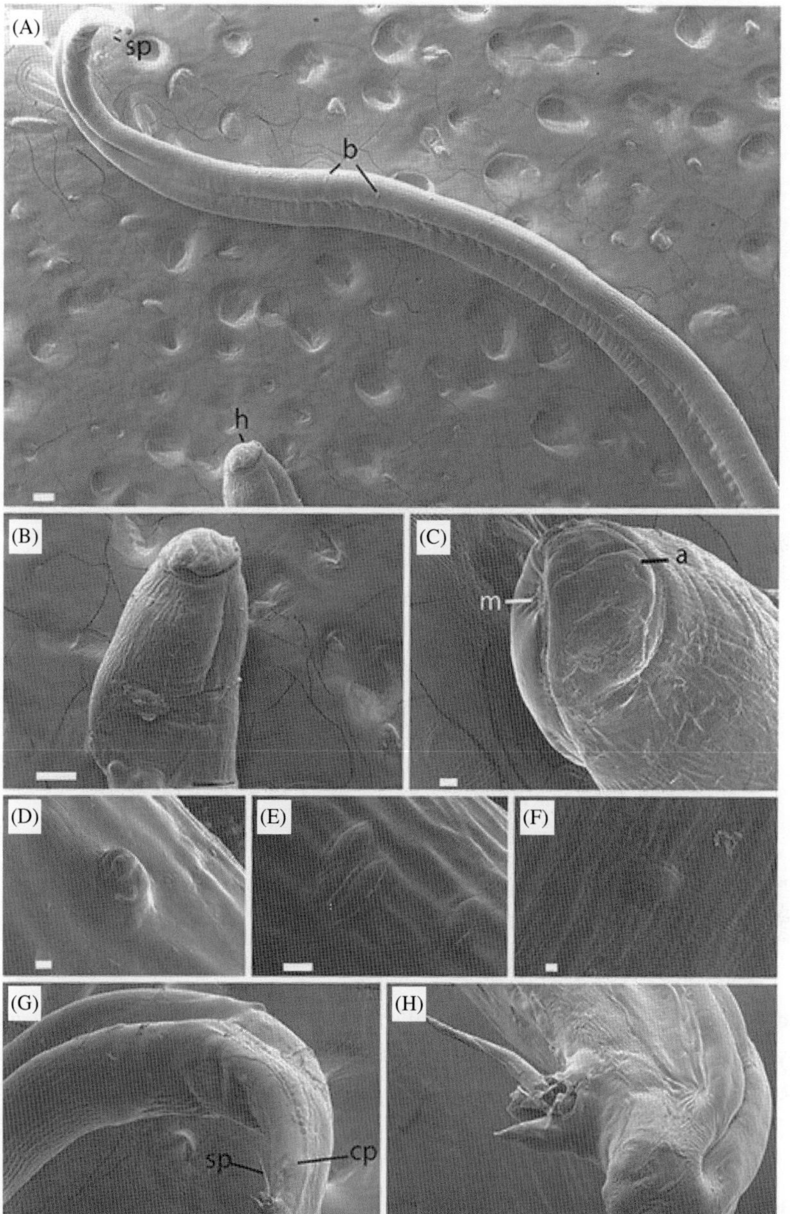

Fig. 19.3 ■ Morphology of adult *Loa loa* by scanning electron microscopy. Scanning electron microscopy. (A) *Loa loa* with head (h), spines (s), and ellipsoid bosses (b) (scale = 100 μm). (B) Head and cervical region (scale = 100 μm). (C) Oral region with mouth (m) amphid (a) (scale = 20 μm). (D) Tubercle (scale = 3 μm). (E) Ellipsoid bosses (scale = 10 μm). (F) Dome-shaped boss (scale = 2 μm). (G) Tail region with caudal papillae (cp) and genital spines (sp) (scale = 20 μm). (H) Genitalia and caudal end (scale = 20 μm). Courtesy: Juul *et al. Case Rep Ophthalmol* 2020;11:486–92. Reproduced with permission from *Case Report in Ophthalmology* with Creative Commons Attribution 4.0 (CC-BY) International License and from Jens Juul.

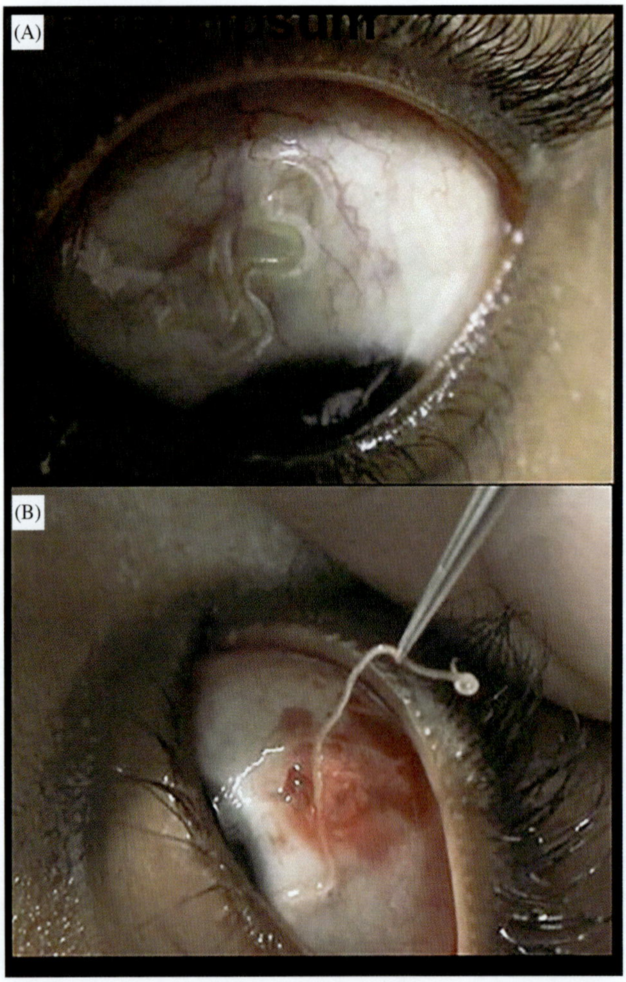

Fig. 19.4 ■ Adult *Loa loa* worm in a patient's eye and its removal. (A) *Loa loa* worm in the patient's left eye (Case 2). (B) The *Loa loa* worm is removed with forceps (Case 2). Courtesy: Bowler *et al. Eye (Lond)* 2011;25:389–91. Reproduced with permission from Springer Nature.

came to France and was hospitalized to explore a lytic lesion of the right humerus. CT scan showed a fracture of surgical neck of his right humerus with numerous osteolytic lesions. Microfilariae were seen in blood smears after Giemsa stain. His blood samples were analyzed by flow cytometry: based on the forward and the side scatter delineated two populations: one for leucocytes, and the other for *Loa* microfilariae. The patient recovered after treatment with ivermectin and corticosteroids (prednisone). "The current report highlights the potential of flow cytometry to assess microfilarial *L. loa* load from a patient with loiasis infection" (Mouri *et al.* 2019).

"Loiasis is a vector-borne parasitic infection endemic across many areas of Central and West Africa. Its treatment is tricky due to the risk of serious neurologic adverse events occurring after the administration of microfilaricidal drugs, like DEC or ivermectin, in subjects with high pre-treatment microfilarial load. Albendazole is currently recommended to slowly reduce microfilaremia before curative regimen is prescribed" (Volpicelli *et al.* 2020). A case of treatment-related *Loa loa* encephalopathy induced by albendazole was documented in Italy. A 25-year-old man from Guinea's capital city Conakry but had been in Italy for 18 months, was incidentally diagnosed with microfilaremic *Loa loa* infection. A 3-week regimen of albendazole was prescribed, with minor neurologic side effects after two weeks and serious encephalopathy developed at week 3 (with clinical and electroencephalographic features resembling an immune-mediated encephalitis). The patient recovered after steroid treatment (methylprednisolone). "Administration of either DEC or IVM, in individuals with elevated basal level of microfilaremia, imply significant risk of life-threatening encephalopathy.... In order to reduce the incidence of DEC-related neurologic SAEs, CDC presently recommends a 3-week regimen of albendazole (ALB), a benzimidazole drug, to safely reduce microfilaremia before curative DEC treatment is prescribed in subjects with high pre-treatment level of microfilaremia (≥8,000 mf/mL). ... The patient agreed an informed consent form giving us his approval to publish a case report" (Volpicelli *et al.* 2020).

Before the albendazole case report, four cases of *Loa* microfilaremia, ivermectin, and serious adverse event (**SAE**) were investigated. "Ivermectin (IVM) is exceptionally safe in humans, and is used for mass treatment of onchocerciasis and lymphatic filariasis. However, cases of encephalopathy, sometimes fatal, have been reported in a small number of individuals who harbored large numbers of *Loa loa* microfilariae (mf). A loss-of-function mutation in the *mdr-1* gene in some dog breeds and in mice leads to accumulation of the drug in the brain, causing coma and death. This hypothesis was tested in four individuals from Cameroon who experienced a post-IVM SAE and in nine non-SAE matched controls. No loss-of-function mutation was detected in *mdr-1* in any subject. However, haplotypes, associated with altered drug disposition, were present as homozygotes in two of the SAE patients (50%), but absent as homozygotes in the controls (0%). An association of high *Loa* mf load and a genetic predisposition to altered IVM distribution could be involved in IVM SAEs" (Bourguinat *et al.* 2010).

19.2.4 Diagnosis

Loa loa can be diagnosed by identifying microfilariae in peripheral blood smears, or adult worms in the subconjunctiva.

19.2.5 Therapy

Treatment is diethylcarbamazine (**DEC**). Antibacterial treatment is not helpful because *Loa loa* does not possess *Wolbachia*, which is an endosymbiont bacterium of other filarial worms.

19.2.6 Genome

The genome of *Loa loa* was determined first from whole-genome shotgun sequencing and later improved with single molecule sequencing (Desjardins *et al.* 2013; Tallon *et al.* 2014). It has **14,908** protein-coding genes. There are six **hyaluronidase** genes, corresponding to the active mobility and tissue penetration of these worms (*Brugia malayi* and *Wuchereria bancrofti* both only have 2). Interestingly, many cytokine and chemokine mimics and antagonists are found in the worm genome, such as suppressor of cytokine signaling 7 (**SOCS7**), as well as serpins and cystatins (protease inhibitors that can interfere with antigen processing and presentation to T cells), and indolamine dioxygenase (**IDO**) (for immunomodulatory function).

Loa loa has no bacterial endosymbiont, but there has been no change in the analyzed biosynthetic pathways (such as heme, riboflavin and purine pathways). Exact role played by the bacterial endosymbiont remains to be discovered ("deepen the mystery surrounding the 'essential nature' of *Wolbachia* for many filarial worms"). There is the finding of nuclear *Wolbachia* transfers (**nuwts**) in various filarial genomes, including the one from *Loa loa*. This finding suggests that *Loa loa* at one time possessed the bacteria which was subsequently lost.

19.3 *Onchocerca*

Onchocerca volvulus (onkos means node or swelling, kerkos means tail, volvulus means rolled in) causes river blindness. Onchocerciasis is a neglected tropical disease. The prevalence estimate is **20.9 million**, including 14.6 million with skin disease and 1.15 million with vision loss. A total of 205 million people are at risk. The majority of the disease is in Africa (99% in 31 countries). The disease is also present in South America (Brazil and Venezuela) and has been introduced in Yemen.

For onchocerciasis, there are dermatitis-causing nodules (**onchocercoma**), and disease of the eye, leading to river blindness. The disease name river blindness is due to the vector, female black fly (*Simulium*) preferring the fast flowing rivers as its niche.

Mass drug administration (MDA) to treat onchocerciasis has been "on" in many countries in Africa, but there is a case of "off" in Nigeria (Evans 2020). "Plateau and Nasarawa states in central Nigeria were endemic for onchocerciasis. The rural populations of these two states received annual ivermectin MDA for a period of 8–26 years (1992–2017). Ivermectin combined with albendazole was given for 8–13 of these years for lymphatic filariasis (LF); the LF MDA program successfully concluded in 2012, but ivermectin MDA continued in areas known to have a baseline meso-/hyperendemic onchocerciasis. … Only two of 6,262 children were OV16 IgG4 antibodies positive, and none of 19,056 vector heads were positive for parasite DNA. Therefore, both states were able to meet WHO stop-MDA thresholds of an infection rate in children of <0.1% and a rate of infective blackflies of <1/2,000, with 95% statistical confidence. Transmission of onchocerciasis was declared interrupted in Plateau and Nasarawa states by the Federal Ministry of Health, and 2.2 million ivermectin treatments/year were stopped in 2018" (Richards *et al.* 2020). There was post-treatment surveillance. Thus, "an apparent positive impact of the LF MDA program on eliminating hypo-endemic onchocerciasis was observed. This is the first stop-MDA decision for onchocerciasis in Nigeria and the largest single stop-MDA decision for onchocerciasis yet reported. This achievement, along with the process used in adapting and implementing the 2016 WHO stop-MDA guidelines, will be important as a potential model for decision makers and national onchocerciasis elimination committees in other African countries that are charged with advancing their programs" (Richards *et al.* 2020). So, here, we have a success story.

19.3.1 History

In 1874, the Irish naval surgeon John O'Neill found microfilariae in skin snips from patients suffering from **craw craw** (kru kru) in Ghana. Craw craw is a Creole word used by freed slaves settled in Sierra Leone describing skin disease with chronic lesions and intense itching. In 1893 Patrick Manson described the adult worms, based on his communication with the German parasitologist Friedrich Rudolf Leuckart, worms within tumor nodules that Leuckart had received from missionaries working in Gold Coast, West Africa. Manson gave full credit for discovery of the new species to Leuckart. "Happy it is to see such cooperation between two giants of medical parasitology" (Kean *et al.* 1978). *Onchocerca* is believed to have been transported to the Americas via the slave trade. In 1917, the Paris-educated Guatemalan physician Rodolfo Robles described the Latin American onchocerciasis. In 1927 the Scottish physician Donald Blacklock reported the insect vector of this disease while working in Sierra Leone to be *Simulium* (the black fly).

19.3.2 Life cycle

Please see Figure 19.5 for the life cycle, from CDC.[2]

Life cycle is humans bitten by *Simulium*, whose larval stages require clean, fast running water. Adults live for 8–10 years. Females are 33–50 cm and males are small, only 2–4 cm. Humans are the only definitive host. There are nodules known as onchocercomas, which are caused by host immune response and may contain several female worms inside. Males migrate in search of females. After fertilization females produce non-sheathed microfilariae. There may be 1 to over 100 nodules, leading to loss of tissue elasticity, even causing hanging groins. Microfilariae migrate to places including the lymphatic system, eyes, and even present in urine. Eye infection, scarring keratitis and

[2] https://www.cdc.gov/dpdx/onchocerciasis/index.html

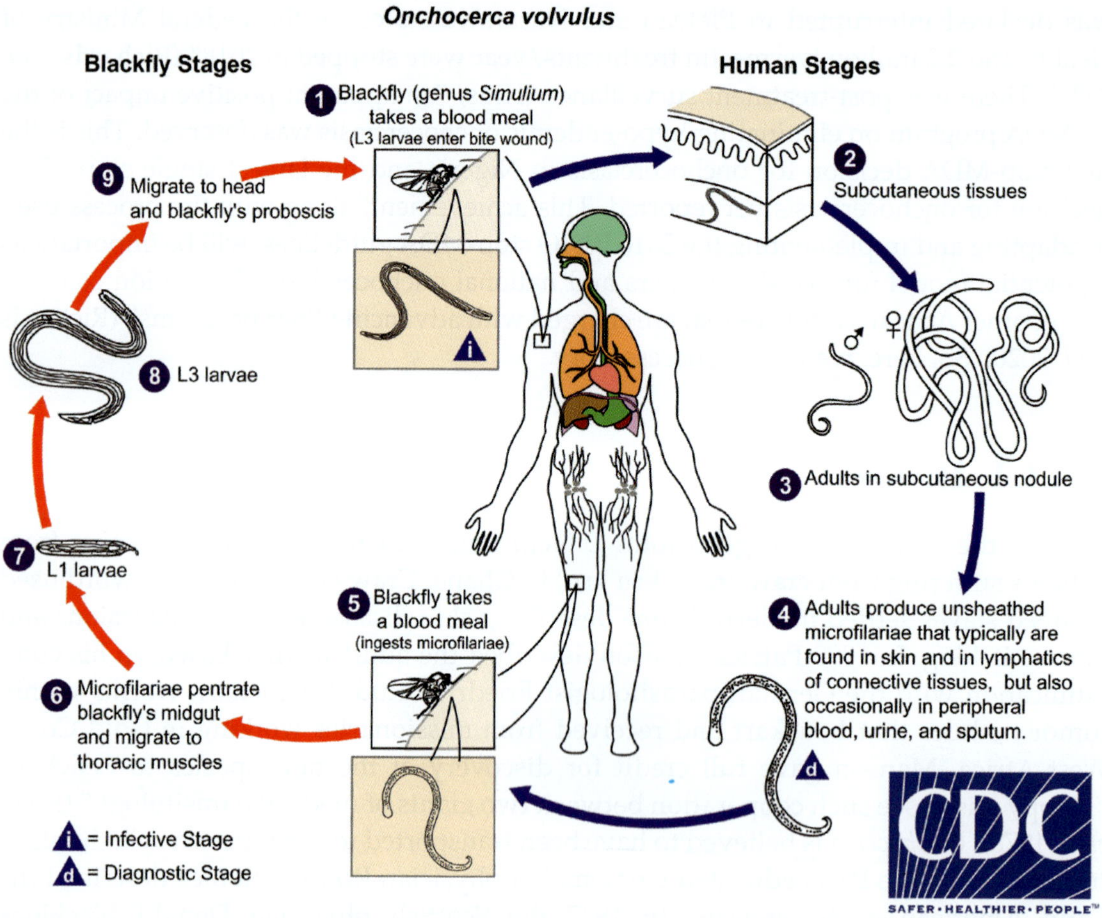

Fig. 19.5 ■ Life cycle of *Onchocerca volvulus*. During a blood meal, an infected blackfly (genus *Simulium*) introduces third-stage filarial larvae onto the skin of the human host, where they penetrate into the bite wound ❶. In subcutaneous tissues the larvae ❷ develop into adult filariae, which commonly reside in nodules in subcutaneous connective tissues ❸. Adults can live in the nodules for approximately 15 years. Some nodules may contain numerous male and female worms. Females measure 33–50 cm in length and 270–400 μm in diameter, while males measure 19–42 mm by 130–210 μm. In the subcutaneous nodules, the female worms are capable of producing microfilariae for approximately 9 years. The microfilariae, measuring 220–360 μm by 5–9 μm and unsheathed, have a life span that may reach 2 years. They are occasionally found in peripheral blood, urine, and sputum but are typically found in the skin and in the lymphatics of connective tissues ❹. A blackfly ingests the microfilariae during a blood meal ❺. After ingestion, the microfilariae migrate from the blackfly's midgut through the hemocoel to the thoracic muscles ❻. There the microfilariae develop into first-stage larvae ❼ and subsequently into third-stage infective larvae ❽. The third-stage infective larvae migrate to the blackfly's proboscis ❾ and can infect another human when the fly takes a blood meal ❶. Courtesy of the CDC. Reproduced from https://www.cdc.gov/dpdx/onchocerciasis/index.html

further development to blindness takes time, 7–9 years, so these symptoms are mostly seen in adults over 40 years of age.

19.3.3 Pathology

River blindness is the second leading infectious cause of human blindness. The first is **trachoma** due to infection of the prokaryote *Chlamydia trachomitis*. Here, eradication would not involve the so-called parasitologist's dilemma, just alleviating the economic burden of the affected countries. Whereas it takes decades for vision loss to occur, skin disease is much more frequent (seen as nodules named onchocercomas).

In a case study of onchocerciasis, a 59-year-old man from an onchocerciasis-endemic area in eastern Ghana was enrolled in a clinical trial to assess the impact of ivermectin on microfilariae (**Mf**) in the skin and eyes (Gyasi *et al*. 2020). He had palpable subcutaneous nodules consistent with onchocerciasis and a high Mf burden in skin snips (170/mg of skin). He reported mild generalized pruritus and blurry vision in both eyes. A cell-phone video was able to record the motile Mf in the anterior chamber using a slit lamp. After 3 months of ivermectin treatment, his ocular Mf were still present but decreased in number and motility. However, the patient's vision did not improve after treatment, presumably because of irreversible effects of onchocerciasis.

Onchocerciasis may mimic metastatic breast cancer. A 42-year-old female from Cameron, with a history of invasive ductal mammary carcinoma, had right mastectomy but showed 1-cm peri-scapular lesion. Although position emission tomography (PET) scan showed a lesion suspicious for metastasis, histologic examination of skin biopsy revealed *Onchocerca volvulus*. The patient was treated with ivermectin (Nava *et al*. 2020).

19.3.4 Nodding syndrome

Onchocerciasis is known as river blindness, because the black fly vector needs flowing waters for breeding. Actually, there are multiple symptoms associated with infection by *Onchocerca volvulus*. Please see Figure 19.6 for onchocerciasis symptoms (Colebunders *et al*. 2016). After decades of infection, there is blindness. At a younger age, there is onchocerciasis-associated epilepsy (**OAE**), alias nodding syndrome.

The disease nodding syndrome affect young African children in Tanzania, Uganda and South Sudan; they get seizures. Nodding syndrome is a rare and distinct form of pediatric epilepsy. This syndrome may be related to their *Onchocerca volvulus* worm infection and worm burden. It may be a neurological complication of the worm infection. Host immune response to worm antigens leads to an autoantibody, for the host protein **leiomodin** (Johnson *et al*. 2017). There is amino acid sequence similarity between the human leiomodin and the worm proteins tropomyosin and tropomodulin. In immunological terms this is molecular mimicry. However, it should be pointed out that while this is an

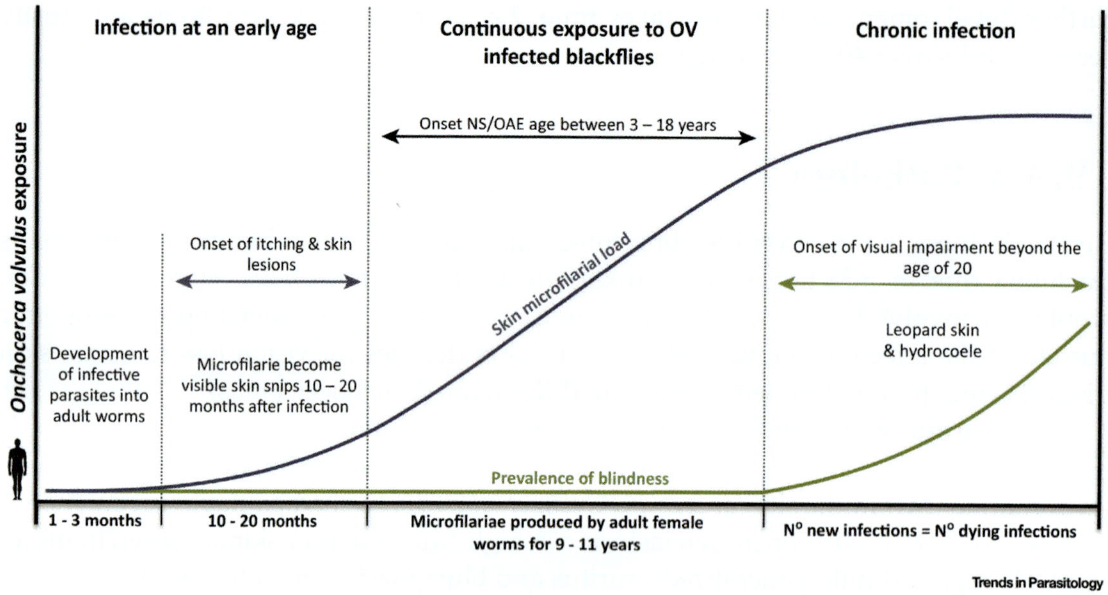

Fig. 19.6 ■ Onchocerciasis symptoms. Onchocerciasis-associated epilepsy in relation to onset of infection, increasing microfilarial load, and other clinical manifestations of onchocerciasis. Courtesy: Colebunders *et al. Trends Parasitol* 2016;32:581–3. Reproduced with permission from Elsevier.

interesting finding, not all investigators agree this as the cause of the epileptic disorder. Please see Figure 19.7 for leiomodin, from Johnson *et al.* (2017). Please see Figure 19.8 for potential pathway of nodding syndrome, from Idro *et al.* (2016).

"Despite efforts to understand the etiology and pathogenesis of nodding syndrome, absolute answers to why and how this disease occurs remain enigmatic, although the process of molecular mimicry between *O. volvulus* and brain antigens has been implicated as has the involvement of tau accumulation" (Johnson *et al.* 2020). "One hypothesis proposes that parasite-induced immune responses cross-react with human leiomodin-1 resulting in immune-mediated central nervous system (CNS) damage" (Nauen *et al.* 2020). The presence of leiomodin in brain and neurons has been demonstrated by qPCR and immunoblot techniques (Nauen *et al.* 2020).

"Nodding syndrome is an uncommon epileptic disorder of childhood onset, which appears to occur exclusively in clusters in sub-Saharan Africa. It was first reported in the 1960s, in what is now southern Tanzania, then in Liberia, and later in South Sudan and northern Uganda, with both epidemic and endemic patterns described. The cause remains unknown" (Olum *et al.* 2020). "The cause of the disorder has hitherto eluded scientists. Neuroimaging studies show involvement of the nervous system with associated severe cortical atrophy in the affected children. The affected communities have generated a number of perceived causes including some conspiracy theories related to intentional poisoning of water sources and foods, and causes related to fumes and

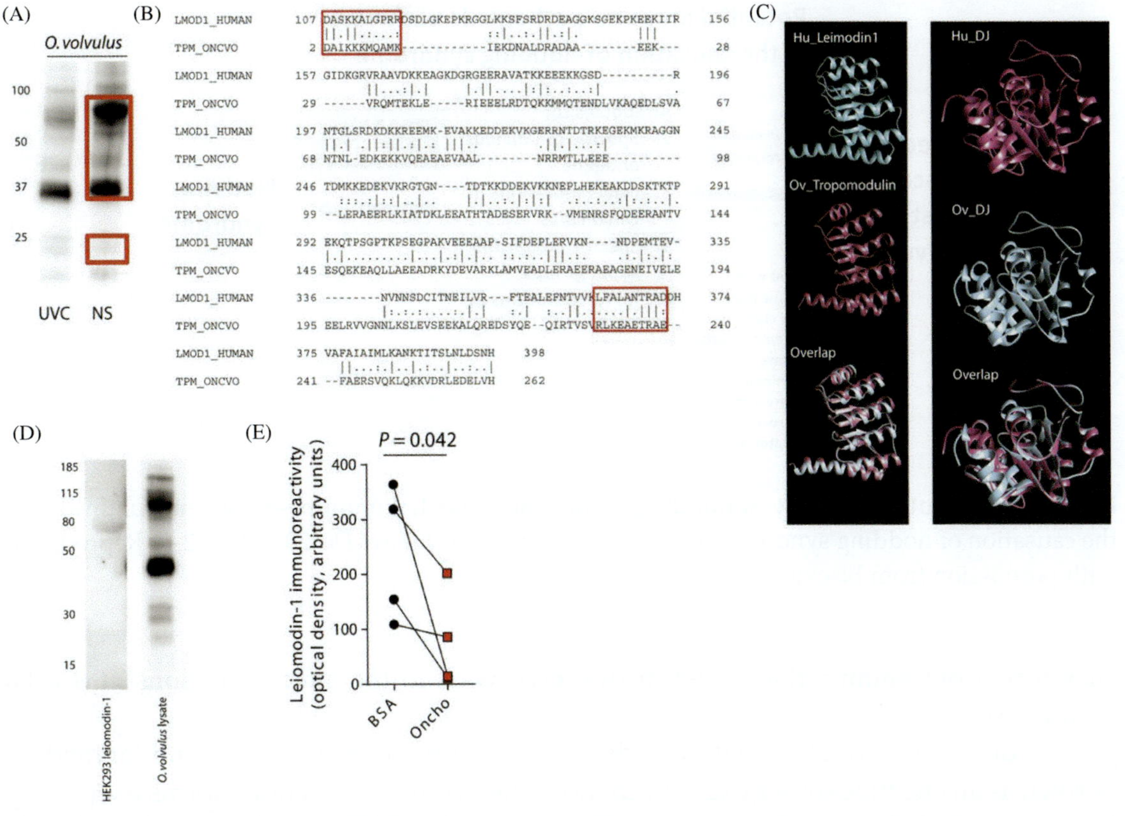

Fig. 19.7 ■ Nodding syndrome & leiomodin. Leiomodin-1 autoantibodies from the CSF of patients with nodding syndrome cross-react with *O. volvulus* proteins. (A) Western blot analyses of *O. volvulus* lysates probed with sera from unaffected village controls and patients with nodding syndrome. Red boxes indicate the region of the corresponding gel that was excised and analyzed by mass spectrometry for protein identification. (B) Sequence homology between human leiomodin-1 (accession number NP036266) and *O. volvulus* tropomyosin (accession number Q25632) by pairwise alignment (EMBOSS, EMBL EBI with Smith-Waterman algorithm). Conserved tropomyosin regions 1 and 2 and their corresponding leiomodin-1 sequences are indicated by red boxes. (C) Depiction of structural homology between human leiomodin-1 (Hu_Leiomodin1) and *O. volvulus* tropomodulin (Ov_Tropomodulin) (accession number A0A044S1K6) (left) and between human DJ1 (Hu_DJ) (accession number Q99497) and the *O. volvulus* ortholog (Ov_DJ) (accession number A0A044RAJ4) (right). (D) Leiomodin-1 antibodies purified from patients reacted to a single band in HEK293 cells overexpressing tagged human leiomodin-1 (left). The same purified anti–leiomodin-1 antibodies demonstrated strong immunoreactivity to multiple proteins from *O. volvulus* whole-organism lysate (right). (E) Inhibition of patient sera immunoreactivity to leiomodin-1 by *O. volvulus* whole-organism lysate (oncho) compared to bovine serum albumin (BSA) (n = 4; P = 0.042, one-way Student's unpaired t test). Courtesy: Johnson *et al. Sci Transl Med* 2017;9:eaaf6953. Reproduced with permission from The American Association for the Advancement of Science.

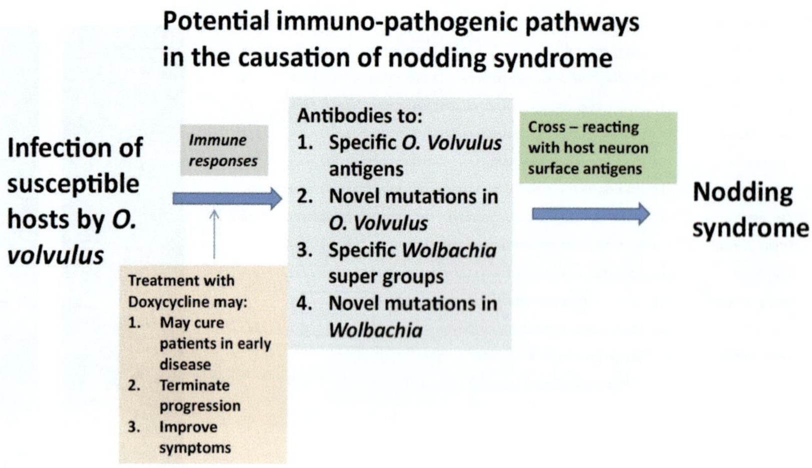

Fig. 19.8 ■ Potential pathway of nodding syndrome. Potential immune-pathogenic pathways in the causation of nodding syndrome. Courtesy: Idro *et al. Int J Infect Dis* 2016;45:112–7. Reproduced with permission from Elsevier.

chemicals from ammunitions used during civil wars in the affected regions" (Mwaka *et al.* 2018).

"A combination of bi-annual mass distribution of ivermectin and ground larviciding of rivers is an effective strategy to prevent nodding syndrome and other forms of epilepsy in onchocerciasis-hyperendemic areas" (Gumisiriza *et al.* 2020). In addition, clinical trials such as using doxycycline are ongoing (Mwaka *et al.* 2018). It should be noted that both onchocerciasis and epilepsy are stigmatizing conditions. "Educating healthcare workers and communities about OAE, strengthening onchocerciasis elimination programs, decreasing the anti-epileptic treatment gap, improving the care of epilepsy-related injuries, and prioritizing epilepsy research is the way forward to decreasing the stigma associated with epilepsy in onchocerciasis-endemic regions" (O'Neill *et al.* 2019).

19.3.5 Diagnosis

Microscopic observation of microfilariae from skin snips is a method of diagnosis.

19.3.6 Therapy

The drug of choice is ivermectin.

The drug maker Merck is donating ivermectin to developing countries to combat river blindness. In 1972 the World Bank president Robert McNamara helped the launching of one of the world's most successful health and humanitarian programs, Onchocerciasis

Control Program (OCP), which was a partnership of the World Bank with World Health Organization (WHO), Food and Agriculture Organization (FAO), and United Nations Development Program (UNDP). From 1974 to 2002, by spraying against black fly larvae, OCP prevented 600,000 cases of river blindness, 18 million children born were free from risk of the disease. For ivermectin, Merck CEO Roy Vagelos donated the drug (brand name Mectizan) free of charge to anyone in need, for as long as needed (to target onchocerciasis and lymphatic filariasis). African Programme for the Control of Onchocerciasis (APOC) started in 1995, with the establishment of self-sustaining community-directed treatment with ivermectin (CDTI), and, where appropriate, vector control with environmentally-safe methods. After mass drug administration (MDA), the aim is moving from control to the elimination of river blindness.

In some countries such as Ghana, resistance to ivermectin may be developing. For patients with *Loa loa* and *Onchocerca volvulus* co-infection in endemic regions, MDA using ivermectin leads to adverse effects and potential deaths. Thus, novel drugs are needed. One example is **moxidectin** (Opoku *et al.* 2018). The drug targets the glutamate-gated chloride channel and disrupts neurotransmission of the worm. In 2018, moxidectin was approved by FDA for onchocerciasis.

19.3.7 Genome

The genome of *Onchocerca volvulus* is known (Cotton *et al.* 2016). The 97 Mb size genome codes for **12,143** protein-coding genes. There is an expansion of **collagen prolyl 4-hydroxylase genes** (16 copies), suggested as required for cuticle remodeling in different stages of the nematode. Mimics of cytokines and chemokines and immune modifiers are found in the genome, as already seen in *Loa loa*. There is lateral gene transfer (LGT) from *Wolbachia* to the worm, with putative 531 nuwts, but all transfers seem to be nonfunctional. For drug repurposing, the diabetic drug **metformin** may target the worm's NADH-ubiquinone oxidoreductase.

MDA of ivermectin has been applied for onchocerciasis. Multiple treatments may have led to changes in the worm's genome. A genome-wide association analyses were done for samples of *Onchocerca volvulus* from Cameroon and Ghana (Doyle *et al.* 2017). Genes involved in neurotransmission are seen as peaks of quantitative trait loci (QTLs). These include genes for ion channels and for acetylcholine signaling and show genetic drifts that may lead to resistance to the drug ivermectin.

19.4 *Dracunculus*

Dracunculus medinensis (dracon is dragon, medinensis means originating from the city Medina in Arabia, now Saudi Arabia) is the **Guinea worm** (Guinea is a country in West Africa). Dracunculiasis is Guinea worm disease. The world is on the verge of eradicating

Guinea worm disease. The only disease that has been eradicated to date is smallpox. There is a difference between eradication and elimination of an infectious disease. For elimination, prevalence of the disease has been reduced and disease transmission has been interrupted, but public health control measures are still needed. For eradication, there is disappearance of the infectious agent to the point that no more public health intervention is necessary. Guinea worm disease is reaching eradication. One major contributor towards this effort is the former United States President Jimmy Carter, with the Carter Center and other organizations (Hopkins *et al.* 2018). Significantly, this feat is being accomplished without any drug or vaccine dedicated to the Guinea worm. There is a data base of Guinea worm worldwide cases; the information is available at the Carter Center website.[3] In 2018, 28 human cases of Guinea worm disease were reported worldwide (17 in Chad, 10 in South Sudan, and 1 in Angola). In 2019, there were 54 cases (48 in Chad, 4 in South Sudan, 1 each in Angola and Cameroon). In 2020, there were 27 cases (1/1/2020 to 11/30/2020, 12 in Chad, 11 in Ethiopia, and 1 each in Angola, Cameroon, Mali and South Sudan). In 2021, there were **14** cases (1/1/2021 to 11/30/2021, 7 in Chad, 4 in South Sudan, 2 in Mali, and 1 in Ethiopia, none in Angola and Cameroon). Carter Center also had records of animal infections: mostly domesticated dog infections of the Guinea worm. In 2019, there were 1,991 cases (1,973 cases in Chad, 9 in Mali, 8 in Ethiopia and 1 in Angola). In 2020, there were **1,550** cases (1,527 cases in Chad, 15 in Ethiopia and 8 in Mali).

19.4.1 History

Dracunculiasis has a long historical record (Tayeh *et al.* 2017). Known since antiquity, the disease was described in Egyptian, Greek, Roman, Arabic, and Persian texts. Persian physicians believed the nature of the disease was due to a vein named the Medina vein. Although others of his time thought the disease due to a rotten vein, the Persian physician Avicenna described the symptom and concluded involvement of a worm. He wrote: "Medina vein is the occurrence of a blister on some part of the body which grows in size and then ruptures; something red to black emerges from it, which grows longer and longer. Probably it has a wormy movement under the skin as an animal's movement. In fact, it is a worm...." The disease was recognized by European travelers to Africa and Asia (hence the name Guinea worm) (Cox 1996).

Dracunculus medinensis may be the fiery serpent of the Bible. "Then the Lord sent fiery serpent among the people, and they bit the people, so that many Israelites died. The people came to Moses and said, 'We have sinned by speaking against the Lord and against you; pray to the Lord to take away the serpent from us.' So Moses prayed for the people. And the Lord said to Moses, 'Make thee a fiery serpent, and set it on a pole; and everyone who is bitten shall look at it and live.' So Moses made a serpent of bronze, and put it upon a pole; and whenever a serpent bit someone, that person would look at the serpent of bronze and live" (Numbers 21:4–8).

[3] https://www.cartercenter.org/health/guinea_worm/case-totals.html

An anonymous painter made a tempera on canvas painting of Saint Roch somewhere between the end of 15th and the beginning of 16th century (currently at the picture gallery of Bari, Puglia, Italy). On the subject's left thigh, a white thin filament comes out of the lesion and almost reaches the knee. While previous art historians have always identified this element as a long drop of pus emerging outside of the infected wound, a new interpretation by Raffaele Gaeta (University of Pisa, Italy) and colleagues was the Guinea worm: "We believe instead that the painter portrayed an ancient case of dracunculiasis." Please see Figure 19.9 for the Saint Roch painting (Gaeta *et al.* 2017).

The classic act to remove the worm by winding it with a wooden stick was written in 1674 by Georgius Hieronymus Velschius. This practice of winding the worm out on a stick as a cure is still being practiced today. It has led to the concept on the rod of Asclepius (or staff of Asclepius). The Greek god Asclepius is associated with healing and medicine, and his staff is a serpent entwined rod. This rod may be confused with the Caduceus, the latter symbol is two snakes twisting around the two-winged staff.

In 1863 the British pathology professor Henry Charlton Bastian gave a first description of the Guinea worm and named it *Filaria medinensis*. In 1870, the Russian Aleksej Pavlovich Fedchenko identified the copepod (*Cyclops*) as its intermediate host. The observation was confirmed by Patrick Manson. In 1907 the British helminthologist Robert Thomson Leiper showed infected copepods were killed by acid but not the parasitic larvae. He further showed by feeding monkeys with banana containing infected copepods and later found adult worms in affected tissues. In 1913, the Indian bacteriologist Dyneshvar Atmaran Turkhud succeeded in infecting human volunteers by drinking water containing infected *Cyclops* (Kean *et al.* 1978). This work completes Koch's postulates; such work, of course, is definitely unethical by today's bioethics standards.

19.4.2 Life cycle

Please see Figure 19.10 for the life cycle, from CDC.[4]

Adult females can be 100 cm long, but males only 40 mm. Males die after mating, so they are not often seen. Females live in tissues, especially in lower extremities. The ovoviviparous females produce larvae, and cause blisters that will burst and release the larvae when in contact with water, for a soothing effect. Copepods such as *Cyclops* ingest the larvae, which molt to infective forms. Humans drink infected copepod-contaminated water and get Guinea worm disease.

19.4.3 Pathology

The worm leads to painful ulcers and blisters, and could be followed by secondary infections.

[4] https://www.cdc.gov/dpdx/dracunculiasis/index.html

Fig. 19.9 ■ Saint Roch. Anonymous painter, Pinacoteca di Bari, Italy. Tempera on canvas; 15th–16th century ca. Courtesy: Gaeta *et al. J Infect* 2017;74:519–21. Reproduced with permission from Elsevier.

Since the Guinea worm is close to eradication, clinical cases are few and far between. Indeed, South Sudan Guinea Worm Eradication Program, during surveillance activities in communities at-risk for cases of Guinea worm disease (dracunculiasis), found two females (23 and 24 years of age) living in two separate villages, each with a live worm emerging from their lower limbs. The worms measured 7 and 8 cm in length and were identified as fourth-stage larvae of *Eustrongylides*. This is the first report of such worms emerging from the skin; all five previous reports of human infection involved surgical removal of worms from the peritoneal cavity (Eberhard and Ruiz-Tiben 2014).

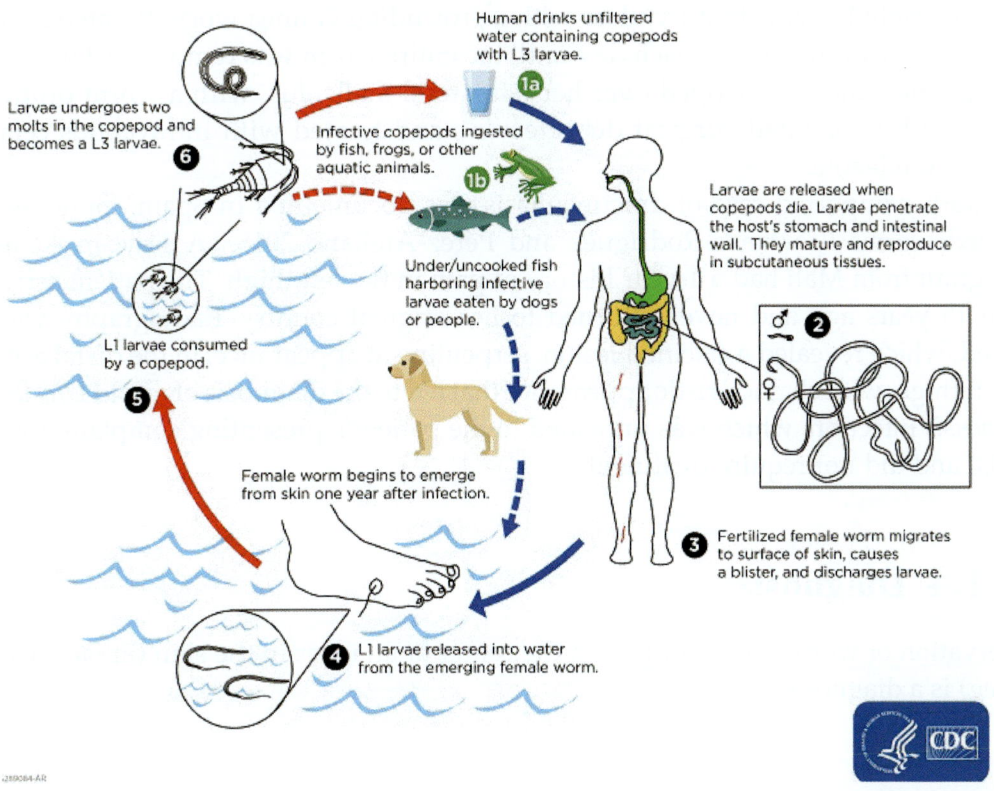

Fig. 19.10 ■ Life cycle of *Dracunculus medinensis*. Humans become infected by drinking unfiltered water containing copepods (small crustaceans) which are infected with larvae of *D. medinensis* 1. Following ingestion, the copepods die and release the larvae, which penetrate the host stomach and intestinal wall and enter the abdominal cavity and retroperitoneal space 2. After maturation into adults and copulation, the male worms die and the females (length: 70–120 cm) migrate in the subcutaneous tissues towards the skin surface 3. Approximately one year after infection, the female worm induces a blister on the skin, generally on the distal lower extremity, which ruptures. When this lesion comes into contact with water, a contact that the patient seeks to relieve the local discomfort, the female worm emerges and releases larvae 4. The larvae are ingested by a copepod 5 and after two weeks (and two molts) have developed into infective larvae 6. Ingestion of the copepods closes the cycle 1. Courtesy of the CDC. Reproduced from https://www.cdc.gov/dpdx/dracunculiasis/index.html

In India, the Rajasthan state was declared free from dracunculiasis in 1997, nevertheless a third case was reported in 2006 (previous two in 2002 and 2003). A 40-years-old male from a tribal village was admitted in the surgical ward with complaint of pain in his shallow ulcer on the left foot with an emerging gravid Guinea worm; the worm was surgically extracted (Choubisa *et al.* 2010).

An imported case of dracunculiasis was documented in USA (Spring and Spearman 1997). A 9-year-old girl from Sudan emigrated to Nashville, Tennessee, in September 1995. Her relocation was precipitated by the ongoing civil war in Sudan. Before arriving, she had a right lower extremity ulcer with a protruding Guinea worm (treated by winding the worm around a stick each day until the entire worm was removed); 3 weeks after arrival, a new ulcer developed over her left lateral malleolus, with a worm protruding from the ulcer. She had surgical debridement, and treated with intravenous cefazolin and metronidazole.

Another imported case of dracunculiasis was documented in Spain, found as dead calcified worms (Carranza-Rodríguez and Pérez-Arellano 2018). A 44-year-old female immigrant from Mali had a 1-year history of pain in the left thigh. The patient arrived in Spain 15 years ago and never returned to her original country. Radiography was performed, which revealed a calcified lesion, serpentine in appearance, in the distal aspect of her left thigh, with characteristic appearance that led to the diagnosis of an old *Dracunculus medinensis* infection, which was unrelated to the patient's presenting complaint (osteoarthritis) and did not require treatment.

19.4.4 Diagnosis

Observation of worm protruding from the center of an ulcer in the skin (in most cases in the leg) is a diagnosis.

19.4.5 Genome

According to the 81 worm genome publication, *Dracunculus medinensis* possesses **10,969** protein-coding genes (International Helminth Genomes Consortium 2019).

19.4.6 Towards eradication

Dracunculus medinensis is the only parasite that is potentially eradicable, via several approaches: (1) Supply of safe drinking water, such as wells; (2) Health education; (3) Early case containment; (4) Vector control, such as temephos (Abate) from American Cyanamid, a chemical that kills copepods at 1 part per million. DuPont has developed a nylon cloth specifically for Guinea worm copepod filtration.

In 1986, the estimate was 3.5 million cases in Africa, Middle East and Asia. A 20-year global dracunculiasis eradication program results in 99% reduction in incidence. Soon, about 25,000 cases remained, mostly in Sudan and Ghana. Annual total worldwide incidence was 892,055 in 1989, and 2,619 in 2008. There was a very successful global Dracunculiasis Eradication Program (DEP). Coordinated efforts by the Ministries of Health in endemic countries, the U.S. Centers for Disease Control (CDC), The Carter Center, and the World Health Organization (WHO) have reduced the number of annual Guinea worm cases from millions in the 1980s to hundreds in the early 2010s. Please see Figure 19.11 for eradication efforts (Hopkins *et al.* 2018).

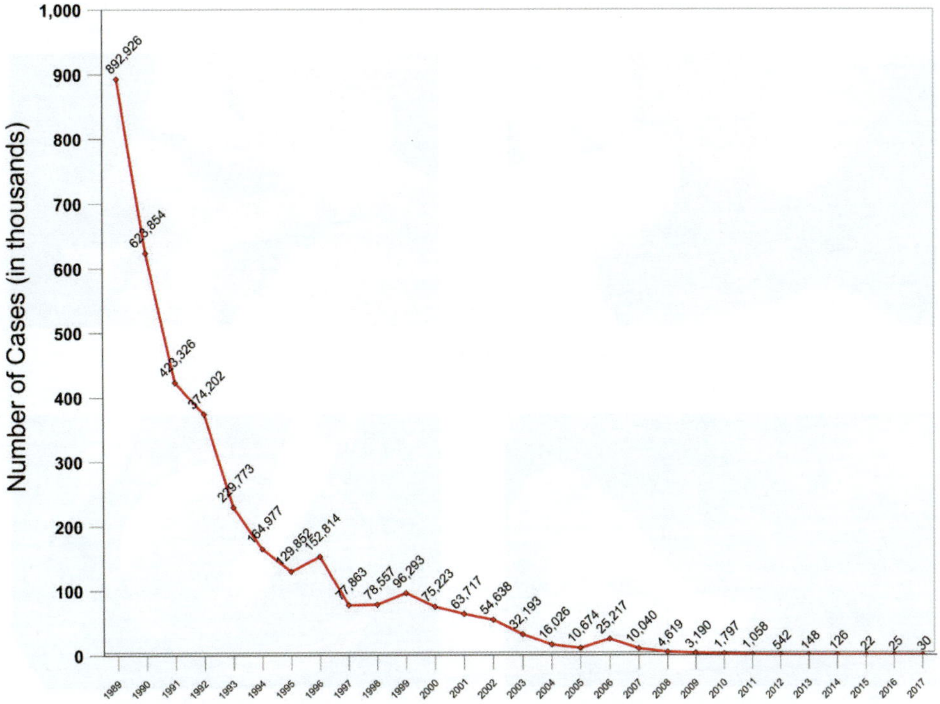

Fig. 19.11 ■ Guinea worm eradication. Number of reported cases of guinea worm disease in humans by year: 1989–2017. Courtesy: Hopkins *et al. Am J Trop Med Hyg* 2018;99:388–95. Reproduced with permission from *American Journal of Tropical Medicine and Hygiene.*

Efforts were spearheaded by Jimmy Carter and the Carter Center. In 1993 Pakistan became the first country to eradicate Guinea worm infection. Even in war-torn Sudan, Jimmy Carter managed to negotiate a 4-month Guinea worm ceasefire in 1995. Gates Foundation and others have funded these efforts by the Carter Center. (The last case of smallpox was recorded in Somalia in 1977, the world was certified smallpox free in 1981.) CDC was looking for a disease to conquer, and suggested Guinea worm disease as target because of relative low prevalence. In 1986 World Health Assembly adopted a resolution to eradicate dracunculiasis, and Jimmy Carter began to champion these efforts. It is the last hundreds of human infection that still stay around. Another concern is the finding of current epidemics in dogs (in Chad), as well as frogs as paratenic/transport host (Hopkins *et al.* 2018; Richards *et al.* 2020). Slightly over 1,000 cases were detected in 2016 and 2018, and over 800 cases for 2017 (Guagliardo *et al.* 2020). Please see Figure 19.12 for treatment of infected dogs (the same way as treating humans) (Guagliardo *et al.* 2020). This situation of canine Guinea worm disease must be mitigated for the eradication of human dracunculiasis.

Relatives of *Dracunculus medinensis* are found in North America, one being *D. insignis*. A study at a plantation site in the southeastern United States was done to evaluate the genetic diversity of parasites and investigate potential paratenic hosts that may be

Fig. 19.12 ■ Treating Guinea worm infected dogs in Chad. Worm extraction in dogs. The identification of pre-emergent worms (A) is challenging because blisters and worms are often obfuscated by dog fur. The "controlled immersion" technique (B) is performed by pouring water over the lesion (left) or submerging the lesion in a bucket of water (right) to allow female adult worms to release larvae within a contained environment. This water is then safely disposed of (e.g., poured on the ground away from any water sources). The worm is finally extracted (C) by gently pulling on the worm (left) or by wrapping it around a wetted gauze. A small stick is also sometimes used to initiate the process (right). Worm extraction in people can range from one day to 2–3 weeks, but Chad Guinea Worm Eradication Program (CGWEP) field staff have reported that worm extraction in dogs is typically quicker than in humans. (Photo credits: Robert Hartwig, The Carter Center.) Courtesy: Guagliardo *et al. PLoS Negl Trop Dis* 2020;14:e0008207.

involved in its transmission (Cleveland *et al.* 2020). *Dracunculus insignis* third-stage larvae were recovered from two different species of frogs (amphibians), but all fish sampled were negative. Adults were found in mammals (raccoon and opossum). "When applied to the global Guinea Worm Eradication Program, and Chad, Africa, in particular, this work increases our knowledge of the potential role of aquatic animals in the transmission of *Dracunculus* species and informs on potential intervention strategies that may be applied to the eradication of Guinea worm in Africa" (Cleveland *et al.* 2020).

Summary & Key Concepts

- *Loa loa* is carried by the day biting fly *Chrysops* and adults live in subcutaneous tissues including the skin and the eye, hence its name, the eye worm of Africa.
- *Onchocercus volvulus* is carried by the black fly *Simulium* and adults live in skin tissues as nodules; long term infection involving the eyes leads to river blindness, disease name reflecting preference for running water by the insect vector.
- MDA is a tool used to support the elimination of river blindness and other parasitic diseases.
- *Dracunculus medinensis* is carried by the crustacean copepod *Cyclops* and adults live in the skin tissues with female worms give viviparous larvae for release into the aquatic environment.
- The practice of winding the Guinea worm on a stick has been used from historical times to today; it is associated with the symbol of healing and medicine.
- Guinea worm disease is almost eradicated with only public health measures and no drug treatment.
- The bacterial endosymbiont *Wolbachia* is only found in *Onchocercus* but absent in the other two species of nematodes.

References

Boden KT, Pérez Guerra N, Szurman P, Simon A, Becker SL. Eosinophilia, iron deficiency anaemia and a subconjunctival worm in a girl from Cameroon. *Travel Med Infect Dis* 2019;29:84–5.

Bourguinat C, Kamgno J, Boussinesq M, *et al.* Analysis of the mdr-1 gene in patients co-infected with *Onchocerca volvulus* and *Loa loa* who experienced a post-ivermectin serious adverse event. *Am J Trop Med Hyg* 2010;83(1):28–32.

Bowler GS, Shah AN, Bye LA, *et al.* Ocular loiasis in London 2008-2009: A case series. *Eye (Lond)* 2011;25(3):389–91.

Carranza-Rodríguez C, Pérez-Arellano JL. Radiological detection of *Dracunculus medinensis*. *Am J Trop Med Hyg* 2018;98(5):12189.

Choubisa SL, Verma R, Choubisa L. Dracunculiasis in tribal region of southern Rajasthan, India: A case report. *J Parasit Dis* 2010;34(2):94–6.

Cleveland CA, Eberhard ML, Garrett KB, *et al. Dracunculus* Species in Meso-mammals from Georgia, United States, and implications for the guinea worm eradication program in Chad, Africa. *J Parasitol* 2020;106(5):616–22.

Colebunders R, Hendy A, van Oijen M. Nodding syndrome in onchocerciasis endemic areas. *Trends Parasitol* 2016;32(8):581–3.

Cotton JA, Bennuru S, Grote A, *et al.* The genome of *Onchocerca volvulus*, agent of river blindness. *Nat Microbiol* 2016;2:16216.

Cox FEG, editor.. *The Wellcome Trust Illustrated History of Tropical Diseases* (1996, The Wellcome Trust, London).

Desjardins CA, Cerqueira GC, Goldberg JM, *et al.* Genomics of *Loa loa*, a Wolbachia-free filarial parasite of humans. *Nat Genet* 2013;45(5):495–500.

Doyle SR, Bourguinat C, Nana-Djeunga HC, *et al.* Genome-wide analysis of ivermectin response by *Onchocerca volvulus* reveals that genetic drift and soft selective sweeps contribute to loss of drug sensitivity. *PLoS Negl Trop Dis* 2017;11(7):e0005816.

Eberhard ML, Ruiz-Tiben E. Cutaneous emergence of Eustrongylides in two persons from South Sudan. *Am J Trop Med Hyg* 2014;90(2):315–7.

Evans DS. Challenges to making the decision to stop mass drug administration for onchocerciasis: Lessons learned from Nigeria. *Am J Trop Med Hyg* 2020;102(3):485–6.

Feasey N, Wansbrough-Jones M, Mabey DC, Solomon AW. Neglected tropical diseases. *Br Med Bull.* 2010;93:179–200.

Foster JM, Landmann F, Ford L, *et al.* Absence of *Wolbachia endobacteria* in the human parasitic nematode *Dracunculus medinensis* and two related *Dracunculus* species infecting wildlife. *Parasit Vectors* 2014;7:140.

Gaeta R, Bruschi F, Giuffra V. The painting of St. Roch in the picture gallery of Bari (15th century): An ancient representation of dracunculiasis? *J Infect* 2017;74(5):519–21.

Guagliardo SAJ, Roy SL, Ruiz-Tiben E, *et al.* Guinea worm in domestic dogs in Chad: A description and analysis of surveillance data. *PLoS Negl Trop Dis* 2020;14(5):e0008207.

Gumisiriza N, Mubiru F, Siewe Fodjo JN, *et al.* Prevalence and incidence of nodding syndrome and other forms of epilepsy in onchocerciasis-endemic areas in northern Uganda after the implementation of onchocerciasis control measures. *Infect Dis Poverty* 2020;9(1):12.

Gyasi ME, Hong AR, Weil GJ. Motile *Onchocerca volvulus* microfilariae in the anterior chamber of the eye. *Am J Trop Med Hyg* 2020;102(5):921.

Hopkins DR, Ruiz-Tiben E, Eberhard ML, *et al.* Dracunculiasis eradication: Are we there yet? *Am J Trop Med Hyg* 2018;99(2):388–95.

Idro R, Opar B, Wamala J, *et al.* Is nodding syndrome an *Onchocerca volvulus*-induced neuroinflammatory disorder? Uganda's story of research in understanding the disease. *Int J Infect Dis* 2016;45:112–7.

International Helminth Genomes Consortium. Comparative genomics of the major parasitic worms. *Nat Genet* 2019;51(1):163–74.

Johnson TP, Sejvar J, Nutman TB, Nath A. The pathogenesis of nodding syndrome. *Annu Rev Pathol* 2020;15:395–417.

Johnson TP, Tyagi R, Lee PR, *et al.* Nodding syndrome may be an autoimmune reaction to the parasitic worm *Onchocerca volvulus. Sci Transl Med* 2017;9(377):eaaf6953.

Juul JA, Forsaa VA, Utheim TP, Willassen E. Scanning electron microscopy observations of *Loa loa* (Nematoda). *Case Rep Ophthalmol* 2020;11(2):486–92.

Kean BH, Mott KE, Russell AJ, editors. *Tropical Medicine and Parasitology: Classic Investigations*, volume I and II (1978, Cornell, Ithaca).

Metzger WG, Mordmüller B. *Loa loa*-does it deserve to be neglected? *Lancet Infect Dis* 2014;14(4):353–7.

Mouri O, Ezzine N, Haddad E, *et al*. New promising method to assess microfilarial *Loa loa* load on the peripheral blood. *Diagn Microbiol Infect Dis* 2019;95(4):114887.

Mwaka AD, Semakula JR, Abbo C, *et al*. Nodding syndrome: Recent insights into etiology, pathophysiology, and treatment. *Res Rep Trop Med* 2018;9:89–93.

Nauen DW, Haffner MC, Kim J, *et al*. Putative autoantigen leiomodin-1 Is expressed in the human brain and in the membrane fraction of newly formed neurons. *Pathogens* 2020;9(12):E1036.

Nava VE, Ejilemele AA. *Onchocerca volvulus* mimicking metastatic breast carcinoma. *Am J Trop Med Hyg* 2020;102(3):487–8.

Ndzeshang LB, Fombad FF, Njouendou AJ, *et al*. Generation of *Loa loa* infective larvae by experimental infection of the vector, *Chrysops silacea*. *PLoS Negl Trop Dis* 2020;14(8):e0008415.

Okonkwo ON, Hassan AO, Alarape T, *et al*. Removal of adult subconjunctival *Loa loa* amongst urban dwellers in Nigeria. *PLoS Negl Trop Dis* 2018;12(11):e0006920.

Olum S, Scolding P, Hardy C, *et al*. Nodding syndrome: A concise review. *Brain Commun* 2020;2(1):fcaa037.

O'Neill S, Irani J, Siewe Fodjo JN, *et al*. Stigma and epilepsy in onchocerciasis-endemic regions in Africa: A review and recommendations from the onchocerciasis-associated epilepsy working group. *Infect Dis Poverty* 2019;8(1):34.

Opoku NO, Bakajika DK, Kanza EM, *et al*. Single dose moxidectin versus ivermectin for *Onchocerca volvulus* infection in Ghana, Liberia, and the Democratic Republic of the Congo: A randomised, controlled, double-blind phase 3 trial. *Lancet* 2018;392(10154):1207–16. Erratum in: *Lancet* 2018;392(10154):1196.

Post R. The chromosomes of the Filariae. *Filaria J* 2005;4:10.

Priest DH, Nutman TB. Loiasis in US traveler returning from Bioko Island, Equatorial Guinea, 2016. *Emerg Infect Dis* 2017;23(1):160–2.

Richards FO, Eigege A, Umaru J, *et al*. The interruption of transmission of human onchocerciasis by an annual mass drug administration program in Plateau and Nasarawa States, Nigeria. *Am J Trop Med Hyg* 2020;102(3):582–92.

Richards RL, Cleveland CA, Hall RJ, *et al*. Identifying correlates of Guinea worm (*Dracunculus medinensis*) infection in domestic dog populations. *PLoS Negl Trop Dis* 2020;14(9):e0008620.

Spring M, Spearman P. Dracunculiasis: Report of an imported case in the United States. *Clin Infect Dis* 1997;25(3):749–50.

Tallon LJ, Liu X, Bennuru S, *et al*. Single molecule sequencing and genome assembly of a clinical specimen of *Loa loa*, the causative agent of loiasis. *BMC Genomics* 2014;15:788.

Tayeh A, Cairncross S, Cox FEG. Guinea worm: From Robert Leiper to eradication. *Parasitology* 2017;144(12):1643–8.

Taylor MJ, Hoerauf A, Bockarie M. Lymphatic filariasis and onchocerciasis. *Lancet* 2010;376(9747):1175–85.

Volpicelli L, De Angelis M, Morano A, *et al*. Encephalopathy in a patient with loiasis treated with albendazole: A case report. *Parasitol Int* 2020;75:102006.

Whittaker C, Walker M, Pion SDS, *et al*. *Loa loa*: More than meets the eye? *Trends Parasitol*. 2018;34(4):261–3.

Winzeler EA. Advances in parasite genomics: From sequences to regulatory networks. *PLoS Pathog* 2009;5(10):e1000649.

20

Soil-Transmitted Helminth Infections

20.1 Introductory Remarks

According to WHO, soil-transmitted helminth (STH) infections are found in over **1.5 billion** people worldwide (**24%** of the world's population), including over 267 million preschool-age children and over 568 million school-age children. Infections by these **geohelminths** are widely distributed in tropical and subtropical areas, with the greatest numbers occurring in sub-Saharan Africa, the Americas, China and East Asia.

The 3 major STHs are **roundworm** (*Ascaris*), **hookworm** (*Ancylostoma, Necator*) and **whipworm** (*Trichiura*). Peter Hotez (2013) mentioned that they were referred as "the unholy trinity" by the Columbia University parasitologist Harold Brown (1902–1988). STHs cause morbidity among the poor of the world population. A child may harbor all three species of worms at the same time. Both the roundworms and hookworms live in the small intestine, whereas the whipworms live in the large intestine. Roundworms are the most abundant among the three STHs. Hookworms cause the most damage, leading to iron-deficiency anemia. Morbidity can be assessed by disability adjusted life years (DALYs) (Jourdan *et al.* 2018; GBD 2017 DALYs and HALE Collaborators 2018).

For ascariasis by *Ascaris lumbricoides*, estimates are: DALY 861,000 to 1 million, deaths 3,000 to 60,000, global prevalence 804 million.

For trichuriasis by *Trichuris trichiura*, estimates are: DALY 213,000 to 500,000, deaths 3,000 to 10,000, global prevalence 477 million.

For hookworm infection by *Necator americanus* or *Ancylostoma duodenale*, estimates are: DALY 845,000 to 4 million, deaths 3,000 to 65,000, global prevalence 472 million.

Infections of ascariasis and trichuriasis are via the fecal-oral route with the intake of eggs, whereas hookworm infections commonly occur via skin penetration by the larvae (stage iL3). The same treatment is used for all STH infections, especially the benzimidazole drugs **albendazole** and **mebendazole**. Periodic mass drug administration (**MDA**) with these drugs to children in endemic areas has been ongoing, although there is a debate on the benefits of this action (Andrews *et al.* 2017). In lieu of MDA, WHO prefers the term preventive chemotherapy (**PC**) and advocates to control the STH infections by distributing albendazole or mebendazole to at-risk populations. "While the overall impact and sustainability of this strategy is disputed, a decrease in moderate and heavy STH infections can be largely attributed to a scale-up of drug distribution. Two factors might jeopardize the success of PC programs. First, the benzimidazoles possess unsatisfactory efficacy against *Trichuris trichiura* infections. Second, increased drug distributions might trigger anthelmintic resistance" (Schulz *et al.* 2018).

STH infections are diseases of poverty. With socioeconomic improvements in many countries, there is a corresponding decrease in these infections. As an example, from 1990 to 2003, STH-infected individuals in China decreased from 536 million to 129 million, showing a decrease of 71% in *Ascaris*, 74% in *Trichuris*, and 61% in hookworm infections (Li *et al.* 2010).

20.2 *Ascaris*

Ascaris lumbricoides is the largest nematode parasitizing the human intestine. Like most nematodes, the females are larger than the males. Females are 20–35 cm (may even reach 40 cm) whereas males are 15–30 cm in length. Because of its great size, abundance and cosmopolitan distribution, this roundworm may well be the first parasite known to humans. Ascariasis is the most common human helminthic infection. It is the world's most common neglected tropical disease (NTD). Children have a higher worm burden; the burden decreases at later ages. The same can be said for the whipworm, but it is not necessarily true for hookworm infection, where all ages can be infected. Chronic ascariasis in children impairs physical growth and development, and even mental capacity, because of parasite-induced malnutrition. Ascariasis leads to ill health and educational deficits.

The infection starts from ingestion of the roundworm eggs. *Ascaris* eggs are very resistant to a variety of chemicals. They can embryonate in 2% formalin, 50% hydrochloric, nitric, or sulfuric acids. Moreover, they survive for long periods of time in the environment. A study in Russia showed their 10-year survival in soil. Therefore, the eggs can contaminate fruits and vegetables. Paratenic hosts include cockroaches and chickens. One study found eggs in paper currencies used in Germany. The basis of this resistance is due to the protective shell containing the sugar **ascarylose**. The special sugar is seen in the lipid layer of the eggshell (containing 25% protein and 75% ascarosides). Ascarosides are glycosides of the sugar ascarylose (3,6-dideoxy-arabinohexose) linking to very long aliphatic side chains (made up with 29 or more carbons). The lipophilic ascarosides form a protective coating of *Ascaris* eggs against various harsh environmental conditions. However, the eggs are water permeable (Clarke and Perry 1980; Roberts *et al.* 2013). [We add here that other ascarosides, especially the smaller soluble ones (via attachment of different side chains to the sugar ascarylose), can serve as pheromones (multifunctional signaling molecules), including action during dauer stage of the free-living nematode *Caenorhabditis elegans* (reviewed by Park *et al.* 2019).]

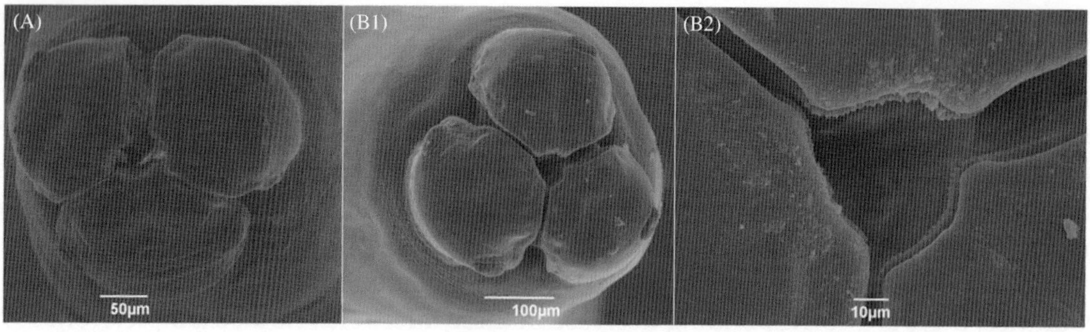

Fig. 20.1 ■ *Ascaris* mouth structure by scanning electron microscopy. Scanning electron micrographs of the buccal orifice of two adult Ascaris specimens obtained from pig necropsy in the city of Teresina, state of Piauí. (A) Six-sided hexagonal shape of the buccal orifice, due to indentations in the three lips. (B1) Two lips have indentations and the third is almost straight. (B2) At higher magnification, the triangular shape of the denticules is observed. Courtesy: Monteiro *et al. PLoS One* 2019;14:e0218867. Reproduced with permission from *PLoS One* with Creative Commons Attribution 4.0 (CC-BY) International License.

Origins of this large roundworm have been postulated. It is possible that *Ascaris* was originally a parasite of pigs, which became adapted to humans when swines were first domesticated. Alternatively, this could be a human parasite that we gave to the swines. For most parasitologists, the human species is *Ascaris lumbricoides*; the pig species is *Ascaris suum*. However, some have suggested the two are the same: "*A. suum* Goeze 1782 should be considered a synonym of *A. lumbricoides* 1758" (Leles *et al.* 2012). A total of 40 ascariasis cases were reported in the state of Maine, United States from 2010 to 2013, with direct or indirect contact with pigs as the single common factor. For one farm in particular, "the timing of illness among the farm workers was consistent with acquisition of *Ascaris* infection from pigs" (Miller *et al.* 2015). Please see Figure 20.1 for *Ascaris* mouth (buccal orifice) by scanning electron microscopy; the worms were isolated from pigs in Brazil (Monteiro *et al.* 2019).

20.2.1 History

For ascariasis, its name *Ascaris lumbricoides* (askaris means intestinal worm, lumbricoides means like lumbicus) was coined by Carl Linnaeus in 1758 (he named a total of six worms), for its resemblance to the common earthworm, *Lumbricus terrestrias*. *Ascaris* eggs were found in human coprolites from Peru dating at 2277 BC, Egyptian mummies dating 1938 BC, and human remains from Ming dynasty China at 1368 AD. In 1683, the Oxford-educated physician Edward Tyson described worm anatomy; he recognized male and female roundworms. The same description was provided by the Italian Francisco Redi in 1684 (famous for his disproval of the theory of spontaneous generation). In 1881, the

Italian scientist Giovanni Battista Grassi infected himself with 100 embryonated eggs and found eggs in his feces 22 days later. In 1916, the Scottish physician Francis Hugh Stewart (working in Hong Kong) fed *Ascaris* eggs from pigs to experimental rats and later dissected the rats to find larvae in their lungs. Stewart wrote: "Ascariasis, both in man and the pig, is of extraordinary frequency in the colony of Hong Kong and in South China generally. I therefore, while stationed in this colony, has an unusual opportunity of studying the subject." In 1922, the Japanese pediatrician Shimesu Koino infected himself and his 21-year-old younger brother. The brother got 500 mature eggs from *Ascaris suum*, the pig species; he gave himself 2,000 *A. lumbricoides* eggs. He found large numbers of larvae in his sputum from days 3 to 11, thus discovering *Ascaris* pneumonitis. He became very sick, took anthelmintic at day 50, ending with the release of 667 worms; he fortunately recovered (Kean *et al.* 1978; Cox 1996).

Human infections by *Ascaris* and other helminths have been identified in archaeological samples. In an analysis of 589 grave samples from seven European sites (Britain, Germany & the Czech Republic) dated between 680 and 1700 CE (Medieval Europe), all seven sites showed evidence for *Ascaris* and *Trichuris*. In addition, from four sites there was evidence of cestodes that humans acquire from eating undercooked red meat (*Taenia* spp.) or freshwater fish (*Diphyllobothrium latum*). "The rates of nematode infection in the medieval populations (1.5–25.6% for *T. trichiura*; 9.3–42.9% for *Ascaris* spp.) were comparable to those reported within modern endemically infected populations ... It is noteworthy that helminths were endemic in historical Europe but were eradicated prior to the development of modern drugs" (Flammer *et al.* 2020). In sum, human-helminth association has a long historical record.

20.2.2 Life cycle

Please see Figure 20.2 for the life cycle, from CDC.[1]

A female can lay 200,000 eggs a day. Its uterus has 27 million eggs at one time. Eggs are passed with feces. Only the fertilized eggs embryonate in moist, warm, and shaded soil. They become infective larvae inside eggs in 2–4 weeks. After ingestion, larvae hatch from eggs, invade the small intestinal mucosa, enter circulation to the lungs (filter out by capillaries of alveoli), where they molt and mature further for another 2 weeks or so, larvae enter the throat where they are swallowed, and reach intestine to mature to adults.

Larval migration of *Ascaris* starts in the intestine and ends back in the intestine: they end up where they begin. Hypotheses have been developed to explain the phenomenon. The route may simulate the ancient migration in an intermediate host. The parasite derived from two-hosts to end up with one-host, but retained the migratory pattern. Another possibility is the selection of a stronger and fitter parasite via the migration, enabling a roundworm with high fecundity and fast growth.

[1] https://www.cdc.gov/dpdx/ascariasis/index.html

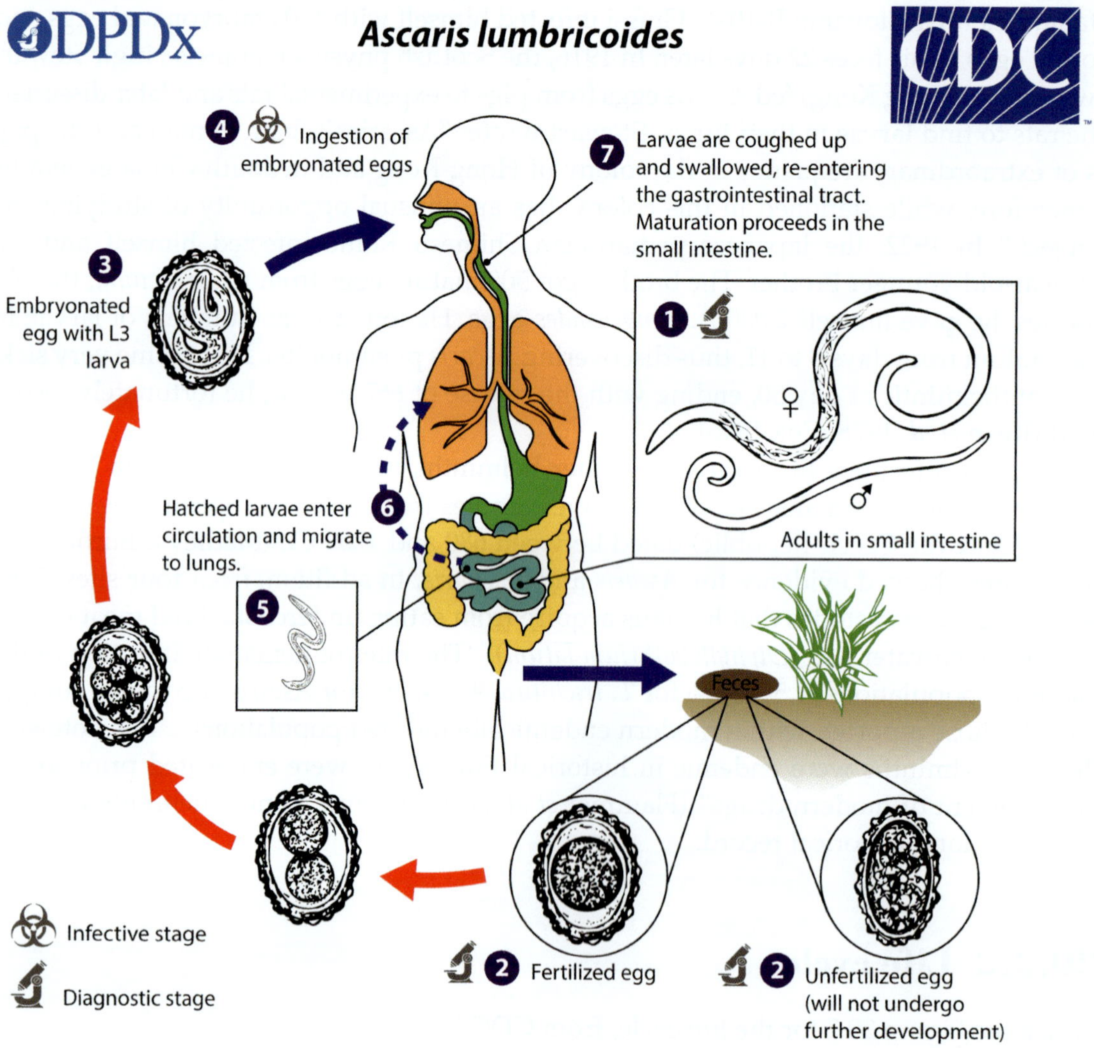

Fig. 20.2 ■ Life cycle of *Ascaris lumbricoides*. Adult worms ❶ live in the lumen of the small intestine. A female may produce approximately 200,000 eggs per day, which are passed with the feces ❷. Unfertilized eggs may be ingested but are not infective. Larvae develop to infectivity within fertile eggs after 18 days to several weeks ❸, depending on the environmental conditions (optimum: moist, warm, shaded soil). After infective eggs are swallowed ❹, the larvae hatch ❺, invade the intestinal mucosa, and are carried via the portal, then systemic circulation to the lungs ❻. The larvae mature further in the lungs (10–14 days), penetrate the alveolar walls, ascend the bronchial tree to the throat, and are swallowed ❼. Upon reaching the small intestine, they develop into adult worms. Between 2 and 3 months are required from ingestion of the infective eggs to oviposition by the adult female. Adult worms can live 1–2 years. Courtesy of the CDC. Reproduced from https://www.cdc.gov/dpdx/ascariasis/index.html

20.2.3 Pathology

Pathology depends on the number of worms. The larval migratory phase causes pneumonitis and eosinophilia. Clinical symptoms of cough, difficult breathing, hemoptysis, eosinophilic pneumonitis are known as **Loeffler's syndrome**, after the Swiss doctor Wilhelm Loeffler (1887–1972) who described eosinophilic pneumonia caused by parasites including *Ascaris* in 1932. The adult intestinal phase with many roundworms can lead to intestinal obstruction. The adult worms can cause hepatobiliary and pancreatic ascariasis, as well as neonatal ascariasis if the worm enters the placenta.

The natural habitat of *Ascaris lumbricoides* is usually in the jejunum, but they can migrate to the biliary tract, causing biliary colic, obstructive jaundice, and cholelithiasis (formation of gallstones). In Korea, a total of 1,198 cases of biliary ascariasis were reported between 1955 and 1989, accounting for over 90% of the overall surgical ascariasis patients (with a subsequent decrease, only 3 case reports since then). A case of biliary ascariasis in a 72-year-old male was documented in 2015. The patient visited the emergency room of a university hospital with complaints of right-upper-quadrant pain. "By endoscopic retrograde cholangiopancreatography (ERCP), a tubular filling defect in the right hepatic duct was detected. The defect was endoscopically removed and diagnosed as an adult female of *Ascaris lumbricoides* worm, of 30 cm length. Upon removal of the worm, the pain subsided, and the patient was discharged without any complication. When treating cases of biliary colic, physicians should not neglect biliary ascariasis as the possible cause" (Choi and Seo 2017).

20.2.4 Diagnosis

Microscopic examination of eggs in the stool is used for diagnosis, because of unique morphology of the eggs. Worms may also be found in the feces.

20.2.5 Therapy

The drugs are **benzimidazole** compounds that target microtubules, notably albendazole and mebendazole. Treatment is the same for all three STH infections.

20.2.6 Genome

From the draft genome of *Ascaris suum*, the roundworm possesses **18,542** protein-coding genes, including excretory/secretory (**E/S**) proteins (775 proteins) (Jex *et al*. 2011). A total of 456 proteases are predicted, with 68 secreted proteases. E/S proteins may play roles in host-parasite interactions. Proteases, protease inhibitors and other proteins may be functional in tissue invasion and immune modulation. Some can be mimics of host proteins for host immune evasion. One example is an IgE receptor. One secreted leucine aminopeptidase may have immunomodulatory activity to induce alternatively activated macrophages (AAMs) and Th2 host immune response. In addition, genes include 272 voltage-gated ion channels (for drugs ivermectin and levamisole) and 98 ligand-gated ion channels (for drug monepantel). A later genomic study has included both *Ascaris suum* and *Ascaris lumbricoides* (Wang *et al.* 2017). The two genomes are highly similar, with over **99%** sequence identity.

20.2.7 Chromatin diminution

One interesting aspect of the roundworm and related species is chromatin diminution. This is **programmed DNA elimination** during development, namely a loss of repetitive sequences and germline-expressed genes in somatic cells (Wang *et al.* 2017). Whereas the *Ascaris* germline genome codes for 18,025 genes, its **soma** genomes codes for 17,102 genes. About 5% DNA coding for about **1,000** germline-expressed genes are eliminated during embryogenesis. In addition to the loss of germline specific genes, there is also loss of repetitive DNA (9% or 30 Mb of genome containing 120 bp sequences). It has been proposed that, in order for this process to occur, there is a sequence-independent mechanism for DNA breakage to be followed by telomere healing. The DNA breakage regions are the same for *Ascaris suum* and *A. lumbricoides*. Please see Figure 20.3 for chromatin diminution (Wang *et al.* 2017).

The phenomenon of chromatin diminution has a long history. It was first discovered by the developmental biologist Theodor Boveri in 1887, using the horse nematode *Parascaris equorum*. The nuclei retaining the original complete chromosomes became germline cells, and all somatic cells had chromatin diminution (known as programmed DNA elimination today). Besides the roundworms mentioned here, it is found in other nematodes, including *Strongyloides* and *Toxicara* (species to be discussed in Chapters 21 and 22, respectively). The phenomenon has also been seen in other multicellular organisms, including copepods (invertebrates) and lampreys (vertebrates). DNA elimination may be viewed as a novel form of gene silencing, dosage compensation, and sex determination (Wang and Davis 2014).

20.3 *Trichuris*

For trichuriasis, the whipworm possesses a structure known as **stichosome** in the anterior portion of esophagus. The stichosome consists of a row of cells (known as stichocytes) each of which partially or completely encloses the esophagus and serves secretory function (as unicellular glands). In addition, the bacillary band, consists of tall columnar cells, forms a thin layer covering the esophagus (Steffield 1963). In the adult, a total of 50,000 bacillary cells serve the function of absorption of molecules from the intestinal epithelium (Tilney *et al.* 2005). The stichosome is also found in *Trichinella* (to be discussed in Chapter 21). The name ***Trichuris trichiura*** (trichos means hair; oura means tail) refers to the human parasite. It has no animal reservoir. Other whipworm species infect other animals,

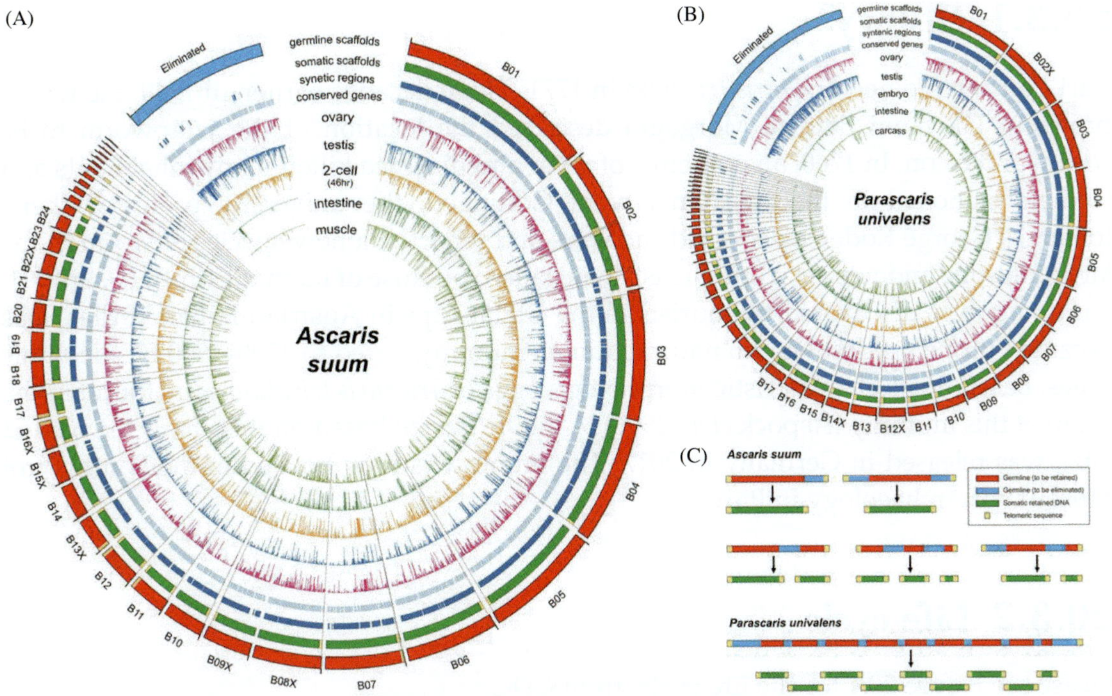

Fig. 20.3 ■ Programmed DNA elimination. *Ascaris* and *Parascaris* programmed DNA elimination genome changes. (A) Breakpoints and eliminated sequences in *Ascaris*. Illustrated are *Ascaris* genomic regions (scaffolds) that are partially or completely eliminated (blue in germline scaffold ring). Scaffolds with DNA breakpoints are shown in red within the germline scaffolds ring (the largest outer circle). The positions for the 40 identified DNA break regions are shown as black lines connecting the largest and smallest circles. Genomic regions (scaffolds) eliminated were concatenated for illustration and are shown as a blue block (ring). The somatic scaffolds track indicates the retained somatic sequences. Telomeres are indicated as yellow boxes. Note that all breaks are healed by new telomere addition. The syntenic regions and conserved genes between *Ascaris* and *Parascaris* are illustrated in the light blue ring/track. Gene transcript levels (derived from RNA-seq data) for the germline, two-cell embryo, and several somatic tissues are illustrated in the inner circles. Note the high level of RNA expression in the testis corresponding to DNA eliminated regions. In addition, a few of the eliminated genes (six out of 921) appear to be expressed in the soma due to paralogous genes that are retained or to low level contamination of highly expressed germline genes. (B) Breakpoints and eliminated sequences in *Parascaris*. Circle plots are not drawn to scale. (C) DNA elimination at the chromosome level in *Ascaris* and *Parascaris*. Courtesy: Wang *et al. Genome Res* 2017;27:2001–14. Reproduced with permission from *Genome Research* with Creative Commons Attribution 4.0 (CC-BY) International License.

such as ***Trichuris suis*** for pigs, *Trichuris ovis* for sheep and *Trichuris muris* for mice. The adult parasite resembles a whip with a handle, from the thin long thread anterior to thicker posterior. However, the name is a misnomer, because the thinner thread is the anterior end (the head). The correct name should be ***Trichocephalus*** (trichos means hair; cephalo means head). Some parasitologists did use *Trichocephalus*, but *Trichuris* takes precedence. It came first in the game of naming species.

20.3.1 History

Carl Linnaeus coined *Trichuris trichiura* in 1771. Three decades earlier, in 1740, the Italian professor Giovanni Battista Morgagni described the location of the whipworm to be cecum and colon. In 1760, an epidemic of fever and diarrhea killed many inhabitants and soldiers stationed in the German city of Gottingen, the university professor there, Johannes George Roderer dissected cadavers and reported a new species of worm in the large intestine and named it "trichuris" (hair-tailed) because of its shape (in 1761). In 1991, a mummy was discovered by tourists in the Otztal Alps in Austrian-Italian border. This became Europe's oldest known natural human mummy, dated to 3200–3300 BC Neolithic times. Based on its characteristic morphology, eggs of *Trichuris trichiura* were found in the colon of this mummy (Aspock *et al*. 1996). A movie *Iceman* based on this character, named Otzi, was released in Germany in 2017. The mummy is now housed in the South Tyrol Museum of Archaeology in Italy.

20.3.2 Life cycle

Please see Figure 20.4 for the life cycle, from CDC.[2]

The whipworm infection is via the fecal-oral route, same as the roundworm. Eggs possess the unique shape, like an American football with both bulged ends. After ingestion, embryonated eggs hatch and release the larvae in the small intestine. Larvae matures and live in the colon and cecum as 4-cm long adults. Adults have a lifespan of 1–2 years (extreme case of 8 years was also known).

Please see Figure 20.5A for *Trichuris trichiura* embryonated egg (Izurieta *et al*. 2018).[3] Please see Figure 20.5B for adult *Trichuris trichiura* as detected by colonoscopy, from CDC.[2]

20.3.3 Pathology

Like other STHs, total worm number is important. Under 100, there can be asymptomatic. For children with heavy infection (200–1,000 worms), there can be bloody diarrhea, abdominal pain, anemia, and even rectal prolapse. Chronic infections cause malnutrition and stunting in children.

A case of incidental diagnosis of trichuriasis was documented in Italy (Peradotto *et al*. 2012). The 52-year-old HIV-positive male, with a family history of colorectal cancer, had a routine colonoscopy. The endoscopy showed the presence of a small whitish, motile nematode in the cecal region; the worm's DNA sample by PCR sequencing of mitochon-

[2] https://www.cdc.gov/dpdx/trichuriasis/index.html

[3] https://www.waterpathogens.org/book/trichuris-trichiura%C2%A0

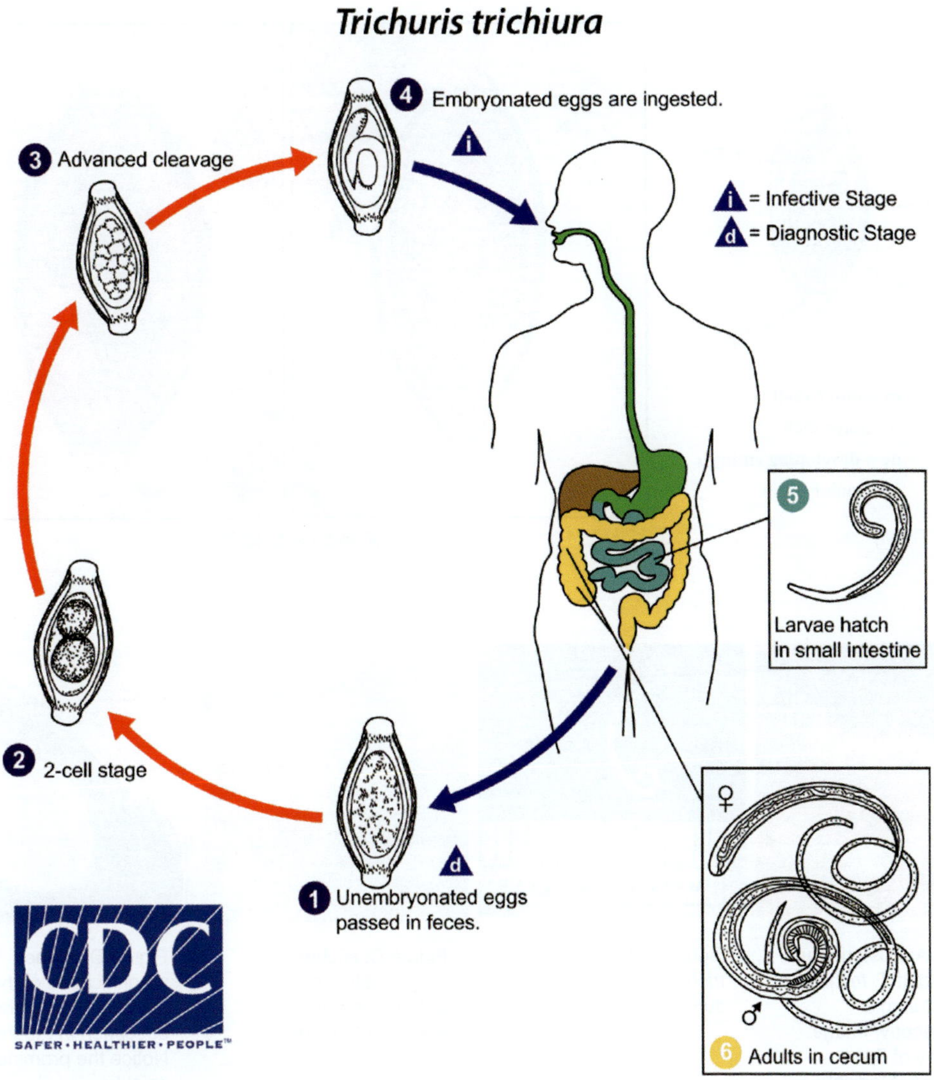

Fig. 20.4 ■ Life cycle of *Trichuris trichiura*. The unembryonated eggs are passed with the stool ❶. In the soil, the eggs develop into a 2-cell stage ❷, an advanced cleavage stage ❸, and then they embryonate ❹; eggs become infective in 15–30 days. After ingestion (soil-contaminated hands or food), the eggs hatch in the small intestine, and release larvae ❺ that mature and establish themselves as adults in the colon ❻. The adult worms (approximately 4 cm in length) live in the cecum and ascending colon. The adult worms are fixed in that location, with the anterior portions threaded into the mucosa. The females begin to oviposit 60–70 days after infection. Female worms in the cecum shed between 3,000 and 20,000 eggs per day. The life span of the adults is about 1 year. Courtesy of the CDC. Reproduced from https://www.cdc.gov/dpdx/trichuriasis/index.html

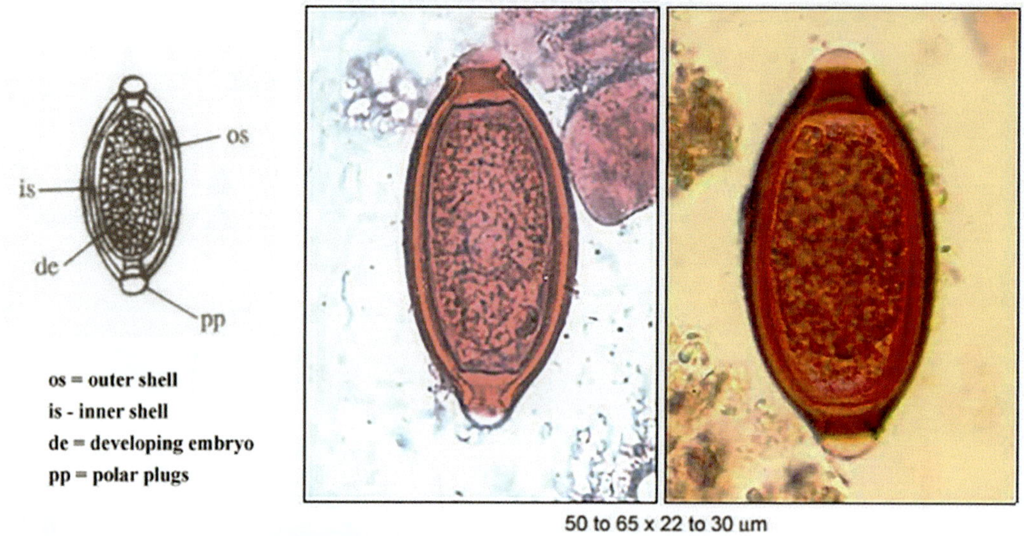

(A)

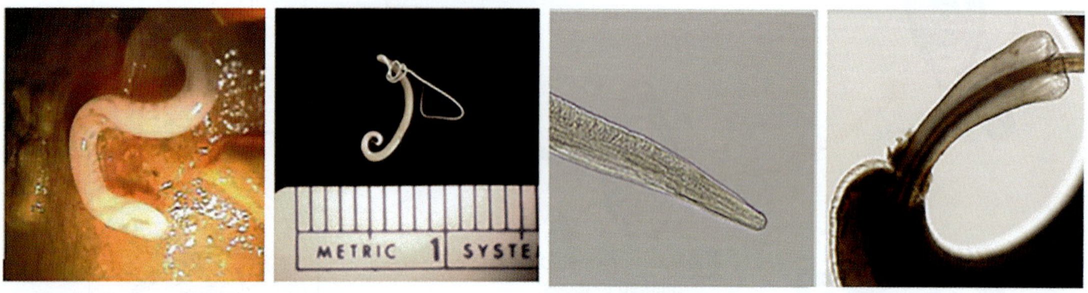

Figure A: Posterior end of an adult *T. trichiura*, taken during a colonoscopy. Image courtesy of Duke University Medical Center.

Figure B: Adult if *T. trichiura* removed during a colonoscopy.

Figure C: Higher magnification of the anterior end of the speciment in Figure B.

Figure D: Higher magnification of the posterior end of the specimen in Figure B. Notice the prominent spicule.

(B)

Fig. 20.5 ■ *Trichuris* morphology. (A) *Trichuris trichiura* embryonated egg. *Trichuris trichiura* ova structure. (Courtesy of University of South Florida Donald Price Center). Reproduced from https://www.waterpathogens.org/book/trichuris-trichiura%C2%A0 with permission from UNESCO with Creative Commons Attribution 3.0 (CC-BY) International License. (B) **Adult *Trichuris trichiura* as detected by colonoscopy.** Adult males of *Trichuris trichiura* are 30–45 mm long, with a coiled posterior end. Adult females are 35–50 mm with a straight posterior end. Both sexes have a long, whip-like anterior end. Adults reside in the large intestine, cecum and appendix of the host. Courtesy of the CDC. Reproduced from https://www.cdc.gov/dpdx/trichuriasis/index.html

drial cytochrome *b* identified it to be *Trichura* sp. and the patient was prescribed oral albendazole. This patient resided in a non-endemic area (Turin, Italy); he admitted frequent raw fish consumption during a trip to Antigua 6 months before colonoscopy (thus brought himself "an unpleasant souvenir"). "Overall, this case highlights the importance of improving parasitic diseases diagnosis through cutting-edge clinical and laboratory diagnostic tools alongside advanced training of specialists in the area of parasitology" (Peradotto *et al.* 2021).

Adult *Trichuris trichiura* worms have been detected by sigmoidoscopy (Niyas *et al.* 2019). The procedure was performed on a 30-year-old female from Kerala, India who had diarrhea and fever for 2 weeks. After whipworm detection the patient was treated with albendazole.

20.3.4 Diagnosis

Detection of eggs or worms in the stool is used as the diagnosis. The eggs show unique morphology distinguishable from other parasites. Colonoscopy is also available for worm detection.

20.3.5 Therapy

The drugs are benzimidazole compounds that target microtubules, albendazole and mebendazole, the same as other STH infections.

20.3.6 *Trichuris* as potential therapy

One interesting aspect is the application of *Trichuris* to treat autoimmune disorders, as seen in reports using *Trichuris suis* ova (**TSO** from the pig whipworm) for patients of inflammatory bowel disease (IBD), multiple sclerosis, and even autism. TSOs are commercially available from the German company OvaMed. There is a study of TSO therapy of Crohn's disease, using 2,500 live TSOs every 3 weeks for 24 weeks, with positive response in 79% patients (total of 23) (Summers *et al.* 2005a). A similar study was done for ulcerative colitis, using 2,500 live TSOs every 2 weeks for 12 weeks, with positive responses for 43% of patients (13 out of 30 total) (Summers *et al.* 2005b). In an article titled "Opening a can of worms," with a sample size of 1, the highly autistic 13-year-old Lawrence Johnson of Brooklyn, New York, was treated with TSOs and had decreased symptoms (no more bashing his head against the wall) (Grant 2011). A clinical trial has shown safety profile in treating 7,500 TSOs to humans (Sandborn *et al.* 2013). From genomes and transcriptomes of *T. suis*, potential gene products that can target inflammation have been identified (Cantacessi *et al.* 2011). These molecules should be more attractive in lieu of the whole fertilized egg.

Since TSOs have been applied to humans, the relationship between human and pig whipworms is of interest. Based on ribosomal DNA ITS sequence comparison, the helminth that infects primates and swines are different species (Cutillas *et al.* 2009). By analyzing specific mitochondrial genes for phylogenetic relationship from samples from different regions from humans, pigs and baboons, it has been proposed for an African origin of *Trichuris trichiura* that was transmitted to human ancestors in Asia and further to South America. A host shift to pigs possibly occurred in Asia and *T. suis* was then transmitted worldwide (Hawash *et al.* 2016).

20.3.7 Genome

The chromosomes of whipworms have a haploid number $n = 4$, with **XX-XO** sex determination mechanism (females are diploid with 8 chromosomes and XX; males are diploid with 7 chromosomes and XO) (Goswami 1978). Several draft genomes of whipworms are known, *Trichuris trichiura, T. muris* (Foth *et al.* 2014) and *T. suis* (Jex *et al.* 2014). *Trichuris trichiura* possesses **9,650** protein-coding genes, whereas *T. muris* codes for 11,004 genes. For *Trichuris suis*, the male codes for 14,781 genes, whereas the female codes for 14,470 genes. From the genome of *T. trichiura*, there is an expansion of chymotrypsin A-like **serine proteases** (75 genes). This is the single largest group of proteases of the human whipworm. There are 111 genes for protease inhibitors, including secretary leukocyte proteinase inhibitors (**SLPIs**) that may exert immunomodulatory, anti-inflammatory properties for innate immunity and wound healing. Transcriptomes have been analyzed in the whipworms. DNase II-like proteins are expressed in the anterior region of the worm, they may be functional in host DNA degradation during tissue invasion (in order to limit host immune response to undigested host DNA). Males express major sperm protein (**MSP**) used in the amoeboid movement of the nematode sperm. The pig whipworm genome is "the first study to characterize the genomes of male and female individuals of a dioecious nematode" (Jex *et al.* 2014). How the whipworm modulates the host immune response is a key area for study, especially in the light of its potential therapeutic applications in anti-inflammatory therapy.

20.4 Hookworms

Among the hookworms infecting humans and sucking human blood, the two major species are ***Ancylostoma duodenale*** (ankylos means hook-like, stoma means mouth, duodenale means duodenum) and ***Necator americanus*** (Necator means killer, americanus means American). It is believed that *A. duodenale* originated in Asia and *N. americanus* originated in Africa, but there are overlaps in species distribution. Today, *Necator americanus* is the most common species in humans in most parts of the world, but *Ancylostoma duodenale* is the more severe species in human infections. The two species can be differentiated by their mouth parts: two pair of teeth (four **teeth**) for *Ancylostoma duodenale* and two semi-lunar shaped **cutting plates** for *Necator americanus*. A zoonotic species *Ancylostoma ceylanicum* infects cats, dogs and humans in Asia (Traub 2013).

MDA has been practiced for hookworm infections, sometimes together with related activities, especially **Footwear** Campaign and water, sanitation, and hygiene (**WASH**) interventions. "Historically, successful STH elimination has only been achieved in regions with concomitant significant economic growth. Since 2001, control of the STHs has been attempted via single-dose mass deworming of at-risk school-aged and preschool-aged children within STH-endemic countries, with the goal of morbidity reduction. Research questioning this strategy has grown in recent years, and current studies are evaluating the effectiveness of novel deworming strategies, including multidrug regimens and expansion of deworming to entire communities. While footwear campaigns may be associated with reduced odds of hookworm infection, the evidence supporting the impact of WASH interventions upon hookworm is mixed" (Haldeman *et al.* 2020).

20.4.1 History

Human infections by hookworm in the Old World have been ongoing for over 5,000 years. Whether the hookworm in the Americas came before or after Christopher Columbus, or due to slave trade from Africa, is highly debated. However, there are ova and eggs of hookworm found in coprolite dated from 3,350 BC to 480 AD in the Americas. A case of hookworm infection in a 900 AD Tiahuanaco mummy from the coastal southern Peru was determined likely to be *Ancylostoma duodenale* (by morphology); the investigators wrote: "This is the first reported case of hookworm infestation in the Americas prior to the coming of Europeans" (Allison *et al.* 1974).

Papyrus record in ancient Egypt and the work of Hippocrates had recorded symptoms of hookworm infection, namely intestinal disorders and yellow skin pallor (color, due to anemia). Yellow pallor in miners was noted by Lucretius in 50 BC. The real connection between hookworm disease and miners was established by the Italian veterinarian Edoardo Perroncito in 1880, during the building of Saint Gothard tunnel (linking Switzerland and Italy in the Swiss Alps). Feces from contaminated workers allowed spread of infection. Conditions in mines and tunnels favored hookworm larval development: warm and damp. Strict hygiene control prevented infection. In 1904 the famous British scientist J.B.S. Haldane reported workers in a tin mine in Cornwall with 95% infection and 5% anemia. This finding led to the British Home Secretary to rule that buckets be provided in mines to forbid indiscriminate defecation (Cox 1996).

The link between hookworm infection and anemia was first proposed by the German physician Wilhelm Griesinger working in Cairo in 1854. He noted the presence of "*Ancylostoma duodenale* … in Egypt … often the worm itself, engorged with blood … the involved section of the intestine is often filled with blood from the numerous wound … as 'Egyptian chlorosis'…." However, iron-deficiency anemia linking to hookworms was not accepted until confirmation made by Otto Wucherer in 1866, from Brazil: the cause of tropical anemia was infection by hookworms (Kean *et al.* 1978).

Hookworm larvae transmission via the skin route was investigated by Arthur Looss, working in Egypt. In 1898, he accidentally dropped larvae on his hand when orally feeding larvae to guinea pigs. He felt an itch, had reddish skin, and then looked for eggs in his own feces, which he found after several weeks. In 1901 a 13-year-old Egyptian boy needed his leg amputated. Before this process Looss put infective larvae on the leg; afterwards, he found penetration of worm larvae into skin of the boy's leg. This became the discovery of cutaneous route of infection. In 1911, Looss described a new species collected from a civet cat in Ceylon (now Sri Lanka) and named the hookworm *Ancylostoma ceylanicum*.

The presence of the actual worm in the intestines was credited to the Persian physician Avicenna in 1000. The Italian physician Angelo Dubini first described hookworms from autopsy of a peasant woman in Milan, in 1843 and named *Agchyostoma duodenale* (today's *Ancylostoma duodenale*). The American zoologist Charles Wendell Stiles described a new species, the new world hookworm and named *Uncinaria americana* (today's *Necator americanus*), in 1902. At that time, hookworm infection was common in southern United States and Puerto Rico. Stiles convinced Frederick Gates, a Baptist minister, to convince John D. Rockefeller to donate $1 million in 1909 to set up the Rockefeller Sanitary Commission for the Eradication of Hookworm Disease (RSC). Gates also advised in the setting up of the Rockefeller Foundation. There was the Rockefeller Institute for Medical Research, which later became the Rockefeller University. With the aim to eradicate the hookworm, there was indeed a decrease in hookworm infection. Actually, this was due to economic development (no more poverty) rather than commission efforts. However, this event also resulted in the establishment of schools of public health in the United States, with the flagship school of public health at Johns Hopkins University.

The Rockefeller donation, announced on October 28, 1909, was known to the American writer and humorist Mark Twain, pen name of Samuel Clemens (1835–1910).[4] Twain, author of *Adventures of Huckleberry Finn* (1884),[5] wrote about hookworm in *Letters from the Earth* (1909), posthumously published as collated by Bernard DeVoto (in 1962). Taking a sarcastic look at religion and morality, Twain commented on the hookworm disease: "The very latest of these blessed triumphs of science is the discovery and identification of the ambuscaded assassin which goes by the name of the hookworm ... The disease induced by the hookworm had been doing its evil work here and there in the earth ever since Shem landed on Ararat, but it was never suspected to *be* a disease at all. The people who had it were merely supposed to be *lazy*, and were therefore despised and made fun of, when they should have been pitied. The hookworm is a peculiarly sneaking and underhanded invention ... God is back of this. He has been thinking about it for six thousand years, and making up his mind. The idea of exterminating the hookworm was his. He came very near doing it before Dr. Charles Wardell Stiles did. But he is in time to get the credit of it. He always is. It is going to cost a mil-

[4] https://en.wikipedia.org/wiki/Mark_Twain

[5] https://contentserver.adobe.com/store/books/HuckFinn.pdf

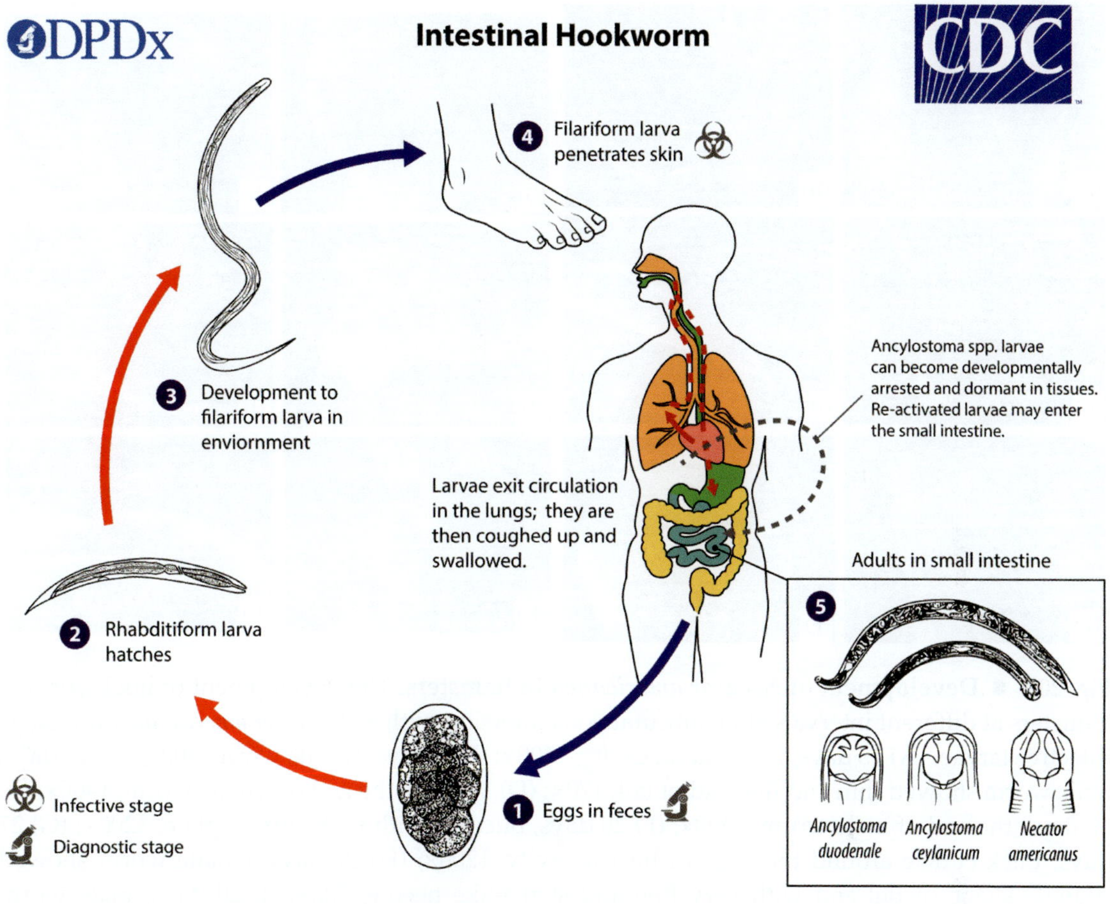

Fig. 20.6 ■ Life cycle of intestinal hookworms. Eggs are passed in the stool ❶, and under favorable conditions (moisture, warmth, shade), larvae hatch in 1–2 days and become free-living in contaminated soil. These released rhabditiform larvae grow in the feces and/or the soil ❷, and after 5–10 days (and two molts) they become filariform (third-stage) larvae that are infective ❸. These infective larvae can survive 3–4 weeks in favorable environmental conditions. On contact with the human host, typically bare feet, the larvae penetrate the skin and are carried through the blood vessels to the heart and then to the lungs. They penetrate into the pulmonary alveoli, ascend the bronchial tree to the pharynx, and are swallowed ❹. The larvae reach the jejunum of the small intestine, where they reside and mature into adults. Adult worms live in the lumen of the small intestine, typically the distal jejunum, where they attach to the intestinal wall with resultant blood loss by the host ❺. Most adult worms are eliminated in 1–2 years, but the longevity may reach several years. Some *A. duodenale* larvae, following penetration of the host skin, can become dormant (hypobiosis in the intestine or muscle). These larvae are capable of re-activating and establishing patent, intestinal infections. In addition, infection by *A. duodenale* may probably also occur by the oral and the transmammary route. *A. ceylanicum* and *A. caninum* infections may also be acquired by oral ingestion. *A. caninum*-associated eosinophilic enteritis is believed to result following oral ingestion of larvae, not percutaneous infection. *N. americanus* does not appear to be infective via the oral or transmammary route. Courtesy of the CDC. Reproduced from https://www.cdc.gov/dpdx/hookworm/index.html

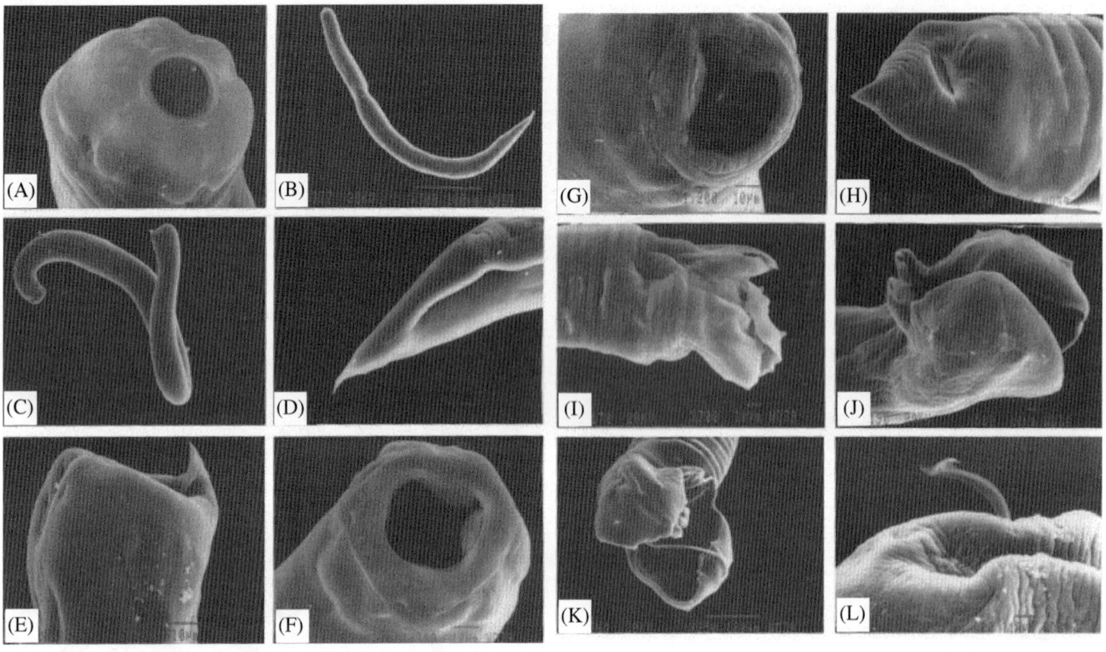

Fig. 20.7 ■ Development of *Necator americanus* in hamsters. The development of hookworm in hamsters at different intervals after subcutaneous infection with 250 *Necator americanus* third stage infective larvae. (A) 15 days, false buccal cavity, 1500×; (B) 7 days, female worm, 300×; (C) 15 days, male worm showed thin and fine end of tail, 170×; (D) 14 days, the end of female worm, 1400×; (E) 15 days, the end of male worm, 1300×; (F) 20 days, buccal cavith with cutting plate, 1200×; (G) 27 days, thick cuticle around the edge of buccal cavity, 1200×; (H) 27 days, female worm showed triangle shape of tail end with very fine and sharp-like needle, 700×; (I) 20 days, male worm showed formation of dorsal and ventral part of copulatory bursa, 700×; (J) 27 days, more strong and thick of dorsal and ventral part of copulatory bursa with two pairs of papillae on the dorsal surface revealed in triangle shape, 500×; (K) 55 days, male worm showed opened copulatoruy bursa, 250×; (L) 63 days, male worm showed a copulatory spicule, 1000×. Courtesy: Jian *et al. Exp Parasitol* 2003;105:192–200. Reproduced with permission from Elsevier.

lion dollars. He was probably just in the act of contributing that sum when a man pushed in ahead of him — as usual. Mr. Rockefeller. He furnishes the million, but the credit will go elsewhere — as usual."[6]

20.4.2 Life cycle

Please see Figure 20.6 for the life cycle, from CDC.[7]

[6] https://www.cs.umd.edu/~mvz/bible/ltrs-from-earth.pdf

[7] https://www.cdc.gov/dpdx/hookworm/index.html

An adult hookworm female is bigger than the male. A male worm has, at its terminal posterior end, a copulatory bursa composed of structures known as rays. *Ancylostoma* females are 10–13 mm and lay 10,000–30,000 eggs per day; males, 8–11 mm. *Necator* females are 9–11 mm and lay 5,000–10,000 eggs per day; males, 7–9 mm. Adult lifespan is 1–5 years, although 15 years have been noted. Pigs can be paratenic hosts but humans are the only definitive hosts. Animal models have been developed for the hookworms. *Necator americanus* was adapted to the golden hamster through 100 passages (Jian *et al.* 2003). The hamster model of *N. americanus* is potentially useful for studying the development of new anthelminthic drugs and vaccines. Please see Figure 20.7 for the development of *Necator americanus* in hamsters (Jian *et al.* 2003).

Eggs are mixed with feces, at 2, 4 or more cell stages. In 1 to 2 days the eggs hatch and the L1 or rhabditiform larvae come out. L1 larvae live in the soil; they feed on bacteria and debris. For 5–10 days they molt twice to infective L3 larvae (iL3). These non-feeding infective stages can live for several weeks and seek out the human skin.

The L3 filariform hookworm larvae infect humans by penetration of bare skin. The skin route is common for all hookworm species. However, additional routes have been found later, for *Ancylostoma duodenale* larvae. Some larvae, following penetration of the host skin, can become dormant (**hypobiosis**) in the intestine or muscle. These larvae are capable of re-activating and establishing patent, intestinal infections. *Ancylostoma* infection may also occur by oral and trans-mammary routes (via the mouth and milk, respectively).

20.4.3 Pathology

Adult worms live in the small intestine. They produce anticoagulants and eat red blood cells, using hemoglobinase and other protease cascades. An adult *Ancylostoma* worm takes in 0.1 to 0.2 mL of blood per worm per day. An adult *Necator* worm takes in 0.01 to 0.02 mL blood per worm per day (10-fold less). A patient with heavy infection can lose 200 mL of blood a day, leading to **iron-deficiency anemia**. Hookworm patients may like to eat soil, **geophagy**, especially clay, presumably to replenish iron (another example of parasite-induced host behavioral change).

It is important to differentiate **hookworm infection** and **hookworm disease**. A lower parasite number leads to infection but a higher number leads to disease. For *Necator*, less than 25 worms is asymptomatic, 25–100 light, 100–500 moderate, 500–1000 severe symptoms, over 1000 can be fatal. For *Ancylostoma*, 100 worms cause severe symptoms, as *Ancylostoma* adults take in 10-fold more blood than *Necator* adults.

Morbidity is directly correlated with the intensity of hookworm infection. Intensity of infection can be expressed as eggs per gram of feces (**EPG**). The WHO categorizes hookworm infections as light (≤1,999 EPG), moderate (2,000–3,999 EPG) and heavy (≥4,000 EPG). Heavy infections are found in places with high hookworm prevalence.

Pathology is divided into three phases: **cutaneous** or invasion phase, migration or **pulmonary** phase, and **intestinal** phase. Non-feeding iL3 filariform larvae enter the skin. After entrance they resume feeding by activation of cyclic GMP (cGMP), insulin, and transforming growth factor *beta* (TGF β) signal pathways. Skin penetration is followed by blood capillaries to bring the larvae to the heart and then to the lung. From lung the larvae enter pharynx and are swallowed, to mature in the small intestine. Adults produce products with immunomodulatory activities, such as neutrophil inhibitory factors. In addition, *Necator* secretes acetyl cholinesterase to inhibit gut peristalsis.

A case of hookworm infection caused acute intestinal bleeding was reported in Hunan province, China (Tan *et al.* 2017). A 46-year-old male complaining of edema for 2 months and exertional dyspnea and chest pain for 2 weeks was admitted to a university hospital at Changsha (Hunan Province). The patient had primary nephrotic syndrome and pulmonary embolism. During the treatment with steroids and anticoagulants, he had acute massive hemorrhage of the gastrointestinal tract. Capsule endoscopy revealed fresh blood and multiple hookworms in the jejunum and ileum; the patient was successfully treated with albendazole. "Hence, hookworm infection should be considered in the differential diagnosis of a patient with obscure gastrointestinal bleeding" (Tan *et al.* 2017).

20.4.4 Diagnosis

Examination of eggs in feces can be diagnostic. Eggs may contain 2–8 embryonic cells.

20.4.5 Therapy

Drugs of choice are the benzimidazoles: albendazole and mebendazole. These compounds target beta tubulin. However, overuse in cattle and veterinary medicine leads to drug resistance. Human hookworm resistance to benzimidazole has been reported in Mali.

Benzimidazoles may not be safe for pregnancy and infants. Another drug **pyrantel pamoate** can be used. This compound is a depolarizing neuromuscular blocking agent. It inhibits cholinesterase, and halts the release of acetylcholine leading to worm paralysis. Another drug is ivermectin, but *Necator* is less sensitive to ivermectin than *Ancylostoma*.

Here, we introduce China's contribution to anthelmintic (Hu *et al.* 2009; Xiao *et al.* 2013). The Chinese CDC has developed an anthelmintic, **tribendimidine**. The compound is an L-type (levamisole and pyrantel) nicotinic acetylcholine receptor agonist. So, it is useful for benzimidazole-resistant species, but not for pyrantel-resistance species. Tribendimidine is active against all three groups of STHs (including hookworms) as well as *Clonorchis*, *Taenia* and *Strongyloides*, but not *Fasciola*, *Paragonimus* and *Schistosoma*.

The drug for parasitic protozoa **nitazoxanide** is also active against hookworms and other nematodes (Somvanshi *et al.* 2014). It targets a glutamate-gated chloride ion channel, like ivermectin. It may be synergistic with other drugs (albandazole and pyrantel).

Similar to other STHs, periodic, single dose MDA can be useful to control hookworm infections in endemic areas.

20.4.6 Hookworms as potential therapy

Relevant to the concept of hygiene hypothesis (discussed in Chapter 3), whipworms and hookworms have shown potential therapeutic applications in inflammatory disorders. Epidemiological studies suggest that a hookworm infection producing 50 eggs per gram of feces may protect against asthma. Investigators at the University of Nottingham treated 10 volunteers with 10, 25, 50, 100 *Necator americanus* larvae administered double blind on the arm, and tested for fecal egg count afterwards for 12 weeks, and followed by mebendazole treatment. Eight completed this study, at 10 larvae can produce 50 eggs per gram in feces, suggesting this dose as potentially suitable for use in preliminary clinical therapeutic trials (Mortimer *et al.* 2006). However, in a subsequent study the investigators reported that such a trial was not successful. Using 32 individuals with asthma, they used 10 larvae and followed the patients for 16 weeks. This was this first clinical trial of experimental hookworm infection in people with allergic asthma, however, only resulted in a non-significant improvement in airway responsiveness. They suggested that further study that mimics more closely to natural infection would be feasible and worthwhile (Feary *et al.* 2010).

Celiac disease is caused by intolerance of gluten that leads to inflammation of the gut. It has been shown that infection of 20 *Necator americanus* larvae would allow patients to tolerate gluten (by gradual challenge) to doses that correspond to a bowl of pasta daily (finally at 3 g gluten) (Loukas *et al.* 2016). Hookworm infection also restores the diversity of gut microbiome (Giacomin *et al.* 2016).

"The notion of live helminth therapy is unpalatable to many people" (Loukas *et al.* 2016). Instead of the whole worm, the aim is to search for worm products with anti-inflammatory and other beneficial functions. Noting the recombinant hirudin from the leech, as an animal salivary protein useful for coagulation disorders, similar excretory/secretory (E/S) molecules from hookworms may also be discovered for their medicinal potential. There was earlier development on hookworm proteins neutrophil inhibitory factor and nematode anticoagulant peptide (derived from the dog hookworm *Ancylostoma caninum*) but the commercial developments were currently suspended (Navarro *et al.* 2013). A recombinant dog hookworm secretory product anti-inflammatory protein-2 (**AIP-2**) expressed in yeast (AIP-2 amino acid sequence 17–244) has been shown to work in suppressing asthma using an experimental murine model, by activity on dendritic cells and regulatory T cells (Navarro *et al.* 2016). Additional novel and potentially useful products may be generated with knowledge from the hookworm genomes.

20.4.7 Genome

The chromosomes of hookworms have a haploid number n = **6**, with **XX-XO** sex determination mechanism (females are diploid with 12 chromosomes and XX; males are diploid with 11 chromosomes and XO) (Blaxter 2000). The genome of *Necator americanus* and *Ancylostoma ceylanicum* have been published and the genome of *Ancylostoma duodenale* has been included in a comparative genomics study of parasitic worms (Tang *et al.* 2014; Schwarz *et al.* 2015; International Helminth Genomes Consortium, 2019). From these first publications, *Necator americanus* possesses **19,151** genes. *Ancylostoma ceylanicum* expresses 30,738 genes. *Ancylostoma duodenale* possesses **27,485** genes.

From the genome of *Necator americanus*, expansion of immunomodulatory genes is seen. There are **operons** and **trans-splicing** (3,223 genes) and the host-parasite interaction protein family known as **SCP** (sperm-coating protein) with 137 genes. A third (33%) of the predicted proteins (proteome) are excretory/secretory (**secretome**). Drug target genes are confirmed, such as nicotinic acetylcholine receptor for levamisole and monepantel sensitivity, and ivermectin insensitivity for sequence diversity of the glutamate-gated chloride channel. Transcriptomic analysis shows differential gene expression at the iL3 (infective larval 3) stage, and the activation of transcription factors for rapid gene expression after host invasion.

From the genome of *Ancylostoma ceylanicum*, iL3 stage shows upregulation of protease, protease inhibitors, nucleases and protein synthesis genes; expressed proteins can function in digesting host proteins and suppressing host immune response. There is an expansion of **ASPs** (activation-associated secreted protein) and **ASPR** (ASP-related) genes, these are cysteine-rich proteins that can function in blocking the host immune response and blood clotting. Genomes can lead to potential drug targets ("we search for genes that were conserved by diverse parasites but absent from mammals," Schwarz *et al.* 2015); one candidate is **trehalose-6-phosphate synthase**. An interesting comparison between free-living and parasitic nematodes has been mentioned by the group that presented this zoonotic hookworm genome. "Parasitism allows adult nematodes to grow larger and live longer than their free-living relatives (*N. americanus* adults are ~1 cm long and live for 3–10 years, whereas *C. elegans* adults are ~1 mm long and live for 3 weeks), but the genomic changes underlying these adaptations are essentially unknown" (Schwarz *et al.* 2015).

SCPs, ASPs, and ASPRs are related proteins. ASP can also mean *Ancylostoma*-secreted protein; they are abundant secretory proteins in the iL3 stage of hookworms, to play a role in their transition to the parasitic life style (Cantacessi and Gasser 2012). Although these proteins are found in many eukaryotic species, current attempts are using them as hookworm vaccine candidates.

20.4.8 Towards hookworm vaccine

One group actively studying hookworm vaccine development is under the leadership of Peter Hotez (Esch 2007). Beginning his career as a junior faculty member at Yale, Hotez started on hookworm vaccine. He had iL3 larvae but could not get any secretory protein. He hired as post doc John Hawdon, who had developed a method of treating L3 with dog serum to stimulate them to resume development. So, they treated larvae with a fractionated dog serum and glutathione. Secreted proteins were found, and a cDNA library was made (for *Necator americanus*). This became their ASP1; the paper was published in 1996. This idea of human vaccine came to Hotez based on old experiments in the 1930s: if give small inoculum of larvae to dogs, orally or subcutaneously, live *Ancylostoma caninum* L3 over several months, the animals became resistant to the challenge infection. A hookworm vaccine for dogs was indeed available commercially for some time.

The human hookworm vaccine initiative is a program of the Sabin Vaccine Institute at Washington DC, under the direction of Peter Hotez, then at George Washington University Medical Center. (Hotez later moved to Baylor University in Houston, Texas.) Founded in 2000 with Gates Foundation funds, the aim was to develop a bivalent vaccine comprised of recombinant protein antigens from infective larval stage and adult blood feeding stage. The hookworm antigen was expressed in yeast (*Pichia pastoris)* and formulated with Alhyrogel as adjuvant, together with CpG oligodeoxycucleotides (in some cases, for toll-like receptor engagement). (Alhydrogel is a sterilized aluminium hydroxide wet gel suspension which has been tested free of pyrogenicity.) Alhydrogel tolerates re-autoclaving, but can be destroyed if frozen. When the pH is maintained at 5–7, normal for vaccine production, Alhydrogel has a positive charge so they readily adsorb negatively charged antigens (e.g. proteins with acidic isoelectric points kept at neutral pH). There will be technology transfer from the United States (Walter Reed Army Institute of Research pilot bioproduction facility GMP) to Brazil (Sao Paulo Instituto Butantan, and Oswaldo Cruz Foundation, FIOCRUZ).

Their initial targets include Na-ASP2 (*Necator americanus-Ancylostoma* secreted protein 2), possible chemotaxis mimic (attenuates larval migration through tissues), Na-APR1 aspartic protease hemoglobinase (blocks enzyme in hookworm digestive tract), Na-GST1 glutathione S-transferase (blocks detoxification of host heme), Na-CP2 cysteine protease (blocks enzyme in hookworm digestive tract), Ac-16 and Ac-SAA1 (larval and adult immune-dominant surface antigens, attenuates larval migration).

When Na-ASP-2 was tested in 36 human volunteers (unexposed adults) in the United States, high antibody titer was seen after 3rd vaccination in 8 months, suggesting future trial in endemic regions. Unexpectedly, when undergoing field trial in Brazil (an endemic area), there were generalized urticarial reactions (hives and rashes) in volunteers (7 out of 9), due to prior exposure of hookworms, and these adults had pre-existing Na-ASP2 IgE. Thus, replacement targets would be preferred (Schneider *et al.* 2011).

Na-GST was tested in a hamster hookworm model, with 32–39% reduction in worm burden by larval challenge. Currently, a vaccine containing two components, Na-GST and Na-APR1 are undergoing clinical trials in Africa and America. Target enzymes that are essential for the hookworm: APR for hemoglobin digestion, and GST for heme detoxification. Recombinant GST is still made in yeast but APR is made in the tobacco (*Nicotiana*) plant. These two are lead candidates for clinical development (Hotez *et al.* 2016). Expanding from the hookworm vaccine, Hotez and colleagues have proposed a multivalent "pan-anthelmintic" vaccine by adding a larval antigen from *Ascaris lumbricoides* and an adult antigen form the stichosome of *Trichuris trichiura* (Zhan *et al.* 2014).

Other potential vaccine candidates are available from hookworm excretory/secretory (E/P) products, especially the ones from iL3. Whereas some can be vaccines, other may show immunomodulatory capacity potentially useful for the treatment of immunological disorders (Abuzeid *et al.* 2020).

Summary & Key Concepts

- STHs are the unholy trinity of roundworms, whipworms and hookworms.
- High worm burden in children leads to malnutrition and cognitive defects.
- *Ascaris lumbricoides* is the most abundant STH infection; ascariasis is the most common NTD.
- *Trichuris trichiura* lives in the colon; it can cause rectal relapse.
- Hookworms include *Necator americanus* and *Ancylostoma duodenale*; they cause anemia.
- Whipworm and hookworm components (*Trichuris suis* ova) show beneficial anti-inflammatory effects.
- STH treatments include the anti-microtubule benzimidazole drugs albendazole and mebendazole.
- Hookworm vaccine and pan-anthelmintic vaccine are currently being developed.

References

Abuzeid AMI, Zhou X, Huang Y, Li G. Twenty-five-year research progress in hookworm excretory/secretory products. *Parasit Vectors* 2020;13(1):136.

Allison MJ, Pezzia A, Hasegawa I, Gerszten E. A case of hookworm infestation in a Precolumbian American. *Am J Phys Anthropol* 1974;41(1):103–6.

Andrews JR, Bogoch II, Utzinger J. The benefits of mass deworming on health outcomes: New evidence synthesis, the debate persists. *Lancet Glob Health* 2017;5(1):e4–e5.

Aspock H, Auer H, Picher O. *Trichuris trichiura* eggs in the neolithic glacier mummy from the Alps. *Parasitol Today* 1996;12:255–6.

Bethony JM, Simon G, Diemert DJ, *et al.* Randomized, placebo-controlled, double-blind trial of the Na-ASP-2 hookworm vaccine in unexposed adults. *Vaccine* 2008;26(19):2408–17.

Blaxter M. Genes and genomes of *Necator americanus* and related hookworms. *Int J Parasitol* 2000;30(4):347–55.

Cantacessi C, Gasser RB. SCP/TAPS proteins in helminths — where to from now? *Mol Cell Probes* 2012;26(1):54–9.

Cantacessi C, Young ND, Nejsum P, *et al.* The transcriptome of *Trichuris suis* — first molecular insights into a parasite with curative properties for key immune diseases of humans. *PLoS One* 2011;6(8):e23590.

Choi JH, Seo M. A case of biliary ascariasis in Korea. *Korean J Parasitol* 2017;55(6):659–60.

Clarke AJ, Perry RN. Egg-shell permeability and hatching of *Ascaris suum*. *Parasitology* 1980;80(3):447–56.

Cox FEG, editor. *The Wellcome Trust Illustrated History of Tropical Diseases* (1996, The Wellcome Trust, London).

Cutillas C, Callejón R, de Rojas M, *et al*. *Trichuris suis* and *Trichuris trichiura* are different nematode species. *Acta Trop* 2009;111(3):299–307.

Diemert DJ, Bethony JM, Hotez PJ. Hookworm vaccines. *Clin Infect Dis* 2008;46(2):282–8.

Esch GW. *Parasites and Infectious Disease* (2007, Cambridge).

Feary JR, Venn AJ, Mortimer K, *et al*. Experimental hookworm infection: A randomized placebo-controlled trial in asthma. *Clin Exp Allergy* 2010;40(2):299–306.

Flammer PG, Ryan H, Preston SG, *et al*. Epidemiological insights from a large-scale investigation of intestinal helminths in Medieval Europe. *PLoS Negl Trop Dis* 2020;14(8):e0008600.

Foth BJ, Tsai IJ, Reid AJ, *et al*. Whipworm genome and dual-species transcriptome analyses provide molecular insights into an intimate host-parasite interaction. *Nat Genet* 2014;46(7):693–700.

GBD 2017 DALYs and HALE Collaborators. Global, regional, and national disability-adjusted life-years (DALYs) for 359 diseases and injuries and healthy life expectancy (HALE) for 195 countries and territories, 1990–2017: A systematic analysis for the Global Burden of Disease Study 2017. *Lancet* 2018;392(10159):1859–1922.

Giacomin P, Zakrzewski M, Jenkins TP, *et al*. Changes in duodenal tissue-associated microbiota following hookworm infection and consecutive gluten challenges in humans with coeliac disease. *Sci Rep* 2016;6:36797.

Goswami U. Some cytogenetical aspects of genus *Trichuris* (Nematoda). *Curr Sci.* 1978;47(11): 368–371.

Grant B. Opening a can of worms. *The Scientist* 2011;25:42–7.

Haldeman MS, Nolan MS, Ng'habi KRN. Human hookworm infection: Is effective control possible? A review of hookworm control efforts and future directions. *Acta Trop* 2020;201:105214.

Hawash MB, Betson M, Al-Jubury A, *et al*. Whipworms in humans and pigs: Origins and demography. *Parasit Vectors* 2016;9:37.

Hotez PJ. *Forgotten People, Forgotten Diseases*, 2nd ed., ASM Press, 2013.

Hotez PJ, Brown AS. Neglected tropical disease vaccines. *Biologicals* 2009;37(3):160–4.

Hotez PJ, Beaumier CM, Gillespie PM, Strych U, Hayward T, Bottazzi ME. Advancing a vaccine to prevent hookworm disease and anemia. *Vaccine* 2016;34(26):3001–5.

Hu Y, Xiao SH, Aroian RV. The new anthelmintic tribendimidine is an L-type (levamisole and pyrantel) nicotinic acetylcholine receptor agonist. *PLoS Negl Trop Dis* 2009;3(8):e499.

International Helminth Genomes Consortium. Comparative genomics of the major parasitic worms. *Nat Genet* 2019;51(1):163–74.

Izurieta R, Reina-Ortiz M, Ochoa-Capello T. *Trichuris trichiura*. In: Rose JB, Jiménez-Cisneros B, editors. *Water and Sanitation for the 21st Century: Health and Microbiological Aspects of Excreta and Wastewater Management (Global Water Pathogen Project)*. (Robertson L, editor. Part 3: *Specific Excreted Pathogens: Environmental and Epidemiology Aspects* — Section 4: Helminths), Michigan State University, E. Lansing, MI (2018, UNESCO).

Jex AR, Nejsum P, Schwarz EM, *et al*. Genome and transcriptome of the porcine whipworm *Trichuris suis*. *Nat Genet* 2014;46(7):701–6.

Jex AR, Liu S, Li B, *et al. Ascaris suum* draft genome. *Nature* 2011;479(7374):529–33.

Jian X, Shu-Hua X, Hui-Qing Q, *et al. Necator americanus*: Maintenance through one hundred generations in golden hamsters (Mesocricetus auratus). II. Morphological development of the adult and its comparison with humans. *Exp Parasitol* 2003;105(3–4):192–200.

Jourdan PM, Lamberton PHL, Fenwick A, Addiss DG. Soil-transmitted helminth infections. *Lancet* 2018;391(10117):252–65.

Kean BH, Mott KE, Russell AJ. editor. *Tropical Medicine and Parasitology. Classic Investigations*, volume I and II (1978, Cornell, Ithaca).

Leles D, Gardner SL, Reinhard K, Iñiguez A, Araujo A. Are *Ascaris lumbricoides* and *Ascaris suum* a single species? *Parasit Vectors* 2012;5:42.

Loukas A, Hotez PJ, Diemert D, *et al.* Hookworm infection. *Nat Rev Dis Primers* 2016;2:16088.

Li T, He S, Zhao H, Zhao G, Zhu XQ. Major trends in human parasitic diseases in China. *Trends Parasitol* 2010;26(5):264–70.

Miller LA, Colby K, Manning SE, *et al.* Ascariasis in humans and pigs on small-scale farms, Maine, USA, 2010–2013. *Emerg Infect Dis* 2015;21(2):332–4.

Monteiro KJL, Calegar DA, Santos JP, *et al.* Genetic diversity of *Ascaris* spp. infecting humans and pigs in distinct Brazilian regions, as revealed by mitochondrial DNA. *PLoS One* 2019;14(6):e0218867.

Mortimer K, Brown A, Feary J, *et al.* Dose-ranging study for trials of therapeutic infection with *Necator americanus* in humans. *Am J Trop Med Hyg* 2006;75(5):914–20.

Navarro S, Ferreira I, Loukas A. The hookworm pharmacopoeia for inflammatory diseases. *Int J Parasitol* 2013;43(3-4):225–31.

Navarro S, Pickering DA, Ferreira IB, *et al.* Hookworm recombinant protein promotes regulatory T cell responses that suppress experimental asthma. *Sci Transl Med* 2016;8(362):362ra143.

Niyas VKM, Balasubramanian P, Thulaseedharan NK. *Trichuris trichiura. QJM* 2019;112(7):537.

Park JY, Joo HJ, Park S, Paik YK. Ascaroside pheromones: Chemical biology and pleiotropic neuronal functions. *Int J Mol Sci* 2019;20(16):3898.

Roberts LS, Janovy J Jr, Nadler S. *Foundations of Parasitology*, 9th edition (2013, McGraw Hill).

Sandborn WJ, Elliott DE, Weinstock J, *et al.* Randomised clinical trial: The safety and tolerability of *Trichuris suis* ova in patients with Crohn's disease. *Aliment Pharmacol Ther* 2013;38(3):255–63.

Schneider B, Jariwala AR, Periago MV, *et al.* A history of hookworm vaccine development. *Hum Vaccin* 2011;7(11):1234–44.

Schulz JD, Moser W, Hürlimann E, *et al.* Preventive chemotherapy in the fight against soil-transmitted Helminthiasis: Achievements and limitations. *Trends Parasitol* 2018;34(7):590–602.

Schwarz EM, Hu Y, Antoshechkin I, Miller MM, Sternberg PW, Aroian RV. The genome and transcriptome of the zoonotic hookworm *Ancylostoma ceylanicum* identify infection-specific gene families. *Nat Genet* 2015;47(4):416–22.

Somvanshi VS, Ellis BL, Hu Y, Aroian RV. Nitazoxanide: Nematicidal mode of action and drug combination studies. *Mol Biochem Parasitol* 2014;193(1):1–8.

Sheffield HG. Electron microscopy of the bacillary band and stichosome of *Trichuris muris* and *T. vulpis. J Parasitol.* 1963;49:998–1009.

Summers RW, Elliott DE, Urban JF Jr, Thompson R, Weinstock JV. *Trichuris suis* therapy in Crohn's disease. *Gut* 2005a;54(1):87–90.

Summers RW, Elliott DE, Urban JF Jr, Thompson RA, Weinstock JV. *Trichuris suis* therapy for active ulcerative colitis: A randomized controlled trial. *Gastroenterology* 2005b;128(4):825–32.

Tan X, Cheng M, Zhang J, *et al.* Hookworm infection caused acute intestinal bleeding diagnosed by capsule: A case report and literature review. *Korean J Parasitol* 2017;55(4):417–420.

Tang YT, Gao X, Rosa BA, *et al.* Genome of the human hookworm *Necator americanus. Nat Genet* 2014;46(3):261–9.

Tilney LG, Connelly PS, Guild GM, Vranich KA, Artis D. Adaptation of a nematode parasite to living within the mammalian epithelium. *J Exp Zool A Comp Exp Biol* 2005;303(11):927–45.

Traub RJ. *Ancylostoma ceylanicum*, a re-emerging but neglected parasitic zoonosis. *Int J Parasitol* 2013;43(12–13):1009–15.

Ubelaker JE, Allison VF. Scanning electron microscopy of the eggs of *Ascaris lumbricoides, A. suum, Toxocara canis*, and *T. mystax*. *J Parasitol* 1975;61(5):802–7.

Wang J, Davis RE. Programmed DNA elimination in multicellular organisms. *Curr Opin Genet Dev* 2014;27:26–34.

Wang J, Gao S, Mostovoy Y, *et al.* Comparative genome analysis of programmed DNA elimination in nematodes. *Genome Res* 2017;27(12):2001–14.

Xiao SH, Utzinger J, Tanner M, Keiser J, Xue J. Advances with the Chinese anthelminthic drug tribendimidine in clinical trials and laboratory investigations. *Acta Trop* 2013;126(2):115–26.

Zhan B, Beaumier CM, Briggs N, *et al.* Advancing a multivalent 'Pan-anthelmintic' vaccine against soil-transmitted nematode infections. *Expert Rev Vaccines* 2014;13(3):321–31.

Zhan B, Perally S, Brophy PM, *et al.* Molecular cloning, biochemical characterization, and partial protective immunity of the heme-binding glutathione S-transferases from the human hookworm *Necator americanus*. *Infect Immun* 2010;78(4):1552–63.

21

Strongyloidiasis, Trichinellosis and Enterobiasis (Pinworm)

21.1 Introductory Remarks

In addition to the filariae and soiled-transmitted nematodes (STHs) covered in the previous chapters, the other nematodes whose adult stages are found in humans include the genera *Strongyloides*, *Trichinella*, and *Enterobius* (pinworm). As these nematodes are found worldwide, even in the Arctic region, therefore they are not known as agents of neglected tropical diseases (NTDs), like the ones discussed in previous chapters. *Strongyloides* is grouped as a STH, but its uniqueness lies in its capacity to also be free-living. Thus, with respect to parasitism, the fact that this nematode possesses a free-living stage suggests that it may still be towards further adaptation for total parasitism. *Trichinella* is a foodborne pathogen, transmitted to humans by consuming undercooked contaminated meat from pigs or games (such as bears and boars). *Enterobius* is commonly known as the pinworm. As an infectious agent, the pinworm is found in children and people confined within institutions. Both *Ascaris lumbricoides* and *Enterobius vermicularis* are common and readily transmissible helminthic infections. The two are among the top with respect to the number of people affected. Some parasites can increase their number within the host by autoinfection. This condition is seen in *Enterobius* and *Strongyloides*. For *Trichinella*, the intermediate host can be skipped, as the juveniles live in one environment (muscles) and the adults in another (gut), in the same host.

21.2 *Strongyloides*

Although not a member of the "unholy trinity," ***Strongyloides stercoralis*** (strongylos means round, oides means similar, stercoralis means inside feces) is also a STH. It has a worldwide distribution, especially in tropical and subtropical regions. The prevalence of strongyloidiasis by *Strongyloides stercoralis* has been estimated to be 30 to **100 million** people (this may be an underestimate) (Greaves *et al.* 2013; Nutman 2017). A study in Japan has found a total of 865 cases of soil-transmitted nematodiasis from 2000 to 2017, with 279 cases due to *Strongyloides stercoralis* (32.3% of all cases), the most prominent but restricted to southern Japan. Other STHs were 30.7% from *Ascaris lumbricoides* and 23.1% from *Trichuris trichiura*. "At least 15.5 cases of strongyloidiasis occurred on average each year" in Japan (Ikuno *et al.* 2020). *Strongyloides* has been found in a low-income community in Texas. "Given continued poverty and that nearly one in five American homes are lacking proper sanitation systems, many U.S. regions are at risk for intestinal parasites. A central Texas community was chosen as the study site, given previous reports of widespread sanitation failure, degree of poverty, and community willingness to participate. A total of 92 households were surveyed and residents tested for nine intestinal parasites using a multi-parallel quantitative real-time polymerase chain reaction and ELISA serology. From 43 stool samples, 27 (62.8%) tested positive for *Blastocystis* spp. and one (2.3%) for *Giardia lamblia*. From 97 serum samples, *Strongyloides* serology detected 16 (16.5%) positive individuals. … Residents without access to functioning and sustainable sanitation infrastructure should be provided that access as a basic human right and to promote public health" (Singer *et al.* 2020).

A related species, *Strongyloides fuelleborni*, can cause "swollen belly syndrome" (**SBS**) in infants in New Guinea and sub-Sahara Africa. Current classification has split *Strongyloides fuelleborni* into two subspecies, with *Strongyloides fuelleborni fuelleborni* as a parasite of Old World apes and monkeys (zoonosis) and ***Strongyloides fuelleborni kellyi*** as a human pathogen, causing SBS (Barratt *et al.* 2019).

21.2.1 History

For French soldiers returning from Southeast Asia, they suffered from "diarrhea of Cochin China." The port physician Louis Normand and his colleague Arthur Bavay, working at Toulon, France, discovered the parasitic worm and named it *Anguillula stercoralis* (today *Strongyloides stercoralis*) in 1876. In 1900, the German professor Max Askanazy described "a case of infection with *Anguillula (strongyloides) intestinalis*" in a forester, with worm larvae in his stool, and adult worms found in his gastrointestinal tract at autopsy. In 1902, for his thesis at the Liverpool School of Tropical Medicine, Paul van Dume described skin penetration of *Strongyloides intestinalis* larvae on shaved guinea pig skin from surface to the dermis. The German professor Friedrich Fulleborn extended the life cycle study using dogs in 1914 and reported autoinfection in human patients in 1926. Fulleborn wrote: "The penetration into the surrounding skin of filariform *Strongyloides* larvae, which developed in the anal cleft, not only causes urticaria but also must be a cause for permanent new infection of the *Strongyloides* carrier." Working in Taipei, Taiwan, the Japanese pathologist Masao Nishigori made extensive study of autoinfection in dogs, made them constipated with drugs (morphine and bismuth), to pass filariform larvae instead of rhabditiform ones, and resulted in a greater number in the parasitic infection (**hyper-infection**) (Kean *et al.* 1978).

21.2.2 Life cycle

Please see Figure 21.1 for the life cycle, from CDC.[1]

For *Strongyloides*, its unique biology involves either a free living stage with male and female adult worms, or a parasitic stage involves a 2–2.5 mm **parthenogenetic** female. For the direct cycle (**homogonic cycle**), eggs in soil go through 2 molts to filariform larvae that invades the skin, pass through the circulation, to heart, lung and settle in the small intestine. For the indirect cycle (**heterogonic cycle**), eggs undergo 4 molts into 1 mm adult males and 2 mm females in the soil. Free living occurs under favorable conditions, such as ambient temperature. At 34°C or higher, they prefer parasitic cycle. Thus, there is alternative generations of the *Strongyloides* life cycle. Parasitic females have longer lifespan than free living forms. For the rat parasite *Strongyloides ratti*, there is 80-fold difference in lifespan: 5 days for free living; 403 days for parasitic females (Gardner *et al.* 2006).

Please see Figure 21.2 for developmental stages of *Strongyloides stercoralis* as seen by light microscopy (Page *et al.* 2018).

21.2.3 Pathology

Infection of strongyloidiasis can be divided into 3 phases: **cutaneous**, **pulmonary**, and **intestinal**. These steps are similar to ones seen in other STHs, from larval migration to adult settlement. Acute strongyloidiasis leads to diarrhea, but chronic strongyloidiasis is generally asymptomatic. In humans there is **autoinfection**, some World War II veterans harbored the infection for decades. There was a record of an 83-year-old French male who had lived for several years in Vietnam (plus a 10-day trip to Canary Islands) found to have *Strongyloides* infection 75 years after his Vietnam stay (Prendki *et al.* 2011). For individuals undergoing drug treatment (such as corticosteroids) that suppresses immune response (or in AIDS patients), there can be hyper-infection and **disseminated infection**. Autoinfection is amplified, with an increase in the number of larvae and their migration go to various organs. As the larvae may carry bacteria with them, there can be localized infection leading to systemic sepsis. Such situations are potentially fatal.

Strongyloidiasis can be asymptomatic. A case of *Strongyloides stercoralis* infection was discovered incidentally (Bhasin *et al.* 2020). A 71-year-old male was presented to the emergency department of Northwestern University, Chicago, with fevers, abdominal pain, nausea, and diarrhea. He was not immunosuppressed but several months before presentation had a subtotal cystectomy with the creation of an ileal conduit to treat

[1] https://www.cdc.gov/dpdx/strongyloidiasis/index.html

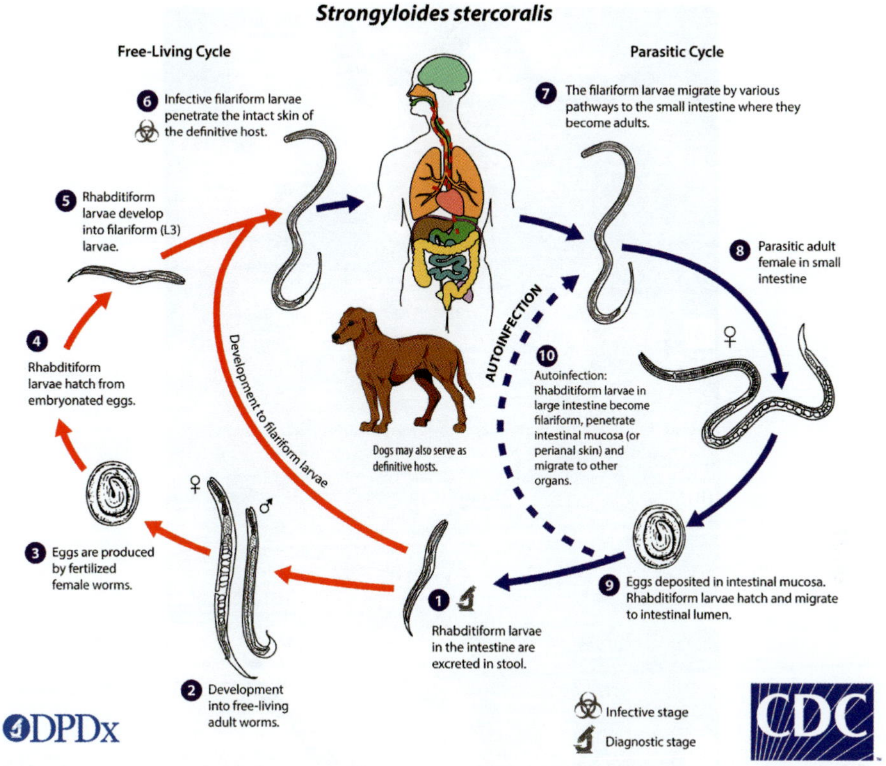

Fig. 21.1 ■ Life cycle of *Strongyloides stercoralis*. The *Strongyloides stercoralis* life cycle is complex, alternating between free-living and parasitic cycles and involving autoinfection. In the **free-living cycle:** Rhabditiform larvae are passed in the stool of an infected definitive host ❶, develop into either infective filariform larvae (direct development) ❻ or free-living adult males and females ❷ that mate and produce eggs ❸ , from which rhabditiform larvae hatch ❹ and eventually become infective filariform (L3) larvae ❺. The filariform larvae penetrate the human host skin to initiate the parasitic cycle (see below) ❻. This second generation of filariform larvae cannot mature into free-living adults and must find a new host to continue the life cycle. **Parasitic cycle:** Filariform larvae in contaminated soil penetrate human skin when skin contacts soil ❻, and migrate to the small intestine ❼. It has been thought that the L3 larvae migrate via the bloodstream and lymphatics to the lungs, where they are eventually coughed up and swallowed. However, L3 larvae appear capable of migrating to the intestine via alternate routes (e.g. through abdominal viscera or connective tissue). In the small intestine, the larvae molt twice and become adult female worms ❽. The females live embedded in the submucosa of the small intestine and produce eggs via parthenogenesis (parasitic males do not exist) ❾, which yield rhabditiform larvae. The rhabditiform larvae can either be passed in the stool ❶ (see "Free-living cycle" above), or can cause autoinfection ❿. Rhabditiform larvae in the gut become infective filariform larvae that can penetrate either the intestinal mucosa or the skin of the perianal area, resulting in autoinfection. Once the filariform larvae reinfect the host, they are carried to the lungs, pharynx and small intestine as described above, or disseminate throughout the body. The significance of autoinfection in *Strongyloides* is that untreated cases can result in persistent infection, even after many decades of residence in a non-endemic area, and may contribute to the development of hyperinfection syndrome. Courtesy of the CDC. Reproduced from https://www.cdc.gov/dpdx/strongyloidiasis/index.html

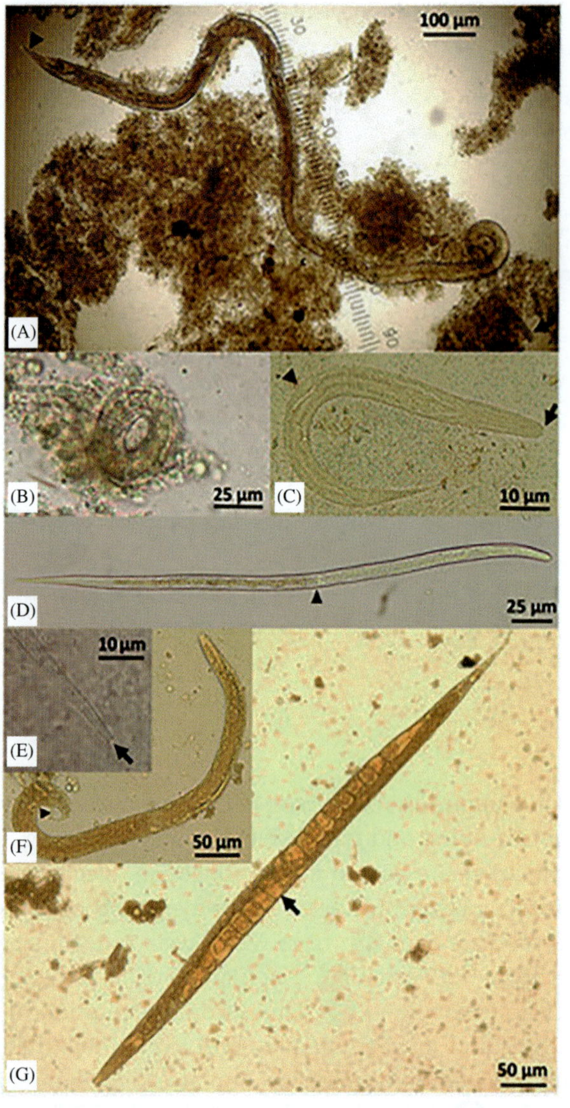

Fig. 21.2 ■ Developmental stages of *Strongyloides stercoralis*. The life stages of *Strongyloides stercoralis*; (A) parasitic female with tapering anterior (arrow) and pointed caudal extremity (dart); (B) embryonated egg; (C) rhabditiform larva in feces with short buccal cavity (arrow) and rhomboid genital primordium (dart); (D) filariform larva with oesophago-intestinal junction at midbody (dart); (E) notched tail of the filariform larva (arrow); (F) free-living male with prominent spicule (dart); and (G) gravid free-living female with eggs in uterus (arrow). *Note*: A,B are from feces of a patient with hyperinfection; these life stages are not seen in patient feces in the absence of severe hyperinfection. Figure attributions: (A, B, E): Dr Richard Bradbury, Central Queensland University; (D): Emeritus Professor John Goldsmid, University of Tasmania; (C, F, G): CDC DPDx web site (https://www.cdc.gov/dpdx/). Courtesy: Page *et al. Trop Med Infect Dis* 2018;3:53. Reproduced with permission from *Tropical Medicine and Infectious Disease* with Creative Commons Attribution 4.0 (CC-BY) International License.

urinary incontinence secondary to complications from prior prostate cancer treatment. Repeat urine microscopy showed the presence of small roundworms, with morphology as rhabditiform (not filiariform) larvae. The patient was treated with ivermectin for 5 days, with confirmed clearance of parasites in urine and stool analyses. The investigators noted that his was not a disseminated disease; creation of the ileal conduit had transplanted the intestinal infection to his urinary tract. His symptoms likely were secondary to bacterial infection and surgical complications. The *Strongyloides* were likely an "innocent bystander" and discovered incidentally. Previously the patient had lived in a rural region of Puerto Rico on a small farm and often walked barefoot there. "This is the first case of *Strongyloides* infection of the urinary tract secondary to ileal loop conduit creation and not as a result of hyperinfection" (Bhasin *et al.* 2020).

In immunocompromised individuals, strongyloidiasis may cause persistent diarrhea. A 61-year-old male with known HIV infection presented with a 3-month history of diarrhea was positive for *Strongyloides stercoralis* infection (but negative for *Clostridium difficile, Cryptosporidium, Giardia, Cyclospora*). The patient was successfully treated with oral ivermectin. "Parasitic infections, such as *S. stercoralis,* should be considered among HIV-infected patients with persistent diarrhea and eosinophilia regardless of ethnicity or recent travel history" (Vazquez Guillamet *et al.* 2017).

In USA, *Strongyloides stercoralis* is found in warm and moist rural agricultural areas, particularly Puerto Rico, Appalachia, and the Southeastern United States. Socioeconomically disadvantaged and institutionalized populations are at higher risk.

21.2.4 Diagnosis

Demonstration of larvae in the stool is a means of diagnosis.

21.2.5 Therapy

Albendazole and ivermectin are drugs for *Strongyloides* infections.

Thinking along the line of hygiene hypothesis, strongyloidiasis may or may not affect other diseases. An initial investigation suggests that the nematode infection protects against diabetes among the Australian aborigines. However, among Bangladesh immigrants in East London, only a close association between *Strongyloides* infection and diabetes has been noted (McGuire *et al.* 2019). A different investigation has concluded that *Strongyloides* infection may be protective by alleviating severity of diabetic symptoms, possibly by lowering the pro-inflammatory cytokines (Th1, Th17) (Rajamanickam *et al.* 2018). Therefore, the relationship between this STH and diabetes needs further clarification.

21.2.6 Genome

From the genomes of *Strongyloides stercoralis* and related species, including parasitic (*S. ratti* for rats, *S. papillosus* for sheep) and free-living species, the evolution towards parasitism has been deduced (Hunt *et al.* 2016). The STH *Strongyloides stercoralis* possesses **XX-XO** sex chromosomes (females with two pairs of autosomes and XX, **6** chromosomes; males with XO, 5 chromosomes). Like the other STH *Ascaris lumbricoides*, *Strongyloides stercoralis* shows **chromatin diminution** (Nemetschke *et al.* 2010). The genome of *Strongyloides stercoralis* is AT-rich and compact, due to intron loss and shorter intergenic regions (43 Mb). The genome contains **13,098** genes, including ones in operons. There is an expansion of **astacin**-like (metalloprotease) and **SCP** (sperm coating protein) gene families (clustered in regions of chromosome 2), with differential expression of these genes between free-living and parasitic species. These genes may be the ones among parasitism-associated genes. **Parasitism-associated genes** are necessary for adaptation to parasitism, with repeated gene duplications associated with adaptation to different hosts.

Parasitism-associated genes found in *Strongyloides* should be common to ones seen in other nematode parasites. From genomics, transcriptomics and proteomics, gene families have been found to serve specific functions. Whereas astacins and SCPs are immunomodulatory, others are protease inhibitors. Proteases are needed for protein digestion (including hemoglobin) and larval penetration of the host tissue. Acetylcholine esterases are needed to inhibit gut expulsion mechanisms (Hunt *et al.* 2017). Please see Figure 21.3 for gene families (Hunt *et al.* 2017).

21.3 *Trichinella*

This parasitic roundworm has its own web site,[2] started by the Columbia University emeritus professor Dickson Despommier, consultant to Animal Planet shows, green farming, and author of *Parasitic Diseases*, 7th edition[3] and YouTube videos.[4,5]

Trichinella is the world's largest intracellular parasite. Actually, it is an intra-multi-cellular organism. It also happens to be among the smallest nematode parasite in humans. A typical cyst of larva inside a nurse cell is 0.25–0.5 mm. A typical adult male is 1.5 mm in length; the female is bigger, 2.2 mm. Juveniles live in the skeletal muscle, inducing trans-differentiation from muscle cell to nurse cell. Adults live among the villi of the small intestine. Juveniles and adults can live in different compartments of the same animal host.

Trichinella spiralis (trichos means tiny hair, spira means spiral) is the major species, and there are other species. The *Trichinella* genus is undergoing revision, with sibling species and subspecies. Currently, there are at least 8 species; besides which, there are four

[2] www.trichinella.org

[3] http://www.parasiteswithoutborders.com/books

[4] https://www.youtube.com/watch?v=-nTSQxqcamg

[5] https://www.youtube.com/watch?v=5PQXm1t-hvQ

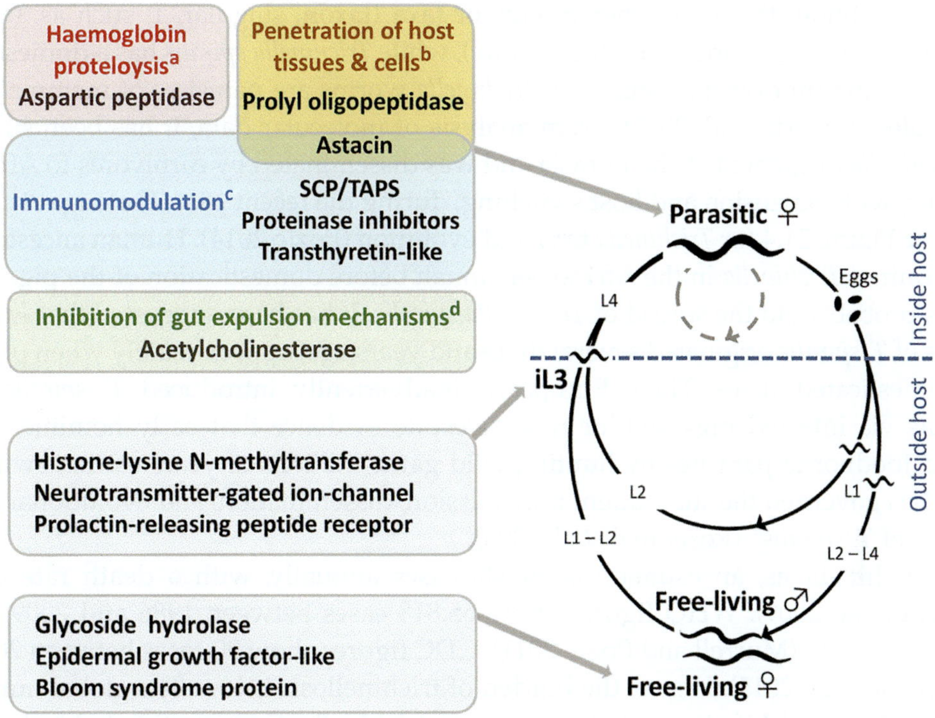

Fig. 21.3 ■ *Strongyloides* life cycle and protein families. The *Strongyloides* life cycle and the protein families associated with the parasitic adult female, free-living adult female and third stage infective larvae (iL3), and their putative roles in nematode parasitism. The coloured boxes represent the different putative roles of protein families in parasitism, including haemoglobin proteolysis (red), penetration of host tissues and cells (orange), immunomodulation (blue) and inhibition of gut expulsion mechanisms (green). These putative roles are based on empirical evidence of proteins from parasitic nematodes and other parasites. Mostly, protein families are associated with a single putative role, apart from astacins where there is evidence for roles of astacin proteins in host tissue penetration and immunomodulation. Little is known about the role of these protein families and further investigation may reveal that other protein families also have multiple roles in parasitism. Courtesy: Hunt *et al. Parasitology* 2017;144:343–58. Reproduced with permission from Cambridge University Press.

additional genotypes (**T1–T12**). While all are morphologically similar, they are differentiated by molecular data such as rDNA and isozyme analysis. For some species, their larval stage nurse cells are protected by a collagenous capsule; for other species, they are not (thus known as unencapsulated *Trichinella* species).

The eight species are: (1) *Trichinella spiralis*, worldwide, carnivores and omnivores (swine, rats) (2) *T. pseudospiralis*, worldwide, mammals and birds (unencapsulated) (3) *T. nativa*, Arctic bears (4) *T. nelsoni*, African predators and scavengers (5) *T. britovi*, carnivores of West Africa and Europe (Bruschi and Pozio 2020) (6) *T. murrelli*, US carnivores and horses (7) *T. papuae*, reptiles and mammals of Papua New Guinea (unencapsulated) (8) *T. zimbabwensis*, African reptiles, crocodiles and experimentally mammals (unencapsulated). In addition, there are other groups or taxa (**taxon**, singular, T, such as T8). Most species go through sylvatic cycles (in wildlife), while *Trichinella spiralis* has a domestic cycle of transmission (in domestic animals). *Trichinella* worms are parasites of mammals, birds and reptiles (Roberts *et al.* 2013). From analysis of molecular data, it has been suggested that *Trichinella* originated in the Eurasia and was disseminated by carnivores to Africa and the Arctic, with expansion and host switching, during the recent past (Zarlenga *et al.* 2006). Please see Figure 21.4 for *Trichinella* taxa and evolution (Pozio 2014). Human ancestors may have acquired *Trichinella* in the African savannah before domestication of the pig. In turn, humans probably aid the spread of *Trichinella spiralis*. It has been suggested that European lineages of *T. spiralis* originated several thousand years ago, approximately when pigs were first domesticated there. Then, Europeans inadvertently introduced *T. spiralis* to the Americas via infected pigs and/or rats. "Despite evidence that early hominid hunters ingested foodborne parasites by hunting wild game millions of years earlier, swine husbandry has governed the subsequent transmission, dissemination, and evolutionary diversification of *T. spiralis*" (Rosenthal *et al.* 2008).

For trichinellosis, an estimate is **10,000** cases annually, with a death rate of 0.2% (Gottstein *et al.* 2009). WHO figures show 65,818 cases between 1986 and 2009, with a death rate of 0.4% (Murrell and Pozio 2011). CDC figures show 90 cases between 2008 and 2012 (Wilson *et al.* 2015). Hence, the burden of trichinellosis is low. The global number of Disability-Adjusted Life Years (DALYs) due to trichinellosis was estimated to be 76 per billion persons per year (Devleesschauwer *et al.* 2015). In addition, there are occasional reports of outbreaks. One such case involved pork sausages from Corsica in 2015, when a 59-year-old French female in Nice consumed raw sausage (a delicacy named *figatelli*) and got sick, as well as her two friends; but 14 other individuals ate the same batch of cooked sausage and were fine (Ruetsch *et al.* 2016).

In sum, trichinellosis is one of the most important foodborne zoonotic diseases with worldwide distribution. While human risk for trichinellosis has historically been linked to pork, modern pork production systems and slaughter inspection programs have reduced or eliminated pork as a source for trichinellosis in many countries. Trichinellosis may occur to humans who consume meat from animal species such as wild boar and bear, with wild boar being the second most important source of human trichinellosis (Rostami *et al.* 2017).

Trichinellosis is a meat-borne hazards in need for surveillance. Risk-based surveillance systems apply risk analysis principles to set priorities, and allocate resources effectively and efficiently. The latter is done through a focus on the cost-effectiveness ratio in sampling and prioritization. With the use of a surveillance design tool, "examples are given covering three meat-borne parasites for which risk-based surveillance is (1) either in place in the European Union (EU) (*Trichinella* spp.), (2) to be officially implemented in December 2019 (*Taenia saginata*) or (3) only carried out by one abattoir company in the EU as there is no official EU requirement (*Toxoplasma gondii*). … Collaboration with the food business operator, consumers, NGOs and other organizations in the food system should be considered by identification of values, common interests, sharing of data and joint action" (Alban *et al.* 2020).

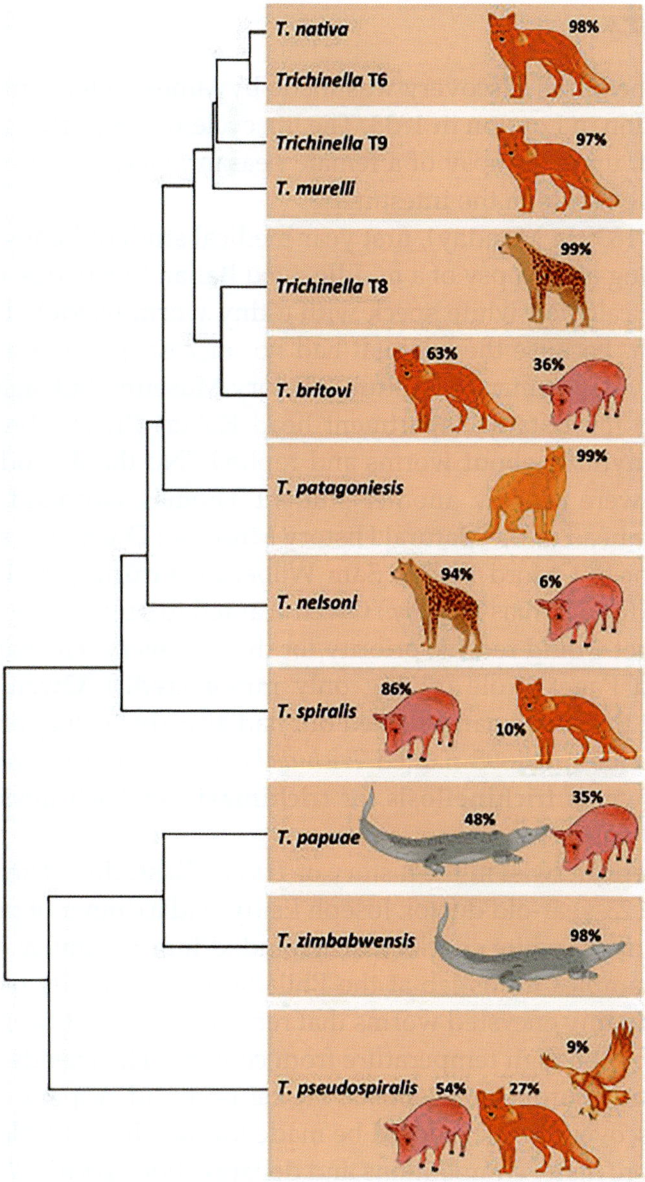

Fig. 21.4 ■ Evolution of *Trichinella* species and genotypes. *Trichinella* taxa and their main hosts. The fox and hyena are shown as representatives of carnivores of the American, Asian, and European continents, and of Africa, respectively. The pig is meant to represent all domestic and wild swine races and species. The crocodile represents the Nile crocodile (for *Trichinella zimbabwensis*) or the saltwater crocodile (for *Trichinella papuae*). The raptorial bird represents carnivorous birds. The percentages refer to the probability of detecting the *Trichinella* taxon in a host group. Host groups of minor epidemiological importance are not shown. Data on the relationships between *Trichinella* spp. and hosts, and the maximum likelihood tree of the genus *Trichinella* are from Pozio E, Zarlenga D, *Int J Parasitol* 2013;43:983–97. Courtesy: Pozio E. *Trends Parasitol* 2014;30:4–11. Reproduced with permission from Elsevier.

21.3.1 History

For trichinellosis, the initial discovery was made by James Paget, a medical student during cadaver dissection in London in 1835. The life cycle was reported in 1860 by Friedrich Zenker, who found, upon autopsy of a female peasant, larval stages in the muscles and adult stage with live larvae in the intestine.

On February 2, 1835 (a Monday), first year medical student James Paget, 21 years old at the time, was doing an autopsy of a middle-aged Italian (death due to tuberculosis). He found trichinae (as calcified white speck with a tiny worm inside) at St. Bartholomew's Hospital in London. Because the hospital had no microscopist nor a microscope, Paget went to the Zoology department of Natural History Museum, but, again, no microscope. He was referred to the Botany department head Robert Brown. Brown was asked by Paget if he knew anything about worms and replied "No thank God." Specimens from the same cadaver were sent by another student Thomas Wormald to Richard Owen. (Owen later became head of the Natural History Museum; Owen was archrival to Charles Darwin and advisor to Oxford Bishop Sam Wilberforce during the clergyman's debate with Darwin's bulldog Thomas Huxley.) Owen wanted to publish the finding and agreed with Paget that Paget would receive priority for the discovery. The paper was published; Owen downplayed Paget's role (giving only minor credit). Owen named the worm *Trichina spiralis*, but the genus name turned out had already been applied to a fly in 1830. So, Louis-Joseph Railliet in 1895 named *Trichinella spiralis*, and the name has remained. The disease is known as **trichinellosis,** or **trichiniasis,** or **trichinosis**. (Paget was later knighted to be Sir James.)

There is an American twist in the history of *Trichinella* studies. The father of American parasitology, then a 23-year-old doctor, Joseph Leidy, had a dinner of pork in Philadelphia in 1846. He found many white specks that reminded him of similar ones in cadavers at autopsy. He took samples to his lab at the Philadelphia Academy of Sciences. Under a microscope he found tiny encysted worms that reminded him of Owen's publication. The larvae were killed by the high temperature from cooking. His friends urged him to enter the priority race with European scientists. He refused and responded: "The important thing is that the discovery or fact should be made known. It is of little consequence who made it." (There were many competitions and debates about *Trichinella*. Some believed as larvae of *Trichuris trichiura*. Both are indeed related, both adult *Trichuris* and *Trichinella* worms possess stichocytes) (Esch 2007).

The major discovery of the complete life cycle was made by the German pathology professor Friedrich Zenker in 1860: clinical significance of the infection and conclusion that humans become infected by eating raw pork. In December 1859, a 20-year-old servant girl was admitted to a hospital at Dresden with muscle pain, fever and she supposedly had typhoid fever. She died two weeks later; Zenker immediately removed muscle tissues and found the muscle crawling with tiny worms that he recognized as trichinae. "The first clinical case of trichinosis ever recognized was also the first known fatal case," was the comment by William Campbell (who received a Nobel prize for the discovery of ivermectin). A few weeks later Zenker examined the mucous tissues of the woman's gut and found adult worms, together with larvae of the same kind that he found in muscle tissues (**ovoviviparous**). He sent samples to other parasitologists (including Rudolf Virchow and Rudolf Leuckart) who fed the worms and larvae to dogs and hogs, and the animals developed infections as well. Zenker knew that the dead woman had worked on a farm 80 miles from Dresden. He went there, and found the farmer's wife ill with the same symptoms as the dead woman, so was the butcher who prepared the pig. He found the Christmas celebration ham and sausage still on the site, with trichinae in them (Kean *et al.* 1978).

Many trichinellosis cases were found in Germany at the time. Virchow recognized the role of the pig in the transmission of trichinellosis to humans; he advocated and campaigned for control measures, much to the displeasure of butchers and veterinarians. Meat inspection rules were set up. The US pork was sold to Europe. US Congress passed the rule for inspection of exported pork in 1890; it was signed into law by President Benjamin Harrison. Still, France had an embargo of US pork and Germany required re-inspection. With trained inspectors, the level of trichinellosis in Germany in 1870 was lower than those in the US in 1970. In the first half of the 20th century, the level of trichinellosis was high in US. Passage of a law banning the feeding of uncooked garbage to hogs to control hog cholera reduced the prevalence of trichinellosis, however, still the disease remained. "*Trichinella spiralis* is destined to remain with us, both in nature and in the laboratory. It is not an endangered species" (Campbell, quoted by Esch, 2007).

Cooking at 58.5°C for 10 minutes, or freezing at −20°C for 3 days will kill the L1 larvae of the common *Trichinella spiralis*. However, the cold-adapted species, *T. native*, is resistant to freezing.

21.3.2 Life cycle

Please see Figure 21.5 for the life cycle, from CDC.[6]

With various sylvatic and urban or domestic life cycles, *Trichinella* has a unique and interesting biology. It actually requires only one host, with larvae and adults living in different organs (muscle and gut). An infected animal serves as a definitive host and potential intermediate host. A second host is required to perpetuate the life cycle of *Trichinella*. The domestic cycle most often involves pigs and anthropophilic rodents, but other domestic animals such as horses can be involved. (This association with pigs, rats, and humans in the domestic cycle reminds one of the Wilbur and Templeton pair in *Charlotte's Web*, the novel by E. B. White in 1952.) In the sylvatic cycle, the range of infected animals is great, but animals most often associated as sources of human infection are bear, moose and wild boar.

[6] https://www.cdc.gov/dpdx/trichinellosis/index.html

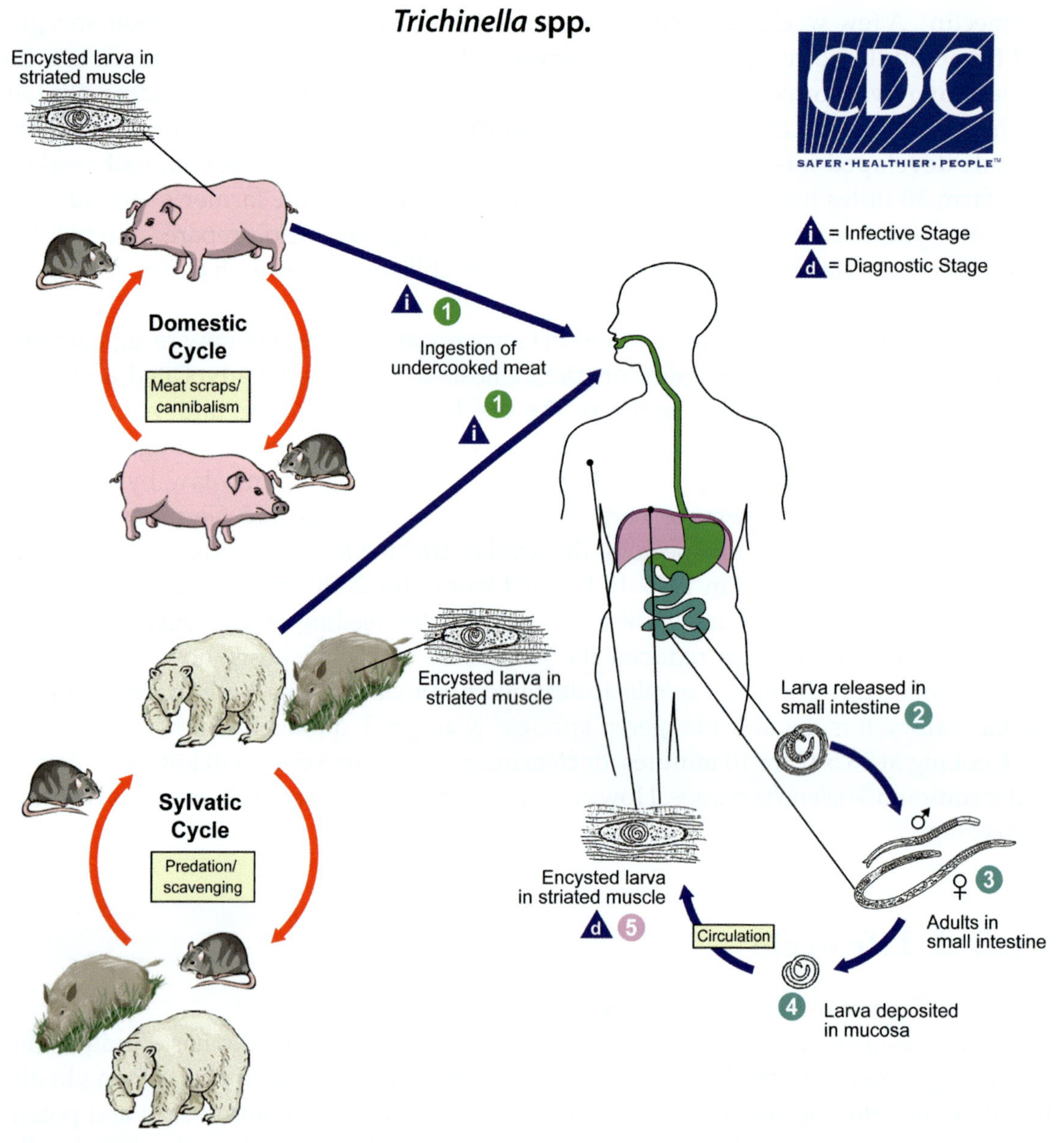

Fig. 21.5 ■ Life cycle of *Trichinella spiralis*. Depending on the classification used, there are several species of *Trichinella: T. spiralis, T. pseudospiralis, T. nativa, T. murelli, T. nelsoni, T. britovi, T. papuae, and T. zimbabwensis*, all but the last of which have been implicated in human disease. Adult worms and encysted larvae develop within a single vertebrate host, and an infected animal serves as a definitive host and potential intermediate host. A second host is required to perpetuate the life cycle of *Trichinella*. The domestic cycle most often involved pigs and anthropophilic rodents, but other domestic animals such as horses can be involved. In the sylvatic cycle, the range of infected animals is great, but animals most often associated as sources of human infection are bear, moose and wild boar. Trichinellosis is caused by the ingestion of undercooked meat containing

21.3.3 Pathology

Ingestion of meats with larvae leads to their release by pepsin and gastric acid in the stomach. Larvae move into the small intestine and develop into female and male adults (4 molts in 30 hours). Adult males have two lobed appendages known as alae. Their life span is about 4 weeks. After 1 week, females release larvae, and the larvae are carried via the bloodstream to various sites. The larvae migrate and invade different cells. The newborn larva possesses a sword-like stylet at its anterior end to poke holes in cells. Larvae can cause heart failure and central nervous system (CNS) damage. Many invaded cells die and the larvae leave. However, in skeletal muscle, larvae induce a **transdifferention** (reprogramming) of terminally differentiated cell. Muscle genes are shut down while collagen genes are expressed. Nuclei have DNA synthesis to become 4N. Smooth endoplasmic reticulum expands while mitochondria degenerate, to yield an anaerobic environment favorable to the larva. It eventually becomes **a nurse cell** with an infective L1 larva within. Even vascular endothelial growth factor (VEGF) is secreted to induce angiogenesis for new blood vessel to surround the nurse cell to allow nutrient entrance. Molecular studies have shown the induced changes in gene expression of primary myoblast cultures after treatment with excretory/secretory products of *Trichinella* muscle larvae (isolated from skeletal muscle) (Hernández-Ancheyta *et al.* 2018). The primary mouse myoblasts undergo increased proliferation, decreased expression of MHC and up-regulation of α-actin, as well as changes in muscle transcription factors (such as Myf5). Thus, these *Trichinella* larvae alter the normal process of skeletal muscle repair after their invasion to accomplish nurse cell formation. The encapsulated larvae may survive with the lifespan of the host; or they can die and the capsule becomes calcified. In the small intestine, adult worms live under the villi of intestinal epithelial cells. They thread through intestinal epithelium. In this sense, the adult *Trichinella* nematode is an **intra-multi-cellular parasite**. Please see Figure 21.6 for images of adults, newborns, and larvae in nurse cells (Gao *et al.* 2014). Please see the illustrations Figure 21.7(A) for *Trichinella* larva nurse cell angiogenesis (Despommier 1998) and Figure 21.7(B) for adult female demonstrating its nature as an intra-multi-cellular parasite by winding through the villi from several intestinal epithelial cells (Despommier *et al.* 2019).[7]

Fig. 21.5 (Figure on facing page) ■ encysted larvae (except for *T. pseudospiralis* and *T. papuae*, which do not encyst) of *Trichinella* species ❶. After exposure to gastric acid and pepsin, the larvae are released from the cysts ❷ and invade the small bowel mucosa where they develop into adult worms ❸. Females are 2.2 mm in length; males 1.2 mm. The life span in the small bowel is about four weeks. After 1 week, the females release larvae ❹ that migrate to striated muscles where they encyst ❺. Diagnosis is usually made based on clinical symptoms, and is confirmed by serology or identification of encysted or non-encysted larvae in biopsy or autopsy specimens. Courtesy of the CDC. Reproduced from https://www.cdc.gov/dpdx/trichinellosis/index.html

[7] https://parasiteswithoutborders.com/books/

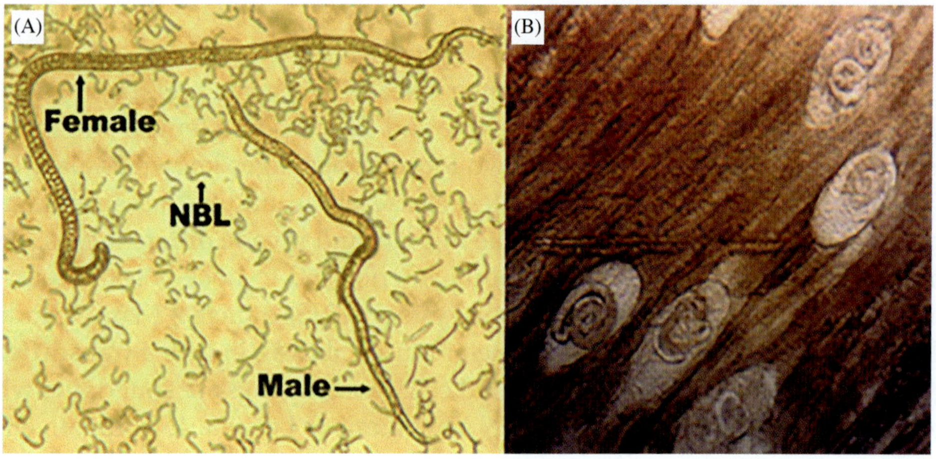

Figure 21.6: ■ Trichinella images: adults, newborns, and larvae in nurse cells. Three main life-stage forms of *T. spiralis*. (A) Adults and new born larvae (NBL) and (B) infective muscle larvae. Female adults, which develop in the small intestine, will produce new-born larvae, which then disseminate through the blood stream, invade skeletal muscles, and encyst in a collagen capsule to form a new generation of muscle larvae. Courtesy: Gao *et al. Front Physiol* 2014;4:410. Reproduced with permission from *Frontiers in Physiology* with Creative Commons Attribution 4.0 (CC-BY) International License.

Trichinellosis symptoms include fever, muscle pain, pneumonia and eosinophilia. *Trichinella* infection may also be asymptomatic. A 51-year-old man with metastatic papillary thyroid cancer underwent modified neck dissection with excision of the strap muscle at Baylor College of Medicine. Histopathology demonstrated a 275-μm encapsulated cyst containing a larva 27 μm in diameter with bacillary bands within the skeletal muscle consistent with *Trichinella* species. The patient was originally from Mexico City, Mexico, and moved to Houston, Texas, 17 years before presentation without further travel, but he had eaten raw pork 10 years ago while in Texas but denied any wild animal consumption. He mostly likely had chronic trichinellosis and was treated with albandazole, afterwards his eosinophil count showed a decrease (Kaplan *et al*. 2020).

21.3.4 Diagnosis

Muscle biopsy can be used to check parasites. Serology assays to detect anti-parasite antibodies are also available.

21.3.5 Therapy

Treatment are steroids and benzimidazoles (mebendazole and albendazole). Rapid destruction of larvae without the anti-inflammatory steroids may exacerbate host inflammatory response and worsen the disease.

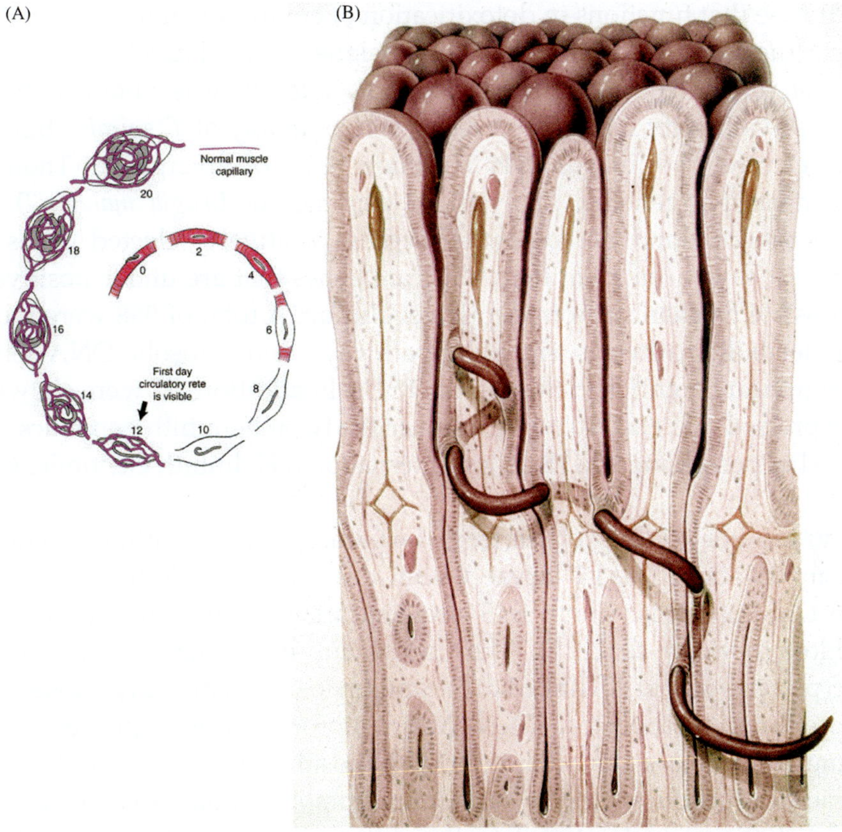

Figure 21.7: ■ *Trichinella* illustrations. (A) *Trichinella* larva and nurse cell angiogenesis. Angiogenesis and nurse cell formation. Angiogenesis begins on about Day 12 after the larva invades the muscle cell and ceases by Day 26. Courtesy: Despommier D. *Parasitol Today* 1998;14:318–23. Reproduced with permission from Elsevier. (B) **An adult female *T. spiralis*, depicted *in situ*.** The nematode is winding through villi of intestinal epithelial cells. Drawing by Karapelou J. Courtesy: Despommier *et al. Parasitic Diseases*, 7th edition (2019). Reproduced from https://parasiteswithout-borders.com/books/ with permission from Parasites Without Borders and Daniel Griffin.

21.3.6 Genome

Similar to *Strongyloides stercoralis*, *Trichinella spiralis* also has **XX-XO** chromosome structure (females with five pairs of autosomes and XX, **12** chromosomes; males five pairs and X, 11 chromosomes). The 64 Mb size genome possesses **15,808** protein-coding genes. Unexpectedly, operons are not found, the "existence of operons in this nematode remains an open question" (Mitreva *et al*. 2011). Compared to the free-living *Caenorhabditis elegans* genome, there are less gene numbers, and more gene family deaths in this parasitic nematode. However, there is an expansion of **secreted DNase II-like protein** family (125 gene copies), which may be functional in host-parasite interactions and immune modulation. In addition, there is evidence of lateral gene transfer (LGT), notably the **cyanase,** cyanate hydratase that functions in detoxification of environmental cyanate. Whether the same works in the worm, or cyanase has been assigned a novel function, is not yet known (Zarlenga *et al.* 2016). The genome of *Trichinella murrelli* was obtained by long-read sequencing. Its availability not only corrects prior assembly of *T. spiralis*, but also shows synteny between the two linages over 7 million years of divergence (Thompson *et al.* 2017). By comparative genomic analysis for genomes of *Brugia malayi, Trichuris suis, Ancylostoma ceylanicum* and *Caenorhabditis elegans*, positively selected genes (**PSGs**) of *Trichinella spiralis* have been identified. PSGs are genes that are under positive selection, as well as possible mechanisms of adaptive evolution. A total of **968** were found. Genes involved in metabolic pathways, signaling pathways, and cytosolic DNA-sensing pathways were significantly enriched among the PSGs. In addition, 57 were shown to be differentially expressed (Qu *et al.* 2019). In another study on helminth genomics, ***Trichinella nativa*** is listed as possessing **10,175** genes (International Helminth Genomics Consortium 2019).

Excretory/secretory **(E/S)** proteins from the parasite serve multiple functions, including immunomodulation. The L1 larvae within the nurse cells induce gene reprogramming of host muscle cells. Their E/S proteins are thus of interest to investigators (Sofronic-Milosavljevic *et al.* 2015). They show anti-inflammatory capacity. Juveniles produce E/S proteins (about 40) linked to the antigenic sugar named **tyvelose** (3,6-dideoxy arabinohexose) from stichocytes. These juvenile-produced E/S products can induce changes in muscle cells towards nurse cells. Both the adult worm E/S products (AES) and muscle larvae E/S products (MES) have immunomodulation capacity, as shown in a mouse model. E/S products stimulate the differentiation of host regulatory T cells through activating dendritic cells. These are $CD4^+CD25^+Foxp3^+$ and $CD4^+CD25^-Foxp3^+$ Treg cells expressing IL-10 and TGFβ, resulting in the creation of a regulatory environment that benefits the survival of the parasite in the host (Sun *et al.* 2019).

21.4 *Enterobius*

Enterobius vermicularis (enteron means intestine, bios means life, vermacularis means worm-like) is commonly known as the pinworm or seatworm. It has the largest geographic range of any helminth. Enterobiasis is the most common nematode infection of humans in temperate climate. Contracting pinworm is the most prevalent nematode infection in the United States. Estimates of the prevalence of pinworm varies from 209 million to almost **1 billion** people worldwide from all socioeconomic classes. If the higher estimate is accurate, pinworm would be a close second to the roundworm *Ascaris lumbricoides* in nematode infection of humans worldwide. In the United States, prevalence is estimated at 20–42 million people. More than 30% of children worldwide are infected. Pinworm infection is common in day care centers, elementary schools, orphanages, and mental hospitals (Vermund and Wilson 2000; Lohiya *et al.* 2000; Kucik *et al.* 2004).

Humans are the only known host of *Enterobius vermicularis*. Close association between humans and *Enterobius vermicularis* existed for a long time. Humans have been known to contract pinworms since the early days in Africa. Pinnworm ova in human **coprolites** have been seen in archaeological sites; *Enterobius* DNA has been detected from North and South American human coprolites.

In northern Chile, the archaeological site Lluta 57 in the Lluta Valley, provides a chronology of settlements: from pre-Inca or Late Intermediate Period (LIP) (1200–1400 CE), through the Inca or Late period (LP) (1400–1530 CE), ending with Hispanic conquest and the Inca State collapse (1530–1600 CE) known as the Hispanic contact period (HCP). In a paleoparasitological investigation using the coprolites to gain insight into the dynamics of parasitism, 14 human coprolites from the three time periods were rehydrated, submitted to spontaneous sedimentation, and examined by light microscopy for the presence of intestinal parasite eggs and pollen grains. Pinworm eggs were absent in LIP but present as a hyper-infection in LP, interpreted as the result of transition from living in isolated hamlets to larger, more densely populated villages. In this site, 21% of analyzed coprolites of the LP and HCP were positive for *Enterobius vermicularis*. A prevalence of 21% could be considered a pinworm hyper-infection. Pinworms are transmitted by direct person-to-person contact, by retro-infection, and through air-borne environmental contamination. Overcrowding facilitates transmission and, consequently, increases prevalence (de Souza *et al.* 2018).

The study of coprolites has been a theme of archaeology in the American Southwest. In a coprolite from a cave in Utah, United States, has shown "*Enterobius vermicularis*: 10,000-year-old human infection" (Fry and Moore 1969). "A feature of archaeoparasitology on the Colorado Plateau is the ubiquity of pinworm infection. As a crowd parasite, this ubiquity signals varying concentrations of populations. Our recent analysis of coprolite deposits from 2 sites revealed the highest prevalence of infection ever recorded for the region. … Both sites can be placed in the Ancestral Pueblo III occupation (AD 1100–1300) …" (Reinhard and Camacho 2019). In sum, the presence of evidence of pinworms corresponds with the rise of agricultural activity, versus pre-agricultural hunter-gatherer activity (Reinhard *et al.* 2016).

A pinworm egg was discovered in coprolite of an ancestor of mammals in Brazil. The cynodont is considered to be a stem group mammal and the pinworm egg is 240 million years old, shedding "light on the early origin of pinworms in vertebrates" (Hugot *et al.* 2014). Such an achievement for paleoparasitology!

If you can access this internet site,[8] you can have an intimate view on pinworms, in a case study of a 32-year old woman and her 5-year-old daughter, in South Korea. "The patient and her family members were treated with oral albendazole, and at follow-up 2

[8] https://www.nejm.org/doi/10.1056/NEJMicm1811156

months later the anal pruritus in the patient and her daughter had disappeared" (Kang and Lee, 2019).

An interesting fact about the pinworm is **haplodiploidy**: male worms are haploid, female worms are diploid. *Enterobius vermicularis* the only known endoparasite with haplodiploidy. This feature will be discussed in a later section.

21.4.1 History

Linnaeus named the worm in 1758 (he named a total of six, the names of three are still the same today: *Ascaris lumbricoides, Taenia solium, Fasciola hepatica*; the other three have changed). He named the pinworm *Ascaris vermicularis*, today it is *Enterobius vermicularis.*

In 1824, the curator of the Natural History Museum in Vienna Johann Bremer gave a detailed description of the pinworm and distinguished it from the other roundworm groups including *Ascaris*. He wrote: "The *Oxyuris vermicularis* lives in the large intestine, principally in the rectum. ... The oxyurids are equally tapered toward their anterior extremity, but they are terminated at the other end by a point (this is especially true of the females) ..." (Kean *et al.* 1978).

21.4.2 Life cycle

Please see Figure 21.8 for the life cycle, from CDC.[9]

The typical pinworm lifespan is 2 months. Adult females are 1 cm in size, with long but small posterior end (hence the term pinworm); males are smaller at 0.2–0.5 cm (Robinson 2004). Males die after copulation; females die after egg laying (up to 15,000 eggs). Within the thin shells, pinworms embryonate and become infective within 6 hours (iL3, infective L3 larvae). This allows autoinfection (retrofection or **retroinfection)**.

Please see Figure 21.9 for pinworm eggs and adults as seen under light microscopy.[8]

21.4.3 Pathology

Pinworm eggs are deposited along perianal folds, they can also be airborne contaminating the environments (clothing, etc.). A child may scratch the anal area and then put her/his finger in the mouth to allow eggs to be swallowed. The iL3 will migrate from the anal skin back into the rectum. In addition, the wandering worms can migrate along the vagina for ectopic infection. There was a case of viable pinworm eggs present in the ovary of a 31-year-old woman (Powell *et al.* 2013).

[9] https://www.cdc.gov/dpdx/enterobiasis/index.html

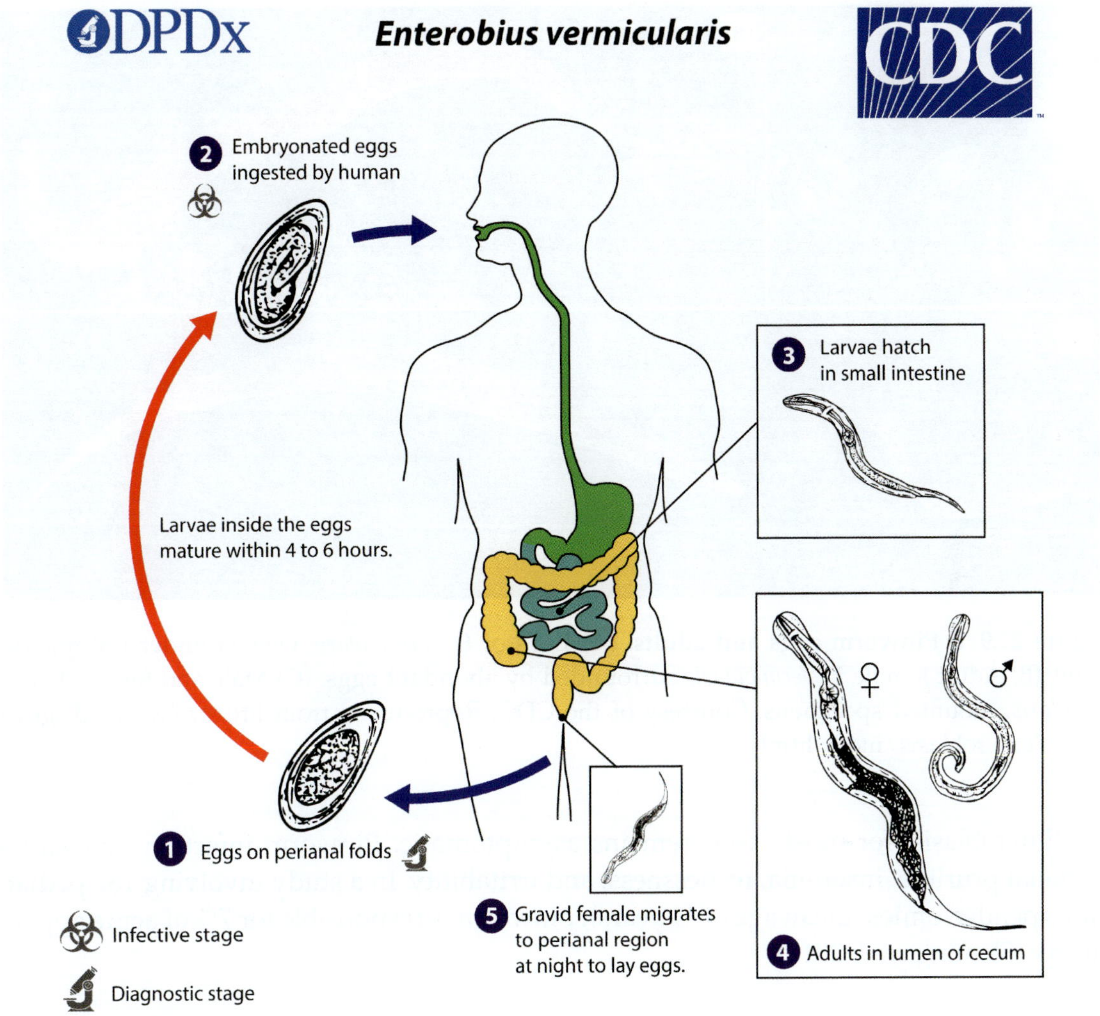

Figure 21.8 ■ Life cycle of *Enterobius vermicularis*. Gravid adult female *Enterobius vermicularis* deposit eggs on perianal folds ❶. Infection occurs via self-inoculation (transferring eggs to the mouth with hands that have scratched the perianal area) or through exposure to eggs in the environment (e.g. contaminated surfaces, clothes, bed linens, etc.) ❷. Following ingestion of infective eggs, the larvae hatch in the small intestine ❸ and the adults establish themselves in the colon, usually in the cecum ❹. The time interval from ingestion of infective eggs to oviposition by the adult females is about one month. At full maturity adult females measure 8 to 13 mm, and adult males 2 to 5 mm; the adult life span is about two months. Gravid females migrate nocturnally outside the anus and oviposit while crawling on the skin of the perianal area ❺. The larvae contained inside the eggs develop (the eggs become infective) in 4 to 6 hours under optimal conditions ❶. Rarely, eggs may become airborne and be inhaled and swallowed. Retroinfection, or the migration of newly hatched larvae from the anal skin back into the rectum, may occur but the frequency with which this happens is unknown. Courtesy of the CDC. Reproduced from https://www.cdc.gov/dpdx/enterobiasis/index.html

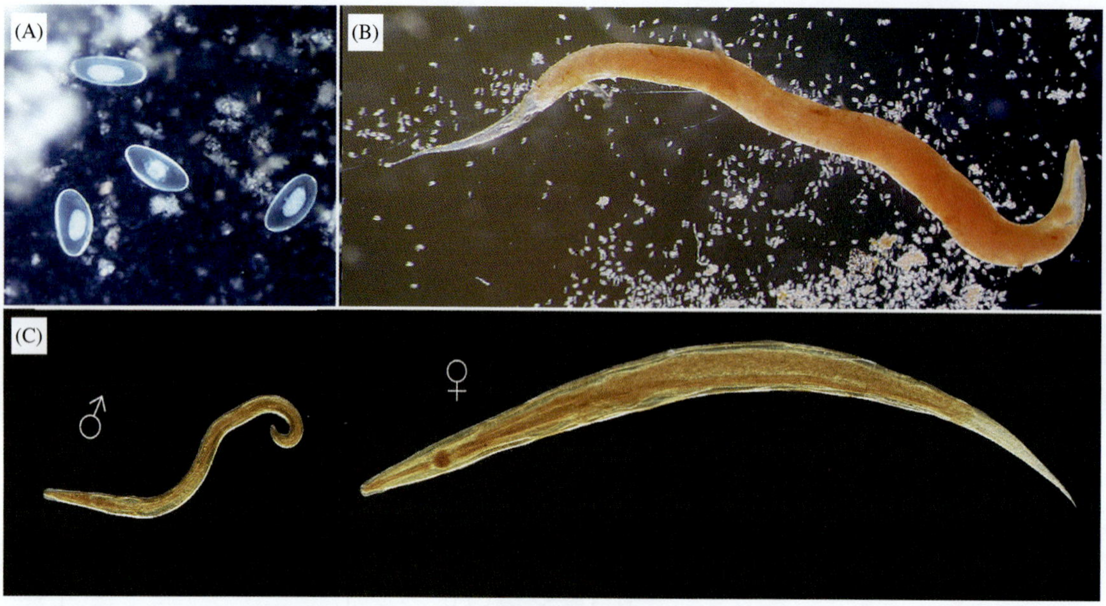

Figure 21.9 ■ Pinworm eggs and adults. (A) Eggs of *E. vermicularis* viewed under UV microscopy. (B) Adult female *E. vermicularis* surrounded by abundant eggs. (C) Male and female *E. vermicularis*, mounted specimens. Courtesy of the CDC. Reproduced from https://www.cdc.gov/dpdx/enterobiasis/index.html

Enterobiasis, for most cases, remains asymptomatic. Pinworm infection may cause perianal pruritus, insomnia, restlessness, and irritability. In a study involving 182 pediatric appendectomies (mean age of 11 years), pinworm is responsible for 7% of acute appendicitis (Fleming *et al.* 2015).

21.4.4 Diagnosis

A perianal sticky tape test is performed on the suspected individual. Microscopic identification of eggs collected in the perianal area is the method of choice for diagnosing enterobiasis. To improve sensitivity, collection should be done in the morning, before defecation and washing, by pressing transparent cellulose tape ("Scotch test", cellulose tape slide test) on the perianal skin and then examining the tape placed on a microscope slide.

21.4.5 Therapy

Treatment is pyrantel pamoate, albendazole or mebendazole. A repeat treatment is necessary and family members may also be needed for test and treatment.

21.4.6 Genome

Enterobius vermicularis possesses **12,895** genes, as listed in a study on helminth genomics (International Helminth Genomics Consortium 2019).

21.4.7 Haplodiploidy

Pinworms are the only known endoparasites with haplodiploidy. Males are haploid and develop parthenogenetically from unfertilized eggs. Females are diploid and develop from fertilized eggs. Pinworms are the only endoparasitic group in which this form of reproduction has been found.

Enterobius vermicularis only infects humans. Other pinworms infect other species. A total of 52 species of pinworms can infect primates, such as the orangutan (Foitová *et al.* 2014). Pinworm species infect mammals (especially rodents and lagomorphs, rabbits), birds, reptiles, amphibians; however, pinworms are rare in fish. Pinworms, belonging to the group named Oxyurida, have 850 species and are found in intestines of vertebrates and arthropods (especially cockroaches) (Adamson 1994).

As pinworms are highly host-specific, co-evolution between the parasite and its host may take place. An analysis between pinworms and their primate hosts was performed to test the hypothesis on the positive covariation between parasite body size (reflecting its longevity) and host longevity. The finding was that female parasite body length positively correlates with host longevity (but not the males), suggesting that host longevity may represent a constraint on the evolution of body size of the pinworms (Sorci *et al.* 1997).

Haplodiploidy is a sex determination system. It is found in insects: bees, ants, and wasps (Hymenoptera). In honeybees, drones are haploid, but workers and the queen bee are diploids (but only "royal jelly" as food for the queen). The same sex determination system is found in the pinworms. For example, for a frog pinworm, females have eight chromosomes and males with four chromosomes. Other pinworm species females have 6, 8, 10, or 12 chromosomes (and males half the number). To our knowledge, the chromosome number of *Enterobius vermicularis* is not yet known. As haplodiploid organisms, pinworms tend to have life histories that involve high levels of inbreeding. Parasitism may be originated from bacterial feeding ancestors through oral contamination. Thus, no extra-intestinal migration is necessary (as found in other STHs). Although pinworms show little variety in the life cycle, they have been able to colonize a greater diversity of hosts than other parasites. Pinworms are the only lineage to have radiated in arthropods and vertebrates (Adamson 1994).

Host-parasite interactions may be related to the evolution of ploidy. Sarah Otto (University of British Columbia, Vancouver) and colleagues have reported "a discovery that emerged from host–parasite models in which ploidy levels were allowed to evolve:

selection is more likely to favor diploidy in host species and haploidy in parasite species. Essentially, when parasites must evade a host's immune system or defense response, selection favors parasitic individuals that express a narrow array of antigens and elicitors, thus favoring haploid parasites over diploid parasites. Conversely, when hosts must recognize a parasite before mounting a defensive response, selection favors hosts with a broader arsenal of recognition molecules, thus favoring diploid hosts over haploid hosts. These results are consistent with the predominance of haploidy among parasitic protists" (Nuismer and Otto 2004). "Theoretical studies have clarified many important genetic advantages to haploidy (for example, lower mutation load, more rapid spread of beneficial alleles) and to diploidy (for example, protection from somatic mutation, heterozygote advantage). More and more, these advantages are being experimentally tested and validated. … Experiments exploring fitness and adaptation of haploids and diploids across a range of environments promise to shed some light on the relative importance of genetics and the environment in shaping the patterns of life cycle diversity surrounding us" (Otto and Gerstein 2008).

Summary & Key Concepts

- The life cycle of *Strongyloides stercoralis* can alter between free-living stage with both male and female adult worms and parasite cycle which is involved in autoinfection in humans with only parthenogenetic female adult worms.
- Infection of strongyloidiasis can be divided into 3 phases: cutaneous, pulmonary, and intestinal. In people with immunodeficiency, autoinfection is amplified, which can cause hyper-infection and disseminated infection.
- *Trichinella* is the world's largest intracellular parasite, at the same time, the smallest nematode parasite in humans, with *Trichinella spiralis* as the major species.
- *Trichinella* is a foodborne pathogen, transmitted to humans by consuming undercooked contaminated meat from pigs or game animals.
- *Trichinella* larvae induces transdifferention (reprogramming) of terminally differentiated skeletal muscle cell to turn the muscles cell into nurse cell for the larval parasite and to allow nutrient entrance.
- *Enterobius vermicularis* the only known endoparasite with haplodiploidy: male worms are haploid, female worms are diploid.
- *Enterobiasis* is the most common nematode infection of humans in the temperate climate.

References

Adamson M. Evolutionary patterns in life histories of Oxyurida. *Int J Parasitol* 1994;24(8):1167–77.

Alban L, Häsler B, van Schaik G, Ruegg S. Risk-based surveillance for meat-borne parasites. *Exp Parasitol* 2020;208:107808.

Barratt JLN, Lane M, Talundzic E, *et al.* A global genotyping survey of *Strongyloides stercoralis* and *Strongyloides fuelleborni* using deep amplicon sequencing. *PLoS Negl Trop Dis* 2019;13(9):e0007609.

Bhasin A, Yura E, Boyd D, Kuksuk L, Flaherty JP. Case report: Incidentally discovered *Strongyloides stercoralis* infection after urinary diversion. *Am J Trop Med Hyg* 2020;102(6):1396–8.

Bruschi F, Pozio E. *Trichinella britovi. Trends Parasitol* 2020;36(2):227–8.

Cox FE. History of human parasitology. *Clin Microbiol Rev* 2002;15(4):595–612.

Cox FEG, editor. *The Wellcome Trust Illustrated History of Tropical Diseases* (1996, The Wellcome Trust, London).

de Souza MV, da Silva LGR, Silva-Pinto V, *et al.* New paleoparasitological investigations from the pre-inca to hispanic contact period in northern Chile. *Acta Trop* 2018;178:290–6.

Despommier DD. How does *Trichinella spiralis* make itself at home? *Parasitol Today* 1998;14(8): 318–23.

Despommier DD, Griffin DO, Gwadz RW, Hotez PJ, Knirsch CA. *Parasitic Diseases*, 7th edition (2019). Parasites Without Borders. https://parasiteswithoutborders.com/books/

Devleesschauwer B, Praet N, Speybroeck N, *et al.* The low global burden of trichinellosis: Evidence and implications. *Int J Parasitol* 2015;45(2–3):95–9.

Esch GW, *Parasites and Infectious Disease* (2007, Cambridge).

Fleming CA, Kearney DE, Moriarty P, Redmond HP, Andrews EJ. An evaluation of the relationship between *Enterobius vermicularis* infestation and acute appendicitis in a paediatric population — A retrospective cohort study. *Int J Surg* 2015;18:154–8.

Foitová I, Civáňová K, Baruš V, Nurcahyo W. Phylogenetic relationships between pinworms (Nematoda: Enterobiinae) parasitising the critically endangered orang-utan, according to the characterisation of molecular genomic and mitochondrial markers. *Parasitol Res* 2014;113(7): 2455–66.

Fry GF, Moore JG. *Enterobius vermicularis*: 10,000-year-old human infection. *Science* 1969; 166(3913):1620.

Gao F, Wang R, Liu M. *Trichinella spiralis*, potential model nematode for epigenetics and its implication in metazoan parasitism. *Front Physiol.* 2014;4:410.

Gardner MP, Gems D, Viney ME. Extraordinary plasticity in aging in *Strongyloides ratti* implies a gene-regulatory mechanism of lifespan evolution. *Aging Cell* 2006;5(4):315–23.

Gottstein B, Pozio E, Nöckler K. Epidemiology, diagnosis, treatment, and control of trichinellosis. *Clin Microbiol Rev* 2009;22(1):127–45.

Greaves D, Coggle S, Pollard C, Aliyu SH, Moore EM. *Strongyloides stercoralis* infection. *BMJ* 2013;347:f4610.

Hernández-Ancheyta L, Salinas-Tobón MDR, Cifuentes-Goches JC, *et al. Trichinella spiralis* muscle larvae excretory-secretory products induce changes in cytoskeletal and myogenic transcription factors in primary myoblast cultures. *Int J Parasitol* 2018;48(3–4):275–85.

Hugot JP, Gardner SL, Borba V, *et al.* Discovery of a 240 million year old nematode parasite egg in a cynodont coprolite sheds light on the early origin of pinworms in vertebrates. *Parasit Vectors* 2014;7:486.

Hunt VL, Tsai IJ, Selkirk ME, Viney M. The genome of *Strongyloides* spp. gives insights into protein families with a putative role in nematode parasitism. *Parasitology* 2017;144(3):343–58.

Hunt VL, Tsai IJ, Coghlan A, *et al.* The genomic basis of parasitism in the *Strongyloides clade* of nematodes. *Nat Genet* 2016;48(3):299–307.

Ikuno H, Ishikawa T, Norose K. Status of strongyloidiasis in Japan, 2000–2017. *Am J Trop Med Hyg* 2020;103(2):727–34.

International Helminth Genomes Consortium. Comparative genomics of the major parasitic worms. *Nat Genet* 2019;51(1):163–74.

Kang WH, Jee SC. *Enterobius vermicularis* (pinworm) infection. *N Engl J Med* 2019;381(1):e1.

Kaplan J, Finch CJ, Weatherhead JE. Coiled encapsulated *Trichinella* larva. *Am J Trop Med Hyg* 2020;103(5):1754.

Kean BH, Mott KE, Russell AJ, editors, *Tropical Medicine and Parasitology. Classic Investigations* volume I and II (1978, Cornell, Ithaca).

Kucik CJ, Martin GL, Sortor BV. Common intestinal parasites. *Am Fam Physician*. 2004;69(5):1161–8.

Lohiya GS, Tan-Figueroa L, Crinella FM, Lohiya S. Epidemiology and control of enterobiasis in a developmental center. *West J Med* 2000;172(5):305–8.

McGuire E, Welch C, Melzer M. Is *Strongyloides seropositivity* associated with diabetes mellitus? A retrospective case-control study in an East London NHS Trust. *Trans R Soc Trop Med Hyg* 2019;113(4):189–94.

Mitreva M, Jasmer DP, Zarlenga DS, *et al.* The draft genome of the parasitic nematode *Trichinella spiralis. Nat Genet* 2011;43(3):228–35.

Murrell KD, Pozio E. Worldwide occurrence and impact of human trichinellosis, 1986–2009. *Emerg Infect Dis* 2011;17(12):2194–202.

Nemetschke L, Eberhardt AG, Hertzberg H, Streit A. Genetics, chromatin diminution, and sex chromosome evolution in the parasitic nematode genus *Strongyloides*. *Curr Biol* 2010;20(19): 1687–96.

Nuismer SL, Otto SP. Host-parasite interactions and the evolution of ploidy. *Proc Natl Acad Sci USA* 2004;101(30):11036–9.

Nutman TB. Human infection with *Strongyloides stercoralis* and other related *Strongyloides* species. *Parasitology* 2017;144(3):263–73.

Otto SP, Gerstein AC. The evolution of haploidy and diploidy. *Curr Biol* 2008;18(24):R1121–4.

Page W, Judd JA, Bradbury RS. The unique life cycle of *Strongyloides stercoralis* and implications for public health action. *Trop Med Infect Dis* 2018;3(2):53.

Powell G, Sarmah P, Sethi B, Ganesan R. *Enterobius vermicularis* infection of the ovary. *BMJ Case Rep* 2013;2013:bcr2013201146.

Pozio E. Searching for *Trichinella*: Not all pigs are created equal. *Trends Parasitol* 2014;30(1):4–11.

Prendki V, Fenaux P, Durand R, Thellier M, Bouchaud O. Strongyloidiasis in man 75 years after initial exposure. *Emerg Infect Dis* 2011;17(5):931–2.

Qu Z, Li W, Zhang N, *et al.* Comparative genomic analysis of *Trichinella spiralis* reveals potential mechanisms of adaptive evolution. *Biomed Res Int* 2019;2019:2948973.

Rajamanickam A, Munisankar S, Bhootra Y, *et al.* Metabolic consequences of concomitant *Strongyloides stercoralis* infection in Type 2 diabetes mellitus. *Clin Infect Dis* 2018.

Reinhard KJ, Camacho M. Pinworm infection at salmon ruins and Aztec Ruins: Relation to Pueblo III Regional Violence. *Korean J Parasitol* 2019;57(6):627–33.

Reinhard KJ, Araújo A, Morrow JJ. Temporal and spatial distribution of *Enterobius vermicularis* (Nematoda: Oxyuridae) in the Prehistoric Americas. *Korean J Parasitol* 2016;54(5):591–603.

Roberts, LS, Janovy, J Jr, Nadler S. *Foundations of Parasitology*, 9th edition (2013, McGraw Hill).

Robinson E. Microscopic photography of a pinworm. *J Audiov Media Med* 2004;27(1):35–6.

Rosenthal BM, LaRosa G, Zarlenga D, *et al.* Infect human dispersal of *Trichinella spiralis* in domesticated pigs. *Infect Genet Evol* 2008;8(6):799–805.

Rostami A, Gamble HR, Dupouy-Camet J, Khazan H, Bruschi F. Meat sources of infection for outbreaks of human trichinellosis. *Food Microbiol* 2017;64:65–71.

Ruetsch C, Delaunay P, Armengaud A, *et al.* Inadequate labeling of pork sausages prepared in Corsica causing a trichinellosis outbreak in France. *Parasite* 2016;23:27.

Singer R, Xu TH, Herrera LNS, *et al.* Prevalence of intestinal parasites in a low-income Texas community. *Am J Trop Med Hyg* 2020;102(6):1386–95.

Sofronic-Milosavljevic L, Ilic N, Pinelli E, Gruden-Movsesijan A. Secretory products of *Trichinella spiralis* muscle larvae and immunomodulation: Implication for autoimmune diseases, allergies, and malignancies. *J Immunol Res* 2015;2015:523875.

Sorci G, Morand S, Hugot JP. Host-parasite coevolution: comparative evidence for covariation of life history traits in primates and oxyurid parasites. *Proc Biol Sci* 1997;264(1379):285–9.

Sun XM, Guo K, Hao CY, Zhan B, Huang JJ, Zhu X. *Trichinella spiralis* excretory-secretory products stimulate host regulatory T cell differentiation through activating dendritic cells. *Cells* 2019;8(11):1404.

Thompson PC, Zarlenga DS, Liu MY, Rosenthal BM. Long-read sequencing improves assembly of *Trichinella* genomes 10-fold, revealing substantial synteny between lineages diverged over 7 million years. *Parasitology* 2017;144(10):1302–15.

Vazquez Guillamet LJ, Saul Z, Miljkovich G, *et al. Strongyloides stercoralis* infection among Human Immunodeficiency Virus (HIV)-infected patients in the United States of America: A case report and review of literature. *Am J Case Rep* 2017;18:339–46.

Vermund SH, Wilson CM. Pinworm (*Enterobius vermicularis*). *Semin Pediatr Infect Dis* 2000;11(4):2526.

Wilson NO, Hall RL, Montgomery SP, Jones JL. Trichinellosis surveillance--United States, 2008–2012. *MMWR Surveill Summ* 2015;64(1):1–8.

Zarlenga D, Wang Z, Mitreva M. *Trichinella spiralis*: Adaptation and parasitism. *Vet Parasitol* 2016;231:8–21.

Zarlenga DS, Rosenthal BM, La Rosa G, Pozio E, Hoberg EP. Post-Miocene expansion, colonization, and host switching drove speciation among extant nematodes of the archaic genus *Trichinella*. *Proc Natl Acad Sci U S A* 2006;103(19):7354–9.

22

Juvenile Nematode Infections

22.1 Introductory Remarks

Many species of mammals serve as the definitive host of parasitic nematodes. Sometimes, eggs and larvae of mammalian nematodes may inadvertently enter humans (a child may pick up the eggs at play, or a larva may penetrate the human skin in error by assuming it to be its proper host). The major types of diseases caused by juvenile nematodes are cutaneous larva migrans (**CLM**) and visceral larva migrans (**VLM**). Whereas many species of animal nematode larvae have been documented in humans, here we only cover the major species involved in these "aberrant" nematode infections.

CLM is mostly caused by infective third stage larvae (iL3) of the hookworm species *Ancylostoma braziliense*, which is normally an intestinal parasite of cats and dogs. The juvenile worms come in contact with the exposed human body, they penetrate the skin and then migrate/move under the human skin.

VLM is caused by juveniles of other nematode species targeting animals, including **toxocariasis**, **angiostrongyliasis** and **anisakiasis**. Toxocariasis is caused by the roundworms *Toxocara canis* and *Toxocara cati*, which normally prefer dogs and cats, respectively. Children ingest the eggs of these species on the playground, and the larvae hatch in the body and migrate to different organs. This can include the eye, which leads to blindness as the result of ocular larva migrans (**OLM**). Angiostrongyliasis is caused by the rat lungworm *Angiostrongylus cantonensis*. The individuals ingest an intermediate host (gastropods: a snail or a slug) containing the iL3 and the larvae migrate to the brain. Anisakiasis is caused by the intake of undercooked or raw fish contaminated with the larvae of *Anisakis simplex* and the larvae migrate to the stomach.

22.2 *Ancylostoma*

Human hookworm infections (*Ancylostoma duodenale, Necator americanus*) are important soil-transmitted helminths (STHs) that can cause iron-deficiency anemia. However, animal hookworm infections of humans cause CLM (cutaneous means skin, larva means juvenile, migrans means migration, movement). CLM is also known as **creeping eruption**. CLM is often regarded as a syndrome while creeping eruption is the clinical sign of infection. Creeping eruption is defined as a linear or serpiginous, slightly elevated, erythematous track that moves forward in the skin in an irregular pattern. Although other helminths (such as *Loa loa*) can cause this symptom, the most common cause of creeping eruption is infection by iL3 of dog and cat hookworms; sometimes the disease is known as hookworm-related CLM **(HrCLM)** (Bowman *et al.* 2010; Feldmeier and Schuster 2012). Distribution of the disease is worldwide. It is endemic in many resource-poor communities in the developing world. HrCLM infection is more frequent in the tropical and subtropical countries of Southeast Asia, Africa, South America, Caribbean, and the southeastern part of the United States. HrCLM is of concern to the unfortunate tourists returning from tropical areas (**travel medicine**) (Hochedez and Caumes 2007).

As an example of resource-poor community with HrCLM, a study was done in a community located in the outskirts of the city Manausthe, Amazonas state, Brazil. Infection rate in the area was at 8%. For monthly observation on 476 children over 6 months, 10–15 years old, especially males, walking barefoot on sandy ground had the highest infection rate. Seasonal variability is noted, with the most infection during the rainy season. "Children from the poorest families in the resource-poor community were most vulnerable to HrCLM" (Reichert *et al.* 2018).

22.2.1 History

The first report of a child with a creeping lesion in the skin was described in England by R.J. Lee in 1874, using the name creeping eruption for the disease. In a later case, an insect larva was found in the lesion (maggot of bot fly; the fly that lays eggs on hairs of horses), hence the name larva migrans. In a study by J.L. Kirby-Smith in a free clinic in Florida in 1926, iL3 larvae were found in the lesions, and some individuals had cats and dogs in their families (as pets). HrCLM was found among all ages: for a total of 301 individuals, 14 were under 3 years of age, 242 were under 15, 148 were between 5 and 9, and 57 were between 15 and 61. There were no cases between 61 and 71, but there were 2 that were more than 71 (Kirby-Smith *et al.* 1929).

22.2.2 Life cycle

Please see Figure 22.1 for the life cycle, from CDC.[1]

The life cycle of cat and dog hookworms is similar to that of human hookworms. The most common species is ***Acylostoma braziliense*** (ankylose means hook-like, stoma

[1] https://www.cdc.gov/dpdx/zoonotichookworm/index.html

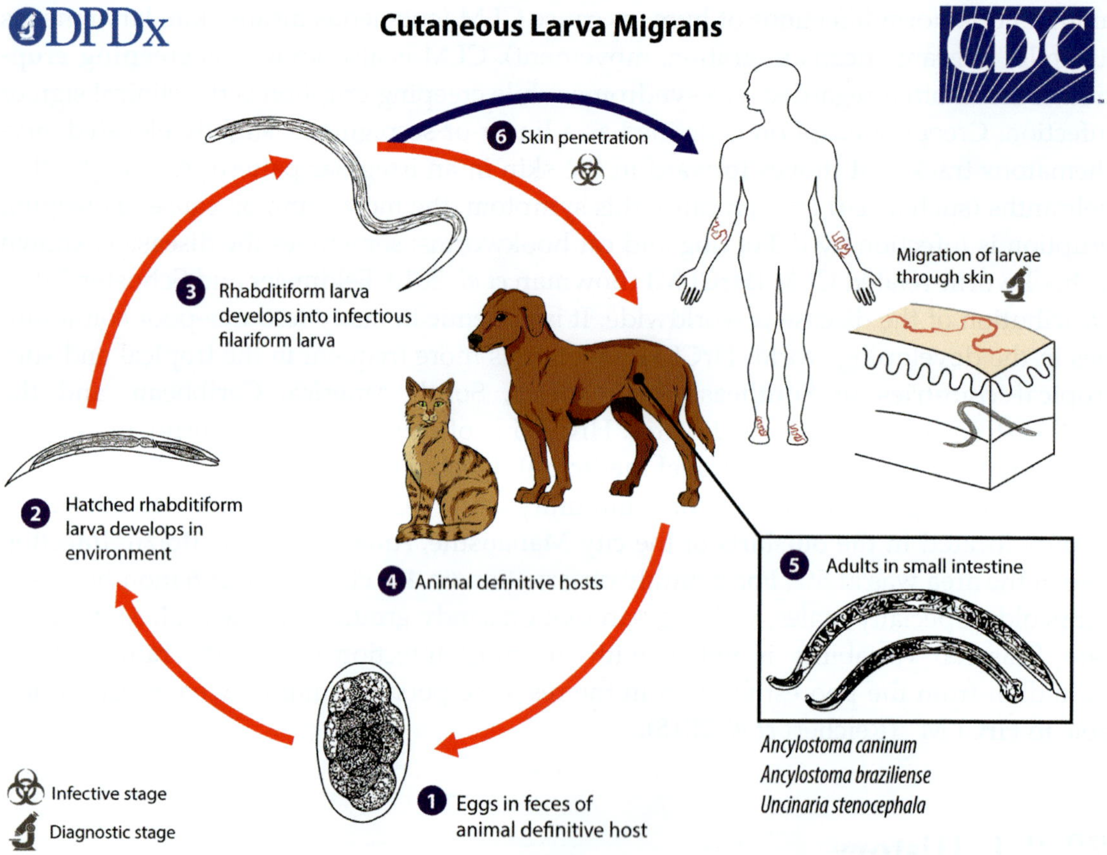

Fig. 22.1 ■ CDC Life cycle of cutaneous larval migrans. Cutaneous larva migrans (also known as creeping eruption) is a zoonotic infection with hookworm species that do not use humans as a definitive host, the most common being *Ancylostoma braziliense* and *A. caninum*. The cycle in the definitive host is very similar to the cycle for the human species, which involves tracheal migration to the small intestine. Some larvae become arrested in the tissues and serve as the source of infection for pups via transmammary (and possibly transplacental) routes. Mature hookworms reproduce in the small intestine, and eggs are passed in the animal definitive host's stool ❶, and under favorable conditions (moisture, warmth, shade), larvae hatch in 1–2 days. The released rhabditiform larvae grow in the feces and/or the soil ❷, and after 5–10 days (and 2 molts) they become filariform (third-stage) larvae that are infective ❸. These infective larvae can survive 3–4 weeks in favorable environmental conditions. On contact with the animal host ❹, the larvae penetrate the skin and are carried through the blood vessels to the heart and then to the lungs. They penetrate into the pulmonary alveoli, ascend the bronchial tree to the pharynx, and are swallowed. The larvae reach the small intestine, where they reside and mature into adults. Adult worms live in the lumen of the small intestine, where they attach to the intestinal wall. Some larvae become arrested in the tissues, and serve as source of infection for pups via transmammary (and possibly transplacental) routes ❻. Humans become infected when filariform larvae penetrate the skin ❼. With most species, the larvae cannot mature further in the human host and migrate aimlessly within the epidermis, sometimes as much as several centimeters a day. Some larvae may become arrested in deeper tissue after skin migration. Courtesy of the CDC. Reproduced from https://www.cdc.gov/dpdx/zoonotichookworm/index.html

means mouth, braziliense means Brazil). This species is found along the southeastern Atlantic coast of North America, the Gulf of Mexico and the Caribbean Sea, down to Uruguay in South America, in Africa (South Africa, Somalia, Democratic Republic of Congo, Sierra Leone), Australia, and Asia (Malaysia, Indonesia, Thailand). Other species that can cause CLM include the dog hookworm *Ancylostoma caninum* and the cat hookworm *Uncinaria stenocephala*.

22.2.3 Pathology

The larvae migrate under the skin; they cannot penetrate the dermis. The defining sign of creeping eruption is the host inflammatory response and pruritus: an unpleasant sensation that induces the individual to scratch or rub the skin. The symptom may survive for a week or so. Itching and scratching may cause secondary bacterial infection.

Creeping eruption usually appears 1–5 days after a skin penetration, but the incubation period may be ≥1 month. Typically, a serpiginous, erythematous track appears in the skin and is associated with intense itchiness and mild swelling. Usual locations are the foot and buttocks, although any skin surface encountering contaminated soil can be affected.

A 28-year-old woman returned to London from a scuba-diving holiday in Thailand; she had an intensely itchy rash on her anterior abdominal wall and buttocks, plus eosinophilia. With a diagnosis of follicular CLM, she was cured with a single dose of oral ivermectin; her pruritus settled within 4 days and palpable eruption 10 days later. "Cutaneous larva migrans is a common skin infestation in travelers returning from tropical destinations, although it can be acquired in cooler climates and even in the United Kingdom" (Lander *et al.* 2020).

22.2.4 Diagnosis

Diagnosed is based on characteristic skin lesions.

22.2.5 Therapy

Ivermectin and albendazole are administered as treatment; both oral and topical versions are available. A report has shown a 4-year-old who was playing naked in the Caribbean during vacation and got CLM in the penis; he was cured with topical ivermectin (Gelmetti *et al.* 2019).

22.2.6 Genome

Ancylostoma caninum possesses **30,918** genes (International Helminth Genomes Consortium 2019). The genome of *Acylostoma braziliense* is not yet known.

22.3 *Toxocara*

Humans are accidental hosts of toxocariasis. Normally, our pets are definite hosts. Similar to the human roundworm *Ascaris lumbricoides*, the dog roundworm is ***Toxocara canis*** (toxon means arch or bow, kara means head, worms with a bent anterior end, canis means dog), and the cat roundworm is ***Toxocara cati*** (catta means cat). These roundworms cannot complete the life cycle in the humans. They wander viscerally, and the degree of damage depends on the tissues being invaded: liver, lung, CNS, eye, as well as the number of roundworm eggs ingested by the individual. This can cause VLM and OLM, which are more severe than CLM just discussed. "Parasitic nematodes of the genus *Toxocara* are socioeconomically important zoonotic pathogens. These parasites are usually directly transmitted to the human host via the fecal–oral route and can cause toxocariasis and associated complications, including allergic and neurological disorders" (Ma *et al.* 2018).

Distribution of *Toxocara canis* and *T. cati* is worldwide, so is toxocariasis. Children with pets, or playing in areas with fecal contamination of cats and dogs, may ingest embryonated *Toxocara* eggs and get infected. In the United States, *Toxocara* may be the second most common infection after the pinworm (*Enterobius vermicularis*). (Please see Chapter 21 for pinworm.) The infection is found in rural areas, communities with poverty, and children with pets. An estimate of toxocariasis shows over 2.8 million African Americans infected; toxocariasis can lead to diminished cognitive function and epilepsy (Hotez 2014). In a study on the prevalence of toxocariasis in the United States, National Health and Nutrition Examination Survey (NHANES) for 2011–2014, the overall **seroprevalence** (seropositive result) was 5.1%, a decrease from a previous result of 13.9% for 1988–1994. The data came from 13,509 individuals (3,337 children and 10,172 adults). Adults with anti-*Toxocara* antibodies are typically males, non-White, less than college-educated, with low income. These adults and children also have increased blood lead level. "Persistent **disparities** appear to be associated with at-risk populations such as minority ethnicity and low socioeconomic status" for toxocariasis (Farmer *et al.* 2017).

Since environmental contamination with *Toxocara* eggs is a major risk factor for toxocariasis, Yadolah Fakhri (then Shahid Beheshti University of Medical Sciences, Tehran; now Hormozgan University of Medical Sciences, Bandar Abbas, Iran) and colleagues conducted a systematic literature review and meta-analysis to assess the global prevalence of *Toxocara* eggs in public places, including beaches, parks and playgrounds.

From a total of 109 studies in 40 countries, 13,895 were positive among 42,797 soil samples, yielding the pooled global prevalence of *Toxocara* eggs in public places at **21%**. The investigators also found regional differences that range from 13% to 35%. Soil samples from North and Central America had a prevalence of 13% (4,481 positives among 10,792 samples) (Fakhri *et al.* 2018). The 13% egg prevalence corresponds with the older 13.9% seroprevalence in the US (Farmer *et al.* 2017).

22.3.1 History

The first description of human infection was reported by the pioneering ophthalmic pathologist Helenor Campbell Wilder Foerster in 1950. Foerster discovered *Toxocara* larva within a child's retinal granuloma. "She is best known for her twin discoveries of the protozoal organism *Toxoplasma gondii* as the cause of a form of blinding retinal inflammation previously attributed to tuberculosis, and of the presence of the larval form of the nematode *Toxocara canis* in enucleated eyes suspected of harboring retinoblastoma" (Spencer and Zimmerman 1999).[2]

In 1952, Paul Chester Beaver at Tulane University, New Orleans, Louisiana, linked chronic eosinophilia to VLM. Three cases were reported: M.M., a 16-month white boy who had eaten dirt and also had a pet dog, P.T., a 26-month black girl with low grade fever and limping, and J.G., a 2.5-year white girl with fever and weight loss. All had eosinophilia and showed liver VLM. Parasites seen in liver sections were described: "the head end was viewed slightly obliquely and in all evident details resembled the infective stage of *Toxocara canis* or *T. cati*" (Beaver *et al.* 1952).[3]

22.3.2 Life cycle

Please see Figure 22.2 for the life cycle, from CDC.[4]

Toxocara spp. develop to third stage (L3) larvae in ovo. This dog roundworm can infect transplacentally (vertical transmission), so 100% puppies can be infected at birth. Humans ingest eggs that develop into larvae but cannot develop into adults. Humans may also be infected by consuming undercooked meat (beef, lamb, chicken, duck liver), since many mammals and birds can serve as paratenic hosts.

Dog walking may bring *Toxocara* eggs to people's homes. Olga Panova and Alexander Khrustalev (All-Russian Research Institute of Fundamental and Applied Parasitology of Animals and Plants of Name K.I. Scriabina, Moscow) conducted a small study in Moscow,

---

[2] https://jamanetwork.com/journals/jamaophthalmology/fullarticle/412049

[3] https://libguides.tulane.edu/famousalumni/PCBeaver

[4] https://www.cdc.gov/dpdx/toxocariasis/index.html

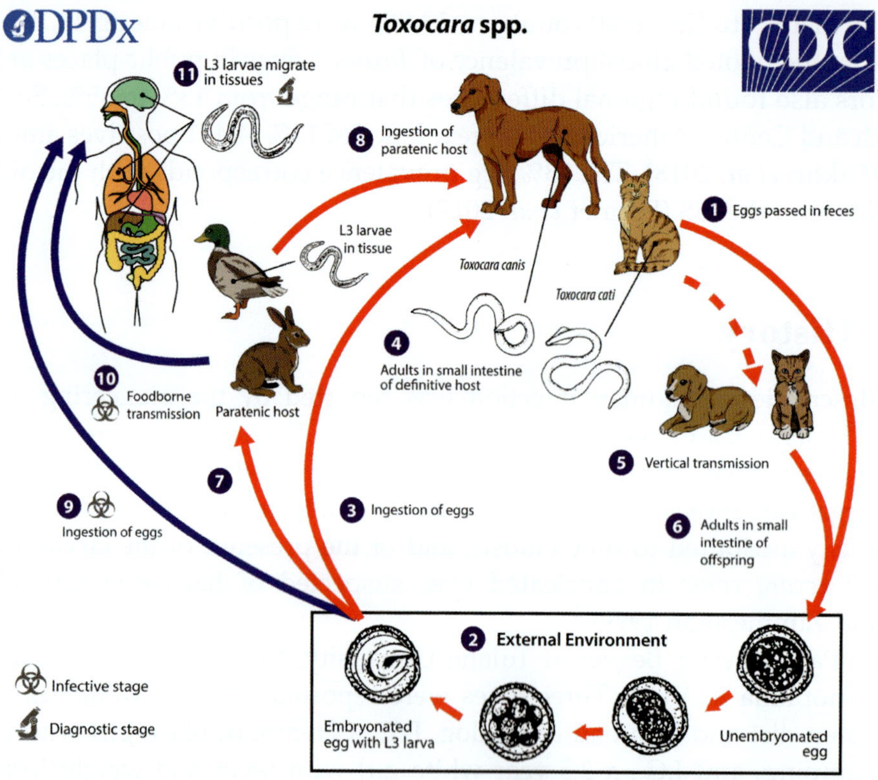

Fig. 22.2 ■ CDC Life cycle of *Toxocara species*. *Toxocara* spp. can follow a direct (one host) or indirect (multiple host) life cycle. Unembryonated eggs are shed in the feces of the definitive host (canids: *T. canis;* felids: *T. cati*) ❶. Eggs embryonate over a period of 1 to 4 weeks in the environment and become infective, containing third-stage (L3) larvae ❷. Following ingestion by a definitive host ❸, the infective eggs hatch and larvae penetrate the gut wall. In younger dogs (*T. canis*) and in cats (*T. cati*), the larvae migrate through the lungs, bronchial tree, and esophagus, where they are coughed up swallowed into the gastrointestinal tract; adult worms develop and oviposit in the small intestine ❹. In older dogs, patent (egg-producing) infections can also occur, but larvae more commonly become arrested in tissues. Arrested larvae are reactivated in female dogs during late gestation and may infect pups by the transplacental (major) and transmammary (minor) routes ❺ in whose small intestine adult worms become established ❻. In cats, *T. cati* larvae can be transmitted via the transmammary route ❺ to kittens if the dam is infected during gestation, but somatic larval arrest and reactivation does not appear to be important as in *T. canis*. *Toxocara* spp. can also be transmitted indirectly through ingestion of paratenic hosts. Eggs ingested by suitable paratenic hosts hatch and larvae penetrate the gut wall and migrate into various tissues where they encyst ❼. The life cycle is completed when definitive hosts consume larvae within paratenic host tissue ❽, and the larvae develop into adult worms in the small intestine. Humans are accidental hosts who become infected by ingesting infective eggs ❾ or undercooked meat/viscera of infected paratenic hosts ❿. After ingestion, the eggs hatch and larvae penetrate the intestinal wall and are carried by the circulation to a variety of tissues (liver, heart, lungs, brain, muscle, eyes) ⓫. While the larvae do not undergo any further development in these sites, they can cause local reactions and mechanical damage that causes clinical toxocariasis. Courtesy of the CDC. Reproduced from https://www.cdc.gov/dpdx/toxocariasis/index.html

with 8 dogs and their owners walking on grass in the house yards of residential areas or in city parks. Immediately after walking the dogs' paws and shoes of their owners were washed with warm water and the washings were checked for the presence of *Toxocara* eggs. The number of eggs found on the paws was about twice as high as ones on the shoes (19.4% from 36 paw washings versus 11.0% from 44 shoe washings). Within the positive samples, eggs of *T. cati* were found in 83%, and *T. canis*, 42% (species identified by size and egg-shell structure). In the washings from shoes of people that do not own dogs, parasite eggs were not found. The investigators concluded that *Toxocara* eggs can be transferred from contaminated soil to people's homes on animal paws and human shoe soles (Panova and Khrustalev 2018).

22.3.3 Pathology

The dog or cat roundworm cannot complete the life cycle in humans. Four forms of toxocariasis have been noted: VLM, OLM, neural larva migrans (**NLM**) or neurotoxocariasis (including eosinophilic meningoencephalitis), and covert toxocariasis (**CT**) or common toxocariasis. Whereas CT shows mild symptoms (coughs, headache, abdominal pain), NLM shows larval migration to the brain (Moreira *et al.* 2014). Young children tend to get VLM and older children skew towards OLM. This may be due to different worm strains preferring different tissues (tissue tropism), or due to repeated infections and host immune response.

Ingested embryonated eggs develop into larvae. Larvae invade the eyes, liver, lungs, and CNS. After weeks to months of migration, the larvae die, followed by host immediate-type and delayed-type hypersensitivity responses, as defined by the formation of eosinophilic granulomas. In the eyes, the granuloma may be responsible for blindness.

A case of VLM was documented at a university hospital in Marrakech, Morocco (Gakosso *et al.* 2020). The 9-year-old child "living in countryside, with a notion of cohabitation with canids" had abdominal pain for 15 days, and was diagnosed with VLM and eosinophilia, possessing anti-*Toxocara canis* antibodies, hepatomegaly and liver damage (from ultrasound and radiology). He was treated with oral albendazole.

A case of *T. canis*-related gastroenteritis and peritonitis was reported at a university hospital in Kadıköy/İstanbul, Turkey (Arslan *et al.* 2019). The 29-year-old female had abdominal distention, for which an abdominal drainage catheter was inserted in the left lower quadrant at the outpatient clinic. Her symptoms had started 1 month before: anorexia, nausea, vomiting, stinging abdominal pain, and swelling in the abdomen. "She also had no contact with new pets or animals. However, she stated that she ate fish and salad in a restaurant 1 day before the first symptoms began." The patient had eosinophilia, but tested negative for *Entamoeba histolytica, Fasciola hepatica*, and hydatid cysts. Her serum IgG levels for *Strongyloides* sp., *Ascaris* sp., and *Schistosoma mansoni* were slightly positive above the upper limit, but her *T. canis* IgG was elevated. She was treated with oral albendazole for 5 days; her ascites and peripheral eosinophilia regressed completely within a week (Arslan *et al.* 2019).

Most cases of ocular toxocariasis are caused by *Tococara canis* larvae in the eye. A case involving *T. cati* was documented in Iran. The 6-year-old child, with complaint of blurred vision in his right eye, was found to have lesions in the peripheral retina. For his serological assays, ELISA using *T. canis* excretory/secretory (E/S) antigen showed low antibody titer, whereas using *T. cati* E/S protein revealed high antibody titer. "Hence, we believe that ocular toxocariasis is caused by *T. cati*" (Zibaei *et al.* 2014). The child was treated with oral albendazole and prednisolone for 3 weeks; he showed improvement.

22.3.4 Diagnosis

Serological assays are used for diagnostic purposes, such as enzyme-linked immunosorbent assay (ELISA) based on *Toxocara* excretory/secretory (**TES**) products.

22.3.5 Therapy

Treatment are anti-inflammatory drugs and benzimidazoles.

22.3.6 Genome

The draft genome of *Toxocara canis* was first published by Chinese scientists with international collaborators (Zhu *et al.* 2015). The genome is 317 Mb in size, 13.5% repetitive DNA, with **18,596** protein-coding genes. Transcriptomes were also studied, in both larval and adult stages. They reported mucins that can induce host Th2 response, immunomodulatory molecules (transforming growth factor *beta* and neutrophil inhibitors), SCP (sperm coating protein), and a secretome (870 molecules). Korean scientists also investigated the *T. canis* genome and reported **20,178** genes (Kong *et al.* 2016). Genes involved in cuticle metabolism have been proposed as potential drug targets.

Toxocara cati is the most common parasitic nematode of cats. With sponsorship from the Cornell Feline Health Center Program, Dwight Bowman (Cornell University) and colleagues are currently sequencing its genomic DNA using Oxford Nanopore (long-read) and Illumina (short-read) technologies.[5]

Proteomics aspects of *Toxocara canis* have been explored. **TES** products have been investigated. A total of **646** TES proteins has been identified by gel electrophoresis and

[5] https://www.vet.cornell.edu/research/awards/201904/genomictranscriptomic-analysis-toxocara-cati-most-common-parasitic-nematode-cats

mass spectrophotometry. These proteins may be useful as potential diagnostics and vaccines. Please see Figure 22.3 for TES (da Silva *et al.* 2018).

22.4 *Angiostrongylus*

Angiostrongylus cantonensis is the rat lungworm. It can cause meningoencephalitis in humans who have ingested contaminated water and vegetables containing larvae (iL3), or infected molluscs. In fact, it is now recognized as the leading cause of **eosinophilic meningitis** worldwide. This is an emerging disease expanded from south China to other parts of Asia, Australia, Brazil, Caribbean, Pacific Islands, and continental United States (Louisiana, Texas, Oklahoma, and Florida). Over **2,800** cases of human infection have been reported in 30 countries (Barratt *et al.* 2016). Hawaii Island is the epicenter of angiostrongyliasis in the United States: with 2.4 human cases per year for 2010–2014, 9 cases in 2015, and 21 cases in 2016, showing an upward trend (Jarvi *et al.* 2017).

Meningoencephalitis can be fatal. A tragic case happened to an individual in Australia. Sam Ballard, a 19-year-old rugby player had swallowed a slug on a dare in 2010. He ended up in intensive care, suffered brain damage, and became paralyzed due to angiostrongyliasis. In 2018 he died at the age of 28.

22.4.1 History

In 1935, H.T. Chen described a nematode in the lung of rats in China. Its capacity for human infections was soon reported in Taiwan, in 1944. The life cycle involving mollusc as an obligatory intermediate host was discovered in Australia in 1955. Commonly known as **rat lungworm disease**, the agent is now known as *Angiostrongylus cantonensis* (angeion means vessel, strongylus means round, cantonensis means Canton, a city in south China, today's name is Guangzhou).

22.4.2 Life cycle

Please see Figure 22.4 for the life cycle, from CDC.[6]

The normal host of *A. cantonensis* is a rat (black rat or brown rat). Snails and slugs (gastropod molluscs) are intermediate hosts. There can be many paratenic or transport hosts including crustaceans, pigs, and cattle.

There are 20 species of *Angiostrongylus*, with only two infecting humans. *A. cantonensis* causes eosinophilic meningitis; another species, ***A. costaricensis*** stays in the mesenteric arterioles and causes peritonitis in infected humans.

[6]https://www.cdc.gov/dpdx/angiostrongyliasis_can/index.html

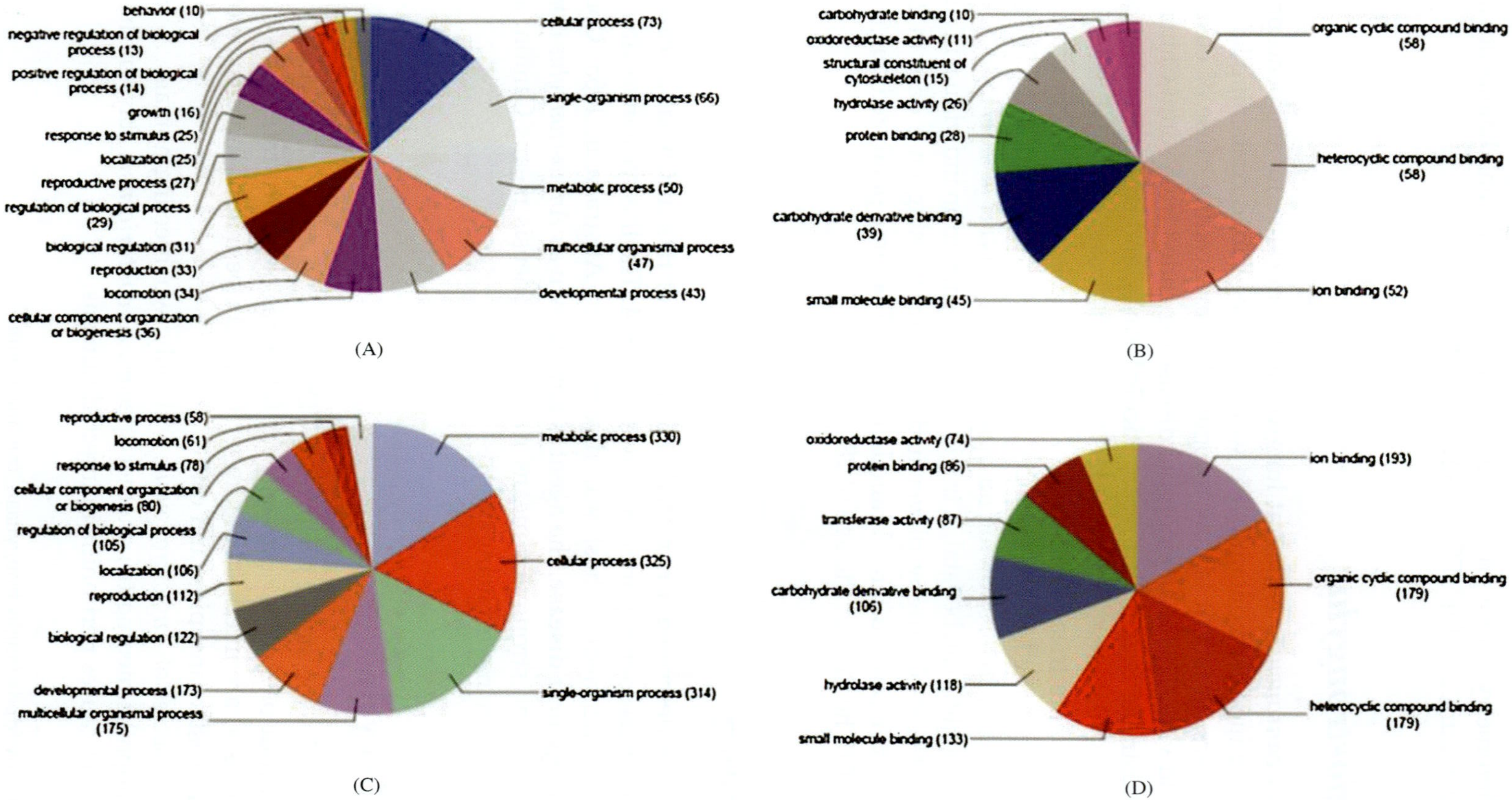

Fig. 22.3 ■ ***Toxocara canis* TES.** GO pie chart shows representation of the proteins categorized according to biological process (A and C) and molecular function (B and D) in the TES and larval extract of *T. canis*, respectively. Courtesy: da Silva *et al. Vet Parasitol* 2018;259:25–34. Reproduced with permission from Elsevier.

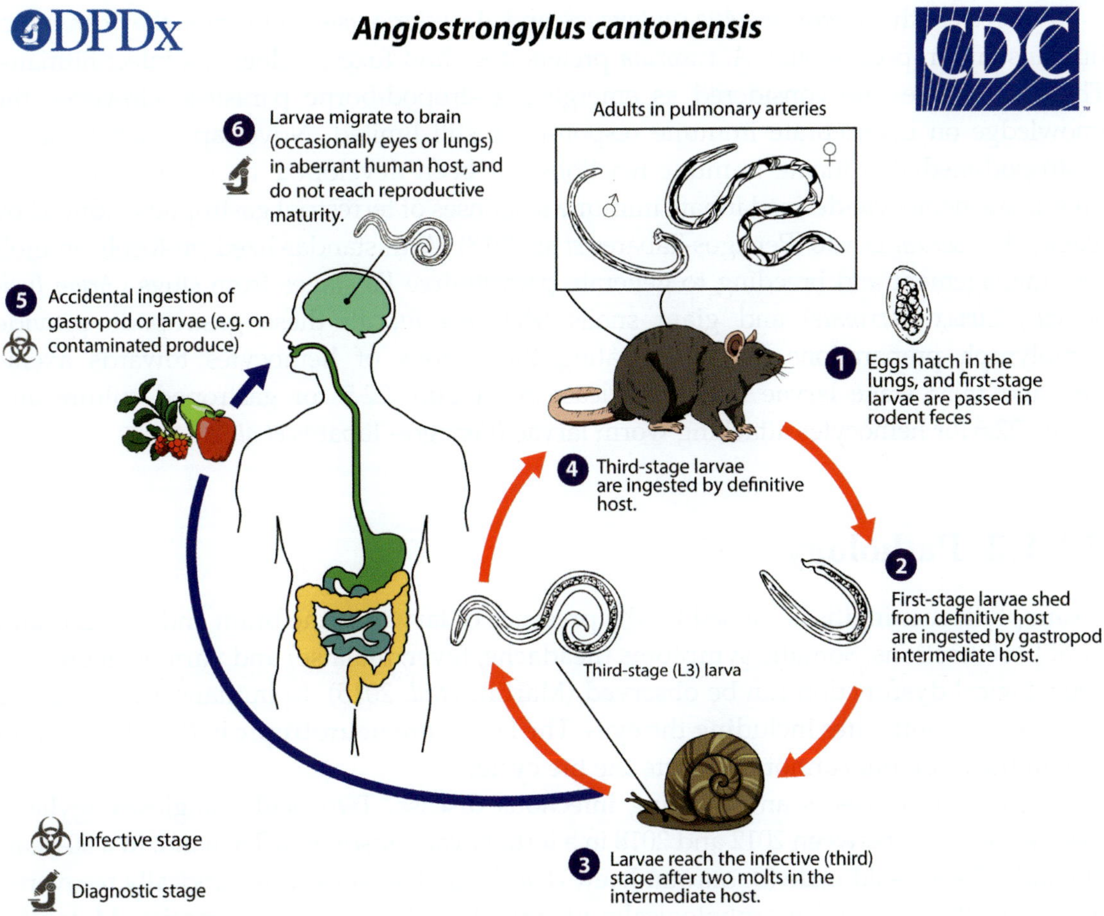

Fig. 22.4 ■ CDC Life cycle of *Angiostronylus cantonensis*. Adult worms of *A. cantonensis* live in the pulmonary arteries and right ventricle of the normal definitive host ❶. The females lay eggs that hatch in the terminal branches of the pulmonary arteries, yielding first-stage larvae. The first-stage larvae migrate to the pharynx, are swallowed, and passed in the feces. They penetrate or are ingested by a gastropod intermediate host ❷. After two molts, third-stage larvae are produced ❸ which are infective to mammalian hosts. When the infected gastropod is ingested by the definitive host, the third-stage larvae migrate to the brain where they develop into young adults ❹. The young adults return to the venous system and then the pulmonary arteries where they become sexually mature. Of note, various animals act as paratenic (transport) hosts: after ingesting the infected snails, they carry the third-stage larvae which can resume their development when the paratenic host is ingested by a definitive host. Humans can acquire the infection by eating raw or undercooked snails or slugs infected with the parasite; they may also acquire the infection by eating raw produce that contains a small snail or slug, or part of one ❺. There is some question whether or not larvae can exit the infected gastropods in slime (which may be infective to humans if ingested, for example, on produce). Infection may also be acquired by ingestion of invertebrate paratenic hosts containing L3 larvae (e.g. crabs, freshwater shrimp). In humans, larvae migrate to the brain, or rarely to the lungs, where the worms ultimately die ❻. Larvae may develop to fourth or fifth stage in the human host, but seem to be incapable of maturing fully. Courtesy of the CDC. Reproduced from https://www.cdc.gov/dpdx/angiostrongyliasis_can/index.html

Whereas both *Angiostrongylus cantonensis* and *A. costaricensis* prefer rats, they can infect humans (anthropozoonotic). *A. vasorum* prefers dogs and foxes; it does not infect humans. These nematodes are considered as emerging gastropod-borne parasites. However, the knowledge on invertebrate immune responses is still limited. Novel approach to study gastropod-mediated innate immune reactions has been developed: an in vitro system to investigate hemocyte-derived innate immune responses of terrestrial gastropods induced by axenic *A. vasorum* larvae (Penagos-Tabares *et al.* 2018). With standardized protocols on mollusc management and breeding to generate parasite-free F0 stages from slugs (*Arion lusitanicus*, *Limax maximus*) and giant snails (*Achatina fulica*), these gastropods provide hemolymph preparations for investigating the actions of hemocytes towards axenic first and third stage larvae (L1, L3). Please see Figure 22.5 for gastropod culture and Figure 22.6 for hemocytes attacking worm larvae (Penagos-Tabares *et al.* 2018).

22.4.3 Pathology

Eosinophilic meningitis is caused by the presence of larvae in the brain and the resultant local host reactions. Somatic symptoms (headache, fever, malaise) and various degrees of neurological dysfunction can be observed (Martins *et al.* 2015). In humans, the L3 larvae migrate to various sites including the eyes. The larvae are **neurotropic** in that they go and stay in the brain but cannot complete the life cycle.

Angiostrongyliasis is an emerging infectious disease. Two ocular angiostrongyliasis cases were found between 2012 and 2018 in a tertiary care hospital in Thailand, in a 50-year-old and a 70-year-old male (Boonroumkaew *et al.* 2020). Parasites were surgically recovered from patients' eyes and morphologically identified as *Angiostrongylus* species. Molecular analysis allowed species identification to be *A. cantonensis*, by PCR of the small subunit ribosomal RNA internal transcribed spacer region and cytochrome c oxidase subunit 1.

Similar to the case of Sam Ballard in Australia mentioned before, a case of eosinophilic meningitis due to *A. cantonensis* was reported in a 9-month-old male baby from Vietnam, presented with fever and seizures (Pham Thu *et al.* 2020). The baby lived in a rural area where farming was widespread. His blood and cerebrospinal fluid (CSF) ELISA were positive for *A. cantonensis*, and a mobile worm was seen in the CSF. The patient was treated (albendazole, dexamethasone, mannitol, prednisolone) and gained full recovery. Likewise, in the Caribbean, the first cases (a total of 8) of laboratory-confirmed **neuroangiostrongyliasis** were reported between 2002 and 2017 on the island of Martinique, French West Indies (Dard *et al.* 2020). So, *Angiostrongylus cantonensis* is on the move (its range is spreading).

22.4.4 Diagnosis

Diagnosis is difficult, but patient history can be helpful (eating contaminated food, visiting endemic areas like tourists returning from Hawaii). A definitive diagnosis is the

Fig. 22.5 ■ Gastropod culture. Terrestrial gastropods maintained under controlled standardized conditions. Adult specimens of (A) the Iberian slug (*Arion lusitanicus*), (B) the giant garden slug (*Limax maximus*), and (C) the giant African snail (*Achatina fulica*). (D) Glass container used for reproduction of *L. maximus*. (E) *Limax* slugs chasing one another (due to their special mating behaviour) in reproduction container. (F) Eggs and freshly hatched F0 specimens of *L. maximus*. (G) Slugs were maintained in plastic containers with humidified absorption paper and fed lettuce, cucumber fruits, carrot roots, champignons, rabbit pelleted food and dry dog food. (H) Giant snails were maintained in plastic containers on terrarium soil and fed in the same manner as the slugs with addition of a calcium supplement. Courtesy: Penagos-Tabares *et al. Parasitol Res* 2018;117:1211–24. Reproduced with permission from Springer Nature.

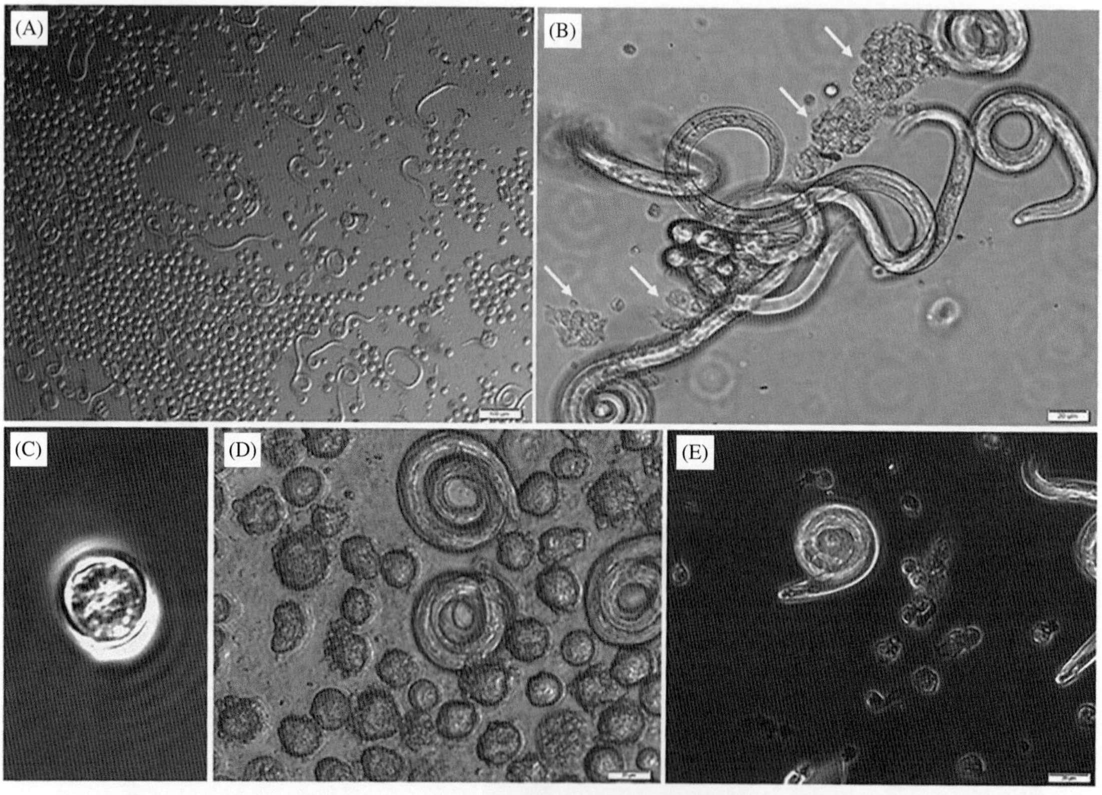

Fig. 22.6 ■ Gastropod hemocytes attacking worm larvae. Co-cultures of gastropod hemocytes and *A. vasorum* larvae. (A) *Limax maximus* hemocytes co-cultured with axenic and viable *A. vasorum* L1. (B) Cluster of *Arion lusitanicus* hemocytes acting against *A. vasorum* L1s forming aggregated material (arrows, 30 min). (C) Non-activated *Limax maximus* hemocyte. (D) *Limax maximus* hemocytes reacting against *A. vasorum* L1 showing activated cell surface (arrows, 30 min). (E) *Achatina fulica* hemocytes acting against *A. vasorum* L1 at an early time point in the reaction (arrows, 5 min). Courtesy: Penagos-Tabares *et al. Parasitol Res* 2018;117:1211–24. Reproduced with permission from Springer Nature.

detection of *Angiostrongylus cantonensis* larvae in the cerebrospinal fluid (CSF) or the eye of suspected patients.

22.4.5 Therapy

Albendazole and mebendazole plus corticosteroids are used as anti-parasitic and anti-inflammatory treatments.

22.4.6 Genome

Transcriptomes and genomes of *A. cantonensis* were published by several groups: Brazilian and American scientists (Morassutti *et al.* 2013), Taiwanese scientists (Wang *et al.* 2013), and Malayan and Thai scientists (Yong *et al.* 2015). The first study concentrated on gene transcription and proteome, and a total of **28,080** open reading frames (ORFs) were obtained. In addition, immune-diagnostic and vaccine candidates such as the **galectins**, sugar-binding proteins with affinity for β-galactoside sugars, such as N-acetyllactosamine (6 gene copies) were identified. In the second study, transcriptome from the L5 larvae (first isolating L3 from infected snails and then feeding L3 to rats, finally isolating L5 from rat brain 21-day post-infection) was analyzed. There were **31,487** unique genes, with expression of antioxidant, heat shock protein and protease genes in the L5 larvae. In the third study, 260 Mb DNA was analyzed, yielding **17,482** predicted genes. There were **7,737** predicted proteins, including 34 excretory/secretory (E/S) proteins.

22.5 *Anisakis*

For the nematode ***Anisakis simplex*** (aniso means different, akon means hook, simplex means simple), its normal hosts are marine mammals. Humans eat infected raw fish and the L3 larvae stay in the stomach wall, leading to eosinophilic granuloma. Repeat contact with the larvae induces host sensitization, with the production of IgE and potential anaphylactic shock.

With increased awareness of less red meat (beef and pork) and more seafood (marine fish, squids and octopi), human anisakiasis has become an emerging disease. Since the 1960s, over **20,000** cases have been reported worldwide (most likely an underestimate, due to unreported cases). Raw fish is a beloved cuisine in many cultures (think ceviche in Peru, sushi and sashimi in Japan); when imported elsewhere these dishes become popular in the new locations (think sushi in the US). In Japan, there are 2,000 to 3,000 cases of anisakiasis annually (Baird *et al.* 2016). Approximately 60 cases of anisakiasis have been described in the US (Li *et al.* 2015).

Cooking fish kills the larvae (to 63–74°C). However, larvae of *Anisakis* species have been observed to be alive if frozen for a short period at −20°C. The US Food and Drug Administration (FDA) has recommended that fish be kept frozen at −20°C for at least 168 hours or blast-frozen at −35°C for at least 15 hours (Aibinu *et al.* 2019).

Since commercial blast freezing of caught fish kills nematode larvae, there is no need to avoid sushi and sashimi. Indeed, there may even be benefits. It has been shown that gut microbiome in the Japanese contain novel genes for unique carbohydrate degrading enzymes, *Bacteroides* have genes via horizontal gene transfer (HGT) from marine microbes associated with seaweed (nori used to wrap sushi). "Consumption of hyper hygienic, mass produced, highly processed and calorie-dense foods is testing how rapidly the microbiota of individuals in industrialized countries can adapt while being deprived of the environment reserves of microbial genes that allow adaptation by lateral transfer" (Hehemann *et al.* 2010).

The presence of parasites, including *Anisakis* spp. larvae in fishery products jeopardizes their safety and quality, which is a matter of concern and a challenge for government authorities, as well as for food business operators, and a potential health risk to consumers. Paula Ramos (Portuguese Institute for the Sea and Atmosphere, Lisbon) has proposed laboratory and education strategies towards the control of parasite in food products. She wrote: "The two complementary parts of this work, the laboratorial activity component that provided support to fish supply chain and the educational component that helped disseminate information concerning parasites, were essential in furnishing improved data to assess and minimize the level of risk to humans, associated with the consumption of fish" (Ramos 2020). In this 10-year study, no *Anisakis* larvae were collected from the farmed fish. The practice of freezing trash fish used to feed farmed fish, and the placement of nets at the water entry points of the earth ponds, in order to avoid wild fish introduction, were simple and important measures that were implemented to prevent *Anisakis* and other parasites entering fish farms.

However, fishery products containing parasites are being commercialized. The majority are dead *Anisakis* iL3 larvae, with the exception of live larvae collected from fresh fish. Live larvae can give the consumers a risk of anisakiasis. Dead larvae are associated with an allergenic potential to sensitized individuals (*Anisakis* allergens are thermostable). "More research is needed with regard to the potential allergenicity of dead parasites, collected from dried salted cod and cans of cod, since this specimen constitute one of the most preferred fish by the Portuguese" (Ramos 2020). (For Portuguese cuisine, have you tried bacalao?)

22.5.1 History

In 1960, Pieter Hendrik van Thiel (University of Leiden, the Netherlands) reported 11 cases (accumulated in the previous decade) of acute abdominal syndrome in previously healthy adults, with juvenile nematode worms boring deep into the gut wall, requiring their endoscopic removal within 24 hr of appearance of symptom. This became the first report on anisakiasis. Since the larvae are found in cod, haddock, herring, and mackerel, the agent has been named **herring worm**, or cod worm. Many other marine fishes can carry the nematode, their definitive hosts are marine mammals, including cetaceans (dolphins, whales) and pinnipeds (seals) (Van Thiel 1962; Audicana and Kennedy 2008).

22.5.2 Life cycle

Please see Figure 22.7 for the life cycle, from CDC.[7]

[7] https://www.cdc.gov/dpdx/anisakiasis/index.html

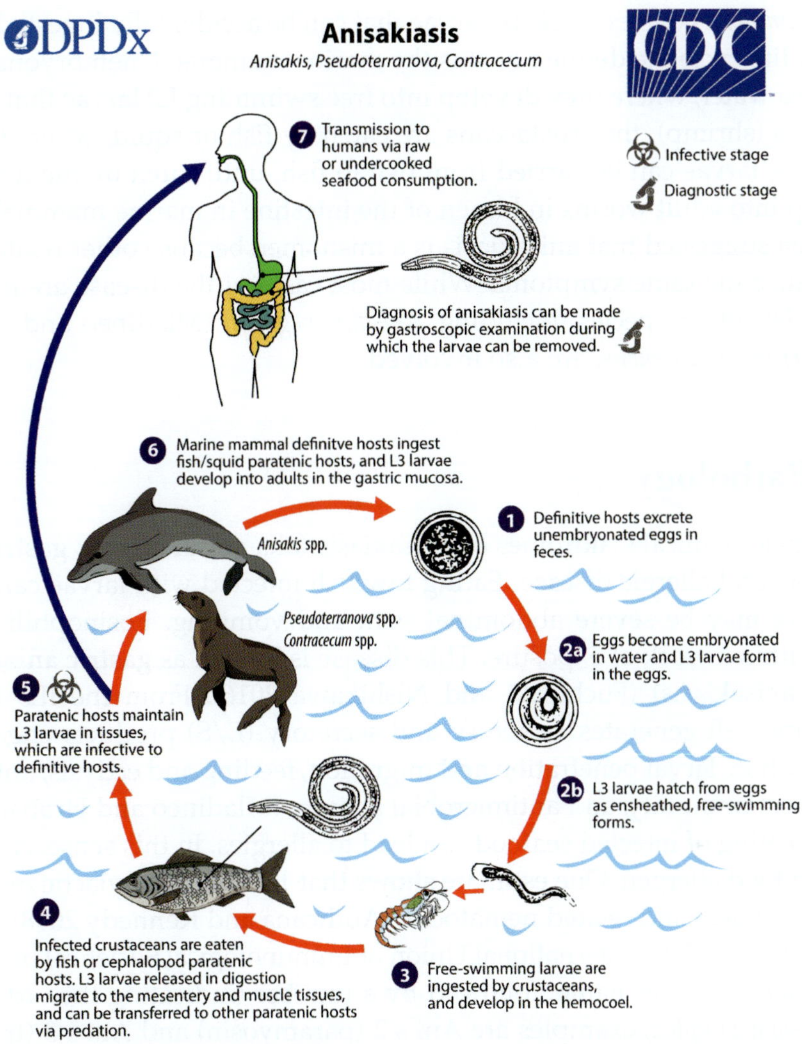

Fig. 22.7 ■ CDC Life cycle of *Anisakis simplex*. Adult stages of anisakid nematodes reside in the stomach of marine mammals, where they are embedded in the mucosa in clusters. Unembryonated eggs produced by adult females are passed in the feces of marine mammals ❶. The eggs become embryonated in water, undergoing two developmental molts ❷a, and hatch from the eggs as free-swimming ensheathed third-stage (L3) larvae ❷b. These free-swimming larvae are then ingested by crustaceans ❸. The ingested larvae grow within the crustacean hemocoel, and become infective to fish and cephalopod paratenic hosts. After preying upon infected crustaceans, the digested L3 larvae migrate from the paratenic host intestine into the abdominal cavity, and eventually to the tissues of the mesenteries and skeletal muscle. Through predation, tissue-stage L3 larvae can be transmitted among paratenic hosts ❹. Fish and squid maintain L3 larvae that are infective to humans and marine mammals ❺. When fish or squid containing third-stage larvae are ingested by definitive host marine mammals, the larvae molt twice and develop into adult worms ❻. After ingestion by humans, the anisakid larvae penetrate the gastric and intestinal mucosa, causing the symptoms of anisakiasis ❼. Courtesy of the CDC. Reproduced from https://www.cdc.gov/dpdx/anisakiasis/index.html

Anisakis simplex is one example of larvae that can be accidentally ingested by humans. In its normal life cycle the definite host is the marine mammal. Unembryonated eggs are released to sea water, where they develop into free swimming L2 larvae that can be taken by crustaceans (shrimp), the crustaceans are eaten by fish or squid, where they develop to 3 cm in size, larvae can be carried from fish to fish, until eaten by the definitive host. They develop into adult worms in lumen of the intestine in marine mammals.

It has been suggested that anisakiasis is a misnomer, because other related nematode larvae can cause the same symptoms. While most cases of the disease are indeed due to *Anisakis simplex*, other species, including *Anisakis pegreffii* (Mladineo and Hrabar 2020) and *Pseudoterranova decipiens*, are also involved.

22.5.3 Pathology

There are 4 major clinical syndromes of anisakiasis (aka anisakidosis): gastric, intestinal, extraintestinal, and allergic disease. Eating raw fish infected with larvae can lead to anisakiasis. There may be severe abdominal pain and vomiting. Eosinophilic granuloma may occur within 1 week of exposure. This disease is known as **gastric anisakiasis** (gastrointestinal anisakiasis) (Fuchizaki and Nishikawa 2016). From the iL3 larvae, their excretory gland cell generates excretory and secretory (E/S) products engaged in host tissue degradation, larval penetration and migration, feeding and ecdysis, antigenic interaction with host immunity, and antimicrobial activity (Mladineo and Hrabar 2020).

Frequent eating of infected seafood can lead to allergies. In this sense, *Anisakis* can be classified as a food allergen. One estimate shows that 10% of anaphylactic response could be caused by *Anisakis* and related nematodes (Audicana and Kennedy 2008). For allergen classification, WHO/IUIS (International Union of Immunological Societies) uses the 3-letter genus and 1-letter species name, followed by a number (indicating the order of discovery). For *Anisakis simplex*, examples are Ani s 2 (paramyosin) and Ani s 3 (tropomyosin). Cross-reactivity of the nematode allergens to allergens from other invertebrates have been shown: Ani s 2 to an allergen of dust mite, and Ani s 3 to a different dust mite allergen and an allergen of cockroach. A total of **14** *Anisakis simplex* allergens have approved IUIS names (Aibinu *et al.* 2019). This disease is known as **allergic anisakiasis**. The most severe symptom, anaphylactic shock, can be fatal.

The ingestion of raw seafood infected with nematode larvae of the Anisakidae family can cause gastric anisakiasis. The majority of the infections involve a single larva, however, there were instances of multiple infection, as documented in 14 cases in Japan — most with 2 or 3 larvae, and most due to consumption of raw mackerel (Shimamura *et al.* 2016). An extreme case of gastric hyperinfection was reported in Portugal: "A 43-year-old Portuguese woman living in Lisbon was admitted to the emergency department complaining of the sudden onset of nausea, epigastric pain, asthenia, intense cold, and low blood pressure (67/45 mmHg), 24 h after consuming a grilled scabbard fish.... Over 140 anisakid larvae were removed by gastroscopy" (Baptista-Fernandes *et al.* 2017).

Endoscopists should therefore be aware of the potential for multiple infections by *Anisakis* and the need for a thorough inspection of all parts of the stomach when encountering such cases.

Besides gastrointestinal anisakiasis, *Anisakis simplex* is etiologic agent responsible for food allergy, as already discussed. This condition was seen in a case study of a 61-year-old female presented to the emergency department of a Japanese hospital with generalized itchy, erythematous hives 2 hr after ingestion of raw mackerel (in sashimi). From generalized urticarial and subsequent anaphylaxis, she rapidly recovered with administration of epinephrine and endoscopic extraction of an *A. simplex* larva. Serologic testing revealed specific IgE antibody to *A. simplex* was positive whereas that to mackerel was negative, thus the diagnosis as IgE-mediated hypersensitivity to *A. simplex*. "Patients diagnosed as fish-related or idiopathic allergy should be examined for evidence of *Anisakis*-induced allergy" (Hoshino and Narita 2011). There is a relationship between anaphylaxis and cardiovascular events. Anaphylaxis can trigger atrial fibrillation, as seen in a 42-year-old male with a history of dyslipidemia but with no other remarkable medical records. He was admitted to the university hospital, Madrid, Spain, for having general discomfort, itching, facial angioedema, and tachycardia 45 minutes after eating fresh grilled fish (a hake). He showed atrial fibrillation, was treated (dexchlorpheniramine, dexamethasone, atenolol, flecainide), recovered and had diet recommendations for *Anisakis simplex* allergy. No new allergic events or atrial fibrillation were observed at 1-year follow-up. "We emphasize the importance of the priority of establishing protocols between cardiologist and allergist in treatment of cardiac complications during anaphylaxis" (Rojas-Perez-Ezquerra *et al.* 2017).

22.5.4 Diagnosis

Detection of larvae is done via endoscopy.

22.5.5 Therapy

Endoscopic or surgical removal of larvae is needed for therapy.

22.5.6 Genome

Both the transcriptome and genome of *Anisakis simplex* are known. Transcriptome sequencing shows **18,842** proteins and 34 putative allergens for *A. simplex* (Baird *et al.* 2016). Polish scientists provide the draft genome of the L3 stage of *Anisakis simplex* sensu lato (Łopieńska-Biernat *et al.* 2019a). A total of **7,607** protein-coding genes have been predicted.

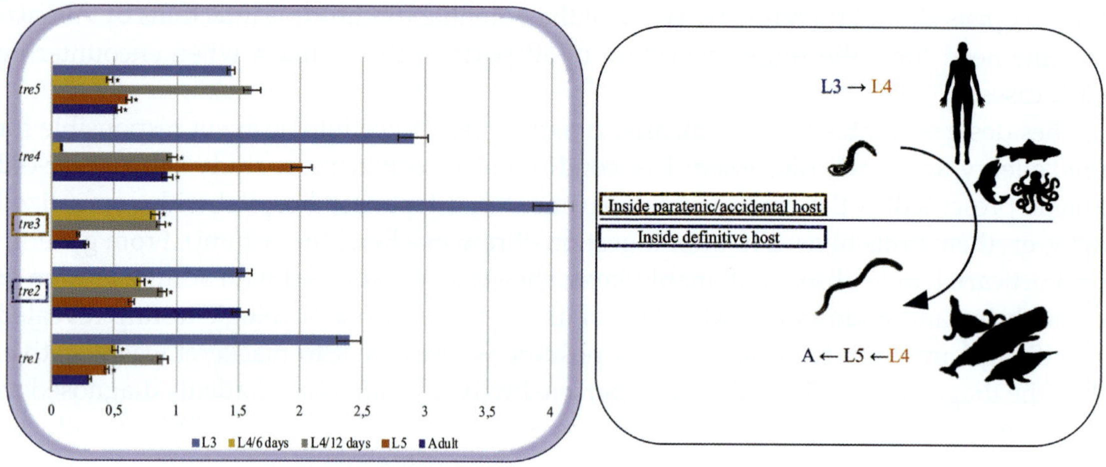

Fig. 22.8 ■ Stage-specific expression of different trehalases. Quantitative PCR, expression genes of trehalase during *in vitro* developmental of *Anisakis simplex*. The reference gene used: *ef1α*. The bars represent "mean (SD)", stars indicate $P < 0.01$. Courtesy: Łopieńska-Biernat *et al. Int J Biol Macromol* 2019;129:957–64. Reproduced with permission from Elsevier.

The role of carbohydrate metabolism in *Anisakis simplex* has been stressed, especially trehalose metabolism (Łopieńska-Biernat *et al.* 2019a). Trehalose anabolism and glycogen catabolism are predominant in larval stages L4 and L5. The enzyme trehalase plays an important role in the catabolism of trehalose, a disaccharide which is one of the most widespread carbohydrates in nematode tissues. Trehalase might be a major adaptation of the nematode to parasitic lifestyle. In *Anisakis*, a total of **5 trehalase** genes are found in the parasite and they show differential expression during development. Please see Figure 22.8 for stage-specific expression of different trehalases (Łopieńska-Biernat *et al.* 2019b). As trehalases may be important for parasitism, they are potential target for controlling the parasitic disease anisakiasis.

In contrast to *Anisakis*, humans have no trehalose but possess a single, functional trehalase gene. The presence of trehalase in mammals has been found to indicate diet diversification. Among the mammals, bats represent the largest dietary radiation, with independent origins of frugivory, nectarivory, carnivory, omnivory, and even sanguivory in an otherwise insectivorous clade. The trehalase gene (*Treh*) encodes an enzyme capable of digesting trehalose present in insects. Enzymatic assays of intestinal trehalase in bats suggest that trehalase activity tends to be lost or markedly reduced in noninsectivorous bats compared with their insectivorous relatives. A survey of *Treh* in 119 mammal species also shows a number of other independent losses of *Treh* in noninsectivorous species, recapitulating the evolutionary pattern found in bats. Please see Figure 22.9 for phylogenetic tree of mammals showing species with a pseudogenized *Treh* (Jiao *et al.* 2019). The trehalase gene serves as a molecular signature of dietary diversification in mammals. Hengwu Jiao (Wuhan University, Wuhan, China) and colleagues stated: "Diet is a key factor in determining and structuring animal diversity and adaptive radiations" (Jiao *et al.* 2019).

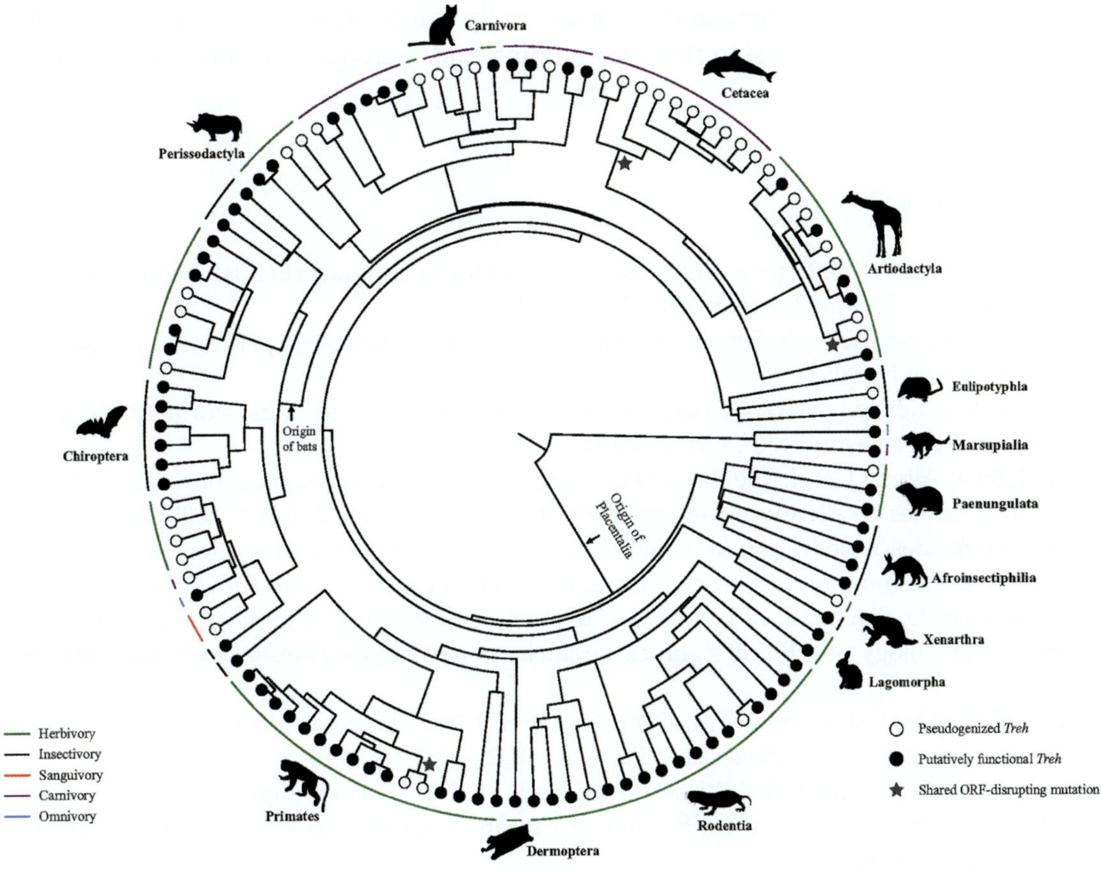

Fig. 22.9 ■ Phylogenetic tree of mammals showing species with a pseudogenized *Treh*. Tree topology is based on multiple recent studies of mammalian phylogeny. Dietary preferences were indicated with various colors as indicated. Silhouettes of mammals were taken from phylopic.org. Courtesy: Jiao *et al. Mol Biol Evol* 2019;36:2171–83. Reproduced with permission from Oxford University Press.

Summary & Key Concepts

- While juvenile nematodes normally infect nonhuman species, they cause CLM or VLM if they enter a human host.
- CLM is classified by a creeping eruption that moves forward in a track under epidermis of the skin in an irregular pattern and can cause painful lesions and secondary bacterial infection.
- VLM includes toxocariasis, angiostrongyliasis and anisakiasis.
- Toxocariasis is caused by cat or dog roundworms making their way into humans and wander viscerally, causing varying amounts of damage depending on the tissues invaded (including CNS and the eye).
- Angiostrongyliasis due to rat lungworm infection can cause eosinophilic meningitis and various degrees of neurological dysfunction.

- Anisakiasis involves a nematode that normally infects marine mammals, though in humans it can cause eosinophilic granuloma and anaphylactic shock (in sensitized individuals).

References

Aibinu IE, Smooker PM, Lopata AL. *Anisakis* nematodes in fish and shellfish- from infection to allergies. *Int J Parasitol Parasites Wildl* 2019;9:384–93.

Arslan F, Baysal NB, Aslan A, Simsek BC, Vahaboglu H. *Toxocara* related peritonitis: A case report and review of literature. *Parasitol Int* 2019;73:101950.

Audicana MT, Kennedy MW. *Anisakis simplex*: From obscure infectious worm to inducer of immune hypersensitivity. *Clin Microbiol Rev* 2008;21(2):360–79.

Baird FJ, Su X, Aibinu I, *et al*. The *Anisakis* transcriptome provides a resource for fundamental and applied studies on allergy-causing parasites. *PLoS Negl Trop Dis* 2016;10(7):e0004845.

Baptista-Fernandes T, Rodrigues M, Castro I, *et al*. Human gastric hyperinfection by *Anisakis simplex*: A severe and unusual presentation and a brief review. *Int J Infect Dis* 2017;64:38–41.

Barratt J, Chan D, Sandaradura I, *et al*. *Angiostrongylus cantonensis*: A review of its distribution, molecular biology and clinical significance as a human pathogen. *Parasitology* 2016;143(9):1087–118.

Beaver PC, Snyder CH, Carrera GM, Dent JH, LaffertY JW. Chronic eosinophilia due to visceral larva migrans; report of three cases. *Pediatrics* 1952;9(1):7–19.

Boonroumkaew P, Sanguansak T, Visaetsilpanonta S, *et al*. Two ocular angiostrongyliasis cases in Thailand with molecular identification of causative parasite species. *Am J Trop Med Hyg* 2020;102(6):1399–403.

Bowman DD, Montgomery SP, Zajac AM, Eberhard ML, Kazacos KR. Hookworms of dogs and cats as agents of cutaneous larva migrans. *Trends Parasitol* 2010;26(4):162–7.

da Silva MB, Urrego A JR, Oviedo Y, *et al*. The somatic proteins of *Toxocara canis* larvae and excretory-secretory products revealed by proteomics. *Vet Parasitol* 2018;259:25–34.

Dard C, Tessier E, Nguyen D, *et al*. First cases of *Angiostrongylus cantonensis* infection reported in Martinique, 2002–2017. *Parasite* 2020;27:31.

Fakhri Y, Gasser RB, Rostami A, *et al*. *Toxocara* eggs in public places worldwide — A systematic review and meta-analysis. *Environ Pollut* 2018;242(Pt B):1467–75.

Farmer A, Beltran T, Choi YS. Prevalence of *Toxocara* species infection in the U.S.: Results from the National Health and Nutrition Examination Survey, 2011–2014. *PLoS Negl Trop Dis* 2017;11(7):e0005818.

Feldmeier H, Schuster A. Mini review: Hookworm-related cutaneous larva migrans. *Eur J Clin Microbiol Infect Dis* 2012;31(6):915–8.

Fuchizaki U, Nishikawa M. Images in clinical medicine. Gastric anisakiasis. *N Engl J Med* 2016;375(7):e11.

Gakosso LGC, Baadi F, Abakka FZ, Basraoui D, Jalal H. The visceral larva migrans caused by *Toxocara canis*: A case report. *Pan Afr Med J* 2020;36:150.

Gelmetti C, Brena M, Veraldi S. Hookworm-related cutaneous larva migrans of the penis successfully treated with topical ivermectin. *Pediatr Dermatol* 2019;36(3):3912.

Hehemann JH, Correc G, Barbeyron T, Helbert W, Czjzek M, Michel G. Transfer of carbohydrate-active enzymes from marine bacteria to Japanese gut microbiota. *Nature*. 2010;464(7290): 908–12.

Hochedez P, Caumes E. Hookworm-related cutaneous larva migrans. *J Travel Med* 2007;14(5): 326–33.

Hoshino C, Narita M. *Anisakis simplex*-induced anaphylaxis. *J Infect Chemother* 2011;17(4):544–6.

Hotez PJ. Neglected infections of poverty in the United States and their effects on the brain. *JAMA Psychiatry* 2014;71(10):1099–100.

International Helminth Genomes Consortium. Comparative genomics of the major parasitic worms. *Nat Genet*. 2019;51(1):163–74.

Jarvi SI, Quarta S, Jacquier S, *et al*. High prevalence of *Angiostrongylus cantonensis* (rat lungworm) on eastern Hawai'i Island: A closer look at life cycle traits and patterns of infection in wild rats (*Rattus* spp.). *PLoS One* 2017;12(12):e0189458.

Jiao H, Zhang L, Xie HW, Simmons NB, Liu H, Zhao H. Trehalase gene as a molecular signature of dietary diversification in mammals. *Mol Biol Evol* 2019;36(10):2171–83.

Kirby-Smith JL, Dove WE, White GF. Some observations on creeping eruption. *Am J Trop Med Hyg* 1929;s1-9:179–93.

Kong J, Won J, Yoon J, Lee U, Kim JI, Huh S. Draft genome of *Toxocara canis*, a pathogen responsible for visceral larva migrans. *Korean J Parasitol* 2016;54(6):751–8.

Lander M, Checkley AM, Walker SL. Cutaneous larva migrans presenting with folliculitis. *Am J Trop Med Hyg* 2020;102(5):919–20.

Li SW, Shiao SH, Weng SC, Liu TH, Su KE, Chen CC. A case of human infection with *Anisakis simplex* in Taiwan. *Gastrointest Endosc* 2015;82(4):757–8.

Łopieńska-Biernat E, Paukszto Ł, Jastrzębski JP, Makowczenko K, Stryiński R. Genes expression and in silico studies of functions of trehalases, a highly dispersed *Anisakis simplex* s. l. specific gene family. *Int J Biol Macromol* 2019a;129:957–64.

Łopieńska-Biernat E, Paukszto Ł, Jastrzębski JP, Myszczyński K, Polak I, Stryiński R. Genome-wide analysis of *Anisakis simplex* sensu lato: The role of carbohydrate metabolism genes in the parasite's development. *Int J Parasitol* 2019b;S0020-7519(19):30212–7.

Ma G, Holland CV, Wang T, *et al*. Human toxocariasis. *Lancet Infect Dis* 2018;18(1):e14-e24.

Martins YC, Tanowitz HB, Kazacos KR. Central nervous system manifestations of *Angiostrongylus cantonensis* infection. *Acta Trop* 2015;141(Pt A):46–53.

Mladineo I, Hrabar J. *Anisakis pegreffii*. *Trends Parasitol* 2020;36(8):717–8.

Morassutti AL, Perelygin A, DE Carvalho MO, *et al*. High throughput sequencing of the *Angiostrongylus cantonensis* genome: A parasite spreading worldwide. *Parasitology* 2013;140(10):1304–9.

Moreira GM, Telmo Pde L, Mendonça M, *et al*. Human toxocariasis: Current advances in diagnostics, treatment, and interventions. *Trends Parasitol* 2014;30(9):456–64.

Panova OA, Khrustalev AV. Dog walking brings *Toxocara* eggs to people's homes. *Vet Parasitol* 2018;262:16–19.

Penagos-Tabares F, Lange MK, Seipp A, *et al*. Novel approach to study gastropod-mediated innate immune reactions against metastrongyloid parasites. *Parasitol Res* 2018;117(4):1211–24.

Pham Thu H, Đao Huu N, Thi Thu TL, Van LN. Case report: *Angiostrongylus cantonensis* meningoencephalitis in a 9-month-old baby in Vietnam. *Am J Trop Med Hyg* 2020;103(2):723–6.

Ramos P. Parasites in fishery products — Laboratorial and educational strategies to control. *Exp Parasitol* 2020;211:107865.

Reichert F, Pilger D, Schuster A, *et al.* Epidemiology and morbidity of hookworm-related cutaneous larva migrans (HrCLM): Results of a cohort study over a period of six months in a resource-poor community in Manaus, Brazil. *PLoS Negl Trop Dis* 2018;12(7):e0006662.

Rojas-Perez-Ezquerra P, Noguerado-Mellado B, Morales-Cabeza C, Zambrano Ibarra G, Datino Romaniega T. Atrial fibrillation in anaphylaxis. *Am J Med* 2017;130(9):1114–16.

Shimamura Y, Ishii N, Ego M, *et al.* Multiple acute infection by *Anisakis*: A case series. *Intern Med* 2016;55(8):907–10.

Spencer WH, Zimmerman LE. Helenor Campbell Wilder Foerster, 1895–1998. *Arch Ophthalmol* 1999;117(6):849–50.

Van Thiel PH. Anisakiasis. *Parasitology* 1962;52:16–7.

Wang LC, Chen KY, Chang SH, *et al.* Transcriptome profiling of the fifth-stage larvae of *Angiostrongylus cantonensis* by next-generation sequencing. *Parasitol Res* 2013;112(9):3193–202.

Yong HS, Eamsobhana P, Lim PE, *et al.* Draft genome of neurotropic nematode parasite *Angiostrongylus cantonensis*, causative agent of human eosinophilic meningitis. *Acta Trop* 2015;148:51–7.

Zhu XQ, Korhonen PK, Cai H, *et al.* Genetic blueprint of the zoonotic pathogen *Toxocara canis*. *Nat Commun* 2015;6:6145.

Zibaei M, Sadjjadi SM, Jahadi-Hosseini SH. *Toxocara cati* larvae in the eye of a child: A case report. *Asian Pac J Trop Biomed* 2014;4(Suppl 1):S53–5.

23

Introduction to Arthropods

23.1 Arthropoda

Arthropods are members of the phylum Arthropoda; they are exceedingly successful invertebrates. Some arthropods are human ectoparasites, others (such as insects) are vectors for human pathogens (viruses, bacteria, protozoa, helminths). Disciplines involving arthropods include **entomology** (for all insects), **medical entomology** (for insects and human diseases), and **acarology** (for ticks and mites). Insects go through metamorphosis and have cuticles as exoskeleton. They are the most abundant arthropods. For treatment of arthropod infections, ivermectin is active against fleas, flies, lice, mites, ticks as well as parasitic helminths (filariae and *Onchocerca*).

What is the relationship of arthropods to other organisms? Based on the Adl classification, they belong to Opisthokonta, Metazoa (Adl *et al.* 2019). Based on Ruggiero classification, under the kingdom Animalia, arthropods belong to the superphylum **Ecdysozoa** and the phylum **Arthropoda**. Many phyla are under this superphylum, which means organisms that undergo molts. One phylum that includes parasitic helminths is Nematoda. Arthropoda has several subphyla, including Chelicerata (scorpions, spiders, ticks, mites, horseshoe crab), Crustacea (copepods, shrimps, crabs), Myriapoda (centipedes, millipedes) and Hexopoda. The phylum **Hexapoda** (six legs) includes the class Insecta (insects). The class **Insecta** includes the order **Diptera** (two wings, flies and mosquitoes are examples) (Ruggiero *et al.* 2015).

The above classification of arthropods has been supplemented with data from phylogenomics (comparing entire genomes or large portion of genomes among organisms to establish evolutionary relationships), morphology (extant, current species), and paleontology (ancient, fossil records, such as the famous trilobites). Arthropods are ecdysozoans, a group (clade) of invertebrates that also includes the roundworms (Nematoda). Within Ecdysozoa, one clade is named Panarthropoda, for animals with paired segmental ventrolateral appendages. **Panarthropoda** includes Tardigrada (water bear), Onychophora (velvet worm), and Arthropoda (aka Euarthropoda). The panarthropod body is divided into a head and a trunk, with structurally and functionally distinct batches of segments known as tagmata (singular is tagma). In insects, the tagmata include a head, thorax, and abdomen. One phenomenon involved here is the process of **arthropodization:** the appearance of appendages with sclerotization or tanning and separated by a ring of unsclerotized cuticles (forming joints or hinges) distinguish arthropods from organisms with only soft cuticles. Hence the name is arthropod (arthro means joint, pod means foot). This feature is absent in velvet worms and water bears. Arthropods are divided into two clades: Chelicerata and Mandibulata (named for their biting appendages). Then, within the Mandibulata are two clades: Myriapoda and Pancrustacea. **Pancrustacea** includes multiple lineages of crustaceans, one of which is the hexapods, a clade that includes the insects. In this phylogenetic analysis, insects are a just a subset of hexapods and of pancrustaceans, "albeit a phenomenally diverse one!" (Giribet and Edgecombe 2019). Please see Figure 23.1 for phylogeny of arthropods (Giribet and Edgecombe 2019).

Arthropods are exceedingly successful animals on earth. How many are there? Current estimates suggest a total of 7 million species of terrestrial arthropods, 5.5 million species of insects, 1.5 million species of beetles, and 1 million species of mites (Stork 2018). For described extant species, there are 1,214,295 species of arthropods; **1,013,825** of which are **insects**. The latter includes beetles or the order Coleoptera (387,000), butterflies or the order Lepidoptera (157,000), flies or the order Diptera (155,000) and bees or order Hymenoptera (117,000) (Stork 2018).

A tale on the abundance of species of beetles by the famous British geneticist and evolutionary biologist J. B. S. (John Burdon Sanderson) Haldane was told by another famous British ecologist G. (George) Evelyn Hutchinson: "there is a story, possibly apocryphal, of the distinguished British biologist, J. B. S. Haldane, who found himself in the company of a group of theologians. On being asked what one could conclude as to the nature of the Creator from a study of his creation, Haldane is said to have answered, 'An inordinate fondness for beetles'" (Hutchinson 1959).

23.2 Cuticle & other structures

"The evolutionary success of arthropods, including insects, is attributable to the development of the cuticle, which is a complex exoskeleton with diverse functions. The composition of the cuticle is dictated by the desired physicochemical and mechanical properties for each anatomical part of the organism. The main structural components of the cuticle are chitin, a large assortment of cuticular proteins, lipids, catecholamines, and minerals" (Zhu *et al.* 2016). The components are secreted by a sheet of epidermal cells across their apical membranes. Above the epidermis are cuticular layers, namely **endocuticle**, **exocuticle**, and **epicuticle**. [As discussed at the beginning of this chapter, the superphylum Ecdysozoa includes Arthropoda and Nematoda. A similar statement on the evolutionary success of nematodes can also be attributed to the development of their cuticle. Please see Chapter 17 for a description of nematode cuticle.]

Chitin is the major component of cuticle. It is the most widespread amino polysaccharide in nature. The annual global amount of chitin is believed to be only one order of

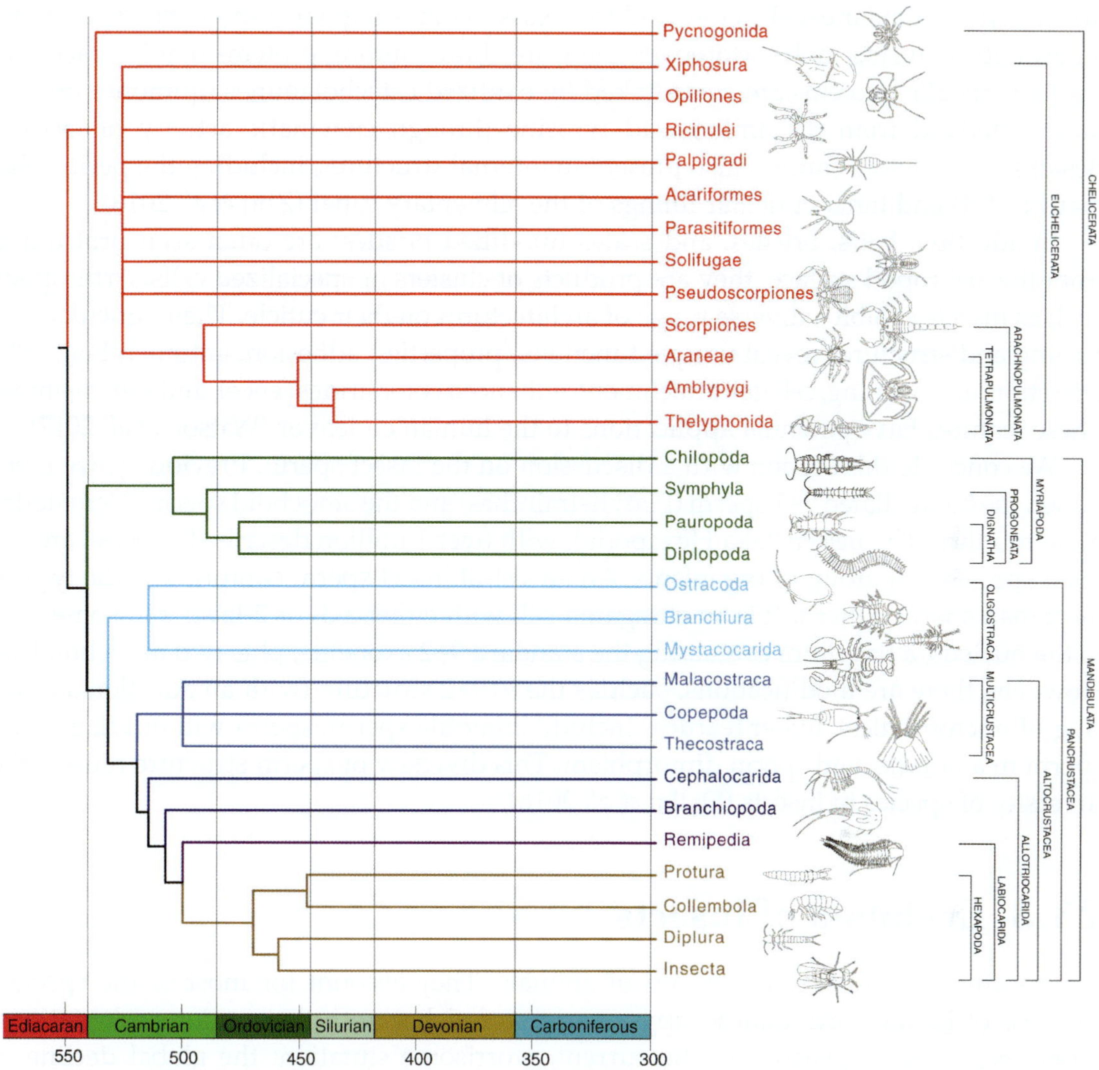

Fig. 23.1 ■ Phylogeny of arthropods. Summary chronogram of the major arthropod lineages. Topology is largely based on phylogenomic analyses [9, 10, 11]; divergence dates mainly based on [9, 10, 111, 112]. Line drawings based on [33, 80, 113, 114]; Mystacocarida line drawing by Triton — Own work, CC BY-SA 4.0, https://commons.wikimedia.org/w/index.php?curid=69989974. Courtesy: Giribet G, Edgecombe G. *Curr Biol* 2019;29:R592–602. Reproduced with permission from Elsevier.

magnitude less than that of cellulose. It is mainly synthesized by arthropods, fungi, and nematodes (Merzendorfer 2006). In arthropods, chitin is the major cuticular component. It is a linear polysaccharide of glucosamine and N-acetyl-glucosamine that forms microfibrils by the enzymatic activity of chitin synthase (an integral membrane glycosyltransferase). During molting, chitin is degraded by N-acetyl-glucosaminidase and endochitinase. Its synthesis is vital for both growth and development, since chitin forms much of the arthropod's cuticular exoskeleton, and the exoskeleton is regularly shed and replaced by a new cuticle during molts. Moreover, there are chitin binding proteins that interact with chitin. Cuticular proteins are cross-linked by oxidized catecholamines (quinones or phenolics) derived from the amino acid tyrosine through enzymatic activity of laccase. Besides exoskeleton, chitin is also present in internal structures, including the peritrophic matrix (**PM**) and inner cuticular linings of the alimentary canal (Zhu *et al.* 2016).

In addition, hairs, bristles, and scales (modified bristles) are often seen protruding from the arthropod surface; they are products of clusters of specialized cells. Arthropods such as insects exhibit a diverse range of architectures on their cuticle. Their cuticular patterning and structures reveal unique functions/properties: adhesion, antimicrobial, antireflection, anti-wetting, cell-cell attachment, enhanced color (iridescence), and self-cleaning. These features have potential applications to the human endeavor (Watson *et al.* 2017).

We conclude this section with a discussion on the insect sperm. Previously, we mentioned the biflagellated 9+1 sperm (Platyhelminthes) and the amoeboid sperm (Nematoda) of helminthes. The insects (aka Hexapoda), with over 1 million described species, are the most species-rich group of organisms. An ancestral insect sperm conforms to the typical metazoan sperm pattern. It is an elongated cell with either a 3- or 2-layer acrosome next to the nucleus, a flagellum containing the standard 9+2 axoneme, plus two mitochondria. However, there are modifications, such as the 9+9+2 structure (with an additional outer ring of microtubules). Other features include immotile sperm, sperm without flagellum, sperm in a bundle, and sperm dimorphism. This diversity of sperm structure reflects the diversity of species in insects (Dallai *et al.* 2016).

23.3 Evolution of Insects

Insects are the most speciose group of animals. They account for most of the species-richness of life on earth and occupy a variety of niches with their unique adaptations. [Here, we must emphasize on the current, worrisome situation: the global decline of insects, involving both species extinction and decrease in population abundance (Sanchez-Bayo and Wyckhuys 2019).] The diversity of insect forms has become the basis of morphological systematics, and current insect systematics has been improved by molecular data from insects and other arthropods. One example is the recognition of hexapods as a crustacean lineage within the Pancrustacea, as mentioned earlier (Trautwein *et al.* 2012).

A phylogeny of insects has been constructed from analysis of 1,478 protein-coding genes, together with correspondence to dates from the fossil records. The origin of insects has been dated to 479 million years ago (mya) (Ordovician period); insect flight to 401 mya (Devonian); major holometabolous insect diversification to **145 mya** (Cretaceous) (insect metamorphosis to be discussed in the next section). Based on this phylogeny, many common insects are included, with the order **Diptera** (true flies) as the most advanced insects. Many dipterans are involved in human parasitic diseases. Please see Figure 23.2 for the phylogeny of insects (Misof *et al.* 2014).

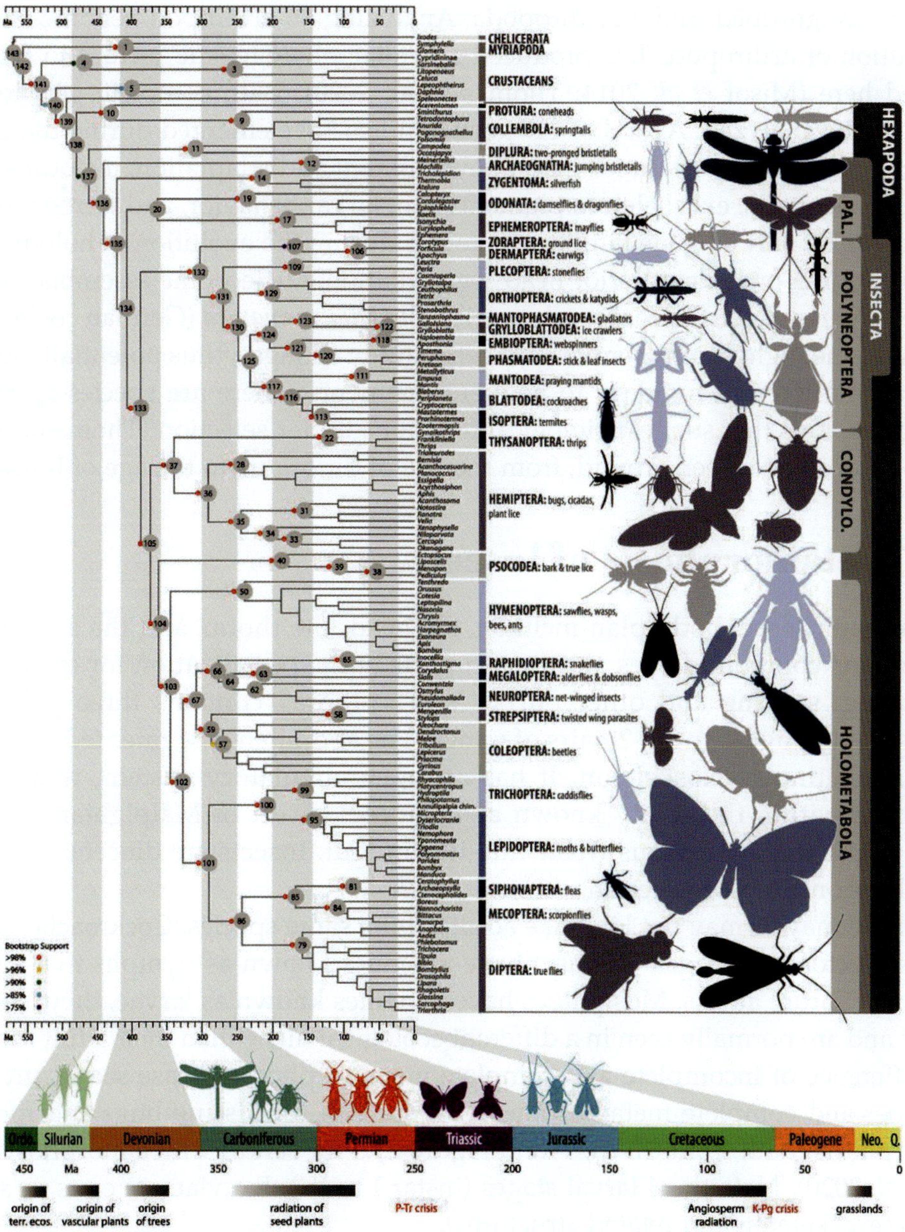

Fig. 23.2 ■ Phylogeny of insects. Dated phylogenetic tree of insect relationships. The tree was inferred through a maximum-likelihood analysis of 413,459 amino acid sites divided into 479 metapartitions. Branch lengths were optimized and node ages estimated from 1,050,000 trees sampled from trees separately generated for 105 partitions that included all taxa (**5**). All nodes up to orders are labeled with numbers (gray circles). Colored circles indicate bootstrap support (**5**) (left key). The time line at the bottom of the tree relates the geological origin of insect clades to major geological and biological events. CONDYLO, Condylognatha; PAL, Palaeoptera. Courtesy: Misof *et al. Science* 2014;346:763–7. Reproduced with permission from the American Association for the Advancement of Science.

Insects are grouped under Arthropoda. Analyzing 76 arthropod genomes to explore the evolution of arthropods has produced a similar phylogenetic picture to Figure 23.2 presented here (Misof *et al.* 2014; Thomas et al. 2020). With complete genomes, gene families can be analyzed. A total of **147** gene families have emerged during the evolution of insects. Some are important for insect development and adaptation, including ones for wing morphogenesis, exoskeleton, pigmentation, larval behavior, and terrestrial adaptation. In contrast, only 10 gene families are found during the evolution of holometabolous insects, including ones for anterior head segmentation, nucleosome assembly, and serine proteases. Interestingly, the cockroach species, *Blattella germanica* (German cockroach) has experienced the highest number of rapid gene family changes, thus potentially indicating its increased capability to adapt to new environments. There are species-specific gene family expansions that suggest biological functions under selection (Thomas *et al.* 2020). Roaches have always been around, from the age of dinosaurs to the age of humans.

23.4 Metamorphosis of Insects

A typical adult insect body plan includes the head, the thorax and the abdomen. The head contains compound eyes and mouth parts with specialization for cutting, chewing, piercing, sucking and other purposes. The thorax contains three pairs of legs (walking appendages) and 1–2 pairs of wings. The abdomen is segmented. It is covered with hard chitinous exoskeleton. It has an open circulatory system, with the fluid hemolymph within the cavity known as hemocoel. A set of Malpighian tubules are present to excrete nitrogenous waste into its hindgut. Insects are dioceous, with internal fertilization for reproduction.

Juveniles may or may not look like adults of the same species. Cockroaches and kissing bugs (vector for Chagas' disease) have juveniles known as nymphs that somewhat look like miniature adults. Mosquitoes have juveniles known as larvae, they look totally different and are normally seen in a different ecological niche than their adult forms. This is the difference of incomplete and complete metamorphosis. Please see Figure 23.3 for mosquitoes and complete metamorphosis, Figure 23.4 for kissing bugs and incomplete metamorphosis (both from CDC),[1–2] and Figure 23.5 for sand fly metamorphosis (Sousa-Paula *et al.* 2020). Note the 4 larval stages (instar I to IV). Exuviae are casts or sloughed off skins (exoskeleton and related structures).

For Holometabola, the insects that undergo complete metamorphosis, this process has made insects the most diverse lineage of life on Earth. Approximately 80% of their species richness is concentrated in four super-radiations: beetles, flies, bees and wasps, and moths and butterflies (as mentioned before). The more evolved or higher insects such as Diptera undergo complete metamorphosis, egg to larva to pupa to adult, known as holo-

[1] https://www.cdc.gov/mosquitoes/about/life-cycles/culex.html

[2] https://www.cdc.gov/parasites/chagas/gen_info/vectors/triatomine_stages_lg.html

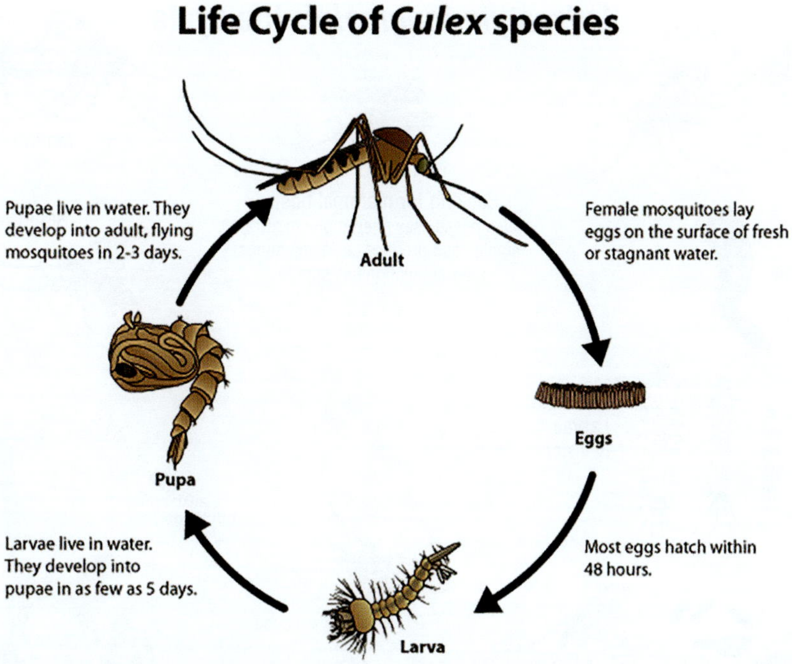

Fig. 23.3 ■ Mosquitoes as examples of complete metamorphosis. Life Cycle of *Culex* Species Mosquitoes. Life stages of *Culex pipiens, Cx. quinquefasciatus,* and *Cx. Tarsalis.* It takes about 7–10 days for an egg to develop into an adult mosquito. Courtesy of the CDC. Reproduced from https://www.cdc.gov/mosquitoes/about/life-cycles/culex.html

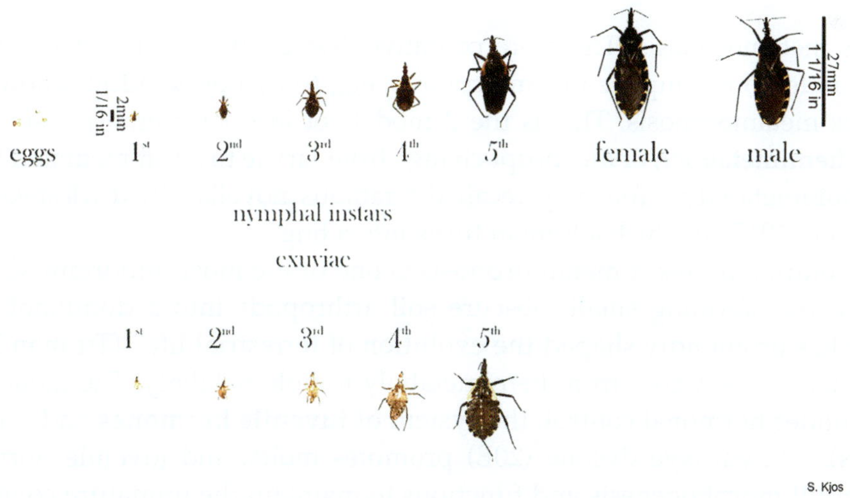

Fig. 23.4 ■ Kissing bugs as examples of incomplete metamorphosis. Various triatomine bugs in all life stages, from eggs to nymphs to fully grown adults. A variety of bug species, that share similar traits, are pictured. Courtesy of the CDC. Reproduced from https://www.cdc.gov/parasites/chagas/gen_info/vectors/triatomine_stages_lg.html

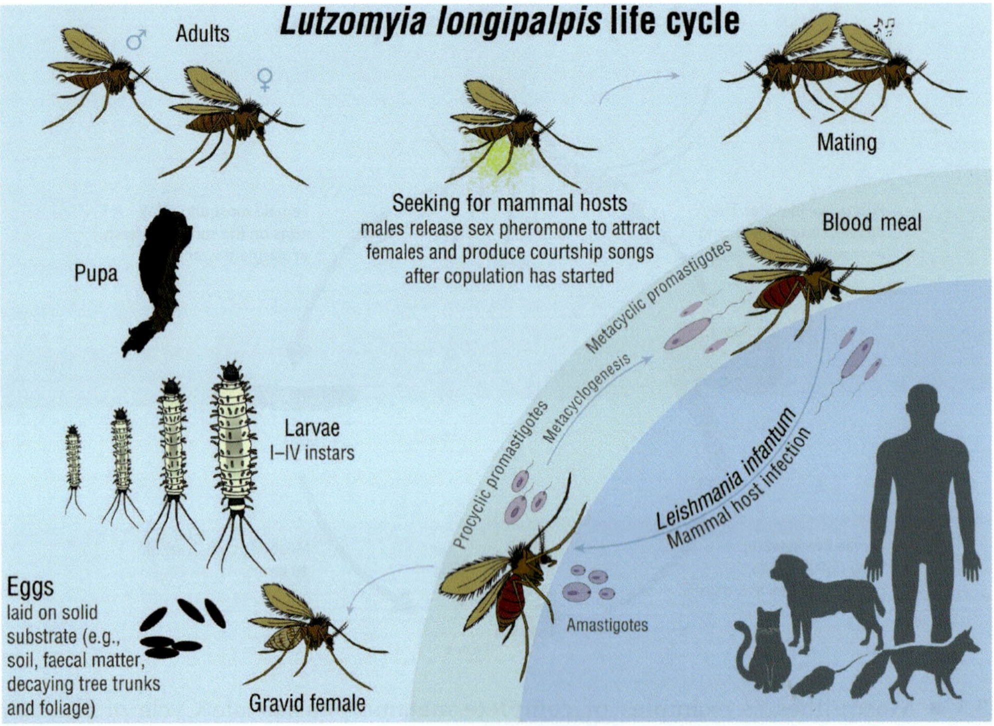

Fig. 23.5 ■ Sand fly metamorphosis. *Lutzomyia longipalpis* life cycle. Courtesy: Sousa-Paula *et al.* *Trends Parasitol* 2020;36:796–7. Reproduced with permission from Elsevier.

metabolous metamorphosis. The more primitive, less evolved or lower insects such as cockroach undergo incomplete metamorphosis, egg to nymph to adult, known as hemimetabolous metamorphosis. This is the 2 models of insect metamorphosis, a gradual change for **hemimetaboly**, or an abrupt change from larvae to adult mediated by a pupal stage for **holometaboly**. (You may recall the famous novella, titled *Metamorphosis*, by Frank Kafka in 1915, in which a human turns into a bug.)

"The evolution of insect metamorphosis is one of the most important sagas in animal history, transforming small, obscure soil arthropods into a dominant terrestrial group that has profoundly shaped the evolution of terrestrial life" (Truman 2019). It is believed the evolution goes from hemimetaboly to holometaboly. The metamorphosis process is under hormonal control, the system of **juvenile hormones** and ecdysteroids (**ecdysones**): 20-hydroxyecdysone (20E) promotes molts, and juvenile hormone (JH) represses adult morphogenesis and functions to maintain the immature condition. The hormones activate stage-specifying master transcription factors; three important genes are Krupel homolog 1 (**Kr-h1**), **broad** and **E93**. For holometabolous life stages: Kr-h1 is active in the larva, broad in the pupa and E93 in the adult. Kr-h1 mediates JH action and is found whenever JH acts, while the other two genes direct the formation of their corresponding stages. In hemimetabolous forms, there is broad expression through the nymphal molts and a switch to E93 to form the adult. The ecdysones act through the nuclear hormone receptor named ecdysone receptor (EcR) which acts to initiate a network of other transcription factors to regulate the expression of stage-specific genes (Truman 2019; Rolff *et al.* 2019).

The evolution of insect flight is thought to initiate the process of metamorphosis. As the only invertebrate group that had evolved to possess powered flight, insects had flown for over 100 million years before the reptilian Pterosaurs appearing in the Triassic (and Aves, including insect-eating birds, even much later, after the dinosaurs). With flight, insects can undertake long-range dispersals, they can easily travel between different food source locations, and they can fly to avoid predators. Today's **winged insects** are the Pteryogota. The aim is to make the wing as light as possible, weight reduction by apoptosis of the epidermal cells that secrete the cuticle of the wing membrane after adult emergence from the pupa (Truman 2019). In addition to the benefits of flight, the evolution of metamorphosis has been linked to the decoupling of life stages. The main adaptive benefit of complete metamorphosis is decoupling between growth and differentiation. This facilitates the exploitation of different resources and enhances the probability of the metamorphic transition escaping developmental size thresholds. However, whereas the pupa stage allows complete remodeling of adult structures, it comes with a cost. Pupae can be susceptible to predators, parasites and pathogens. Complete metamorphosis also poses a challenge for the maintenance of symbionts (gut microbiome), although it may also offer the benefit of allowing an extensive change in microbiome between the larval and adult stages (Rolff *et al.* 2019). As mentioned before, a selective advantage of holometaboly is: within one species the two forms (larva and adult) with different lifestyles can exploit diverse habitats. This environmental adaptation and specialization of larvae, primarily the delay and internalization of wing development, is believed to lead to the eventual requirement of the pupal intermediate stage (Jindra 2019).

23.5 Arthropods & Diseases

Arthropods can be carriers of vector-borne diseases, or they themselves can be ectoparasites of humans (Mathison and Pritt 2014). The human pathogens they carry include viral, bacterial, protozoal and helminthic species. Arthropod borne viruses are known as arboviruses. Examples of viruses include yellow fever and West Nile viruses which are carried by mosquitoes (from older to newer human infections). Historical record showed the 14th century Black Death and the Great Plague of London in 1665 (bubonic plague in both cases). Examples of bacteria include fleas carrying the plague pathogen (*Yersinia pestis*) and ticks carrying Rocky Mountain spotted fever (*Rickettsia rickettsii*) and Lyme disease (*Borrelia burgdorferi*) pathogens (again, from older to newer human infections). Ticks and mites are arthropods but they are not insects; they have eight legs whereas insects have

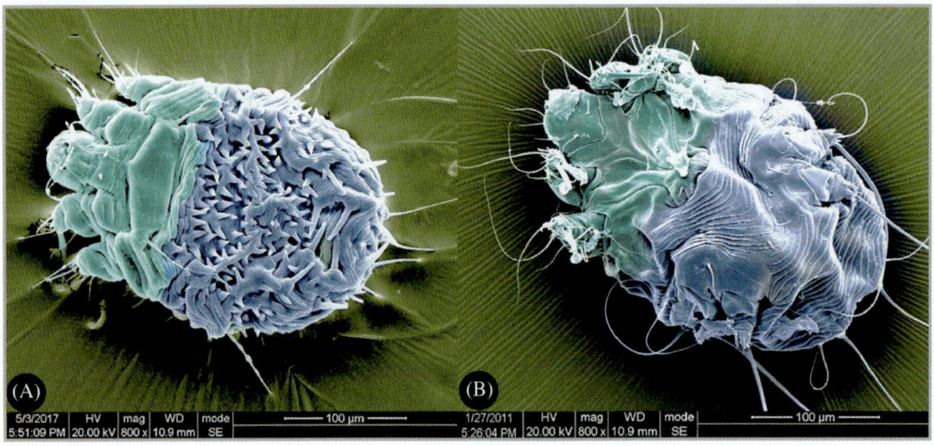

Fig. 23.6 ■ *Sarcoptes scabiei* scabes mite under scanning electron microscope. The manifestation of adult mite *Sarcoptes scabiei* under scanning electron microscope. A is dorsal view and B is ventral view of the mite. Courtesy: Ran *et al. Br J Dermatol* 2018;179:545–6. Reproduced with permission from John Wiley and Sons.

six. Mites are more versatile than ticks. Whereas ticks only feed on the blood of reptiles, birds and mammals, mites feed on decaying animal matter, feces, plants, animal secretions, and blood. One example comes from the human hair, with two species of hair follicle mites: "a larger, *Demodex folliculorum* (Simon), located primarily in the hair follicle, and a smaller species, D. *brevis* Akbulatova, in the main residing in the sebaceous glands" (Nutting 1976). In 1976, the legendary mite specialist William Nutting (University of Massachusetts Amherst) (1918–1994) wrote: "One can conclude that wherever mankind is found, hair follicle mites will be found and that the transfer mechanism is 100% effective! (One of my students noted it was undoubtedly the first invertebrate metazoan to visit the moon!)"[3]

Ticks are grouped into hard ticks and soft ticks. Tick paralysis, a rare disease, is believed to be due to toxin in the tick saliva. Mites can be ectoparasites; scabies is caused by the human itch mite (*Sarcoptes scabiei*). Please see Figure 23.6 for adult scabes mite and Figure 23.7 for *Ixodes ricinus* complex ticks (adult males and females) seen as images by scanning electron microscopy (Ran *et al.* 2018; Saracho-Bottero *et al.* 2020). As an example, the first reported case in Korea on the diagnosis and treatment of a tick bite in the ear canal documented the successful recovery of an oval-shaped mass from the right auditory canal of a 22-month-old male infant under a surgical microscope, and the identification within the recovered specimen one hard tick of the family Ixodidae (based on gross and histological findings) (Sung and Kim 2017).

Various parasitic protozoa are carried by different species of arthropods. Ticks carry *Babesia*. The higher insects belonging to the class Diptera are important vectors/carriers

[3] https://www.discovermagazine.com/planet-earth/everything-you-never-wanted-to-know-about-the-mites-that-eat-crawl-and-have-sex-on-your-face

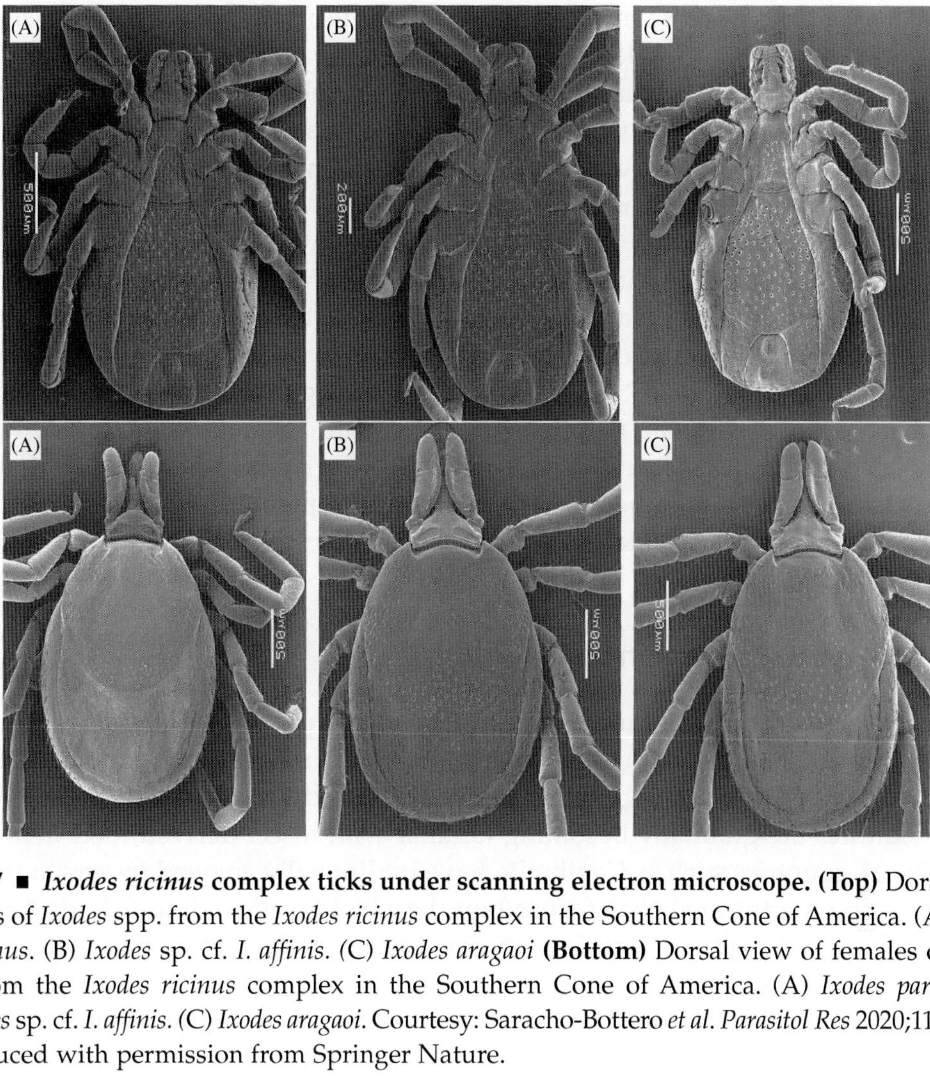

Fig. 23.7 ■ *Ixodes ricinus* complex ticks under scanning electron microscope. (Top) Dorsal view of males of *Ixodes* spp. from the *Ixodes ricinus* complex in the Southern Cone of America. (A) *Ixodes pararicinus*. (B) *Ixodes* sp. cf. *I. affinis*. (C) *Ixodes aragaoi* **(Bottom)** Dorsal view of females of *Ixodes* spp. from the *Ixodes ricinus* complex in the Southern Cone of America. (A) *Ixodes pararicinus*. (B) *Ixodes* sp. cf. *I. affinis*. (C) *Ixodes aragaoi*. Courtesy: Saracho-Bottero *et al. Parasitol Res* 2020;119:43–54. Reproduced with permission from Springer Nature.

of human parasitic diseases caused by protozoa and helminths. Many dipteran insects carry protozoa: mosquitoes for *Plasmodium*, tsetse flies for *Trypanosoma brucei*, kissing bugs for *Trypanosoma cruzi*, and sand flies for *Leishmania*. Many dipteran insects carry helminths: mosquitoes for *Wuchereria*, black flies for *Onchocerca*, and deer flies for *Loa*.

As hosts to human protozoan and helminthic parasites, insects can be intermediate or definitive hosts. They also act as vectors for the spread of human pathogens. In this sense, they can be mechanical or biological vectors. An example of mechanical vector is the *Entamoeba* cysts in human feces carried by flies and cockroaches. For biological vectors, the species may undergo growth or differentiation within the vector carrier. For **cyclopropagative** biological transmission, there is both reproduction and cyclic changes, such as *Plasmodium* in mosquitoes. For **cyclodevelopmental** biological transmission, there is cyclic changes but no increase in the number of individuals. An example is microfilariae in mosquitoes (Bogitsh *et al.* 2019).

Insects can be human ectoparasites. There are lice, which include the pubic louse (or crab louse, *Phthirus pubis*) and the head-and-body louse (*Pediculus humanus*). There are fleas, bedbugs, and others such as wasps, spiders (black widow) and scorpions that have toxins against humans (Mathison and Pritt 2014).

Species of fly larvae (maggots) can infect and live in human tissues as **myiasis**. The first imported case of furuncular myiasis caused by *Cordylobia anthropophaga* (mango fly) in a Korean overseas traveler was reported in 2017, with the fly maggot recovered from a lesion on the left leg of a 33-year-old male (previously worked in Uganda for 8 months) and species identification by 28S rRNA sequencing (Song *et al.* 2017). A second case was reported in a 55-year-old male who had spent 1 month at Equatorial Guinea, with two larvae isolated and morphologically identified. "Although rarely described in Korea until now, cutaneous myiasis may be encountered more frequently with increasing international travel and exchange workers to tropical areas" (Ko *et al.* 2018).

23.6 Genomes of Arthropods

Arthropods, including insects, are diverse in species and population mass. World populations use crustaceans as food sources (shrimps, crabs). Due to the concern of raising cattle and the toll on global warming, entomology should introduce **entomophagy**. Whereas western cultures are gradually becoming familiar with insect-derived food items (think cricket flour), countries such as Cambodia have traditionally enjoyed insects in their cuisine. Research on arthropods has focused on their biology, including fisheries, aquaculture, apiculture and pollination biology (bees), diseases and genetics. Before the selection of the free-living nematode *Caenorhabditis elegans* (by Sydney Brenner), the fruit fly *Drosophila melanogaster* has been the model species for genetics and developmental biology. Like the nematode, the fruit fly genome has been sequenced before the human genome (Adams *et al.* 2000). Many arthropod genomes have been or are being investigated. Over 470 genomes are currently available, representing 175 of about 3,000 arthropod families.[4] (Giribet *et al.* 2018). An initiative known as the 5,000 arthropod genomes initiative (**i5K**) is ongoing, including the suggestion for new species to be sequenced.[4]

Insects are the most abundant arthropods. Scientists from China have started a data base dedicated to the insects. **InsectBase** encompasses 138 insect genomes, 116 insect transcriptomes, with additional insect gene sets, gene families, miRNAs (microRNAs) and other data (Yin *et al.* 2016).[5]

Only a small number of arthropods play significant roles in human diseases. They act as ectoparasites and as vectors of parasitic protozoa and helminths. There is a dedicated

[4] http://i5k.github.io/arthropod_genomes_at_ncbi
[5] http://www.insect-genome.com/

scientific journal on this topic: ***Parasites & Vectors*** is an open-access journal published by BioMed Central (part of Springer), covering the biology of parasites, parasitic diseases, intermediate hosts, vectors, and vector-borne pathogens. It was established in 2008 (a merger of two formal journals — *Filaria Journal* and *Kinetoplastid Biology*). In addition to the journal, there is also a dedicated data base. **VectorBase** is a National Institute of Allergy and Infectious Diseases (NIAID)-supported Bioinformatics Resource Center. Scientists from the University of Notre Dame (Indiana, USA), European Molecular Biology Laboratory (EMBO), and Imperial College London are currently involved in its maintenance. Their aim is to provide genomic, phenotypic and population-centric data to the scientific community for invertebrate vectors of human pathogens (Giraldo-Calderon *et al.* 2015).[6]

Among the dipteran insects, mosquitoes are important vectors. Genome of the malaria parasite carrying mosquito, *Anopheles gambiae*, was first published in 2002. Soon, genomes of other species followed: the yellow fever (arbovirus) carrying *Aedes aegypti* in 2007, and the elephantiasis microfilariae carrying *Culex quinquefasciatus* in 2010 (Holt *et al.* 2002; Nene *et al.* 2007; Arensburger *et al.* 2010). These three species are popular organisms at the VectorBase web site. Genomes of other mosquito species have been studied, including 16 species of anopheline mosquitoes. Noted dynamics in their genes "may contribute to their flexible capacity to take advantage of new ecological niches, including adapting to humans as primary hosts" (Neafsey *et al.* 2015). *Plasmodium falciparum* and other malaria parasites complete their reproductive cycle within the mosquitos (definitive host). Only adult females take blood meals. Further analyses of the anopheline genome are in progress, including the search for genetic diversity among native mosquito populations with an aim to accelerate the development of new strategies/tools for vector control. The *Anopheles gambiae* 1000 Genomes Project has reported genomes of 765 specimens of *Anopheles gambiae* and *Anopheles coluzzii* sampled from 15 locations across Africa, and identified over 50 million single nucleotide polymorphisms (Anopheles gambiae 1000 Genomes Consortium 2017).[7]

The first genome of ***Anopheles gambiae*** showed a size of 278 Mb, over 400,000 single nucleotide polymorphisms (SNPs), 13,683 predicted genes (current gene count is **13,796** at VectorBase), 40 types of transposons, expansion in gene families for cell adhesion and immunity (compared to *Drosophila*, for serine protease genes and cadherin domain-containing genes), plus a 19-member odorant receptor family (absent in fruit fly). The genome of ***Aedes aegypti*** shows a large genome of 1,376 Mb, 5X the size of *A. gambiae*, with 50% of DNA as transposable elements, and codes for 15,419 genes (**19,763** at VectorBase). There is an increase in genes coding for odorant receptors, cytochrome P450 and cuticle domains. *A. aegypti* is a vector for the etiologic agents of yellow fever, dengue fever and chikungunya fever. The largest genome size for a mosquito belongs to another vector for the agents of dengue fever and chikungunya fever, the Asian tiger mosquito ***Aedes albopictus***. This

[6] https://www.vectorbase.org/

[7] https://www.malariagen.net/mosquito/ag1000g

mosquito is a highly adaptive species. From its origin in Asia, it has established itself on every continent except Antarctica. It has a genome size of 1,967 Mb and has 17,539 predicted protein-encoding genes (**18,294** at VectorBase). There are expansions of gene family members involved in insecticide resistance, diapause, sex determination, immunity, and olfaction (Chen *et al.* 2015). The genome of ***Culex quinquefasciatus*** shows a size of 579 Mb with 18,883 predicted protein-coding genes (**19,793** at VectorBase). Again, there are multiple gene family expansions, for olfactory and gustatory receptors, salivary gland genes, and genes associated with xenobiotic detoxification. This mosquito carries the West Nile virus as well as the agents for lymphatic filariasis. In mosquito biology, major groups are divided into *Anopheles* or *Culex* related species, because their larvae behave differently in the aquatic environment. *Anopheles* larvae do not have breathing tubes, so they must lie parallel to the surface and breathe through holes in their sides called spiracles. *Culex* larvae can lie at an angle to the surface. Larvae of *Culex* mosquito are bottom feeders whereas larvae of *Anopheles* mosquito are surface feeders. In addition, eggs of *Culex* are vertically laid in clusters on the surface of the water whereas eggs of *Anopheles* are laid singly and horizontally on the surface of the water. Looking at the genes and genome sizes among mosquito species available at VectorBase, their DNA sizes are variable, less for *Anopheles* (172–445 Mb) but more for *Aedes* (1,278–1,923 Mb). Predicted protein-coding genes also differ, varying from **11,000 to 19,800** depending on individual mosquito species. [The American Mosquito Control Association is dedicated to the suppression of mosquitoes.[8]]

Different species of dipteran flies are vectors of diseases such as sleeping sickness and leishmaniasis. The tsetse fly is the vector for human African trypanosomiasis (HAT). The genome of ***Glossina morsitans*** is available (International Glossina Genome Initiative 2014). The genome is 366 Mb in size and codes for 12,308 predicted genes (**12,869** at VectorBase). Tsetse flies are the sole vectors of HAT throughout sub-Saharan Africa. Both male and female tsetse flies take blood meals. Females are viviparous; they also provide lactation to their young. This phenomenon is known as **adenotrophic viviparity**: intrauterine larval development, nourishment by glandular secretions, and live birth. The genome data also note the presence of specific opsin (Rh5) and its photoreceptor, which is the basis of the tsetse fly's attraction to color **blue/black**, a feature being exploited in the development of tsetse fly traps. In addition to visual cues, the tsetse fly also uses olfactory cues to locate its mammalian hosts. This knowledge has been applied to a novel vector control strategy, known as the tsetse repellent technology. Use of repellents (either synthetic or natural), first characterized from the non-preferred vertebrate hosts (zebras and waterbucks), can disrupt the disease transmission cycle and vector-host contact. As an example, **blend K**, composed of acetophenone, geranyl acetone, and 6-methyl-5-hepten-2-one (three compound combination mimicking zebra skin odor), has been shown to repel both riverine and savannah tsetse fly species (Olaide *et al.* 2020). Thus, animal skin odors are important to the tsetse fly for its host-seeking behavior.

[8] https://www.mosquito.org/page/biology

The tsetse fly carries bacterial endosymbionts. The genome data shows chromosomal integration of the bacterial genome sequences from ***Wolbachia***. *Wolbachia* bacteria are found in ovarian tissues and have been implicated in cytoplasmic incompatibility in the tsetse. Thus, *Wobachia* is bad for insects (including tsetse fly). The tsetse fly also possesses two endosymbionts: the primary endosymbiont, ***Wigglesworthia glossinidia***, and the secondary endosymbiont, ***Sodalis glossinidius***. Removal of endosymbiont bacteria with antibiotics has an impact on fly fecundity and pupal emergence (Dale and Welburn 2001). The tsetse fly can also be host to a large DNA hytrosavirus. Please see Figure 23.8 for the endosymbionts of tsetse fly (International Glossina Genome Initiative 2014). Genomes of other tsetse flies are listed in the VectorBase. In addition, a dedicated website for the tsetse fly is being maintained by scientists from the Liverpool School of Tropical Medicine.[9]

The sand fly is the insect vector of leishmaniasis. Many species are involved in the transmission of different species of the protozoan parasite (Ready 2013). Genomes of several species are listed in the VectorBase: **11,821** genes for ***Phlebotomus papatasi***, and **10,760** genes for ***Lutzomyia longipalpis***. Formal publications are not yet available. Transcriptome analysis of the sand fly *Phlebotomus perniciosus*, agent of *Leishmania infantum*, has shown sex-specific genes and pathways (Petrella *et al.* 2015). MicroRNA (21 in total) of *Lutzomyia longipalpis* has been detected by bioinformatics analysis (Yang and Wu 2019).

Other vector genomes are available in the VectorBase. One notable insect is the bed bug, *Cimex lectularius*, with 14,220 predicted genes (**15,292** at VectorBase). It is a ubiquitous human ectoparasite with a global resurgence likely linked to increased international travel and commerce, and widespread insecticide resistance. The bed bug has been shown to be able to transmit *Trypanosoma cruzi*, the agent of Chagas disease, experimentally, in mice (Benoit *et al.* 2016). The more common vector for Chagas is the kissing bug. One species, ***Rhodnius prolixus***, with **15,738** genes, is listed in the VectorBase.

Besides insects, genomes of mites and ticks are known. The scabies mite ***Sarcoptes scabiei*** has two predicted gene numbers: 10,644 protein-coding genes (Rider *et al.* 2015) and 13,226 protein-coding genes (Mofiz *et al.* 2016) (**10,797** at VectorBase). As there has been fragmentation in these samples, a high quality genome has followed, aided by transcriptomics data, investigators have annotated 9,174 protein-encoding genes consisting of ~4.0 exons per gene (Korhonen *et al.* 2020). Ticks are vectors of *Borrelia burgdorferi*, the agent of Lyme disease. Genome of the hard tick ***Ixodes scapularis*** has 20,486 protein-coding genes (Gulia-Nuss *et al.* 2016) (**23,340** at VectorBase); the genome of *Ixodes ricinus* has 25,263 protein-coding genes (Cramaro *et al.* 2017). Tick-pathogen interactions based on gene expression have been investigated. Please see Figure 23.9 for an example: the tick is *Ixodes scapularis*, the pathogen is *Anaplasma phagocytophilum*, the bacterium that is the infectious agent of human granulocytic anaplasmosis (**HGA**) (de la Fuente *et al.* 2016).

[9] https://www.tsetse.org/

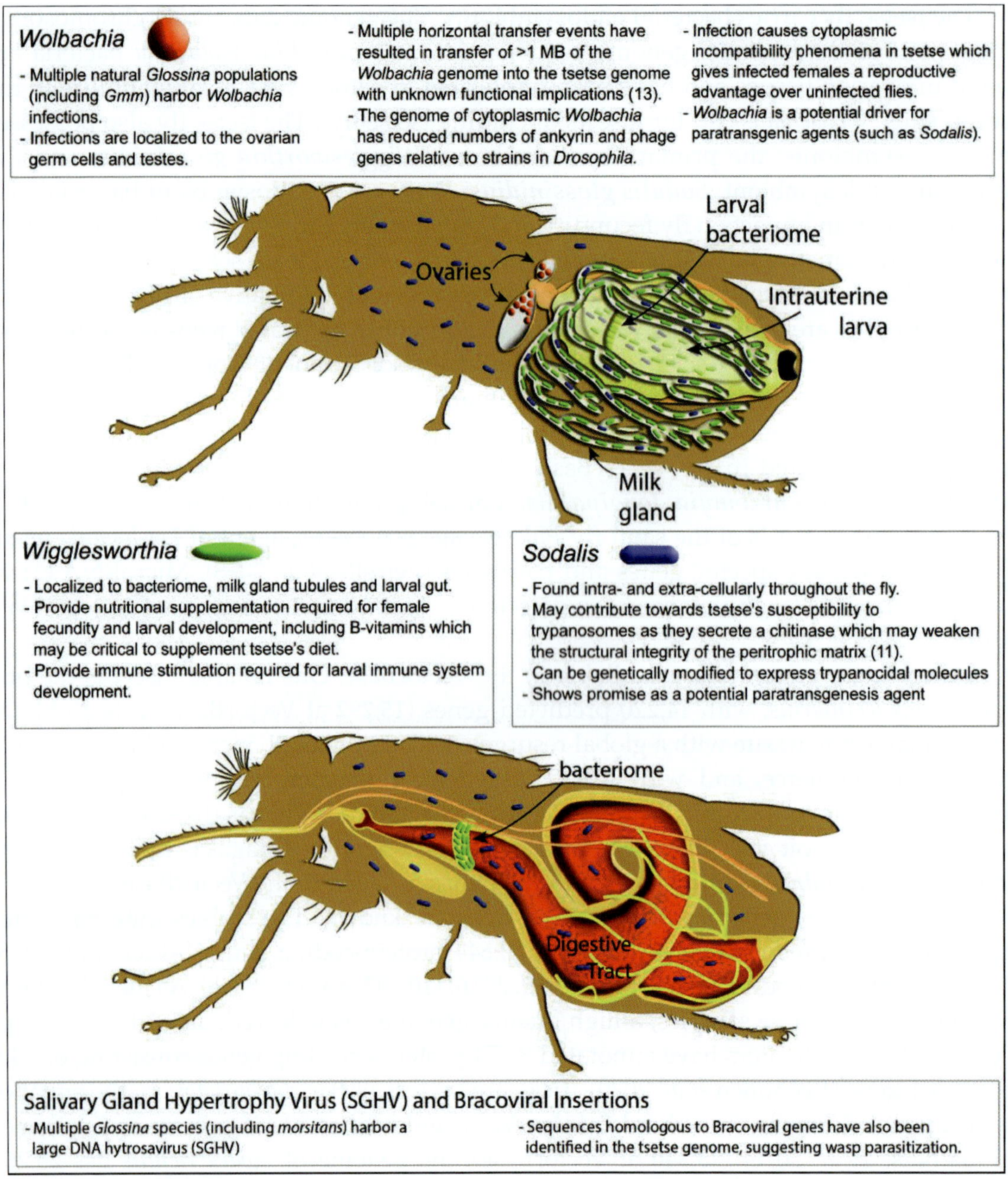

Fig. 23.8 ■ Endosymbionts of tsetse fly. Diagrammatic presentation of the *Glossina* microbiome, tissue localization of bacterial symbionts, physiological importance, and summary of genomic interactions. (Top) *Glossina* reproductive physiology and associated symbiont localizations. (Bottom) *Glossina* digestive physiology and the associated symbiont localizations. Associated text describes significant findings regarding the *Glossina* microbiome and the associated impacts in terms of *Glossina* immunity, nutrition, vectorial capacity, and vector control. Associated satellite references are listed within the figure as numbers in parentheses and correspond to the reference list (*11, 13*). Courtesy: International Glossina Genome Initiative. *Science* 2014;344:380–6. Reproduced with permission from the American Association for the Advancement of Science.

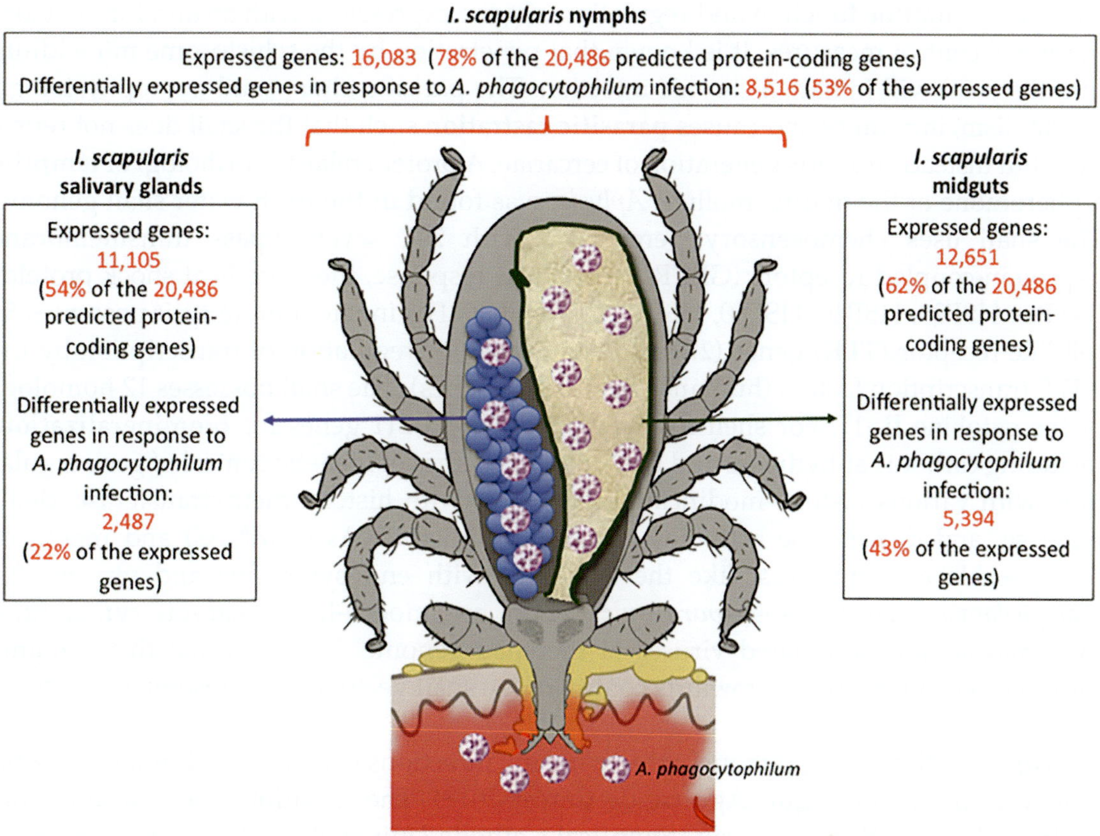

Fig. 23.9 ■ Tick-pathogen interaction based on gene expression: the tick is *Ixodes scapularis*, the pathogen is *Anaplasma phagocytophilum*, causative agent of human granulocytic anaplasmosis (HGA). Example of the advance in the characterization of tick-pathogen interactions based on the sequence and assembly of the *I. scapularis* genome. Transcriptomics data was obtained from Ayllon *et al.* (2015). Courtesy: de la Fuente *et al. Front Cell Infect Microbiol* 2016;6:103. Reproduced with permission from *Frontiers in Cellular and Infection Microbiology* with Creative Commons Attribution 4.0 (CC-BY) International License.

23.7 Genome of a Mollusc (Not an Arthropod)

Schistosomiasis is an important vector borne neglected tropical disease. Hence, VectorBase includes the snail ***Biomphalaria glabrata***. This neotropical fresh water gastropod mollusc is the intermediate host for *Schistosoma mansoni*. "With the World Health Organization's goal to eliminate schistosomiasis as a global health problem by 2025, there is now renewed emphasis on snail control" (Adema *et al.* 2017). The genome with an estimated size of 916 Mb. There are 18 chromosomes and 14,423 predicted genes (the number has become **31,985** in VectorBase). The investigators studied phero-perception, stress responses, immune function and regulation of gene expression, with an aim for developing novel control measures. It is known that penetration by the schistosome miracidium into the snail will initiate a chronic infection. The parasite alters snail neurophysiology, metabolism, immunity and causes **parasitic castration** such that the snail does not reproduce but instead supports generation of cercariae. A protein relative (ortholog) of **temptin**, a pheromone of the marine mollusc *Aplysia*, was found in the fresh water snail genome. The snail uses chemosensory perception, with 241 seven-bypass transmembrane G-protein-coupled receptors (GPCRs). For stress response, there are heat shock proteins (**HSPs**): HSP20, HSP40, HSP60, HSP70, and HSP90. For innate immunity, it possesses 56 toll-like receptor (**TLR**) genes (**27** complete genes) for regulation of transcription by the NF*k*B transcription factors (humans have 10 TLR genes). The snail possesses 12 homologs of the cytokine IL-17. For shell formation there are 1,211 genes for **biomineralization**, including carbonic anhydrases and tyrosinases. There is epigenetic control of gene regulation, with various histone modification enzymes (with histone methytransferase, demethylase, and deacetylase activities), as well as microRNAs (miRNAs) and repetitive transposable elements. Just like the tsetse fly with endosymbionts and viruses, for *Biomphalaraia*, there is ***Capsaspora owczarzaki***, an amoeba-like eukaryote symbiont, a mycoplasma, and associated viruses in the snail genome. It is expected this genomic information will be applied towards control of the snail vector of schistosomiasis (Adema *et al*. 2017).

We have discussed previously that parasitic infections can alter the human microbiome, especially in the gut (Aguirre de Cárcer 2018). The situation is also true for the gastropod. Joana Borges Osório (Pontifical Catholic University of Rio Grande do Sul , Porto Alegre, Brazil) and colleagues reported on mollusc microbiome shift due to infection by the rat lung worm *Angiostrongylus cantonensis*. (Angiostrongyliasis has been presented in Chapter 22.) They experimentally infected the rat lung worm to terrestrial slugs and freshwater snails. For the latter, the species used was *Biomphalaria glabrata*. Snails were infected with L1 larvae (isolated from feces of infected rats) and after 30-day infection, snail feces were collected for microbiome analysis. Fecal DNAs from control and infected groups were extracted and subjected to 16S rRNA high-throughput sequencing survey. In *Biomphalaria* microbiota, control and infected groups were significantly different. "The microbiome of *B. glabrata* infected with *A. cantonensis* showed a significant decline in the abundance of *Flavobacterium*, *Fluviicola*, *Nitrospira*, *Vogesella* and an OTU belonging to the family *Comamonadaceae*, and a significant increase of *Uliginosibacterium* and an OTU belonging to the family *Weeksellaceae* when compared to a control group. Overall, the microbiome data reported here provided valuable information with regard to the diversity of bacterial communities that comprise the gut microbiome of gastropods" (Osório *et al*. 2020). OTU is used here; the concept of operational taxonomic units (OTUs), which constructs "mathematically" defined taxa, is widely accepted and applied to describe bacterial communities using amplicon sequencing of 16S rRNA gene.

Summary & Key Concepts

- Arthropods are exceedingly successful invertebrates.
- The evolutionary success of arthropods is due to development of cuticles, of which chitin is the major component.
- The most abundant species in the arthropods is Hexapoda, the insects.
- Insects can undergo either incomplete or complete metamorphosis.
- Arthropods can be carriers of vector-borne diseases, or they themselves can be human ectoparasites.
- Arthropod genomes have provided insights on their capacity to be parasites or vectors, their versatility to inhabit ecological niches, insecticide resistance, and development of tools to decrease their numbers.
- The genome of snail (a gastropod mollusc, not an arthropod) *Biomphalaria glabrata* is known; this snail is intermediate host for the blood fluke *Schistosoma mansoni*.

References

Adams MD, Celniker SE, Holt RA, *et al.* The genome sequence of *Drosophila melanogaster*. *Science* 2000;287(5461):2185–95.

Adema CM, Hillier LW, Jones CS, *et al.* Whole genome analysis of a schistosomiasis-transmitting freshwater snail. *Nat Commun* 2017;8:15451.

Adl SM, Bass D, Lane CE, *et al.* Revisions to the classification, nomenclature, and diversity of eukaryotes. *J Eukaryot Microbiol* 2019;66(1):4–119.

Aguirre de Cárcer D. The human gut pan-microbiome presents a compositional core formed by discrete phylogenetic units. *Sci Rep* 2018;8(1):14069.

Anopheles gambiae 1000 Genomes Consortium. Genetic diversity of the African malaria vector *Anopheles gambiae*. *Nature* 2017;552(7683):96–100.

Anopheles gambiae 1000 Genomes Consortium. Genome variation and population structure among 1142 mosquitoes of the African malaria vector species *Anopheles gambiae* and *Anopheles coluzzii*. *Genome Res* 2020;30(10):1533–46.

Arensburger P, Megy K, Waterhouse RM, *et al.* Sequencing of *Culex quinquefasciatus* establishes a platform for mosquito comparative genomics. *Science* 2010;330(6000):86–8.

Benoit JB, Adelman ZN, Reinhardt K, *et al.* Unique features of a global human ectoparasite identified through sequencing of the bed bug genome. *Nat Commun* 2016;7:10165.

Bogitsh BJ, Carter CE, Oeltmann TN. *Human Parasitology*, 5th ed., Academic Press, Elsevier, 2019.

Chen XG, Jiang X, Gu J, *et al.* Genome sequence of the Asian Tiger mosquito, *Aedes albopictus*, reveals insights into its biology, genetics, and evolution. *Proc Natl Acad Sci USA* 2015;112(44): E5907–15. Erratum in: *Proc Natl Acad Sci U S A* 2016;113(4):E489.

Cramaro WJ, Hunewald OE, Bell-Sakyi L, *et al.* Genome scaffolding and annotation for the pathogen vector *Ixodes ricinus* by ultra-long single molecule sequencing. *Parasit Vectors* 2017;10(1):71.

Dale C, Welburn SC. The endosymbionts of tsetse flies: Manipulating host-parasite interactions. *Int J Parasitol* 2001;31(5–6):628–31.

Dallai R, Gottardo M, Beutel RG. Structure and evolution of insect sperm: New interpretations in the age of phylogenomics. *Annu Rev Entomol* 2016;61:1–23.

de la Fuente J, Waterhouse RM, Sonenshine DE, *et al.* Tick genome assembled: New opportunities for research on tick-host-pathogen interactions. *Front Cell Infect Microbiol* 2016;6:103.

Giraldo-Calderón GI, Emrich SJ, MacCallum RM, *et al.* VectorBase: An updated bioinformatics resource for invertebrate vectors and other organisms related with human diseases. *Nucleic Acids Res* 2015;43(Database issue):D707–13.

Giribet G, Edgecombe GD. The phylogeny and evolutionary history of arthropods. *Curr Biol* 2019;29(12):R592–R602.

Gulia-Nuss M, Nuss AB, Meyer JM, *et al.* Genomic insights into the *Ixodes scapularis* tick vector of Lyme disease. *Nat Commun* 2016;7:10507.

Holt RA, Subramanian GM, Halpern A, *et al.* The genome sequence of the malaria mosquito *Anopheles gambiae*. *Science* 2002;298(5591):129–49.

Hutchinson GE. Homage to Santa Rosalia or why are there so many kinds of animals? *Am Nat* 1959;93:145–59.

International Glossina Genome Initiative. Genome sequence of the tsetse fly (*Glossina morsitans*): Vector of African trypanosomiasis. *Science* 2014;344(6182):380–6.

Jindra M. Where did the pupa come from? The timing of juvenile hormone signalling supports homology between stages of hemimetabolous and holometabolous insects. *Philos Trans R Soc Lond B Biol Sci* 2019;374(1783):20190064.

Ko JY, Lee IY, Park BJ, *et al.* A case of cutaneous myiasis caused by *Cordylobia anthropophaga* larvae in a Korean traveler returning from Central Africa. *Korean J Parasitol* 2018;56(2):199–203.

Korhonen PK, Gasser RB, Ma G, *et al.* High-quality nuclear genome for *Sarcoptes scabiei*-A critical resource for a neglected parasite. *PLoS Negl Trop Dis* 2020;14(10):e0008720.

Mathison BA, Pritt BS. Laboratory identification of arthropod ectoparasites. *Clin Microbiol Rev* 2014;27(1):48–67.

Merzendorfer H. Insect chitin synthases: A review. *J Comp Physiol B* 2006;176(1):1–15.

Misof B, Liu S, Meusemann K, *et al.* Phylogenomics resolves the timing and pattern of insect evolution. *Science* 2014;346(6210):763–7.

Mofiz E, Holt DC, Seemann T, *et al.* Genomic resources and draft assemblies of the human and porcine varieties of scabies mites, *Sarcoptes scabiei* var. *hominis* and var. *suis*. *Gigascience* 2016;5(1):23.

Mongin E, Louis C, Holt RA, *et al.* The *Anopheles gambiae* genome: An update. *Trends Parasitol* 2004;20(2):49–52.

Neafsey DE, Waterhouse RM, Abai MR, *et al.* Mosquito genomics. Highly evolvable malaria vectors: The genomes of 16 *Anopheles* mosquitoes. *Science* 2015;347(6217):1258522.

Nene V, Wortman JR, Lawson D, *et al.* Genome sequence of *Aedes aegypti*, a major arbovirus vector. *Science* 2007;316(5832):1718–23.

Nutting WB. Hair follicle mites (Acari: Demodicidae) of man. *Int J Dermatol* 1976;15(2):79–98.

Olaide OY, Tchouassi DP, Yusuf AA, *et al.* Effect of zebra skin-derived compounds on field catches of the human African trypanosomiasis vector *Glossina fuscipes fuscipes*. *Acta Trop* 2020;213:105745.

Osório JB, de Mattos Pereira L, Giongo A, *et al.* Mollusk microbiota shift during Angiostrongylus cantonensis infection in the freshwater snail *Biomphalaria glabrata* and the terrestrial slug *Phillocaulis soleiformis*. *Parasitol Res* 2020;119(8):2495–2503.

Petrella V, Aceto S, Musacchia F, *et al.* De novo assembly and sex-specific transcriptome profiling in the sand fly *Phlebotomus perniciosus* (Diptera, Phlebotominae), a major Old World vector of *Leishmania infantum*. *BMC Genomics* 2015;16:847.

Ran X, Tang JQ, Zheng L, *et al.* Cover image: The manifestation of adult mite *Sarcoptes scabiei* under scanning electron microscope. *Br J Dermatol* 2018;179(2):545–6.

Ready PD. Biology of phlebotomine sand flies as vectors of disease agents. *Annu Rev Entomol* 2013;58:227–50.

Rider SD Jr, Morgan MS, Arlian LG. Draft genome of the scabies mite. *Parasit Vectors* 2015;8:585.

Rolff J, Johnston PR, Reynolds S. Complete metamorphosis of insects. *Philos Trans R Soc Lond B Biol Sci* 2019;374(1783):20190063.

Ruggiero MA, Gordon DP, Orrell TM, *et al.* A higher level classification of all living organisms. *PLoS One* 2015;10(4):e0119248. Erratum in: PLoS One 2015;10(6):e0130114.

Sánchez-Bayo F, Wyckhuys KAG. Worldwide decline of the entomofauna: A review of its drivers. *Biological Conservation* 2019; 232:8–27.

Saracho-Bottero MN, Venzal JM, Tarragona EL, *et al.* The *Ixodes ricinus* complex (Acari: Ixodidae) in the Southern Cone of America: *Ixodes pararicinus*, *Ixodes aragaoi*, and *Ixodes* sp. cf. *I. affinis*. *Parasitol Res* 2020;119(1):43–54.

Song SM, Kim SW, Goo YK, *et al.* A case of furuncular myiasis due to *Cordylobia anthropophaga* in a Korean traveler returning from Uganda. *Korean J Parasitol* 2017;55(3):327–31.

Sousa-Paula LC, Otranto D, Dantas-Torres F. *Lutzomyia longipalpis* (Sand Fly). *Trends Parasitol* 2020;36(9):796–7.

Stork NE. How many species of insects and other terrestrial arthropods are there on earth? *Annu Rev Entomol* 2018;63:31–45.

Sung WJ, Kim YH. A case of engorged female hard tick in the external auditory canal of an infant. *Korean J Parasitol* 2017;55(5):565–8.

Thomas GWC, Dohmen E, Hughes DST, *et al.* Gene content evolution in the arthropods. *Genome Biol* 2020;21(1):15.

Trautwein MD, Wiegmann BM, Beutel R, *et al.* Advances in insect phylogeny at the dawn of the postgenomic era. *Annu Rev Entomol* 2012;57:449–68.

Truman JW. The evolution of insect metamorphosis. *Curr Biol* 2019;29(23):R1252–68.

Watson GS, Watson JA, Cribb BW. Diversity of cuticular micro- and nanostructures on insects: Properties, functions, and potential applications. *Annu Rev Entomol* 2017;62:185–205.

Yang Z, Wu Y. Improved annotation of *Lutzomyia longipalpis* genome using bioinformatics analysis. *PeerJ* 2019;7:e7862.

Yin C, Shen G, Guo D, *et al.* InsectBase: A resource for insect genomes and transcriptomes. *Nucleic Acids Res* 2016;44(D1):D801–7.

Zhu KY, Merzendorfer H, Zhang W, *et al.* Biosynthesis, turnover, and functions of chitin in insects. *Annu Rev Entomol* 2016;61:177–96.

24

Global Collaboration Targeting the Control and Elimination of Parasitic Diseases

24.1 The Current Scene

In this concluding chapter, we begin our discussion on neglected tropical diseases (NTDs) and other parasitic diseases, expand into disease control and elimination, cover ecology and the One Health concept of humans and animals, and then move into new discoveries and current challenges facing the world. We shall close with ideas to motivate you, the reader, towards individual involvement in disease mitigation and public health improvement for the whole world population.

As a start, we want to draw your attention to an article published by Peter Hotez (then at George Washington University, Washington, DC, USA, now founding dean of the National School of Tropical Medicine at Baylor College of Medicine; he was founding editor-in-chief of *PLoS Neglected Tropical Diseases*) and colleagues over a decade ago, titled "Rescuing the bottom billion through control of neglected tropical diseases." These are their two opening sentences: "People in the bottom billion are the poorest in the world; they are often subsistence farmers, who essentially live on no money and are stuck in a poverty trap of disease, conflict, and no education. One of the most potent reinforcements of the poverty trap is the neglected tropical diseases." Actions by public and private agencies on NTDs have led to this conclusion: "With the track record of high return rates on investments in neglected tropical diseases, and recognition that these diseases represent an important challenge to global security and fundamental human rights, this amount is especially small and will address a major development problem and bring hope to the most disenfranchised populations" (Hotez *et al.* 2009). [The amount referred to a sum of $2–3 billion commitment towards NTDs in an almost $100 trillion global economy.]

NTDs represent the most common diseases for the 2.7 billion people living on less than US $2 per day. Some NTDs can be treated very cost-effectively; the control of NTDs can be an efficient way to fight poverty. The four key elements of the **poverty trap** are health (both maternal and child), agriculture, education and infrastructure. As mentioned above, people in the bottom billion of the world population are the poorest and are often subsistence farmers. For a similar view on this topic, the United States Centers for Disease Control and Prevention (CDC) have stated: "Neglected tropical diseases (NTDs) are a group of parasitic and bacterial diseases that cause substantial illness for more than one billion people globally. Affecting the world's poorest people, NTDs impair physical and cognitive development, contribute to mother and child illness and death, make it difficult to farm or earn a living, and limit productivity in the workplace. As a result, NTDs trap the poor in a cycle of poverty and disease."[1]

In addition to the village poor, there are the urban poor, as well as the connection of "poverty and pathogens" (Eisenstein 2016). Developing nations have experienced **urbanization** as the population shifts from rural to urban areas. For example, 85% of the population of Brazil lives in cities. Most are in "informal settlements," aka slums. United Nations Habitat puts the global estimate of slum populations at **881 million** (as of 2014), just under a third of all urban-dwellers in the developing world. Close quarters breed infectious diseases, and vectors tend to follow the inbound city dwellers. Specifically, the vector for Chagas' disease changes from country bug to city bug, accompanying rural migrants to city slums.

NTDs have different definitions. Depending on the context, there are two views. The first emphasizes neglect as the defining characteristic; the second concentrates on the diseases' shared features and their effects on poverty and development. NTDs "persist in conditions of poverty where they cluster and frequently overlap" (Liese *et al.* 2010). In addition, there has been a tendency to broaden the geographic scope of NTDs beyond the tropics. Attempts are being made to connect the neglected diseases in the developing world to those of disenfranchised minorities in the developed world. As an example, while NTDs are known to mostly affect the developing countries, there is a rise of NTDs in Texas, a southern state of USA, with "a high level of parasitic infections, including Chagas' disease, trichomoniasis, and possibly leishmaniasis and toxocariasis," in addition to viral and bacterial diseases (Hotez 2018a). Indeed, "the poor living in G20 nations now account for most of the world's NTDs" (Hotez and Booker 2020). Besides infectious diseases, there are non-communicable diseases (**NCDs**) such as cancer and heart disease, and most "NCDs cause more deaths at every age in low- and middle-income tropical countries than in high-income Western countries" (Ezzati *et al.* 2018). These diseases are a major public health concern of the world population.

Public and private sectors have geared up to target NTDs and other diseases. The World Health Organization (WHO) acts as an international leader with other agencies, such as the World Bank, also contributing to disease treatment and prevention. There are government agencies from developed countries, such as the Agency for International Development (**AID**) in the US and the Department for International Development (**DFID**) in the UK, and developing countries, such as the onchocerciasis focus group of nineteen

---

[1] https://www.cdc.gov/globalhealth/ntd/index.html

African countries forming African Programme for Onchocerciasis Control (**APOC**) and the six countries forming Onchocerciasis Elimination Programme for the Americas (**OEPA**). The APOC countries are Angola, Burundi, Cameroon, Central African Republic, Chad, Congo, Democratic Republic of Congo, Ethiopia, Equatorial Guinea, Gabon, Kenya, Liberia, Malawi, Mozambique, Nigeria, Rwanda, Sudan, Tanzania, and Uganda. The OEPA countries are Brazil, Colombia, Ecuador, Guatemala, Mexico, and Venezuela. Both groups continue to receive ivermectin donations provided by the American multinational pharmaceutical company Merck.

Beyond the government, there is active participation from private philanthropies, notably the Bill and Melinda **Gates Foundation** in the US and the **Wellcome Trust** in the UK. Many public-private partnerships (**PPPs**) have been set up to develop new drugs, vaccines and mitigation methods, such as the Drugs for Neglected Diseases Initiative (**DNDi**). Created in 2003 and headquartered in Geneva, Switzerland, DNDi is a non-profit drug research and development (R&D) organization with a mission to meet patients' needs through collaborative efforts in NTD drug discovery. The organization was set up by key research and health institutions, including ones from the public sector in NTD-endemic countries. Members include the Oswaldo Cruz Foundation from Brazil, the Indian Council of Medical Research, the Kenya Medical Research Institute, the Ministry of Health of Malaysia, France's Pasteur Institute, and Médecins Sans Frontières' (MSF) (Doctors Without Borders). DNDi was set up with seed money from the 1999 Nobel Peace Prize awarded to MSF. It should also be noted that the WHO Special Programme for Research and Training in Tropical Diseases (**TDR**) is permanent observer of the DNDi.

Because of the high costs in developing new drugs and many economically challenged countries are locations where NTDs are found, drugs for NTDs are not attractive to pharmaceutical companies for the lack of profitability. Hence, there are PPPs with the specific purpose of developing NTD drugs. In addition, for drugs already available, there are drug donation programs from pharmaceutical companies for the treatment of NTDs. A total of **seven** NTDs are noteworthy because of high prevalence and amenability to control: soil-transmitted helminth infections (hookworm, ascariasis, trichuriasis), lymphatic filariasis, schistosomiasis, and diseases that can cause blindness (trachoma and onchocerciasis). The aim is to reduce disease burden or interfere with disease transmission through population-based chemotherapy. The idea was introduced in the 1920s, via mass drug administration (**MDA**) of diethylcarbamazine (DEC) or DEC-fortified salt to interrupt the transmission of lymphatic filariasis. MDA is feasible because of free drug donations. In 2005, a low-cost "**rapid impact**" package combining 4 drugs, praziquantel and azithromycin along with either albendazole or mebendazole, and ivermectin or DEC, was developed to simultaneously target the 7 major NTDs. This integration provides cost savings; the estimate is US $0.40 per person per year for **integrated control**. In sub-Saharan Africa there are 162,000 community-based drug distributors to provide MDA service (established from previous interventions such as childhood vaccinations and antimalarial bednet distributions) (Hotez 2013; Hotez *et al.* 2018c). MDA has been termed **preventive chemotherapy** by WHO.

"No other public health initiative has benefited from the availability of donated drugs to such an extent as have neglected tropical diseases. Key enabling factors for these donations are the preventive public health nature of the programs; their large scale, the pre-existence of structured multi-donor, international control efforts, and clearly delineated accountability and evaluation mechanisms. These factors seem to facilitate both the willingness of the pharmaceutical industry to provide such charitable donations and their effective use. Such cooperation between the industry and programs for NTDs is a good example of a public-private partnership" (Liese *et al.* 2010). Many drug manufacturers have donation programs. Merck, with its Mectizan donation program founded in 1987, pledged to contribute as much ivermectin as needed for the treatment of onchocerciasis. In 2014, drug companies donated 41 billion treatments, with a dollar value of nearly $1.5 billion (Cohen *et al.* 2016). Select drug donations by manufacturers are listed in Table 24.1 (Cohen *et al.* 2016; WHO 2020; Bradley *et al.* 2021).[2] It must also be noted that donations are a necessity but there exist underlying issues leading to insufficient patient access to NTD drugs. Still, drug donations have expanded patients' overall access to medicines targeting NTDs. Additional resources must be allocated to ensure the delivery of donated products to patients in order to further expand accessibility needed to combat the NTDs.

Table 24.1 Select pharmaceutical companies drug donation program. [Modified from J. Cohen *et al.*, 2016, *Clin Ther*. 38, 1193-1204; M. Bradley *et al.*, 2021, *Trans R Soc Trop Med Hyg*. 2021;115(2):136–144; and WHO, Ending the Neglect to attain the Sustainable Development Goals: A Road Map for Neglected Tropical Diseases 2021–2030, https://www.who.int/publications/i/item/9789240010352.]

Year start	Year end	Drug name	Disease targeted	Company name
1987	Unlimited	Ivermectin	Onchocerciasis	Merck
1998	Unlimited	Ivermectin	Lymphatic filariasis	Merck
1998	2025	Azithromycin	Trachoma	Pfizer
1998	Unlimited	Albendazole	Lymphatic filariasis	GlaxoSmithKline
2011	Unlimited	Albendazole	Soil-transmitted helminthiasis	GlaxoSmithKline
2006	2025	Mebendazole	Soil-transmitted helminthiasis	Johnson & Johnson
2001	2025	Pentamidine	Human African trypanosomiasis	Sanofi
2001	2025	Eflornithine	Human African trypanosomiasis	Sanofi
2001	2025	Melasoprol	Human African trypanosomiasis	Sanofi
2000	2022	Triclabendazole	Fascioliasis	Norvatis
2000	2025	Multidrug therapy	Leprosy	Norvatis
2002	2025	Suramin	Human African trypanosomiasis	Bayer
2004	2025	Nifurtimox	American trypanosomiasis	Bayer
2014	Unlimited	Diethylcarbamazine	Lymphatic filariasis	Eisai

[2] https://www.who.int/publications/i/item/9789240010352

There are critiques on drug donation and MDA. It has been suggested that the evidence of the efficacy of mass treatment programs is lacking. Furthermore, there is concern that MDA may lead to decreased anthelmintic efficacy (Tinkler 2019). There are alternatives. A more sophisticated approach is mass screening and treatment (**MSAT**), whereby drugs are administered only to individuals who test positive for the pathogen. Whereas both MDA and MSAT rely upon high coverage and repeated interventions to achieve a long-term effect, MSAT also requires the availability and adoption of appropriate diagnostic tools (Croft 2016). While it seems to be a better approach on paper, this option may run into issues in reality. Since medical treatment can be expensive, any cost increase will further restrict accessibility.

Yao Sodahlon (Mectizan Donation Program, Task Force for Global Health, Georgia) and colleagues stated: "Much of the progress toward the control and elimination of NTDs is due to three factors: (1) Countries have committed to reaching more people with NTD interventions, (2) the pharmaceutical industry has donated billions of treatments for NTDs, and (3) philanthropists have provided generous funding to implement NTD interventions." They proposed a call for action: "We are at a unique moment in time. Countries are motivated to increase ownership of and domestic spending for their NTD programs. They are asking for guidance. The community of donors, NGOs, and other stakeholders involved in supporting endemic countries must seize upon this moment by recognizing and acting upon the need to build country capacity to sustain NTD programs and the progress they have made over time" (Sodahlon *et al.* 2020).

Summarizing the current status, the United Nations (UN), individual countries, government agencies, non-governmental organizations (**NGOs**), foundations, philanthropies, drug manufacturers, and both public and private establishments have joined forces towards the development of effective and affordable drugs, vaccines, and diagnostics in targeting human parasitic and infectious diseases.

24.2 Adding Ecology to Parasitic Diseases

Humans come in contact with protozoan and metazoan parasites during their daily activities, as many parasites thrive within the ecosystem. If feasible, humans, domesticated, and wild animals would prefer to avoid these parasites. The trait is known as the **landscape of disgust** (Weinstein *et al.* 2018). Analogous to the landscape of fear known to the prey in the predator-prey relationship, the host avoids the parasite in the parasite-host relationship. However, there are overlapping landscapes of disgust and fear (Weinstein *et al.* 2018). Please see Figure 24.1 for stimuli of fear and disgust (Buck *et al.* 2018). Disgust and fear stimuli induce different responses.

Disgust is a basic human emotion typically experienced as revulsion accompanied by a desire to avoid contact with the stimulus. Once believed to be a cultural construct, disgust is now considered to be an adaptive system for infection avoidance. Almost all disgust elicitors could be mapped onto agents of infectious disease. As an example, humans

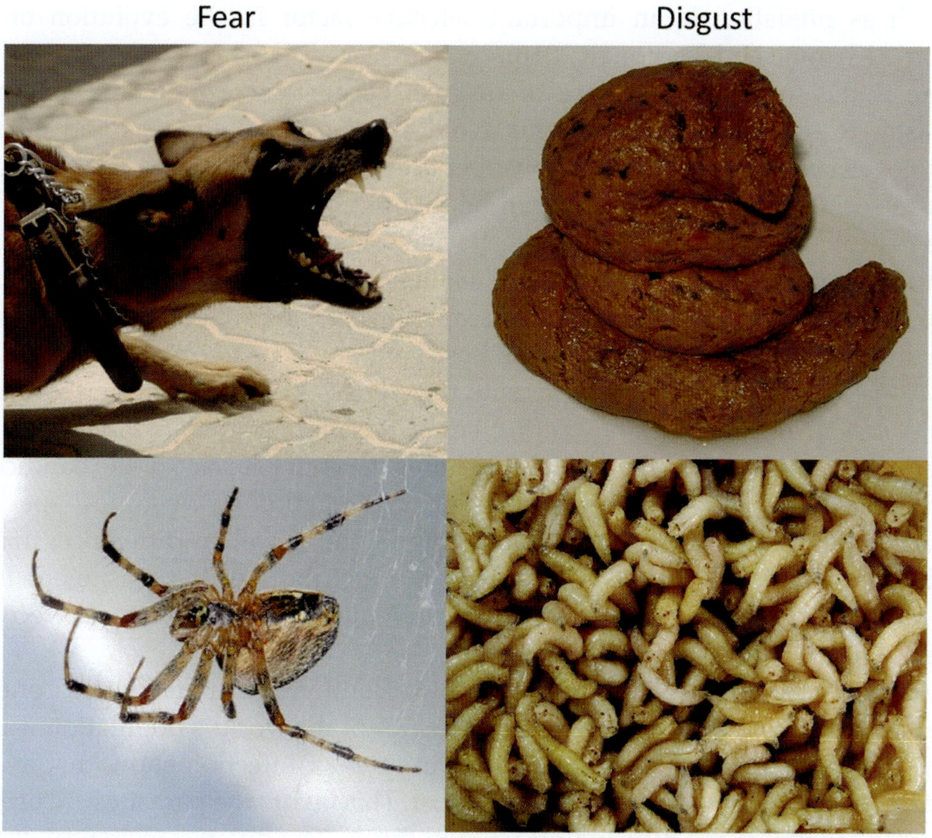

Fig. 24.1 ■ The stimuli of fear and disgust. Fear-Inducing Stimuli and Disgust-Inducing Stimuli Cause Different Responses. Photo credit: feces: Cacetudo; spider: Michael Gäbler; maggots: Dalius Baranauskas. Courtesy: Buck *et al. Trends Ecol Evol* 2018;33:619–32. Reproduced with permission from Elsevier.

may elicit disgust in the sight of feces ("stinky poops"), a potential source of parasitic cysts and eggs. Both predator-prey and parasite-host relationships can be generalized in the framework of consumers and resources (Buck *et al.* 2018).

The landscape of disgust is a feature of infection avoidance behavior. "The Queen of Hygiene" Val Curtis (1958–2020) of the London School of Hygiene and Tropical Medicine wrote: "**Parasites create problems for all animals**. Potential hosts can respond by learning to live with parasites (tolerance), actively fighting them (resistance), or they can avoid becoming infected in the first place (avoidance)" and she suggested, "a new classification of animal disease-avoidance behavior according to the epidemiology of parasite infection risk: (i) conspecifics, (ii) parasites and their vectors, (iii) places and objects likely to harbor parasites — which can be avoided or, (iv) modified to avoid parasite risk arising" (Curtis 2014). Parasite avoidance is a learned behavior, as shown in an example of fish-trematode interaction. For example, sea trouts are capable of learning to avoid visual cues associated with the presence of parasites. Thus, "parasitism, in addition to other biological interactions such as predation is an important selective factor in the evolution of animal cognition" (Klemme and Karvonen 2016).

There is the social neuroscience of disgust. Disgust incorporates social cognitive mechanisms to regulate, anticipate, and avoid exposure to pathogens and toxins. The neurobiological aspects of disgust involve peptide and hormone (oxytocin, estrogens) in relation to social cognition. "Disgust can be thought of as an affective system that has evolved to detect signs of pathogens, parasite and toxins as well as to stimulate behaviors that reduce the risk of their acquisition" (Kavaliers *et al.* 2019).

A concept of "Landscapes within landscapes" has been proposed, for a parasite that utilizes different ecological niches on the host landscapes of two host species. The tick *Ixodes holocyclus* is a generalist ectoparasite that infects both the long-nosed bandicoot (*Perameles nasuta*) and the black rat (*Rattus rattus*). It is more aggregated in the rat population. At the host landscape scale, its niche includes the entire surface of the bandicoot, but only on the head of the rat. "Differences in tick aggregation between host species may reflect tick habitat suitability at the host landscape scale, as well as differences in ecological and evolutionary histories. By exploring the distribution of parasites at multiple scales, including host landscapes, we can better understand the complex ecology of parasites" (Lydecker *et al.* 2019).

As we have discussed NTDs and poverty, we continue to quote Curtis: "one billion (people) have to defecate in the open. Less than 17% of the world's population wash their hands with soap after the toilet. Inequalities in rates of infection show that avoidance behavior has failed in the places that need it most. This favors the parasites" (Curtis 2014).

Another concept is the **dilution effect** hypothesis. The diverse ecological communities limit the spread of disease because a parasite is less likely to encounter its suitable host among the presence of a multitude of species. Biodiversity losses could worsen epidemics that harm humans and wildlife. "**Biodiversity inhibits parasites**" (Civitello *et al.* 2015). Human-induced declines in biodiversity could increase human and wildlife diseases and decrease crop and forest production.

24.3 One Health Philosophy

Humans and animals live within the ecosystem. Healthy humans, healthy animals, and a healthy environment are combined to form the One Health philosophy. Humans, animals, and the ecosystem form the "One Health" **triad**. Please see Figure 24.2 for the triad (Thompson 2013). One Health needs to consider humans, domestic animals, wildlife and the changing ecosystems in which they live in a holistic manner. One Health is defined as "an approach to address a health threat at the human-animal-environment interface based on collaboration, communication, and coordination across all relevant sectors and disciplines, with the ultimate goal of achieving optimal health outcomes for both people and animals; a One Health approach is applicable at the subnational, national, regional, and global level;" it "joins the three interdependent sectors — animal health, human health, and ecosystems — with the goal to holistically address health issues such as

Fig. 24.2 ■ The One Health Triad. The 'One Health' triad, encompassing the collaborative goals of providing optimal health for people, animals (domestic and wild) and the environment by considering interactions between all three systems. Courtesy: Thompson R. *Int J Parasitol* 2013;43:1079–88. Reproduced with permission from Elsevier.

zoonotic diseases, antimicrobial resistance, foodborne diseases and environmental conditions" (Humboldt-Dachroeden *et al.* 2020). Agencies of the United Nations are involved in the One Health framework: WHO (World Health Organization), TDR (WHO Special Programme for Research and Training in Tropical Diseases), FAO (Food and Agriculture Organization), OIE (World Organization for Animal Health), UNDP (United Nations Development Programme), UNEP (United Nations Environment Programme), UNFPA (United Nations Population Fund), UNICEF (United Nations Children's Fund), and WMO (World Meteorological Organization) (Mackey *et al.* 2014).

"The One Health (OH) approach to research ensures that human, animal, and environmental health questions are evaluated in an integrated and holistic manner to provide a more comprehensive understanding of the problem and potential solutions than would be possible with siloed approaches" (Lebov *et al.* 2017). A One Health research project incorporates elements from all 3 domains: human health, animal health, and environmental health (Lebov *et al.* 2017). As an example, Kwang Poo Chang (Chicago Medical School/ Rosalind Franklin University of Medicine and Science) and colleagues are interested in "New 'light' for one-world (One Health) approach toward safe and effective control of animal diseases and insect vectors from leishmaniac perspectives" (Chang *et al.* 2016). Using photodynamic therapy (PDT), *Leishmania*-based "photodynamic vaccination"

(PDV) is possible for leishmaniasis and other infectious diseases (by adding pathogen genes to the *Leishmania* carrier). In addition, photosensitizer (PS)-mediated photodynamic insecticides (PDIs) are under investigation. "The ongoing work is patterned after the one-world approach by enlisting the participation of experts in medicinal chemistry, cell/molecular biology, immunology, parasitology, entomology, cancer research, tropical medicine and veterinary medicine. The availability of multidisciplinary expertise is indispensable for implementation of the necessary studies to move the project toward product development" (Chang *et al.* 2016).

Historically, One Health developed from an earlier concept known as One Medicine (Thompson 2013; Zinsstag *et al.* 2011). Medications for humans, domestic, and wild animals tend to be the same. Ivermectin is one such example. It was first used in veterinary medicine and then used to treat humans experiencing ecto- and endo-parasitic infections.

Surveillance and control of zoonotic diseases are required, to make "a significant impact on human health of the most marginalized populations characteristically dependent on livestock," as noted by David Molyneux (Liverpool School of Tropical Medicine) and colleagues: "Many endemic zoonoses have a dual impact on human health and livestock production. Human populations dependent on livestock are not only most at direct risk from zoonotic disease but are most vulnerable to the indirect impacts on health of reduced production on livelihoods and food security, which exacerbates the poverty cycle. It is estimated that over 600 million people globally are livestock-dependent, and represent up to 70% of the population in the most marginal areas" (Molyneux *et al.* 2011).

One Health has a long history. The current initiative has its roots in the colonial era, a time rich in attempts to link human, animal, and environmental health, as well as marked by a strong distinction between the colonial administrators and the local populations they controlled. Please see Figure 24.3 for the colonial scientific network of environmental management (Lainé and Morand 2020). [We have mentioned previously that European schools of tropical medicine were established due to the then novel diseases, especially African sleeping sickness.]

Now, interactions between humans and life on earth need closer attention. Humans, animals, and the environment should be linked together to form a decolonized and more-than-human approach to One Health. Animals do act and think in their environment. As an example, a mahout (elephant whisperer) in Laos knows that the pachyderms possess a rich knowledge of the forest world, which they express by looking for specific plant specimens for food and healing. Therefore, **multispecies ethnography**, an approach that aims at considering the agency of nonhumans and their multiple (social, historical, and ecological) connectivities with humans, may be preferable than the classic anthropocentric view. "Applying this perspective to a One Health approach allows us to engage in innovative results which could benefit humans, animals, and their shared environment. … Humans should no longer be considered as the sole repositories of knowledge imposed on nature. On the contrary, they must learn to collaborate with non-humans. This means changing our view of wildlife and domesticated animals, and not necessarily consider them as passive objects, or in the case of health as victims of pathogens or guilty of trans-

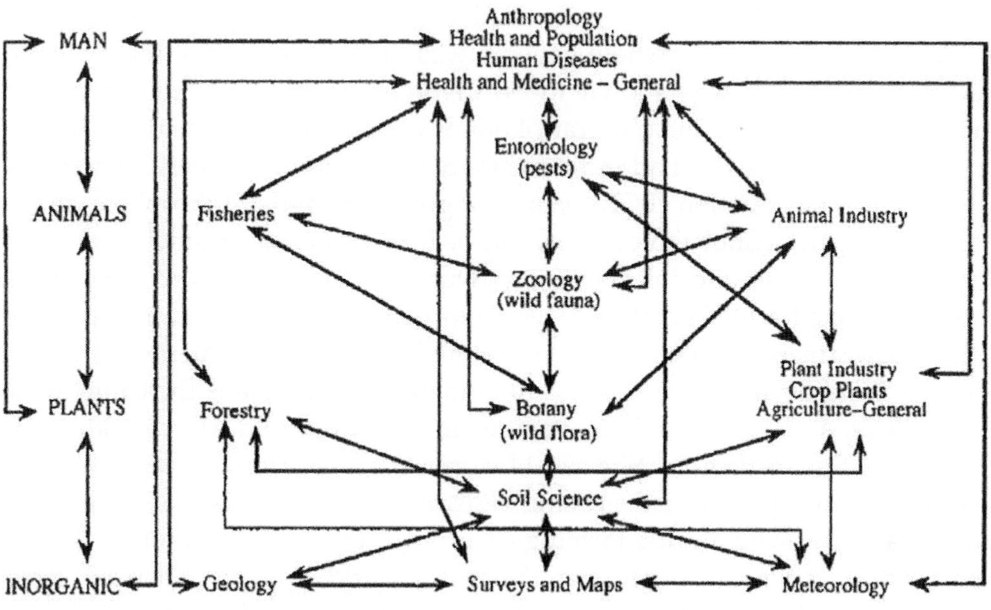

Fig. 24.3 ■ The colonial scientific network of environmental management. The colonial scientific network of environmental management in Worthington (see also Tilley, Morand & Lajaunie). Courtesy: Lainé N, Morand S. *Parasite* 2020;27:55. Reproduced with permission from *Parasite* with Creative Commons Attribution 4.0 (CC-BY) International License.

mitting them. Potentially, they are co-producers of knowledge on biodiversity. Recent developments in social science methodologies allow us to take the agency of animals and highlight the interdependencies of living beings in shared territories. This type of perspective sheds light on how social and ecological processes interact with each other and build precious **ecological solidarity** (including plants, animals, microbes, insects and other species) that can help prevent the next epidemic" (Lainé and Morand 2020).

24.4 New Pathogens & Novel Targets

Humans face novel pathogens all the time. Human infectious agents may originate from wildlife or domestic animals. Quite a few are viruses that cross the species barrier and propagate in humans. The year 2020 has seen the worldwide pandemic of coronavirus disease 2019 (COVID-19), the virus originally from bats that may have gone through an intermediate animal (maybe pangolin) and then to humans. Some governments' response (the lack/inadequacy in response) has been rated as "**The COVID-19 Catastrophe**" (Horton 2020; Abutaleb and Paletta 2021).

Like viruses, animal parasites cross the species barrier and infect humans, especially individuals possessing defective immune responses. In the following, we give three examples. With our interest in *Leishmania*, we start with trypanosomatid protozoa. In

2012, a HIV-negative 65-year-old male died of visceral leishmaniasis-like disease in Brazil. When the protozoan's whole genome was finally sequenced, the closest resemblance of the pathogen was shown to be ***Crithidia fasciculata***, an insect pathogen (Maruyama *et al.* 2019). Similarly, in Iran, 4 out of 167 samples of patients with cutaneous leishmaniasis symptoms also had the presence of only *Crithidia* species, as demonstrated by polymerase chain reaction (PCR) using the glyceraldehyde 3-phosphate dehydrogenase (GAPDH) gene (Ghobakhloo *et al.* 2019). Like protozoa, multicellular helminths cross the species barrier and infect humans. During our discussion of tapeworm infections, we mentioned a HIV-positive 41-year-old male who died of cancer cells derived from the tapeworm *Hymenolepis nana* in Colombia in 2013 (Muehlenbachs *et al.* 2015). Parasites of domestic animals also cross to humans; an example is the cattle eye worm, ***Thelazia gulosa***. A case of thelaziasis was seen in the 26-year-old Abby Beckley, acquired in the western US state Oregon.[3] She had 14 worms removed from her left eye; the worms "were morphologically identified as being *Thelazia gulosa*" (after she had practiced horsemanship in a region where cattle farming occurred). "Previously, only two *Thelazia* spp. have been implicated as causing human thelaziasis worldwide, these being *T. californiensis* (in the western United States) and *T. callipaeda* (in Europe and Asia). In this report, we add a third species, *T. gulosa*, an endemic eye worm of cattle in North America, Europe, Central Asia, and Australia as a novel agent of human thelaziasis in the United States of America" (Bradbury *et al.* 2018).

To deal with the old and new parasites infecting humans, standard approaches are drugs, vaccines, diagnostics, and vector control (for vector-borne diseases). Overuse of drugs have led to resistant strains of parasites. Thus, there is an urgent need for new therapeutic drugs. "Diseases caused by helminth infections affect more than a quarter of the population of the world, but the therapeutic arsenal is limited. The approval of **moxidectin** in 2018 and **triclabendazole** in 2019 by the FDA marked an important moment in the fight against diseases of poverty, such as helminthiases" (de Moraes and Geary 2020). Moxidectin, a macrocyclic lactone from the bacterium *Streptomyces*, targets the glutamate gated chloride channel and is approved for use against onchocerciasis (river blindness). Triclabendazole, a benzimidazole, is approved for fascioliasis (sheep liver fluke). Going beyond approved drugs, there are others in the pipeline. As examples are the compounds targeting the endosymbiotic bacterium *Wolbachia* (for lymphatic filariasis and river blindness). A safe macrofilaricide drug based on the antibiotic **tylosin A** targeting *Wolbachia* is undergoing preclinical development. This immediate future drug is being developed by the company AbbVie (with international academic collaborators) and currently named ABBV-4083 (Taylor *et al.* 2019; von Geldern *et al.* 2019). For parasitic diseases, there are efforts at repurposing existing drugs (aka drug repositioning). One example is **auranofin**, from current use in arthritis to potential future applications to parasitic protozoan and helminthic infections (Feng *et al.* 2020). Future drug possibilities will be based on genomic

[3] https://www.npr.org/sections/goatsandsoda/2018/02/13/584490122/you-don-t-want-to-know-what-was-in-abby-beckley-s-eye

data of human parasites. One obvious example is targeting of biosynthetic pathway of the disaccharide trehalose. This pathway is of great interest for the development of novel therapeutics because trehalose is important to microbes and invertebrates but nonessential to vertebrates (including humans). One target is trehalose-6-phosphate phosphatase (**TPP**), a key enzyme in trehalose biosynthesis. Recombinant enzymes from parasitic nematodes (including the zoonotic roundworms *Ancylostoma ceylanicum* and *Toxocara canis*) have been generated in bacteria for the screening of specific inhibitors. After testing a total of 5,452 compounds (collected from Compounds Australia/Queensland Compound Library, the public-private partnership Medicines for Malaria Venture, and other sources), ***N*-(phenylthio)phthalimide** has been identified as an inhibitor of nematode TPPs. This compound serves as a lead for further development of an anti-parasitic drug targeting their trehalose pathway. Moreover, TPP is expected to be a broad-spectrum therapeutic target against both eukaryotic and prokaryotic pathogens (Cross *et al.* 2017 and 2019). Therefore, we eagerly anticipate that genomes from parasitic protozoa and helminths, for comparison to the human host and their non-parasitic counterparts, will yield many novel targets for drugs and vaccines. As an example, the TPP enzyme itself may be applicable for use as a vaccine.

24.5 Developing Technologies & Future Challenges

The vaccine approach has been applied to human parasites, with some success. To date, the only vaccine being used is against the malaria parasite *Plasmodium falciparum*: **RTSS**. The "R" stands for the central repeat region of *Plasmodium falciparum* circumsporozoite protein (CSP); the "T" represents the T-cell epitopes of the CSP; and the "S" is for hepatitis B surface antigen (HBsAg). Vaccines for other parasitic protozoa are being developed, notably ones against *Leishmania* species (Palatnik-de-Sousa and Nico 2020). Vaccines against helminths are also being investigated. One example is the ongoing work towards vaccines for hookworms and blood flukes by Peter Hotez and colleagues. A product development partnership (**PDP**) has been set up, and current efforts towards recombinant vaccines (protein synthesized by yeast or the tobacco plant) plus adjuvant and innate immunity enhancers (to activate toll-like receptors). With previous experience in IgE and allergic reactions in people with prior exposure to the hookworm parasite, current vaccine candidates are aspartate protease and glutathione S-transferase from *Necator americanus* and tetraspanin (tegument component) from *Schistosoma mansoni* (Diemert *et al.* 2018). We look forward towards the availability of anti-parasite vaccines for the world's population.

For any infectious disease, one needs drugs, vaccines, diagnostics, and vector control (for vector-borne diseases). We applaud the improvements in diagnostics of parasitic diseases. Take *Leishmania* as an example. There are multiple diagnostic tests to identify the species for appropriate clinical treatment (Akhoundi *et al.* 2017). *Leishmania* species, as well as other protozoan and helminthic parasites, have been tagged (such as adding the green fluorescent protein, GFP) and investigated in animal models in vivo for studies including pathology and therapy (Chan *et al.* 2003; Novobilský and Höglund 2020). As a non-invasive test, the patient's urine may be a potential source for *Leishmania* DNA isolation and analysis (Bezerra *et al.* 2019). Similarly, diagnosis to identify *Echinococcus granulosus*-derived cell-free DNA (cfDNA) in the urine of cystic echinococcosis (CE) patients by PCR has been established (Toribio *et al.* 2020). Matrix-assisted laser desorption/ionization-time of flight (MALDI-TOF) mass spectrometry (MS) is a widely used technique for the rapid and accurate identification of bacterial and fungal pathogens in the clinical microbiology laboratories. It is being applied to parasitic helminths (such as *Trichinella*) for the identification of adult helminths, larvae and eggs shed in fecal samples, and to detect helminth-related proteins in serum or body fluids of infected individuals (Feucherolles *et al.* 2019). Using MALDI-TOF mass spectrometry together with an in-house reference database, identification of the leishmaniasis insect vector phlebotomine sand flies has been achieved (Arfuso *et al.* 2019).

Ideally, diagnostics should be simple to use, rapid, and affordable, all of which lead to increased availability. Along this line, cell phones are popular; "smart diagnosis" of parasitic diseases are possible via smartphones (Saeed and Jabbar 2017). As an example, scientists at Kathmandu, Nepal have developed and optimized an affordable smartphone microscopic method for simultaneous detection of *Cryptosporidium* and *Giardia* oocysts in food and water samples. They transformed a smartphone (Samsung Galaxy J7 prime) into a smartphone microscope, using "a ball lens of 1 mm diameter, white LED as illumination source and Lugols's iodine staining provided magnification and contrast capable of distinguishing (oo)cysts of *Cryptosporidium* and *Giardia*" (Shrestha *et al.* 2020).

On a wider scale, there is Global Information Systems (**GIS**) technology that is useful in public health applications, including parasitology (Fletcher-Lartey and Caprarelli 2016). Global Positioning Systems (**GPS**) uses satellites that orbit the Earth to send information to GPS receivers that are on the ground to help people determine their location. GIS is a software program that helps people use the information collected from GPS satellites. GPS and GIS combine to find the location of people, parasites, and vectors to be tracked and monitored, whereas molecular biology allows information on individual parasitic species. At the level of species and strains, knowledge of parasites' genome and secretory products for host-parasite interactions, as well as advances in molecular technology such as single cell transcriptomics, allow a deeper understanding for novel approaches to their control (Marzano *et al.* 2017; McVeigh 2020). Similarly, genomes of vector species allow translational science to design specific methods of control. However, for vector control, "the pipeline for new insecticides is limited" (Hotez *et al.* 2016). So, we turn to **biological control**. This is purposeful introduction of a biological agent (an antagonistic species) to control a pathogen or vector (the targeted species). Ideally, biological control can offer a relatively economical and possibly self-sustaining means of disrupting the transmission of parasitic diseases. Current approaches of biological control management involve detailed interactions of multiple traits/characteristics, as well as the inclusion of genomic information (Perovi *et al.* 2018; Leung *et al.* 2020). "Biological control is widely successful at controlling pests, but effective biocontrol agents are now more difficult to import from countries of origin due to more restrictive international trade laws (the Nagoya Protocol). Coupled with increasing demand, the efficacy of existing and new biocontrol agents needs to be improved with genetic and genomic approaches" (Leung *et al.* 2020).

Potential novel control agents are being discovered. As an example, a specific bacterial species can destroy parasitic nematodes (including the ruminant nematode barber's pole worm, *Haemonchus contortus*): "The golden death bacillus ***Chryseobacterium nematophagum*** is a novel matrix digesting pathogen of nematodes" (Page *et al.* 2019). Another example is the use of genetically modified male mosquito release into the environment to control vector transmitted viral diseases (Zika, dengue), as in Florida and Cayman Islands using CRISPR/Cas9 gene drive modified *Aedes aegypti*. However, it must be emphasized that deliberate human action of biological control may result in unexpected outcomes and adversely impact the ecosystem.[4]

Human activities already have a major impact on all living organisms. In the current Anthropocene epoch, first there is human population increase. The world's population is projected to grow from 7.7 billion in 2019 to 8.5 billion in 2030 (10% increase) and to almost 10 billion by 2050.[5]

In addition to population growth, there are population movements, some being forced migration to leave areas of war and conflicts (refugees), others being economical to seek better opportunities in the cities (urbanization and "slums"). For human survival, there is an absolute need for food, water, and shelter. The UN Sustainable Development Goal 6 (SDG 6) is oriented around clean water and sanitation. Universal, affordable, and sustainable access to **WASH** ("water, sanitation and hygiene") is a key public health issue. Current estimates include 2.3 billion without sanitation facilities and 844 million without access to safe and clean drinking water. Human activities lead to climate change (aka greenhouse effect, a warming world with carbon dioxide and other gases in the atmosphere), resulting in droughts, famines, and forest fires in many locations. This situation has been referred to as the global syndemic of obesity, undernutrition and climate change (Swinburn *et al.* 2019). A **syndemic** (synergistic epidemic) is the aggregation of two or more concurrent or sequential epidemics or disease clusters in a population with biological interactions, which exacerbate the prognosis and burden of disease. Climate change leads to changes in disease patterns including the NTDs. "A changing climate is associated with spatiotemporal variation in exposure and transmission of each species of infection" (Booth 2018). Human consumption of meat requires intensive rearing of cattle. As a result, livestock contribute to increased carbon dioxide and methane emissions. One view of the changes in total biomass of humans and animals throughout time is shown in Figure 24.4 (Pozio 2020). Increase in total mass of humans and domestic animals (cattle,

---

[4] https://www.genengnews.com/news/florida-approves-mosquito-release-to-curb-spread-of-viruses/

[5] https://population.un.org/wpp/Publications/Files/WPP2019_Highlights.pdf

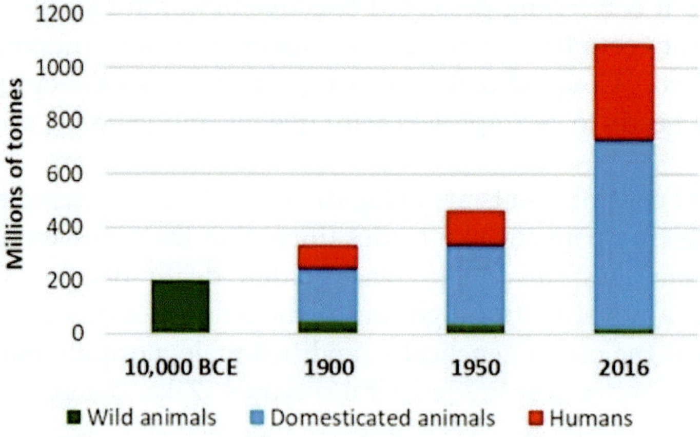

Fig. 24.4 ■ Changes in total biomass of humans and animals throughout time. Changes of terrestrial vertebrate biomass in the last 12,000 years according to Smil (2011). Courtesy: Pozio E. *Exp Parasitol* 2020;208:107807. Reproduced with permission from Elsevier.

pigs, chickens) and the concept of the global village (**globalization**) allowing easy worldwide access and person-to-person contact (including travel and tourism) will impact the foodborne parasites. Edorado Pozio (Istituto Superiore di Sanità/Italian National Institute of Health, Rome) wrote: "Since both domesticated and wild animals play an important role as reservoirs of these pathogens the increase/decrease of their biomasses, migration, and passive introduction by humans can change their epidemiological patterns" (Pozio 2020). This again reminds us of the One Health concept.

"The global response to neglected tropical diseases has been mounted to expressly help the poor and pull their poverty-related health problems out of neglect. Driven by novel thinking and boosted by strong public-private partnership the effort has taken proportions that are unmatched in scope today. Yet there is no room for complacency.... The year 2020 will be crucial for the future of the global response to NTDs" (Engels and Zhou 2020).

In this regard WHO has published *Ending the neglect to attain the Sustainable Development Goals: A road map for neglected tropical diseases 2021–2030.*[2] As a continuation of the previous roadmap in 2012, the current road map tackles 20 NTDs and disease groups that affect hundreds of millions of people. It aims to improve coordination and collaboration among health partners, integrate and mainstream approaches, and promote greater ownership by governments and communities. The road map, agreed upon by the World Health Assembly (WHA) during its 73rd meeting in November 2020, was the work of Dr. Mwelecele Ntuli Malecela (Director of WHO's Department of Control of Neglected Tropical Diseases since 2018) and her colleagues.

The current road map sets global targets and milestones to prevent, control, eliminate or eradicate 20 diseases and disease groups as well as cross-cutting targets aligned with the Sustainable Development Goals (SDGs).[2] In addition, there were changes in strategy. "As the NTD community began to plan and develop the 2021–2030 road map, it became clear that fundamental shifts in strategy were indicated. Three shifts, in fact, form its pillars. The first is a shift from measuring process to measuring impact. The second is a shift from vertical programming to horizontal, cross-cutting programming. The third shift, and potentially the most significant, calls for a move away from partner-led to country-driven and country-owned work" (Malecela and Ducker 2021).

The overarching 2030 global targets are to:

- reduce by 90% the number of people requiring treatment for NTDs;
- eliminate at least one NTD in 100 countries;
- eradicate 2 diseases (dracunculiasis and yaws);
- reduce by 75% the disability-adjusted life years (DALYs) related to NTDs.[6]

24.6 Parting Thoughts

In this textbook on human parasites, we began with a discussion on NTDs in Chapter 1 and have gone full circle to conclude with this same topic at the end. David Molyneux still put NTDs as an emerging challenge: "Recognition of global burden of NTDs, including higher mortality estimated at 350,000 deaths annually rather than that attributed in Global Burden of Disease studies" (Molyneux 2016). NTDs have been grouped as "**the chronic pandemic**" (Molyneux *et al.* 2017). Both emerging and reemerging infectious pathogens bring challenges and opportunities for human innovation, insight, and behavior change to face these infectious agents (Mackey *et al.* 2014; Molyneux *et al.* 2018). In 2020, we experienced the COVID-19 pandemic, by the novel severe acute respiratory syndrome coronavirus 2 (SARS-CoV-2). Many viruses jump from animals to humans on many occasions. "Infectious diseases prevalent in humans and animals are caused by pathogens that once emerged from other animal hosts.... Disease emergence reflects dynamic balances and imbalances, within complex globally distributed ecosystems comprising humans, animals, pathogens, and the environment" (Morens and Fauci 2020). [Vaccines for COVID-19 have been rapidly developed ("Operation Warp Speed") and received Emergency Use Authorization (EUA) from the US Food and Drug Administration (FDA) by December 2020, including two novel mRNA-based vaccines (by Pfizer and Moderna) targeting the viral spike protein (the gene being engineered with 2 additional prolines to stabilize the protein for high levels of expression, based on knowledge gained from prior studies with seasonal coronavirus and the Middle East respiratory syndrome, MERS, coronavirus (Krammer 2020). Time magazine Heroes of the Year 2021 celebrated 'Vaccine scientists and the miracle of mRNA.' The 4 researchers honored are Katalin

[6] https://www.who.int/news/item/12-11-2020-neglected-tropical-diseases-world-health-assembly-endorses-bold-new-road-map-targets-for-2030

Kariko (Temple, to University of Pennsylvania, to BioNTech), Drew Weissman (University of Pennsylvania), Barney Graham (Vaccine Research Center, VRC, National Institute of Allergy and Infectious Diseases, NIAID, National Institutes of Health, NIH) and Kizzmekia Corbett (VRC, to Harvard T.H. Chan School of Public Health). The Oxford-AstraZeneca DNA vaccine (also target the viral spike protein, with the gene for spike protein in chimpanzee adenovirus ChAd) was approved by Britain's Medicines and Healthcare Products Regulatory Agency in December 2020 (after RNA vaccines' approval in the US) (Gilbert and Green 2021). The Janssen–Johnson & Johnson DNA vaccine (the gene of spike protein in adenovirus type 26, Ad26) was approved as EUA by FDA in February 2021.]

One concern is that malaria and parasitic NTDs can be potential syndemics with COVID-19. "Current models suggest that low- and middle-income countries (LMICs) will have a similar incidence but substantially lower mortality rate than high-income countries. However, malaria and NTDs are prevalent in LMICs, and coinfections are likely. Both malaria and parasitic NTDs can alter immunologic responses to other infectious agents. Malaria can induce a cytokine storm and procoagulant state similar to that seen in severe COVID-19. Consequently, coinfections with malaria parasites and SARS-CoV-2 could result in substantially worse outcomes than monoinfections with either pathogen, and could shift the age pattern of severe COVID-19 to younger age-groups" (Gutman *et al.* 2020). Please see Table 24.2 for a summary of key symptoms of COVID-19, malaria and key NTDs (Gutman *et al.* 2020).

Co-infection cases have been reported for COVID-19 with parasites, including *Trypanosoma cruzi* (protozoan) and *Strongyloides* species (helminth). Two patients, a 74-year-old female and a 68-year-old male with prior diagnosis of Chagas' disease, were treated in a reference center for COVID-19 treatment in the metropolitan region of São Paulo, a city in the Southeast of Brazil. Confirmed positive for SARS-CoV-2 RNA by RT-PCR of nasopharyngeal samples, the case report described their hospitalization and death (Alberca *et al.* 2020). One patient, a 68-year-old male immigrated from Ecuador to USA 20 years ago, living in the state of Connecticut, was admitted to Yale University hospital for COVID-19. With confirmed presence of viral RNA, he was treated with steroid (methylprednisolone) and antibiotics for bacterial infections. On day 18, his sputum culture grew *Pseudomonas aeruginosa* and methicillin-sensitive *Staphylococcus aureus*. The next day, serpiginous tracks were detected on the agar surface, made by helminth larvae that were found to be *Strongyloides* infection. He was treated with ivermectin and albendazole for disseminated strongyloidiasis. "On day 38, repeat *Strongyloides* serology was positive. He currently awaits placement to a skilled nursing facility" (Lier *et al.* 2020). *Strongyloides stercoralis* can have auto-infection and there can be hyper-infection or disseminated strongyloidiasis after corticosteroid treatments (as previously discussed, please see Chapter 21). "Screening for *Strongyloides* infection should be pursued in individuals with COVID-19 who originate from endemic regions before initiating immunosuppressive therapy" (Lier *et al.* 2020).

TABLE 24.2: Summary of key symptoms of COVID-19, malaria and key NTDs. Summary of principal characteristics of COVID-19, malaria, and key neglected tropical diseases. Courtesy: Gutmen *et al.* *Am J Trop Med Hyg* 2020;103:572–7. Reproduced with permission from the American Society of Tropical Medicine and Hygiene.

Characteristic	COVID-19	Malaria	Soil-transmitted helminths	Schistosomiasis	Chagas
Infectious agent	SARS-CoV-2	*Plasmodium falciparum, Plasmodium vivax, Plasmodium ovale, Plasmodium malariae,* and *Plasmodium knowlesi*	*Ascaris lumbicoides, Trichuris trichiura*, and hookwom (*Ancylostoma duodenale* and *Necator americanus*)	*Schistosoma mansoni, S. haematobium*, and *S. japonicum*	*Trypanosoma cruzi*
Principal symptoms of clinical disease	Fever, cough, and shortness of breath	Fever	*Ascaris* and hookworm: transient pneumonitis. Hookworm and *Trichuris*: abdominal pain, nausea, diarrhea, and anemia	Often asymptomatic; acute infection causes fever, cough, abdominal pain, diarrhea, hepatosplenomegaly, and eosinophilia.	Fever, edema, malaise, lymphadenopathy, hepatosplenomegaly, and chagoma (skin nodule at the inoculation site)
Severe clinical disease manifestation	Acute respiratory distress syndrome	Cerebral malaria, severe anemia, and acute respiratory distress syndrome	*Ascaris*: acute intestinal obstruction and peritonitis. Hookworm: anemia. *Trichuris*: colitis, anemia, growth restriction, and dysentery	*S. mansoni* and *japonicum*: cirrhosis and portal hypertention. *S. hematobium*: hematuria and squamous cell carcinoma of the bladder; rarely, central nervous system lesions	Chronic heart disease, dilated cardiomyopathy, megacolon, and megaesophagus
Mode of transmission	Person-to-person, primarily by respiratory droplets	Mosquito vector	*Ascaris* and *Trichuris*: ingestion of eggs. Hookworm: larvae penetrate the unprotected skin	Exposure to water containing larval forms of the parasite which penetrate the skin	Triatomine vector
Age-group most affected	Adults	Children	Children and pregnant women	School-aged children for infection and adults for severe disease	Children for infection and adults for severe disease

At the time of a pandemic, one needs urgency and empathy, as well as timely and accurate scientific facts. Instead, COVID-19 has unleashed a "tsunami of hate and xenophobia, scapegoating and scaremongering," according to UN Secretary General Antonio Guterres (as quoted in Horton 2020). An avalanche of **infodemic** has appeared with the epidemic that one needs to deal with (Eysenbach 2020; Zarocostas 2020). Infodemic, a blend of "information" and "epidemic," typically refers to a rapid and far-reaching spread of both accurate and inaccurate information about something, such as COVID-19. There is an excessive amount of information concerning the problem such that the solution is made more difficult. In addition, there can be wide and rapid spread of misinformation (and the deliberate disinformation). Fact checking the "fake news" is crucial. To verify a claim, one must "dig to the source." In USA and in some European countries, there is an **antiscience** movement. Peter Hotez wrote: "In the United States and in some areas of Europe there has been a rise in antiscience sentiments reflected as climate denial or an antivaccine movement. Globalization of the antivaccine movement or its expansion to middle-income countries could lead to reversals in public health gains or Sustainable Development Goals" (Hotez 2018b). Therefore, one must select consistent and reliable information. For NTDs and parasitic diseases, an essential source is PubMed.[7]

Furthermore, we have an obligation to engage the public. As President Abraham Lincoln (1858) said: "Public sentiment is everything. With public sentiment, nothing can fail. Without it, nothing can succeed." To the public, we must accurately and effectively communicate on science, including NTDs and parasitic diseases. For this, the reader may be interested in the report from the US National Academy of Sciences on *Communicating Science Effectively*.[8]

In previous chapters we include select stories of discovery, ecology, evolution, life cycles, and transmission of parasites, as well as molecular cell biology, genomes, and host parasite interactions, such as parasitic excretory/secretory products modulating host immune response. In our opinion, such a presentation gives a more complete picture of the parasitic life on earth. John Tyler Bonner (Princeton University) (1920–2019) has elegantly commented: "Both the reductionist approach of molecular biology and the holistic approach of ecology and evolution go hand-in-hand in biology; both are essential. It is looking for the big picture, for the generalizations that underlie the major processes of ecology and evolution on the one hand and the molecular details of all life processes on the other. **Holism** and **reductionism** are both required ways of thinking about biology; the two essential ways look through different ends of the telescope" (Bonner 2020).[9]

We have mentioned the control and eradication of human parasites. Guinea worm disease, aka dracunculiasis, is fast racing towards the end. Previously, only smallpox has been eradicated (in the year 1977), and only two stocks of the smallpox variola virus (VARV) are kept in high-security laboratories (CDC, Atlanta, USA & Novosibirsk, Russia) (Smith and McFadden 2002). The idea of parasite conservation, that eradicated

---

[7] https://pubmed.ncbi.nlm.nih.gov/?otool=njrutulib

[8] https://www.nap.edu/catalog/23674/communicating-science-effectively-a-research-agenda

[9] https://en.wikipedia.org/wiki/John_Tyler_Bonner

parasites should still be preserved ("equal right" for parasites), has been presented for the sake of biodiversity. Scientists have already perfected cryopreservation techniques for embryos and cell lines of fruit fly and mouse. We give another example: Frozen Ark project, a frozen zoo project created jointly by the Zoological Society of London, the Natural History Museum, and the University of Nottingham, with the aim of preserving the DNA and living cells of endangered species to retain the genetic knowledge for the future.[10] The world's first cloned Przewalski's horse was born in 2020 at the San Diego Zoo. Named Kurt, after Kurt Benirschke (created the world's first Frozen Zoo for the cryopreservation of genetic material from endangered species), this rare, endangered Przewalski's horse was created from cells taken in 1980 from a stallion that had sat frozen at the San Diego Zoo for 40 years before they were fused with an enucleated egg from a domestic horse. Another success story was the cloning of black-footed ferret (long thought to be extinct until rediscovery in 1981 in Wyoming) by scientists of US Fish and Wildlife Service (black-footed ferret breeding facility in Fort Collins, Colorado). Born in December 2020 and named Elizabeth Ann, she was cloned using frozen cells from Willa (one of the originally captured ferrets who had died in 1988 without any offspring). This is the first clone of an endangered animal native to North America (Anonymous 2021).

It is easy for people to want to conserve animals such as the tiger and the giant panda because they have species charisma (appeal). Conservation of parasites, however, is a hard sell, because most people's interactions with parasites are unpleasant, and parasites are neither cute nor beautiful. Acknowledging that "Metazoan parasites are among the most diverse, threatened, and under-protected animals on Earth ... a working group of parasitologists and ecologists propose a formal action plan for conserving parasites that do not threaten human health or domesticated species, which the conservation community can leverage over the upcoming decade (2020–2030) to minimize the loss of parasite biodiversity" (Carlson *et al.* 2020). The document was presented by Colin Carlson (Georgetown University) and a group of international colleagues. They have identified 12 goals that could advance parasite biodiversity conservation through an ambitious mix of research, advocacy, and management. Please see Figure 24.5 for the 12 goals of **parasite conservation** (Carlson *et al.* 2020). In our opinion, the approach should include parasitic protozoa and helminths, like the cryopreservation of smallpox viruses.

The SARS CoV-19 COVID-19 pandemic leads to a lack of global **food security**, as David Laborde (International Food Policy Research Institute, Washington DC) and colleagues observed: "The pandemic is affecting all four pillars of food security: availability (is the supply of food adequate?), access (can people obtain the food they need?), utilization (do people have enough intake of nutrients?), and stability (can people access food at all times?). COVID-19 is most directly and severely impacting access to food, even though impacts are also felt through disruptions to availability; shifts in consumer demand toward cheaper, less nutritious foods; and food price instability" (Laborde *et al.* 2020). The ongoing COVID-19 pandemic has resulted in economic fallouts and disrup-

[10] https://www.frozenark.org/

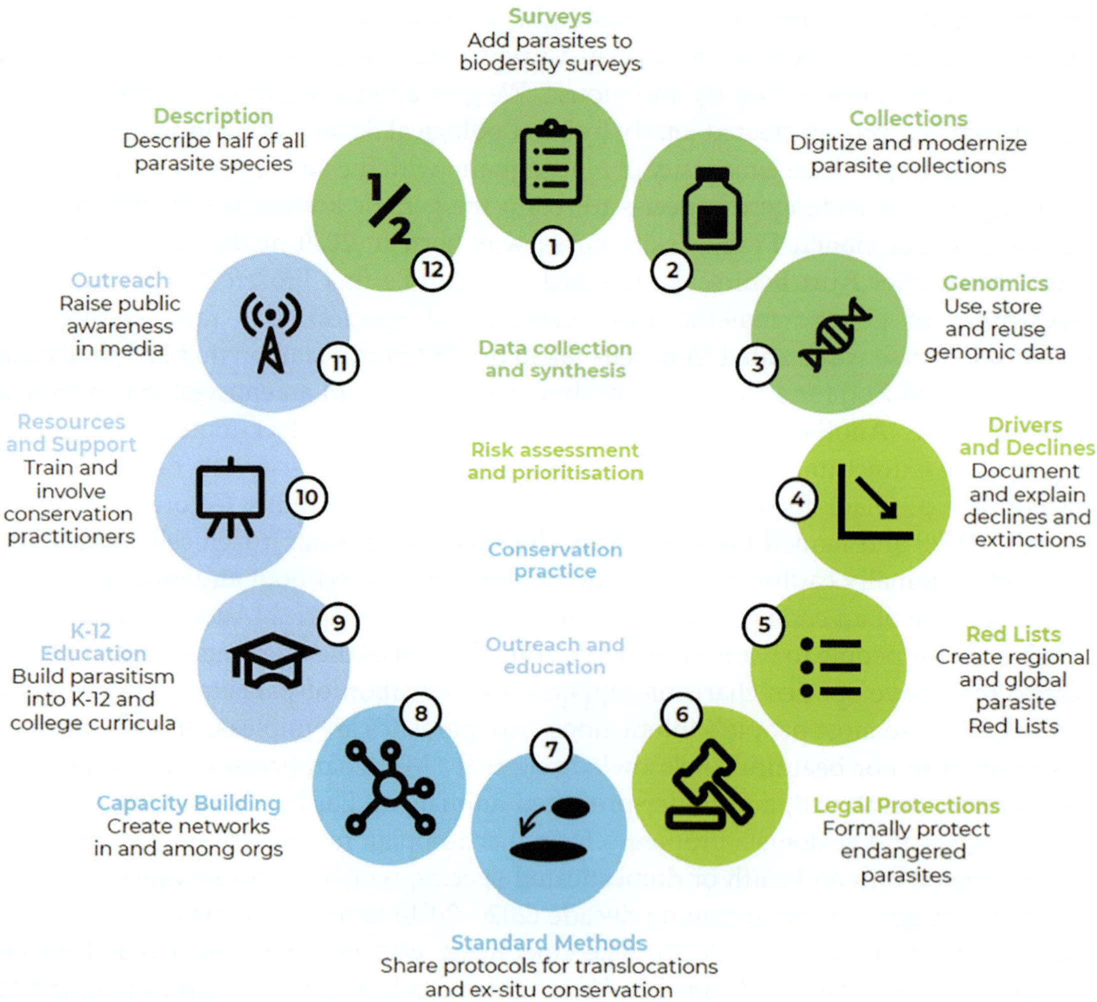

Fig. 24.5 ■ Twelve goals for parasite conservation. The twelve major goals in the parasite conservation plan. Courtesy: Carlson *et al. Biol Conserv* 2020;250:108596. Reproduced with permission from Elsevier.

tions of food supply chains. Whether it is during a global pandemic or regional famine, climate change causes more frequent droughts that proceed to worsen the issue of food insecurity. In 2019, the United Nations World Food Program (WFP), the Rome-based organization, assisted around 100 million people in 88 countries who were victims of acute food insecurity and hunger. As the world's biggest humanitarian group addressing hunger and promoting food security, WFP was awarded the 2020 Nobel Peace Prize for its efforts to combat hunger and food insecurity around the globe.

In regard to survival and global public health, can an individual make a difference? Let us ponder this question concerning food supply. We are advised to consume more fresh produce because fruits and vegetables are beneficial to our health. An increase in their production is possible via **vertical farming**, a practice to grow crops in vertically stacked layers that incorporate controlled-environment agriculture, with aims to optimize plant growth, and soilless farming techniques such as hydroponics.

A decrease in red meat intake is good for both the wellbeing of people and the climate. US fast food-chains are bringing forth plant-based burgers (Impossible Whopper from Burger King; Beyond Sausage sandwich from Dunkin in collaboration with Beyond Meat); these improved plant-based meat is also available in US supermarkets. [Impossible Foods was founded by Patrick Brown (formerly at Stanford) (Leeming 2021).] Another source of meat is from the laboratory. In lieu of the classic livestock farm, now it is "real, high-quality meat created directly from animal cells for safe human consumption" (such as animal skeletal muscle cell culture; cell cultured beef burger may be tasty but cost-prohibitive; cell culture chicken, developed by East Just, a company in San Francisco, California, has received approval from the Singapore government in December 2020 for chicken nuggets, the cost, previously estimated at US$50 per nugget, will be at "price parity for premium chicken you'd enjoy at a restaurant." Singapore's action is "the world's world's first regulatory approval for a cultivated meat product."[11] [The process for growing meat in a bioreactor has been named **cellular agriculture**.][11]

One existing and widely available source of protein is insects. As included in the 2019 edition of *The Joy of Cooking*, John Becker and Megan Scott stated: "Insects are not really eaten in the United States with any great gusto, but they are beloved in cuisines around the world and have been for a very long time. … The chief advantage to insects as food is that they are plentiful as well as an excellent source of nutrition, thus providing a sustainable source of protein and fat." Well, some Americans are using cricket flour. Extending from food choice to other affairs and attitudes, we quote Hope Jahren, *The Story of More*, who said, "Using less and sharing more is the biggest challenge our generation will ever face." In a resource-restricted world, with human activities causing climate change, pollution and habitat loss (less biodiversity), these are global challenges that every individual has a duty to respond (Cable *et al.* 2017). For the sake of sustainability, we must reflect and act when it comes to reducing, reusing, recycling, and respecting.

In a time of crisis, during the pandemic, we must find happiness in hard times; we need to feel more gratitude, hope, kindness, and love. The founder of World Central Kitchen (providing free meals to the disaster-affected people worldwide, including at Puerto Rico after Hurricane Maria in 2017, as shown in the 2018 book *We Fed an Island*) was the celebrity chef, Jose Andres, and he commented: "There is a world of difference between wanting to do good and knowing how to make it happen." President Bill Clinton had this assessment for the chef: "If you spend more time on your fears than your hopes, on your resentments than your compassions, and you divide people up, in an interdependent world, bad things are going to happen. … If that's all you do, you're not helping the people who have been victimized or left behind or overlooked. He's a walking model of what the 21st century citizen should be" (April 8/13 2020 *Time Magazine*). Please, **be**

[11] https://www.nytimes.com/2020/12/02/business/singapore-lab-meat.html

the 21st century citizen: compassionate, creative, competent. Be resourceful and resilient. Speak up, get involved, build the community. Keep engaged. Be the voice of change. Embrace the campaign for a more just and equitable society because: "Yes we can" (as spoken by President Barack Obama on November 4, 2008).

Greta Thunberg, at age 16, from Sweden, was Time magazine Person of the Year for 2019, for bringing global warming/climate change to a wide audience. Gitanjali Rao, at age 15, from Colorado, USA, has become the first ever Time magazine Kid of the Year (in partnership with Nickelodeon). "Observe, brainstorm, research, build, and communicate," this young scientist/inventor/STEM (science, technology, engineering, mathematics) promoter told her interviewer, the actress Angelina Jolie, about her process, over Zoom (December 14, 2020 *Time Magazine*). She won the 3M Young Scientist Challenge in 2017; she has conducted "innovation workshops" across the globe.[12] We must embrace the views on science and climate from Gita and Greta. You may also remember Roald Dahl (author of *Charlie and the Chocolate Factory* 1964, *James and the Giant Peach* 1961, *Matilda* 1988, and others) (1916–1990). This is Roald's advice to all readers: "And above all, watch with glittering eyes the whole world around you because the greatest secrets are always hidden in the most unlikely places" (The *Minpins* 1991, quoted by Davis, 2018). Watch, and change the world!

Summary & Key Concepts

- NTDs trap the poor in a cycle of poverty and disease.
- An available "rapid impact" package targeting seven NTDs is composed of 4 drugs: azithromycin, praziquantel, albendazole or mebendazole, and ivermectin or diethylcarbamazine.
- For NTDs, there are mass drug administration (MDA) and mass screening and treatment (MSAT).
- The landscape of disgust indicates parasite avoidance behavior of humans and animals.
- There is an urgent need for parasite conservation to maintain species biodiversity.
- Humans, animals, and the ecosystem form the One Health philosophy.
- Traditional approaches to parasitic diseases involve drugs, vaccines, diagnostics, and vector control.
- Malaria and parasitic NTDs may be potential syndemics with COVID-19.
- Ongoing climate change yields the warming earth, with famines and droughts, fires and floods.
- In times of a pandemic or other crises, be a responsible 21st century citizen.

References

Abutaleb Y, Paletta D. *Nightmare Scenario*. Harpers 2021.

Akhoundi M, Downing T, Votýpka J, *et al*. *Leishmania* infections: Molecular targets and diagnosis. *Mol Aspects Med* 2017;57:1–29.

[12] https://www.youtube.com/watch?v=f2RQMOft5w8

Alberca RW, Yendo TM, Leuzzi Ramos YÁ, *et al.* Case report: COVID-19 and Chagas disease in two coinfected patients. *Am J Trop Med Hyg* 2020.

Arfuso F, Gaglio G, Abbate JM, *et al.* Identification of phlebotomine sand flies through MALDI-TOF mass spectrometry and in-house reference database. *Acta Trop* 2019;194:47–52.

Bezerra GSN, Barbosa WL Júnior, Silva EDD, Leal NC, Medeiros ZM. Urine as a promising sample for *Leishmania* DNA extraction in the diagnosis of visceral leishmaniasis — a review. *Braz J Infect Dis* 2019;23(2):111–20.

Bonner JT. *Biology at Princeton (1947–2012)* (2020, Middletown, DE).

Booth M. Climate change and the neglected tropical diseases. *Adv Parasitol* 2018;100:39–126.

Bradbury RS, Breen KV, Bonura EM, Hoyt JW, Bishop HS. Case report: Conjunctival infestation with *Thelazia gulosa*: A novel agent of human thelaziasis in the United States. *Am J Trop Med Hyg* 2018;98(4):1171–4.

Bradley M, Taylor R, Jacobson J, *et al.* Medicine donation programmes supporting the global drive to end the burden of neglected tropical diseases. *Trans R Soc Trop Med Hyg*. 2021;115(2):136–144.

Buck JC, Weinstein SB, Young HS. Ecological and evolutionary consequences of parasite avoidance. *Trends Ecol Evol* 2018;33(8):619–32.

Cable J, Barber I, Boag B, *et al.* Global change, parasite transmission and disease control: Lessons from ecology. *Philos Trans R Soc Lond B Biol Sci* 2017;372(1719):20160088.

Carlson CJ, Hopkins S, Bell KC, *et al.* Wood, a global parasite conservation plan. *Biol Conserv* 2020;250:108596.

Chan MM, Bulinski JC, Chang KP, Fong D. A microplate assay for *Leishmania amazonensis* promastigotes expressing multimeric green fluorescent protein. *Parasitol Res* 2003;89(4):266–71.

Chang KP, Kolli BK, New Light Group. New "light" for one-world approach toward safe and effective control of animal diseases and insect vectors from leishmaniac perspectives. *Parasit Vectors* 2016;9(1):396.

Civitello DJ, Cohen J, Fatima H, *et al.* Biodiversity inhibits parasites: Broad evidence for the dilution effect. *Proc Natl Acad Sci U S A* 2015;112(28):8667–71.

Cohen JP, Silva L, Cohen A, Awatin J, Sturgeon R. Progress report on neglected tropical disease drug donation programs. *Clin Ther* 2016;38(5):1193–204.

Croft SL. Neglected tropical diseases in the genomics era: Re-evaluating the impact of new drugs and mass drug administration. *Genome Biol* 2016;17:46.

Cross M, Rajan S, Biberacher S, *et al.* Trehalose-6-phosphate phosphatase as a broad-spectrum therapeutic target against eukaryotic and prokaryotic pathogens. *Emerg Top Life Sci* 2017;1(6):675–83.

Cross M, York M, Długosz E, *et al.* A suicide inhibitor of nematode trehalose-6-phosphate phosphatases. *Sci Rep* 2019;9(1):16165.

Curtis VA. Infection-avoidance behaviour in humans and other animals. *Trends Immunol* 2014;35(10):457–64.

Davis DM. *The Beautiful Cure: The Revolution in Immunology and What It Means for Your Health*, 2018, The University of Chicago Press.

de Moraes J, Geary TG. FDA-approved antiparasitic drugs in the 21st century: A success for helminthiasis? *Trends Parasitol* 2020;36(7):573–5.

Diemert DJ, Bottazzi ME, Plieskatt J, Hotez PJ, Bethony JM. Lessons along the critical path: Developing vaccines against human helminths. *Trends Parasitol* 2018;34(9):747–58.

Eisenstein M. Disease: Poverty and pathogens. *Nature* 2016 Mar;531(7594):S61–3.

Engels D, Zhou XN. Neglected tropical diseases: An effective global response to local poverty-related disease priorities. *Infect Dis Poverty* 2020;9(1):10.

Eysenbach G. How to fight an infodemic: The four pillars of infodemic management. *J Med Internet Res* 2020;22(6):e21820.

Ezzati M, Pearson-Stuttard J, Bennett JE, Mathers CD. Acting on non-communicable diseases in low- and middle-income tropical countries. *Nature* 2018;559(7715):507–16.

Feng L, Pomel S, Latre de Late P, *et al.* Repurposing auranofin and evaluation of a new Gold(I) compound for the search of treatment of human and cattle parasitic diseases: From protozoa to helminth infections. *Molecules.* 2020;25(21):5075.

Feucherolles M, Poppert S, Utzinger J, Becker SL. MALDI-TOF mass spectrometry as a diagnostic tool in human and veterinary helminthology: A systematic review. *Parasit Vectors* 2019;12(1):245.

Fletcher-Lartey SM, Caprarelli G. Application of GIS technology in public health: Successes and challenges. *Parasitology* 2016;143(4):401–15.

Ghobakhloo N, Motazedian MH, Naderi S, Ebrahimi S. Isolation of *Crithidia* spp. from lesions of immunocompetent patients with suspected cutaneous leishmaniasis in Iran. *Trop Med Int Health* 2019;24(1):116–26.

Gilbert S, Green C. *Vaxxers: The Inside Story of the Oxford AstraZeneca Vaccine and the Race Against the Virus*, Hodder & Stoughton. London.

Gutman JR, Lucchi NW, Cantey PT, *et al.* Malaria and parasitic neglected tropical diseases: Potential syndemics with COVID-19? *Am J Trop Med Hyg* 2020;103(2):572–7.

Horton R. *The COVID-19 Castastrophe.* Polity 2020.

Hotez PJ. *Forgotten People, Forgotten Diseases*, 2nd edition (2013, ASM Press).

Hotez PJ. The rise of neglected tropical diseases in the "new Texas". *PLoS Negl Trop Dis* 2018a18;12(1):e0005581.

Hotez PJ. Human parasitology and parasitic diseases: Heading towards 2050. *Adv Parasitol* 2018b;100:29–38.

Hotez PJ, Booker C. STOP: Study, Treat, Observe, and Prevent neglected diseases of poverty act. *PLoS Negl Trop Dis* 2020;14(2):e0008064.

Hotez PJ, Fenwick A, Savioli L, Molyneux DH. Rescuing the bottom billion through control of neglected tropical diseases. *Lancet* 2009;373(9674):1570–5.

Hotez PJ, Fenwick A, Ray SE, Hay SI, Molyneux DH. "Rapid impact" 10 years after: The first "decade" (2006–2016) of integrated neglected tropical disease control. *PLoS Negl Trop Dis* 2018c;12(5):e0006137.

Hotez PJ, Pecoul B, Rijal S, *et al.* Eliminating the neglected tropical diseases: Translational science and new technologies. *PLoS Negl Trop Dis* 2016;10(3):e0003895.

Humboldt-Dachroeden S, Olivier Rubin O, Frid-Nielsen SS. The state of One Health research across disciplines and sectors — A bibliometric analysis. *One Health* 2020;10:100146.

Kavaliers M, Ossenkopp KP, Choleris E. Social neuroscience of disgust. *Genes Brain Behav* 2019;18(1):e12508.

Klemme I, Karvonen A. Learned parasite avoidance is driven by host personality and resistance to infection in a fish-trematode interaction. *Proc Biol Sci* 2016;283(1838):20161148.

Krammer F. SARS-CoV-2 vaccines in development. *Nature* 2020;586(7830):516–27.

Laborde D, Martin W, Swinnen J, Vos R. COVID-19 risks to global food security. *Science* 2020;369(6503):500–2.

Lainé N, Morand S. Linking humans, their animals, and the environment again: A decolonized and more-than-human approach to "One Health". *Parasite* 2020;27:55.

Lebov J, Grieger K, Womack D, *et al.* A framework for One Health research. *One Health* 2017;3:44–50.

Leeming J. Meet the food pioneer whose meat replacements are rocking the gravy boat. *Nature* 2021;590(7844):176.

Leung K, Ras E, Ferguson KB, *et al.* Next-generation biological control: The need for integrating genetics and genomics. *Biol Rev Camb Philos Soc* 2020;95(6):1838–54.

Lier AJ, Tuan JJ, Davis MW, *et al.* Case report: Disseminated strongyloidiasis in a patient with COVID-19. *Am J Trop Med Hyg* 2020;103(4):1590–92.

Liese B, Rosenberg M, Schratz A. Programmes, partnerships, and governance for elimination and control of neglected tropical diseases. *Lancet* 2010;375(9708):67–76.

Lydecker HW, Etheridge B, Price C, Banks PB, Hochuli DF. Landscapes within landscapes: A parasite utilizes different ecological niches on the host landscapes of two host species. *Acta Trop* 2019;193:60–65.

Mackey TK, Liang BA, Cuomo R, Hafen R, Brouwer KC, Lee DE. Emerging and reemerging neglected tropical diseases: A review of key characteristics, risk factors, and the policy and innovation environment. *Clin Microbiol Rev* 2014;27(4):949–79.

Malecela MN, Ducker C. A road map for neglected tropical diseases 2021–2030. *Trans R Soc Trop Med Hyg.* 2021;115(2):121–123.

Maruyama SR, de Santana AKM, Takamiya NT, *et al.* Non-leishmania parasite in fatal visceral leishmaniasis-like disease, Brazil. *Emerg Infect Dis* 2019;25(11):2088–92.

Marzano V, Mancinelli L, Bracaglia G, *et al.* "Omic" investigations of protozoa and worms for a deeper understanding of the human gut "parasitome". *PLoS Negl Trop Dis* 2017;11(11): e0005916.

McVeigh P. Post-genomic progress in helminth parasitology. *Parasitology* 2020;147(8):835–40.

Molyneux DH. The London declaration on neglected tropical diseases: 5 years on. *Trans R Soc Trop Med Hyg* 2016;110(11):623–5.

Molyneux DH, Savioli L, Engels D. Neglected tropical diseases: Progress towards addressing the chronic pandemic. *Lancet* 2017;389(10066):312–25.

Molyneux DH, Dean L, Adekeye O, Stothard JR, Theobald S. The changing global landscape of health and disease: Addressing challenges and opportunities for sustaining progress towards control and elimination of neglected tropical diseases (NTDs). *Parasitology* 2018;145(13):1647–54.

Molyneux D, Hallaj Z, Keusch GT, *et al.* Zoonoses and marginalised infectious diseases of poverty: Where do we stand? *Parasit Vectors* 2011;4:106.

Morens DM, Fauci AS. Emerging Pandemic Diseases: How We Got to COVID-19. *Cell* 2020;182(5):1077–92.

Muehlenbachs A, Bhatnagar J, Agudelo CA, *et al.* Malignant transformation of *Hymenolepis nana* in a human host. *N Engl J Med* 2015;373(19):1845–52.

National Academy of Sciences USA. Communicating Science Effectively. A research agenda. Consensus study report (2017). https://www.nap.edu/catalog/23674/communicating-science-effectively-a-research-agenda

Novobilský A, Höglund J. Small animal in vivo imaging of parasitic infections: A systematic review. *Exp Parasitol* 2020;214:107905.

Page AP, Roberts M, Félix MA, Pickard D, Page A, Weir W. The golden death bacillus *Chryseobacterium nematophagum* is a novel matrix digesting pathogen of nematodes. *BMC Biol* 2019;17(1):10.

Palatnik-de-Sousa CB, Nico D. The delay in the licensing of protozoal vaccines: A comparative history. *Front Immunol* 2020;11:204.

Perovi DJ, Gámez-Virués S, Landis DA, *et al.* Managing biological control services through multi-trophic trait interactions: Review and guidelines for implementation at local and landscape scales. *Biol Rev Camb Philos Soc* 2018;93(1):306–21.

Pozio E. How globalization and climate change could affect foodborne parasites. *Exp Parasitol* 2020;208:107807.

Saeed MA, Jabbar A. "Smart Diagnosis" of parasitic diseases by use of smartphones. *J Clin Microbiol* 2017;56(1):e01469–17.

Shrestha R, Duwal R, Wagle S, Pokhrel S, Giri B, Neupane BB. A smartphone microscopic method for simultaneous detection of (oo)cysts of *Cryptosporidium* and *Giardia*. *PLoS Negl Trop Dis* 2020;14(9):e0008560.

Smith GL, McFadden G. Smallpox: Anything to declare? *Nat Rev Immunol* 2002;2(7):521–7.

Sodahlon Y, Ross DA, McPhillips-Tangum C, *et al.* Building country capacity to sustain NTD programs and progress: A call to action. *PLoS Negl Trop Dis* 2020;14(10):e0008565.

Swinburn BA, Kraak VI, Allender S, *et al.* The global syndemic of obesity, undernutrition, and climate change: The Lancet Commission report. *Lancet* 2019;393(10173):791–846.

Taylor MJ, von Geldern TW, Ford L, *et al.* Preclinical development of an oral anti-*Wolbachia* macrolide drug for the treatment of lymphatic filariasis and onchocerciasis. *Sci Transl Med* 2019;11(483):eaau2086.

Thompson RC. Parasite zoonoses and wildlife: One Health, spillover and human activity. *Int J Parasitol* 2013;43(12–13):1079–88.

Tinkler SH. Preventive chemotherapy and anthelmintic resistance of soil-transmitted helminths — Can we learn nothing from veterinary medicine? *One Health* 2019;9:100106.

Toribio L, Santivanez S, Scott AL, *et al.* Diagnostic urinary cfDNA detected in human cystic echinococcosis. *Mol Biochem Parasitol* 2020;239:111314.

von Geldern TW, Morton HE, Clark RF, *et al.* Discovery of ABBV-4083, a novel analog of Tylosin A that has potent anti-*Wolbachia* and anti-filarial activity. *PLoS Negl Trop Dis* 2019;13(2):e0007159.

Weinstein SB, Buck JC, Young HS. A landscape of disgust. *Science* 2018;359(6381):12134.

Zarocostas J. How to fight an infodemic. *Lancet* 2020;395(10225):676.

Zinsstag J, Schelling E, Waltner-Toews D, Tanner M. From "one medicine" to "one health" and systemic approaches to health and well-being. *Prev Vet Med* 2011;101(3–4):148–56.

Index